Basic Applied Reservoir Simulation

SPE Textbook Series

The Textbook Series of the Society of Petroleum Engineers was established in 1972 by action of the SPE Board of Directors. The Series is intended to ensure availability of high-quality textbooks for use in undergraduate courses in areas clearly identified as being within the petroleum engineering field. The work is directed by the Society's Books Committee, one of the more than 40 Society-wide standing committees. Members of the Books Committee provide technical evaluation of the book. Below is a listing of those who have been most closely involved in the final preparation of this book.

Book Editors

Allan Spivak, Duke Engineering & Services Co., Los Angeles
John E. Killough, Landmark Graphics Corp., Houston

Books Committee (2001)

Hans Juvkam-Wold, Texas A&M U., College Station, Texas, Chairman
J. Ben Bloys, Texaco Upstream Technology, Houston
Anil Chopra, PetroTel Inc., Plano, Texas
Rafael Guzman, BP Exploration Colombia Ltd., Bogota, Colombia
William C. Miller, Consultant, Houston
Susan Peterson, J Murtha & Assocs., Houston
Cem Sarica, The Pennsylvania State U., University Park, Pennsylvania
Arlie M. Skov, Arlie M. Skov Inc., Santa Barbara, California
Sally Thomas, Conoco Inc., Houston

Basic Applied Reservoir Simulation

Turgay Ertekin
George E. Trimble Chair
Professor of Petroleum and Natural Gas Engineering
The Pennsylvania State U.

Jamal H. Abou-Kassem
Professor of Petroleum Engineering
United Arab Emirates U.

Gregory R. King
Petroleum Engineering Adviser
Chevron Overseas Petroleum Inc.

Henry L. Doherty Memorial Fund of AIME
Society of Petroleum Engineers
Richardson, Texas USA

Printed in the United States of America.

ISBN 978-1-55563-089-8

Society of Petroleum Engineers
222 Palisades Creek Drive
Richardson, TX 75080-2040 USA

http://store.spe.org/
books@spe.org
1.972.952.9393

Dedication

This book is dedicated to our mentors and friends,
C. Drew Stahl and S.M. Farouq Ali.

Introduction

High-speed computers have now been part of our lives, in so many different ways, for almost half a century. The electronic explosion that we have been witnessing over the past two decades has transformed reservoir simulation from a somewhat esoteric approach to a practical toolbox of immense importance. With the use of the tools from this toolbox, today's engineering community has an opportunity to better understand not only the intricacies of fluid-flow dynamics in increasingly complex reservoirs, but also the characteristics of fluid-flow dynamics in wellbores, flow patterns developing within the immediate vicinity of perforations, the interaction of vertical, slanted, horizontal, and multilateral wells and the reservoir, and the complexities of reservoir characterization. These areas represent only a small portion of a list that includes some challenging issues playing critical roles in the optimum development of hydrocarbon reservoirs, and in the optimized implementation of capital-intensive projects that can be investigated with numerical simulation.

The conduct of a reservoir-simulation study should not simply imply making a few computer runs and writing a report based on the computer-generated results. In our view, the conduct of a simulation study covers much more. First, the simulation engineer must set the objectives for the study. Envisaging a judicious set of objectives will assist the simulation engineer in selecting an adequate approach that is in parity with the scope of the study as well as with the characteristics of the reservoir and its fluids. The third step of the process involves the preparation of the input data. The time invested in looking for good-quality data represents time well spent; an internally consistent set of data will save a great deal of time later. The fourth step of the simulation study involves careful planning of computer runs. It is again the simulation engineer's responsibility to ensure that each run conducted does not represent a "shot in the dark." The final step of a simulation study involves the analysis of results and report preparation. An experienced simulation engineer will not subscribe immediately to the results presented within the output files. To avoid becoming a hostage to computer-generated results, it is necessary to ask questions and ponder the implications of those results. Therefore, it is very important to remember that every simulation study carries the signature of the simulation engineer, but not the computing device and the computer code used in the study.

I guess the take-home lesson from it all is that the most important thing for the success of an exhaustive simulation study is not the hardware or software... It's the individuals from different disciplines that you work with. If the people are compatible and can get along, then it will be a successful simulation study. *

Preface

This text is written for senior undergraduate students and first-year graduate students studying petroleum engineering. The text evolved from the courses that we presented in university settings. The examples and exercises presented are from the examinations and homework sets that we prepared over the course of several years. The contents of this book can be taught in three successive courses. In our own teaching experience, we were able to cover various single-phase reservoir simulation topics and applications, included mainly in Chaps. 1 through 8, during a one-semester undergraduate senior-level course. We have followed a similar coverage, in greater depth, in the first graduate-level course. The second graduate-level course dwells mainly on multiphase-flow-simulation problems, as covered in Chap. 9. A third course, which deals mainly with the practical application of reservoir simulation (as covered in Chap. 10), can be given as either an undergraduate senior-level course or as a graduate course to practicing engineers.

Chap. 1 provides an overview of numerical reservoir simulation. In Chap. 2, we present a brief review of some fundamental reservoir engineering concepts as well as reservoir rock and fluid properties that comprise the building blocks of a reservoir simulator. Chap. 3 is written to serve as a refresher in mathematics and presents an introductory treatment of finite-difference calculus as it forms the backbone of reservoir simulation. In this chapter, we also hope to establish a bridge between mathematical reasoning and jargon and reservoir-engineering concepts. In Chap. 4, rectangular and cylindrical coordinate systems are introduced and various forms of the single-phase flow equations are developed. In Chap. 5, protocols used in obtaining the finite-difference analogs of linear-flow equations are discussed. Chap. 6 introduces various well models and their coupling to the reservoir-flow equations. Some direct and iterative algorithmic protocols, used in solving linear-difference equations presented in their increased rigor, are discussed in Chap. 7. In Chap. 8, transmissibility groups are defined and coefficient matrices for incompressible, slightly compressible, and compressible flow problems are formed. After solving the system of equations, incremental and cumulative material-balance checks are introduced as internal checks that monitor the accuracy level of the solutions generated. Chap. 9, in its entirety, is devoted to multiphase flow and its simulation. In this chapter, procedures and algorithms introduced in the first eight chapters are generalized so that they become applicable to multiphase-flow problems. In Chap. 10, our intent is to bring the practical aspects of reservoir simulation to the forefront. Topics such as data analysis, model construction, history matching, and forecasting are discussed. Finally, Chap. 11 ties the reservoir simulation equations back to classical reservoir engineering approaches and shows that the latter are simply the subsets of the former. The book concludes with three appendices. Appendix A provides a thorough treatment of interpolation techniques that are often used in reservoir simulation for data handling. Appendix B shows the similarities between the single-phase and multiphase flow problems at the level of the coefficient matrices generated by the finite-difference representation. Appendix C presents a brief overview of the architectures of scalar, vector, and parallel processors.

Our discussion of the topical material in each chapter typically concludes with a section identified as "Chapter Project." Starting with Chap. 1, these sections provide a large field-scale example. In this way, we are able to construct a field example throughout the book. As the reader progresses through the chapters of the book, the chapter projects will provide an opportunity to apply some of the salient topics discussed in each chapter in a more realistic setting. Furthermore, the discussions and results provided through this "marching" example can be used as benchmark solutions if the reader is engaged in reservoir simulator development.

* Adapted from astronaut Shannon Lucid's statement upon her return to earth after 6 months aboard Russia's Mir space station. Her original statement reads, "I guess the take-home lesson from it all is that the most important thing for the success of a long-duration space flight is not the hardware... It's the people you fly with. If the people are compatible and can get along, then it will be a great flight."

Throughout the book, numerous examples that have been specifically designed to be solved by hand calculations are dispersed. With these examples, our goal is to create an opportunity for the reader to better and more effectively understand some of the fine details of reservoir simulation. The additional exercises are designed to redrill basics and improve the reader's understanding as well as to test their innovation for more difficult problems.

When we started this book, we neither wanted to produce a handbook on reservoir simulation, nor did we envisage how to write a user's manual that comes together with a simulation package. Our goal was to create a textbook that would help in breaking the ice between neophyte simulation students (or engineers) and the mathematical nature of reservoir simulation. In our simulation courses, we always draw an analogy between developing a reservoir model and raising a child. The time and effort expended during the development phase of a simulator would determine our expectations for the simulator. We hope that the readership of this book will acquire basic understanding of the mechanics involved in developing and applying reservoir simulators. In our classrooms, we have always thought that students who go through the rigor of developing a reservoir simulator, even a simple one, would develop a much better appreciation for the strengths and weaknesses of the tool. Thus, even if they are confronted with the request of only implementation of a predeveloped simulation package (not its modification), they will be able to demonstrate that they are much more informed and confident users.

In this book the reader will find that our approach is to proceed through the various stages of model development so that solutions to the problems in increasingly more complicated domains can be sought. In this way, we create opportunities for the treatment and discussion of more sophisticated procedures and algorithms. Over the years, for pedagogical reasons, we have found the modeling "from the bottom up" approach to be effective in a classroom environment. We hope that the readers of this book will agree with our philosophy.

We would like to close this preface with. a quotation from *Calculus Made Easy* by Silvanus P. Thompson:**

Considering how many fools can calculate, it is surprising that it should be taught either a difficult or a tedious task for any other fool to learn how to master the same tricks. Some calculus tricks are quite easy. Some are enormously difficult. The fools who write the textbooks of advanced mathematics—and they are most clever fools—seldom take the trouble to show you how easy the calculations are. On the contrary, they seem to desire to impress you with their tremendous cleverness by going about it in the most difficult way. Being myself a remarkably stupid fellow, I have had to unteach myself the difficulties, and now beg to present to my fellow fools the parts that are not hard. Master these thoroughly, and the rest will follow. What one fool can do, another can.

Turgay Ertekin
Jamal H. Abou-Kassem
Gregory R. King

**Thompson, S.P. and Martin Gardner, M.: *Calculus Made Easy*, St. Martin's Press, New York City (1998) 38. The original edition of *Calculus Made Easy* was written by Silvanus P. Thompson and published in 1910, with subsequent editions in 1914 and 1946.

Acknowledgments

We have enjoyed the pleasure of teaching the material covered in this text to students at The Pennsylvania State U. and the United Arab Emirates U. for more than two decades. We gratefully acknowledge their patience, suggestions, and comments, all of which have been instrumental in bringing this book to reality.

During the writing of this book, we have benefited from the kind assistance of many colleagues and friends. First, we would like to thank Peggy L. Conrad and Timothy E. Kohler for their most skillful typing and for designing the page layouts of the original draft of the manuscript from our almost illegible writings. We are also grateful to Connie DiAndreth and Mohammed Safargar for their assistance in typing several sections of the manuscript at various stages of revision. Special thanks are due to Nor Azlan Nordin, who drew most of the artwork. We are indebted to Y. Serdar Dogulu, who helped us structure the Chapter Project sections of the book during the summer of 1995. We express our gratitude to our colleagues S. Tanju Obut, Kemal Anbarci, and Adwait Chawathe for their multitude of suggestions and critiques. We are indebted to Gabriel Falade for his review of the first six chapters of the book.

We are also indebted to our SPE Books Committee editors Allan Spivak and John E. Killough for their critical review of the manuscript. We extend our acknowledgments to James R. Gilman for his suggestions as the symbols editor. Bringing this book to reality took almost a decade, during which we have worked with several SPE editors. We value the fine work and cooperation of Flora Cohen, Carla Atwal, Nikki Blair, and Amanda Stites throughout the publication process.

Finally, but most deeply, we thank all of our "teachers," from whom we have learned all that we know, and our family members, who walked with us through the tortuous paths of writing a book. Without their constant encouragement, support, and most importantly their tolerance, the journey never would have ended.

Contents

Chapter 1
Introduction

1.1 Introduction

Reservoir simulation combines physics, mathematics, reservoir engineering, and computer programming to develop a tool for predicting hydrocarbon-reservoir performance under various operating conditions. This book is limited to the basics of this subject and is aimed at developing understanding of and insight into the mechanics of this powerful tool. Chap. 1 presents a review of the prediction techniques available to petroleum engineers, with an emphasis on practical limitations. To develop appreciation for the role of reservoir simulation in optimizing the development and production of hydrocarbon resources, the chapter also presents an overview of reservoir simulation and its applications in hydrocarbon recovery.

1.2 The Need for Reservoir Simulation

The need for reservoir simulation stems from the requirement for petroleum engineers to obtain accurate performance predictions for a hydrocarbon reservoir under different operating conditions. This need arises from the fact that in a hydrocarbon-recovery project (which may involve a capital investment of hundreds of millions of dollars), the risk associated with the selected development plan must be assessed and minimized. Factors contributing to this risk include the complexity of the reservoir because of heterogeneous and anisotropic rock properties; regional variations of fluid properties and relative permeability characteristics; the complexity of the hydrocarbon-recovery mechanisms; and the applicability of other predictive methods with limitations that may make them inappropriate. The first three factors are beyond the engineer's control; they are taken into consideration in reservoir simulation through the generality of input data built into reservoir-simulation models and the availability of simulators for various enhanced-oil-recovery techniques. The fourth factor can be controlled through proper use of sound engineering practices and judicious use of reservoir simulation.

1.3 Traditional Modeling Approaches

Traditional methods of forecasting reservoir performance generally can be divided into three categories: analogical methods, experimental methods, and mathematical methods. Analogical methods use properties of mature reservoirs that are either geographically or petrophysically similar to the target reservoir to attempt to predict reservoir performance of a target zone or reservoir. Experimental methods measure physical properties (such as rates, pressures, or saturations) in laboratory models and scale these results to the entire hydrocarbon accumulation. Finally, mathematical methods use equations to predict reservoir performance. The remaining sections of this chapter provide more detailed discussions of these methods.

1.3.1 Analogical Methods. Before drilling, when limited or no data are available, the only method reservoir engineers can use to perform economic analysis is that of analogy. In this method, reservoirs in the same geologic basin or province or reservoirs with similar petrophysical properties are used to predict the performance of the target reservoir. This method can be used to estimate recovery factors, initial production rates, decline rates, well spacing, and recovery mechanisms. The analogical method can yield reliable results when two similar reservoirs are compared and similar development strategies are used. The method suffers, however, if different development strategies are considered. In addition, "what-if" sensitivities cannot be investigated.

One form of analogy, the staged field trial, provides the most reliable predictions for secondary- and tertiary-recovery operations. In this method, representative well patterns in a field that is a candidate for secondary or tertiary recovery are converted to the new process and the production performance is monitored. The results of the field trial, which may take 1 or 2 years to obtain, are applied to the remaining well patterns, and field performance can be predicted. Managements are generally confident with decisions made on the basis of results of a staged field test.

1.3.2 Experimental Methods. Experimental methods, both analog and physical, play a key role in understanding petroleum reservoirs. While analog models are seldom used today, physical models in the form of corefloods, sandpacks, and slim tubes are run often.

Analog Models. Analog models are rarely used in modern reservoir studies, but two points about them are worthy of discussion. First, from a historical point of view, analog models were important in early studies, particularly in incorporating sweep efficiencies into waterflood calculations. Second, the difference between resistance-capacitance (RC) networks and potentiometric models illustrates the difference between discrete and continuous models.

Analog models use similarities between the phenomenon of fluid flow through porous media and other physical phenomena (such as those **Table 1.1** shows) to simulate reservoir performance. Analog models based on the governing equations listed in the table are built to represent the reservoir, and the appropriate quantities (those representing pressure and flow rate) are measured. These quantities can be translated through the governing equations into their porous-medium analogs. Three analog methods—RC networks, potentiometric models, and the Hele-Shaw[1] models—are discussed next.

TABLE 1.1—PHYSICAL PHENOMENA ANALOGOUS TO FLUID FLOW THROUGH POROUS MEDIA				
Phenomenon	Fluid Flow Through Porous Media	Fluid Flow Through Parallel Plates	Electricity Flow Through Circuitry	Heat Flow by Conduction
Governing equation	Darcy's law* $q=\frac{\beta_c kA}{\mu}\frac{\Delta p}{\Delta L}$	Hagen-Poiseuille law $q=\frac{w^2A}{12a_c\mu}\frac{\Delta p}{\Delta L}$	Ohm's law, $I=(1/R)\Delta E$	Fourier's law, $Q=\frac{KA\Delta T}{\Delta L}$
Properties	Volumetric rate, q	Volumetric rate, q	Current, I	Heat flow rate, Q
	Transmissibility, $\frac{\beta_c kA}{\mu\Delta L}$	Hydraulic conductance, $\frac{w^2A}{12a_c\mu\Delta L}$	Electrical conductance, $1/R$	Thermal conductance, $\frac{KA}{\Delta L}$
	Fluid mobility, $\frac{\beta_c k}{\mu}$	Hydraulic conductivity, $\frac{w^2}{12a_c\mu}$	Electrical conductivity,** $1/r$	Thermal conductivity, K
	Pressure, p	Pressure, p	Voltage, E	Temperature, T

*Horizontal flow.
** $R=\frac{r\Delta L}{A}$

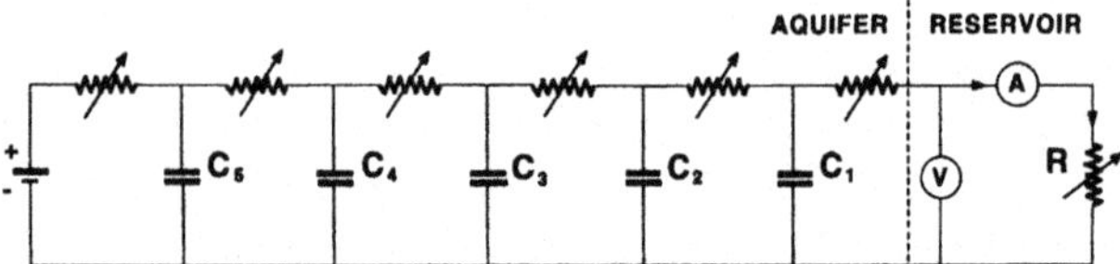

Fig. 1.1—Electric-circuit analog for a simple hydrocarbon reservoir/aquifer system.[3] (C_1 through C_5 = capacitors; R = resistor; A = ampmeter; and V = voltmeter.)

RC networks use the analogy between fluid flow through porous media and electrical flow to model reservoir performance. Bruce[2] introduced this method to the petroleum industry to simulate the unsteady-state performance of undersaturated oil reservoirs under waterdrive. **Fig 1.1** shows the RC network for this problem. In these models, capacitance is used to model fluid storage at a point in space, while resistance is used to model the transmissibilities between points. Capacitor discharge represents the unsteady-state behavior of the reservoir in accordance with the properties listed in Table 1.1. As a final note on RC networks, although these circuits simulate unsteady-state behavior (and, therefore, may represent reservoirs undergoing primary depletion), they are discrete models. That is, the capacitors represent the storage at discrete points in the reservoir.

A continuous form of the electrical analog is the potentiometer. A potentiometer is a scaled model of a reservoir or well pattern constructed with a continuous electrical conducting material. Voltages are applied at wellsites and voltage measurements can be made at any point within the model. This is in contrast to the RC circuit, where measurements can be made at only discrete points in the reservoir. A second difference between RC networks and potentiometers is that potentiometers can simulate only steady-state flow. Most early studies on sweep efficiencies of waterflood patterns were conducted on models like that depicted in **Fig. 1.2**.

In general, electrical analog models must be custom built for individual reservoirs, making them very difficult to adapt to other reservoirs. The discrete RC-network models also suffer from inadvertent malfunction of electrical components (capacitors, meters, resistors) and the huge space they usually occupy (several rooms). Aside from these deficiencies, these analogs are limited to modeling single-phase flow in porous media or, at best, two-phase flow with a unit mobility ratio.

The Hele-Shaw[1] model is an analog model that allows for nonunit mobility ratios. Hele-Shaw models use the analogy between fluid flow through porous media and fluid flow between parallel plates to simulate the behavior of regular pattern elements in secondary- and tertiary-recovery operations. These models are constructed with two transparent plates spaced at a uniform distance from each other. The gap between the plates is filled with the fluid to be displaced, while the displacing fluid is introduced at the injection wellsites. The sweep efficiencies of the reservoir patterns are then determined visually.

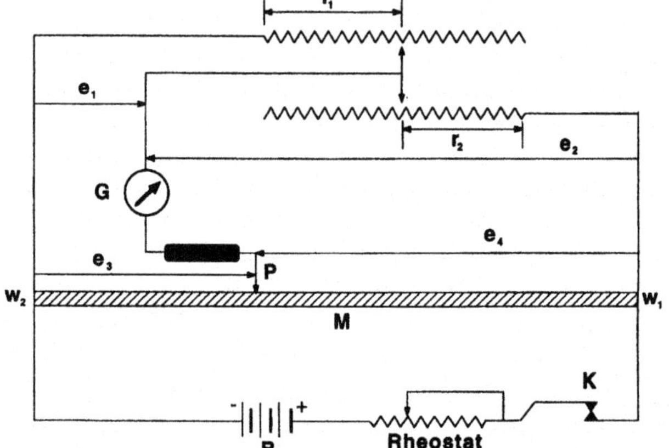

Fig. 1.2—Electrical circuit for determining the potential distributions in 2D flow systems.[4] (B = battery; r_1 and r_2 = resistors; G = galvanometer; e_1 through e_4 = potential drops; M = potentiometer; w_1 and w_2 = electrodes representing the injectors and producers; P = exploring electrode; and K = key.)

Physical Models. As opposed to analog models, physical models are used to make direct measurements of flow properties in porous media. Two types of physical models are in use in the petroleum industry. The first does not account for the flow geometry occurring in the reservoir. Coreflood experiments fall into this category. These experiments, generally run on linear cores, are probably the most common physical models used in the oil industry today. They are run on virtually every oil and gas field to determine reservoir properties, such as porosity and permeability, and to establish mechanisms of oil recovery. One detrimental feature of these models is that the experiments are conducted at a scale that is not representative of actual reservoir scale. Consequently, the results of these experiments must be scaled up to more representative scales. Other physical models that fall into this category include slim tubes and sandpacks.

The second type of physical model uses geometrical-, mechanical-, and thermal-similarity concepts. That is, the areal geometry, thickness, porosity, and permeability of the model and the fluid properties are scaled so that the shape and dimensions of the model (as well as the ratios of active forces in the model) are the same as those in the reservoir. The performance of this type of scaled model reflects that of the reservoir. One example is Sobocinski and Cornelius's[5] single-well coning model (**Fig. 1.3**). This type of model can determine critical coning rates, water-breakthrough times, and post-breakthrough water cuts. Note, however, that, in reservoir-engineering problems, it is generally impossible to scale all physical characteristics of the reservoir, so the use of truly scaled models is very limited. Adequately

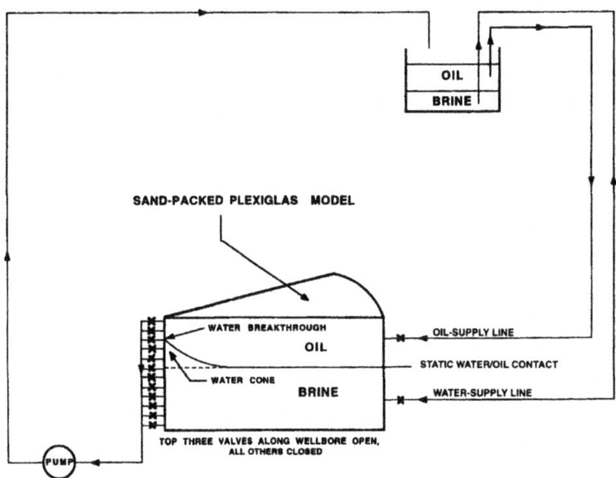

Fig. 1.3—A laboratory water-coning model.[5]

scaled models, in which only the most important characteristics are considered in the scaling process, are used instead.

1.3.3 Mathematical Methods. Mathematical models are probably the methods used most commonly by modern petroleum engineers. These models include material-balance, decline-curve, statistical, and analytical (well-test) methods. Hand calculations or graphical procedures are generally sufficient when these methods are used; however, with the proliferation of personal computers, many software packages that perform these tasks are available. The following sections focus on the theoretical bases and practical limitations of each of these methods, and Chap. 11 demonstrates the relationship between these models and numerical reservoir simulation.

Material-Balance Equations. The classic material-balance equation, or tank model, is a mathematical representation of reservoir or drainage volume. This model's basic principle is the conservation of mass: that the amount of material (gas, oil, or water) remaining in the reservoir after a production interval is equal to the amount of material originally in the reservoir minus the amount of material removed from the reservoir (because of production), plus the amount of material added to the reservoir (because of injection and encroachment). The material-balance method is simply an inventory of all fluids entering, leaving, and remaining in the reservoir. The literature has presented many forms of the material-balance equation, all of which can be derived from a single, generalized form.

Table 1.2 shows common forms of the generalized material-balance equation, illustrating that the material-balance equation contains much of the physics (in the form of drive mechanisms) that governs production from petroleum reservoirs. The reliability of material-balance analysis, however, depends on the accuracy of available data and the degree to which the underlying assumptions are met. The material-balance equation does not take into consideration spatial variations of rock and fluid properties, hydrodynamics of fluid flow in the porous media, fluid segregation, geometrical configuration of the reservoir, location of wells, or rate of production of various fluids. It also assumes that the pressure/volume/temperature (PVT) data used in the material-balance equation are obtained with the same gas-liberation process (flash vs. differential) that is active in the reservoir. The material-balance equation is also sensitive to inaccuracies in measured reservoir pressure; the model breaks down when no appreciable decline occurs in reservoir pressure, as in pressure-maintenance operations.

Decline-Curve Analysis. One of three mathematical forms—exponential, hyperbolic, and harmonic decline[7,8]—can often describe the rate of oil-production decline. The general form of the decline-curve equation is

TABLE 1.2—MATERIAL-BALANCE EQUATIONS FOR SPECIFIC APPLICATIONS.[6]

Reservoir Type	Material-Balance Equation	Unknowns
Oil reservoir with gas cap		
Active waterdrive	$N=\dfrac{N_p\left[B_t+B_g\left(R_p-R_{si}\right)\right]-\left(W_e-W_p\right)}{mB_{oi}\left(\dfrac{B_g}{B_{gi}}-1\right)+\left(B_t-B_{oi}\right)}$	N, W_e, m
No active waterdrive ($W_e=0$)	$N=\dfrac{N_p\left[B_t+B_g\left(R_p-R_{si}\right)\right]+W_p}{mB_{oi}\left(\dfrac{B_g}{B_{gi}}-1\right)+\left(B_t-B_{oi}\right)}$	N, m
Initially undersaturated oil reservoir ($m=0$); active waterdrive		
Above bubblepoint	$N=\dfrac{\left[N_p\left(1+\Delta p_R c_o\right)-\dfrac{W_e-W_p}{B_{oi}}\right]\left(1-S_{wi}\right)}{\Delta p_R\left[c_o+c_R-S_{wi}\left(c_o-c_w\right)\right]}$	N, W_e
Below bubblepoint	$N=\dfrac{N_p\left[B_t+B_g\left(R_p-R_{si}\right)\right]-\left(W_e-W_p\right)}{B_t-B_{oi}}$	N, W_e
Initially undersaturated oil reservoir ($m=0$); no active waterdrive ($W_e=0$)		
Above bubblepoint	$N=\dfrac{\left[N_p\left(1+\Delta p_R c_o\right)+\dfrac{W_p}{B_{oi}}\right]\left(1-S_{wi}\right)}{\Delta p_R\left[c_o+c_R-S_{wi}\left(c_o-c_w\right)\right]}$	N
Below bubblepoint	$N=\dfrac{N_p\left[B_t+B_g\left(R_p-R_{si}\right)\right]+W_p}{B_t-B_{oi}}$	N
Gas reservoir; active waterdrive	$G=\dfrac{G_pB_g-\left(W_e-W_p\right)}{B_g-B_{gi}}$	G, W_e
Gas reservoir; no active waterdrive ($W_e=0$)	$G=\dfrac{G_pB_g+W_p}{B_g-B_{gi}}$	G

TABLE 1.3—FORMS OF DECLINE-CURVE EQUATION.[7,8]

Decline Type	Exponential Decline	Hyperbolic Decline	Harmonic Decline
Basic characteristic	Decline constant, $b=0$	Decline proportional to a fractional power (b) of the production rate, $0<b<1$	Decline proportional to production rate, $b=1$
	$D = Kq^o = -\frac{dq/dt}{q}$	$D = Kq^b = -\frac{dq/dt}{q}$ for initial conditions,	$D = Kq^1 = -\frac{dq/dt}{q}$ for initial conditions,
	$K=D$	$K = \frac{D_i}{q_i^b}$	$K = \frac{D_i}{q_i}$
	$\int_o^t D dt = -\int_{q_i}^q \frac{dq}{q}$	$\int_o^t \frac{D_i}{q_i^b} dt = -\int_{q_i}^q \frac{dq}{q^{b+1}}$	$\int_o^t \frac{D_i}{q_i} dt = -\int_{q_i}^q \frac{dq}{q^2}$
	$-Dt = \log_e \frac{q}{q_i}$	$\frac{bD_i t}{q_i^b} = q^{-b} - q_i^{-b}$	$\frac{D_i t}{q_i} = \frac{1}{q} - \frac{1}{q_i}$
Rate/time relationship	$q = q_i e^{-Dt}$	$q = q_i\left(1 + bD_i t\right)^{-(1/b)}$	$q = q_i\left(1 + D_i t\right)^{-1}$
	$N_p = \int_o^t q dt = \int_o^t q_i e^{-Dt} dt$	$N_p = \int_o^t q dt = \int_o^t q_i\left(1 + bD_i t\right)^{-(1/b)} dt$	$N_p = \int_o^t q dt = \int_o^t q_i\left(1 + D_i t\right)^{-1} dt$
	$N_p = \frac{q_i - qe^{-Dt}}{D}$	$N_p = \frac{q_i}{(b-1)D_i}\left[\left(1 + bD_i t\right)^{\frac{b-1}{b}} - 1\right]$	$N_p = \frac{q_i}{D_i}\left[\log_e\left(1 + D_i t\right)\right]$
	Substitute from rate/time equation, $q_i e^{-Dt} = q$, to find	Substitute from rate/time equation, $\left(1 + bD_i t\right) = \left(\frac{q_i}{q}\right)^b$, to find	Substitute from rate/time equation, $\left(1 + D_i t\right) = \frac{q_i}{q}$, to find
Rate-cumulative relationship	$N_p = \frac{q_i - q}{D}$	$N_p = \frac{q_i^b}{(1-b)D_i}\left(q_i^{1-b} - q^{1-b}\right)$	$N_p = \frac{q_i}{D_i}\log_e\frac{q_i}{q}$

$$D = Kq^b = -(dq/dt)/q, \qquad (1.1)$$

where $b=0$ for exponential decline, $0<b<1$ for hyperbolic decline, $b=1$ for harmonic decline, and $K=D_i/q_i^b$.

In decline-curve analysis, historical production data are matched to the appropriate rate/time equation resulting from Eq. 1.1 (see **Table 1.3**). Once a decline model has been selected, historical data are matched by selecting decline parameters, D_i and b, that minimize the error (usually the least-squares error) between the data and the rate/time equation. Extrapolating the historical data into the future by use of the matched equation allows predictions to be made. Other common extrapolation techniques that do not fit Eq. 1.1 include the logarithm of water/oil ratio vs. cumulative oil production and x plots.[9]

The principal assumption of any extrapolation technique is that all processes occurring in the past will continue in the future. Therefore, it is a very powerful technique for reservoir-performance prediction when operational practices are not expected to change in the future. If operational practices will change, decline-curve analysis cannot be used. Consequently, decline-curve analysis cannot be used for "what-if" analyses.

Statistical Approach. The statistical approach uses empirical correlations that are statistically derived by use of the past performance of numerous reservoirs to predict the future performance of others. This approach, therefore, can be considered a formal extension of the analogical method (Sec. 1.3.1). A correlation is derived with data from mature reservoirs located in the same region (e.g., Texas or California), with the same lithology (e.g., sandstone or carbonate), and operating under the same driving mechanism (e.g., waterdrive or solution-gas drive). For example, Guthrie and Greenberger[10] presented an oil-recovery-factor correlation as a function of permeability, porosity, formation thickness, oil viscosity, and initial water saturation for sandstone reservoirs that were producing (wholly or partially) under waterdrive conditions. **Table 1.4** lists several examples of empirical correlations based on statistical analysis.

For an empirical correlation to be used with confidence, reservoir properties must be within the limits of the regression database used to develop such a correlation. Statistical correlations may give a reasonably accurate estimate for a reservoir as a whole, but the same correlations may produce unrealistic estimates when applied to a particular lease or portion of a reservoir because of fluid migration within the reservoir. Forecasting errors with these techniques can often be as high as 20 to 50%. In addition, these correlations can be used only to estimate the ultimate recovery and not to develop a rate/time relationship.

Analytical Methods. Analytical methods are based on the exact solutions of theoretically derived models. Pressure-transient analysis and Buckley-Leverett analysis[16] are examples of analytical models. The derivation of these models preserves the physical description of the processes occurring in the reservoir but often results in very complex equations that, in general, cannot be solved with current mathematical procedures. To solve these equations analytically, simplifying assumptions must be applied to reduce the complexity of the model. Consequently, analytical methods represent exact solutions to simplified problems. The simplifying assumptions used in pressure-transient analysis include horizontal reservoir, uniform thickness, single-phase flow, small pressure gradients, and laminar flow conditions, while the simplifying assumptions used in Buckley-Leverett analysis include incompressible linear flow, negligible capillary and gravity effects, and voidage-balanced production.

Although these assumptions must be applied for mathematical solutions, the physics of the problem is preserved, so analytical methods are often used to determine how various parameters affect reservoir performance. Furthermore, these methods provide much of the important data required by simulation studies.

TABLE 1.4—STATISTICAL RELATIONSHIPS IN HYDROCARBON RECOVERY

Empirical Relationship	Comments
$N_p^* = 3244\left[\frac{\phi(1-S_{wi})}{B_{ob}}\right]^{1.1611}\left(\frac{k}{\mu_{ob}}\right)^{0.0979}(S_{wi})^{0.3722}\left(\frac{p_b}{p_a}\right)^{0.1741}$	Solution-gas-drive reservoirs;[11] convert N_p^* to R_o by dividing by the oil-in-place term, $\frac{7758}{100}\left[\frac{\phi(1-S_{wi})}{B_{ob}}\right]$.
or $R_o = 41.815\left[\frac{\phi(1-S_{wi})}{B_{ob}}\right]^{0.1611}\left(\frac{k}{\mu_{ob}}\right)^{0.0979}(S_{wi})^{0.3722}\left(\frac{p_b}{p_a}\right)^{0.1741}$	All equations are valid for production below the bubblepoint pressure.
$N_p^* = 4259\left[\frac{\phi(1-S_{wi})}{B_{oi}}\right]^{1.0422}\left(\frac{k\mu_{wi}}{\mu_{oi}}\right)^{0.077}(S_{wi})^{-0.1903}\left(\frac{p_b}{p_a}\right)^{-0.2159}$	Waterdrive reservoirs;[11] convert N_p^* to R_o by dividing by the oil-in-place term, $\frac{7758}{100}\left[\frac{\phi(1-S_{wi})}{B_{oi}}\right]$.
or $R_o = 54.898\left[\frac{\phi(1-S_{wi})}{B_{oi}}\right]^{0.0422}\left(\frac{k\mu_{wi}}{\mu_{oi}}\right)^{0.077}(S_{wi})^{-0.1903}\left(\frac{p_b}{p_a}\right)^{-0.2159}$	All equations are valid for production from initial conditions.
$N_p^* = 3244\left[\frac{\phi(1-S_{wi})}{B_{ob}}\right]^{1.312}\left(\frac{k}{\mu_{ob}}\right)^{0.0816}(S_{wi})^{0.463}\left(\frac{p_b}{p_a}\right)^{0.249}$	Solution-gas-drive reservoirs;[12] convert N_p^* to R_o by dividing by the oil-in-place term, $\frac{7758}{100}\left[\frac{\phi(1-S_{wi})}{B_{ob}}\right]$.
or $R_o = 41.815\left[\frac{\phi(1-S_{wi})}{B_{ob}}\right]^{0.312}\left(\frac{k}{\mu_{ob}}\right)^{0.0816}(S_{wi})^{0.463}\left(\frac{p_b}{p_a}\right)^{0.249}$	All equations are valid for production below the bubblepoint pressure.
$R_o = 11.4 + 27.2\log_{10}(1000k) + 25.6S_{wi} - 13.6\log_{10}(\mu_o) - 153.8\phi - 0.035h$	Waterdrive and sandstone reservoirs.[10]
$N_p^* = -0.061743 + \frac{143.55}{R_{pi}} + 0.00012184T + 0.0010114(°\text{API})$	Gas-condensate reservoirs;[13] units of N_p^* are STB/RB hydrocarbon pore volume (HCPV).
and $G_p^* = -2229.4 + 148.43\left(\frac{R_{pi}}{100}\right)^{0.2} + \frac{124130}{T} + 21.831(°\text{API}) + 0.26356\,p_s$	All equations are valid for production to an abandonment pressure of 500 psia.
$E_{ABT} = 0.54602036 + \frac{0.03170817}{M} + \frac{0.30222997}{e^M} - 0.00509693M$	Waterflood areal sweep efficiency at breakthrough for a five-spot pattern.
$E_A = E_{ABT} + 0.633\log_{10}(W_i/W_{iBT})$	Waterflood areal sweep efficiency after breakthrough for a five-spot pattern.[14]
$E_{CO_2} = 0.33 - 0.035\,N_c - 4.5\times10^{-5}\mu + 1.6\times10^{-4}p_t + 1.3\times10^{-9}p_t^2 + 4.3\times10^{-2}k - 0.013S_{oi} - 0.69V_{CO_2}$	CO_2 flood efficiency of CO_2 cyclic-stimulation process.[15]

1.4 Reservoir-Simulation Approach

The use of reservoir simulation as a predictive tool is becoming standard in the petroleum industry. Its widespread acceptance can be attributed to advances in computing facilities (particularly the speed of computation and the increase in computer memory/storage); advances in numerical techniques for solving partial-differential equations (PDE's); the generality built into reservoir simulators, which makes them useful in modeling field cases; advances in reservoir-characterization techniques; and the development of increasingly complicated oil-recovery techniques that would otherwise be impossible to analyze. A set of algebraic mathematical equations developed from a set of PDE's with appropriate initial and boundary conditions approximates reservoir behavior in the reservoir-simulation approach. These equations incorporate the most important physical processes taking place in the reservoir system, including, among other things, the flow of fluids partitioned into as many as three phases (oil, water, and gas), and mass transfer between the various phases. The effects of viscous, capillary, and gravity forces on fluid flow are taken into consideration by use of a generalized form of Darcy's law. The advantages of this approach lie in the fact that the least number of simplifying assumptions is used for reservoir heterogeneity, mass transfer between phases, and the forces/mechanisms responsible for flow. In addition, spatial variations of rock properties, fluid properties, and relative permeability characteristics can be represented accurately in a reservoir simulator.

1.4.1 Numerical Models. Numerical models use high-speed computers to solve the mathematical equations describing the physical behavior of the processes in a reservoir to obtain a numerical solution to the reservoir behavior of the field. **Fig. 1.4** depicts the major steps involved in development of a reservoir simulator. In this figure, the formulation process outlines the basic assumptions inherent to the simulator, states these assumptions in precise mathematical terms, and applies them to a control volume in a heterogeneous reservoir. The result of the formulation process is a set of coupled, nonlinear PDE's that describes fluid flow through porous media.

The equations derived during the formulation process, if solved analytically (exactly), would give the pressure, saturation, and production rates as continuous functions of time and location. Because of the nonlinear nature of the equations, analytical techniques cannot be used and solutions must be obtained with numerical (approximate) methods. In contrast to analytical solutions, numerical solutions give the values of pressure and saturation only at discrete points in the reservoir. Discretization is the process of converting the PDE's into algebraic equations. In general, analytical methods provide exact solutions to simplified problems, while numerical methods yield approximate solutions to exact problems.

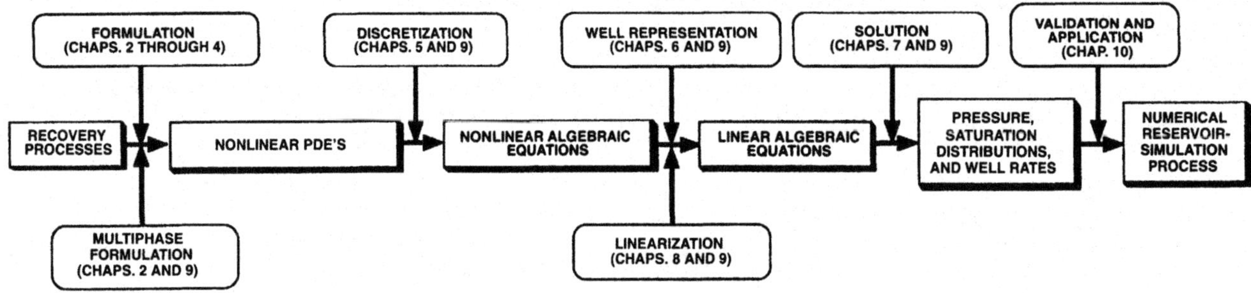

Fig. 1.4—Major steps used to develop reservoir simulators. (Redrawn from Ref. 17.)

Several numerical methods can be used to discretize the fluid-flow equations; however, the most common approach in the oil industry is the finite-difference method. The discretization process results in a system of nonlinear algebraic equations. These equations cannot, in general, be solved with algebraic techniques and must be linearized (put in the form of linear equations) before solutions can be obtained. Once the simulator equations have been linearized, one of several linear-equation-solving techniques can be used to solve them. These techniques fall into two categories: direct methods and iterative methods. In direct methods, an exact solution is obtained (subject to machine round-off error) after a fixed number of mathematical operations. The direct methods discussed in this book are all forms of Gaussian elimination. In iterative methods an initial estimate of the solution is improved successively until it is reasonably close to the exact solution. The number of mathematical operations required to reach this approximate solution is not fixed but depends on the initial estimate, the definition of what is reasonably close (tolerance), and the properties of the system of equations. The iterative-solution methods discussed in this book include Jacoby's method, the Gauss-Seidel method, successive-over-relaxation methods, the alternating-direction implicit procedure, the strongly implicit procedure, and the conjugate gradient method.

1.4.2 Reservoir-Simulator Classification. Reservoir simulators can be classified in several ways. The most common criteria for classifying reservoir simulators are the type of reservoir and reservoir fluids to be simulated and the recovery processes occurring in the subject reservoir. Reservoir simulators can also be classified according to the coordinate system used in the model, the number of dimensions in space, and the number of phases.

Classifications based on reservoir and fluid type may include gas-, black-oil-, and compositional-reservoir simulators. Classifications based on recovery processes include simulators categorized into conventional-recovery, chemical-flood, thermal-recovery, and miscible-displacement simulators. In this book, conventional-recovery simulators and black-oil simulators are synonomous. **Fig. 1.5** shows groupings of specific recovery methods under any of these categories.

Reservoir simulators based on reservoir and fluid descriptions fall into two categories: black-oil and compositional simulators. Black-oil simulators are used in situations where recovery processes are insensitive to compositional changes in the reservoir fluids. In black-oil simulators, mass transfer is assumed to be strictly pressure dependent. In these simulators, the fluid properties B_o, B_g, and R_s govern PVT behavior.

Compositional simulators are used when recovery processes are sensitive to compositional changes. These situations include prima-

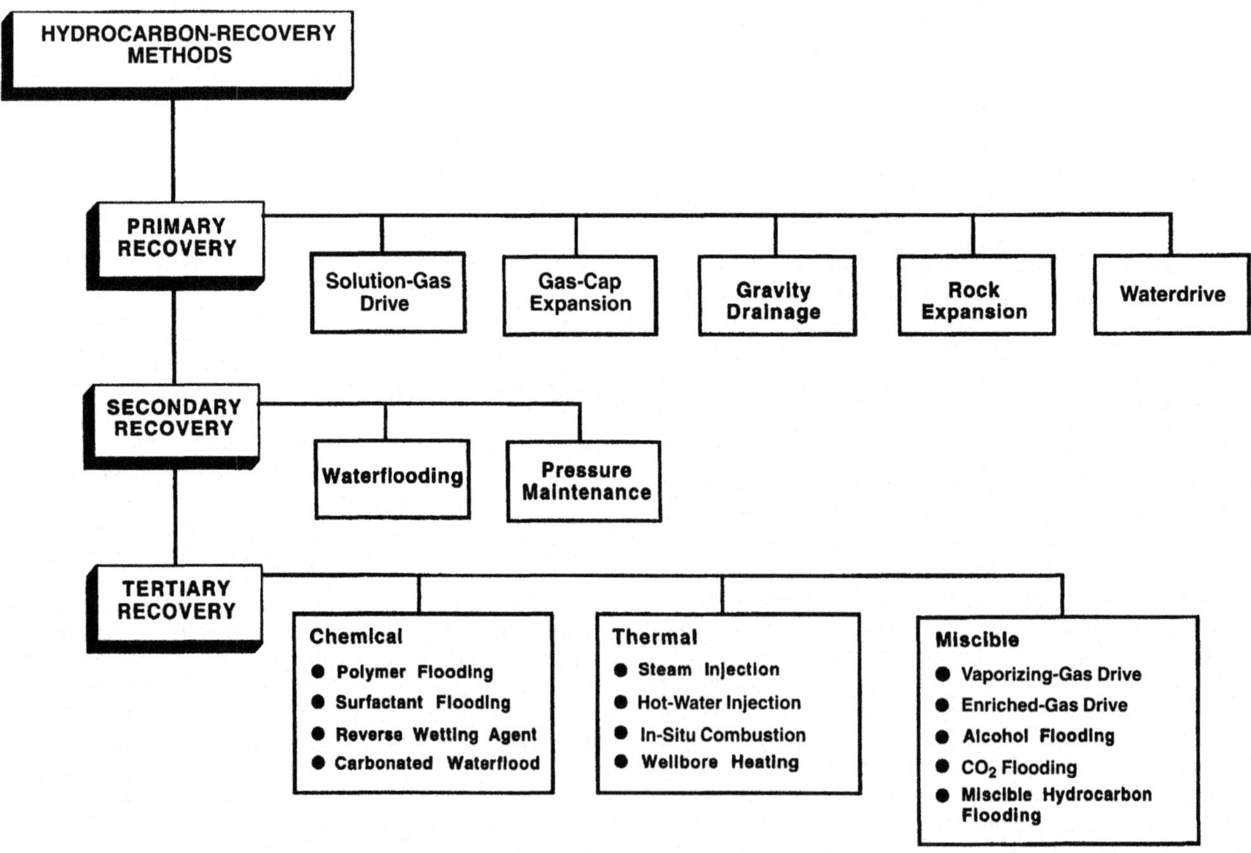

Fig. 1.5—Hydrocarbon-recovery methods.

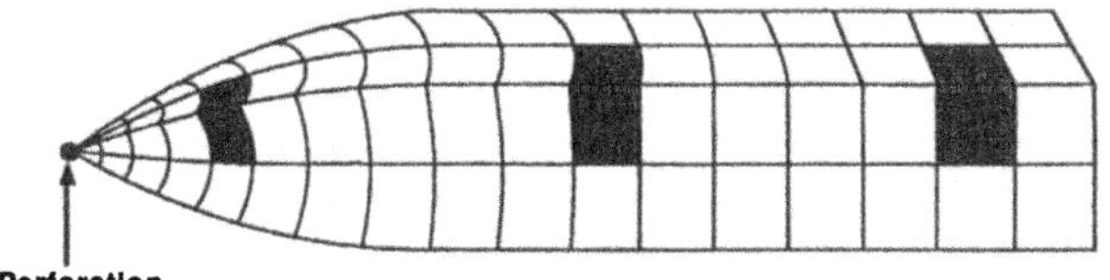

Fig. 1.6—Metamorphosis of flow geometries.

ry depletion of volatile-oil and gas-condensate reservoirs, as well as pressure-maintenance operations in these reservoirs. Also, multiple-contact-miscible processes are generally modeled with compositional simulators. In compositional simulators, a cubic equation of state governs the PVT behavior.

When classifying reservoir simulators by recovery processes, primary-oil-recovery mechanisms, such as solution-gas drive, gas-cap expansion, gravity drainage, and waterdrive, can all be modeled with a conventional or black-oil simulator. In addition, secondary-recovery mechanisms, such as water or gas injection (where mass-transfer effects are negligible), can also be modeled with a black-oil simulator. Chemical-flooding processes, such as polymer or surfactant floods, require a chemical-flooding simulator. These simulators differ from black-oil simulators in that additional conservation equations are used to track the individual chemical species used in the flood. Thermal-recovery processes, such as steamfloods and in-situ-combustion processes, require thermal-recovery simulators for reservoir forecasts. These simulators use an energy-balance equation in addition to the mass-balance equations. Generally, thermal-recovery simulators use a compositional approach. A recent development in reservoir simulation has been the multipurpose reservoir simulator. These simulators generally are developed with the most flexible assumptions and algorithms, so they are capable of modeling all the recovery mechanisms discussed earlier.

Reservoir simulators and their applications can also be classified by their geometry and dimensionality. For example, three-dimensional (3D) simulation models in rectangular coordinates (x,y,z) can be used for full-field applications. Also, two-dimensional (2D) models in rectangular coordinates can be used for areal (x,y) applications or for cross-sectional (x,z) applications. Two-dimensional models in cylindrical coordinates (r,z) can be used for single-well coning applications. Finally, one-dimensional models can be used for applications involving laboratory corefloods.

Although the geometry and dimensionality of simulation models and their traditional applications are listed earlier, no single flow geometry can adequately describe fluid flow in a hydrocarbon reservoir. **Fig. 1.6** shows the changes in flow geometry as oil is produced. Away from the well, fluid flow is nearly linear and rectangular flow is prevalent. As fluids move near a wellbore, the flow geometry distorts to cylindrical flow, so cylindrical coordinates are appropriate. Finally, as the fluids move near individual perforations, spherical flow dominates and spherical coordinates are appropriate. Therefore, whenever a single coordinate system is used, the results will always be approximate.

The use of geometry and dimensionality to classify simulators is not as common as it once was. This is because as the power of computers increased in the late 1960's and early 1970's, most numerical-simulation programs added the capability for 3D problems. Today, all commercial simulators have this capability.

1.4.3 Reservoir-Simulation Application. Reservoir simulation is generally performed in several steps.

1. Set the study objectives. The first step of any successful simulation study is to set clear, achievable objectives. These objectives must be compatible with available data and production history. Objectives are used to set goals, define basic strategy, identify available resources, and determine what is to be learned from the study.

2. Acquire and validate all reservoir data. Once the study objectives have been defined, reservoir and production data are gathered. Only the data required to meet the objectives of the study should be incorporated into the simulation model. Incorporating additional detail that does not add to understanding the objectives leads to overkill.

3. Construct the reservoir model. After the data have been gathered and validated, the simulation model is built. In this step the reservoir is divided into gridblocks, as in **Figs. 1.7 and 1.8**. Formation properties, such as porosity, directional permeabilities, and net-pay thickness, are assigned to these grid cells. The different grid cells can have different reservoir properties; however, reservoir properties are assumed to be homogeneous within a grid cell. Because dif-

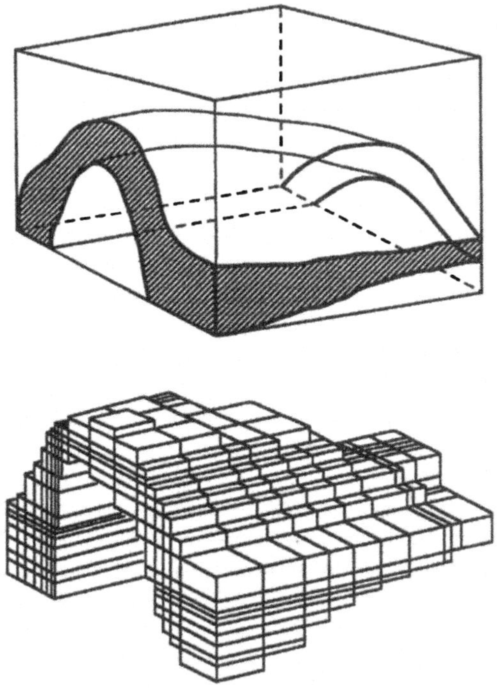

Fig. 1.7—Three-dimensional gridblock arrangement for an anticline.

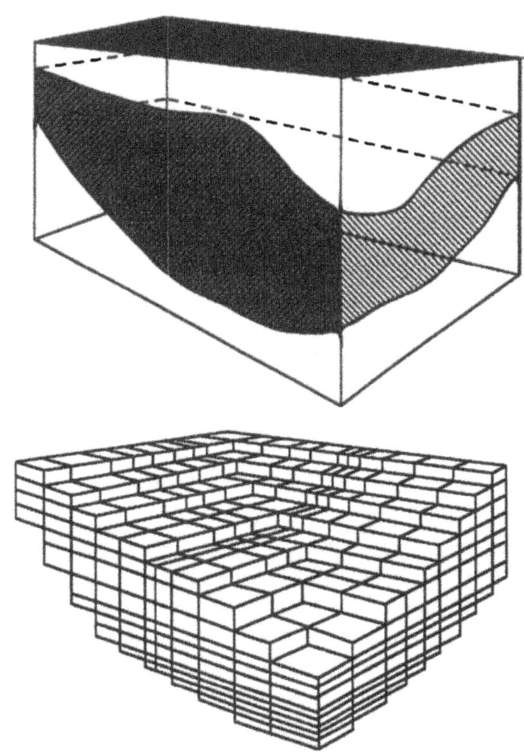

Fig. 1.8—Three-dimensional gridblock arrangement for a blanket sand with varying thickness.

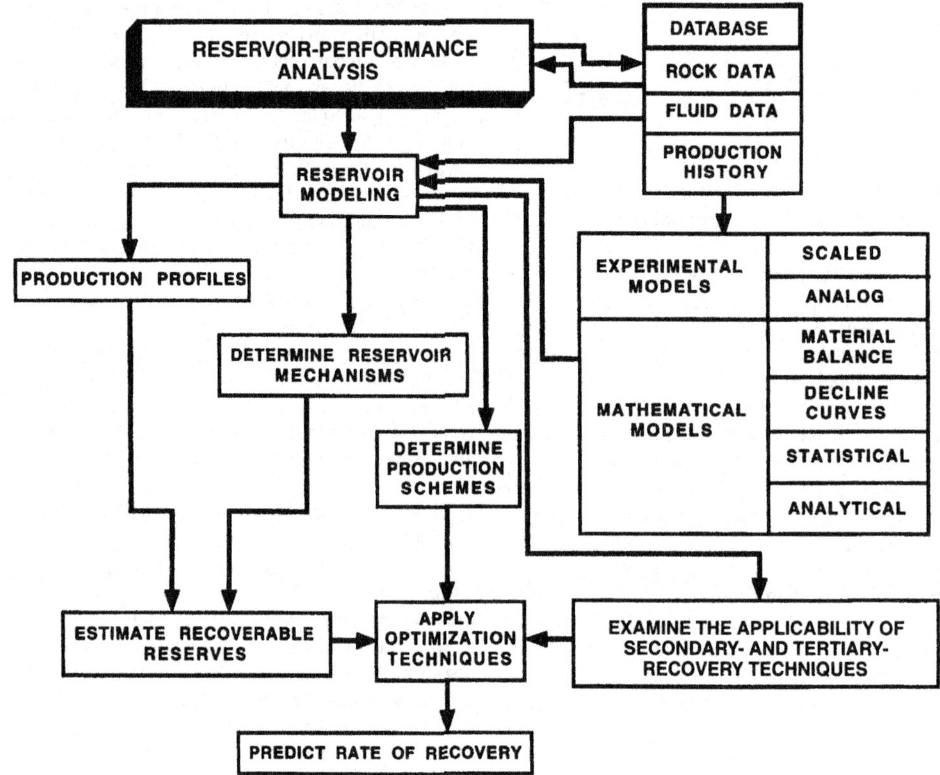

Fig. 1.9—Interaction of methods used to predict reservoir performance.

ferent cells can have different properties, areal and vertical trends in data can be incorporated into the model. At this stage of the study, all data must be properly scaled for the simulation grid.

4. History match the reservoir model. Once the simulation model has been built it must be tuned, or history matched, with available production data because much of the data in a typical simulation model is not known for certain but is the result of engineers' and geologists' interpretations. Although these interpretations are generally the best representation of available data, they are still subjective and may require modifications.

5. Run prediction cases. The final step in the simulation process is the prediction phase, in which various production schemes are evaluated and sensitivity analyses of various production and reservoir parameters are performed.

The main objective of any simulation study is to gain knowledge of the subject reservoir. In most simulation studies, most of the knowledge is gained during the data-gathering, history-matching, and prediction phases. During the data-gathering and history-matching phases, all relevant reservoir data are collected, validated, and synthesized into a coherent field model. This process will inevitably yield information about the reservoir that was unknown before the study. During the prediction phase, questions concerning the subject reservoir can be addressed and most of the study objectives are met.

1.5 Concluding Remarks

Although reservoir simulation is the most comprehensive method of forecasting reservoir performance, it does not replace the classic reservoir-engineering approach. In fact, a properly conducted simulation study will always use results from several classic methods to obtain input to the simulator. **Fig. 1.9** summarizes the intricate interaction of various methods used to predict reservoir performance. For example, during the reservoir-characterization phase of a simulation study, pressure-buildup analysis is the preferred method of obtaining formation permeabilities; and during the history-matching phase, material-balance methods can be used to obtain information about water encroachment and aquifer size.

After reviewing the study objectives, it may even be determined that a simulation study is not warranted because of time, cost, manpower, or machine constraints. The simplest and least-expensive method for meeting the study objectives should always be used. The detailed data required by the reservoir simulator are often unavailable or are uneconomical to obtain. Finally, analog, experimental, and analytical methods are the only methods available to validate a numerical simulator. Without these, we could not confidently use the results generated by a simulation study.

1.6 Chapter Project

Using computer modeling to simulate hydrocarbon-reservoir behavior is an arduous task. This book introduces a variety of topics, including techniques for developing reservoir simulators and procedures for conducting reservoir-simulation studies. Through the book, it will become evident that simulator-development engineers and reservoir engineers conducting modeling studies should possess diverse engineering experience with an understanding of transport phenomena, fluid-flow dynamics in porous media, physics, and advanced mathematics. Furthermore, engineers must be conversant with computers.

To facilitate understanding of presented topics, key chapters will conclude with "Chapter Project" sections that present a large-scale field example. Depending on chapter contents, new data and relevant analyses will be provided, and the project in each chapter will highlight the principles discussed. In this way, a field example will be constructed throughout the book. The goal of this large-scale example is two-fold. First, it will provide a platform from which some of the more salient topics can be reiterated and reinforced. Second, as the results of the analyses (with some intermediate observations) are presented, important information that can be used for benchmarking is provided. In this way, it will be possible for development engineers to test their software using the data presented in this project to check the validity of their simulators.

Fig. 1.10 presents the isopach and structural maps for the project field, which will be referred to as the A-1 reservoir. This reservoir is not a completely hypothetical field. The isopach and the structural maps in Fig. 1.10 are for the Plum Bush Creek field, located in Washington County, Colorado. Some reservoir and fluid data are altered to make the example more compatible with the contents of this book. The isopach and structural maps of the Plum Bush Creek field

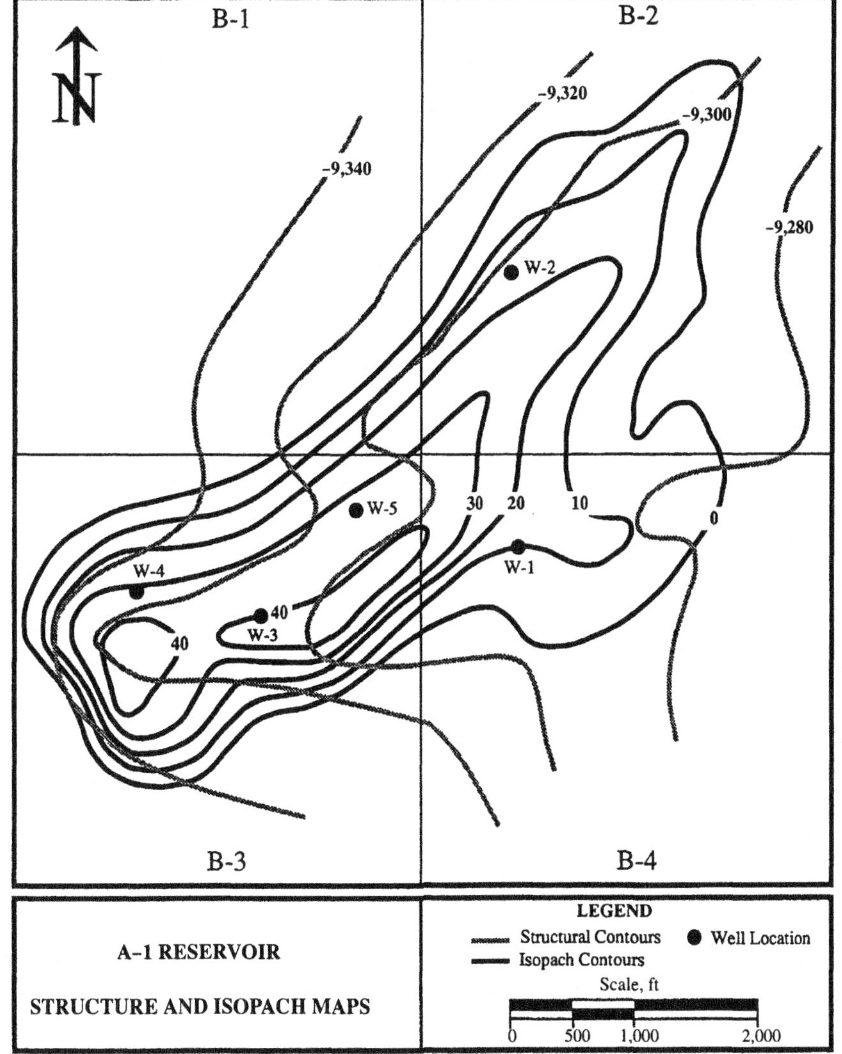

Fig. 1.10—Structural and isopach maps of the A-1 reservoir.

are obtained from Ref. 18. The information on the A-1 reservoir that is available at this stage describes it as a gently west-dipping sandstone reservoir of Cretaceous age. The reservoir rock is a channel sand and the trapping mechanism for the field is a permeability pinchout updip on a slight structural nose.

Exercises

1.1 What are the different ways a reservoir can be modeled?

1.2 What are the differences between a mathematical, a numerical, and a computer model?

1.3 Match the following.

Physical model	Simulator
Conceptual model	Partial-differential equations
Geological model	Material-balance equations
Mathematical model	Laboratory sandpacks
Computer model	Potentiometric model
Analog model	Depositional model
Numerical model	Empirical-correlation equations
Statistical model	Finite-difference equations

1.4 Put the following in sequential order to summarize the basic steps of a simulation study.

Preparing the data
Constructing the geological model
Defining the study objectives
History matching
Analyzing the results
Reporting
Predicting performance

1.5 The equation $q = 2\pi\beta_c hk\Delta p/\mu\log_e(r_e/r_w)$ represents the steady-state radial flow of a fluid in a cylindrical porous medium. What are the analog representations describing the heat and current flows in similar cylindrical systems? Identify the analogous terms and/or groups.

1.6 Comment about the accuracy of the statement "The material-balance equation is considered to be a zero-dimensional model because time dependency is not incorporated into it."

Nomenclature

A = cross-sectional area normal to flow, L^2, ft^2 [m^2]
b = constant in decline-curve equation
B_g = gas formation volume factor (FVF), L^3/L^3, RB/scf [m^3/std m^3]
B_{gi} = gas FVF at initial conditions, L^3/L^3, RB/scf [m^3/std m^3]
B_o = oil FVF, L^3/L^3, RB/STB [m^3/std m^3]
B_{ob} = oil FVF at bubblepoint conditions, L^3/L^3, RB/STB [m^3/std m^3]
B_{oi} = oil FVF at initial conditions, L^3/L^3, RB/STB [m^3/std m^3]
B_t = total (two-phase) FVF, L^3/L^3, RB/STB [m^3/std m^3]
c_o = oil compressibility, Lt^2/m, psi^{-1} [kPa^{-1}]

c_R = reservoir rock compressibility, Lt^2/m, psi^{-1} [kPa^{-1}]
c_w = water compressibility, Lt^2/m, psi^{-1} [kPa^{-1}]
D = decline-rate constant, day^{-1}
D_i = initial decline rate, day^{-1}
e^{-Dt} = exponential decline coefficient, dimensionless
E = voltage, V
E_A = areal sweep efficiency after waterflood breakthrough, dimensionless
E_{ABT} = areal sweep efficiency at waterflood breakthrough, dimensionless
E_{CO_2} = efficiency of CO_2 cyclic-stimulation process
ΔE = voltage difference, V
G = original gas in place, L^3, scf [std m^3]
G_p = cumulative gas production, L^3, scf [std m^3]
G_p^* = cumulative gas production per unit HCPV, L^3/L^3, scf/RB HCPV [std m^3/m^3 HCPV]
h = thickness (general and individual bed), L, ft [m]
I = electrical current, q/t, A
k = permeability, L^2, darcy [μm^2]
K = constant in generalized decline curve
ΔL = segment length, L, ft [m]
m = gas-cap/oil-zone ratio, fraction
N_c = capillary number, dimensionless
N = initial oil in place, L^3, STB [std m^3]
N_p = cumulative oil production, L^3, STB [std m^3]
N_p^* = cumulative oil production per unit volume of reservoir, L^3/L^3, STB/acre-ft [std $m^3/(ha \cdot m)$]
p = pressure, m/Lt^2, psia [kPa]
p_a = abandonment pressure, m/Lt^2, psia [kPa]
p_b = bubblepoint pressure, m/Lt^2, psia [kPa]
p_s = saturation pressure, m/Lt^2, psia [kPa]
p_t = tubinghead pressure, m/Lt^2, psia [kPa]
Δp = pressure difference, m/Lt^2, psi [kPa]
Δp_R = change in reservoir pressure, m/Lt^2, psi [kPa]
q = production rate or flow rate, L^3/t, B/D [m^3/d]
q = production rate or flow rate in hyperbolic decline relationship in Table 1.3, L^3/t, B/D [m^3/d]
q_{oi} = initial oil production rate, L^3/t, STB/D [std m^3/d]
q_i = initial production rate or flow rate in hyperbolic decline relationship in Table 1.3, L^3/t, B/D [m^3/d]
q^o = initial production rate, L^3/t, B/D [m^3/d]
Q = rate of heat transfer, m/t^3T, Btu/hr [kW]
r = distance in the radial direction in cylindrical coordinate system, L, ft [m]
r = electrical resistivity in Table 1.1, mL^4/tq^2, $\Omega \cdot m$
r_e = radius of external boundary, L, ft [m]
r_w = well radius, L, ft [m]
R = electrical resistance, mL^3/tq^2, Ω
R_o = oil-recovery factor, %
R_p = cumulative produced gas/oil ratio, L^3/L^3, scf/STB [std m^3/std m^3]
R_{pi} = producing gas/oil ratio at initial conditions, L^3/L^3, scf/STB [std m^3/std m^3]
R_s = solution-gas/oil ratio, L^3/L^3, scf/STB [std m^3/std m^3]
R_{si} = initial solution-gas/oil ratio, L^3/L^3, scf/STB [std m^3/std m^3]
S_{oi} = initial oil saturation, fraction
S_{wi} = initial water saturation, fraction
t = time, t, days
T = absolute temperature, T, °R [K]
ΔT = temperature difference, T, °R [K]
V_{CO_2} = volume of CO_2 injected per cycle per foot of sand, L^3/(cycle-L), MMscf/cycle-ft [std m^3/(cycle.m)]
w = width, L, ft [m]
W_e = cumulative volume of water influx, L^3, RB [m^3]
W_i = cumulative volume of water injected, L^3, RB [m^3]
W_{iBT} = volume of water injected at breakthrough, L^3, RB [m^3]
W_p = cumulative volume of produced water, L^3, RB [m^3]
x = distance in the x direction in the Cartesian coordinate system, L, ft [m]
y = distance in the y direction in the Cartesian coordinate system, L, ft [m]
z = distance in the z direction in the Cartesian coordinate system, L, ft [m]
α_c = volume conversion factor whose numerical value is given in Table 2.1
β_c = transmissibility conversion factor whose numerical value is given in Table 2.1
Δ = difference operator
μ = viscosity, m/Lt, cp [$Pa \cdot s$]
μ_o = oil viscosity, m/Lt, cp [$Pa \cdot s$]
μ_{ob} = oil viscosity at bubblepoint pressure, m/Lt, cp [$Pa \cdot s$]
μ_{oi} = oil viscosity at initial pressure, m/Lt, cp [$Pa \cdot s$]
μ_{wi} = initial water viscosity, m/Lt, cp [$Pa \cdot s$]
ϕ = porosity, fraction

References

1. Hele-Shaw, H.S.: "Experiments on the Nature of the Surface Resistance in Pipes and on Ships," *Trans.*, Inst. of Naval Architects (1897) **39,** 145.
2. Bruce, W.A.:"An Electrical Device for Analyzing Oil-Reservoir Behavior," *Trans.*, AIME (1943) **157,** 112.
3. Craft, B.C. and Hawkins, M.F.: *Applied Petroleum Reservoir Engineering*, Prentice-Hall Inc., Englewood Cliffs, New Jersey (1959) 236.
4. Muskat, M.: *Flow of Homogeneous Fluids*, McGraw-Hill Book Co. Inc., New York City (1937) (reprinted by Intl. Human Resources Development Corp. in 1982) 575.
5. Sobocinski, D.P. and Cornelius, A.J.: "A Correlation for Predicting Water Coning Time," *JPT* (May 1965) 594; *Trans.*, AIME, **234.**
6. Garb, F.A.: "Oil and Gas Reserves Classification, Estimation, and Evaluation," *JPT* (March 1985) 373.
7. Arps, J.J.: "Analysis of Decline Curves," *Trans.*, AIME (1945) **160,** 228.
8. Arps, J.J. and Smith, A.E.: "Practical Use of Bottom-hole Pressure Build-up Curves," *Drill. & Prod. Prac.* (1949) 155.
9. Ershaghi, I. and Omoregie, O.: "A Method for Extrapolation of Cut vs. Recovery Curves," *JPT* (February 1978) 203.
10. Guthrie, R.K. and Greenberger, M.K.: "The Use of Multiple Correlation Analyses for Interpreting Petroleum-Engineering Data," *Drill. & Prod. Prac.* (1955) 135.
11. Arps, J.J. *et al.*: "Statistical Analysis of Crude Oil Recovery and Recovery Efficiency," Bulletin, D14, American Petroleum Inst., Washington, D.C. (October 1967).
12. "Statistical Analysis of Crude Oil Recovery and Recovery Efficiency,"American Petroleum Inst., Dallas (April 1984).
13. Jacoby, R.H., Koeller, R.C., and Berry, V.J. Jr.: "Effect of Composition and Temperature on Phase Behavior and Depletion Performance of Rich Gas-Condensate Systems," *JPT* (July 1959) 58; *Trans.*, AIME, **216.**
14. Craig, F.F. Jr., Geffen, T.M., and Morse, R.A.: "Oil Recovery Performance of Pattern Gas or Water Injection Operations from Model Tests," *JPT* (January 1955) 7; *Trans.*, AIME, **204.**
15. Patton, J.T., Coats, K.H., and Spence, K.: "Carbon Dioxide Well Stimulation: Part 1—A Parametric Study," *JPT* (August 1982) 1798.
16. Buckley, S. E. and Leverett, M.C.: "Mechanism of Fluid Displacement in Sands," *Trans.*, AIME (1942) **146,** 107.
17. Odeh, A.S.: "An Overview of Mathematical Modeling of the Behavior of Hydrocarbon Reservoirs," *Soc. of Industrial and Applied Mathematics Review* (July 1982) **24,** No. 3, 263.
18. *Oil and Gas Fields of Colorado/Nebraska & Adjacent Areas*, M.C. Crouch III (ed.), Rocky Mountain Assn. of Geologists. Denver, Colorado (1982) **2,** 390.

SI Metric Conversion Factors

acre	× 4.046 873	E − 01	= ha
bbl	× 1.589 873	E − 01	= m^3
ft	× 3.048*	E − 01	= m
ft^2	× 9.290 304*	E − 02	= m^2
ft^3	× 2.831 685	E − 02	= m^3
psi	× 6.894 757	E + 00	= kPa

*Conversion factor is exact.

Chapter 2
Basic Reservoir-Engineering Concepts and Reservoir-Fluid and -Rock Properties

2.1 Introduction

Mathematical modeling of a given system requires understanding of the behavior of the different elements that make up the system under study. In reservoir simulation, this system comprises the reservoir rock and the various fluids (oil, water, and gas) flowing through it. Reservoir-rock properties of interest include those related to the capacity of the rock to transmit and store fluids in its pores. The dependence of fluid properties on primary simulation unknowns (pressure and saturation) is required in black-oil simulation. A thorough understanding of the pressure dependence of fluid densities, viscosities, formation volume factors (FVF's), solution-gas/liquid ratios, and the saturation dependence of relative permeability and capillary pressure is very helpful for both model developers and users.

This chapter discusses rock properties, fluid properties, fluid/rock interactions, basic reservoir-engineering concepts (such as fluid potential, steady- and unsteady-state phenomena, rock heterogeneity and rock anisotropy), and basic reservoir-engineering laws (such as Darcy's law and the law of mass conservation).

2.2 Basic Reservoir-Engineering Concepts

Understanding basic reservoir-engineering concepts for modeling flow problems in porous media is very important. This section includes discussions of fluid-flow potential, Darcy's law, and steady- and unsteady-state phenomena. Capillary pressure and relative permeability and the law of mass conservation are presented in context of their applications to single- and multiphase fluid flow in porous media.

2.2.1 Fluid Potential. In earth sciences other than petroleum engineering (for example, geology or hydrology), fluid potential at a point is defined as the work required by a frictionless process to transport a unit mass of fluid from a state of atmospheric pressure and zero elevation (absolute datum) to the point in question. Defined this way, fluid potential expressed mathematically as the fluid head (h_f) for an incompressible fluid is

$$h_f = \frac{p}{\gamma} + D, \quad \text{(2.1)}$$

where D is positive in the vertical upward direction and

$$\gamma = \gamma_c \rho g \quad \text{(2.2)}$$

is the fluid density in terms of pressure per distance (usually called fluid gravity). In Eq. 2.2, γ_c = gravity conversion factor (**Table 2.1** gives unit definitions). Multiplying both sides of Eq. 2.1 by γ gives

$$\gamma h_f = p + \gamma D. \quad \text{(2.3)}$$

The term (γh_f) has pressure units and is frequently referred to as the datum pressure. In reservoir simulation and petroleum engineering, this term is referred to as fluid potential, Φ, so

$$\Phi = p + \gamma D. \quad \text{(2.4)}$$

In reservoir engineering, an arbitrary and convenient datum (other than the absolute datum) is used as a reference for all reservoir pressures. This arbitrary datum can be sea level or the middle, top, or base of the reservoir. The level of this new datum is not important because flow rate depends on potential gradient (see Sec. 2.2.2) rather than absolute potentials. To demonstrate this point, calculate the potential difference between Points A and B in **Fig. 2.1**. By use of the absolute datum as a reference level, the potentials at Points A and B are given by applying Eq. 2.4 as

$$\Phi_A = p_A + \gamma D_A \quad \text{(2.5)}$$

and $\Phi_B = p_B + \gamma D_B$, $\quad$ (2.6)

then $\Phi_A - \Phi_B = (p_A - p_B) + \gamma(D_A - D_B)$. $\quad$ (2.7)

From Fig. 2.1,

$$(D_B - D_A) = (Z_A - Z_B). \quad \text{(2.8)}$$

Substituting Eq. 2.8 into Eq. 2.7 yields

$$\Phi_A - \Phi_B = (p_A - p_B) - \gamma(Z_A - Z_B). \quad \text{(2.9)}$$

Using the new datum as a reference level,

$$\Phi_A - \Phi^\circ = (p_A - p^\circ) - \gamma Z_A \quad \text{(2.10)}$$

and $\Phi_B - \Phi^\circ = (p_B - p^\circ) - \gamma Z_B$, $\quad$ (2.11)

where $\Phi^\circ = p^\circ + \gamma D^\circ$ $\quad$ (2.12)

and p° = pressure at the new datum.

TABLE 2.1—UNITS FOR VARIABLES IN DARCY'S LAW*

Variable	System of Units: Customary	Metric
α_c	5.614583	1
β_c	1.127	86.4×10^{-6}
γ_c	0.21584×10^{-3}	10^{-3}
q	RB/D	m^3/d
A	ft^2	m^2
u	RB/(D-ft^2)	$m^3/(d\cdot m^2)$
k	darcy	μm^2
k_r	fraction	fraction
μ	cp	Pa·s
∇p	psi/ft	kPa/m
∇Z	ft/ft	m/m
γ	psi/ft	kPa/m
ρ	lbm/ft^3	kg/m^3
g	ft/sec^2	m/s^2

*Extracted from Table 4.1

Subtracting Eq. 2.11 from Eq. 2.10, both Φ° and p° drop out, resulting in

$$\Phi_A - \Phi_B = (p_A - p_B) - \gamma(Z_A - Z_B). \quad (2.13)$$

Eqs. 2.9 and 2.13 are identical. This implies that the potential difference between two points does not depend on the datum depth used in the computations.

The potential at any arbitrary point with the new datum can be expressed as

$$\Phi - \Phi^\circ = (p - p^\circ) - \gamma Z, \quad (2.14)$$

where p and Z = pressure and elevation, respectively, at the arbitrary point. The potential gradient, obtained by differentiating Eq. 2.14, is

$$\vec{\nabla}\Phi = \vec{\nabla}p - \gamma\vec{\nabla}Z, \quad (2.15)$$

where Z is positive in the downward vertical direction.

Although Eq. 2.15 derived for incompressible fluids assumes that the fluid density used to define the hydrostatic gradient, γ, is constant, it is applicable to compressible fluids as well. To derive an expression for the gradient of flow potential of a slightly compressible or compressible fluid, write an energy-conservation equation for the mechanical energy to translate a unit mass from some reference level to an arbitrary level. In doing so, consider the total work done on the fluid that is composed of collection work, potential energy gained (or lost), compression work, and rejection work. Such a treatment yields the definition of Hubbert's[1] potential, Φ_h, which is valid for both compressible and incompressible fluids,

$$\Phi_h = \int_{p^\circ}^{p} \frac{dp}{\gamma(p)} - Z. \quad (2.16)$$

The potential gradient can then be obtained from Eq. 2.16 as

$$\vec{\nabla}\Phi_h = \vec{\nabla}\left[\int_{p^\circ}^{p} \frac{dp}{\gamma(p)} - Z\right] = \frac{1}{\gamma}\vec{\nabla}p - \vec{\nabla}Z. \quad (2.17)$$

Then the potential gradient defined in Eq. 2.15 is

$$\vec{\nabla}\Phi = \gamma\vec{\nabla}\Phi_h = \vec{\nabla}p - \gamma\vec{\nabla}Z, \quad (2.18)$$

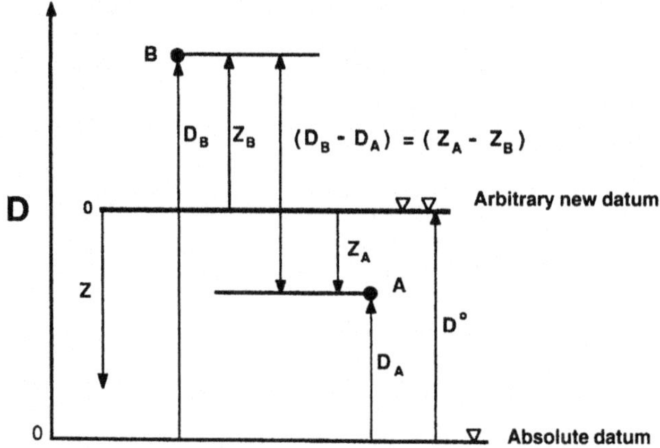

Fig. 2.1—Absolute datum and arbitrary datum.

which simply indicates that $\vec{\nabla}\Phi$ is related to $\vec{\nabla}\Phi_h$ through γ. In a simulation study, a constant-density assumption may not be applied to certain fluids, such as an oil phase with solution gas or a gas phase. To remove the nonlinearity introduced by the pressure-dependent density term, the γ term in Eq. 2.15 is updated as the new pressure values become available at a given timestep (or if necessary at a given iteration level) to recalculate the fluid density. Furthermore, during the initialization step, γ is continuously updated at new depth levels as the hydrostatic pressure is calculated.

Alternatively, the hydrostatic fluid gradient, γ, in Eq. 2.15 is calculated with the average fluid density in the elevation interval ΔZ. In other words, Eq. 2.15 is applicable for both incompressible and compressible fluids. While γ is constant for an incompressible fluid, it is an average that takes into consideration the variation of γ with pressure over the elevation interval ΔZ for a compressible fluid. In Eq. 2.15, the operator $\vec{\nabla}$ is defined by Eq. 3.99.

For multiphase flow, the potential gradient for each phase (o, w, and g) is

$$\vec{\nabla}\Phi_l = \vec{\nabla}p_l - \gamma_l\vec{\nabla}Z, \quad (2.19)$$

where $l = o$, w, or g;

$$\gamma_l = \gamma_c \rho_l g; \quad (2.20)$$

and Z is positive in the vertical downward direction. Note that, if the coordinate system used in the computation is chosen to be positive in the vertical upward direction, the minus sign in Eq. 2.19 must be changed to a plus sign.

2.2.2 Darcy's Law. Darcy's law is an empirical relationship between fluid flow rate through a porous medium and potential gradient.[2] For single-phase, one-dimensional (1D) flow, this law can be expressed in a differential form as

$$\frac{q}{A_x} = u_x = -\beta_c\frac{k_x}{\mu}\frac{d\Phi}{dx}, \quad (2.21)$$

where β_c = unit conversion factor for the transmissibility coefficient, k = absolute rock permeability in the direction of flow, μ = fluid viscosity, Φ = fluid potential, and u = fluid flow rate per unit cross-sectional area perpendicular to the flow direction (superficial velocity). For three-dimensional (3D) flow the differential form of Darcy's law is

$$\vec{u} = -\beta_c\frac{k}{\mu}\vec{\nabla}\Phi. \quad (2.22)$$

With the definition for potential gradient (Eq. 2.15), the velocity vector $\vec{u}$ becomes

$$\vec{u} = -\beta_c\frac{k}{\mu}\left(\vec{\nabla}p - \gamma\vec{\nabla}Z\right). \quad (2.23)$$

When using this form of Darcy's law, engineers should be aware of some implicit assumptions and limitations.[3,4]

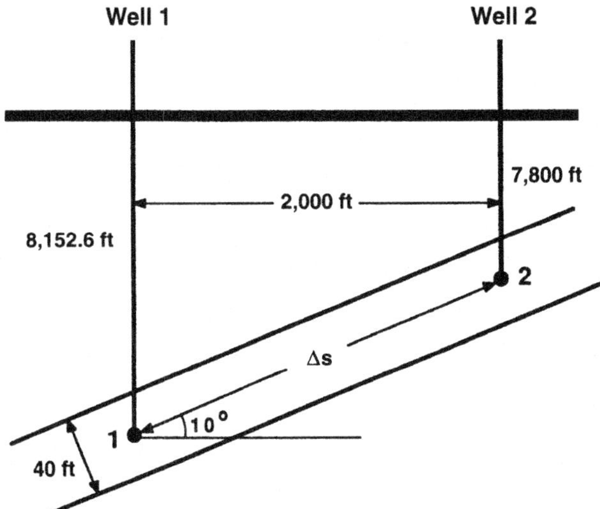

Fig. 2.2—Cross section of reservoir described in Example 2.1.

1. The fluid is homogeneous, single-phase, and Newtonian.
2. There is no chemical reaction between the fluid and the porous medium.
3. Laminar-flow conditions prevail.
4. Permeability is a property of the porous medium that is independent of pressure, temperature, and the flowing fluid.
5. There is no slippage effect (Klinkenberg[5] phenomenon).
6. There is no electrokinetic effect.

For multiphase flow the extended form of Darcy's law for each phase can be expressed as

$$\vec{u}_l = -\beta_c \frac{kk_{rl}}{\mu_l}\vec{\nabla}\Phi_l, \quad\text{(2.24)}$$

where $l = o$, w, or g. Combining with Eq. 2.19 gives

$$\vec{u}_l = -\beta_c \frac{kk_{rl}}{\mu_l}\left(\vec{\nabla}p_l - \gamma_l\vec{\nabla}Z\right), \quad\text{(2.25)}$$

where $l = o$, w, or g and k_{rl}, μ_l, p_l, and γ_l = relative permeability, viscosity, pressure, and fluid gravity for Phase l, respectively.

Darcy's law can be considered an empirical law[2] or an analytical expression derived from the Navier and Stokes equation.[1] In either case, Darcy's law is a cornerstone to reservoir simulation.

Example 2.1 An oil formation dips with a 10° angle. Its permeability is 100 md and its thickness is 40 ft. Its oil density and viscosity are 40 lbm/ft^3 and 0.6 cp, respectively. Two observation wells are drilled at Points 1 and 2. The two points are separated horizontally by 2,000 ft; **Fig. 2.2** shows where they fall on the formation. The bottom of Observation Well 1 is 8,152.6 ft below sea level, and that of Well 2 is 7,800 ft below sea level. The bottomhole pressure of Well 1 is 3,600 psia, and that of Well 2 is 3,570 psia. Determine the fluid velocity between the two observation points.

Solution. The positive direction is from Point 1 to Point 2. Fluid velocity for single-phase flow is

$$\vec{u} = -\beta_c \frac{k}{\mu}\left(\vec{\nabla}p - \gamma\vec{\nabla}Z\right). \quad\text{(2.23)}$$

For 1D flow in the s direction, this equation becomes

$$u = -\beta_c \frac{k}{\mu}\left(\frac{dp}{ds} - \gamma\frac{dZ}{ds}\right). \quad\text{(2.26)}$$

Correlating the field units indicated in Fig. 2.2 with the information in Table 2.1, $\beta_c = 1.127$, $k = 0.100$ darcy, $\mu = 0.60$ cp, $\rho = 40$ lbm/ft^3, $g = 32.174$ ft/s^2, $\gamma_c = 0.21584 \times 10^{-3}$, $\gamma = \gamma_c \rho g$ or 0.2776 psi/ft $[(0.21584 \times 10^{-3})(40)(32.17)]$,

$$\frac{dp}{ds} = \frac{p_2 - p_1}{s_2 - s_1} = \frac{p_2 - p_1}{\Delta s}$$

$$= \frac{3,570 - 3,600}{2,000/\cos 10°} = -0.0148 \text{ psi/ft}, \quad\text{(2.27)}$$

and $\dfrac{dZ}{ds} = \dfrac{Z_2 - Z_1}{s_2 - s_1} = \dfrac{Z_2 - Z_1}{\Delta s}$.

$$= \frac{7,800 - 8,152.6}{2,000/\cos 10°} = -0.1736 \text{ ft/ft}. \quad\text{(2.28)}$$

Substituting into Eq. 2.26 yields

$$u = -\frac{1.127 \times 0.1}{0.6}[-0.0148 - (0.2776)(-0.1736)]$$

or $u = -0.0063$ $\text{RB/(D-ft}^2)$. Because u is negative, the direction of fluid flow is in the direction opposite to the direction of increasing s. Therefore, oil flows from Point 2 to Point 1 and the magnitude of the Darcy velocity is 0.0063 $\text{RB/(D-ft}^2)$ or 0.0353 ft/D.

It is important to recognize that Eq. 2.23 in this example gives the apparent, or Darcy, velocity. Because of the tortuosity of the flow paths (a result of the conspicuous nature of the pore structure), the actual fluid velocity will vary from point to point within the rock and result in an average velocity. In other words, the actual fluid velocity is a local microscopic velocity as defined at the microscopic scale. The average velocity, a property at the core scale, can be found by dividing the apparent velocity by the porosity of the rock. The average velocity becomes equal to the actual velocity if the porous medium is assumed to consist of a bundle of uniform capillary tubes (homogeneous porosity distribution). In reservoir engineering, the apparent fluid velocity is used to calculate the volume of fluid passing through a section of a porous medium. On the other hand, it is essential to use the average velocity to consider the movement of particles and/or fluid interfaces. Because actual velocities are difficult to measure, they are rarely used in reservoir-engineering calculations.

2.2.3 Steady- and Unsteady-State Flow. Steady- and unsteady-state flow are basic concepts required by both practicing engineers and students. For example, the unsteady-state nature of a waterflood is the reason that oil production from a reservoir does not respond immediately to changes in water injection. Fluid compressibility, c_f, and the manner in which fluid density, ρ, responds to pressure are the main factors responsible for this behavior.

For an incompressible fluid (see Types of Reservoir Fluids in Sec. 2.3.2), pressure response is felt instantly with equal intensity at any point in the reservoir, provided that the reservoir rock is incompressible. Mathematically stated,

$$\rho \neq f(p) \quad\text{(2.29)}$$

when $c_f = 0$ or ρ is constant for all p and

$$\frac{\partial\rho}{\partial t}\Big|_s = 0 \quad\text{(2.30a)}$$

and $\dfrac{\partial p}{\partial t}\Big|_s = 0.$ (2.30b)

In terms of fluid velocity,

$$\frac{\partial u}{\partial t}\Big|_s = 0. \quad\text{(2.31)}$$

Flow problems involving incompressible fluids and porous media have solutions that are independent of time (because all derivatives with respect to time are zero) and dependent on space only. Such flow is called steady-state flow because all properties are steady, or constant, with time.

For slightly compressible and compressible fluids, the pressure shock (or at least part of it) will be absorbed initially by fluid compression until the fluids can no longer compress. The remainder of the energy will then be transmitted to the next point in space, and so on. The energy stored in the compressed fluid will be released later and transmitted from one point to the next. In time, the pressure shock (or at least part of it) will be felt at any observation point. That is to say that there is transient, or time-dependent, behavior occurring in the porous medium. In this case, we have

$$\rho = f(p) \quad \text{.......} \quad (2.32)$$

when $c_f > 0$ and

$$\frac{\partial \rho}{\partial t}|_s \neq 0 \quad \text{.......} \quad (2.33a)$$

and $\frac{\partial p}{\partial t}|_s \neq 0.$ .... (2.33b)

In terms of fluid velocity,

$$\frac{\partial u}{\partial t}|_s \neq 0. \quad \text{.......} \quad (2.34)$$

Flow problems involving compressible or slightly compressible fluids have solutions that are dependent on both space and time. For these problems, the solution at any given time is obtained by advancing the solution from $t_0 = 0$ to $t_1 = t_0 + \Delta t$ and then from t_1 to $t_2 = t_1 + \Delta t$, and so on, until the final time is reached. The process of advancing the solution in time can either be continuous, as in pressure-transient analysis, or discrete, as in numerical reservoir simulation. Such flow is called transient or unsteady-state flow.

2.3 Reservoir-Rock and -Fluid Properties

The properties of reservoir rock, the physical properties of the fluids [such as pressure/volume/temperature (PVT) behavior], and rock/fluid-interaction properties (such as capillary pressures and relative permeabilities) strongly influence multiphase flow in porous media. The following sections give some of the basics of these properties.

2.3.1 Rock Properties. This section introduces basic reservoir-rock properties, such as porosity and permeability, which are assumed to be independent of fluid content, provided that the rock and fluid are nonreactive. The concepts of rock heterogeneity and anisotropy are also introduced.

Porosity and the Concept of Heterogeneity. The pore spaces of reservoir rock contain the fluids in petroleum reservoirs. Some of these pore spaces are isolated, while others are interconnected. The ratio of the pore space in a rock sample to the total volume of the rock sample is called porosity. Two primary types of porosity can be encountered in a real reservoir rock: total porosity and effective porosity. Total porosity includes both isolated and interconnected pore spaces, while effective porosity includes only interconnected pores. Because only interconnected pores produce fluids, we are concerned mainly with effective porosity; therefore, in the remainder of this text, the term porosity is used to mean only effective porosity. Porosity in this sense is a measure of the capacity of the reservoir rock to store producible fluids in its pores.

Variation of pore volume (PV) with pore pressure can be accounted for by the pressure dependence of porosity. Porosity is dependent on pressure because of rock compressibility, which is usually assumed to be constant (generally about 10^{-6} to 10^{-7} psi^{-1}). Rock porosity at any pressure can be expressed as

$$\phi = \phi^\circ\left[1 + c_\phi(p - p^\circ)\right], \quad \text{.......} \quad (2.35)$$

where p° = reference pressure at which the porosity is ϕ°. The reference pressure is usually atmospheric pressure or initial reservoir pressure. Eq. 2.35 reveals that porosity increases as the pressure of the fluids contained in the pore space increases. Furthermore, porosity decreases in relation to reference porosity when pore pressure decreases, as with pressure decline during primary production.

A reservoir-rock property (such as porosity) often varies in space from one point to another or from one region to another. If a property is constant and independent of location, the reservoir rock is called homogeneous. If, however, a property varies with location, it is called heterogeneous. In reality, homogeneous reservoirs are rare, so the concept of homogeneity is generally used for ideal porous media. Idealization is used to simplify otherwise intractable problems to obtain analytical solutions.

Example 2.2 Prove that the effective compressibility of an oil-filled (single-phase) reservoir is given by

$$c_e = c_o\phi + c_R(1 - \phi). \quad \text{.......} \quad (2.36)$$

Solution. The bulk volume of a reservoir equals the sum of the PV and rock-solids volume; that is,

$$V_b = V_p + V_s \quad \text{.......} \quad (2.37a)$$

or $V_b = V_o + V_s$, ... (2.37b)

because the oil fills the PV. Differentiating the relationship in Eq. 2.37b with respect to reservoir pressure yields

$$\frac{dV_b}{dp} = \frac{dV_o}{dp} + \frac{dV_s}{dp}. \quad \text{.......} \quad (2.38)$$

From the definition of compressibility,

$$c = -\frac{1}{V}\frac{dV}{dp}, \quad \text{.......} \quad (2.39)$$

comes $\frac{dV}{dp} = -cV,$ .... (2.40)

so $\frac{dV_b}{dp} = -c_bV_b$ .... (2.41)

for bulk volume;

$$\frac{dV_o}{dp} = -c_oV_o \quad \text{.......} \quad (2.42)$$

for oil; and

$$\frac{dV_s}{dp} = -c_RV_s \quad \text{.......} \quad (2.43)$$

for rock solids. Substituting Eqs. 2.41 through 2.43 into Eq. 2.38 results in

$$-c_bV_b = -c_oV_o - c_RV_s, \quad \text{.......} \quad (2.44)$$

and solving for c_b gives

$$c_b = c_o\frac{V_o}{V_b} + c_R\frac{V_s}{V_b}. \quad \text{.......} \quad (2.45)$$

With Eq. 2.37b to substitute for V_s, Eq. 2.45 can be simplified further to give

$$c_b = c_o\frac{V_o}{V_b} + c_R\left(\frac{V_b - V_o}{V_b}\right)$$

$$= c_o\phi + c_R(1 - \phi), \quad \text{.......} \quad (2.46)$$

which is

$$c_e = c_b = c_o\phi + c_R(1 - \phi). \quad \text{.......} \quad (2.36)$$

Note that in Eq. 2.46, for a single phase, the volume V_o is identical to the effective PV.

Permeability and the Concept of Anisotropy. Permeability is the capacity of a porous medium to transmit fluids through its interconnected pores. This capacity is called absolute permeability or simply permeability if the medium is 100% saturated with a single liquid phase. For a gas phase, permeability is a function of pressure because of the Klinkenberg[5] effect. For gases, absolute permeability is measured at infinite pressure, where the Klinkenberg effect vanishes. If two or more phases are saturating the porous medium, the reservoir capacity to transmit any phase is called the effective permeability to that phase. Relative Permeability in Sec. 2.3.3 discusses effective and relative permeabilities.

Permeability varies from one point to another and, even at the same point, may depend on the flow direction. In many practical problems, it is sufficient to assume that permeability can be represented by three

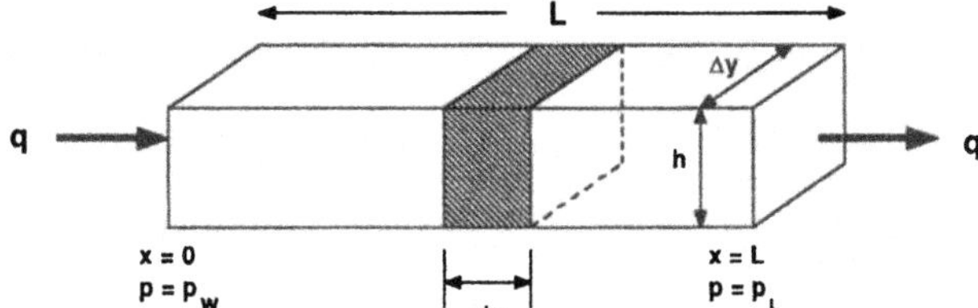

Fig. 2.3—One-dimensional reservoir described in Example 2.3.

values (k_x, k_y, and k_z) in three principal directions (x, y, and z). It is often possible to assume that $k_H = k_x = k_y$ in the horizontal plane because in many depositional environments directional trends are not apparent. In addition, the vertical permeability, k_V, is often different from the horizontal permeability, k_H, because even very thin shale stringers significantly affect vertical permeability. In general, vertical permeability is lower than horizontal permeability. If $k_x = k_y = k_z$, the porous medium is called isotropic; however, it is called anisotropic if the permeability shows a directional bias.

Some parameters used in reservoir simulation exhibit directional dependency. A reservoir exhibits an isotropic property distribution if that property has the same value regardless of the direction in which it is measured. On the other hand, if the value varies with direction, the reservoir is anisotropic with respect to that property. Only those properties that are not volume-based can exhibit directional dependency. Porosity, for example, is volume-based by definition; it uses all three dimensions, so it has zero degrees of freedom in terms of directional variation. Permeability, by contrast, has only the dimension of area, leaving one direction in which it can vary. Therefore, all possible permutations of isotropic and anisotropic and homogeneous and heterogeneous systems can exist for multidimensional cases.

Homogeneity and heterogeneity and isotropy and anisotropy are each related to a single property, so these terms should always be used in reference to a specific property. For example, a reservoir can display homogeneous distribution with respect to porosity but heterogeneous distribution with respect to thickness.

Example 2.3 Consider the following 1D horizontal porous medium in which steady-state flow of oil is taking place in the positive x direction. Let the permeability of the system vary according to

$$k_x = 1{,}000/(980 + 0.04x), \quad \text{(2.47)}$$

where x is in feet and k is in darcies. At $x = 0, p = p_W$, and at $x = L, p = p_L$. If the viscosity of oil is μ_o and the dimensions of the porous medium, h, Δy, and L (**Fig. 2.3**), are in feet, obtain an expression that describes the average permeability of the porous medium.

Solution. To find the average permeability of the porous medium in the x direction, k_x must be integrated according to Darcy's law. Choose an element of the reservoir with a cross-sectional area perpendicular to flow of $A_x = h\Delta y$, a length of dx, and permeability of k_x at Point x along the x direction.

For 1D horizontal flow, Darcy's law written for a differential element reduces to

$$q = -\beta_c \frac{k_x A_x}{\mu_o} \frac{dp}{dx}. \quad \text{(2.48)}$$

Separating the variables and integrating over the length of the porous medium, (0, L), results in

$$\int_0^L \frac{q\mu_o}{k_x A_x} dx = \int_{p_W}^{p_L} -\beta_c dp. \quad \text{(2.49)}$$

The terms $q, \mu_o, A_x = h\Delta y$, and β_c are independent of x and can be taken outside of the integrals, giving

$$\frac{q\mu_o}{h\Delta y}\int_0^L \frac{dx}{k_x} = -\beta_c \int_{p_W}^{p_L} dp. \quad \text{(2.50)}$$

Substituting for β_c and k_x results in

$$\frac{q\mu_o}{h\Delta y}\int_0^L \frac{dx}{[1{,}000/(980 + 0.04x)]} = -1.127\int_{p_W}^{p_L} dp \quad \text{(2.51)}$$

$$\text{or } \frac{q\mu_o}{h\Delta y}\int_0^L \frac{980 + 0.04x}{1{,}000} dx = -1.127\int_{p_W}^{p_L} dp. \quad \text{(2.52)}$$

Integrating gives

$$\frac{q\mu_o}{h\Delta y}\left[0.980x + \frac{1}{2}\left(\frac{0.04}{1{,}000}\right)x^2\right]_0^L = -1.127p \Big|_{p_W}^{p_L} \quad \text{(2.53)}$$

$$\text{or } \frac{q\mu_o}{h\Delta y}\left\{\left[0.980L + 2(10^{-5})L^2\right] - \left[0.980(0) + 2(10^{-5})(0^2)\right]\right\}$$

$$= -1.127(p_L - p_W). \quad \text{(2.54)}$$

It follows that

$$\frac{q\mu_o}{h\Delta y}\left[0.980L + 2(10^{-5})L^2\right] = -1.127(p_L - p_W), \quad \text{(2.55)}$$

resulting in

$$q = 1.127\left[\frac{1}{0.980 + 2(10^{-5})L}\right]\frac{h\Delta y}{\mu_o}\left(\frac{p_W - p_L}{L}\right). \quad \text{(2.56)}$$

With average properties, Darcy's law for the system can be written

$$q = 1.127\bar{k}\,\frac{h\Delta y}{\mu_o}\left(\frac{p_W - p_L}{L}\right). \quad \text{(2.57)}$$

Comparison of Eqs. 2.56 and 2.57 gives the average permeability for the porous medium,

$$\bar{k} = \frac{1{,}000}{980 + 0.02L}. \quad \text{(2.58)}$$

2.3.2 Fluid Properties. Fluid properties of interest in reservoir modeling include fluid compressibilities and gas-compressibility factors, solution-gas/liquid ratios, fluid densities, fluid FVF's, and fluid viscosities. The dependence of oil, water, and gas properties on pressure at reservoir temperature will be discussed to gain insight into the role they play in reservoir modeling.

In general, oil, water, and gas can be produced simultaneously from hydrocarbon reservoirs. These fluids coexist in equilibrium at reservoir pressure and temperature. The produced gas is composed of solution gas and free gas. Most of the solution gas comes from the gas dissolved in oil, and the remainder comes from the gas dissolved in water. Therefore, considering that oil and water are immiscible, the properties of the oil phase at reservoir conditions are strongly affected by the gas in solution. Likewise, the properties of water are affected (though to a much lesser extent) by the gas dissolved in water. It is also generally assumed that, for black-oil systems, neither oil nor water vaporizes in gas in any significant quantity. The presence of oil and water in black-oil systems does not affect the properties of the gas phase at reservoir conditions.

Types of Reservoir Fluids. Oil, gas, and water are the fluids produced from petroleum reservoirs. These fluids can be classified as incompressible, slightly compressible, or compressible, depending on how they behave when subjected to external pressure. An incompressible fluid, as the name implies, has zero compressibility; therefore, it has constant density regardless of pressure. This type of fluid is an idealization for gas-free (or dead) oil and water. A slightly compressible fluid has a small but constant compressibility that usually ranges from 10^{-5} to 10^{-6} psi^{-1}. The dashed line in **Fig. 2.4** shows that the density of a slightly compressible fluid varies linearly with pressure. Under reservoir conditions, dead oil, undersaturated oil, and

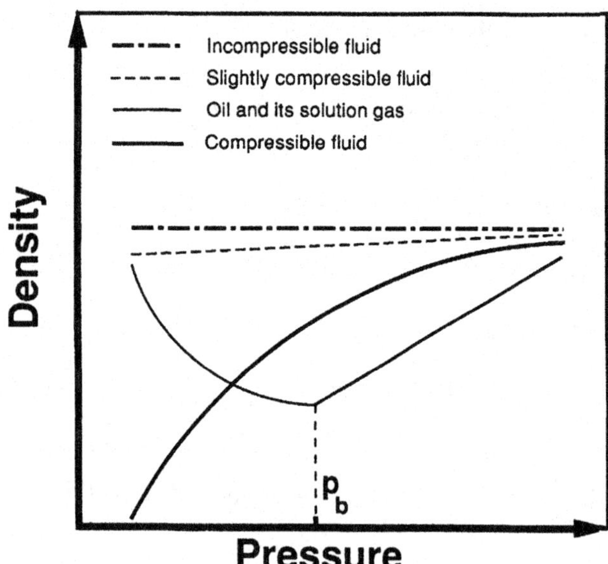

Fig. 2.4—Density behavior of various types of fluids as a function of pressure.

water behave as slightly compressible fluids. A compressible fluid has a higher compressibility than a slightly compressible fluid, usually approximately 10^{-3} to 10^{-4} psi^{-1}. The density of a compressible fluid increases as pressure increases but tends to level off at high pressures. At reservoir pressures and temperatures, gas is a good example of a compressible fluid.

In multiphase flow in petroleum reservoirs, water is treated either as incompressible or slightly compressible and natural gas is treated as compressible. Oil and its solution gas are treated as slightly compressible when reservoir pressure is higher than the oil bubblepoint pressure and as compressible when reservoir pressure falls below bubblepoint pressure. Because of the pressure dependence of density, single-phase flow problems involving incompressible fluids lead to steady-state solutions, while those involving slightly compressible and compressible fluids lead to unsteady-state solutions.

Fluid Compressibility and Gas-Compressibility Factor. Fluid compressibility is defined as the relative volumetric change of a given mass to pressure change at constant temperature. Mathematically, compressibility can be expressed as

$$c_l = -\frac{1}{V}\frac{\partial V}{\partial p}\Big|_T, \quad (2.59)$$

where $l = o, w,$ or g. With the definition of fluid density, $\rho = m/V$, an equivalent expression for fluid compressibility is

$$c_l = \frac{1}{\rho_l}\frac{\partial \rho_l}{\partial p}\Big|_T. \quad (2.60)$$

As discussed previously, fluids can be classified as incompressible ($c_f = 0$ psi^{-1}), slightly compressible (10^{-6} psi$^{-1} < c_f < 10^{-5}$ psi^{-1}), or compressible ($c_f > 10^{-4}$ psi^{-1}).

For gas, Eq. 2.60 may be written in another form with the real-gas law,

$$\rho_g = \frac{pM}{zRT}. \quad (2.61)$$

Substituting Eq. 2.61 into Eq. 2.60 ($c_l = c_g$ when $\rho = \rho_g$) yields

$$c_g = \frac{1}{p} - \frac{1}{z}\frac{\partial z}{\partial p}\Big|_T. \quad (2.62)$$

Example 2.4 provides the mathematical detail required to go from Eq. 2.59 to Eq. 2.62. Eq. 2.62 can also be expressed in a reduced form as

$$c_r = \frac{1}{p_{pr}} - \frac{1}{z}\frac{\partial z}{\partial p_{pr}}\Big|_{T_{pr}}, \quad (2.63)$$

$$\text{where } c_r = c_g p_{pc}. \quad (2.64)$$

Trube[6] presented a graphical correlation for reduced compressibility, c_r, of gas as a function of pseudoreduced pressure, p_{pr}, and pseudoreduced temperature, T_{pr}, based on Eq. 2.63, using the Brown *et al.*[7] z-factor chart for natural gas. This correlation is useful for hand calculations, but it is not suited to computer usage. On the basis of manipulation of Eq. 2.63, Mattar *et al.*[8] reported the expression for c_r,

$$c_r = \frac{1}{p_{pr}} - \frac{0.270}{z^2 T_{pr}}\left[\frac{(\partial z/\partial \rho_r)|_{T_{pr}}}{1 + (\rho_r/z)(\partial z/\partial \rho_r)|_{T_{pr}}}\right], \quad (2.65)$$

where an analytical expression for $(\partial z/\partial \rho_r)|_{T_{pr}}$ was derived from the Dranchuk *et al.*[9] z-factor equation for natural gas. Abou-Kassem *et al.*[10] pointed out that the reduced compressibility for natural gas can be obtained from the definition of compressibility (Eq. 2.60) and that c_r can be obtained by taking the inverse of the product $(\rho_r)(\partial p_{pr}/\partial \rho_r)|_{T_{pr}}$ where both ρ_r and $(\partial p_{pr}/\partial \rho_r)|_{T_{pr}}$ are embedded in the calculation of z factors by use of equations of state (EOS's).

The z, or gas-compressibility, factor is the empirical factor that accounts for the deviation of a real gas from ideal-gas behavior. **Fig. 2.5** shows the Standing and Katz[11] z-factor chart for natural gases. At any given T_{pr}, the z factor is a function of p_{pr}. The reduced (or pseudoreduced) properties are

$$p_{pr} = \frac{p}{p_{pc}} \quad (2.66)$$

$$\text{and } T_{pr} = \frac{T}{T_{pc}}. \quad (2.67)$$

For natural gas, p_{pc} and T_{pc} are the pseudocritical pressure and temperature calculated as the molal average of the critical properties of the gas components. Dranchuk and Abou-Kassem[12] reported correlations for p_{pc} and T_{pc} of natural gases as functions of gas gravity that are useful when gas composition is not available. For sour natural gas, these pseudocriticals must be modified as suggested by Wichert and Aziz.[13]

Several methods are available to generate the Standing and Katz z-factor chart with computers.[14] The more powerful methods use EOS's, such as those based on the Benedict-Webb-Rubin[15] (BWR) EOS. The BWR EOS's may be written in a reduced form as

$$p_{pr} = \frac{1}{z_c}\Big[T_r\rho_r + C_0\rho_r^2 + C_2\rho_r^3 + C_3\rho_r^6 + C_4\rho_r^3\left(1 + C_5\rho_r^2\right) \times \exp\left(-C_5\rho_r^2\right)\Big], \quad (2.68)$$

where the coefficients C_0, C_2 through C_5 are defined for both the Dranchuk *et al.*[9] and Dranchuk and Abou-Kassem[16] equations in **Table 2.2**. (**Table 2.3** lists the values of coefficients A_1 through A_8 and A_1 through A_{11} for both equations.) This gas-compressibility factor can be obtained from the reduced form of the real-gas law (Eq. 2.61) as

$$z = 0.270\frac{p_{pr}}{\rho_r T_{pr}}. \quad (2.69)$$

For a given T_{pr} and p_{pr}, the reduced density ρ_r that satisfies Eq. 2.68 is first found by use of the Newton-Raphson iteration. At convergence both ρ_r and $(\partial p_{pr}/\partial \rho_r)|_{T_r}$ are calculated. Furthermore, z and c_r can be calculated with Eq. 2.69 and the reduced form of Eq. 2.60, respectively. FORTRAN computer programs that calculate both z and c_r with the Dranchuk *et al.*[9] and Dranchuk and Abou-Kassem[16] z-factor equations can be found in the literature.[10]

Example 2.4. Derive the equation for reduced compressibility of a real gas, Eq. 2.63, from the basic definition of compressibility. Also find the compressibility of an ideal gas.

Solution. The definition of compressibility is

$$c_l = -\frac{1}{V}\frac{\partial V}{\partial p}\Big|_T. \quad (2.59)$$

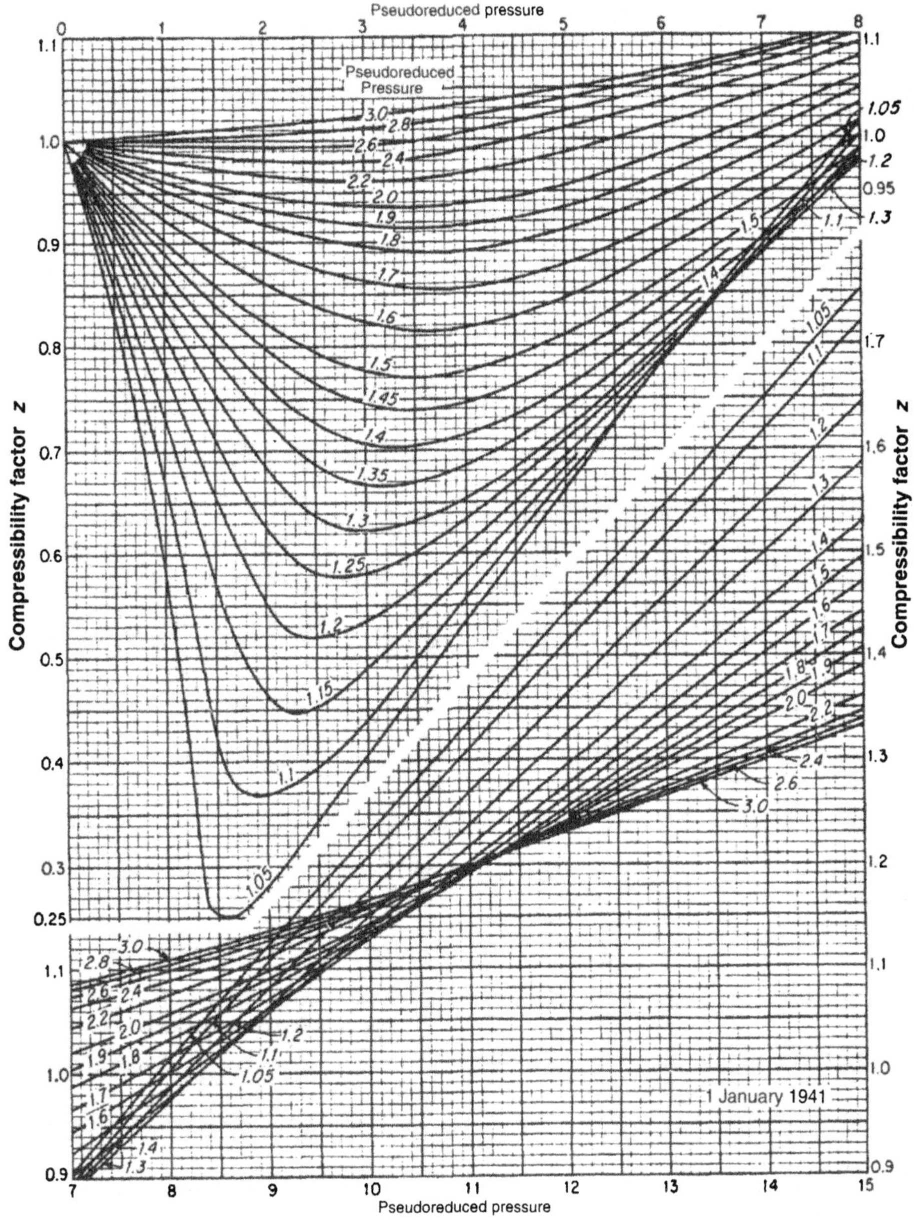

Fig. 2.5—Standing and Katz *z*-factor chart for natural gas (from Ref. 11).

Dividing and multiplying the right side of Eq. 2.59 by the mass of the gas that occupies volume V at pressure p and absolute temperature T results in

$$c_l = -\frac{m}{V}\frac{\partial(V/m)}{\partial p}|_T$$

$$= -\rho_l\frac{\partial}{\partial p}\left(\frac{1}{\rho_l}\right)|_T$$

$$= -\rho_l\left(\frac{-1}{\rho_l^2}\frac{\partial \rho_l}{\partial p}|_T\right)$$

$$= \frac{1}{\rho_l}\frac{\partial \rho_l}{\partial p}|_T \quad \text{(2.70)}$$

or, for $l = g$,

$$c_g = \frac{1}{\rho_g}\frac{\partial \rho_g}{\partial p}|_T. \quad \text{(2.71)}$$

In Eq. 2.71, $\rho_g = m/V$ is gas density at p and T. Gas density is given by the real-gas law,

$$\rho_g = \frac{pM}{zRT}. \quad \text{(2.61)}$$

Eq. 2.61 can be used to obtain $(\partial\rho_g/\partial p)|_T$.

$$\frac{\partial \rho_g}{\partial p}|_T = \frac{M}{RT}\frac{\partial}{\partial p}\left(\frac{p}{z}\right)|_T$$

$$= \frac{M}{RT}\left(\frac{z - p(\partial z/\partial p)|_T}{z^2}\right)$$

$$= \frac{Mp}{zRT}\left(\frac{1}{p} - \frac{1}{z}\frac{\partial z}{\partial p}|_T\right)$$

$$= \rho_g\left(\frac{1}{p} - \frac{1}{z}\frac{\partial z}{\partial p}|_T\right). \quad \text{(2.72)}$$

TABLE 2.2—DEFINITION OF COEFFICIENTS OF EQ. 2.68 FOR THE DRANCHUK *et al.*[9] AND DRANCHUK AND ABOU-KASSEM[16] EQUATIONS

Coefficient	Dranchuk *et al.* Equation	Dranchuk and Abou-Kassem Equation
C_0	$T_r\left(A_1 + \frac{A_2}{T_r} + \frac{A_3}{T_r^3}\right)$	$T_r\left(A_1 + \frac{A_2}{T_r} + \frac{A_3}{T_r^3} + \frac{A_4}{T_r^4} + \frac{A_5}{T_r^5}\right)$
C_2	$T_r\left(A_4 + \frac{A_5}{T_r}\right)$	$T_r\left(A_6 + \frac{A_7}{T_r} + \frac{A_8}{T_r^2}\right)$
C_3	$-A_6(A_5)$	$-A_9\left(A_7 + \frac{A_8}{T_r}\right)$
C_4	$\frac{A_7}{T_r^2}$	$\frac{A_{10}}{T_r^2}$
C_5	A_8	A_{11}

TABLE 2.3—VALUES OF COEFFICIENTS A_1 THROUGH A_{11} FOR THE DRANCHUK *et al.*[9] AND DRANCHUK AND ABOU-KASSEM[16] EQUATIONS

Coefficient	Dranchuk *et al.* Equation	Dranchuk and Abou-Kassem Equation
A_1	0.31506237	0.3265
A_2	−1.0467099	−1.070
A_3	−0.57832729	−0.5339
A_4	0.53530771	0.01569
A_5	−0.61232032	−0.05165
A_6	0.10488813	0.5475
A_7	0.68157001	−0.7361
A_8	0.68446549	0.1844
A_9	—	0.1056
A_{10}	—	0.6134
A_{11}	—	0.7210

Substituting Eq. 2.72 into Eq. 2.71 and simplifying gives

$$c_g = \frac{1}{p} - \frac{1}{z}\frac{\partial z}{\partial p}\Big|_T . \quad (2.73)$$

From the definition of pseudoreduced pressure, $p_{pr} = p/p_{pc}$ and $p = p_{pc}p_{pr}$ may be substituted into Eq. 2.73 to obtain

$$c_g = \frac{1}{p_{pc}p_{pr}} - \frac{1}{z}\frac{\partial z}{p_{pc}\partial p_{pr}}\Big|_{T_{pr}} \quad (2.74)$$

$$\text{or } c_g p_{pc} = \frac{1}{p_{pr}} - \frac{1}{z}\frac{\partial z}{\partial p_{pr}}\Big|_{T_{pr}}. \quad (2.75)$$

From Eq. 2.64,

$$c_r = c_g p_{pc}, \quad (2.64)$$

$$\text{comes } c_r = \frac{1}{p_{pr}} - \frac{1}{z}\frac{\partial z}{\partial p_{pr}}\Big|_{T_{pr}}, \quad (2.63)$$

which is the desired definition for c_r.

For an ideal gas (gas at low pressures), $z = 1$ and

$$\frac{\partial z}{\partial p_{pr}}\Big|_{T_{pr}} = 0. \quad (2.76)$$

Substituting these into Eq. 2.63 gives

$$c_r = \frac{1}{p_{pr}} \quad (2.77)$$

$$\text{or } c_g = \frac{1}{p}; \quad (2.78)$$

therefore, the compressibility of an ideal gas is equal to the reciprocal of the pressure.

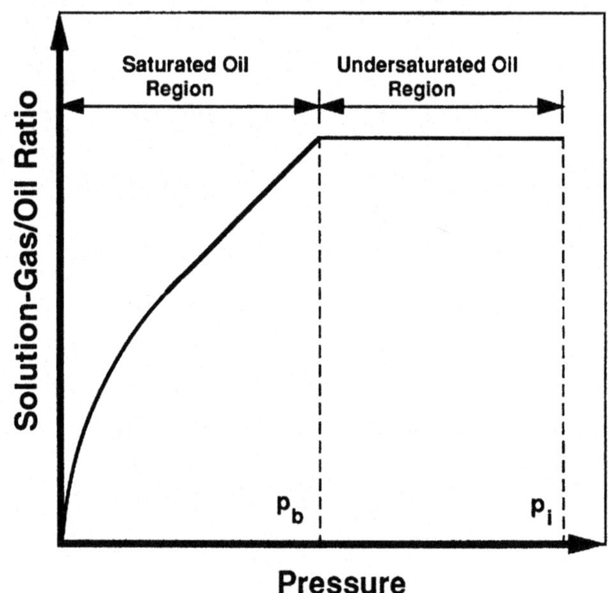

Fig. 2.6—Solution-gas/oil ratio.

Solution-Gas/Liquid Ratio. At reservoir temperature and pressure, the thermodynamic equilibrium of a gas/liquid system is achieved by the transfer of mass between the two phases. In a black-oil system, this mass transfer can be described by the solution-gas/liquid ratio. The solution-gas/liquid ratio is the volume of gas (at standard conditions) that must dissolve into a unit volume of liquid (at standard conditions) for the liquid and gas system to reach equilibrium at reservoir temperature and pressure. Equilibrium in this context means that the liquid is saturated with gas. In black-oil reservoirs there are two solution-gas/liquid ratios: solution-gas/oil ratio and solution-gas/water ratio. The solution-gas/water ratio can, for all practical purposes, be assumed to be zero; therefore, this section is devoted to the solution-gas/oil ratio.

Fig. 2.6 shows the pressure dependence of the solution-gas/oil ratio, R_s, for a constant-bubblepoint-pressure reservoir at reservoir temperature. This is primary depletion, when the reservoir is initially undersaturated and the pressure decreases everywhere during the producing life of the reservoir. As pressure decreases from initial pressure, p_i, no gas evolves from solution and R_s remains constant until the pressure reaches the bubblepoint pressure, p_b. The reservoir is undersaturated when its pressure is greater than the p_b ($p_b < p \leqq p_i$). At $p = p_b$, the first gas bubble evolves from solution. As the pressure drops below p_b, gas evolves from solution and a free-gas phase develops. In this pressure region ($p \leqq p_b$), the reservoir is called saturated; both the oil and gas phases coexist in thermodynamic equilibrium.

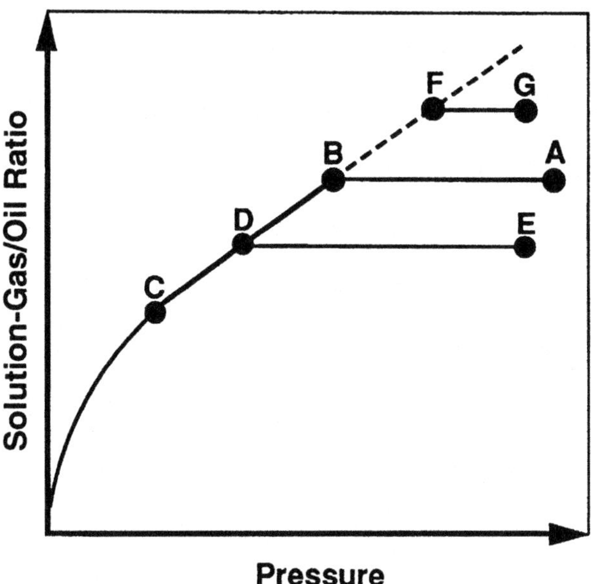

Fig. 2.7—Production and injection operations leading to variable bubblepoint pressures in thick reservoirs. (Redrawn from Ref. 17.)

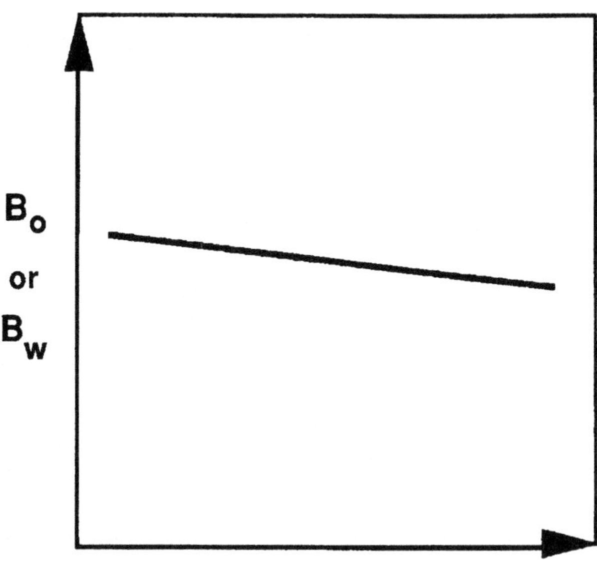

Fig. 2.8—Water and gas-free oil FVF's.

Several practical instances exist when treatment of a black oil as a constant-bubblepoint fluid is not realistic.[17] One example is a reservoir with a large oil column where, because of gravity effects, the bubblepoint pressure of oil varies with depth. Another example is an undersaturated reservoir undergoing gas injection, where different regions of the reservoir may have different bubblepoint pressures because of the different levels of available gas. Primary depletion followed by a pressure-maintenance scheme that uses water (or gas) injection may also result in different bubblepoints in different parts of the reservoir. Consider an undersaturated reservoir, represented by Point A in **Fig. 2.7**. During primary depletion, the pressure declines below the original bubblepoint pressure (Point B) to Point C. Because of gas percolation (vertical gas migration), the bottom portion of the reservoir will have less free gas available to it than the upper portion. If water is injected at Point C, the reservoir pressure increases and gas goes into solution, giving new bubblepoints (Points D and F, respectively) for the lower and upper portions of the reservoir. Further repressurization may lead to the conditions indicated by Points E and G for the lower and upper portions of reservoir. In contrast, if gas is injected at Point C, abundant gas is available to many parts of the reservoir, resulting in areas of the reservoir with bubblepoint pressures falling on the dashed line in Fig. 2.7. The variable-bubblepoint formulation can be used in all black-oil situations and, consequently, is the most common formulation in commercial reservoir simulators.

FVF. A fixed mass of a reservoir fluid occupies a different volume at different reservoir pressures. FVF's are used to convert volumes at reservoir pressure and temperature to their equivalent volumes at standard conditions. These factors take into consideration volume changes caused by fluid compressibility for the water and gas phases and those caused by fluid compressibility and mass transfer of solution gas for the oil phase. The phase FVF is the ratio of the volume that the phase occupies at reservoir pressure and temperature to that at standard conditions,

$$B = \frac{V}{V_{sc}}. \quad \text{(2.79)}$$

For a single phase (water, gas, or dead oil) Eq. 2.79 may be written in terms of densities.

$$B_l = \frac{\rho_{lsc}}{\rho_l}, \quad \text{(2.80)}$$

where $l = o$, w, or g. For slightly compressible fluids, such as water and gas-free (dead) oil, Eq. 2.60 can be integrated and the effect of temperature can be incorporated. The resulting ratio in Eq. 2.80 may be approximated by

$$B_l = B_l^\circ/\left[1 + c_l(p - p^\circ)\right] = 1/\left[1 + c_l(p - p_{sc}) - c_{Tl}(T - T_{sc})\right], \quad \text{(2.81)}$$

where $l = o$ or w, and where c_{Tl} = coefficient of thermal expansion of the fluid. **Fig. 2.8** shows this relationship. For pressures greater than the bubblepoint pressure, the FVF of an undersaturated oil can be obtained with Eq. 2.59 in the vicinity of the bubblepoint pressure and approximating the derivative by first-order Taylor series expansion (see Example 3.17). The resulting expression is

$$B_o = B_{ob}\left[1 - c_o(p - p_b)\right], \quad \text{(2.82)}$$

where $p > p_b$. Comparing Eqs. 2.81 and 2.82 indicates a disparity of the isothermal definition of FVF. Eq. 2.82 is developed assuming a linear relationship above bubblepoint pressure, while Eq. 2.81 represents a nonlinear relationship for isothermal conditions. Both approximations have similar degree of accuracy.

For the gas phase, the real-gas law expressed by Eq. 2.61 can be applied at reservoir conditions and at standard conditions, and combined with Eq. 2.80 to give the expression for B_g,

$$B_g = \frac{\rho_{gsc}}{\alpha_c \rho_g} = \frac{p_{sc}}{\alpha_c T_{sc}} T \frac{z}{p}. \quad \text{(2.83)}$$

Fig. 2.9 shows the gas-phase FVF for a typical gas.

Eqs. 2.81 and 2.83 (and Figs. 2.8 and 2.9), respectively, express the water and gas FVF's for three-phase-flow problems. The oil FVF for a crude oil must be treated differently because of the mass transfer between the gas and oil phases (**Fig. 2.10**). The oil FVF increases as pressure decreases in the undersaturated region ($p > p_b$) as a result of the expansion of the oil and its solution gas. As pressure decreases in the saturated region ($p < p_b$), the oil phase shrinks because of gas evolution, causing a decrease in the oil FVF. In this region, the shrinkage of the oil phase is a result of gas evolution dominating oil expansion because of pressure drop.

For a variable-bubblepoint formulation, the oil FVF follows the saturated curve (solid line) in **Fig. 2.11** when the oil pressure is below its bubblepoint pressure. For pressures greater than the bubblepoint pressure, the FVF follows the undersaturated curve (dashed line), which begins at the bubblepoint pressure. This bubblepoint pressure is not static but may vary from location to location or throughout time in the same location in the reservoir.

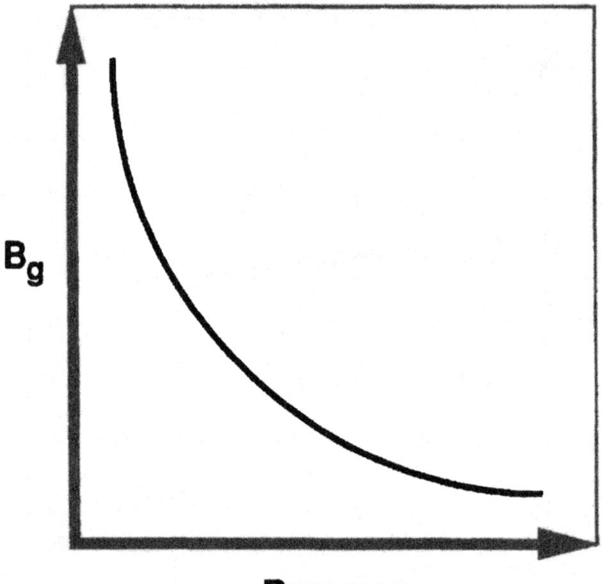

Fig. 2.9—Gas-phase FVF.

Example 2.5. Derive the expression for gas FVF (Eq. 2.83).

Solution. The FVF of any gas or liquid is defined by Eq. 2.79, so

$$B = \frac{V|_{p,T}}{V|_{p_{sc},T_{sc}}} = \frac{V}{V_{sc}}; \quad (2.84)$$

or, for a gas where the units of B_g are RB/scf,

$$B_g = \frac{V_g}{\alpha_c V_{gsc}}; \quad (2.85)$$

or, multiplying and dividing by the mass of the fluid,

$$B_g = \left(\frac{m}{\alpha_c V_{gsc}}\right)\left(\frac{V_g}{m}\right)$$

$$= \frac{\rho_{gsc}}{\alpha_c \rho_g}, \quad (2.86)$$

where m = mass of gas occupying V_g or V_{gsc}. Gas density at p and T and at p_{sc} and T_{sc} can be obtained by applying the real-gas law at two conditions,

$$\rho_{gsc} = \frac{p_{sc} M}{z_{sc} RT_{sc}} \quad (2.87)$$

and $\rho_g = \frac{pM}{zRT}$. (2.61)

Substituting these two equations into Eq. 2.86 results in

$$B_g = \frac{p_{sc} M}{\alpha_c z_{sc} RT_{sc}} \frac{zRT}{pM} \quad (2.88)$$

or $B_g = \frac{p_{sc}}{\alpha_c p} \frac{T}{T_{sc}} \frac{z}{z_{sc}}$, (2.89)

or $B_g = \frac{p_{sc}}{\alpha_c T_{sc}} T \frac{z}{p}$ (2.90)

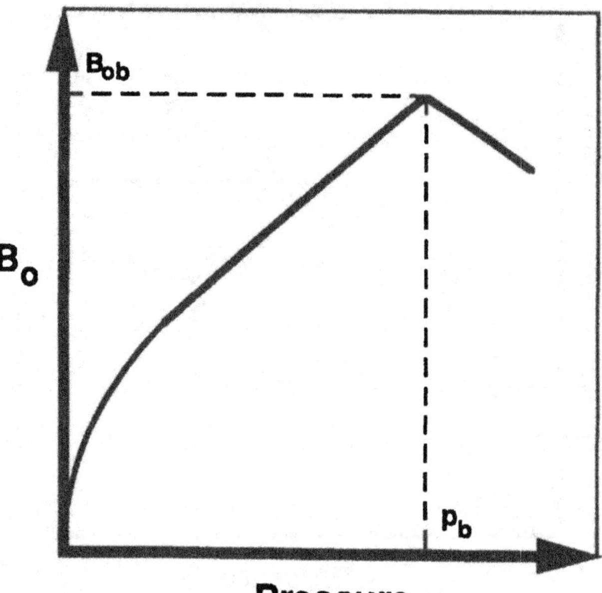

Fig. 2.10—Oil FVF for constant-bubblepoint-pressure oil.

(because $z_{sc} = 1$). The units of B_g are RB/scf.

Fluid Density. The pressure dependence of density of black-oil-reservoir fluids is shown in Fig. 2.4. For single-phase flow, the density of water, gas, and gas-free oil can be obtained from Eq. 2.80, so

$$\rho_l = \frac{\rho_{lsc}}{B_l}, \quad (2.91)$$

where $l = o, w,$ or g. If B_l is estimated with Eq. 2.81 for water and gas-free oil, then the density of these two liquid phases can be expressed as

$$\rho_l = \rho_{lsc}\left[1 + c_l(p - p_{sc}) - c_{Tl}(T - T_{sc})\right], \quad (2.92)$$

where $l = o$ or w. The real-gas law gives the density of gas.

$$\rho_g = \frac{pM}{zRT}. \quad (2.61)$$

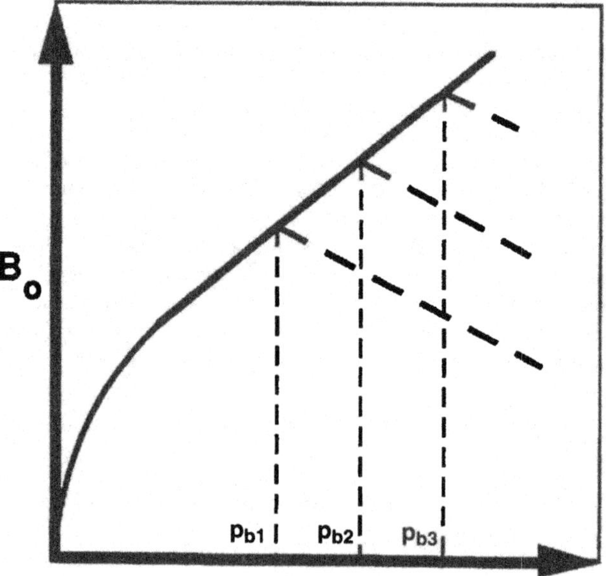

Fig. 2.11—Oil FVF for variable-bubblepoint-pressure oil.

Eq. 2.91 gives the water-phase density for multiphase flow in oil reservoirs by use of the appropriate FVF or with Eq. 2.92. Eq. 2.61 gives the gas-phase density. If ideal mixing of oil and solution gas is assumed, then the oil-phase density (stock-tank oil plus the solution gas dissolved in it) is estimated by

$$\rho_o = \left(\rho_{osc} + \frac{1}{\alpha_c}\rho_{gsc} R_s\right)/B_o, \quad\text{.......}\quad (2.93)$$

where $p \leqq p_b$, or

$$\rho_o = \rho_{ob}\left[1 + c_o(p - p_b)\right], \quad\text{.......}\quad (2.94)$$

where $p > p_b$ and ρ_{ob} is estimated with Eq. 2.93 at the bubblepoint-pressure conditions, c_o = compressibility of stock-tank oil and its solution gas at p_b, B_o = input from PVT-data analysis when $p \leqq p_b$, and α_c = a volumetric conversion factor defined in Table 2.1.

Example 2.6. Derive an expression for the density of slightly compressible fluids at reservoir pressure and temperature (Eq. 2.92). Then use the resulting expression to derive Eq. 2.81 for the FVF.

Solution. From the definition of fluid compressibility,

$$c_l = \frac{1}{\rho_l}\frac{\partial \rho_l}{\partial p}\Big|_T, \quad\text{.......}\quad (2.60)$$

where $l = o$ or w for slightly compressible fluids and c_l = constant over the pressure range of interest. Eq. 2.60 can be integrated at reservoir temperature by separation of variables as

$$c_l \partial p = \frac{\partial \rho_l}{\rho_l} \quad\text{.......}\quad (2.95a)$$

$$\text{and } c_l \int_{p^\circ}^{p} \partial p = \int_{\rho^\circ}^{\rho} \frac{\partial \rho_l}{\rho_l}, \quad\text{.......}\quad (2.95b)$$

where $\overset{\circ}{\rho_l} = \rho_l|_{p^\circ,T}$, or as

$$c_l(p - p^\circ) = \log_e\left(\frac{\rho_l}{\overset{\circ}{\rho_l}}\right). \quad\text{.......}\quad (2.95c)$$

Taking the exponential of both sides of Eq. 2.95c and rearranging yields

$$\rho_l = \rho_l^\circ \exp\left[c_l(p - p^\circ)\right], \quad\text{.......}\quad (2.96)$$

where $l = o$ or w. Eq. 2.96 is one of the forms of the desired expression. To obtain an expression for B, divide Eq. 2.96 by $\rho_{lsc} = \rho_l|_{p_{sc},T_{sc}}$ so that

$$\frac{\rho_l}{\rho_{lsc}} = \frac{\overset{\circ}{\rho_l}}{\rho_{lsc}}\exp\left[c_l(p - p^\circ)\right], \quad\text{.......}\quad (2.97)$$

where $l = o$ or w. With the definition of B_l given in Eq. 2.80,

$$\frac{1}{B_l} = \frac{1}{\overset{\circ}{B_l}}\exp\left[c_l(p - p^\circ)\right] \quad\text{.......}\quad (2.98a)$$

$$\text{or } B_l = \overset{\circ}{B_l}/\exp\left[c_l(p - p^\circ)\right], \quad\text{.......}\quad (2.98b)$$

(where $l = o$ or w), which is one of the forms for the FVF for a slightly compressible fluid.

The exponential term, $\exp[c_l(p - p^\circ)]$, can be expanded with Taylor's series expansion (see Example 3.15) about p° as

$$\exp\left[c_l(p - p^\circ)\right] = 1 + c_l(p - p^\circ) + \frac{1}{2!}c_l^2(p - p^\circ)^2 + \ldots \quad\text{.......}\quad (2.99)$$

Considering only the first two terms of this expansion,

$$\exp\left[c_l(p - p^\circ)\right] \approx 1 + c_l(p - p^\circ), \quad\text{.......}\quad (2.100)$$

(where $l = o$ or w) because c_l is small (10^{-5} to 10^{-6} psi^{-1}).

Substituting Eq. 2.100 into Eqs. 2.96 and 2.98b, one obtains other forms of the sought expression,

$$\rho_l = \overset{\circ}{\rho_l}\left[1 + c_l(p - p^\circ)\right] \quad\text{.......}\quad (2.101)$$

$$\text{and } B_l = \overset{\circ}{B_l}/\left[1 + c_l(p - p^\circ)\right], \quad\text{.......}\quad (2.102)$$

where $l = o$ or w.

The last step in this example involves expressing $\overset{\circ}{\rho_l} = \rho_l|_{p^\circ,T}$ in terms of $\rho_{lsc} = \rho_l|_{p_{sc},T_{sc}}$.

First, let $p^\circ = p_{sc}$, then $\overset{\circ}{\rho_l} = \rho_l|_{p_{sc},T}$, then include the effect of temperature change from T to T_{sc} on $\overset{\circ}{\rho_l}$ by considering the fluid-expansion coefficient

$$c_{Tl} = \frac{1}{V_l}\frac{\partial V_l}{\partial T}\Big|_{p^\circ} = -\frac{1}{\rho_l}\frac{\partial \rho_l}{\partial T}\Big|_{p^\circ}, \quad\text{.......}\quad (2.103)$$

where $l = o$ or w and c_{Tl} = both constant in the temperature range (T_{sc}, T) and is small.

Integrating Eq. 2.103 by separation of variables yields

$$c_{Tl}\partial T = -\frac{\partial \rho_l}{\rho_l}, \quad\text{.......}\quad (2.104a)$$

$$c_{Tl}\int_{T_{sc}}^{T} \partial T = -\int_{\rho_{sc}}^{\rho^\circ} \frac{\partial \rho_l}{\rho_l}, \quad\text{.......}\quad (2.104b)$$

$$\text{and } \overset{\circ}{\rho_l} = \rho_{lsc}\exp\left[-c_{Tl}(T - T_{sc})\right], \quad\text{.......}\quad (2.104c)$$

where $l = o$ or w.

Again, the exponential term in Eq. 2.104c may be approximated by the first two terms of Taylor's series expansion (because c_{Tl} is small) to give

$$\overset{\circ}{\rho_l} = \rho_l|_{p_{sc},T} \approx \rho_{lsc}\left[1 - c_{Tl}(T - T_{sc})\right], \quad\text{.......}\quad (2.105)$$

where $l = o$ or w.

Combining Eqs. 2.101 and 2.105 gives

$$\rho_l = \rho_{lsc}\left[1 + c_l(p - p_{sc})\right]\left[1 - c_{Tl}(T - T_{sc})\right]$$

$$= \rho_{lsc}[1 + c_l(p - p_{sc}) - c_{Tl}(T - T_{sc})$$

$$- c_l c_{Tl}(p - p_{sc})(T - T_{sc})]. \quad\text{.......}\quad (2.106)$$

The last term in Eq. 2.106 is small because of the product of c_l and c_{Tl}, so for engineering purposes it can be neglected; therefore,

$$\rho_l = \rho_{lsc}\left[1 + c_l(p - p_{sc}) - c_{Tl}(T - T_{sc})\right], \quad\text{.......}\quad (2.92)$$

where $l = o$ or w.

Eq. 2.92 can be arranged to give

$$B_l = \frac{\rho_{lsc}}{\rho_l}$$

$$= 1/\left[1 + c_l(p - p_{sc}) - c_{Tl}(T - T_{sc})\right], \quad\text{.......}\quad (2.81)$$

where $l = o$ or w.

Fluid Viscosity. Fluid viscosity is a measure of the ease with which the fluid flows as a result of an applied pressure gradient. For a dilute (gaseous) fluid, the molecules are far apart and offer low resistance to flow as a consquence of their random motions. In contrast, a dense fluid offers high resistance to flow because the fluid molecules are close to each other and their random motions retard flow. Fluid viscosity is a function of both pressure and temperature; however, we are only interested in the pressure dependence of viscosity in isothermal reservoirs.

One can analyze the variation of water and gas viscosities with pressure by considering the effect of pressure on their densities. Water

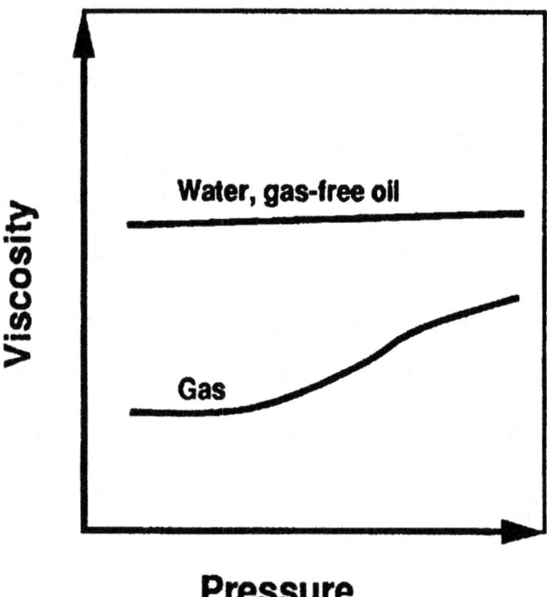

Fig. 2.12—Viscosity of slightly compressible fluids and gas.

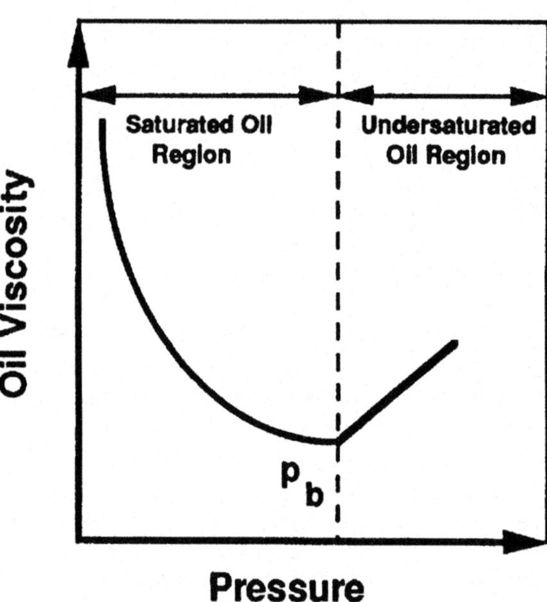

Fig. 2.13—Viscosity of constant-bubblepoint-pressure oil.

is slightly compressible; therefore, as pressure increases, water viscosity increases slightly or remains almost constant (see **Fig. 2.12**). Gas is a compressible fluid, and its viscosity is low at low pressures. Gas viscosity increases as pressure increases but tends to level off at high pressures (Fig. 2.12) because gas under high pressure begins to behave as if it is a liquid.

The pressure/viscosity relationship for gas-free (dead) oil is analogous to that of water, whereas that of the oil phase in a gas/oil system must account for mass transfer (**Fig. 2.13**). Fig. 2.13 shows the viscosity behavior, which can be explained by considering the effect of pressure on oil-phase density and solution-gas/oil ratio on oil-phase dilution. In the undersaturated oil region ($p > p_b$), oil dilution remains unchanged because R_s is constant (Fig. 2.6), and only the oil-component density decreases as pressure decreases from p_i to p_b. As a result, the oil-phase viscosity in this region decreases as pressure decreases. In the saturated oil region ($p \leqq p_b$), both oil-phase dilution and density change in response to pressure changes. As pressure decreases, gas evolves from the oil phase, leaving it less diluted by gas. On the other hand, the oil component and the associated solution gas expand as pressure drops. The effect of gas liberation on viscosity dominates the effect of oil expansion; therefore, the oil phase becomes more viscous as the reservoir pressure drops.

For variable-bubblepoint formulations, the oil-phase viscosity follows the solid line in **Fig. 2.14** as long as the oil is saturated with gas. Once the oil becomes undersaturated, the oil-phase viscosity follows one of the dashed lines, depending on its corresponding bubblepoint pressure. Mathematically,

$$\mu_o = \mu_{ob}/\left[1 - c_\mu(p - p_b)\right] \quad \text{.................. (2.107)}$$

for $p > p_b$, where μ_{ob} = oil viscosity at p_b and c_μ = fractional change of viscosity per unit change of pressure. The value of c_μ in Eq. 2.107 may either be constant (i.e., the dashed lines in Fig. 2.14 are parallel) or a function of the solution-gas/oil ratio.

The behavior of viscosity is related to that of density because density is a measure of the mean free path of liquid and gas molecules and, consequently, a measure of random molecular motions and interactions that affect viscosity.

2.3.3 Fluid/Rock Properties. This section presents basic definitions of fluid saturations encountered in multiphase flow and introduces the concepts of capillary pressure and relative permeability, as well as the most widely used relative permeability models in reservoir simulation.

Fluid Saturation. Fluid saturation of a particular fluid is the fraction of the pore space that is occupied by that fluid. For single-phase flow, fluid saturation, S_l, is unity. For two-phase flow of oil and water, the oil saturation, S_o, is the fraction of void space occupied by the oil phase, and the water saturation, S_w, is the remaining fraction that is occupied by the water phase. These two saturations are interdependent; that is,

$$S_o + S_w = 1. \quad \text{.............................. (2.108)}$$

The water saturation at which water becomes immobile is called the irreducible water saturation, S_{iw}. During water displacement, the oil saturation at which oil becomes immobile is called the residual oil saturation (ROS) to water, S_{orw}. The value $S_{w\max} = 1 - S_{orw}$ is the maximum water saturation that can be achieved during water displacement.

For two-phase flow of oil and gas there are similar definitions for S_o; gas saturation, S_g; critical gas saturation, S_{gc}; and ROS to gas, S_{org}. In general, the ROS in an oil/gas system, S_{org}, is not equal to the ROS in oil/water system, S_{orw}. Again,

$$S_o + S_g = 1. \quad \text{.............................. (2.109)}$$

In two-phase systems, the wetting phase adheres to the pore walls and occupies the fine pores. The nonwetting phase occupies the center of the pores.

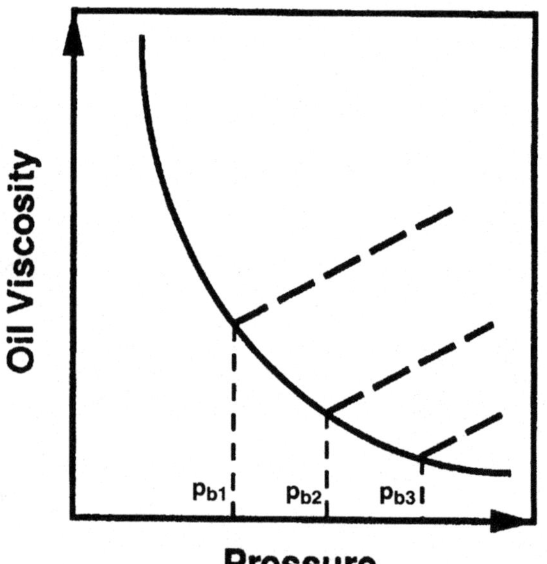

Fig. 2.14—Viscosity of variable-bubblepoint-pressure oil.

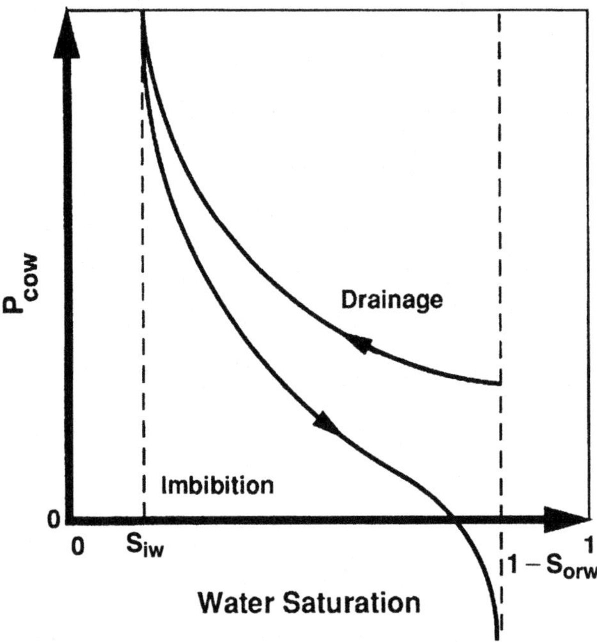

Fig. 2.15—Capillary pressure in oil/water system (water wet).

For three-phase flow of oil, water, and gas, the sum of oil and water saturations is frequently referred to as liquid saturation, S_L. The three saturations are related through the constraint equation

$$S_o + S_w + S_g = 1. \quad (2.110)$$

In three-phase systems, the wetting phase adheres to the walls of the solid rock and fills the fine pores, the nonwetting phase occupies the center of large pores, and the remaining phase fills the space left unoccupied by the other two phases.

Example 2.7. For a two-phase oil/water system, show that the effective liquid compressibility is given by

$$c_{Le} = c_R(1-\phi) + \phi\left(c_o S_o + c_w S_w\right) \quad (2.111)$$

and how the effective oil compressibility in a single-phase oil reservoir can be derived from Eq. 2.111.

Solution. The bulk volume is the PV plus the rock-solids volume,

$$V_b = V_p + V_s. \quad (2.37a)$$

We also have

$$\phi = \frac{V_p}{V_b}. \quad (2.112)$$

As the pore pressure varies, both V_p and V_s vary so that

$$\frac{dV_b}{dp} = \frac{dV_p}{dp} + \frac{dV_s}{dp}. \quad (2.113)$$

Using the definition of compressibility, we have

$$\frac{dV_b}{dp} = -c_b V_b, \quad (2.114a)$$

$$\frac{dV_b}{dp} = -c_p V_p, \quad (2.114b)$$

$$\text{and } \frac{dV_s}{dp} = -c_R V_s = -c_R\left(V_b - V_p\right). \quad (2.114c)$$

Substituting these three relationships into Eq. 2.113 yields

$$-c_b V_b = -c_p V_p - c_R\left(V_b - V_p\right), \quad (2.115)$$

and dividing through by V_b and using Eq. 2.112 gives

$$c_b = c_p\phi + c_R(1-\phi). \quad (2.116)$$

This is the effective compressibility of pores saturated with liquid (oil and water) and is also the effective compressibility of the system; that is,

$$c_{pe} = c_{Le} = c_p\phi + c_R(1-\phi). \quad (2.117)$$

We now have

$$V_p = V_o + V_w, \quad (2.118a)$$

$$S_o = \frac{V_o}{V_p}, \quad (2.118b)$$

$$\text{and } S_w = \frac{V_w}{V_p}. \quad (2.118c)$$

Differentiating Eq. 2.118a with respect to pressure gives

$$\frac{dV_p}{dp} = \frac{dV_o}{dp} + \frac{dV_w}{dp}. \quad (2.119)$$

Using the definition of compressibility gives

$$\frac{dV_p}{dp} = -c_p V_p, \quad (2.114b)$$

$$\frac{dV_o}{dp} = -c_o V_o, \quad (2.120a)$$

$$\text{and } \frac{dV_w}{dp} = -c_w V_w. \quad (2.120b)$$

Combining Eqs. 2.119, 2.114b, and 2.120 results in

$$c_p = c_o\frac{V_o}{V_p} + c_w\frac{V_w}{V_p}$$

$$= c_o S_o + c_w S_w. \quad (2.121)$$

Substituting Eq. 2.121 into Eq. 2.117 yields

$$c_{Le} = \phi\left(c_o S_o + c_w S_w\right) + c_R(1-\phi), \quad (2.111)$$

which is the desired relationship, and

$$c_{oe} = c_o\phi + c_R(1-\phi) \quad (2.122)$$

can be derived from Eq. 2.111.

For two-phase oil and water, $S_o + S_w = 1$, and for single-phase oil, $S_w = 0$ and $S_o = 1$. In this case, Eq. 2.111 reduces to

$$c_{Le} = c_{oe} = \phi\left[c_o(1) + c_w(0)\right] + c_R(1-\phi)$$

$$= \phi c_o + c_R(1-\phi). \quad (2.123)$$

Capillary Pressure. Capillary pressure exists whenever pores (capillaries) are saturated with two or more phases. In a two-phase system, capillary pressure is, by definition, the pressure of the nonwetting phase minus the pressure of the wetting phase.

$$P_{cow} = p_o - p_w = f(S_w) \quad (2.124)$$

for a water-wet system, and

$$P_{cgo} = p_g - p_o = f\left(S_g\right) \quad (2.125)$$

for a two-phase oil and gas system.

Capillary pressure is a function of saturation and saturation history (that is, drainage or imbibition) for a given reservoir rock and fluids at a constant temperature and composition.[18] **Fig. 2.15** shows the functional dependence of P_{cow} on water saturation and saturation history. The wetting-phase saturation at which the wetting phase (typi-

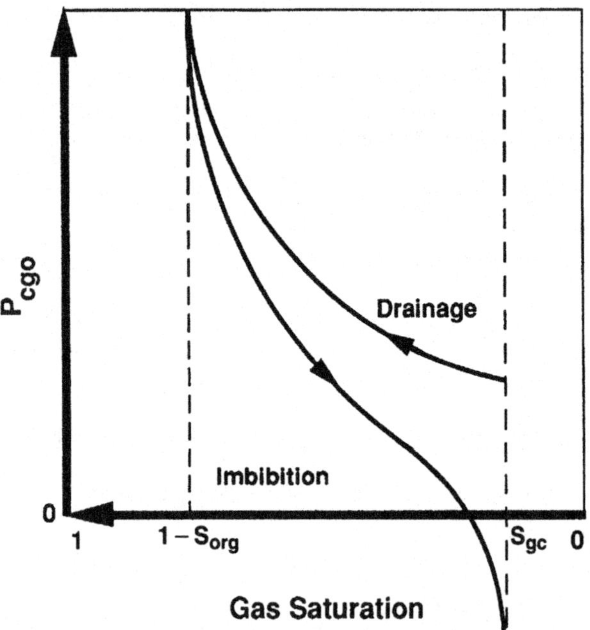

Fig. 2.16—Capillary pressure in oil/gas system (oil wet).

cally water) can no longer be displaced by an applied pressure gradient during drainage is S_{iw}. The nonwetting-phase saturation at which the nonwetting phase (typically oil) can no longer be displaced by an applied pressure gradient during imbibition is S_{orw}. S_{iw} and S_{orw} are congruent to the endpoint saturations of the two-phase oil/water relative permeability curves.

Fig. 2.16 shows the dependence of P_{cgo} on gas saturation and saturation history. In this case, oil is always the wetting phase and gas is always the nonwetting phase. Here, the irreducible wetting-phase saturation is S_{org} and the irreducible nonwetting-phase saturation is S_{gc}. Again, the endpoint saturations of capillary pressure curve are congruent with the endpoint saturations of the gas/oil relative permeability curves.

For a three-phase oil, water, and gas system, P_{cow} and P_{cgo} are functions of both S_w and S_g, respectively; however, Leverett and Lewis[19] found some justification for using P_{cow} and P_{cgo} derived from two-phase systems in three-phase flow problems.

In practice, obtaining a high degree of accuracy when evaluating the change in saturation with depth is often impossible. Under these conditions, the capillary pressure data are used to evaluate initial vertical saturation distribution in a reservoir. Qualitatively, the capillary pressure curves indicate the degree of rock wettability, the nature of the pore-size distribution (uniform or nonuniform, large or small pores), and the connate-water saturation.

Relative Permeability. Originally, Darcy's law was derived for single-phase flow where the permeability of the porous medium to the fluid is the absolute permeability of the medium. When two or more fluids flow simultaneously through the porous medium, Darcy's law can be modified to calculate the flow rate of each phase. The necessary modifications include the use of effective phase permeability (instead of absolute permeability), phase potential (which includes the effects of phase density and capillary pressure), and phase viscosity. With these modifications, the flow rates of oil and water in a two-phase flow system can be written as

$$q_{ox} = -\beta_c \frac{k_{ox} A_x}{\mu_o} \frac{d\Phi_o}{dx} \quad \text{(2.126)}$$

and $$q_{wx} = -\beta_c \frac{k_{wx} A_x}{\mu_w} \frac{d\Phi_w}{dx}, \quad \text{(2.127)}$$

where the effective permeabilities, k_{ox} and k_{wx}, are saturation dependent. The effective permeability to oil, for example, can be expressed as

$$k_{ox} = k_x\left(\frac{k_{ox}}{k_x}\right) = k_x k_{row}, \quad \text{(2.128)}$$

where k_x = absolute permeability of the porous medium in the x-direction and k_{row} = relative permeability to oil. Similarly, for the water phase,

$$k_{wx} = k_x k_{rw}. \quad \text{(2.129)}$$

Substituting Eqs. 2.128 and 2.129 into Eqs. 2.126 and 2.127 results in

$$q_{ox} = -\beta_c k_x A_x \frac{k_{row}}{\mu_o} \frac{d\Phi_o}{dx} \quad \text{(2.130)}$$

and $$q_{wx} = -\beta_c k_x A_x \frac{k_{rw}}{\mu_w} \frac{d\Phi_w}{dx}. \quad \text{(2.131)}$$

Similarly, the flow rates of oil and gas in a two-phase flow system can be expressed

$$q_{ox} = -\beta_c k_x A_x \frac{k_{rog}}{\mu_o} \frac{d\Phi_o}{dx} \quad \text{(2.132)}$$

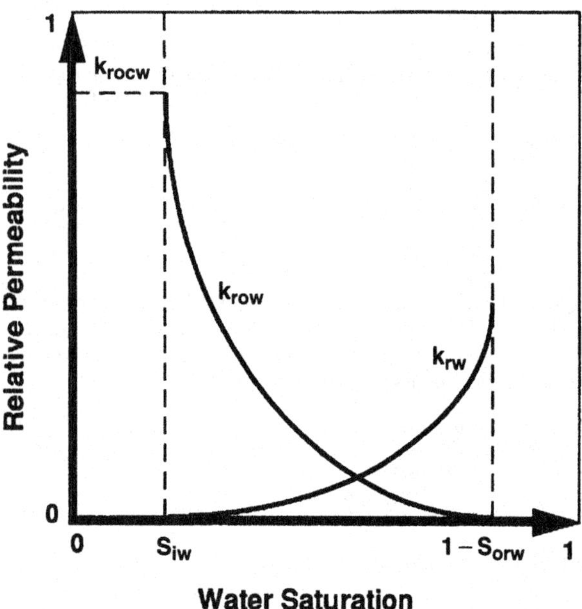

Fig. 2.17—Relative permeabilities for an oil/water system (imbibition curves).

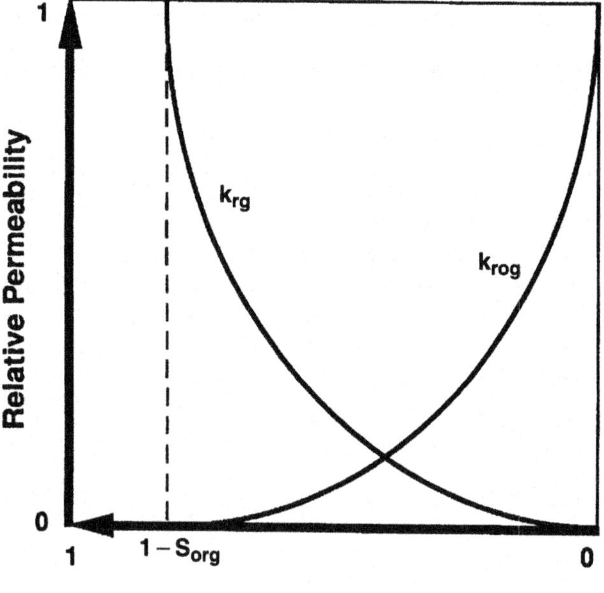

Fig. 2.18—Relative permeabilities for an oil/gas system (drainage curves).

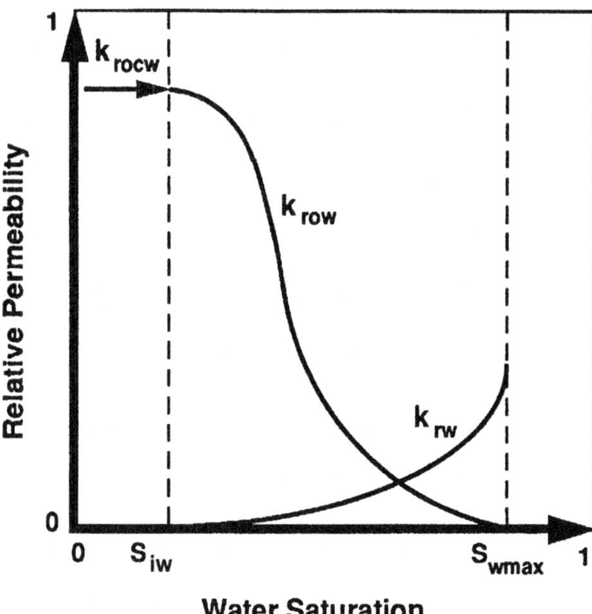

Fig. 2.19—Oil/water relative permeability.

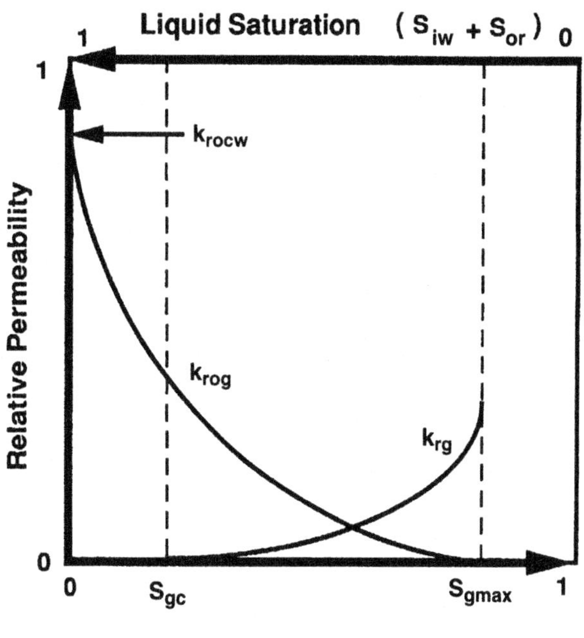

Fig. 2.20—Oil/gas relative permeability.

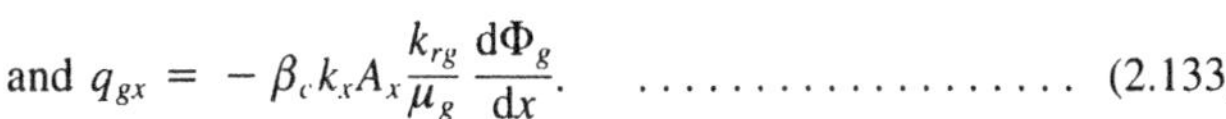

$$\text{and } q_{gx} = -\beta_c k_x A_x \frac{k_{rg}}{\mu_g} \frac{d\Phi_g}{dx}. \quad \text{(2.133)}$$

Figs. 2.17 and 2.18 show the relative permeabilities k_{row} and k_{rw} as functions of S_w for an oil/water system and k_{rog} and k_{rg} as functions of S_g for an oil/gas system, respectively. Note that the relative permeability of a phase falls between zero and one when the base permeability is the absolute permeability, and that the individual sums of k_{row} and k_{rw} at any S_w (and k_{rog} and k_{rg} at any S_g) are always less than or equal to one. This latter effect is caused by the interfacial tension between the two resident fluids.

In summary, for multiphase flow in porous media, the flow rates of the various phases are given by

$$q_{wx} = -\beta_c k_x A_x \frac{k_{rw}}{\mu_w} \frac{d\Phi_w}{dx}, \quad \text{(2.134)}$$

$$q_{gx} = -\beta_c k_x A_x \frac{k_{rg}}{\mu_g} \frac{d\Phi_g}{dx}, \quad \text{(2.135)}$$

$$\text{and } q_{ox} = -\beta_c k_x A_x \frac{k_{ro}}{\mu_o} \frac{d\Phi_o}{dx}, \quad \text{(2.136)}$$

where k_{rw}, k_{rg}, and k_{ro} = relative permeabilities to water, gas, and oil in a three-phase system, respectively. (Note that k_{ro} in Eq. 2.136 is the three-phase relative permeability. This quantity is dependent on S_w, S_g, k_{row}, and k_{rog}, and is discussed in detail in Sec. 2.3.5, Three-Phase Relative Permeability Models.)

2.3.4 Two-Phase Relative Permeability Models. Two-phase relative permeability data are generally obtained from laboratory measurements on suitable cores. In some cases these data may be missing, and reasonable approximations are necessary. These approximations are called models when they are available in an algebraic form. This section presents two models that are often used in reservoir simulation.

Corey's[20] Two-Phase Model. Corey's two-phase model is applicable for the drainage process in consolidated rocks. The normalized wetting-phase saturation is defined as

$$S_{wn} = \frac{S_w - S_{iw}}{1 - S_{iw}}, \quad \text{(2.137)}$$

where S_w and S_{iw} = saturation and irreducible saturation of the wetting phase, respectively. The relative permeability of the wetting phase is approximated by

$$k_{rw} = S_{wn}^4, \quad \text{(2.138)}$$

while the relative permeability of the nonwetting phase is approximated by

$$k_{rnw} = (1 - S_{wn})^2 (1 - S_{wn}^2). \quad \text{(2.139)}$$

Naar and Henderson's[21] Two-Phase Model. The Naar-Henderson model is statistically derived for oil/water systems for the imbibition process. Both oil and water relative permeabilities are approximated as functions of S_{wn}.

$$S_{wn} = \frac{S_w - S_{iw}}{1 - S_{iw}}. \quad \text{(2.140)}$$

The water-phase relative permeability is

$$k_{rw} = S_{wn}^4, \quad \text{(2.141)}$$

while the oil-phase relative permeability is approximated by

$$k_{row} = (1 - 2S_{wn})^{3/2} \left[2 - (1 - 2S_{wn})^{1/2}\right]. \quad \text{(2.142)}$$

Examination of Eq. 2.142 reveals that $k_{row} = 0$ for all values of $S_{wn} \geqq 0.5$.

2.3.5 Three-Phase Relative Permeability Models. The functional dependence of three-phase relative permeabilities can be approximated by[22,23]

$$k_{rw} = f(S_w), \quad \text{(2.143)}$$

$$k_{rg} = f(S_g), \quad \text{(2.144)}$$

$$\text{and } k_{ro} = f(S_w, S_g). \quad \text{(2.145)}$$

The assumptions in Eqs. 2.143 through 2.145 are that water is the wetting phase, gas is the nonwetting phase, and oil is the intermediate wetting phase in a three-phase system. Therefore, $k_{rw} = f(S_w)$ represents the relative permeability of the wetting phase (obtained from measured two-phase data or a two-phase relative permeability model), and $k_{rg} = f(S_g)$ represents the relative permeability of the nonwetting phase (also obtained from two-phase data or model).

In practice, the form of the function $f(S_w, S_g)$ in Eq. 2.145 is rarely known. It is possible, however, to estimate k_{ro} with two sets of two-phase relative permeability data (oil/water system and oil/gas system in the presence of irreducible water). The function $k_{row} = f(S_w)$ in **Fig. 2.19** can be thought of as the relative permeability of the nonwetting phase (oil and gas), while the function $k_{rog} = f(S_g)$ in **Fig. 2.20** can be thought of as that of the wetting phase (oil and water). With this idealization, the point on the saturation axis in Fig. 2.19 where $k_{row}=0$ denotes the maximum water saturation rather than ROS because a further decrease in oil saturation below $S_{orw}=1-S_{w\max}$ is possible by increasing the gas saturation. Experimental evidence shows, however, that ROS in a three-phase system never reaches zero.

The following sections present the three most commonly used models to predict three-phase relative permeabilities.

Naar, Henderson, and Wygal's[21,24] Three-Phase Model. The relative permeabilities of individual reservoir phases are expressed as

$$k_{rw}=\left(\frac{S_w-S_{iw}}{1-S_{iw}}\right)^4, \quad (2.146)$$

$$k_{ro}=\frac{S_o^3\left(1-S_g+2S_w-3S_{iw}\right)}{\left(1-S_{iw}\right)^4}, \quad (2.147)$$

and $$k_{rg}=\frac{S_g^3\left(2-S_g-2S_{iw}\right)}{\left(1-S_{iw}\right)^4}. \quad (2.148)$$

Because this model does not incorporate S_{or} or S_{gc}, the following cutoffs must be imposed on the model predictions (Eqs. 2.147 and 2.148):

$$k_{ro}=0 \quad (2.149)$$

for $S_o\leqq S_{or}$ and

$$k_{rg}=0 \quad (2.150)$$

for $S_g\leqq S_{gc}$.

Stone's[25] Three-Phase Model 1. Stone's first three-phase model uses two sets of two-phase relative permeability data (Figs. 2.19 and 2.20) and the knowledge of S_{or} in a three-phase system to approximate f(S_w, S_g) in Eq. 2.145.[17] In other words, this model is only concerned with the prediction of the relative permeability to the oil phase.

Normalized saturations are defined as

$$S_{wn}=\frac{S_w-S_{iw}}{1-S_{iw}-S_{or}}, \quad (2.151)$$

where $S_w\geqq S_{iw}$;

$$S_{on}=\frac{S_o-S_{or}}{1-S_{iw}-S_{or}}, \quad (2.152)$$

where $S_o\geqq S_{or}$; and

$$S_{gn}=\frac{S_g}{1-S_{iw}-S_{or}}=1-S_{wn}-S_{on}. \quad (2.153)$$

Then,

$$\frac{k_{ro}}{k_{rocw}}=S_{on}\beta_w\beta_g, \quad (2.154)$$

where $$\beta_w=\frac{k_{row}/k_{rocw}}{1-S_{wn}}, \quad (2.155)$$

$$\beta_g=\frac{k_{rog}/k_{rocw}}{1-S_{gn}}, \quad (2.156)$$

$k_{row}=f(S_w)$ is obtained from two-phase oil/water data (Fig. 2.19), $k_{rog}=f(S_g)$ is obtained from two-phase oil/gas data in the presence of irreducible water (Fig. 2.20), and

$$k_{rocw}=k_{row}|_{S_w=S_{iw}}=k_{rog}|_{S_g=0}. \quad (2.157)$$

In other words, k_{rocw} is the oil-phase relative permeability at S_{iw}.

Stone's[26] Three-Phase Model 2. Stone's second model is a probability model based on channel flow considerations.[17] Like Stone's first model, the second model approximates f(S_w, S_g) in Eq. 2.145 using two sets of two-phase relative permeability data (Figs. 2.19 and 2.20) but does not require the knowledge of S_{or} in a three-phase system. The model equation is

$$\frac{k_{ro}}{k_{rocw}}=\left(k_{row}/k_{rocw}+k_{rw}\right)\left(k_{rog}/k_{rocw}+k_{rg}\right)-\left(k_{rw}+k_{rg}\right), \quad (2.158)$$

where $k_{ro}\geqq 0$, k_{row} and k_{rw} are obtained at S_w by use of two-phase oil/water relative permeability data (Fig. 2.19), and k_{rog} and k_{rg} are obtained at S_g by use of two-phase oil/gas relative permeability data in the presence of irreducible water (Fig. 2.20). Again, Eq. 2.157 gives k_{rocw}.

Both Stone's Models 1 and 2 reduce to the two-phase oil and water relative permeability data at $S_g=0$ and to the two-phase oil and gas relative permeability data at $S_w=S_{iw}$.

Example 2.8. Show that Stone's Model 1 reduces to the two-phase relative permeability data at $S_g=0$ and $S_w=S_{iw}$.

Solution. At $S_g=0$, $S_{gn}=0$, and $k_{rog}=k_{rocw}$, Eq. 2.153 with $S_{gn}=0$ gives

$$S_{on}+S_{wn}=1 \quad (2.159)$$

or $$S_{on}=1-S_{wn}. \quad (2.160)$$

Combining Eqs. 2.155 and 2.160 gives

$$\beta_w=\frac{k_{row}/k_{rocw}}{S_{on}} \quad (2.161)$$

for all values of S_w.

Substituting $S_{gn}=0$ and $k_{rog}=k_{rocw}$ into Eq. 2.156 yields

$$\beta_g=\frac{k_{rocw}/k_{rocw}}{1-0}=\frac{1}{1}=1. \quad (2.162)$$

Substituting Eqs. 2.161 and 2.162 into Eq. 2.154 results in

$$\frac{k_{ro}}{k_{rocw}}=S_{on}\left(\frac{k_{row}/k_{rocw}}{S_{on}}\right)(1), \quad (2.163)$$

which simplifies to

$$k_{ro}=k_{row} \quad (2.164)$$

for all values of S_w.

At $S_w=S_{iw}$,

$$S_{wn}=0 \quad (2.165a)$$

and $$k_{row}=k_{rocw}. \quad (2.165b)$$

Eq. 2.153 and $S_{wn}=0$ gives

$$S_{on}=1-S_{gn}. \quad (2.166)$$

Combining Eqs. 2.155 and 2.165 yields

$$\beta_w=\frac{k_{rocw}/k_{rocw}}{1-0}$$

$$=1. \quad (2.167)$$

Combining Eqs. 2.156 and 2.166 yields

$$\beta_g=\frac{k_{rog}/k_{rocw}}{S_{on}} \quad (2.168)$$

for all values of S_g.

Substituting Eqs. 2.167 and 2.168 into Eq. 2.154 results in

$$\frac{k_{ro}}{k_{rocw}}=S_{on}(1)\left(\frac{k_{rog}/k_{rocw}}{S_{on}}\right), \quad (2.169)$$

which simplifies to give $k_{ro}=k_{rog}$ for all values of S_g.

Eq. 2.164 states that Model 1 predicts relative permeability to oil in a two-phase oil/water system when $S_g=0$. Also, Eq. 2.169 states that Model 1 predicts relative permeability to oil in a two-phase oil/gas system in presence of irreducible water (when $S_w=S_{iw}$). Therefore, Stone's Model 1 reduces to the original two-phase relative permeability data.

Example 2.9.

Show that Stone's Model 2 reduces to two-phase relative permeability data under the same conditions as Example 2.8.

Solution.

Predict k_{ro} at $S_g = 0$ using Eq. 2.158.

At $S_g = 0$, $k_{rg} = 0$ and $k_{rog} = k_{rocw}$, regardless of the values of S_w; substituting these into Eq. 2.158 yields

$$\frac{k_{ro}}{k_{rocw}} = (k_{row}/k_{rocw} + k_{rw})(k_{rocw}/k_{rocw} + 0) - (k_{rw} + 0); \quad (2.170)$$

therefore, it follows that

$$\frac{k_{ro}}{k_{rocw}} = (k_{row}/k_{rocw} + k_{rw})(1) - k_{rw}$$

$$= k_{row}/k_{rocw} + k_{rw} - k_{rw}$$

$$= k_{row}/k_{rocw} \quad (2.171)$$

or $k_{ro} = k_{row}$ for all values of S_w.

That is to say, the relative permeability to oil predicted by Stone's Model 2 at $S_g = 0$ is for oil in a two-phase oil and water system.

Predict k_{ro} at $S_w = S_{iw}$ using Eq. 2.158.

At $S_w = S_{iw}$, $k_{rw} = 0$ and $k_{row} = k_{rocw}$, regardless of the values of S_g. Substituting these into Eq. 2.158 yields

$$\frac{k_{ro}}{k_{rocw}} = (k_{rocw}/k_{rocw} + 0)(k_{rog}/k_{rocw} + k_{rg}) - (0 + k_{rg}). \quad (2.172)$$

Again, this can be simplified to

$$\frac{k_{ro}}{k_{rocw}} = (1 + 0)(k_{rog}/k_{rocw} + k_{rg}) - k_{rg}$$

$$= k_{rog}/k_{rocw} + k_{rg} - k_{rg}$$

$$= k_{rog}/k_{rocw} \quad (2.173)$$

or $k_{ro} = k_{rog}$ for all values of S_g and $S_w = S_{iw}$.

In other words, Stone's Model 2 predicts values for k_{ro} equal to those for oil in an oil, gas, and irreducible water system.

2.4 Law of Mass Conservation

The law of conservation of mass is a material-balance equation written for a component in a control volume of the system to be modeled. In petroleum reservoirs, the control volume is made up of a porous medium containing one, two, or three fluid phases. This section concerns single-phase fluid. The porous medium is treated as a continuum whose physical properties at any point are those of a representative element of the medium. The control volume, whose shape depends on the coordinate system used in the model, is chosen and a material balance for the component is written over it. The material-balance equation for any component, c, in the system may be expressed as

$$(m_i - m_o)_c + (m_s)_c = m_{a_c}, \quad (2.174)$$

where m_i = "mass in" = the mass of the component entering the control volume from other parts of reservoir; m_o = "mass out" = the mass of the component leaving the control volume to other parts of reservoir; m_s = "sink/source" = the mass of the component leaving or entering the control volume externally (through wells); and m_a = "mass accumulated" = the mass of excess material stored in or depleted from the control volume over a time interval. Allowing the finite dimensions of the control volume and the time interval to approach zero and taking the limits in Eq. 2.174 result in a mass-conservation equation

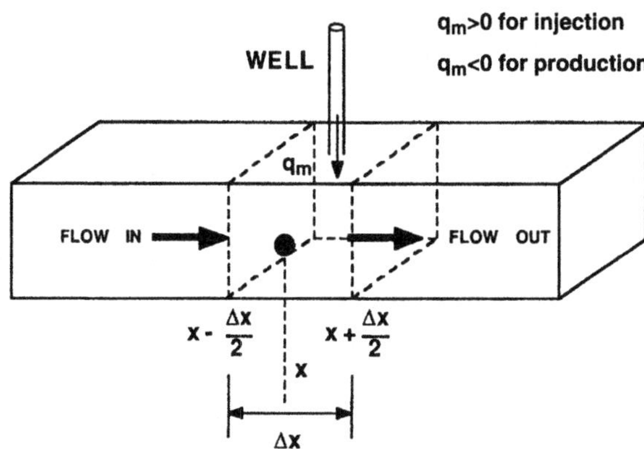

Fig. 2.21—Control volume for 1D flow in rectangular coordinates.

for the component under consideration. The following sections discuss this process in detail.

2.4.1 Mass Conservation for Single-Phase Flow in One Dimension.

Fig. 2.21 shows the finite-control volume with a cross-sectional area A_x perpendicular to the direction of flow, length Δx in the direction of flow, and volume V_b.

Point x represents the center of the control volume. The fluid enters the control volume across its surface at $x - \Delta x/2$ and leaves across its surface at $x + \Delta x/2$ at the mass rates of $w_x|_{x-\Delta x/2}$ and $w_x|_{x+\Delta x/2}$, respectively. The fluid also enters the control volume through a well at a mass rate of q_m. Therefore, the material balance in this case can be written as

$$m_i|_{x-\Delta x/2} + m_s|_x - m_o|_{x+\Delta x/2} = m_a \quad (2.175)$$

$$\text{or } w_x|_{x-\Delta x/2}\Delta t + q_m\Delta t - w_x|_{x+\Delta x/2}\Delta t = \Delta_t(V_b m_v), \quad (2.176)$$

$$\text{where } w_x|_{x-\Delta x/2} = (\dot{m}_x A_x)|_{x-\Delta x/2}, \quad (2.177a)$$

$$w_x|_{x+\Delta x/2} = (\dot{m}_x A_x)|_{x+\Delta x/2}, \quad (2.177b)$$

$$\text{and } \Delta_t(V_b m_v) = V_b(m_v|_{t+\Delta t} - m_v|_t). \quad (2.177c)$$

The terms $\dot{m}_x$, m_v, and q_m = x component of the mass flux vector (mass flow per unit time per unit area), mass of fluid contained in a unit volume of reservoir, and mass production rate through the well (mass per unit time), respectively.

Substituting Eq. 2.177 into Eq. 2.176 and rearranging terms yields

$$-\left[(\dot{m}_x A_x)|_{x+\Delta x/2} - (\dot{m}_x A_x)|_{x-\Delta x/2}\right]\Delta t + q_m\Delta t$$

$$= V_b(m_v|_{t+\Delta t} - m_v|_t). \quad (2.178)$$

Dividing both sides of Eq. 2.178 by Δt and multiplying and dividing the first term on the left side of the equation by Δx, where $\Delta x \neq 0$, yields

$$-\left[\frac{(\dot{m}_x A_x)|_{x+\Delta x/2} - (\dot{m}_x A_x)|_{x-\Delta x/2}}{\Delta x}\right]\Delta x + q_m$$

$$= V_b\left[\frac{m_v|_{t+\Delta t} - m_v|_t}{\Delta t}\right]. \quad (2.179)$$

As Δx and Δt approach zero (that is, $\Delta x \rightarrow 0$ and $\Delta t \rightarrow 0$), the limits of the terms between the brackets in Eq. 2.179 become partial derivatives (see The Partial Derivative in Sec. 3.2.2 of Chap. 3) and the resulting equation becomes the desired expression for mass conservation in rectangular coordinates.

$$-\frac{\partial}{\partial x}(\dot{m}_x A_x)\Delta x = V_b\frac{\partial}{\partial t}(m_v) - q_m. \quad (2.180)$$

Eq. 2.180 appears in the literature in different forms. For example, if A_x is independent of x, then $V_b = A_x\Delta x$ and this equation reduces to

$$-\frac{\partial}{\partial x}(\dot{m}_x) = \frac{\partial}{\partial t}(m_v) - \frac{q_m}{V_b}. \quad \text{(2.181)}$$

For single-phase flow, $m_v = \phi\rho$; therefore

$$-\frac{\partial}{\partial x}\left(\dot{m}_x\right) = \frac{\partial}{\partial t}(\phi\rho) - \frac{q_m}{V_b}. \quad \text{(2.182)}$$

Also, the mass flux can be expressed as the product of the fluid density and velocity, that is $\dot{m}_x = \alpha_c \rho u_x$.

$$-\frac{\partial}{\partial x}(\rho u_x) = \frac{1}{\alpha_c}\frac{\partial}{\partial t}(\phi\rho) - \frac{q_m}{\alpha_c V_b}. \quad \text{(2.183)}$$

2.4.2 Mass Conservation for Single-Phase Flow in Multidimensions. The steps involved in the derivation of the mass-conservation equation for single-phase flow in three dimensions in a rectangular coordinate system are similar to those carried out in Sec. 2.4.1 for 1D flow. Differences appear only in the definitions of m_i and m_o and in the limiting process, specifically,

$$m_i = \left[(\dot{m}_x A_x)|_{x-\Delta x/2} + (\dot{m}_y A_y)|_{y-\Delta y/2} + (\dot{m}_z A_z)|_{z-\Delta z/2}\right]\Delta t \quad \text{(2.184)}$$

and $m_o = \left[(\dot{m}_x A_x)|_{x+\Delta x/2} + (\dot{m}_y A_y)|_{y+\Delta y/2} + (\dot{m}_z A_z)|_{z+\Delta z/2}\right]\Delta t.$ (2.185)

The limits are $\Delta x \rightarrow 0$, $\Delta y \rightarrow 0$, $\Delta z \rightarrow 0$, and $\Delta t \rightarrow 0$.

The mass-conservation equation for 3D rectangular flow (similar to Eq. 2.180) becomes

$$-\frac{\partial}{\partial x}(\dot{m}_x A_x)\Delta x - \frac{\partial}{\partial y}(\dot{m}_y A_y)\Delta y - \frac{\partial}{\partial z}(\dot{m}_z A_z)\Delta z$$

$$= V_b \frac{\partial}{\partial t}(m_v) - q_m. \quad \text{(2.186)}$$

The number of terms on the left side of Eq. 2.186 depends on the dimensionality of the flow problem. For 1D flow, there is only one term; for 2D flow, there are two terms; and for 3D flow, there are three terms. The right side of Eq. 2.186 does not depend on the dimensionality of the flow problem.

In Eq. 2.186 it is also possible to express mass flux, $\vec{\dot{m}}$, as the product of fluid density and Darcy's velocity, fluid concentration or mass per unit volume of reservoir, m_v, as the product of fluid density and porosity, and mass flow rate, q_m, as the product of fluid density and volumetric flow rate.

$$\dot{m}_x = \alpha_c \rho u_x, \quad \text{(2.187)}$$

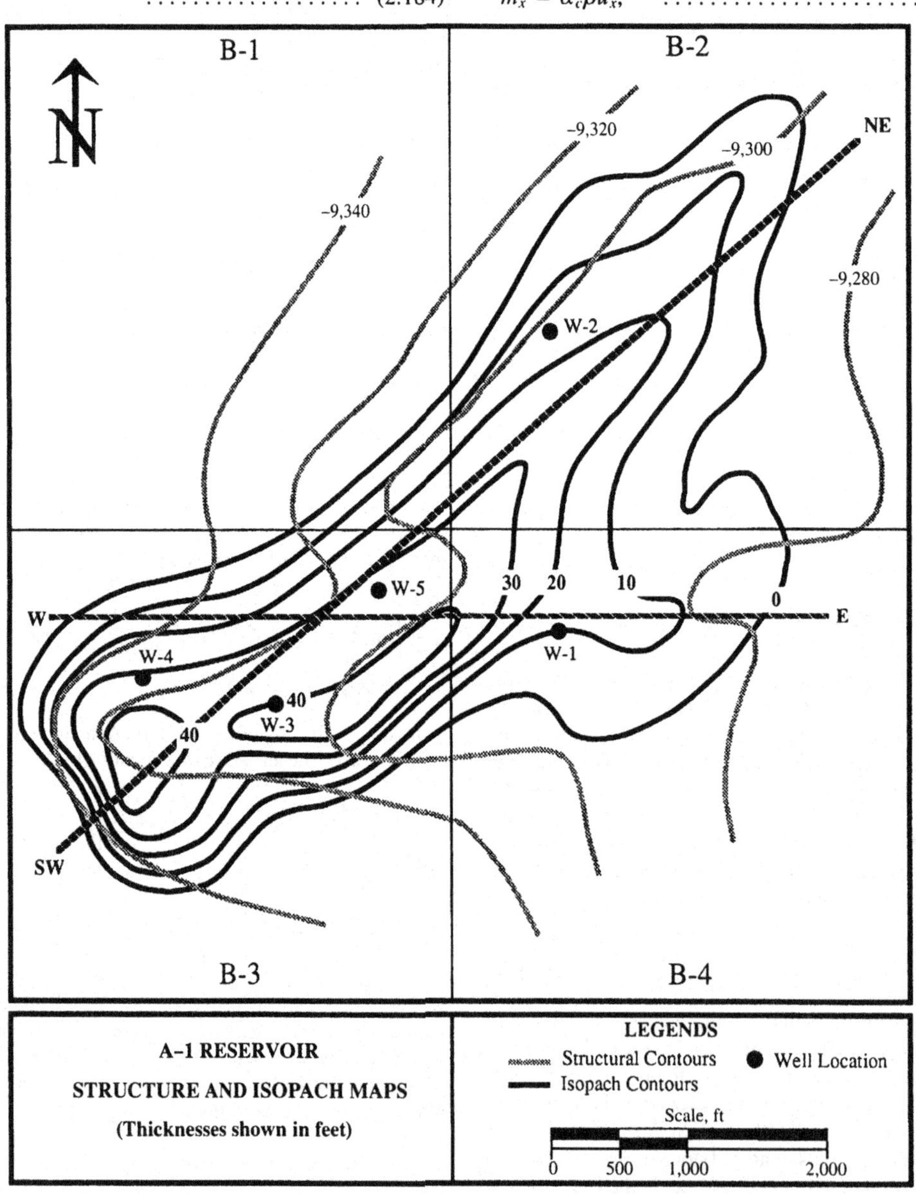

Fig. 2.22—Structural and isopach maps for the A-1 reservoir.

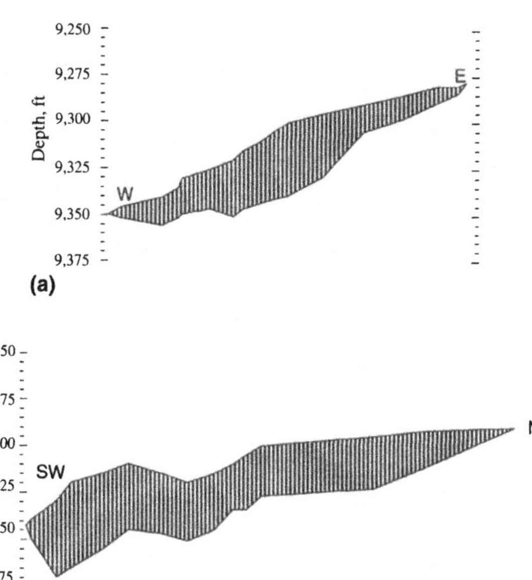

Fig. 2.23—Structural cross sections for the A-1 reservoir: (a) west-east and (b) southwest-northeast.

$$\dot{m}_y = \alpha_c \rho u_y, \quad \text{(2.188)}$$

$$\dot{m}_z = \alpha_c \rho u_z, \quad \text{(2.189)}$$

$$m_v = \rho \phi, \quad \text{(2.190)}$$

$$\text{and } q_m = \alpha_c \rho q. \quad \text{(2.191)}$$

Substituting Eqs. 2.187 through 2.191 into Eq. 2.186 and dividing the resulting equation by $\alpha_c \rho_{sc}$ and using the definition of $B_l = \rho_{lsc}/\rho_l$ (where $l = o$, w, or g) yields another form of the mass-conservation equation.

$$-\frac{\partial}{\partial x}\left(A_x \frac{u_{lx}}{B_l}\right)\Delta x - \frac{\partial}{\partial y}\left(A_y \frac{u_{ly}}{B_l}\right)\Delta y - \frac{\partial}{\partial z}\left(A_z \frac{u_{lz}}{B_l}\right)\Delta z$$

$$= \frac{V_b}{\alpha_c}\frac{\partial}{\partial t}\left(\frac{\phi}{B_l}\right) - q_{lsc}, \quad \text{(2.192)}$$

where $l = o$, w, or g.

2.5 Basic Single-Phase-Flow Equation

The flow equation for single-phase flow can be obtained by combining the appropriate form of Darcy's law and the mass-conservation equation. Fluid density is usually expressed in the implicit form of the FVF as a function of pressure.

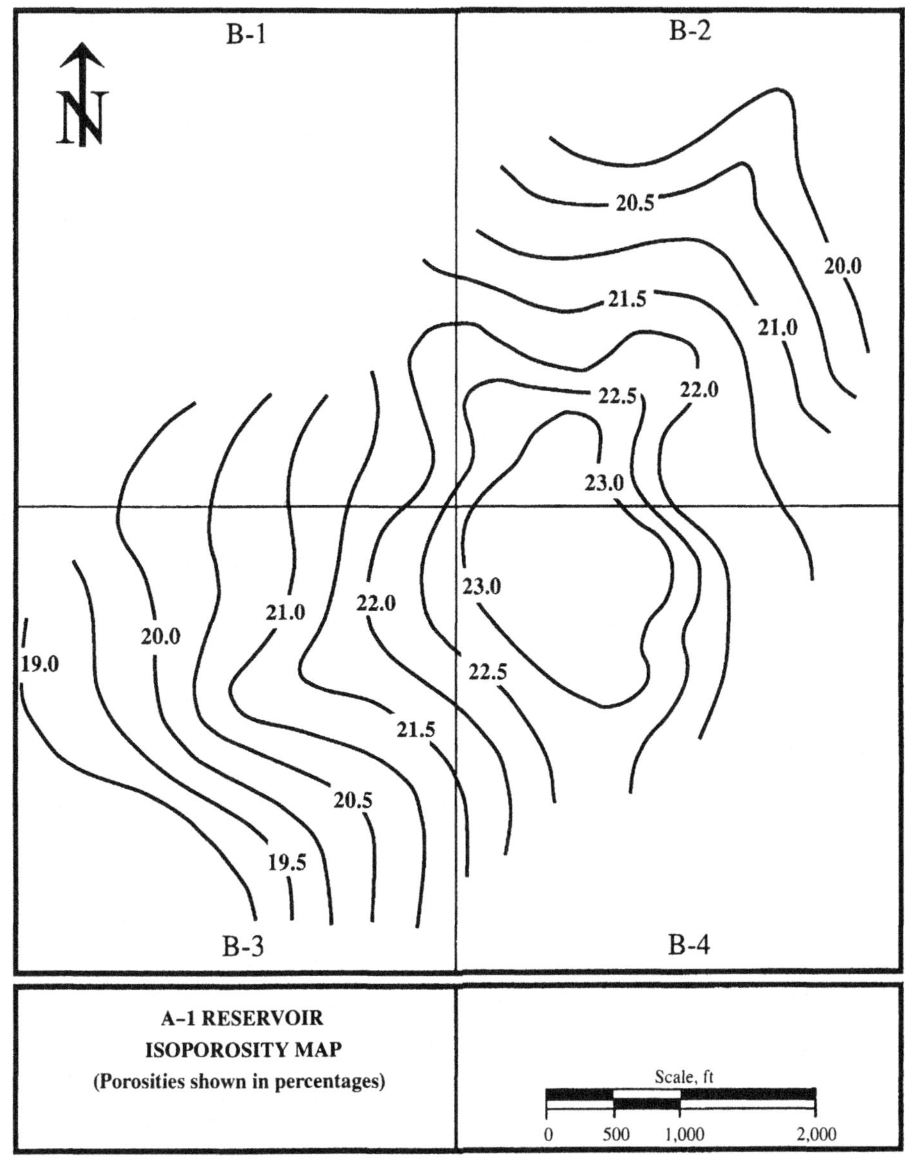

Fig. 2.24—Porosity distribution for the A-1 reservoir.

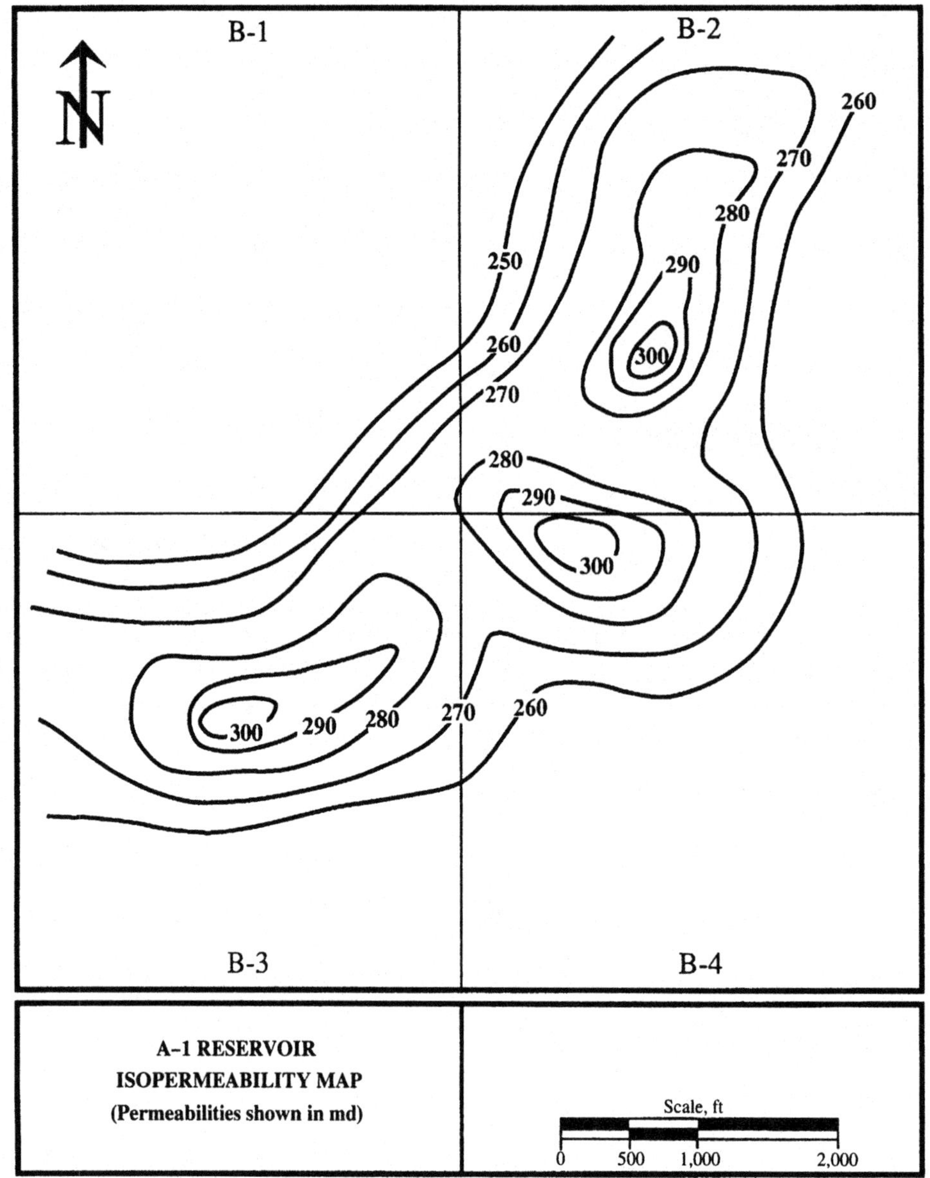

Fig. 2.25—Permeability distribution for the A-1 reservoir (reported permeabilities are along the southwest-northeast direction).

Combining Darcy's law for single-phase flow, Eq. 2.23, and the mass-conservation equation, Eq. 2.192, yields the flow equation for single-phase flow.

$$\frac{\partial}{\partial x}\left[\beta_c \frac{k_x A_x}{\mu_l B_l}\left(\frac{\partial p}{\partial x} - \gamma_l \frac{\partial Z}{\partial x}\right)\right]\Delta x + \frac{\partial}{\partial y}\left[\beta_c \frac{k_y A_y}{\mu_l B_l}\left(\frac{\partial p}{\partial y} - \gamma_l \frac{\partial Z}{\partial y}\right)\right]\Delta y$$

$$+ \frac{\partial}{\partial z}\left[\beta_c \frac{k_z A_z}{\mu_l B_l}\left(\frac{\partial p}{\partial z} - \gamma_l \frac{\partial Z}{\partial z}\right)\right]\Delta z = \frac{V_b}{\alpha_c}\frac{\partial}{\partial t}\left(\frac{\phi}{B_l}\right) - q_{lsc}, \quad \text{(2.193)}$$

where $l = o, w,$ or g. Chap. 4 provides the details of this development in various coordinate systems. Eq. 2.193 is the fundamental equation used in reservoir simulation. In developing Eq. 2.193, no assumptions regarding the fluid type (incompressible, slightly compressible, or compressible) were made. Therefore, this equation is valid for the single-phase flow of oil, water, or gas.

2.6 Chapter Project

Following is more detailed information about the geology and rock and fluid properties of the A-1 reservoir introduced in Sec. 1.6 of Chap. 1.

2.6.1 Reservoir Description. The geometry of the A-1 reservoir rock is that of a channel sand. As **Fig. 2.22** shows, the A-1 sand has a gently west-dipping slope. The maximum elevation difference within the structure is approximately 60 ft, which translates to a drop of approximately 1 ft every 100 ft. The thickest section of the reservoir is encountered in the B-3 quarter and is approximately 40 to 50 ft thick. The average net-pay thickness is 20 ft. **Fig. 2.23** gives two structural cross sections that are studied along the longitudinal axis (southwest-northeast cross section) and along the west-east axis (west-east cross section).

The formation compressibility is determined to be approximately 3.0×10^{-6} psi^{-1}. Initial saturation distributions at 9,290-ft reference depth are estimated to be $S_{oi} = 50\%$, $S_{gi} = 8\%$, and $S_{wi} = 42\%$. At the reference depth of 9,290 ft, initial formation pressure is measured to be 4,800 psia.

2.6.2 Porosity and Permeability. The A-1 formation consists of poorly- to well-sorted Cretaceous Dakota J sands. The reservoir sands exhibit excellent reservoir quality, with an average effective porosity of 22%, and a permeability range of 250 to 300 md. **Figs. 2.24 and 2.25** show the porosity and permeability distributions derived from core analysis and well-test data. The permeability distribution in Fig. 2.25 represents the permeability values along the longitudinal axis of the structure (southwest-northeast direction). The permeability values along the direction orthogonal to the longitudinal axis (southeast-

TABLE 2.4—GAS COMPOSITION OF THE A-1 RESERVOIR

Component	mol%	M	T_c (°R)	p_c (psia)
N_2	1.10	28.013	227.29	493.0
CO_2	5.60	44.010	547.57	1071.0
H_2S	9.20	34.076	672.37	1306.0
CH_4	74.10	16.042	343.06	667.8
C_2H_6	1.90	30.070	549.78	707.8
C_3H_8	1.70	44.097	665.70	616.3
i-C_4H_{10}	5.20	58.124	734.67	529.1
n-C_4H_{10}	1.20	58.124	765.34	550.7

northwest direction) are reported to be approximately 80% of the former. Therefore, the main flow directions are parallel to the southwest-northeast and southeast-northwest directions.

2.6.3 Fluid Properties. The A-1 reservoir has been produced by primary production. The formation produces approximately 50°API gravity oil with no significant sulfur content. The compressibility of gas-free oil is 5×10^{-6} psi^{-1}. The produced water contains primarily NaCl. Other dissolved cations besides Na^+ are K^+, Ca^{++}, and Mg^{++}. The heavy metals such as Ba^{++}, Li^+, Fe^{++}, and St^{++} are found in trace amounts. Besides the Cl^- anion, other anions found in the analysis are SO_4^{--}, HCO_3^-, CO_3^{--}, NO_3^{--}, B^-, I^-, and S^{--}. The compressibility of water is determined to be 3.0×10^{-6} psi^{-1}. **Table 2.4** gives the composition of the associated gas, and **Table 2.5** provides a comprehensive description of the fluid PVT data to be used during the simulation study. **Fig. 2.26** shows the entries of Table 2.5, together with some other properties.

2.6.4 Relative Permeability. Table 2.6 gives two-phase relative permeability data sets, and **Fig. 2.27** shows these experimentally derived oil/water and oil/gas relative permeabilities. Oil relative permeability characteristics are generated with Stone's Three-Phase Model 2 (see Stone's Three-Phase Model 2 in Sec. 2.3.5) from the two sets of two-phase data presented in Table 2.6. **Fig. 2.28** gives the oil isoperms as they appear on a ternary relative permeability diagram.

2.6.5 Capillary Pressure. Table 2.7 and Fig. 2.29 provide the capillary pressure data sets for the A-1 reservoir in tabular and graphical forms, respectively.

Exercises

2.1 In Fig. 2.1 the arbitrary new datum is above the absolute datum. Show that Eqs. 2.13 and 2.14 hold true if the arbitrary new datum falls below the absolute datum.

2.2 Fig. 2.30 shows a water formation dipping with a 15° angle. Points A, B, and C fall on the dip and are separated as shown in the figure. The water density at reservoir conditions is 60 lbm/ft^3. The pressure at Point B is 2,000 psia and water is under hydrodynamic equilibrium at the time of discovery. What are the pressures at Points A and C?

2.3 In Exercise 2.2, the water viscosity at reservoir conditions is 0.95 cp and the permeability of the formation is 300 md. What is the rate of water flow between Points A and C, if the formation width along the strike is 950 ft and the pressures at Points A and C are maintained at 1,500 and 1,300 psia, respectively?

2.4 A reservoir-rock sample has a porosity of 0.18 measured at 14.7 psia. The rock compressibility is 0.77×10^{-5} psi^{-1}. What would the rock porosity be at 2,000 and at 3,000 psia? Plot the relationship between ϕ and p in a pressure range of 14.7 to 5,000 psia.

2.5 Obtain a flow-rate expression for the equivalent of linear flow that takes place between Points 1 and 2 in **Fig. 2.31**. Note that the two blocks have different dimensions and permeabilities and that flow rates at Points 1 and 2 are equal but that $p_1 > p_2$.

2.6 Use the Dranchuk and Abou-Kassem[16] z-factor correlation (discussed in Fluid Compressibility and Gas-Compressibility Factor in Sec. 2.3.2) to plot z and c_r vs. p_{pr} in the pseudoreduced-pressure range of 1 to 10 for $T_{pr} = 1.1$ and 1.5.

2.7 Table 2.8 lists the properties of gas and saturated oil at reservoir temperature. Calculate oil- and gas-phase properties (B, μ, and ρ) at the following reservoir conditions, when $\rho_{osc} = 49.098$ lbm/ft^3, $M = 22.94$ (gas molecular weight), $c_o = 23.2 \times 10^{-6}$ psi^{-1}, $c_\mu = 46 \times 10^{-6}$ psi^{-1}, $p_{sc} = 14.7$ psia, and $T_{sc} = 520$°R.

1. $p = 3{,}014.7$ psia and $R_s = 930$ scf/STB.
2. $p = 3{,}014.7$ psia and $R_s = 800$ scf/STB.

2.8 With the information in Exercise 2.7, calculate the oil- and gas-phase properties for the following reservoir conditions. Use linear interpolation for pressure entries not listed in the table of properties.

1. $p = 4{,}514.7$ psia and $R_s = 1{,}444$ scf/STB.
2. $p = 4{,}514.7$ psia and $R_s = 1{,}000$ scf/STB.

2.9 Plot k_{row} vs. S_w in the range $0 \leqq S_w \leqq 1$ with Eqs. 2.139 and 2.142, when $S_{iw} = 0.15$. Examine the plots and provide comments on the prediction of k_{row} by Corey's[20] and Naar and Henderson's[21] two-phase models.

2.10 The two sets of two-phase relative permeability data given in **Table 2.9** are reported by Coats *et al.*[27] If, at a certain instant in time, phase saturations in a three-phase flow system are $S_w = 0.320$, $S_g = 0.250$, and $S_o = 0.430$, calculate the relative permeability for the three phases using Stone's Three-Phase Models 1 and 2.

TABLE 2.5—FLUID PVT DATA AS INPUT TO THE SIMULATOR

	FVF			Density			Viscosity				
Pressure (psia)	Water (RB/bbl)	Oil (RB/STB)	Gas (RB/scf)	Water (lbm/ft^3)	Oil (lbm/ft^3)	Gas (lbm/ft^3)	Water (cp)	Oil (cp)	Gas (cp)	Solution-Gas/ Oil Ratio (scf/STB)	z factor
1,500	1.02527	1.20413	0.0018	62.2280	49.0113	5.8267	0.5200	1.7356	0.0150	292.75	0.84274
2,000	1.02224	1.23210	0.00133	62.4127	48.5879	8.0573	0.5200	1.5562	0.0167	368.00	0.81258
2,500	1.01921	1.26054	0.00105	62.5968	48.1774	10.2279	0.5200	1.4015	0.0185	443.75	0.80017
3,000	1.01621	1.29208	0.00088	62.7819	47.6939	12.2084	0.5200	1.2516	0.0204	522.71	0.80443
3,500	1.01321	1.32933	0.00077	62.9680	47.1788	13.9421	0.5200	1.1024	0.0222	619.00	0.82180
4,000	1.01024	1.37193	0.00069	63.1531	46.5899	15.4313	0.5200	0.9647	0.0241	724.92	0.84856
4,500	1.00731	1.42596	0.00064	63.3374	45.5756	16.7051	0.5200	0.9180	0.0260	818.60	0.88184
5,000	1.00506	1.46387	0.00060	63.5225	45.1925	17.7994	0.5200	0.9200	0.0278	923.12	0.91958
5,500	1.00170	1.44983	0.00057	63.7077	45.4413	18.7475	0.5200	0.9243	0.0296	965.28	0.96039
6,000	0.99856	1.43831	0.00055	63.8928	45.7426	19.5772	0.5200	0.9372	0.0313	966.32	1.00329

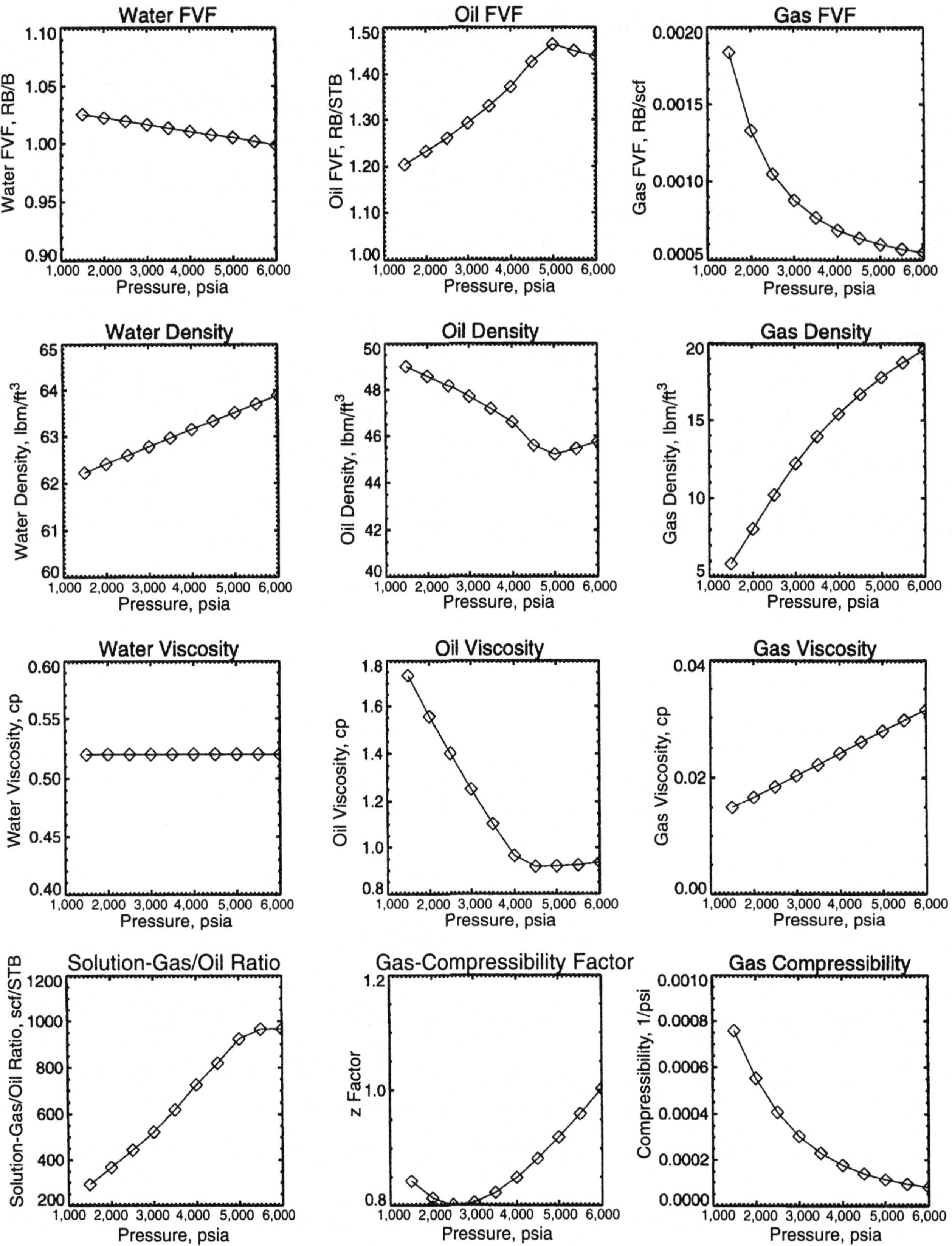

Fig. 2.26—Variation of several reservoir-fluid properties with pressure for the A-1 reservoir.

2.11 Assuming the two-phase relative permeability data sets in Exercise 2.10 are not given, what would the phase relative permeabilities predicted by the Naar, Henderson, and Wygal[21,24] model be if $S_{or} = 0.07$?

2.12 Consider a 3D, thick reservoir in the shape of a perfect rectangular prism. If this reservoir is positioned parallel (along its lateral directions) to the datum plane, would it be possible to replace the potential gradients with the pressure gradients? Show analysis.

2.13 Is $\partial B_g/\partial p = 0$ for an ideal gas? Justify your answer.

2.14 Is compressibility of a real gas always less than that of an ideal gas at a constant temperature but different pressures? Show analysis.

TABLE 2.6—TWO-PHASE RELATIVE PERMEABILITY DATA FOR THE A-1 RESERVOIR					
	Oil/Water			Gas/Oil	
S_w	k_{rw}	k_{row}	S_g	k_{rg}	k_{rog}
0.18	0.00000	1.00000	0.00	0.00000	1.00000
0.21	0.00000	0.92692	0.04	0.01103	0.70778
0.24	0.00002	0.85441	0.08	0.02912	0.55844
0.27	0.00014	0.79288	0.12	0.05138	0.44540
0.30	0.00045	0.71312	0.16	0.07687	0.35562
0.33	0.00111	0.64526	0.20	0.10506	0.28302
0.36	0.00232	0.57980	0.24	0.13561	0.22392
0.39	0.00430	0.51709	0.28	0.16827	0.17574
0.42	0.00733	0.45744	0.32	0.20286	0.13656
0.45	0.01175	0.40110	0.36	0.23923	0.10485
0.48	0.01791	0.34831	0.40	0.27725	0.07938
0.51	0.02623	0.29924	0.44	0.31683	0.05912
0.54	0.03714	0.25403	0.48	0.35788	0.04319
0.57	0.05116	0.21278	0.52	0.40031	0.03084
0.60	0.06882	0.17552	0.56	0.44408	0.02143
0.63	0.09069	0.14228	0.60	0.48911	0.01442
0.66	0.11741	0.11301	0.64	0.53536	0.00933
0.69	0.14963	0.08763	0.68	0.58279	0.00574
0.72	0.18807	0.06603	0.72	0.63134	0.00332
0.75	0.23347	0.04803			
0.78	0.28664	0.03344			
0.81	0.34842	0.02199			
0.84	0.41968	0.01340			
0.87	0.50135	0.00733			
0.90	0.59439	0.00340			

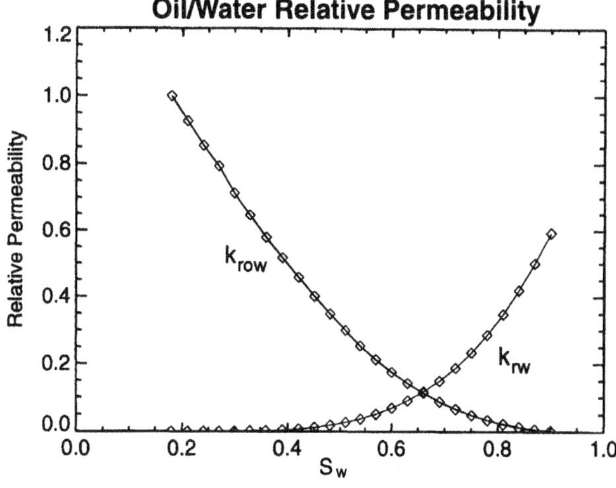

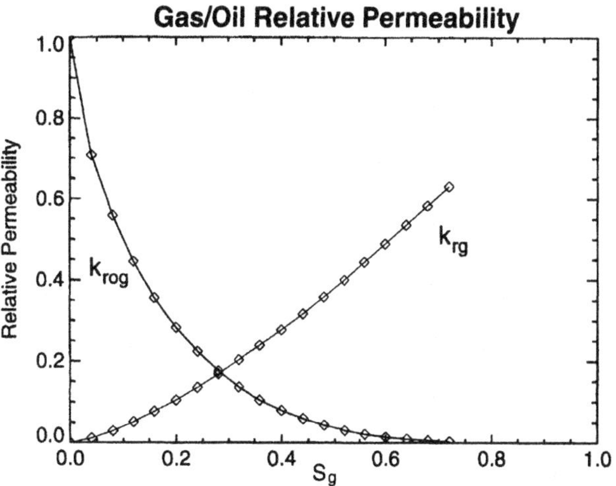

Fig. 2.27—Two-phase relative permeability characteristics for the A-1 reservoir.

2.15 In a two-phase relative permeability data set the summation of relative permeabilities goes through a minimum value. If a third phase is introduced into the system, how will the magnitude of this minimum value change? Explain.

2.16 Table 2.10 shows two-phase relative permeability data to be used in three-phase relative permeability characteristics.

1. On the ternary diagram, indicate the region in which possible saturation combinations can be encountered at any time during the life of the reservoir with the two-phase relative permeability characteristics from the table.
2. Using Stone's Three-Phase Models 1 and 2, calculate the k_{ro}, k_{rw}, and k_{rg} values when $S_o = 27\%$, $S_w = 50\%$, and $S_g = 23\%$.

2.17 Comment on the accuracy of the statement "A hydrocarbon reservoir that initially exhibits isotropic and homogeneous permeability characteristics will have anisotropic and heterogeneous permeability distribution as the reservoir is depleted, if permeability is a function of pressure."

2.18 Is it possible to use the capillary pressure relationships $P_{cow}(S_w) = p_o - p_w$ and $P_{cgo}(S_g) = p_g - p_o$ for oil-wet reservoirs? Explain.

2.19 Derive Eq. 2.82 for the oil FVF above the bubblepoint pressure.

Nomenclature

A = cross-sectional area normal to flow, L^2, ft^2 [m^2]
$A_{1\text{-}11}$ = constants of BWR EOS
A_x = cross-sectional area normal to the x direction, L^2, ft^2 [m^2]
B_g = gas FVF, L^3/L^3, RB/scf [m^3/std m^3]
B_l = FVF of Phase l, L^3/L^3, reservoir volume/volume at standard conditions
B_l^o = FVF of Phase l at reference conditions, L^3/L^3, reservoir volume/volume at standard pressure and reservoir temperature
B_o = oil FVF, L^3/L^3, RB/STB [m^3/std m^3]

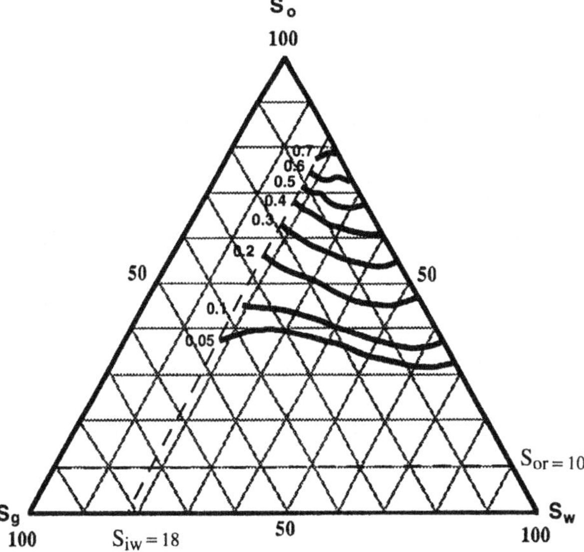

Fig. 2.28—Oil isoperms as generated by the Stone's Three-Phase Model 2.

TABLE 2.7—CAPILLARY PRESSURE DATA			
S_w	P_{cow}	$1-S_g$	P_{cgo}
0.20	8.00	0.21	4.76
0.25	4.30	0.26	2.94
0.30	3.00	0.31	2.22
0.40	1.78	0.41	1.49
0.50	1.21	0.51	1.04
0.60	0.79	0.66	0.51
0.70	0.43	0.76	0.27
0.80	0.10	0.96	0.01
0.90	0.00		

B_{ob} = oil FVF at bubblepoint conditions, L^3/L^3, RB/STB [m^3/std m^3]
B_w = water FVF, L^3/L^3, RB/B [m^3/std m^3]
c = component
c_e = effective compressibility, Lt^2/m, psi^{-1} [kPa^{-1}]
c_f = fluid compressibility, Lt^2/m, psi^{-1} [kPa^{-1}]
c_g = gas compressibility, Lt^2/m, psi^{-1} [kPa^{-1}]
c_l = compressibility of phase l, Lt^2/m, psi^{-1} [kPa^{-1}]
c_{Le} = liquid effective compressibility, Lt^2/m, psi^{-1} [kPa^{-1}]
c_o = oil compressibility, Lt^2/m, psi^{-1} [kPa^{-1}]
c_{oe} = oil effective compressibility, Lt^2/m, psi^{-1} [kPa^{-1}]
c_p = pore compressibility, Lt^2/m, psi^{-1} [kPa^{-1}]
c_{pe} = pore effective compressibility, Lt^2/m, psi^{-1} [kPa^{-1}]
c_R = reservoir-rock compressibility, Lt^2/m, psi^{-1} [kPa^{-1}]
c_r = reduced compressibility, dimensionless
c_{Tl} = thermal expansion coefficient of Phase l, $°F^{-1}$ [$°C^{-1}$]
c_w = water compressibility, Lt^2/m, psi^{-1} [kPa^{-1}]
c_ϕ = porosity compressibility, Lt^2/m, psi^{-1} [kPa^{-1}]
c_μ = relative rate of change of oil viscosity with pressure above bubblepoint
C_0 to C_5 = coefficients in Eq. 2.68, defined in Table 2.2
D = elevation with respect to absolute datum being positive upward, L, ft [m]

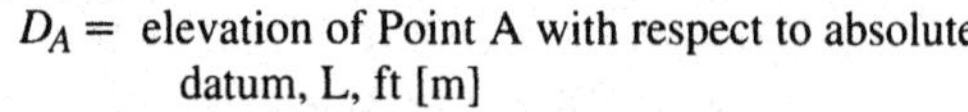
D_A = elevation of Point A with respect to absolute datum, L, ft [m]
D_B = elevation of Point B with respect to absolute datum, L, ft [m]
$D°$ = elevation of datum with respect to absolute datum, L, ft [m]
f = function
g = acceleration of gravity, L/t^2, ft/sec^2 [m/s^2]
h = thickness of porous medium, L, ft [m]
h_f = fluid head, L, ft [m]
k = permeability, L^2, darcy [μm^2]
k_H = horizontal permeability, L^2, darcy [μm^2]
k_{ox} = effective permeability to oil phase in the x direction, L^2, darcy [μm^2]
k_r = relative permeability, fraction
k_{rl} = relative permeability to Phase l, dimensionless
k_{rg} = relative permeability to gas, dimensionless
k_{ro} = relative permeability to oil, dimensionless
k_{rnw} = relative permeability to nonwetting phase, dimensionless
k_{rocw} = relative permeability to oil at irreducible water saturation, dimensionless
k_{rog} = relative permeability to oil in oil/gas system, dimensionless
k_{row} = relative permeability to oil in oil/water system, dimensionless
k_{rw} = relative permeability to wetting phase, dimensionless
k_V = vertical permeability, L^2, darcy [μm^2]
k_{wx} = effective permeability to water phase in the x direction, L^2, darcy [μm^2]
k_x = permeability in the direction of the x axis, L^2, darcy [μm^2]
$\bar{k}$ = average permeability, L^2, darcy [μm^2]
L = distance, displacement, L, ft [m]
m_a = mass accumulated, or mass of excess material stored in or depleted from the control volume over a time interval, m, lbm [kg]
m_i = mass in, or mass of component entering the control volume from other parts of the reservoir, m, lbm [kg]

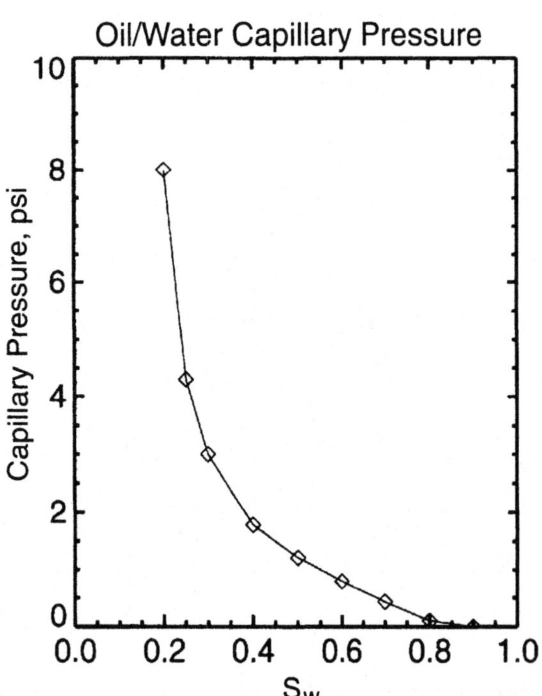

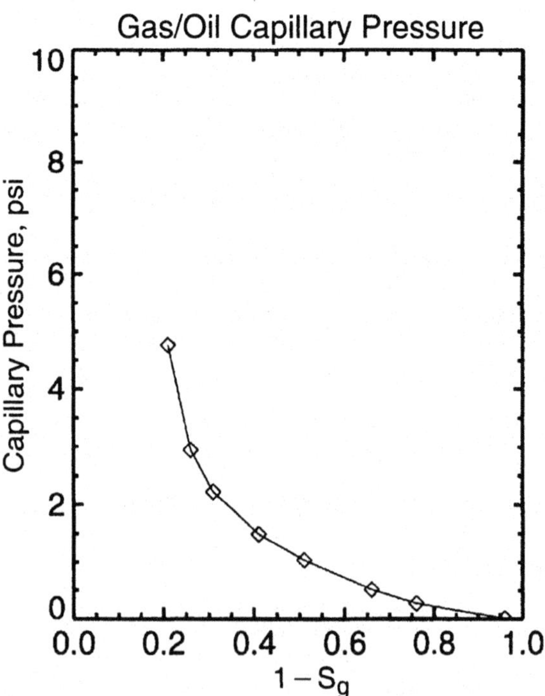

Fig. 2.29—Capillary pressure relations.

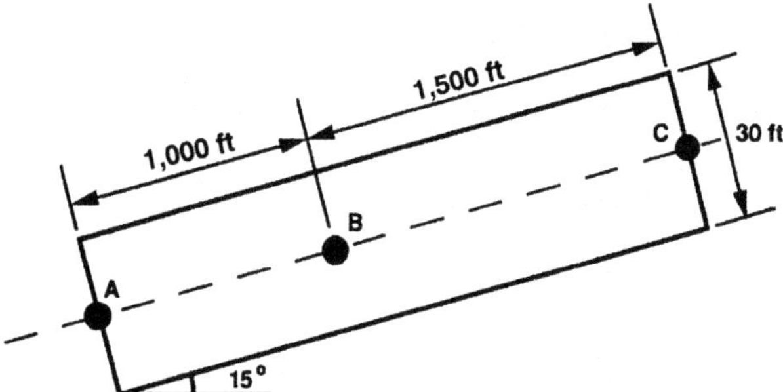

Fig. 2.30—Cross section of reservoir described in Exercise 2.2.

m_o = mass out, or mass of component leaving the control volume to other parts of the reservoir, m, lbm [kg]
m_s = sink/source, or mass of component leaving or entering the control volume externally (through wells), m, lbm [kg]
m_v = mass per unit volume of porous medium, m/L^3, lbm/ft^3 [kg/m^3]
$m_v|_t$ = mass per unit volume of porous media at Time t, m/L^3, lbm/ft^3 [kg/m^3]
$m_v|_{t+\Delta t}$ = mass per unit volume of porous medium at Time $t+\Delta t$, m/L^3, lbm/ft^3 [kg/m^3]
$\dot{m}_x$ = x component of mass flux vector, m/tL^2, lbm/(D-ft^2) [kg/(d·m^2)]
$\dot{m}_y$ = y component of mass flux vector, m/tL^2, lbm/(D-ft^2) [kg/(d·m^2)]
$\dot{m}_z$ = z component of mass flux vector, m/tL^2, lbm/(D-ft^2) [kg/(d·m^2)]
M = gas molecular weight, m, lbm/lbm mol [kg/kg mol]
p = pressure, m/Lt^2, psia [kPa]
p_A = pressure at Point A, m/Lt^2, psia [kPa]
p_b = bubblepoint pressure, m/Lt^2, psia [kPa]
p_B = pressure at Point B, m/Lt^2, psia [kPa]
p_c = critical pressure, m/Lt^2, psia [kPa]
p_g = gas pressure, m/Lt^2, psia [kPa]
p_i = initial pressure, m/Lt^2, psia [kPa]
p_l = pressure of Phase l, m/Lt^2, psia [kPa]
p_L = pressure at $x=L$, m/Lt^2, psia [kPa]
p_o = oil pressure, m/Lt^2, psia [kPa]
p_{pc} = pseudocritical pressure, m/Lt^2, psi [kPa]
p_{pr} = pseudoreduced pressure, dimensionless
p_r = reduced pressure, dimensionless
p_{sc} = standard-condition pressure, m/Lt^2, psia [kPa]
p_w = water pressure, m/Lt^2, psia [kPa]
p_W = pressure at $x=0$, m/Lt^2, psia [kPa]
$p°$ = reference pressure, m/Lt^2, psia [kPa]
P_{cgo} = gas/oil capillary pressure, m/Lt^2, psi [kPa]
P_{cow} = oil/water capillary pressure, m/Lt^2, psi [kPa]
q = production rate or flow rate, L^3/t, B/D [m^3/d]
q_{gx} = gas flow rate along the x direction, L^3/t, RB/D [m^3/d]
q_{lsc} = production rate of Phase l at standard conditions, L^3/t, scf/D or STB/D [std m^3/d]
q_{ox} = oil flow rate along the x direction, L^3/t, RB/D [m^3/d]
q_m = mass production rate, m/t, lbm/D [kg/d]
q_{wx} = water flow rate along the x direction, L^3/t, RB/D [m^3/d]
R = universal gas constant
R_s = solution-gas/oil ratio, L^3/L^3, scf/STB [std m^3/std m^3]
Δs = difference between Points 1 and 2, L, ft [m]
S_g = gas saturation, fraction
S_{gc} = critical gas saturation, fraction
S_{gi} = initial gas saturation, fraction
$S_{g\max}$ = maximum gas saturation, fraction
S_{gn} = normalized gas saturation, fraction
S_{iw} = irreducible water saturation, fraction
S_l = saturation of Phase l, fraction
S_o = oil saturation, fraction
S_{oi} = initial oil saturation, fraction
S_{on} = normalized oil saturation, fraction
S_{or} = ROS, fraction
S_{org} = ROS in gas/oil system, fraction
S_{orw} = ROS in oil/water system, fraction
S_w = water saturation, fraction
S_{wi} = initial water saturation, fraction
$S_{w\max}$ = maximum water saturation, fraction
S_{wn} = normalized water saturation, fraction
s = distance, L, ft [m]
Δt = timestep ($\Delta t = t^{n+1} - t^n$), t, days
T = absolute temperature, T, °R [K]
T_c = critical temperature, T, °R [K]
T_{pc} = pseudocritical temperature, T, °R [K]
T_{pr} = pseudoreduced temperature, dimensionless
T_r = reduced temperature, dimensionless
T_{sc} = standard condition temperature, T, °R [K]
t = time, t, days
t^n = old time, t, days
t^{n+1} = current or new time, t, days
u = volumetric velocity, L/t, RB/(D-ft^2) [m^3/(d·m^2)]
u_l = volumetric velocity of Phase l, L/t, RB/(D-ft^2) [m^3/(d·m^2)]
u_x = volumetric velocity component in the x direction, L/t, RB/(D-ft^2) [m^3/(d·m^2)]

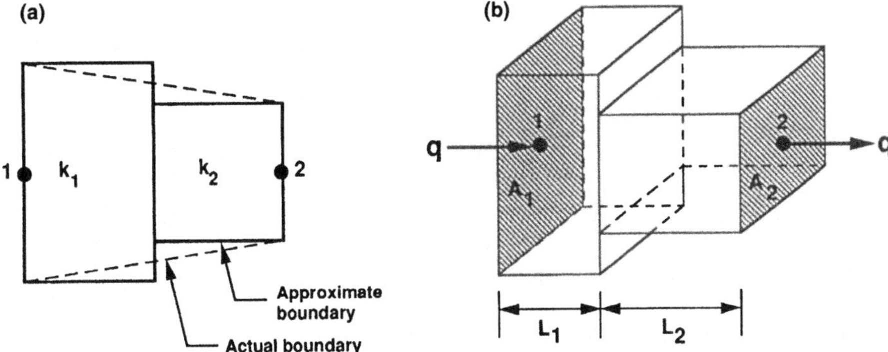

Fig. 2.31—(a) Actual and approximate reservoir boundaries and (b) detailed discretized reservoir between Points 1 and 2 in Exercise 2.5.

TABLE 2.8—SATURATED-OIL AND -GAS PROPERTIES

	Oil			Gas	
p (psia)	R_s (scf/STB)	B_o (RB/STB)	μ_o (cp)	B_g (RB/scf)	μ_g (cp)
14.7	1.0	1.062	1.040	1.6667	0.0080
514.7	180.0	1.207	0.910	0.00627	0.0112
1,014.7	371.0	1.295	0.830	0.00320	0.0140
2,014.7	636.0	1.435	0.695	0.00161	0.0189
3,014.7	930.0	1.565	0.594	0.00108	0.0228
4,014.7	1,270.0	1.695	0.510	0.00081	0.0268
5,014.7	1,618.0	1.827	0.449	0.00065	0.0309

u_y = volumetric velocity component in the y direction, L/t, RB/(D-ft^2) [m^3/(d·m^2)]

u_z = volumetric velocity component in the z direction, L/t, RB/(D-ft^2) [m^3/(d·m^2)]

$\vec{u}_l$ = superficial velocity of Phase l, L/t, RB/(D-ft^2) [m^3/(d·m^2)]

V = volume, L^3, ft^3 [m^3]

V_b = bulk volume, control volume, or gridblock bulk volume, L^3, ft^3 [m^3]

V_g = gas volume, L^3, ft^3 [m^3]

V_{gsc} = gas volume at standard conditions, L^3, scf [std m^3]

V_o = oil volume, L^3, ft^3 [m^3]

V_p = PV, L^3, ft^3 [m^3]

V_s = rock-solids volume, L^3, ft^3 [m^3]

V_{sc} = volume at standard conditions, L^3, STB [std m^3] for liquids, scf [std m^3] for gases

V_w = water volume, L^3, ft^3 [m^3]

w_x = mass flow rate component in the x direction, m/t, lbm/D [kg/d]

x = distance in the x direction in Cartesian coordinate system, L, ft [m]

Δx = difference along x direction ($\Delta x = x_{i+1} - x_i$), L, ft [m]

Δy = difference along y direction ($\Delta y = y_{j+1} - y_j$), L, ft [m]

z = gas-compressibility factor $z = pM/\rho RT$, dimensionless

z_c = critical gas-compressibility factor, 0.270

z_{sc} = gas-compressibility factor at standard conditions, dimensionless

Z = elevation with respect to datum (positive downward), L, ft [m]

Z_A = elevation of Point A with respect to datum, L, ft [m]

TABLE 2.9—TWO-PHASE RELATIVE PERMEABILITY DATA BY COATS *et al.*[27]

Oil/Water Data			Oil/Gas Data		
S_w	k_{rw}	k_{row}	S_g	k_{rg}	k_{rog}
0.130	0.0000	1.0000	0.000	0.0000	1.0000
0.191	0.0051	0.9990	0.101	0.0026	0.5169
0.250	0.0102	0.8000	0.150	0.0121	0.3373
0.294	0.0168	0.7241	0.195	0.0195	0.2919
0.357	0.0275	0.6206	0.250	0.0285	0.2255
0.414	0.0424	0.5040	0.281	0.0372	0.2100
0.490	0.0665	0.317	0.337	0.0500	0.1764
0.557	0.0970	0.3029	0.386	0.0654	0.1433
0.630	0.1148	0.1555	0.431	0.0761	0.1172
0.673	0.1259	0.0956	0.485	0.0855	0.0883
0.719	0.1381	0.0576	0.567	0.1022	0.0461
0.789	0.1636	0.0000	0.605	0.1120	0.0294
			0.800	0.1700	0.0000

Z_B = elevation of Point B with respect to datum, L, ft [m]

α_c = volume conversion factor whose numerical value is given in Table 2.1

β_c = transmissibility conversion factor whose numerical value is given in Table 2.1

Δ_t = difference operator in the time domain

γ = gravity defined by Eq. 2.20, m/L^{2}t^2, psi/ft [kPa/m]

γ_c = gravity conversion factor whose numerical value is given in Table 2.1

γ_l = gravity of Phase l, m/L^{2}t^2, psi/ft [kPa/m]

μ = viscosity, m/Lt, cp [Pa·s]

μ_l = viscosity of Phase l, m/Lt, cp [Pa·s]

μ_o = oil-phase viscosity, m/Lt, cp [Pa·s]

μ_{ob} = oil-phase viscosity at bubblepoint pressure, m/Lt, cp [Pa·s]

ρ = density, m/L^3, lbm/ft^3 [kg/m^3]

ρ_g = gas-phase density, m/L^3, lbm/ft^3 [kg/m^3]

ρ_{gsc} = gas-phase density at standard conditions, m/L^3, lbm/ft^3 [kg/m^3]

ρ_l = density of Phase l, m/L^3, lbm/ft^3 [kg/m^3]

ρ_{lsc} = density of Phase l at standard conditions, m/L^3, lbm/ft^3 [kg/m^3]

ρ_l^o = density of Phase l at reference conditions, m/L^3, lbm/ft^3 [kg/m^3]

ρ_o = oil-phase density, m/L^3, lbm/ft^3 [kg/m^3]

ρ_{ob} = oil-phase density at bubblepoint pressure conditions, m/L^3, lbm/ft^3 [kg/m^3]

TABLE 2.10—TWO-PHASE RELATIVE PERMEABILITY DATA

Water/Oil Data			Oil/Gas Data		
S_w	k_{rw}	k_{row}	S_g	k_{rg}	k_{rog}
0.15	0.000	1.000	0.08	0.000	1.000
0.20	0.00001197	0.830	0.13	0.00066885	0.613
0.25	0.0001197	0.677	0.23	0.01070	0.292
0.30	0.0009698	0.541	0.33	0.03849	0.134
0.40	0.007483	0.321	0.43	0.08926	0.05646
0.50	0.02874	0.169	0.53	0.167	0.02047
0.60	0.07855	0.07500	0.63	0.276	0.005933
0.70	0.175	0.02555	0.73	0.419	0.001182
0.80	0.341	0.005409	0.83	0.600	0.0001132
0.88	0.563	0.00	0.88	1.000	0.000

ρ_{osc} = oil-phase density at standard conditions, m/L^3, lbm/ft^3 [kg/m^3]
ρ_r = reduced density, dimensionless
ρ_{sc} = density at standard conditions, m/L^3, lbm/ft^3 [kg/m^3]
ϕ = porosity, fraction
$\phi°$ = porosity at $p°$, fraction
Φ = potential, m/Lt^2, psia [kPa]
Φ_A = potential at Point A, m/Lt^2, psia [kPa]
Φ_B = potential at Point B, m/Lt^2, psia [kPa]
$\Phi°$ = potential at datum with respect to absolute datum, m/Lt^2, psia [kPa]
Φ_g = gas-phase potential, m/Lt^2, psia [kPa]
Φ_h = Hubbert's potential, L, ft [m]
Φ_l = potential of Phase l, m/Lt^2, psia [kPa]
Φ_o = oil-phase potential, m/Lt^2, psia [kPa]
Φ_w = water-phase potential, m/Lt^2, psia [kPa]

Subscripts

g = gas phase
o = oil phase
w = water phase

References

1. Hubbert, M.K.: "Darcy's Law and the Field Equations of the Flow of Underground Fluids," *Trans.*, AIME (1956) **207,** 222.
2. Darcy, H.: "Les Fontaines Publiques de la Ville de Dijon," Dalmount, Paris (1856), reprinted in Hubbert, M.K.: *The Theory of Ground-Water Motion and Related Papers*, Hofner Publishing, New York City (1969).
3. Scheidegger, A.E.: *Physics of Flow Through Porous Media*, third edition, U. of Toronto Press, Toronto, Canada (1974).
4. Collins, R.E.: *Flow of Fluids Through Porous Materials*, Van Nostrand Reinhold, New York City (1961).
5. Klinkenberg, L.J.: "The Permeability of Porous Media to Liquids and Gases," *Drill. & Prod. Prac.* (1941) 200.
6. Trube, A.S.: "Compressibility of Natural Gases," *Trans.*, AIME (1957) **210,** 355.
7. Brown, G.G. *et al.*: "Natural Gasoline and the Volatile Hydrocarbons," NGAA (1948) 38.
8. Mattar, L., Brar, G.S., and Aziz, K.: "Compressibility of Natural Gases," *J. Cdn. Pet. Tech.* (April 1975) **14,** No. 4, 77.
9. Dranchuk, P.M., Purvis, R.A., and Robinson, D.B.: "Computer Calculations of Natural Gas Compressibility Factors Using the Standing and Katz Correlations," *Inst. Petrol. Tech. Series*, No. IP74-008 (1974) 1.
10. Abou-Kassem, J.H., Mattar, L., and Dranchuk, P.M.: "Computer Calculations of Compressibility of Natural Gas," *J. Cdn. Pet. Tech.* (May 1990) **29,** No. 5, 105.
11. Standing, M.B. and Katz, D.L.: "Density of Natural Gases," *Trans.*, AIME (1942) **146,** 140.
12. Dranchuk, P.M. and Abou-Kassem, J.H.: "Computer Calculation of Heat Capacity of Natural Gases Over a Wide Range of Pressure and Temperature," *Canadian J. Chemical Engineers* (April 1992) **70**, No. 2, 350.
13. Wichert, E. and Aziz, K.: "Compressibility Factor of Sour Natural Gases," *Canadian J. Chemical Engineers* (April 1971) **49,** No. 2, 267.
14. Cox, J.C.: "What You Should Know About Gas Compressibility Factors," *World Oil* (April 1988) **206,** No. 4, 69.
15. Benedict, M., Webb, G.B., and Rubin, L.C.: "An Empirical Equation for Thermodynamic Properties of Light Hydrocarbons and Their Mixtures", *Chemical Engineering Progress* (August 1951) **47,** No. 8, 419.
16. Dranchuk, P.M. and Abou-Kassem, J.H.: "Calculation of *Z* Factors for Natural Gases Using Equations of State," *J. Cdn. Pet. Tech.* (March 1975) **14,** No. 3, 34.
17. Aziz, K. and Settari, A.: *Petroleum Reservoir Simulation*, Applied Science Publishers Ltd., London (1979).
18. Poston, S.W. *et al.*: "The Effect of Temperature on Irreducible Water Saturation and Relative Permeability of Unconsolidated Sands," *SPEJ* (June 1970) 171; *Trans.*, AIME (1970) **249.**
19. Leverett, M.C. and Lewis, W.B.: "Steady Flow of Gas/Oil/Water Mixtures Through Unconsolidated Sands," *Trans.*, AIME (1941) **142,** 107.
20. Corey, A.T.: "The Interrelation Between Gas and Oil Relative Permeabilities," *Producers Monthly* (1954) **19,** 38.
21. Naar, J. and Henderson, J.H.: "An Imbibition Model—Its Application to Flow Behavior and the Prediction of Oil Recovery," *SPEJ* (June 1961) 61.
22. Corey, A.T. *et al.*: "Three-Phase Relative Permeability," *Trans.*, AIME (1956) **207,** 349.
23. Snell, R.W.: "Three-Phase Relative Permeability in Unconsolidated Sand," *J. Inst. Petroleum* (March 1962) **84,** 80.
24. Naar, J., and Wygal, R.J.: "Three-Phase Imbibition Relative Permeability," *SPEJ* (December 1961) 254.
25. Stone, H.L.: "Probability Model for Estimating Three-Phase Relative Permeability," *JPT* (February 1970) 214; *Trans.*, AIME (1970) **249.**
26. Stone, H.L.: "Estimation of Three-Phase Relative Permeability and Residual Oil Data," *J. Cdn. Pet. Tech.* (April 1973) **12,** No. 4, 53.
27. Coats, K.H. *et al.*: "Three-Dimensional Simulation of Steamflooding," *SPEJ* (December 1974) 573; *Trans.*, AIME (1974) **257.**

SI Metric Conversion Factors

°API	141.5/(131.5 + °API)		= g/cm^3
bbl	× 1.589 873	E − 01	= m^3
cp	× 1.0*	E − 03	= Pa·s
ft	× 3.048*	E − 01	= m
ft^2	× 9.290 304*	E − 02	= m^2
ft^3	× 2.831 685	E − 02	= m^3
lbm	× 4.535 924	E − 01	= kg
md	× 9.869 233	E − 04	= μm^2
psi	× 6.894 757	E + 00	= kPa
psi^{-1}	× 1.450 377	E − 01	= kPa^{-1}
°R	× 5/9		= K

*Conversion factor is exact.

Chapter 3
Basic Mathematical Concepts

3.1 Introduction

Mathematical models, such as finite-difference simulators, are built on fundamental physical and mathematical principles. Chap. 2 discussed the physical principles involved in reservoir simulation, including the law of conservation of mass, Darcy's law for fluid flow through porous media, pressure/volume/temperature (PVT) behavior of reservoir fluids, and properties of reservoir rock. The mathematical principles required to develop numerical reservoir simulators include basic differential calculus, differential-equation theory, numerical analysis, finite-difference calculus, and linear algebra.

Differential calculus, which dates back to the time of Newton and Leibnitz, relates the derivative (or tangent slope) of a continuous function to the function itself. This branch of mathematics has many important applications in such diverse fields as engineering, physical sciences, biology, economics, and applied mathematics.

Differential equations involve both known and unknown functions, along with the derivatives of the unknown functions. They have applications in many of the same areas as differential calculus. Examples of differential equations used in petroleum engineering are the pipe-flow equation (Euler's equation), Muskat's[1] method for solution-gas-drive reservoirs, the well-test equation (diffusivity equation), and the equations used in reservoir simulation.

Numerical-analysis methods provide computational techniques (algorithms) for the approximate solutions of exact mathematical problems. Numerical-analysis techniques, or numerical methods, are used to put complex mathematical problems on digital computers and to obtain approximate solutions to otherwise unsolvable problems. One branch of numerical analysis, finite-difference calculus, is used to approximate functional relationships and their derivatives at a series of discrete (discontinuous) points. Such points can be measured in laboratory experiments or field observations, or they can be generated in the numerical solution of differential equations. Finite-difference calculus is related to differential calculus through the Taylor series expansion.

Linear algebra deals with the solution of systems of linear equations. One source of linear-equation problems in reservoir engineering is the approximation of continuous differential equations by finite-difference equations.

3.2 Basic Differential Calculus

Although a complete review of differential calculus is beyond the scope of this book, differential calculus forms the mathematical basis for describing recovery processes observed in hydrocarbon reservoirs. Because practicing simulation engineers rarely directly apply differential calculus techniques, this text does not discuss the theory of differential calculus. It considers only the methods used directly to derive, simplify, and expand reservoir-simulation equations.

3.2.1 Derivatives and Differentiation. ***First Derivative.*** In many engineering applications, knowledge of a function's value is insufficient to solve a given problem. Additional information, such as the rate at which the function changes, is often required before a solution can be obtained. This is apparent in Darcy's law for the steady-state flow of gas to a wellbore,

$$q_{gsc} = \frac{-2\pi\beta_c khr}{\mu_g B_g}\frac{dp}{dr}. \quad\text{(3.1)}$$

Substituting the definition of B_g given in Eq. 2.83 results in

$$q_{gsc} = \frac{-2\pi\alpha_c\beta_c khr}{\mu_g}\frac{T_{sc}}{Tp_{sc}}\frac{p}{z}\frac{dp}{dr}. \quad\text{(3.2)}$$

In this example, the pressure, p, is a function of the spatial variable, r. The gas flow rate, q_{gsc}, cannot be determined from the knowledge of pressure alone. The derivative, dp/dr, must also be known.

To obtain the formal definition of the derivative of a continuous function f(x), let f(x) be a continuous function of x. Then

$$\frac{df}{dx} = \lim_{\Delta x\to 0}\left[\frac{f(x+\Delta x) - f(x)}{\Delta x}\right], \quad\text{(3.3)}$$

where lim = the limiting value inside the brackets as Δx approaches zero. Example 3.1 illustrates this process.

Example 3.1. Determine the derivative of $f(x) = x^2$ using Eq. 3.3.
Solution.

$$\frac{df}{dx} = \lim_{\Delta x\to 0}\left[\frac{f(x+\Delta x) - f(x)}{\Delta x}\right]. \quad\text{(3.3)}$$

$$\text{or } \frac{df}{dx} = \lim_{\Delta x\to 0}\left[\frac{(x+\Delta x)^2 - x^2}{\Delta x}\right]. \quad\text{(3.4)}$$

TABLE 3.1—COMMON FUNCTIONS AND THEIR DERIVATIVES (abridged from Ref. 2)

		Comments
1	$(d/dx)A=0$	$A=$ constant
2	$(d/dx)x=1$	
3	$(d/dx)Ax=A$	$A=$ constant
4	$(d/dx)(u+v-w)=(du/dx)+(dv/dx)-(dw/dx)$	
5	$(d/dx)uv=u(dv/dx)+v(du/dx)$	Product rule
6	$(d/dx)uvw=uv(dw/dx)+uw(dv/dx)+vw(du/dx)$	Product rule
7	$(d/dx)(u/v)=[v(du/dx)-u(dv/dx)]/v^2=(1/v)(du/dx)-(u/v^2)(dv/dx)$	Quotient rule
8	$(d/dx)u^n=nu^{n-1}(du/dx)$	$u=u(x)$
9	$(d/dx)\sqrt{u}=\left[1/\left(2\sqrt{u}\right)\right](du/dx)$	$u=u(x)$
10	$(d/dx)(1/u)=(-1/u^2)(du/dx)$	$u=u(x)$
11	$(d/dx)(1/u^n)=(-n/u^{n+1})(du/dx)$	$u=u(x)$
12	$(d/dx)(u^n/v^n)=(u^{n-1}/v^{n+1})[nv(du/dx)-nu(dv/dx)]$	$u=u(x)$, $v=v(x)$
13	$(d/dx)u^nv^n=(u^{n-1})(v^{n-1})[nv(du/dx)+nu(dv/dx)]$	$u=u(x)$, $v=v(x)$
14	$(d/dx)[(u_1u_2u_3\ldots u_n)/(v_1v_2v_3\ldots v_m)]=[(u_1u_2u_3\ldots u_n)/(v_1v_2v_3\ldots v_m)]$ $\times[(1/u_1)(du_1/dx)+(1/u_2)(du_2/dx)+(1/u_3)(du_3/dx)+\ldots(1/u_n)(du_n/dx)$ $-(1/v_1)(dv_1/dx)-(1/v_2)(dv_2/dx)-(1/v_3)(dv_3/dx)-\ldots(1/v_m)(dv_m/dx)]$	Combined product and quotient rules
15	$(d/dx)[f(u)]=(df/du)(du/dx)$	Chain rule
16	$(d^2/dx^2)[f(u)]=(df/du)(d^2u/dx^2)+(d^2f/du^2)[(du/dx)^2]$	
17	$(du/dx)=1/(dx/du)$	$(dx/du)\neq 0$
18	$(d/dx)\log_A u=(\log_A e)(1/u)(du/dx)$	$A\neq 1$
19	$(d/dx)(\log_e u)=(1/u)(du/dx)$	
20	$(d/dx)A^u=A^u(\log_e A)(du/dx)$	$A=$ constant
21	$(d/dx)e^u=e^u(du/dx)$	$u=u(x)$
22	$(d/dx)u^v=vu^{v-1}(du/dx)+(\log_e u)u^v(dv/dx)$	$u=u(x)$, $v=v(x)$
23	$(d/dx)(\sin u)=(\cos u)(du/dx)$	$u=u(x)$
24	$(d/dx)(\cos u)=-(\sin u)(du/dx)$	$u=u(x)$
25	$(d/dx)(\tan u)=(\sec^2 u)(du/dx)$	$u=u(x)$
26	$(d/dx)(\cot u)=-(\csc^2 u)(du/dx)$	$u=u(x)$
27	$(d/dx)(\sec u)=(\sec u)(\tan u)(du/dx)$	$u=u(x)$
28	$(d/dx)(\csc u)=-(\csc u)(\cot u)(du/dx)$	$u=u(x)$
29	$(d/dx)(\text{arc sin } u)=\left(1/\sqrt{1-u^2}\right)(du/dx)$	$-\pi/2\leqq\text{arc sin } u\leqq\pi/2$
30	$(d/dx)(\text{arc cos } u)=\left(-1/\sqrt{1-u^2}\right)(du/dx)$	$0\leqq\text{arc cos } u\leqq\pi$
31	$(d/dx)(\text{arc tan } u)=[1/(1+u^2)](du/dx)$	$-\pi/2\leqq\text{arc tan } u\leqq\pi/2$
32	$(d/dx)(\text{arc cot } u)=[-1/(1+u^2)](du/dx)$	$0\leqq\text{arc tan } u\leqq\pi$
33	$(d/dx)(\text{arc sec } u)=\left[1/\left(u\sqrt{u^2-1}\right)\right](du/dx)$	$0\leqq\text{arc sec } u\leqq\pi/2$, $-\pi\leqq\text{arc sec } u<-\pi/2$
34	$(d/dx)(\text{arc csc } u)=\left[-1/\left(u\sqrt{u^2-1}\right)\right](du/dx)$	$0\leqq\text{arc csc } u\leqq\pi/2$, $-\pi\leqq\text{arc csc } u\leqq-\pi/2$
35	$(d/dx)(\sinh u)=(\cosh u)(du/dx)$	$u=u(x)$
36	$(d/dx)(\cosh u)=(\sinh u)(du/dx)$	$u=u(x)$
37	$(d/dx)(\tanh u)=(\text{sech}^2 u)(du/dx)$	$u=u(x)$
38	$(d/dx)(\coth u)=(\text{csch}^2 u)(du/dx)$	$u=u(x)$
39	$(d/dx)(\text{sech } u)=-[(\text{sech } u)(\tanh u)(du/dx)]$	$u=u(x)$
40	$(d/dx)(\text{csch } u)=-[(\text{csch } u)(\coth u)(du/dx)]$	$u=u(x)$

Expanding the numerator yields

$$\frac{df}{dx} = \lim_{\Delta x \to 0}\left[\frac{\left\{\left[x^2 + 2x\Delta x + (\Delta x)^2\right] - x^2\right\}}{\Delta x}\right]; \quad \ldots\ldots\ (3.5)$$

simplifying this expression gives

$$\frac{df}{dx} = \lim_{\Delta x \to 0}\left\{\frac{\left[2x\Delta x + (\Delta x)^2\right]}{\Delta x}\right\} \quad \ldots\ldots\ (3.6)$$

$$\text{or } \frac{df}{dx} = \lim_{\Delta x \to 0}(2x + \Delta x). \quad \ldots\ldots\ (3.7)$$

As Δx approaches zero, the second term in the parentheses becomes zero and

$$\frac{df}{dx} = 2x. \quad \ldots\ldots\ (3.8)$$

Calculus textbooks give the standard formula for the first derivative of functions of the form $f(x) = x^n$ as

$$\frac{df}{dx} = nx^{n-1}. \quad \ldots\ldots\ (3.9)$$

Table 3.1 lists several common functions with their first derivatives. Although calculating derivatives of simple functions is beyond the scope of this book, this table is provided to aid in the given examples and exercises. Elementary differential-calculus texts provide more comprehensive tables. Table 3.1 gives several important rules of differentiation, such as the product (multiplication) rule and quotient (division) rule. The following sections discuss these rules in more detail.

Product Rule. The product rule gives the derivative of a function composed of the product of two simple functions. Let

$$f(x) = g(x)h(x), \quad \ldots\ldots\ (3.10)$$

$$\text{then, } \frac{df}{dx} = g(x)\frac{dh}{dx} + h(x)\frac{dg}{dx}. \quad \ldots\ldots\ (3.11)$$

Example 3.2. Use the product rule to calculate the derivative of $f(x) = x^2 \sin(x)$, with respect to x.

Solution. Let

$$f(x) = g(x)h(x), \quad \ldots\ldots\ (3.10)$$

$g(x) = x^2$, and $h(x) = \sin(x)$. From Table 3.1, $dg/dx = 2x$ and $dh/dx = \cos(x)$. Then, from the product rule,

$$\frac{df}{dx} = g(x)\frac{dh}{dx} + h(x)\frac{dg}{dx} \quad \ldots\ldots\ (3.11)$$

$$\text{or } \frac{df}{dx} = x^2\cos(x) + 2x\sin(x). \quad \ldots\ldots\ (3.12)$$

Example 3.3. The Laplace equation,

$$\frac{1}{r}\frac{d}{dr}\left(r\frac{dp}{dr}\right) = 0, \quad \ldots\ldots\ (3.13)$$

describes the steady-state-pressure distribution in the vicinity of a wellbore caused by the withdrawal of an incompressible fluid from a homogeneous reservoir. Use the product rule to expand the left side of this equation.

Solution. Let $f(r) = r(dp/dr)$. Then Eq. 3.13 becomes

$$\frac{1}{r}\frac{df}{dr} = 0. \quad \ldots\ldots\ (3.14)$$

Now, let $g(r) = r$ and $h(r) = dp/dr$. Then $dg/dr = 1$ and $dh/dr = d^2p/dr^2$. From the product rule,

$$\frac{df}{dr} = g(r)\frac{dh}{dr} + h(r)\frac{dg}{dr}. \quad \ldots\ldots\ (3.15)$$

Substituting the definitions of $g(r)$ and $h(r)$ and their derivatives gives

$$\frac{df}{dr} = r\frac{d^2p}{dr^2} + 1\frac{dp}{dr}. \quad \ldots\ldots\ (3.16)$$

Finally, substituting into Eq. 3.14 yields

$$\frac{1}{r}\left(r\frac{d^2p}{dr^2} + 1\frac{dp}{dr}\right) = 0 \quad \ldots\ldots\ (3.17)$$

$$\text{or } \frac{d^2p}{dr^2} + \frac{1}{r}\frac{dp}{dr} = 0, \quad \ldots\ldots\ (3.18)$$

where d^2p/dr^2 = second derivative of pressure with respect to radius. Higher-order derivatives are discussed later.

Quotient Rule. The quotient rule gives the derivative of a function composed of a simple function divided by another simple function. Let

$$f(x) = g(x)/h(x), \quad \ldots\ldots\ (3.19)$$

$$\text{then, } \frac{df}{dx} = \frac{h(x)(dg/dx) - g(x)(dh/dx)}{[h(x)]^2}. \quad \ldots\ldots\ (3.20)$$

Example 3.4. Use the quotient rule to calculate the derivative of $f(x) = \sin(x)/x^2$ for $x > 0$ with respect to x.

Solution. Let

$$f(x) = g(x)/h(x), \quad \ldots\ldots\ (3.19)$$

$g(x) = \sin(x)$, and $h(x) = x^2$. From Table 3.1, $dg/dx = \cos(x)$ and $dh/dx = 2x$. Then, from the quotient rule,

$$\frac{df}{dx} = \frac{h(x)(dg/dx) - g(x)(dh/dx)}{[h(x)]^2}, \quad \ldots\ldots\ (3.20)$$

and substituting the definitions of $g(x)$ and $h(x)$ and their derivatives yields

$$\frac{df}{dx} = \frac{x^2\cos(x) - 2x\sin(x)}{x^4} \quad \ldots\ldots\ (3.21a)$$

$$\text{or } \frac{df}{dx} = \frac{x\cos(x) - 2\sin(x)}{x^3}. \quad \ldots\ldots\ (3.21b)$$

Example 3.5. Use the quotient rule to obtain an expression for the compressibility of a real gas.

Solution. The definition of isothermal compressibility is

$$c_g = -\frac{1}{V}\frac{dV}{dp}\Big|_T. \quad \ldots\ldots\ (3.22)$$

Substituting the real-gas law,

$$pV = znRT, \quad \ldots\ldots\ (3.23)$$

results in

$$c_g = -\frac{p}{z}\frac{d}{dp}\left(\frac{z}{p}\right). \quad \ldots\ldots\ (3.24)$$

Let $f(p)=z/p$. Then

$$c_g = -\frac{1}{f}\frac{df}{dp}. \quad (3.25)$$

Also, let $g(p)=z$ and $h(p)=p$. Then $dg/dp=dz/dp$ and $dh/dp=1$. From the quotient rule, Eq. 3.20,

$$\frac{df}{dp} = \frac{p(dz/dp) - z}{p^2} \quad (3.26)$$

$$\text{and } c_g = -\frac{p}{z}\left(\frac{1}{p}\frac{dz}{dp} - \frac{z}{p^2}\right) = \frac{1}{p} - \frac{1}{z}\frac{dz}{dp}. \quad (3.27)$$

In this example, dz/dp must be determined from laboratory data (table look-up of experimentally derived z factors) or through differentiating z-factor correlations. Gas compressibility is a required property in pressure-transient analysis of gas wells.

Combined Form of the Product and Quotient Rules. A combination of the product and quotient rules gives the derivative of a function composed of the product of several simple functions divided by several other simple functions. Let

$$f(x) = \frac{g_1(x)g_2(x)g_3(x)\ldots g_n(x)}{h_1(x)h_2(x)h_3(x)\ldots h_m(x)}, \quad (3.28)$$

$$\text{then } \frac{df}{dx} = f(x)\left[\frac{(dg_1/dx)}{g_1(x)} + \frac{(dg_2/dx)}{g_2(x)} + \frac{(dg_3/dx)}{g_3(x)} + \ldots + \frac{(dg_n/dx)}{g_n(x)} - \frac{(dh_1/dx)}{h_1(x)} - \frac{(dh_2/dx)}{h_2(x)} - \frac{(dh_3/dx)}{h_3(x)} - \ldots - \frac{(dh_m/dx)}{h_m(x)}\right]. \quad (3.29)$$

Example 3.6. Use the combined product and quotient rules to calculate the derivative of $f(x)=x^2\sin(x)/e^{2x}$ with respect to x.

Solution. Let

$$f(x) = \frac{g_1(x)g_2(x)}{h_1(x)}, \quad (3.30)$$

where $g_1(x)=x^2$, $g_2(x)=\sin(x)$, and $h_1(x)=e^{2x}$.

From Table 3.1, $dg_1/dx=2x$, $dg_2/dx=\cos(x)$, and $dh_1/dx=2e^{2x}$. Then, from the combined product and quotient rules, Eq. 3.29,

$$\frac{df}{dx} = \frac{x^2\sin(x)}{e^{2x}}\left[\frac{2x}{x^2} + \frac{\cos(x)}{\sin(x)} - \frac{2e^{2x}}{e^{2x}}\right]. \quad (3.31)$$

After simplifying,

$$\frac{df}{dx} = \frac{x^2\sin(x)}{e^{2x}}\left[\frac{2}{x} + \cot(x) - 2\right]. \quad (3.32)$$

Example 3.7. The single-phase transmissibility of a porous medium to gas is

$$T_{gx}(p) = \frac{\beta_c\alpha_c A_x k_x}{\mu_g \Delta x}\frac{T_{sc}}{p_{sc}T}\frac{p}{z}, \quad (3.33)$$

where β_c, α_c, A_x, k_x, Δx, T_{sc}, p_{sc}, and T are constant and where μ_g, p, and z are functions of pressure. In reservoir simulation, transmissibility is a measure of the capacity of a fluid to flow through the reservoir rock.

One method of solving reservoir-simulation equations for gas (compressible flow) is the generalized Newton-Raphson method, which is discussed in Chap. 5. The generalized Newton-Raphson method requires the derivative of transmissibility with respect to pressure. Use the combined product rule and quotient rule to obtain this derivative.

Solution. Let

$$T_{gx}(p) = \frac{\beta_c\alpha_c A_x k_x}{\Delta x}\frac{T_{sc}}{p_{sc}T}f(p), \quad (3.34)$$

where $f(p)=p/\mu_g z$. Then

$$\frac{dT_{gx}}{dp} = \beta_c\alpha_c\frac{A_x k_x}{\Delta x}\frac{T_{sc}}{p_{sc}T}\frac{df}{dp}. \quad (3.35)$$

$$\text{Let } f(p) = \frac{g_1(p)}{h_1(p)h_2(p)}, \quad (3.36)$$

$g_1(p)=p$, $h_1(p)=\mu_g$, and $h_2(p)=z$. Then $dg_1/dp=1$, $dh_1/dp=d\mu_g/dp$, and $dh_2/dp=dz/dp$. Then, from the combined product and quotient rules, Eq. 3.29,

$$\frac{df}{dp} = \frac{p}{\mu_g z}\left(\frac{1}{p} - \frac{(d\mu_g/dp)}{\mu_g} - \frac{(dz/dp)}{z}\right) \quad (3.37)$$

or, after simplification,

$$\frac{df}{dp} = \frac{1}{\mu_g z} - \frac{p}{\mu_g^2 z}\frac{d\mu_g}{dp} - \frac{p}{\mu_g z^2}\frac{dz}{dp}. \quad (3.38)$$

Then, the derivative of gas transmissibility becomes

$$\frac{dT_{gx}}{dp} = \frac{\beta_c\alpha_c A_x k_x}{\Delta x}\frac{T_{sc}}{p_{sc}T}\left(\frac{1}{\mu_g z} - \frac{p}{\mu_g^2 z}\frac{d\mu_g}{dp} - \frac{p}{\mu_g z^2}\frac{dz}{dp}\right). \quad (3.39)$$

Chain Rule. The chain rule gives the derivative of a function composed of a complex form of two simple functions. Let

$$f(x) = g[h(x)], \quad (3.40)$$

$$\text{then } \frac{df}{dx} = \frac{dg}{dh}\frac{dh}{dx}. \quad (3.41)$$

Example 3.8. Calculate the derivative of $f(x)=\sin(x^2)$.

Solution. Use Eq. 3.40, where $g(h)=\sin(h)$ and $h(x)=x^2$. From Table 3.1, $dg/dh=\cos(h)$ and $dh/dx=2x$. Then, from the chain rule,

$$\frac{df}{dx} = \frac{dg}{dh}\frac{dh}{dx}, \quad (3.41)$$

$$\frac{df}{dx} = \cos(x^2)2x, \quad (3.42a)$$

$$\text{or } \frac{df}{dx} = 2x\cos(x^2). \quad (3.42b)$$

Example 3.9. The oil stored in an undersaturated reservoir at S_{iw} expressed in field units is

$$N = \frac{S_o\phi V_b}{\alpha_c B_o} \quad (3.43)$$

$$\text{or } N = \frac{(1 - S_{iw})\phi V_b}{\alpha_c B_o}. \quad (3.44)$$

Assuming that both the reservoir rock and irreducible water are incompressible, at what rate will the reservoir pressure decline if oil is removed at a constant rate of q_{osc}?

Solution. First, recall that by definition, oil-production rate equals the rate of removal of oil from the reservoir; that is,

$$q_{osc} = \frac{dN}{dt}. \quad (3.45)$$

Eq. 3.45 implies that the production rate is negative as the amount of oil in the reservoir decreases. Expressing dN/dt with the chain rule,

$$\frac{dN}{dt} = \frac{dN}{dp}\frac{dp}{dt}. \quad (3.46)$$

Differentiating Eq. 3.44 with respect to p and observing that reservoir rock and irreducible water are incompressible yields

$$\frac{dN}{dp} = \frac{(1 - S_{iw})\phi V_b}{\alpha_c}\frac{d}{dp}\left(\frac{1}{B_o}\right). \quad (3.47)$$

Let $f(p) = 1/B_o$ or $f(p) = B_o^{-1}$. Then,

$$\frac{df}{dp} = -\frac{1}{B_o^2}\frac{dB_o}{dp} \quad (3.48)$$

(note the implicit use of the chain rule in this step); therefore,

$$\frac{dN}{dp} = -\frac{(1 - S_{iw})\phi V_b}{\alpha_c}\frac{1}{B_o^2}\frac{dB_o}{dp}. \quad (3.49)$$

Substituting into Eq. 3.46 gives

$$\frac{dN}{dt} = -\frac{(1 - S_{iw})\phi V_b}{\alpha_c}\frac{1}{B_o^2}\frac{dB_o}{dp}\frac{dp}{dt}. \quad (3.50)$$

Substituting into Eq. 3.45 gives

$$q_{osc} = -\frac{(1 - S_{iw})\phi V_b}{\alpha_c}\frac{1}{B_o^2}\frac{dB_o}{dp}\frac{dp}{dt}, \quad (3.51)$$

and solving for dp/dt yields

$$\frac{dp}{dt} = -\frac{\alpha_c B_o^2 q_{osc}}{(1 - S_{iw})\phi V_b \frac{dB_o}{dp}}. \quad (3.52)$$

Above the bubblepoint pressure, the oil-phase formation volume factor (FVF) can be approximated by

$$B_o = \frac{B_{ob}}{1 + c_o(p - p_b)}, \quad (2.81)$$

which, upon differentiation (with Rule 10 in Table 3.1), gives

$$\frac{dB_o}{dp} = -\frac{c_o B_{ob}}{\left[1 + c_o(p - p_b)\right]^2} \quad (3.53)$$

(note that B_{ob} is constant). Substituting Eqs. 2.81 and 3.53 into Eq. 3.52 results in

$$\frac{dp}{dt} = \frac{\alpha_c B_{ob} q_{osc}}{(1 - S_{iw})\phi V_b c_o}, \quad (3.54)$$

which describes the rate of pressure decline in a volumetric, undersaturated oil reservoir.

Higher-Order Derivatives. Higher-order derivatives of a function are defined as derivatives of the function's lower-order derivatives. For example, the second derivative of a function $f(x)$ is the derivative of the first derivative. That is,

$$\frac{d^2f}{dx^2} = \frac{d}{dx}\left(\frac{df}{dx}\right). \quad (3.55)$$

Similarly, derivatives of an order greater than two can be obtained by applying the formula

$$\frac{d^nf}{dx^n} = \frac{d}{dx}\left(\frac{d^{n-1}f}{dx^{n-1}}\right). \quad (3.56)$$

Example 3.10. Find the second derivative of $f(x) = \sin(x)$.

Solution. Let $f(x) = \sin(x)$. From Table 3.1, $df/dx = \cos(x)$ and

$$\frac{d^2f}{dx^2} = \frac{d}{dx}\left(\frac{df}{dx}\right) = \frac{d}{dx}[\cos(x)]. \quad (3.57)$$

Also from Table 3.1, $d^2f/dx^2 = -\sin(x)$.

3.2.2 Partial Differentiation. ***Partial Derivative.*** All the discussion on differentiation so far has been directed toward the functions of one variable. For functions of more than one variable [for example, $f(x,y)$], the concept of partial differentiation must be discussed. The following is the formal definition of the partial derivative of a function of two variables.

Let $f(x,y)$ be a continuous function of the variables x and y. Then

$$\frac{\partial f}{\partial x} = \lim_{\Delta x \to 0}\left[\frac{f(x + \Delta x, y) - f(x,y)}{\Delta x}\right] \quad (3.58)$$

and $$\frac{\partial f}{\partial y} = \lim_{\Delta y \to 0}\left[\frac{f(x, y + \Delta y) - f(x,y)}{\Delta y}\right]. \quad (3.59)$$

These definitions state that the partial derivative of a function of more than one variable with respect to one of the variables can be obtained by fixing all other variables constant and differentiating with respect to the variable of interest. All rules of differentiation discussed earlier are valid for partial differentiation. Examples 3.11 through 3.13 illustrate this principle.

Example 3.11. Find the partial derivatives of $f(x,y) = x^2y^4$ with respect to x and y.

Solution. Holding y constant and differentiating with respect to x leads to $\partial f/\partial x = 2xy^4$. Holding x constant and differentiating with respect to y leads to $\partial f/\partial y = 4x^2y^3$.

Example 3.12. Use the chain rule to find the partial derivatives of $f(x,y) = \sin(x^2y^4)$ with respect to x and y.

Solution. Let $f(x,y) = g[h(x,y)]$, where $g[h] = \sin(h)$ and $h(x,y) = x^2y^4$. From Example 3.11, $\partial h/\partial x = 2xy^4$ and $\partial h/\partial y = 4x^2y^3$.

The chain rule for functions of two variables is

$$\frac{\partial f}{\partial x} = \frac{dg}{dh}\frac{\partial h}{\partial x} \quad (3.60)$$

and $$\frac{\partial f}{\partial y} = \frac{dg}{dh}\frac{\partial h}{\partial y}. \quad (3.61)$$

From Table 3.1, $dg/dh = \cos(h)$; therefore,

$$\frac{\partial f}{\partial x} = 2xy^4\cos(x^2y^4) \quad (3.62)$$

and $$\frac{\partial f}{\partial y} = 4x^2y^3\cos(x^2y^4). \quad (3.63)$$

Example 3.13. Find the partial derivatives of oil in place with respect to pressure and saturation for reservoirs undergoing simultaneous pressure and saturation changes. (Remember that S_{iw} and S_o were assumed constant in Example 3.9.) In this example, let S_o vary with respect to time.

Solution.

$$N = \frac{S_o \phi V_b}{a_c B_o}. \quad \ldots\ldots (3.43)$$

In Eq. 3.43 the only saturation-dependent function is S_o. From Example 3.9,

$$\frac{\partial N}{\partial p} = -\frac{S_o \phi V_b}{a_c} \frac{1}{B_o^2} \frac{dB_o}{dp}. \quad \ldots\ldots (3.64)$$

Note that B_o is a function of pressure only; therefore, its derivative is an ordinary derivative, not a partial derivative. Taking the partial derivative of N (as expressed by Eq. 3.43) with respect to S_o yields

$$\frac{\partial N}{\partial S_o} = \frac{\phi V_b}{a_c B_o} \frac{d}{dS_o}(S_o) \quad \ldots\ldots (3.65)$$

or $$\frac{\partial N}{\partial S_o} = \frac{\phi V_b}{a_c B_o}. \quad \ldots\ldots (3.66)$$

Total Derivative. The chain rule can also give the total derivative of a complicated function of two or more simple functions of a single variable. Let f[g(t),h(t)] be a continuous function of the simple functions g(t) and h(t), then

$$\frac{df}{dt} = \frac{\partial f}{\partial g}\frac{dg}{dt} + \frac{\partial f}{\partial h}\frac{dh}{dt}. \quad \ldots\ldots (3.67)$$

Example 3.14. Find the expression for the production rate from an oil reservoir undergoing simultaneous saturation and pressure changes.

Solution. Because saturation and pressure are both functions of time, Eq. 3.67 applies as

$$q_{osc} = \frac{dN}{dt}$$

$$= \left(\frac{\partial N}{\partial S_o}\frac{dS_o}{dt} + \frac{\partial N}{\partial p}\frac{dp}{dt}\right). \quad \ldots\ldots (3.68)$$

Substituting the results of Example 3.13, Eqs. 3.64 and 3.66, into Eq. 3.68, yields

$$q_{osc} = \frac{\phi V_b}{a_c B_o}\frac{dS_o}{dt} - \frac{S_o \phi V_b}{a_c}\frac{1}{B_o^2}\frac{dB_o}{dp}\frac{dp}{dt}$$

$$= \frac{\phi V_b}{a_c B_o}\left(\frac{dS_o}{dt} - \frac{S_o}{B_o}\frac{dB_o}{dp}\frac{dp}{dt}\right). \quad \ldots\ldots (3.69)$$

3.2.3 Taylor Series Expansion. One of the most useful tools in numerical analysis is the Taylor series expansion, which provides a means for converting most well-behaved functions into simple polynomials. This method is based on the fundamental theorem of calculus coupled with simple integration by parts and has the form

$$f(x) = f(x_o) + \frac{(x - x_o)}{1!}\frac{df}{dx} + \frac{(x - x_o)^2}{2!}\frac{d^2f}{dx^2} + \ldots$$

$$+ \frac{(x - x_o)^N}{N!}\frac{d^Nf}{dx^N} + R_{N+1}, \quad \ldots\ldots (3.70)$$

where f(x) has N+1 continuous derivatives evaluated at $x = x_o$. Eq. 3.70 can be written in a more compact form as

$$f(x) = f(x_o) + \sum_{n=1}^{N}\frac{(x - x_o)^n}{n!}\frac{d^nf}{dx^n} + R_{N+1}. \quad \ldots\ldots (3.71)$$

The remainder term

$$R_{N+1} = \frac{1}{(N+1)!}\int_{x_o}^{x}(x - x_o)^{N+1}\frac{d^{N+1}f}{dx^{N+1}}dx. \quad \ldots\ldots (3.72)$$

When the remainder term is included in the expansion, the Taylor series is an exact representation of f(x). If the expansion is carried out for a finite number of terms and the remainder is ignored, then the Taylor series expansion is only an approximation of f(x). That is,

$$f(x) \approx f(x_o) + \sum_{n=1}^{N}\frac{(x - x_o)^n}{n!}\frac{d^nf}{dx^n}. \quad \ldots\ldots (3.73)$$

Example 3.15. What is the exact Taylor series expansion of f(x) = e^x about the point $x_o = 0$?

Solution. Let f(x) = e^x and $x_o = 0$. From Table 3.1, df/dx = e^x. It can be shown recursively that all the higher-order derivatives of f(x) = e^x are

$$\frac{d^nf}{dx^n} = e^x, \quad \ldots\ldots (3.74)$$

where n = 1,2,3, ... Substituting into Eq. 3.70 yields

$$e^x = e^{x_o} + \frac{(x - x_o)}{1!}e^{x_o} + \frac{(x - x_o)^2}{2!}e^{x_o} + \ldots$$

$$+ \frac{(x - x_o)^N}{N!}e^{x_o} + R_{N+1}. \quad \ldots\ldots (3.75)$$

Evaluating e^x at $x_o = 0$, $e^{x_o} = e^0 = 1$. Substituting into Eq. 3.75 gives

$$e^x = 1 + \frac{x}{1!} + \frac{x^2}{2!} + \frac{x^3}{3!} + \ldots + \frac{x^N}{N!} + R_{N+1} \quad \ldots (3.76a)$$

or $$e^x = 1 + \sum_{n=1}^{N}\frac{x^n}{n!} + R_{N+1}, \quad \ldots\ldots (3.76b)$$

where R_{N+1} is defined by Eq. 3.72.

Example 3.16. Find the fourth-term (N=3) and sixth-term (N=5) approximations of e (the base of the natural logarithm). This is identical to approximating e^x for x = 1.

Solution. From Example 3.15, the fourth-term approximation of e^x becomes

$$e^x = 1 + \frac{x}{1!} + \frac{x^2}{2!} + \frac{x^3}{3!} + R_4. \quad \ldots\ldots (3.77)$$

Ignoring the remainder term and setting x = 1 gives $e = e^1 \approx 1 + 1/1 + 1/2 + 1/6$, or $e \approx 2.66667$. The sixth-term approximation of e is

$$e^x = 1 + \frac{x}{1!} + \frac{x^2}{2!} + \frac{x^3}{3!} + \frac{x^4}{4!} + \frac{x^5}{5!} + R_6. \quad \ldots\ldots (3.78)$$

Ignoring the remainder term and setting x = 1 gives $e = e^1 \approx 1 + 1/1 + 1/2 + 1/6 + 1/24 + 1/120$, or $e \approx 2.71667$. The value of e (to 10 decimal places) is 2.7182818284.

Example 3.17. Find the second-term approximation to the derivative of an arbitrary function, f(x).

Solution. From Eq. 3.70,

$$f(x) = f(x_o) + \frac{(x - x_o)}{1!}\frac{df}{dx} + R_2. \quad \ldots\ldots (3.79)$$

Ignoring the remainder term and solving for df/dx yields

$$\frac{df}{dx} \approx \frac{f(x) - f(x_o)}{(x - x_o)}. \quad \ldots\ldots (3.80)$$

3.3 Basic Differential Equations

Differential equations are equations that relate an unknown function to the derivatives of the function and, possibly, to a known function. The simplest example of a differential equation is

$$\frac{dp}{dt} = f(p,t), \quad (3.81)$$

where $p(t)$ = the unknown function and $f(p,t)$ = the known function. Examples of equations of this type used in the petroleum industry include the pipe-flow equation and Muskat's[1] method for solution-gas-drive reservoirs.

The pipe-flow equation, which is used to model the flow of fluids through a length of pipe or tubing, is derived by performing an energy balance through a control volume of the pipe. For a horizontal pipe (ignoring acceleration effects), the energy balance has the form

$$\frac{dp}{dl} = \frac{f_m \rho v^2}{2Dg_c}. \quad (3.82)$$

A second, more complicated example of a differential equation of the type shown in Eq. 3.81 is Muskat's equation for solution-gas-drive reservoirs. Muskat derived the following equation to predict future reservoir performance of solution-gas-drive reservoirs (see Sec. 11.2.2 of Chap. 11):

$$\frac{dS_o}{dp} = \frac{\dfrac{S_o}{B_o}\dfrac{k_{rg}}{k_{ro}}\dfrac{\mu_o}{\mu_g}\dfrac{dB_o}{dp} - \dfrac{(1-S_o-S_{iw})}{B_g}\dfrac{dB_g}{dp} + \dfrac{B_g S_o}{B_o}\dfrac{dR_s}{dp}}{\dfrac{k_{rg}\mu_o}{k_{ro}\mu_g} + 1}, \quad (3.83)$$

where $S_o(p)$ = the unknown function and the right side of the equation is the known function. The right side includes the derivatives dR_s/dp, dB_o/dp, and dB_g/dp, which are assumed to be known from PVT analyses. Other examples of differential equations used in the petroleum industry, but not of the form shown in Eq. 3.81, include the following.

1. The steady-state-pressure-distribution equation (the Laplace equation).

$$\frac{d^2p}{dr^2} + \frac{1}{r}\frac{dp}{dr} = 0. \quad (3.18)$$

2. The well-test equation (the diffusivity equation).

$$\frac{1}{r}\frac{\partial}{\partial r}\left(r\frac{\partial p}{\partial r}\right) = \frac{\phi \mu c_t}{\beta_c \alpha_c k}\frac{\partial p}{\partial t}. \quad (3.84)$$

3. The equations used in reservoir simulation, including

$$\frac{\partial}{\partial x}\left(\beta_c k_x \frac{k_{ro}}{\mu_o B_o}\frac{\partial p_o}{\partial x}\right) + \frac{\partial}{\partial y}\left(\beta_c k_y \frac{k_{ro}}{\mu_o B_o}\frac{\partial p_o}{\partial y}\right) + \frac{q_{osc}}{V_b} = \frac{1}{\alpha_c}\frac{\partial}{\partial t}\left(\frac{\phi S_o}{B_o}\right). \quad (3.85)$$

3.3.1 Basic Definitions.

Dependent and Independent Variables. Two types of variables, dependent and independent, appear in all differential equations. The unknown functions in the differential equation are the dependent variables of the equation. The derivatives in the differential equations are always taken with respect to the independent variables. In Eq. 3.82, p is the dependent variable and l is the independent variable. The term $f_m \rho v^2/2Dg_c$ is assumed to be a known function of p and l. In Eq. 3.85, p_o and S_o are the dependent variables and x, y, and t are the independent variables. The other terms in Eq. 3.85 (k_{ro}, k_x, k_y, μ_o, B_o, q_{osc}, ϕ, and V_b) are parameters and known functions of the equation.

Order and Degree of a Differential Equation. The order of a differential equation is defined as the order of the highest-order derivative that appears in the equation. Eqs. 3.82 and 3.83 are both first-order differential equations because only the first derivative appears in these equations. Eqs. 3.18, 3.84, and 3.85 are all second-order differential equations because they contain the second derivative of the dependent variables. (Perform the chain rule on the left sides of Eqs. 3.84 and 3.85, as in Example 3.3, to obtain the second derivative explicitly).

The degree of a differential equation is the power of the equation's highest-order derivative. All the previously discussed differential equations are first-degree equations. The degree of a differential equation must be a whole number, not a fraction. Examples of second-degree equations include

$$\left(\frac{d^2f}{dx^2}\right)^2 + \frac{df}{dx} - f = 0 \quad (3.86)$$

and

$$\left(\frac{d^2f}{dx^2}\right)^2 + \left(\frac{df}{dx}\right)^3 - f = 0. \quad (3.87)$$

Ordinary- and Partial-Differential Equations (PDE's). Ordinary-differential equations contain only ordinary derivatives. Eqs. 3.82, 3.83, and 3.18 are all ordinary-differential equations. PDE's contain partial derivatives of the dependent variable with respect to the independent variables. By definition, therefore, PDE's contain more than one independent variable. Eqs. 3.84 and 3.85 are examples of PDE's with independent variables r and t and x, y, and t, respectively.

Linear and Nonlinear Differential Equations. Linear differential equations contain linear differential operators. The formal definition of a linear operator, L, is

$$L(x + y) = L(x) + L(y). \quad (3.88)$$

For the equations we will be working with in reservoir simulation, a less formal definition of a linear differential equation is a differential equation in which all the coefficients are either constant or functions of only the independent variables. Nonlinear differential equations do not satisfy Eq. 3.88. With this definition, Eq. 3.84 is linear (assuming that ϕ, μ, c_t, and k are all constant), while Eq. 3.85 is nonlinear. Linearization is the process of transforming a nonlinear equation into the form of a linear equation.

3.3.2 Solution of Differential Equations.

The solution of a differential equation is a function that does not contain any derivatives with respect to the independent variables, that satisfies any specified conditions, and that satisfies the relationship defined by the differential equation. Example 3.18 illustrates this best.

Example 3.18. The rate of pressure decline in an aquifer under pseudosteady-state conditions may be modeled by the ordinary-differential equation

$$\frac{c_{aq}\phi_{aq}V_{aq}}{\alpha_c}\frac{dp_{aq}}{dt} = -K_{aq}(p_{aq} - p_R), \quad (3.89)$$

where the subscript aq = aquifer, the subscript R = reservoir, K_{aq} = aquifer constant, and all pressures are corrected to a common datum. Determine an equation that defines pressure as a function of time for pseudosteady-state aquifers. For this example, assume an instantaneous pressure drop in the reservoir (i.e., p_R is a constant and $p_R < p_{aq}$).

Solution. Eq. 3.89 can be rewritten as

$$\frac{dp_{aq}}{dt} + C'p_{aq} = C'p_R, \quad (3.90)$$

where

$$C' = \frac{\alpha_c K_{aq}}{c_{aq}\phi_{aq}V_{aq}}. \quad (3.91)$$

In Eq. 3.90, p_{aq} = the dependent variable, t = the independent variable, C' = a parameter, and p_R = a known function that is constant (in this example). For an instantaneous drop in reservoir pressure, the general solution to this equation is

$$p_{aq}(t) = p_R + C_1 e^{-C't}, \quad (3.92)$$

where C_1 = an arbitrary constant (with the units of pressure). This solution can be verified easily by taking the derivative of Eq. 3.92 and substituting both the derivative and Eq. 3.92 into Eq. 3.90.

Note that in this example, Eq. 3.92 represents a family of solutions. This is because the constant C_1 can be chosen arbitrarily and the original differential equation will be satisfied. Each value of C_1 provides a particular solution to the differential equation.

To determine the solution that governs the pressure decline for the aquifer of interest, an additional piece of information is required: the initial value of the aquifer pressure, which is used to determine the appropriate value of C_1. At $t=0$, p_{aq} from Eq. 3.92 must equal the initial reservoir pressure, p_i; therefore,

$$p_{aq} = p_i = p_R + C_1 e^o \quad \text{(3.93)}$$

or $C_1 = p_i - p_R$ . ... (3.94)

Substituting into Eq. 3.92 yields

$$p_{aq}(t) = p_R + (p_i - p_R)e^{-C't}, \quad \text{(3.95)}$$

which is a solution to the equation presented by Eq. 3.90 because it is a function that does not contain any derivative and because it satisfies the initial condition and the differential equation (Eq. 3.90).

3.3.3. Initial and Boundary Conditions. Although the details of obtaining analytical solutions to differential equations are beyond the scope of this book, the basic idea is to integrate the derivative in the equation to obtain an explicit expression for p_{aq} in Example 3.18. The constant C_1 in the general solution (Eq. 3.92 in Example 3.18) is related to the integration constant discussed in most elementary textbooks on integral calculus. Second-order ordinary-differential equations require two such integrations, so they yield two integration constants. Consequently, two additional pieces of information are required to specify the constants and obtain a unique solution to the differential equation. In general, each derivative in the equation requires one integration constant and, in turn, one additional piece of information.

The additional information required to obtain a unique solution to a given differential equation are the initial and/or boundary conditions of the problem. These conditions are so called because they can only be known either initially or on the boundaries. For example, to determine the solution of the diffusivity equation (Eq. 3.84) uniquely, one initial condition (because of the first derivative with respect to time) and two boundary conditions (because of the second-order derivative with respect to radius) are required. In well-test applications, the boundary conditions at the wellbore (either a constant-pressure or -rate well) and at the external radius (infinite-acting reservoir or no-flow or constant-pressure outer boundary) are specified.

For reservoir-simulation problems, the required initial conditions are initial reservoir pressure and saturation distributions. In most simulation studies, the initial conditions are obtained by assuming initial capillary/gravity equilibrium. In this mode of initialization, the pressure distribution is obtained by specifying the pressure at a given datum depth and using the fluid pressure gradients to determine pressures at all other depths. The initial saturation distributions are then obtained with fluid contacts and capillary pressure relationships. Other valid initial conditions may include watered-out (or gassed-out) conditions before an enhanced-oil-recovery project or dynamic initial conditions (such as those required for a tilted oil/water contact).

The boundary conditions used in reservoir simulators can be quite complex because the differential equations solved by reservoir simulators require that all boundaries be specified. This includes both exterior boundaries (reservoir limits) and interior boundaries (production and injection wells). For exterior boundaries, it is generally assumed that a no-flow boundary exists at some distance away from the reservoir. Mathematically, this can be stated as

$$\frac{\partial p_o}{\partial n} = \frac{\partial p_g}{\partial n} = \frac{\partial p_w}{\partial n} = 0, \quad \text{(3.96)}$$

where the variable n = direction normal (perpendicular) to the reservoir boundary. It is obvious that if all gradients across a reservoir boundary are equal to zero, then that boundary is a no-flow boundary. Boundary conditions that specify a derivative on a boundary are referred to as Neumann-type boundary conditions.

For interior boundaries, either well rates or bottomhole pressures can be specified. If a rate is specified for the well, Darcy's law can be used to generate a Neumann-type boundary condition,

$$\frac{\partial p}{\partial r}\Big|_{r=r_w} = -\frac{\mu B q_{sc}}{2\pi\beta_c k h r_w}. \quad \text{(3.97)}$$

If the pressure is specified for the wellbore, then a Dirichlet-type boundary condition is obtained.

$$p|_{r=r_w} = p_{wf}. \quad \text{(3.98)}$$

Well behavior can be specified in many ways. These include specifying the top hole pressures, maximum well rates subject to various constraints, pump and surface facility capacities, and so on. Sophisticated well-management routines, which may take several thousand lines of FORTRAN computer code, are generally incorporated into commercial reservoir simulators to convert the complex well specifications into the simple form of either Eq. 3.97 or Eq. 3.98. Sec. 4.5 in Chap. 4 discusses detailed treatment of initial and boundary conditions in reservoir simulation. Chap. 6 discusses the basics of converting well specifications to the form of Eq. 3.97 or 3.98.

3.3.4 Vector Differential Operators. The vector differential operator, $\vec{\nabla}$, is a compact form for expressing differential operations. It has components similar to vectors (which are discussed later); but, like all operators, it is used to operate on external functions. The gradient operator (which operates on a scalar function of the variables x, y, and z) is

$$\vec{\nabla}s = \frac{\partial s}{\partial x}\vec{i} + \frac{\partial s}{\partial y}\vec{j} + \frac{\partial s}{\partial z}\vec{k}. \quad \text{(3.99)}$$

The gradient operator obeys the distributive law but not the commutative or associative laws. That is,

$$\vec{\nabla}(s_1 + s_2) = \vec{\nabla}s_1 + \vec{\nabla}s_2 \quad \text{(3.100)}$$

but $\vec{\nabla}s \neq s\vec{\nabla}$, ... (3.101)

or $\left(\vec{\nabla}s_1\right)s_2 \neq \vec{\nabla}(s_1 s_2)$. .... (3.102)

The divergence operator, sometimes referred to as the dot product, operates on a vector, $\vec{v} = (v_1, v_2, v_3)$, which is a function of the variables x, y, and z. This operator is defined as

$$\vec{\nabla}\cdot\vec{v} = \frac{\partial v_1}{\partial x} + \frac{\partial v_2}{\partial y} + \frac{\partial v_3}{\partial z}. \quad \text{(3.103)}$$

The divergence operator follows the same laws as the gradient operator.

The Laplacian operator operates on a scalar function of the variables x, y, and z, and is obtained by taking the divergence of the gradient of the scalar function, s. That is,

$$\vec{\nabla}\cdot\left(\vec{\nabla}s\right) = \frac{\partial^2 s}{\partial x^2} + \frac{\partial^2 s}{\partial y^2} + \frac{\partial^2 s}{\partial z^2}. \quad \text{(3.104)}$$

The collection of differential operators operating on the function s on the left side of Eq. 3.104 is called the Laplacian operator, $\vec{\nabla}^2$, or

$$\vec{\nabla}^2 = \frac{\partial^2}{\partial x^2} + \frac{\partial^2}{\partial y^2} + \frac{\partial^2}{\partial z^2}. \quad \text{(3.105)}$$

Again, like the gradient and divergence operators, the Laplacian operator follows the distributive property.

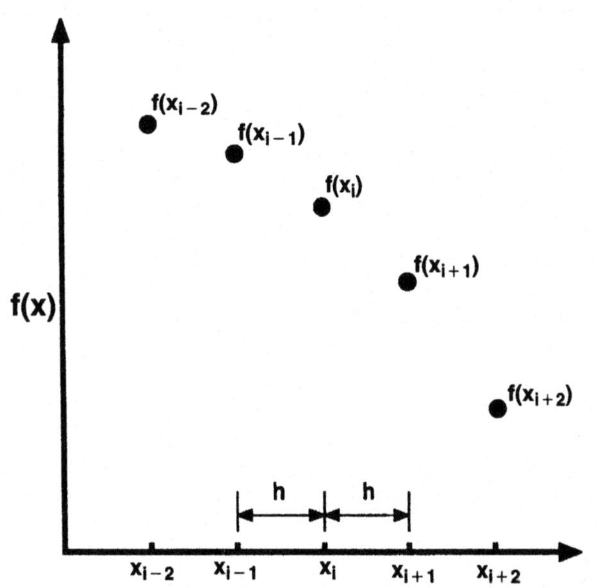

Fig. 3.1—Discrete points used in finite-difference approximations.

With this notation, Eqs. 3.18, 3.84, and 3.85 can be rewritten, respectively, in the compact forms

$$\vec{\nabla}^2_r p = 0, \quad (3.106)$$

$$\vec{\nabla}^2_r p = \frac{\phi \mu c_t}{\beta_c \alpha_c k} \frac{\partial p}{\partial t}, \quad (3.107)$$

and $\vec{\nabla}_{x,y} \cdot \left(\beta_c k \frac{k_{ro}}{\mu_o B_o} \vec{\nabla}_{x,y} p_o \right) + \frac{q_{osc}}{V_b} = \frac{1}{\alpha_c} \frac{\partial}{\partial t} \left(\frac{\phi S_o}{B_o} \right). \quad (3.108)$

Note that the operators described in this section have been assigned the subscripts r in Eqs. 3.106 and 3.107 and x,y in Eq. 3.108 to identify the radial and rectangular coordinate systems, respectively.

3.4 Finite-Difference Calculus

The differential calculus discussed in the previous sections is appropriate for continuous functions only; however, in petroleum reservoir applications, a situation often arises where functional values are known only at discrete points. For example, these discrete points can occur during field measurements where such values as pressures and production rates are measured at fixed time intervals. The values of the measured properties are known only at the instant when they are measured. **Fig. 3.1** illustrates such a series of discrete points.

For discrete points, mathematical techniques are also available to approximate values of functions and their derivatives at points where they are not known. Finite-difference calculus is such a technique. Finite-difference calculus is the branch of mathematics that uses basic arithmetic operations (addition, subtraction, multiplication, and division) to approximate derivatives, differential equations, and other analytical operations performed on continuous functions.

3.4.1 Finite-Difference Operators. The basis of finite-difference calculus is a group of operators that acts on discrete points. An operator is a sequence of mathematical operations performed in a fixed order that acts on any number of the discrete points and results in a final number. The operators used in finite-difference calculus include the forward-difference operator, Δ; the backward-difference operator, ∇; the central-difference operator, δ; the shift (translation) operator, E; and the average operator, A.

Although the finite-difference operators described in this section appear to be very simple, they are the mathematical basis of one of the more powerful predictive tools available to simulation engineers.

TABLE 3.2—TABULATED VALUES OF sin(x) AND cos(x) AT DISCRETE VALUES OF x

Node	x_i	$f(x_i)=\sin(x_i)$	$g(x_i)=\cos(x_i)$
1	0 (0°)	0.0000	1.0000
2	π/12 (15°)	0.2588	0.9654
3	π/6 (30°)	0.5000	0.8660
4	π/4 (45°)	0.7071	0.7071
5	π/3 (60°)	0.8660	0.5000
6	5π/12 (75°)	0.9654	0.2588
7	π/2 (90°)	1.0000	0.0000
8	7π/12 (105°)	0.9659	−0.2588
9	2π/3 (120°)	0.8660	−0.5000
10	3π/4 (135°)	0.7071	−0.7071
11	5π/6 (150°)	0.5000	−0.8600
12	11π/12 (165°)	0.2588	−0.9659
13	π (180°)	0.0000	−1.0000

Forward-Difference Operator. The forward-difference operator, Δ, operating on a function, $f(x_i)$, is defined as

$$\Delta f(x_i) = f(x_{i+1}) - f(x_i). \quad (3.109)$$

In Eq. 3.109, x_i and x_{i+1} = the discrete points and $f(x_i)$ and $f(x_{i+1})$ = the functional values at these discrete points.

Similarly, the second-order forward-difference operator is defined as

$$\begin{aligned} \Delta^2 f(x_i) &= \Delta[\Delta f(x_i)] \\ &= \Delta[f(x_{i+1}) - f(x_i)] \\ &= \Delta f(x_{i+1}) - \Delta f(x_i) \\ &= [f(x_{i+2}) - f(x_{i+1})] - [f(x_{i+1}) - f(x_i)] \\ &= f(x_{i+2}) - 2f(x_{i+1}) + f(x_i). \quad (3.110) \end{aligned}$$

In general, the kth-order forward-difference operator is defined as

$$\Delta^k f(x_i) = \sum_{j=0}^{k} (-1)^j \begin{bmatrix} k \\ j \end{bmatrix} f(x_{i+k-j}), \quad (3.111)$$

where $\begin{bmatrix} k \\ j \end{bmatrix}$ = the binomial coefficient defined as

$$\begin{bmatrix} k \\ j \end{bmatrix} = \frac{k!}{j!(k-j)!}. \quad (3.112)$$

Example 3.19. With the series of values listed in **Table 3.2** give the forward difference of $\sin(x_i)$ at $x=\pi/4$. Note that the values in this table were generated by the formulas $f(x_i)=\sin(x_i)$ and $g(x_i)=\cos(x_i)$.

Solution. For $x=\pi/4$, $i=4$. Then from Table 3.2,

$$\begin{aligned} \Delta f(x_i) &= f(x_{i+1}) - f(x_i) \\ &= f(x_5) - f(x_4) \\ &= f(\pi/3) - f(\pi/4) \\ &= 0.8660 - 0.7071 \\ &= 0.1589. \end{aligned}$$

Example 3.20. Find an expression for $\Delta[g(x_i)f(x_i)]$.
Solution.

$$\Delta[g(x_i)f(x_i)] = g(x_{i+1})f(x_{i+1}) - g(x_i)f(x_i). \quad \text{.......(3.113)}$$

Adding $g(x_i)f(x_{i+1})$ to and subtracting $g(x_i)f(x_{i+1})$ from the right side of Eq. 3.113 gives

$$\Delta[g(x_i)f(x_i)] = [g(x_{i+1})f(x_{i+1}) - g(x_i)f(x_{i+1})]$$
$$- [g(x_i)f(x_i) - g(x_i)f(x_{i+1})], \quad \text{................(3.114)}$$

which can be rearranged to give

$$\Delta[g(x_i)f(x_i)] = f(x_{i+1})\Delta[g(x_i)] + g(x_i)\Delta[f(x_i)]. \quad \text{....(3.115)}$$

Example 3.21. With the values in Table 3.2, use Eq. 3.115 to give the forward difference of $[\sin(x_i)\cos(x_i)]$ at $x = \pi/4$.

Solution. For $x = \pi/4$, $i = 4$. Then from Table 3.2, $\sin(x_i) = 0.7071$, $\sin(x_{i+1}) = 0.8660$, $\cos(x_i) = 0.7071$, and $\cos(x_{i+1}) = 0.5$.

From Example 3.20,

$$\Delta[g(x_i)f(x_i)] = f(x_{i+1})\Delta[g(x_i)] + g(x_i)\Delta[f(x_i)]. \quad \text{....(3.115)}$$

Then $\Delta[\sin(x_i)\cos(x_i)] = \cos(x_{i+1})\Delta\sin(x_i) + \sin(x_i)\Delta\cos(x_i)$

$$\text{....................(3.116)}$$

$$= 0.5(0.8660 - 0.7071) + 0.7071$$
$$\times (0.5 - 0.7071)$$
$$= -0.06699.$$

Backward-Difference Operator. The backward-difference operator, ∇, operating on $f(x_i)$ is defined as

$$\nabla f(x_i) = f(x_i) - f(x_{i-1}). \quad \text{.....................(3.117)}$$

Similarly, the second-order backward-difference operator is defined as

$$\nabla^2 f(x_i) = \nabla[\nabla f(x_i)]$$
$$= \nabla[f(x_i) - f(x_{i-1})]$$
$$= \nabla f(x_i) - \nabla f(x_{i-1})$$
$$= [f(x_i) - f(x_{i-1})] - [f(x_{i-1}) - f(x_{i-2})]$$
$$= f(x_i) - 2f(x_{i-1}) + f(x_{i-2}). \quad \text{............(3.118)}$$

In general, the kth-order backward-difference operator is defined as

$$\nabla^k f(x_i) = (-1)^k \sum_{j=0}^{k} (-1)^j \begin{bmatrix} k \\ j \end{bmatrix} f(x_{i-k+j}), \quad \text{.........(3.119)}$$

where the binomial coefficient $\begin{bmatrix} k \\ j \end{bmatrix}$ is defined by Eq. 3.112.

Example 3.22. With the series of values listed in Table 3.2, give the backward difference of $\sin(x_i)$ at $x = \pi/4$.

Solution. For $x = \pi/4$, $i = 4$, and with Eq. 3.117, $\nabla f(x_i) = 0.7071 - 0.5 = 0.2071$.

Example 3.23. Find an expression for $\nabla[g(x_i)f(x_i)]$.
Solution.

$$\nabla[g(x_i)f(x_i)] = g(x_i)f(x_i) - g(x_{i-1})f(x_{i-1}). \quad \text{......(3.120)}$$

Adding $g(x_i)f(x_{i-1})$ to and subtracting $g(x_i)f(x_{i-1})$ from the right side of Eq. 3.120 yields

$$\nabla[g(x_i)f(x_i)] = [g(x_i)f(x_i) - g(x_i)f(x_{i-1})]$$
$$- [g(x_{i-1})f(x_{i-1}) - g(x_i)f(x_{i-1})], \quad \text{...(3.121)}$$

which can be rearranged to give

$$\nabla[g(x_i)f(x_i)] = g(x_i)\nabla[f(x_i)] + f(x_{i-1})\nabla[g(x_i)]. \quad \text{...(3.122)}$$

Central-Difference Operator. The central-difference operator, δ, operating on $f(x_i)$ is defined as

$$\delta f(x_i) = f(x_{i+\frac{1}{2}}) - f(x_{i-\frac{1}{2}}). \quad \text{..................(3.123)}$$

An alternative definition of the central-difference operator is

$$\delta f(x_i) = f(x_{i+1}) - f(x_{i-1}). \quad \text{...................(3.124)}$$

Similarly, the second-order central-difference operator is defined as

$$\delta^2 f(x_i) = \delta[\delta f(x_i)]$$
$$= \delta[f(x_{i+\frac{1}{2}}) - f(x_{i-\frac{1}{2}})]$$
$$= \delta f(x_{i+\frac{1}{2}}) - \delta f(x_{i-\frac{1}{2}})$$
$$= [f(x_{i+1}) - f(x_i)] - [f(x_i) - f(x_{i-1})]$$
$$= f(x_{i+1}) - 2f(x_i) + f(x_{i-1}). \quad \text{...........(3.125)}$$

Shift (Translation) Operator. The shift (translation) operator, E, operating on $f(x_i)$ is defined as

$$E[f(x_i)] = f(x_{i+1}). \quad \text{.........................(3.126)}$$

Similarly, the inverse of the shift operator, E^{-1}, operating on $f(x_i)$ is defined as

$$E^{-1}[f(x_i)] = f(x_{i-1}). \quad \text{.......................(3.127)}$$

In general, the kth-order shift operator is defined by

$$E^k[f(x_i)] = f(x_{i+k}), \quad \text{........................(3.128)}$$

and the kth inverse of the shift operator is defined as

$$E^{-k}[f(x_i)] = f(x_{i-k}). \quad \text{......................(3.129)}$$

Example 3.24. Show the relationship between the shift and forward-difference operators.

Solution. From the definition of the forward-difference operator,

$$\Delta f(x_i) = f(x_{i+1}) - f(x_i). \quad \text{....................(3.109)}$$

With the definition of the shift operator given by Eq. 3.126, Eq. 3.109 can be written as

$$\Delta f(x_i) = E[f(x_i)] - f(x_i)$$
$$= (E - 1)f(x_i); \quad \text{.....................(3.130)}$$

therefore, $\Delta = E - 1$.

Example 3.25. Show the relationship between the shift and backward-difference operators.

Solution. From the definition of the backward-difference operator,

$$\nabla f(x_i) = f(x_i) - f(x_{i-1}). \quad \text{....................(3.117)}$$

With the definition of the inverse shift operator given by Eq. 3.127, Eq. 3.117 can be rewritten as

$$\nabla f(x_i) = f(x_i) - E^{-1}f(x_i)$$
$$= (1 - E^{-1})f(x_i); \quad \text{...................(3.131)}$$

therefore, $\nabla = 1 - E^{-1}$.

Example 3.26. Show the relationship between the shift and central-difference operators.

Solution. From the definition of the central-difference operator,

$$\delta[f(x_i)] = f(x_{i+½}) - f(x_{i-½}). \quad (3.123)$$

With the definition of the *k*th shift expressed by Eq. 3.128, Eq. 3.123 can be rewritten as

$$\delta f(x_i) = E^{½}[f(x_i)] - E^{-½}[f(x_i)]$$

$$= (E^{½} - E^{-½})[f(x_i)]; \quad (3.132)$$

therefore, $\delta = E^{½} - E^{-½}$.

Examples 3.24 through 3.26 highlight a few identities between the different operators that will generate identical results when operating on a given function.

Average Operator. The average operator, A, operating on $f(x_i)$ is defined as

$$A[f(x_i)] = \frac{f(x_{i+½}) + f(x_{i-½})}{2}. \quad (3.133)$$

Example 3.27. Show the relationship between the central-difference and average operators.

Solution. From the definition of the average operator,

$$A[f(x_i)] = \frac{f(x_{i+½}) + f(x_{i-½})}{2}. \quad (3.134)$$

Rearranging yields

$$2A[f(x_i)] = f(x_{i+½}) + f(x_{i-½}). \quad (3.135)$$

Substituting the definition of the shift operator (Eqs. 3.128 and 3.129) into Eq. 3.135 yields

$$2A[f(x_i)] = E^{½}[f(x_i)] + E^{-½}[f(x_i)]$$

$$= (E^{½} + E^{-½})f(x_i), \quad (3.136)$$

which reduces to

$$2A = E^{½} + E^{-½}. \quad (3.137)$$

Squaring both sides of Eq. 3.137 gives

$$A^2 = ¼(E + 2 + E^{-1}), \quad (3.138)$$

which is one possible solution to this example. Adding 1 to and subtracting 1 from the right side gives

$$A^2 = ¼(E - 2 + E^{-1}) + 1. \quad (3.139)$$

Eq. 3.139 can be written as

$$A^2 = ¼(E^{½} - E^{-½})^2 + 1. \quad (3.140)$$

With the result of Example 3.26, the final result is

$$A^2 = \frac{\delta^2}{4} + 1, \quad (3.141)$$

which is a second, equally valid, solution to this example.

Miscellaneous Properties of Finite-Difference Operators. The finite-difference operators discussed in the previous sections of this chapter obey the following fundamental laws of algebra.

1. The commutative law for sums.

$$\nabla + \Delta = \Delta + \nabla. \quad (3.142)$$

2. The associative law for sums.

$$\delta + (\nabla + \Delta) = (\delta + \nabla) + \Delta. \quad (3.143)$$

3. The commutative law for products.

$$\nabla\delta = \delta\nabla. \quad (3.144)$$

4. The associative law for products.

$$\nabla(\delta\Delta) = (\nabla\delta)\Delta. \quad (3.145)$$

5. The distributive law.

$$\nabla(\delta + \Delta) = \nabla\delta + \nabla\Delta. \quad (3.146)$$

6. The law of exponents.

$$\delta^m\delta^n = \delta^{m+n}, \quad (3.147)$$

where the superscripts indicate the number of applications of δ.

3.4.2 Relationship Between Derivative and Finite-Difference Operators. ***Approximations to the First Derivative.*** *Forward-Difference Approximation.* The finite-difference operators for discrete points are related to the derivative operators of continuous functions through the Taylor series expansion. Evaluating the Taylor series expansion (Eq. 3.70) at $x = x_{i+1}$ and letting $x_o = x_i$ yields

$$f(x_{i+1}) = f(x_i) + \frac{h}{1!}\frac{df}{dx} + \frac{h^2}{2!}\frac{d^2f}{dx^2} + \frac{h^3}{3!}\frac{d^3f}{dx^3} + \ldots$$

$$+ \frac{h^N}{N!}\frac{d^Nf}{dx^N} + R_{N+1}, \quad (3.148)$$

$$\text{where } h = x_{i+1} - x_i \quad (3.149)$$

and the derivatives are evaluated at x_i. If $N = 1$ in Eq. 3.148, then

$$f(x_{i+1}) = f(x_i) + \frac{h}{1!}\frac{df}{dx} + R_2. \quad (3.150)$$

Solving Eq. 3.150 for the first derivative, df/dx, gives

$$\frac{df}{dx} = \frac{f(x_{i+1}) - f(x_i)}{h} - \frac{1}{h}R_2. \quad (3.151)$$

Truncating the series after the second term yields

$$\frac{df}{dx} \approx \frac{f(x_{i+1}) - f(x_i)}{h}, \quad (3.152)$$

where the truncation error is

$$e_t = \frac{1}{h}R_2$$

$$= \frac{1}{h}\left(\frac{h^2}{2!}\frac{d^2f}{dx^2} + R_3\right)$$

$$= \frac{h}{2!}\frac{d^2f}{dx^2} + \frac{1}{h}R_3. \quad (3.153)$$

Substituting the forward-difference operator (Eq. 3.109) into Eq. 3.152 results in

$$\frac{df}{dx} \approx \frac{\Delta f(x_i)}{h}. \quad (3.154)$$

Eq. 3.154 represents the forward-difference approximation to the first derivative. **Fig. 3.2** illustrates the relationship between the first derivative and its forward-difference approximation.

The forward-difference approximation to the first derivative is called a first-order approximation because the truncation error is a function of h^1 (i.e., a second-order approximation would be a function of h^2, and so forth). The truncation error is defined in Eq. 3.153 because the term R_3/h contains terms of higher orders of h (i.e., h^2, h^3, and so forth). If h approaches zero, all terms in e_t would decrease; however, the higher-order terms would decrease more rapidly. Con-

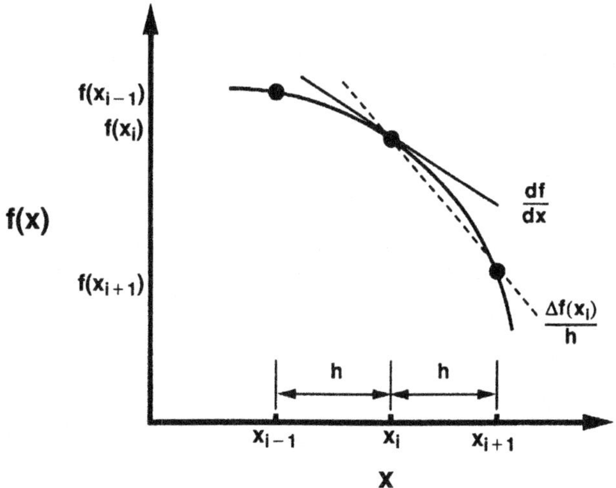

Fig. 3.2—First derivative and its forward-difference approximation.

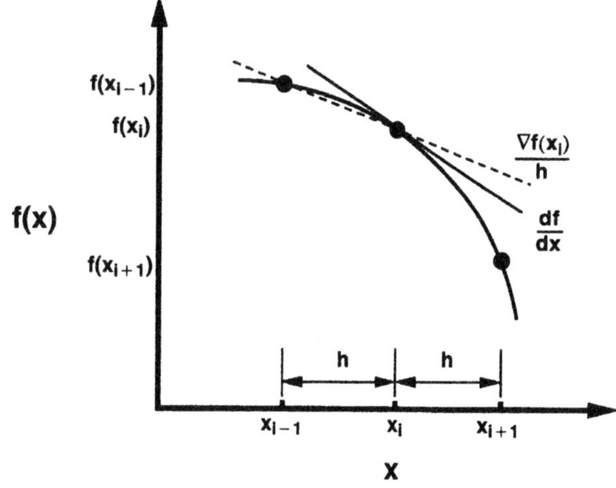

Fig. 3.3—First derivative and its backward-difference approximation.

sequently, most of the error is incorporated into the lowest-order term. In the case of Eq. 3.153, this is in the h^1 term.

Example 3.28. With the series of values listed in Table 3.2, give the forward-difference approximation of the first derivative of sin(x) at $x=\pi/4$.

Solution. Recall the definition of the forward-difference approximation given as

$$\frac{\mathrm{df}}{\mathrm{d}x} \approx \frac{\Delta \mathrm{f}(x_i)}{h}. \quad \text{(3.154)}$$

From Example 3.19, $\Delta f(x_i)=0.1589$ and

$$h=x_{i+1}-x_i=\pi/3-\pi/4=\pi/12. \quad \text{(3.155)}$$

Substituting into Eq. 3.154 yields df/d$x \approx 0.1589/(\pi/12) \approx 0.6070$. The value of the first derivative (to four decimal places) is 0.7071.

Backward-Difference Approximation. Expanding f(x_{i-1}) about x_i (that is, $x=x_{i-1}$ and $x_o=x_i$ in Eq. 3.70) yields

$$\mathrm{f}(x_{i-1}) = \mathrm{f}(x_i) - \frac{h}{1!}\frac{\mathrm{df}}{\mathrm{d}x} + \frac{h^2}{2!}\frac{\mathrm{d^2f}}{\mathrm{d}x^2} - \frac{h^3}{3!}\frac{\mathrm{d^3f}}{\mathrm{d}x^3} + \ldots$$

$$+ (-1)^N\frac{h^N}{N!}\frac{\mathrm{d}^N\mathrm{f}}{\mathrm{d}x^N} + R_{N+1}. \quad \text{(3.156)}$$

Note that, in Eq. 3.156, all even terms in the expansion are positive and all odd terms are negative. This is because in our terminology h is always positive ($h=x_i-x_{i-1}$). Also note that all the derivatives on the right side of the equation are evaluated at x_i.

Following the same procedure as for the forward-difference approximation yields

$$\frac{\mathrm{df}}{\mathrm{d}x} \approx \frac{\nabla \mathrm{f}(x_i)}{h}. \quad \text{(3.157)}$$

Eq. 3.157 is the backward-difference approximation to the first derivative. **Fig. 3.3** illustrates the relationship between the first derivative and its backward-difference approximation. This approximation is also a first-order approximation.

Example 3.29. With the series of values listed in Table 3.2, give the backward-difference approximation of the first derivative of sin(x) at $x=\pi/4$.

Solution. Recall the definition of the backward-difference approximation,

$$\frac{\mathrm{df}}{\mathrm{d}x} \approx \frac{\nabla \mathrm{f}(x_i)}{h}. \quad \text{(3.157)}$$

From Example 3.22, $\nabla f(x_i)=0.2071$ and $h=x_i-x_{i-1}=\pi/4-\pi/6=\pi/12$. Substituting into Eq. 3.157 gives df/d$x \approx 0.2071/(\pi/12) \approx 0.7911$. This is comparable with the exact value of the first derivative [cos($\pi/4$)] of 0.7071.

Central-Difference Approximation. As discussed earlier, both the forward-difference and backward-difference approximations are first-order approximations to the first derivative. A higher-order approximation (for example, second-order) would be preferable because as the spacing size, h, is reduced the truncation error would approach zero more rapidly. In other words, fewer measured or discrete points would give the same accuracy.

The central-difference approximation is a higher-order approximation that is obtained by subtracting Eq. 3.156 from Eq. 3.148. If the spacings, h, in these equations are equal, then

$$\mathrm{f}(x_{i+1}) - \mathrm{f}(x_{i-1}) = \frac{2h}{1!}\frac{\mathrm{df}}{\mathrm{d}x} + \frac{2h^3}{3!}\frac{\mathrm{d^3f}}{\mathrm{d}x^3} + R_5. \quad \text{(3.158)}$$

Note that, because of the alternating signs in the expansion series in Eq. 3.156, all even terms in Eq. 3.158 cancel. Solving for the first derivative in Eq. 3.158 results in

$$\frac{\mathrm{df}}{\mathrm{d}x} \approx \frac{\mathrm{f}(x_{i+1}) - \mathrm{f}(x_{i-1})}{2h}, \quad \text{(3.159)}$$

and the truncation error becomes

$$e_t = R_3 = \frac{h^2}{3!}\frac{\mathrm{d^3f}}{\mathrm{d}x^3} + \frac{1}{2h}R_5. \quad \text{(3.160)}$$

Note that the truncation error defined by Eq. 3.160 is second order.

Substituting the definition of the central-difference operator (Eq. 3.124) into Eq. 3.160 yields

$$\frac{\mathrm{df}}{\mathrm{d}x} \approx \frac{\delta \mathrm{f}(x_i)}{2h}, \quad \text{(3.161)}$$

which is the central-difference approximation to the first derivative. **Fig. 3.4** illustrates the relationship between the first derivative and its central-difference approximation.

Example 3.30. With the series of values listed in Table 3.2, give the central-difference approximation of the first derivative of sin(x) at $x=\pi/4$.

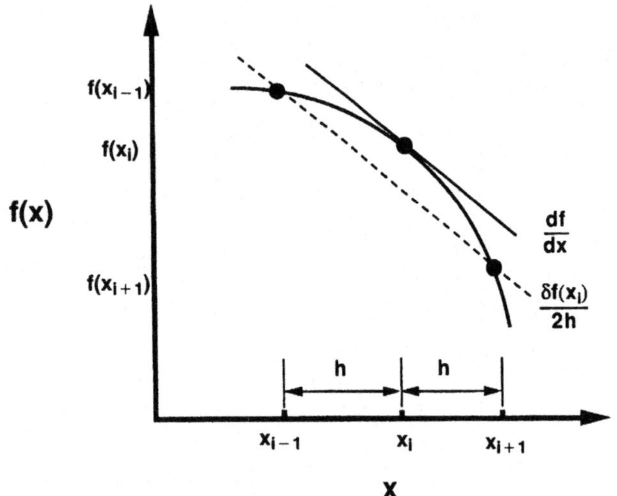

Fig. 3.4—First derivative and its central-difference approximation.

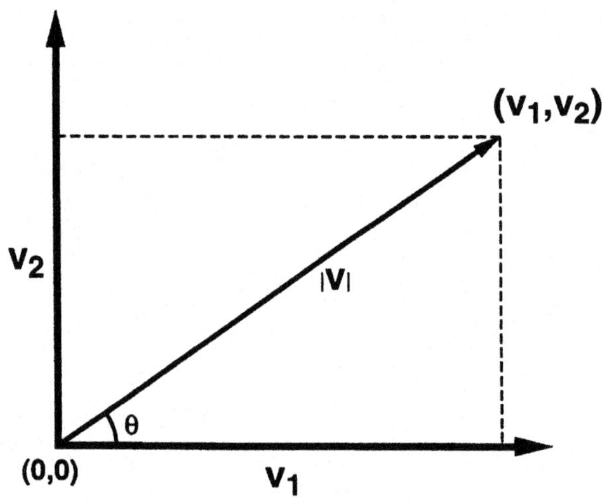

Fig. 3.5—Graphical representation of a vector.

Solution. Recall the definition of the central-difference approximation,

$$\frac{\mathrm{df}}{\mathrm{d}x} \approx \frac{\delta \mathrm{f}(x_i)}{2h}. \qquad (3.161)$$

From Table 3.2 for $i=4$, $\mathrm{f}(x_{i+1})=0.8660$, $\mathrm{f}(x_{i-1})=0.5$, and $h=x_{i+1}-x_i=\pi/12$. Substituting into Eq. 3.161 gives $\mathrm{df}/\mathrm{d}x \approx (0.8660-0.5)/(2[\pi/12]) \approx 0.6990$. This compares very favorably with the exact value of the derivative $[\cos(\pi/4)]$ of 0.7071.

Approximation to the Second Derivative. The central-difference approximation is used almost exclusively to approximate the second derivative in reservoir transport equations because of its higher-order accuracy. This approximation can be obtained by adding Eqs. 3.148 and 3.156, giving

$$\mathrm{f}(x_{i+1}) + \mathrm{f}(x_{i-1}) = 2\mathrm{f}(x_i) + \frac{2h^2}{2!}\frac{\mathrm{d}^2\mathrm{f}}{\mathrm{d}x^2} + \frac{2h^4}{4!}\frac{\mathrm{d}^4\mathrm{f}}{\mathrm{d}x^4} + R_6. \qquad (3.162)$$

Because of the alternating signs in the expansion series in Eq. 3.156, all odd terms in Eq. 3.162 cancel. Solving for the second derivative with Eq. 3.162 results in

$$\frac{\mathrm{d}^2\mathrm{f}}{\mathrm{d}x^2} \approx \frac{\mathrm{f}(x_{i+1}) - 2\mathrm{f}(x_i) + \mathrm{f}(x_{i-1})}{h^2}, \qquad (3.163)$$

and the truncation error becomes

$$e_t = \frac{1}{h^2}R_4 = \frac{2h^2}{4!}\frac{\mathrm{d}^4\mathrm{f}}{\mathrm{d}x^4} + \frac{1}{h^2}R_6. \qquad (3.164)$$

Eq. 3.163 is the central-difference approximation to the second derivative and is a second-order approximation.

3.5 Basic Linear Algebra

Linear algebra is the branch of mathematics that deals with vectors, matrices, and the solution of linear equations. Writing the characteristic linearized finite-difference equation at every unknown node generates a system of linear algebraic equations. This section provides a review of the basic linear algebra that is relevant to solving systems of linear equations.

3.5.1 Scalar Notation and Operations. A scalar quantity, s, is a quantity that has a magnitude; in other words, a scalar quantity is simply a number. Examples of scalar quantities include 1, $1/3$, π, $-e^3$, and $\sin(3\pi/2)$. The scalar quantities most often encountered in reservoir engineering include pressure, temperature, porosity, gas/oil ratio, water/oil ratio, and production rates, among others.

The arithmetical operations of addition, subtraction, multiplication, and division all apply to scalar quantities. The identities defined by the commutative, associative, and distributive laws also all apply to the appropriate scalar operators.

3.5.2 Vector Notation and Operations. A vector, $\vec{v}$, is a set of scalar quantities arranged in a definite order; that is,

$$\vec{v} = (v_1, v_2, v_3, v_4, \ldots, v_I), \qquad (3.165)$$

where $v_1, v_2, v_3, v_4, \ldots, v_I$ are the elements of the vector. The value of the subscript I is often referred to as the vector dimension. A vector has the properties of both magnitude and direction. For a vector with two elements,

$$\vec{v} = (v_1, v_2), \qquad (3.166)$$

the magnitude of the vector is defined as the length of the line segment from the origin (0,0) to the point (v_1, v_2) in the v_1–v_2 plane; that is,

$$|\vec{v}| = \sqrt{(v_1)^2 + (v_2)^2}. \qquad (3.167)$$

The direction of the vector is defined as the direction from the origin to the point (v_1, v_2) in the v_1–v_2 plane; i.e., $\tan\theta = v_2/v_1$. **Fig. 3.5** illustrates these definitions.

For higher-dimension vectors, Eq. 3.167 can be generalized as

$$|\vec{v}| = \sqrt{(v_1)^2 + (v_2)^2 + (v_3)^2 + (v_4)^2 + \ldots + (v_I)^2}. \qquad (3.168)$$

Example 3.31. Give the magnitude and direction of $\vec{v}=(3,4)$.

Solution. With Eq. 3.167, $|\vec{v}| = \sqrt{3^2+4^2} = \sqrt{25} = 5$ and $\tan\theta=(4-0)/(3-0)=4/3$; and $\theta = \tan^{-1}(4/3)$ or $\theta = 53°7'48''$.

Equality of Two Vectors. Two vectors, $\vec{u}$ and $\vec{v}$, with the same dimension are equal if, and only if, all of the corresponding elements are equal. Let

$$\vec{u} = (u_1, u_2, u_3, u_4, \ldots, u_I) \ldots \qquad (3.169)$$

and $\vec{v} = (v_1, v_2, v_3, v_4, \ldots, v_I) \ldots \qquad (3.170)$

Then $\vec{u} = \vec{v}$ implies that

$$u_i = v_i, \qquad (3.171)$$

where $i=1, 2, 3, 4, \ldots, I$.

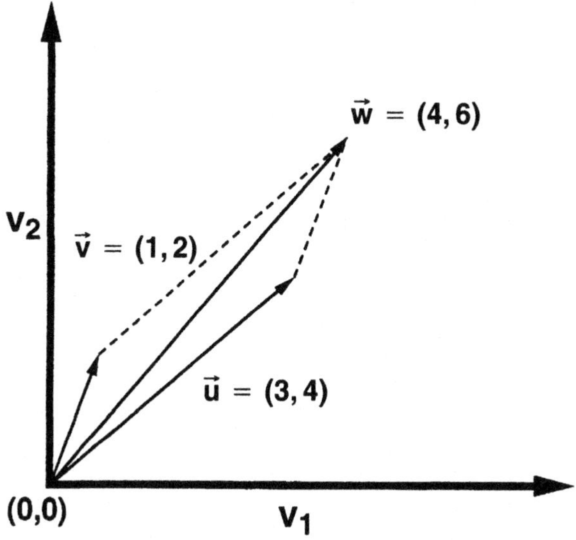

Fig. 3.6—Graphical representation of addition of two vectors.

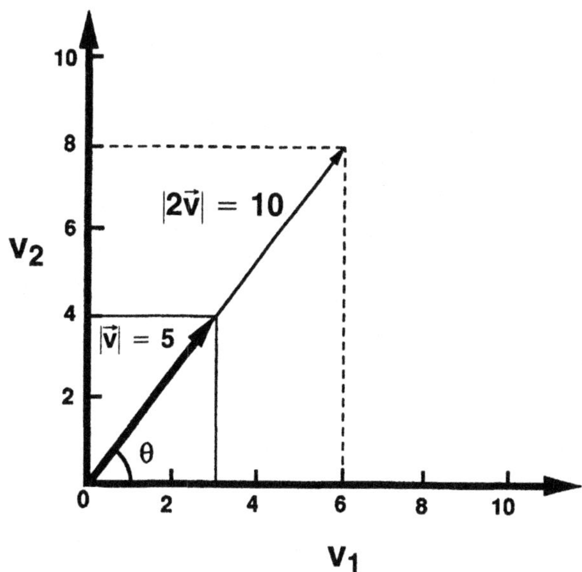

Fig. 3.7—Graphical representation of multiplication of a scalar quantity and a vector.

Addition of Two Vectors. Addition of two vectors, $\vec{u}$ and $\vec{v}$, with the same dimension is performed by adding the corresponding elements of the vectors. Let

$$\vec{u} = (u_1, u_2, u_3, u_4, \ldots, u_I), \quad \ldots\ldots (3.169)$$

$$\vec{v} = (v_1, v_2, v_3, v_4, \ldots, v_I), \quad \ldots\ldots (3.170)$$

and $\vec{w} = (w_1, w_2, w_3, w_4, \ldots, w_I)$. ...... (3.172)

Then $\vec{w} = \vec{u} + \vec{v}$ implies that

$$w_i = u_i + v_i, \quad \ldots\ldots (3.173)$$

where $i = 1, 2, 3, 4, \ldots, I$.

Vector addition follows the commutative, associative, and distributive laws for addition.

Example 3.32. What is the sum of $\vec{u} = (3,4)$ and $\vec{v} = (1,2)$?

Solution. With Eq. 3.173, $\vec{w} = (w_1, w_2)$ where $w_1 = u_1 + v_1$, and $w_2 = u_2 + v_2$; therefore, $\vec{w} = (3+1, 4+2) = (4,6)$. **Fig. 3.6** shows the addition of the two vectors used in this example. Note that the dashed lines in Fig. 3.6 are parallel to the corresponding solid lines.

Multiplication of a Scalar and a Vector. Multiplication of a vector, $\vec{v}$, by a scalar, s, is obtained by multiplying all the elements of the vector by the scalar.

Let s = a scalar value and

$$\vec{v} = (v_1, v_2, v_3, v_4, \ldots, v_I). \quad \ldots\ldots (3.170)$$

Then, $s\vec{v} = (sv_1, sv_2, sv_3, sv_4, \ldots, sv_I)$. ...... (3.174)

Multiplication of a scalar and a vector follows the commutative, associative, and distributive laws for multiplication.

Example 3.33. What is the effect of multiplying a vector by a scalar on the magnitude and direction of the vector?

Solution. To illustrate this effect, use $s = 2$ and $\vec{v} = (3,4)$. From Eq. 3.174, $2\vec{v} = (6,8)$. Substituting these data into the definition of magnitude for a two-dimensional vector (Eq. 3.167) yields $|2v| = \sqrt{(6)^2 + (8)^2} = \sqrt{(2)^2(3)^2 + (2)^2(4)^2} = 2\sqrt{(3)^2 + (4)^2} = 2|\vec{v}|$; tan $\theta = 8/6 = 4/3$. In other words, the magnitude of the vector $2\vec{v}$ is twice the magnitude of $\vec{v}$. **Fig. 3.7** shows this schematically. The figure also illustrates the effect on the direction of the vector; that is, there is no effect on the direction of a vector if it is multiplied by a scalar quantity.

Examples of vector quantities in reservoir engineering include the flow velocities of gas, oil, and water in hydrocarbon reservoirs because these properties include both magnitude and direction. Although this may seem like a somewhat trivial example, these velocities govern practical matters as diverse as lease-line migration, aquifer influx, selection of infill-well locations, and optimized secondary and tertiary recovery and production/injection well realignment.

Scalar Multiplication of Two Vectors. Scalar multiplication of two vectors, $\vec{u}$ and $\vec{v}$ with the same dimension, is obtained by multiplying the corresponding elements of the two vectors and summing the products. The final product of a scalar multiplication of two vectors is a scalar. The operation of multiplication is slightly more complicated than the other operations discussed in this section because it involves two steps. Let

$$\vec{u} = (u_1, u_2, u_3, u_4, \ldots, u_I) \quad \ldots\ldots (3.169)$$

and $\vec{v} = (v_1, v_2, v_3, v_4, \ldots, v_I)$. ...... (3.170)

To find $s = \vec{u} \cdot \vec{v}$, first transpose the original vector, $\vec{u}$, from a column vector to a row vector, $\vec{u}^T$, so that

$$\vec{u}^T = [u_1, u_2, u_3, u_4, \ldots, u_I]. \quad \ldots\ldots (3.175)$$

Second, multiply the elements across $\vec{u}^T$ with the corresponding elements down $\vec{v}$. That is,

$$s = [u_1, u_2, u_3, u_4, \ldots, u_I]\begin{bmatrix} v_1 \\ v_2 \\ v_3 \\ v_4 \\ \vdots \\ v_I \end{bmatrix}$$

$$= \sum_{i=1}^{I} u_i \cdot v_i. \quad \ldots\ldots (3.176)$$

Scalar multiplication of two vectors follows commutative, associative, and distributive laws for products.

Example 3.34. Find the product of scalar multiplication of $\vec{u} = (3,4)$ and $\vec{v} = (1,2)$.

Solution. With Eq. 3.176, $s=3\times1+4\times2=11$.

3.5.3 Matrix Notation and Operations. An $I\times J$ matrix is a rectangular array of scalar elements containing I rows (horizontal lines) and J columns (vertical lines), as in

$$[\mathbf{A}] = \begin{bmatrix} a_{1,1} & a_{1,2} & a_{1,3} & a_{1,4} & \cdots & a_{1,J} \\ a_{2,1} & a_{2,2} & a_{2,3} & a_{2,4} & \cdots & a_{2,J} \\ a_{3,1} & a_{3,2} & a_{3,3} & a_{3,4} & \cdots & a_{3,J} \\ a_{4,1} & a_{4,2} & a_{4,3} & a_{4,4} & \cdots & a_{4,J} \\ \vdots & \vdots & \vdots & \vdots & \vdots & \vdots \\ a_{I,1} & a_{I,2} & a_{I,3} & a_{I,4} & \cdots & a_{I,J} \end{bmatrix}, \quad \ldots\ldots\ldots\ldots (3.177)$$

where all the a_{ij} elements are scalars.

Equality of Two Matrices. Two matrices with the same dimensions, **[A]** and **[B]**, are equal if, and only if, all corresponding elements are equal.

Let **[A]** and **[B]** be two $I\times J$ matrices. Then **[A]** = **[B]** if

$$a_{ij} = b_{ij}, \quad \ldots\ldots\ldots\ldots (3.178)$$

where $i=1, 2, 3, 4, \ldots, I$; and $j=1, 2, 3, 4, \ldots, J$.

Identity Matrix. The identity matrix, **[I]**, is a square matrix ($I=J$) that contains the value 1 on the main diagonal and zeros everywhere else. That is,

$$[\mathbf{I}] = \begin{bmatrix} 1 & 0 & 0 & 0 & \cdots & 0 \\ 0 & 1 & 0 & 0 & \cdots & 0 \\ 0 & 0 & 1 & 0 & \cdots & 0 \\ 0 & 0 & 0 & 1 & \cdots & 0 \\ \vdots & \vdots & \vdots & \vdots & \vdots & \vdots \\ 0 & 0 & 0 & 0 & \cdots & 1 \end{bmatrix}. \quad \ldots\ldots\ldots\ldots (3.179)$$

Transpose of a Matrix. The transpose of a matrix is a matrix in which the rows and columns have been transposed; therefore, the transpose of an $I\times J$ matrix is a $J\times I$ matrix. The transpose of **[A]** defined in Eq. 3.177 is

$$[\mathbf{A}]^T = \begin{bmatrix} a_{1,1} & a_{2,1} & a_{3,1} & a_{4,1} & \cdots & a_{I,1} \\ a_{1,2} & a_{2,2} & a_{3,2} & a_{4,2} & \cdots & a_{I,2} \\ a_{1,3} & a_{2,3} & a_{3,3} & a_{4,3} & \cdots & a_{I,3} \\ a_{1,4} & a_{2,4} & a_{3,4} & a_{4,4} & \cdots & a_{I,4} \\ \vdots & \vdots & \vdots & \vdots & \vdots & \vdots \\ a_{1,J} & a_{2,J} & a_{3,J} & a_{4,J} & \cdots & a_{I,J} \end{bmatrix}. \quad \ldots\ldots\ldots\ldots (3.180)$$

Example 3.35. Find $[\mathbf{A}]^T$ where

$$[\mathbf{A}] = \begin{bmatrix} 1 & 2 & 3 \\ 4 & 5 & 6 \end{bmatrix}.$$

Solution. With Eq. 3.180,

$$[\mathbf{A}]^T = \begin{bmatrix} 1 & 4 \\ 2 & 5 \\ 3 & 6 \end{bmatrix}.$$

Addition of Two Matrices. The addition of two matrices, **[A]** and **[B]**, with the same dimensions is performed by adding the corresponding elements of the matrices.

Let **[A]**, **[B]**, and **[C]** be three $I\times J$ matrices. Then **[C]** = **[A]** + **[B]** if

$$c_{ij} = a_{ij} + b_{ij}, \quad \ldots\ldots\ldots\ldots (3.181)$$

where $i=1, 2, 3, 4, \ldots, I$; and $j=1, 2, 3, 4, \ldots, J$.

Commutative and associative laws for addition apply to matrices.

$$[\mathbf{A}]+[\mathbf{B}]=[\mathbf{B}]+[\mathbf{A}] \quad \ldots\ldots\ldots\ldots (3.182)$$

$$\text{and } ([\mathbf{A}]+[\mathbf{B}])+[\mathbf{C}]=[\mathbf{A}]+([\mathbf{B}]+[\mathbf{C}]). \quad \ldots\ldots\ldots\ldots (3.183)$$

Example 3.36. Find the sum of **[A]** and **[B]** where

$$[\mathbf{A}] = \begin{bmatrix} 1 & 2 & 3 \\ 4 & 5 & 6 \end{bmatrix} \text{ and } [\mathbf{B}] = \begin{bmatrix} 7 & 8 & 9 \\ 0 & 2 & 3 \end{bmatrix}.$$

Solution. With Eq. 3.181,

$$[\mathbf{C}] = \begin{bmatrix} 1+7 & 2+8 & 3+9 \\ 4+0 & 5+2 & 6+3 \end{bmatrix} = \begin{bmatrix} 8 & 10 & 12 \\ 4 & 7 & 9 \end{bmatrix}.$$

Multiplication of a Scalar and a Matrix. The product of a matrix, **[A]**, multiplied by a scalar, s, is another matrix whose elements are obtained by multiplying each element of **[A]** by the scalar value.

Let s be a scalar value and **[A]** and **[B]** be $I\times J$ matrices. Then **[B]** = s**[A]** if

$$b_{ij} = sa_{ij}, \quad \ldots\ldots\ldots\ldots (3.184)$$

where $i=1, 2, 3, 4, \ldots, I$; and $j=1, 2, 3, 4, \ldots, J$.

The laws

$$c([\mathbf{A}]+[\mathbf{B}])=c[\mathbf{A}]+c[\mathbf{B}], \quad \ldots\ldots\ldots\ldots (3.185)$$

$$(c+d)[\mathbf{A}]=c[\mathbf{A}]+d[\mathbf{A}], \quad \ldots\ldots\ldots\ldots (3.186)$$

$$\text{and } (cd)[\mathbf{A}]=c(d[\mathbf{A}]) \quad \ldots\ldots\ldots\ldots (3.187)$$

apply to the multiplication of scalars and matrices.

Multiplication of a Matrix and a Vector. The product of post-multiplying an $I\times J$ matrix, **[A]**, by a J-column vector, $\vec{x}$, is an I-column vector, $\vec{v}$. The elements of $\vec{v}$ are obtained by multiplying the elements across a row of the matrix by the corresponding elements down the column vector and summing the products.

Let **[A]** = an $I\times J$ matrix, $\vec{x}$ = a J-column vector, and $\vec{v}$ = an I-column vector. Then $[\mathbf{A}]\vec{x}=\vec{v}$ if

$$v_i = \sum_{j=1}^{J} a_{ij}\, x_j, \quad \ldots\ldots\ldots\ldots (3.188)$$

where $i=1, 2, 3, 4, \ldots, I$.

Example 3.37. Find the product of post-multiplying matrix **[A]** by $\vec{x}$, where

$$[\mathbf{A}] = \begin{bmatrix} 1 & 2 & 3 \\ 4 & 5 & 6 \end{bmatrix} \text{ and } \vec{x} = \begin{bmatrix} 1 \\ 2 \\ 3 \end{bmatrix}.$$

Solution. With Eq. 3.188,

$$\vec{v} = [\mathbf{A}]\vec{x} = \begin{bmatrix} 1 & 2 & 3 \\ 4 & 5 & 6 \end{bmatrix}\begin{bmatrix} 1 \\ 2 \\ 3 \end{bmatrix}$$

$$= \begin{bmatrix} 1\cdot1+2\cdot2+3\cdot3 \\ 4\cdot1+5\cdot2+6\cdot3 \end{bmatrix}$$

$$= \begin{bmatrix} 14 \\ 32 \end{bmatrix}.$$

Multiplication of Two Matrices. The product of two matrices, **[A]** and **[B]**, is a third matrix, **[C]**. The definition of matrix multiplication requires stringent specifications on the matrices **[A]** and **[B]**. Let **[A]** be an $I_A\times J_A$ matrix and **[B]** be an $I_B\times J_B$ matrix. Then the multiplication, **[A][B]** (in that order), is allowed if, and only if,

$J_A = I_B$. In this case, it is said that **[A]** is post-multiplied by **[B]** or **[B]** is premultiplied by **[A]**.

This multiplication of the two matrices results in an $I_A \times J_B$ matrix, **[C]**, whose elements, c_{ij}, are obtained by multiplying the elements along a row, i, of matrix **[A]** by the elements down a column, j, of matrix **[B]**. That is,

$$c_{ij} = \sum_{k=1}^{I_B} a_{ik} b_{kj}, \quad \text{(3.189)}$$

where $i = 1, 2, 3, 4, \ldots, I_A$ and $j = 1, 2, 3, 4, \ldots, J_B$.

Example 3.38. Find the products **[A][B]** and **[B][A]** if

$$[\mathbf{A}] = \begin{bmatrix} 1 & 2 & 3 \\ 4 & 5 & 6 \end{bmatrix} \text{ and } [\mathbf{B}] = \begin{bmatrix} 1 & 2 \\ 3 & 4 \\ 5 & 6 \end{bmatrix}.$$

Solution. With Eq. 3.189,

$$[\mathbf{A}][\mathbf{B}] = \begin{bmatrix} 1 & 2 & 3 \\ 4 & 5 & 6 \end{bmatrix} \begin{bmatrix} 1 & 2 \\ 3 & 4 \\ 5 & 6 \end{bmatrix}$$

$$= \begin{bmatrix} 1 \cdot 1 + 2 \cdot 3 + 3 \cdot 5 & 1 \cdot 2 + 2 \cdot 4 + 3 \cdot 6 \\ 4 \cdot 1 + 5 \cdot 3 + 6 \cdot 5 & 4 \cdot 2 + 5 \cdot 4 + 6 \cdot 6 \end{bmatrix}$$

$$= \begin{bmatrix} 22 & 28 \\ 49 & 64 \end{bmatrix}$$

$$\text{and } [\mathbf{B}][\mathbf{A}] = \begin{bmatrix} 1 & 2 \\ 3 & 4 \\ 5 & 6 \end{bmatrix} \begin{bmatrix} 1 & 2 & 3 \\ 4 & 5 & 6 \end{bmatrix}$$

$$= \begin{bmatrix} 1 \cdot 1 + 2 \cdot 4 & 1 \cdot 2 + 2 \cdot 5 & 1 \cdot 3 + 2 \cdot 6 \\ 3 \cdot 1 + 4 \cdot 4 & 3 \cdot 2 + 4 \cdot 5 & 3 \cdot 3 + 4 \cdot 6 \\ 5 \cdot 1 + 6 \cdot 4 & 5 \cdot 2 + 6 \cdot 5 & 5 \cdot 3 + 6 \cdot 6 \end{bmatrix}$$

$$= \begin{bmatrix} 9 & 12 & 15 \\ 19 & 26 & 33 \\ 29 & 40 & 51 \end{bmatrix}.$$

Example 3.38 illustrates that matrix multiplication is not commutative. That is, in general,

$$[\mathbf{A}][\mathbf{B}] \neq [\mathbf{B}][\mathbf{A}]; \quad \text{(3.190)}$$

however, the following laws do apply to matrix multiplication.

$$[\mathbf{A}]([\mathbf{B}] + [\mathbf{C}]) = [\mathbf{A}][\mathbf{B}] + [\mathbf{A}][\mathbf{C}]. \quad \text{(3.191)}$$

$$([\mathbf{A}] + [\mathbf{B}])[\mathbf{C}] = [\mathbf{A}][\mathbf{C}] + [\mathbf{B}][\mathbf{C}]. \quad \text{(3.192)}$$

$$c[\mathbf{A}][\mathbf{B}] = (c[\mathbf{A}])[\mathbf{B}] = [\mathbf{A}](c[\mathbf{B}]). \quad \text{(3.193)}$$

$$[\mathbf{A}]([\mathbf{B}][\mathbf{C}]) = ([\mathbf{A}][\mathbf{B}])[\mathbf{C}]. \quad \text{(3.194)}$$

Example 3.39. Show that the post-multiplication of an arbitrary $I \times J$ matrix, **[A]**, by the identity matrix **[I]** results in the original matrix, **[A]**. In this example, use $I = J = 3$.

Solution.

$$\text{Let } [\mathbf{I}] = \begin{bmatrix} 1 & 0 & 0 \\ 0 & 1 & 0 \\ 0 & 0 & 1 \end{bmatrix}$$

$$\text{and } [\mathbf{A}] = \begin{bmatrix} A_{1,1} & A_{1,2} & A_{1,3} \\ A_{2,1} & A_{2,2} & A_{2,3} \\ A_{3,1} & A_{3,2} & A_{3,3} \end{bmatrix}. \quad \text{(3.195a)}$$

$$\text{Then, } \begin{bmatrix} 1 & 0 & 0 \\ 0 & 1 & 0 \\ 0 & 0 & 1 \end{bmatrix} \begin{bmatrix} A_{1,1} & A_{1,2} & A_{1,3} \\ A_{2,1} & A_{2,2} & A_{2,3} \\ A_{3,1} & A_{3,2} & A_{3,3} \end{bmatrix}$$

$$= \begin{bmatrix} A_{1,1} + 0 + 0 & A_{1,2} + 0 + 0 & A_{1,3} + 0 + 0 \\ 0 + A_{2,1} + 0 & 0 + A_{2,2} + 0 & 0 + A_{2,3} + 0 \\ 0 + 0 + A_{3,1} & 0 + 0 + A_{3,2} & 0 + 0 + A_{3,3} \end{bmatrix}$$

$$= \begin{bmatrix} A_{1,1} & A_{1,2} & A_{1,3} \\ A_{2,1} & A_{2,2} & A_{2,3} \\ A_{3,1} & A_{3,2} & A_{3,3} \end{bmatrix}. \quad \text{(3.195b)}$$

Example 3.39 illustrates one important property of the identity matrix: the multiplication of an arbitrary matrix by the identity matrix results in the original matrix. This applies for both pre- and post-multiplication.

Matrix multiplication can be simplified into one of the operations already discussed in this chapter for the following special cases.

If $I_A = J_A = I_B = J_B = 1$, the multiplication of the two matrices is identical to the multiplication of two scalars.

If $I_A = J_B = 1$, the multiplication of the two matrices is identical to the scalar multiplication of two vectors.

If $J_B = 1$, the multiplication of two matrices is identical to the post-multiplication of a matrix by a column vector.

Inverse of a Matrix. The inverse, $[\mathbf{A}]^{-1}$, of a matrix, **[A]**, if it exists, is defined as the matrix that, when pre- or post-multiplied by **[A]**, gives the identity matrix. That is,

$$[\mathbf{A}][\mathbf{A}]^{-1} = [\mathbf{A}]^{-1}[\mathbf{A}] = [\mathbf{I}]. \quad \text{(3.196)}$$

Several methods can be used to obtain the inverse of a matrix, including Gaussian elimination and Crout reduction. These methods are important to the direct solution of systems of linear equations and are discussed in detail in Chap. 7.

3.5.4 Matrix Representation of Algebraic Equations. A system of n linear equations in n unknowns has the form

$$a_{1,1}x_1 + a_{1,2}x_2 + a_{1,3}x_3 + \ldots + a_{1,N}x_n = d_1 \quad \text{(3.197)}$$

$$a_{2,1}x_1 + a_{2,2}x_2 + a_{2,3}x_3 + \ldots + a_{2,N}x_n = d_2 \quad \text{(3.198)}$$

$$\text{and } a_{3,1}x_1 + a_{3,2}x_2 + a_{3,3}x_3 + \ldots + a_{3,N}x_n = d_3 \quad \text{(3.199)}$$

so though n,

$$a_{n,1}x_1 + a_{n,2}x_2 + a_{n,3}x_3 + \ldots + a_{n,N}x_n = d_n. \quad \text{(3.200)}$$

This system of equations can be replaced by a single matrix equation,

$$[\mathbf{A}]\vec{x} = \vec{d}, \quad \text{(3.201)}$$

$$\text{where } [\mathbf{A}] = \begin{bmatrix} a_{1,1} & a_{1,2} & a_{1,3} & \cdots & a_{1,n} \\ a_{2,1} & a_{2,2} & a_{2,3} & \cdots & a_{2,n} \\ a_{3,1} & a_{3,2} & a_{3,3} & \cdots & a_{3,n} \\ \vdots & \vdots & \vdots & \vdots & \vdots \\ a_{n,1} & a_{n,2} & a_{n,3} & \cdots & a_{n,n} \end{bmatrix}, \qquad (3.202)$$

$$\vec{x} = \begin{bmatrix} x_1 \\ x_2 \\ x_3 \\ \vdots \\ x_n \end{bmatrix}, \qquad (3.203)$$

$$\text{and } \vec{d} = \begin{bmatrix} d_1 \\ d_2 \\ d_3 \\ \vdots \\ d_n \end{bmatrix}. \qquad (3.204)$$

This representation can be verified easily by the post-multiplication of the coefficient matrix, **[A]**, by the unknown vector, $\vec{x}$, to obtain the known vector, $\vec{d}$.

The importance of the inverse of a matrix in the solution of linear equations now becomes apparent. Multiplying Eq. 3.201 by $[\mathbf{A}]^{-1}$ (if it exists) gives

$$[\mathbf{A}]^{-1}([\mathbf{A}]\vec{x}) = [\mathbf{A}]^{-1}\vec{d}. \qquad (3.205)$$

Use of Eq. 3.194 yields

$$([\mathbf{A}]^{-1}[\mathbf{A}])\vec{x} = [\mathbf{A}]^{-1}\vec{d}, \qquad (3.206)$$

and, from the definition of the inverse of a matrix (Eq. 3.196),

$$[\mathbf{I}]\vec{x} = [\mathbf{A}]^{-1}\vec{d} \qquad (3.207)$$

$$\text{or } \vec{x} = [\mathbf{A}]^{-1}\vec{d}. \qquad (3.208)$$

In other words, Eq. 3.208 states that, if the inverse of the coefficient matrix in Eq. 3.202 exists and can be found, the solution of the system of equations, $\vec{x}$, can be obtained by premultiplying the known vector, $\vec{d}$, by the inverse of the coefficient matrix, $[\mathbf{A}]^{-1}$.

Exercises

3.1 Show that $(\partial/\partial x)[a(p)(\partial p/\partial x)]$ can be transformed to $\partial^2\psi/\partial x^2$ using the transformation

$$\psi = \int_o^p a(p)dp.$$

Hint: Use the chain rule in conjunction with the Leibnitz rule.

3.2 Use the product rule to expand the expression $(\partial/\partial x)\{[A_x(x) \times k_x(x)]/[\mu(p)B(p)][\partial p(x)/\partial x]\}$.

3.3 Show that the density of a liquid can be expressed as a function of pressure as $\rho = \rho_o[1 + c(p - p_o)]$, where ρ_o = reference density at reference pressure p_o and reservoir temperature and c = compressibility of the liquid (very small). Hint: Use the Taylor series expansion.

3.4 Derive an expression for $\partial B_g/\partial p_g$ for a real gas.

3.5 Identify the following equations as linear or nonlinear PDE's.
1. $(\partial/\partial x)[c(\partial p/\partial x)] = 0$, where c is a constant.
2. $(\partial/\partial x)[c(x)(\partial p/\partial x)] = 0$, where c is a function of x.
3. $(\partial/\partial x)[c(p)(\partial p/\partial x)] = 0$, where c is a function of p.

3.6 Consider a differential equation in the form $k_x(\partial^2 p/\partial x^2) + k_y(\partial^2 p/\partial y^2) = 0$. Use the transformations $X = x/\sqrt{k_x}$ and $Y = y/\sqrt{k_y}$ to transform the given differential equation into Laplace's equation, $(\partial^2 p/\partial X^2) + (\partial^2 p/\partial Y^2) = 0$.

3.7 Use $x = \ln r$ and $y = \theta$ to transform $(1/r)(\partial/\partial r)[r(\partial p/\partial r)] + (1/r^2)[(\partial^2 p)/(\partial\theta^2)] = 0$ to $(\partial^2 p/\partial x^2) + (\partial^2 p/\partial y^2) = 0$.

3.8 Demonstrate the equivalence of the following operations.
1. $\Delta E = E\Delta$.
2. $\Delta b^x = b^x(b^{\Delta x} - 1)$.
3. $D = (1/\Delta x)\sinh^{-1}(A\delta)$, where $D = \partial/\partial x$.
4. $(E-2)(E-1)[f(x)] = -\Delta x$, where $f(x) = (2^{x/\Delta x} + x)$.
5. $\Delta - \nabla = \delta^2$.
6. $\Delta\nabla = \delta^2$.
7. $\nabla = E^{-1}\Delta$.
8. $\Delta\nabla = \nabla\Delta$.
9. $A\delta = ½(\Delta + \nabla)$.
10. $E = \left(\delta/2 + \sqrt{1 + \delta^2/4}\right)^2$.

3.9 Although less common, finite differences can be used to represent integrals. If the operator J is defined as

$$J[f(x_o)] = \int_{x_o}^{x_o+h} f(t)dt,$$

prove that

$$J[f(x_o)] = \frac{h\Delta f(x_o)}{[\Delta - (\Delta^2/2) + (\Delta^3/3) - (\Delta^4/4) + \ldots]}.$$

3.10 Solve $\begin{bmatrix} 3 & 0 \\ 0 & 4 \end{bmatrix}\begin{bmatrix} x_1 \\ x_2 \end{bmatrix} = \begin{bmatrix} 6 \\ 16 \end{bmatrix}$ using the matrix inversion method.

3.11 What is the inverse of a diagonal matrix of the form $\begin{bmatrix} a_{11} & 0 & 0 & 0 \\ 0 & a_{22} & 0 & 0 \\ 0 & 0 & a_{33} & 0 \\ 0 & 0 & 0 & a_{44} \end{bmatrix}$?

3.12 Calculate the coefficient of isothermal compressibility, c_g in psi^{-1} for a real gas at 1,500 psia and 120°F, given that $z = (577.1/T) - 0.00015p$, where p is in psia and T is in °R.

3.13 Function $f(x) = 3x^2 + 6x - 5$ is given.
1. Calculate the value of df/dx at $x = 1$ using the forward-, backward-, and central-difference approximations with $\Delta x = 1$. Compare the results with the exact value of df/dx at $x = 1$.
2. Calculate the value of d^2f/dx^2 at $x = 1$ using the central-difference approximation. Use $\Delta x = 1$ to compare the result against the exact value of d^2f/dx^2 at $x = 1$.

3.14 Consider the function $f(x) = x^3 - 4x^2 + 6$.
1. Calculate the value of df/dx at $x = 2$ using backward-, forward-, and central-difference approximations (let $\Delta x = 1$).
2. Calculate the value of d^2f/dx^2 at $x = 2$ using central-difference approximation (again, let $\Delta x = 1$).
3. Among the four approximations you calculated in Parts 1 and 2, which contain no error? Why?

3.15 Use the transformations $X = (k_y/k_x)^{1/4}x$ and $Y = (k_x/k_y)^{1/4}y$ on the PDE of the form $k_x(\partial^2 p/\partial x^2) + k_y(\partial^2 p/\partial y^2) = 0$. What important observation can be made on the basis of this transformation?

3.16 The differential equation $(\partial^2 p/\partial x^2) + (\partial^2 p/\partial y^2) + (\partial^2 p/\partial z^2) + c = 0$, where c is a constant, is known as the Poisson's equation. Implement the transformation $\psi(x,y,z) = p(x,y,z) + (c/2)x^2$ on the dependent variable p. What is the resulting PDE?

Nomenclature

$a(p)$ = function of p

a_{ij} = the (i,j) element of **[A]**
a_{ik} = the (i,k) element of **[A]**
a_{NN} = the (N,N) element of **[A]**
A = average operator in difference calculus
A = constant in Table 3.1
A_x = cross-sectional area normal to x direction, L^2, ft^2 [m^2]
[A] = coefficient matrix in a matrix equation
$[\mathbf{A}]^T$ = transpose of **[A]**
$[\mathbf{A}]^{-1}$ = inverse of **[A]**
b = constant
b_{ij} = the (i,j) element of **[B]**
b_{kj} = the (k,j) element of **[B]**
B = FVF, L^3/L^3, reservoir volume/volume at standard conditions
B_g = gas FVF, L^3/L^3, scf/STB [m^3/std m^3]
B_o = oil FVF, L^3/L^3, RB/STB [m^3/std m^3]
B_{ob} = oil FVF at bubblepoint pressure, L^3/L^3, RB/STB [m^3/std m^3]
[B] = matrix
c = constant
c_{aq} = aquifer compressibility, Lt^2/m, psi^{-1} [kPa^{-1}]
c_{ij} = the (i,j) element of **[C]**
c_g = gas compressibility, Lt^2/m, psi^{-1} [kPa^{-1}]
c_o = oil compressibility, Lt^2/m, psi^{-1} [kPa^{-1}]
C = constant
[C] = matrix
d = constant
d_n = last entry of the Column Vector d
$\vec{d}$ = right-side vector in a matrix equation
D = pipe diameter, L, ft [m]
e = exponential function
$e^{C't}$ = exponential function of $C't$
e_t = truncation error
e^u = exponential function of u
e^x = exponential function of x
e^{x_0} = exponential function of x_0
e^0 = exponential function of zero = 1
E = shift (or translation) operator in difference calculus
E^k = the kth order shift operator
E^{-k} = the kth inverse of the shift operator
E^{-1} = inverse shift operator in difference calculus
$E^{½}$ = half-shift operator
$E^{-½}$ = inverse half-shift operator
f = function
f_m = Moody's friction factor
g = acceleration of gravity, L/t^2, ft/sec^2 [m/s^2]
g_c = units conversion factor in Newton's law
$g(x)$ = function of x
$g_n(x)$ = nth function of x
h = increment in difference calculus, $h = x_{i+1} - x_i$
h = function
$h(x)$ = function of x
$h_m(x)$ = mth function of x
$\vec{i}$ = unit vector in the x direction
I = dimension of a vector
I_A = number of rows of **[A]**
I_B = number of rows of **[B]**
I_C = number of rows of **[C]**
[I] = identity matrix
j = dummy index
$\vec{j}$ = unit vector in the y direction
J_A = number of columns of **[A]**
J_B = number of columns of **[B]**
k = permeability, L^2, darcy [μm^2]
k_{rg} = relative permeability to gas, dimensionless
k_{ro} = relative permeability to oil, dimensionless
k_x = permeability in the direction of the x axis, L^2, darcy [μm^2]
k_y = permeability in the direction of the y axis, L^2, darcy [μm^2]
$\vec{k}$ = unit vector in the z direction
K_{aq} = aquifer constant, L^2/mt, RB/(D–psi) [m^3/(d · kPa)]
l = distance, L, ft [m]
$L(\,)$ = linear operator in differential calculus
n = number of moles; direction normal to reservoir boundary
N = initial oil in place, L^3, STB [std m^3]
p = pressure, m/Lt^2, psia [kPa]
p_{aq} = aquifer pressure, m/Lt^2, psia [kPa]
p_b = bubblepoint pressure, m/Lt^2, psia [kPa]
p_g = gas pressure, m/Lt^2, psia [kPa]
p_i = initial pressure, m/Lt^2, psia [kPa]
p_o = oil pressure, m/Lt^2, psia [kPa]
p_R = reservoir pressure, m/Lt^2, psia [kPa]
p_{sc} = standard condition pressure, m/Lt^2, psia [kPa]
p_w = water pressure, m/Lt^2, psia [kPa]
p_{wf} = flowing well bottomhole pressure, m/Lt^2, psia [kPa]
p_o = reference pressure, m/Lt^2, psia [kPa]
q_{gsc} = gas production rate at standard conditions, L^3/t, scf/D [std m^3/d]
q_{osc} = oil production rate at standard conditions, L^3/t, STB/D [std m^3/d]
q_{sc} = well flow rate at standard conditions, L^3/t, volume at standard conditions/time
r = radial distance in both cylindrical and spherical coordinate systems, L, ft [m]
r_w = well radius, L, ft [m]
R = universal gas constant, psi-ft^3/(lbm mol-°R) [kPa · m^3/(kg mol · K)]
R_{N+1} = the remainder after considering $N+1$ terms in Taylor series expansion of f(x)
R_s = solution-gas/oil ratio, L^3/L^3, scf/STB [std m^3/std m^3]
s = scalar
s_1 = first scalar
s_2 = second scalar
S_{iw} = irreducible water saturation, fraction
S_o = oil saturation, fraction
t = time, t, days
T = absolute temperature, T, °R [K]
T_{sc} = standard condition temperature, T, °R [K]
u = volumetric velocity, L/t, RB/(D-ft^2) [m^3/(d · m^2)]
u_i = ith element of $\vec{u}$
u_I = Ith element of $\vec{u}$
$\vec{u}$ = vector
$\vec{u}^T$ = transpose of $\vec{u}$
v_i = ith element of $\vec{v}$
v_I = Ith element of $\vec{v}$
$\vec{v}$ = vector
V = volume, L^3, ft^3 [m^3]
V_{aq} = volume of aquifer, L^3, ft^3 [m^3]
V_b = reservoir bulk volume, L^3, ft^3 [m^3]
w_i = ith element of $\vec{w}$
w_I = Ith element of $\vec{w}$
$\vec{w}$ = vector
x = distance in the x direction in the Cartesian coordinate system, L, ft [m]; independent variable
x_i = ith element of $\vec{x}$
x_j = jth element of $\vec{x}$
x_n = nth element of $\vec{x}$
x_o = variable where the function and all of its derivatives are known
$\vec{x}$ = vector
Δx = increment in Variable x

X = normalized x

y = distance in the y direction in the Cartesian coordinate system, L, ft [m]; independent variable

Y = normalized y

z = gas compressibility factor ($z = pM/\rho RT$), dimensionless

α_c = volume conversion factor whose numerical value is given in Table 2.1

β_c = transmissibility conversion factor whose numerical value is given in Table 2.1

Δ = forward difference operator

∇ = backward difference operator

δ = central difference operator

θ = angle in the θ direction in both cylindrical and spherical coordinate systems, rad [rad]

μ = viscosity, m/Lt, cp [Pa · s]

μ_g = gas viscosity, m/Lt, cp [Pa · s]

μ_o = oil viscosity, m/Lt, cp [Pa · s]

ρ = density, m/L^3, lbm/ft^3 [kg/m^3]

T_{gx} = gas-phase transmissibility in the x-direction, scf/(D-psi)[std m^3/(d · kPa)]

ϕ = porosity, fraction

ϕ_{aq} = aquifer porosity, fraction

ψ = defined function

References

1. Muskat, M.: "The Production Histories of Oil Producing Gas-Drive Reservoirs," *J. Applied Physics* (1945) **16**, 147.
2. *CRC Standard Math Tables*, 26th edition, CRC Press, Boca Raton, Florida (1977).

SI Metric Conversion Factors

°F	(°F + 459.67)/1.8		= K
psi	× 6.894 757	E + 00	= kPa
psi^{-1}	× 1.450 377	E − 01	= kPa^{-1}
°R	× 5/9		= K

Chapter 4
Formulation of Basic Equations for Single-Phase Flow

4.1 Introduction

This chapter presents the basic equations that describe the transport of a single-phase fluid through a porous medium. These mathematical equations describe the physical processes of interest in the reservoir and are in the form of partial-differential equations (PDE's) that consider the dynamic relationships between the fluid, the porous medium, and the flow conditions present in the system. In this chapter, we derive a mathematical model that describes the most important aspects of single-phase-fluid flow. The model equations are expressed in different coordinate systems and are developed for the most comprehensive case. Later in the chapter, we reduce the comprehensive, general, differential equation to several special cases that are simple subsets of the original model. **Fig. 4.1** highlights the formulation step in the development of a reservoir simulator.

4.2 Continuity Equation in Various Flow Geometries

The continuity equation (differential mass-conservation equation) can be developed by writing a mass-balance equation over a control volume (stationary volume element) through which the fluid is flowing. The shape of the volume element depends on the coordinate system used to describe the flow problem. The coordinate system should conform as closely as possible to the flow geometry defined by the equipotential lines and streamlines that are, in turn, defined by the shape of the physical boundaries and distribution of reservoir properties. **Figs. 4.2 through 4.4** show three flow geometries commonly used in reservoir modeling. Note that, for homogeneous rock properties, streamlines are defined by the physical boundaries of the volume element in each coordinate system.

It should be noted that rectangular, cylindrical, and spherical flow geometries represent relatively simple, well-defined flow patterns. The rectangular coordinate system represents rectilinear flow systems, while both the cylindrical and spherical coordinate systems represent curvilinear flow systems. In these two curvilinear systems, the flow elements are relatively simple patterns formed from well-defined orthogonal geometric elements, such as cylinders and spheres. When equipotential lines and streamlines are nonuniformly and asymmetrically distorted by the irregularly defined physical boundaries or heterogeneous reservoir properties, a generalized curvilinear coordinate system may be more convenient. **Fig. 4.5**, where a well is located at a distance from an infinite line source (x axis), presents this situation. Any quadrilateral element enclosed within a pair of neighboring equipotential lines and a pair of neighboring streamlines will define a proper, orthogonal volume element in curvilinear coordinates.

Sec. 4.3 shows that it is necessary to define a representative elemental volume to be able to write a mass-balance equation. The continuum approach must be used to define the properties of the elementary volume and the fluid flowing through it. This approach simply treats the porous medium as a continuum concerning rock and fluid properties (such as porosity, permeability, fluid viscosity, and fluid density) assigned to the control volume. These properties describe the overall behavior of the porous medium and the fluid contained in it. **Fig. 4.6** shows the application of the continuum principle to define the porosity of the representative elementary volume.

Applying the continuum approach results in the macroscopic definition of the control volume. The representative elemental volume attempts to summarize the system's macroscopic behavior by taking into consideration the net average of the microscopic effects.

To express the flow of fluids through porous media mathematically, it is necessary to use the following three fundamental laws or rules.

1. The principle of conservation of mass (Eq. 2.174), which states that the total mass of fluid entering a volume element in the reservoir must equal the net increase in the mass of the fluid in the element plus the total mass of fluid leaving the element.
2. An equation of state (EOS) (Eq. 2.91) that describes the density of a fluid as a function of temperature and pressure.
3. The constitutive equation (Eq. 2.23), which describes the rate of fluid movement into or out of the representative elementary volume.

4.3 Derivation of Generalized Flow Equations

4.3.1 Flow Equation in Rectangular Coordinates. The continuity equation is a mathematical expression of material balance. It can be developed by considering the flow of mass through a control volume, as discussed in Sec. 2.4.1 for the simple case of one-dimensional (1D) flow. Because this section is concerned with developing the flow equation in rectangular coordinates, the control volume (shown in **Fig. 4.7**), is a rectangular prism with dimensions Δx, Δy, and Δz, with its sides parallel to the principal directions of the rectangular coordinate system and its center at (x, y, z). For this rectangular prism, one can write a mass-balance equation for a single fluid flowing in the x, y, and z directions. At the $x-\Delta x/2$ face of the rectangular prism, the fluid flow rate and density are $q_{x-\Delta x/2}$ and $\rho_{x-\Delta x/2}$, respectively. Similarly, at the $y-\Delta y/2$ and $z-\Delta z/2$ faces of the rectangular prism, the fluid flow rates and densities are

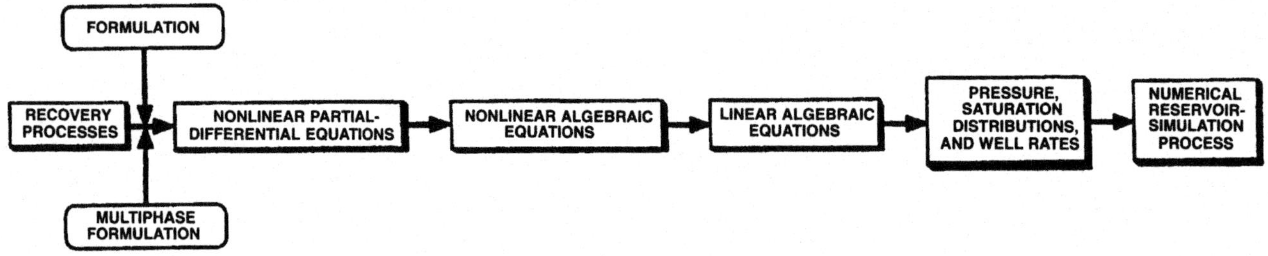

Fig. 4.1—Formulation step in development of a reservoir simulator (redrawn from Ref. 1).

$q_{y-\Delta y/2}$, $\rho_{y-\Delta y/2}$ and $q_{z-\Delta z/2}$, $\rho_{z-\Delta z/2}$, respectively. Likewise, at the $x+\Delta x/2$, $y+\Delta y/2$, and $z+\Delta z/2$ faces of the control volume, the flow rates and densities can be expressed as $q_{x+\Delta x/2}$, $\rho_{x+\Delta x/2}$; $q_{y+\Delta y/2}$, $\rho_{y+\Delta y/2}$; and $q_{z+\Delta z/2}$, $\rho_{z+\Delta z/2}$.

For the control volume shown in Fig. 4.7, one can write a mass-balance equation in the form of Eq. 2.174.

$$(m_i - m_o) + m_s = m_a. \quad (4.1)$$

Obviously, multiplication of the flow rate, q, and density, ρ, gives the amount of mass entering (or leaving) the control volume per unit time because

$$\left[q\left(\frac{L^3}{t}\right)\right]\left[\rho\left(\frac{m}{L^3}\right)\right] = \left[w\left(\frac{m}{t}\right)\right]. \quad (4.2)$$

Fig. 4.7 shows a crosshatched arrow indicating that an additional amount of fluid may be injected into (or produced from) the control volume at a mass rate of q_m(m/t). In this book, we use a positive sign for injection and a negative sign for production. In other words, we consistently use a positive sign to indicate the fluid entering the control volume and a negative sign to indicate the fluid leaving the control volume.

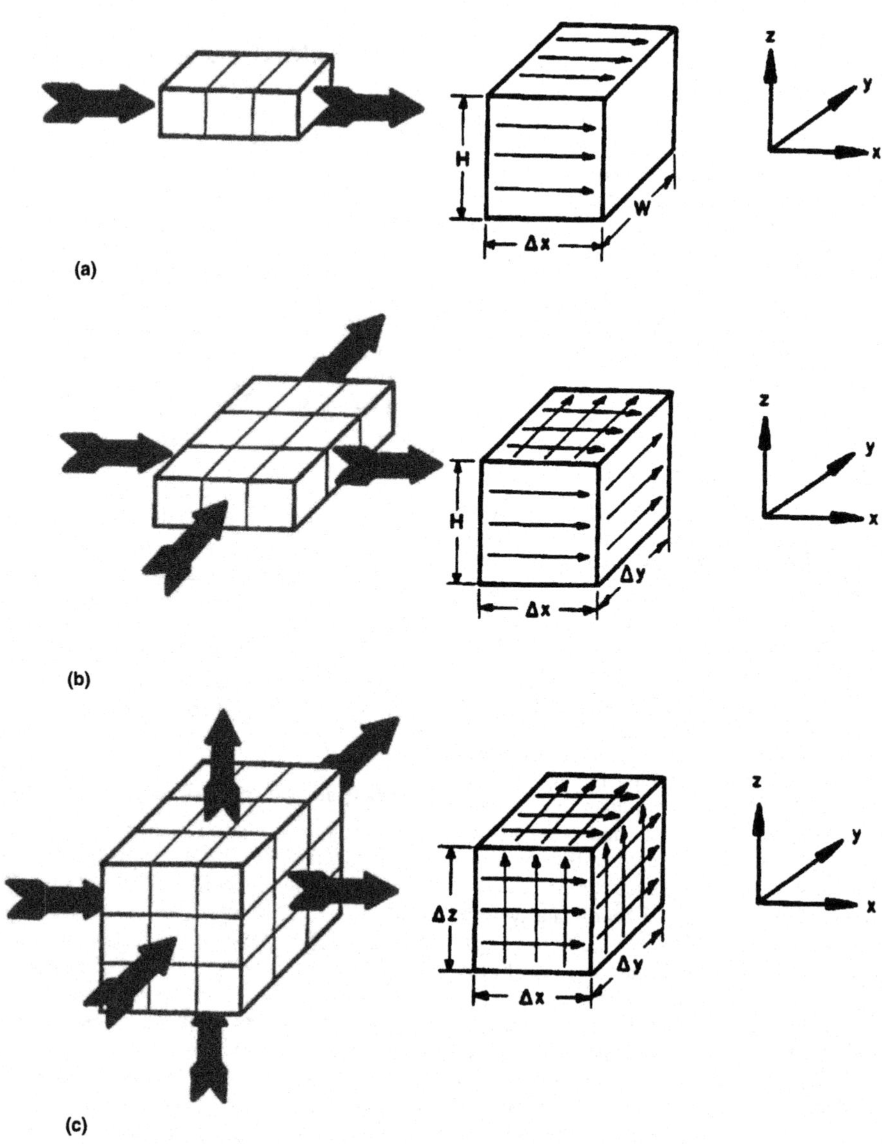

Fig. 4.2—Rectangular flow geometry and volume element details; (a) 1D flow, *x* direction only; (b) 2D flow, *x* and *y* directions only; and (c) 3D flow, *x*, *y*, and *z* directions.

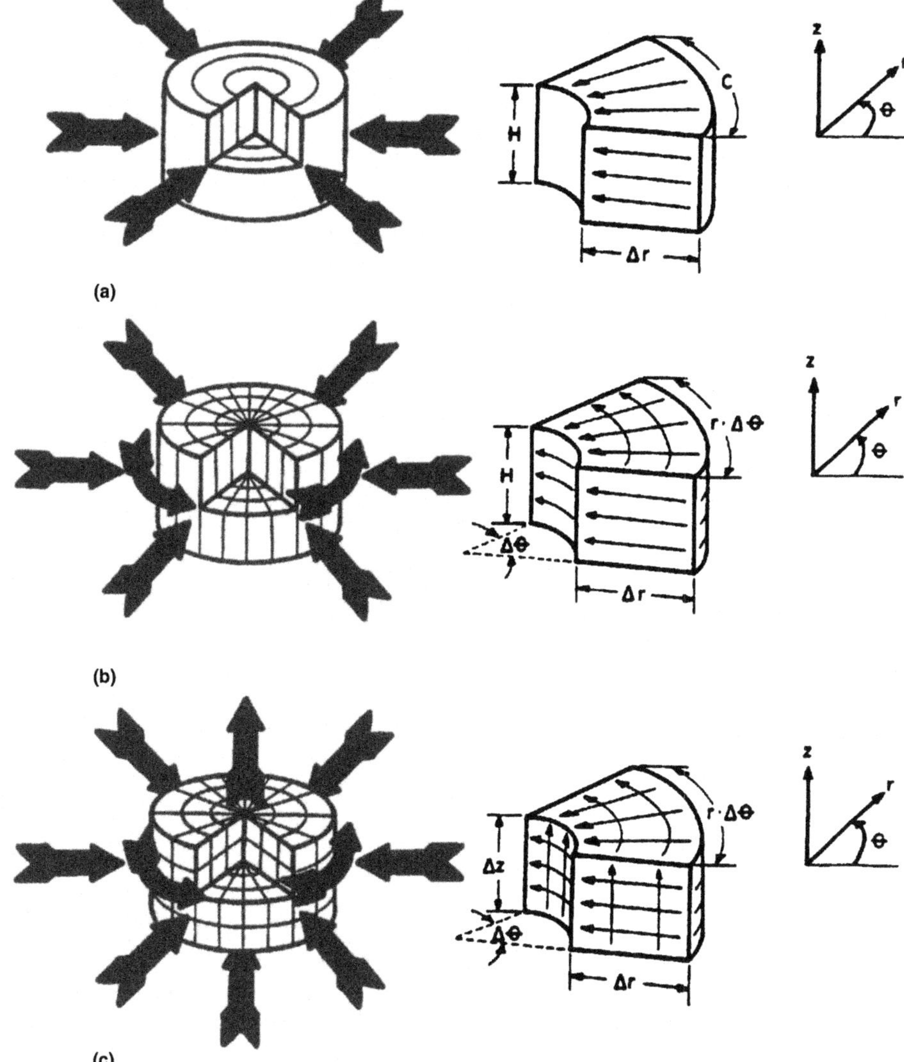

Fig. 4.3—Cylindrical flow geometry and volume element details; (a) 1D flow, *r* direction only; (b) 2D flow, *r* and *θ* directions only; and (c) 3D flow, *r*, *θ*, and *z* directions.

With these definitions, we can write a mass-balance equation over a finite period of time, Δt,

$$\left[(w)_{x-\Delta x/2}\Delta t + (w)_{y-\Delta y/2}\Delta t + (w)_{z-\Delta z/2}\Delta t\right]$$

$$-\left[(w)_{x+\Delta x/2}\Delta t + (w)_{y+\Delta y/2}\Delta t + (w)_{z+\Delta z/2}\Delta t\right] + q_m\Delta t$$

$$= (\phi\Delta x\Delta y\Delta z\rho)_{t+\Delta t} - (\phi\Delta x\Delta y\Delta z\rho)_t. \quad \text{(4.3)}$$

Because mass flux, $\vec{\dot{m}}$, has the dimensions m/L²t, the mass flow rate, $\vec{w}$, can be defined as

$$w_x = \dot{m}_x\Delta y\Delta z = \dot{m}_x A_x, \quad \text{(4.4a)}$$

$$w_y = \dot{m}_y\Delta x\Delta z = \dot{m}_y A_y, \quad \text{(4.4b)}$$

and $w_z = \dot{m}_z\Delta x\Delta y = \dot{m}_z A_z$. .... (4.4c)

The definition of mass flux can be stated in terms of density and volumetric velocity as

$$\dot{m}_x = \alpha_c\rho u_x, \quad \text{(4.5a)}$$

$$\dot{m}_y = \alpha_c\rho u_y, \quad \text{(4.5b)}$$

and $\dot{m}_z = \alpha_c\rho u_z$. .... (4.5c)

Substituting Eq. 4.5 into Eq. 4.4 gives

$$w_x = \alpha_c\rho u_x A_x, \quad \text{(4.6a)}$$

$$w_y = \alpha_c\rho u_y A_y, \quad \text{(4.6b)}$$

and $w_z = \alpha_c\rho u_z A_z$. .... (4.6c)

In Eq. 4.6, A_x, A_y, and A_z = areas perpendicular to flow along the x, y, and z directions, respectively. The new definitions, w_x, w_y, and w_z, can be substituted into Eq. 4.3 to give

$$-\left[(\rho u_x A_x)_{x+\Delta x/2} - (\rho u_x A_x)_{x-\Delta x/2} + (\rho u_y A_y)_{y+\Delta y/2}\right.$$

$$\left. - (\rho u_y A_y)_{y-\Delta y/2} + (\rho u_z A_z)_{z+\Delta z/2} - (\rho u_z A_z)_{z-\Delta z/2}\right] + \frac{q_m}{\alpha_c}$$

$$= \frac{1}{\alpha_c}\frac{(\phi\Delta x\Delta y\Delta z\rho)_{t+\Delta t} - (\phi\Delta x\Delta y\Delta z\rho)_t}{\Delta t}. \quad \text{(4.7)}$$

Dividing Eq. 4.7 through by $\Delta x\Delta y\Delta z$ and noting that $V_b = \Delta x\Delta y\Delta z$ is the bulk volume of the control element gives

$$-\left[\frac{(\rho u_x)_{x+\Delta x/2} - (\rho u_x)_{x-\Delta x/2}}{\Delta x}\right]$$

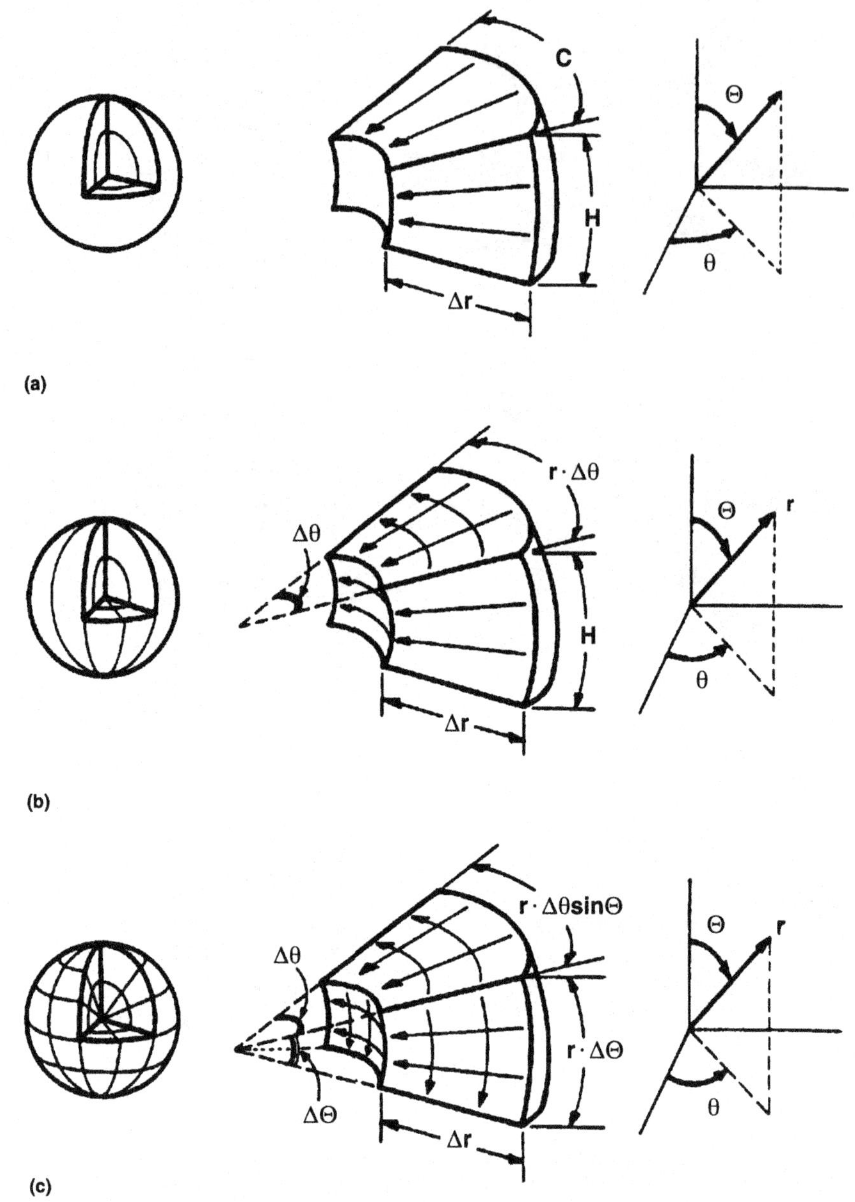

Fig. 4.4—Spherical flow geometry and volume element details; (a) 1D flow, *r* direction only; (b) 2D flow, *r* and *θ* directions only; and (c) 3D flow, *r*, *θ*, and Θ directions.

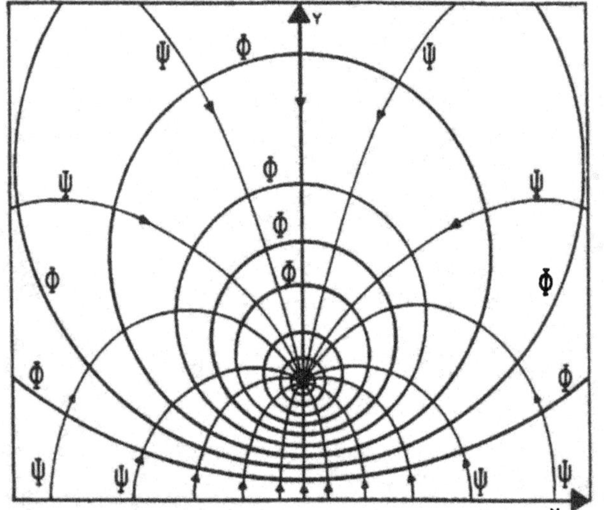

Fig. 4.5—Equipotential lines, Φ, and streamlines, Ψ, describing the flow into a well from an infinite line source at a uniform potential (after Ref. 2).

$$-\left[\frac{(\rho u_y)_{y+\Delta y/2}-(\rho u_y)_{y-\Delta y/2}}{\Delta y}\right]$$

$$-\left[\frac{(\rho u_z)_{z+\Delta z/2}-(\rho u_z)_{z-\Delta z/2}}{\Delta z}\right]+\frac{q_m}{\alpha_c V_b}$$

$$=\frac{1}{\alpha_c}\frac{(\phi\rho)_{t+\Delta t}-(\phi\rho)_t}{\Delta t}. \qquad (4.8)$$

Now take the simultaneous limits over time and space; that is, look at an instant of time as the control volume shrinks to the infinitesimal.

$$\lim_{\substack{\Delta x\to 0\\ \Delta y\to 0\\ \Delta z\to 0\\ \Delta t\to 0}}\left\{\left[-\frac{(\rho u_x)_{x+\Delta x/2}-(\rho u_x)_{x-\Delta x/2}}{\Delta x}\right.\right.$$

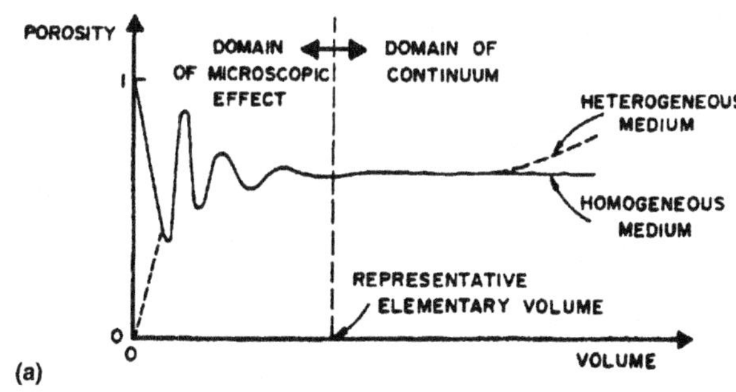

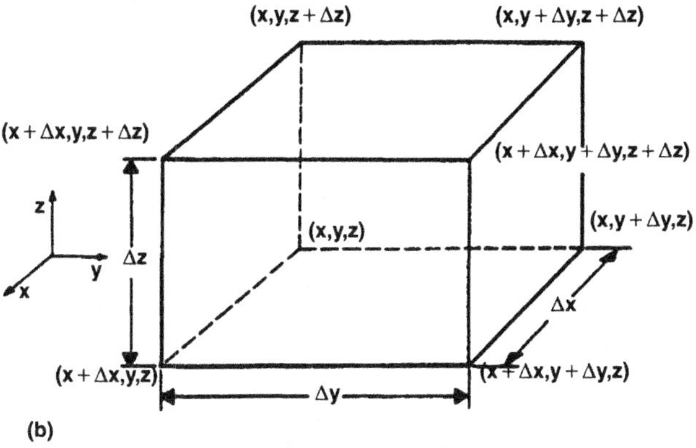

Fig. 4.6—(a) Assignment of porosity with representative elementary volume and (b) elementary volume (redrawn from Ref. 3).

$$-\frac{(\rho u_y)_{y+\Delta y/2} - (\rho u_y)_{y-\Delta y/2}}{\Delta y} - \frac{(\rho u_z)_{z+\Delta z/2} - (\rho u_z)_{z-\Delta z/2}}{\Delta z}\Bigg]$$

$$+\frac{q_m}{\alpha_c V_b}\Bigg\} = \lim_{\substack{\Delta x\to 0\\ \Delta y\to 0\\ \Delta z\to 0\\ \Delta t\to 0}} \left[\frac{(\phi\rho)_{t+\Delta t} - (\phi\rho)_t}{\alpha_c \Delta t}\right]. \quad \text{(4.9)}$$

In Eq. 4.9, we can recognize the definition of the first-order partial derivative with respect to the space and time coordinates (x, y, z, and t, respectively).

For the spatial variables,

$$\frac{\partial f}{\partial s} = \lim_{\Delta s\to 0} \frac{f(s + \Delta s/2) - f(s - \Delta s/2)}{\Delta s},\ s = x,y,z, \quad \text{(4.10)}$$

and for time,

$$\frac{\partial f}{\partial t} = \lim_{\Delta t\to 0} \frac{f(t + \Delta t) - f(t)}{\Delta t}. \quad \text{(4.11)}$$

Therefore, Eq. 4.9 can be written as

$$-\frac{\partial}{\partial x}(\rho u_x) - \frac{\partial}{\partial y}(\rho u_y) - \frac{\partial}{\partial z}(\rho u_z) + \frac{q_m}{\alpha_c V_b} = \frac{1}{\alpha_c}\frac{\partial}{\partial t}(\phi\rho). \quad \text{(4.12)}$$

Multiplying Eq. 4.12 by the bulk volume, V_b, gives

$$-\frac{\partial}{\partial x}(\rho u_x A_x)\Delta x - \frac{\partial}{\partial y}(\rho u_y A_y)\Delta y - \frac{\partial}{\partial z}(\rho u_z A_z)\Delta z + \frac{q_m}{\alpha_c}$$

$$= \frac{V_b}{\alpha_c}\frac{\partial}{\partial t}(\phi\rho). \quad \text{(4.13)}$$

Although some authors prefer to keep the PDE as given in Eq. 4.12 and introduce the bulk volume at the level of finite-difference equations, we will retain the form given in Eq. 4.13 in this book. The only difference between Eqs. 4.12 and 4.13 is that Eq. 4.12 is written per unit bulk volume of the reservoir. Eq. 4.13, on the other hand, provides a basis for including the cross-sectional areas perpendicular to the flow direction in the harmonic averaging of the transmissibility terms as discussed in Sec. 8.2.2.

In Eq. 4.13, we deliberately carried the area terms inside the parentheses. Although this is a mathematical approximation, it makes it possible to accommodate changes in formation thickness in the x, y, and z directions. This equation is a common form of the continuity equation or the mass-conservation equation in three dimensions.

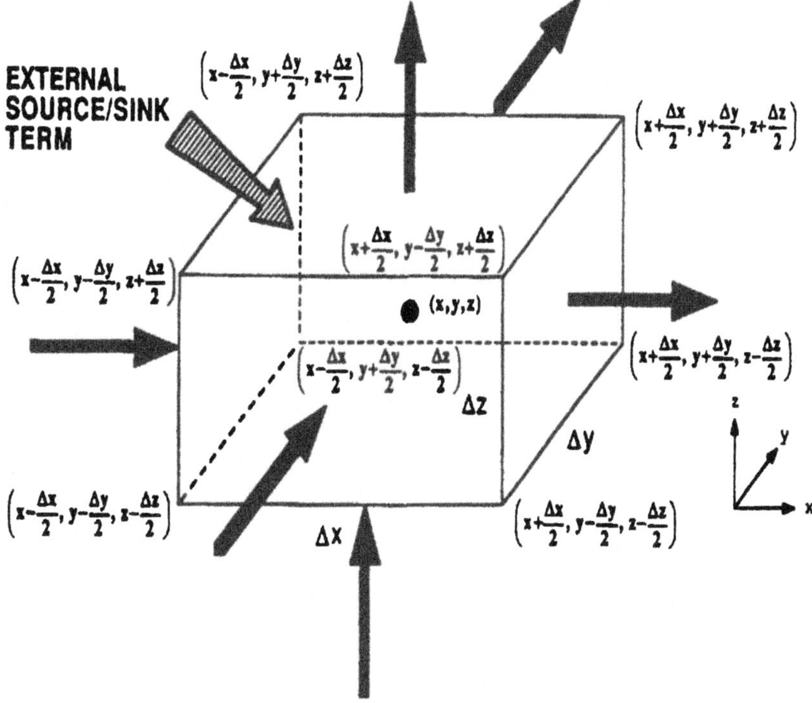

Fig. 4.7—Control volume in rectangular coordinates.

Example 4.1. Show that Eq. 4.13 is dimensionally consistent.

Solution. The dimensions of the differential terms on the left side are

$$\frac{\partial}{\partial x}(\rho u_x A_x)\Delta x \rightarrow \frac{1}{\mathrm{L}}\left(\frac{\mathrm{m}}{\mathrm{L}^3}\frac{\mathrm{L}}{\mathrm{t}}\mathrm{L}^2\right)\mathrm{L} = \left(\frac{\mathrm{m}}{\mathrm{t}}\right), \quad \text{.......... (4.14)}$$

the dimensions of the q_m term are

$$\frac{q_m}{\alpha_c} \rightarrow \left(\frac{1}{\mathrm{L}^3/\mathrm{L}^3}\frac{\mathrm{m}}{\mathrm{t}}\right) = \left(\frac{\mathrm{m}}{\mathrm{t}}\right), \quad \text{.................... (4.15)}$$

and the dimensions of the right side are

$$\frac{V_b}{\alpha_c}\frac{\partial}{\partial t}(\phi\rho) \rightarrow \frac{\mathrm{L}^3}{\mathrm{L}^3/\mathrm{L}^3}\frac{1}{\mathrm{t}}\left(\frac{\mathrm{m}}{\mathrm{L}^3}\right) = \left(\frac{\mathrm{m}}{\mathrm{t}}\right). \quad \text{............. (4.16)}$$

Therefore, Eq. 4.13 is dimensionally consistent.

Now incorporate the remaining two fundamental laws, the EOS, and the constitutive equation into the continuity equation. Remember that an EOS relates the density of a fluid to pressure and temperature. A simple way to express this relationship is through the fluid formation volume factor (FVF), expressed by Eq. 2.80.

$$B = \frac{\rho_{sc}}{\rho}. \quad \text{.................................. (4.17)}$$

In Eq. 4.17, B = FVF, which is the volume at reservoir conditions divided by the volume at standard conditions. Accordingly, ρ_{sc} and ρ = densities of the fluid at standard and reservoir conditions, respectively.

Because Eq. 4.13 is written to describe fluid flow in porous media, the velocity terms can be expressed with Darcy's law, Eq. 2.22, which relates the superficial velocity of the fluid to the potential gradient at the inflow and outflow faces of the control volume.

$$u_x = -\beta_c\frac{k_x}{\mu}\frac{\partial\Phi}{\partial x}, \quad \text{.......................... (4.18a)}$$

$$u_y = -\beta_c\frac{k_y}{\mu}\frac{\partial\Phi}{\partial y}, \quad \text{.......................... (4.18b)}$$

and $$u_z = -\beta_c\frac{k_z}{\mu}\frac{\partial\Phi}{\partial z}, \quad \text{.......................... (4.18c)}$$

where velocities are expressed in RB/D-ft^2 [m^3/(d · m^2)].

Before substituting Eqs. 4.17 and 4.18 into Eq. 4.13, we will express the q_m term as a volumetric rate rather than a mass rate. This is done to conform with industry standard measurement practices that measure and express produced fluids in volumetric units rather than mass flow rates. That is,

$$q_m\left(\frac{\mathrm{m}}{\mathrm{t}}\right) = \alpha_c\left(\frac{\mathrm{L}^3}{\mathrm{L}^3}\right)q_{sc}\left(\frac{\mathrm{L}^3}{\mathrm{t}}\right)\rho_{sc}\left(\frac{\mathrm{m}}{\mathrm{L}^3}\right) \quad \text{............... (4.19a)}$$

or $$q_m = \alpha_c q_{sc}\rho_{sc}. \quad \text{........................... (4.19b)}$$

Now substitute Eqs. 4.17, 4.18, and 4.19b into Eq. 4.13 to obtain

$$\frac{\partial}{\partial x}\left(\beta_c\frac{A_x k_x}{\mu B}\frac{\partial\Phi}{\partial x}\right)\Delta x + \frac{\partial}{\partial y}\left(\beta_c\frac{A_y k_y}{\mu B}\frac{\partial\Phi}{\partial y}\right)\Delta y$$

$$+ \frac{\partial}{\partial z}\left(\beta_c\frac{A_z k_z}{\mu B}\frac{\partial\Phi}{\partial z}\right)\Delta z + q_{sc} = \frac{V_b}{\alpha_c}\frac{\partial}{\partial t}\left(\frac{\phi}{B}\right). \quad \text{..... (4.20)}$$

Eq. 4.20 is the most general form of the single-phase-flow equation. In this form, Eq. 4.20 makes no assumptions regarding the fluid type (incompressible, slightly compressible, compressible) or pressure dependency of the rock and fluid properties. In arriving at Eq. 4.20, porosity is assumed to be a function of pressure and q_{sc} = flow rate at standard conditions.

If Eq. 4.20 is written in terms of pressure rather than potential (assuming horizontal flow and ignoring the gravitational forces in the z direction; that is, $\vec{\nabla}\Phi = \vec{\nabla}p$), it takes the form

$$\frac{\partial}{\partial x}\left(\beta_c\frac{A_x k_x}{\mu B}\frac{\partial p}{\partial x}\right)\Delta x + \frac{\partial}{\partial y}\left(\beta_c\frac{A_y k_y}{\mu B}\frac{\partial p}{\partial y}\right)\Delta y$$

$$+ \frac{\partial}{\partial z}\left(\beta_c\frac{A_z k_z}{\mu B}\frac{\partial p}{\partial z}\right)\Delta z + q_{sc} = \frac{V_b}{\alpha_c}\frac{\partial}{\partial t}\left(\frac{\phi}{B}\right). \quad \text{..... (4.21)}$$

Table 4.1 presents the units of all variables and functions appearing in flow equations.

Example 4.2. Write Eq. 4.20 in customary units.

Solution. Using Table 4.1, enter the values of β_c and α_c and the value of γ_c in the definition of potential. Then Eq. 4.20 in field units is

$$\frac{\partial}{\partial x}\left(\frac{1.127A_x k_x}{\mu B}\frac{\partial\Phi}{\partial x}\right)\Delta x + \frac{\partial}{\partial y}\left(\frac{1.127A_y k_y}{\mu B}\frac{\partial\Phi}{\partial y}\right)\Delta y$$

$$+ \frac{\partial}{\partial z}\left(\frac{1.127A_z k_z}{\mu B}\frac{\partial\Phi}{\partial z}\right)\Delta z + q_{sc} = \frac{V_b}{5.615}\frac{\partial}{\partial t}\left(\frac{\phi}{B}\right).$$

.... 4.22

In this equation, k_x, k_y, and k_z are in darcies, V_b is in cubic feet, and all the other terms are as they appear in Table 4.1 under customary units.

4.3.2 Flow Equation in Cylindrical Coordinates. The continuity equation in cylindrical coordinates can be obtained by considering a cylindrical element whose center is (r,θ,z) as shown in **Fig. 4.8**. The flow equation as expressed in cylindrical coordinates is used exclusively for single-well simulation problems. In these cases, a well is located at the center of a cylindrical drainage volume so that the wellbore and the outer boundaries of the drainage volume are concentric. Note that the external source/sink term that is included as q_m in the rectangular coordinates is often avoided in cylindrical coordinates because the well is at the center of the drainage area and the wellbore specifications and external conditions are incorporated in the form of boundary conditions as is done in classic well-test analysis.

We again write the mass-balance equation as expressed in Eq. 4.1 without an external source/sink term. To simplify the appearance of the equation, write the left side for each direction over a short period of time, Δt.

Flow Term for the r Direction.

$$(m_i - m_o)_r = \left[(w)_{r-\Delta r/2}\Delta t - (w)_{r+\Delta r/2}\Delta t\right]. \quad \text{...... (4.23)}$$

The areas perpendicular to flow along the r direction can be written

$$A_{r-\Delta r/2} = (r\Delta\theta\Delta z)_{r-\Delta r/2} \quad \text{..................... (4.24)}$$

and $$A_{r+\Delta r/2} = (r\Delta\theta\Delta z)_{r+\Delta r/2}. \quad \text{................... (4.25)}$$

Then, mass flow rates along the r direction become

$$w_{r-\Delta r/2} = \alpha_c(\rho u_r A_r)_{r-\Delta r/2} \quad \text{.................. (4.26)}$$

and $$w_{r+\Delta r/2} = \alpha_c(\rho u_r A_r)_{r+\Delta r/2}. \quad \text{.................. (4.27)}$$

Combining Eqs. 4.23 through 4.27 gives

$$(m_i - m_o)_r = \alpha_c\left[(r\rho u_r\Delta\theta\Delta z)_{r-\Delta r/2} - (r\rho u_r\Delta\theta\Delta z)_{r+\Delta r/2}\right]\Delta t.$$

.... (4.28)

Flow Term for the θ Direction.

$$(m_i - m_o)_\theta = \left[(w)_{\theta-\Delta\theta/2}\Delta t - (w)_{\theta+\Delta\theta/2}\Delta t\right]. \quad \text{..... (4.29)}$$

Again, define the areas perpendicular to flow along the θ direction as

$$A_{\theta-\Delta\theta/2} = A_{\theta+\Delta\theta/2} = \Delta r\Delta z. \quad \text{.................. (4.30)}$$

TABLE 4.1—VARIABLES USED IN FLOW EQUATIONS AND DARCY'S LAW

Quantity	Symbol	System of Units: Customary Unit	System of Units: Metric Unit	Conversion Factor*
Length	x, y, z, r	ft	m	0.3048
Area	A	ft^2	m^2	0.09290304
Permeability	k	darcy	μm^2	0.9869233
Phase viscosity	μ	cp	Pa·s	0.001
Gas FVF	B_g	RB/scf**	m^3/std m^3**	5.5519314
Liquid FVF	B_o, B_w	RB/STB**	m^3/std m^3	1.0
Solution-gas/oil ratio	R_s	scf/STB	std m^3/std m^3	0.1801175
Pressure	Φ, p	psia	kPa	6.894757
Pressure gradient	$\vec{\nabla}\Phi$, $\vec{\nabla}p$	psi/ft	kPa/m	22.62059
Phase gravity	γ	psi/ft	kPa/m	22.62059
Gas flow rate	q_{sc}, q_{gsc}	scf/D	std m^3/d	0.02863640
Liquid flow rate	q_{sc}, q_{osc}, q_{wsc}	STB/D	std m^3/d	0.1589873
Volumetric velocity	u, q/A	RB/(D-ft^2)	m^3/(d·m^2)	1.7103717
Gridblock bulk volume	V_b	ft^3	m^3	0.02831685
Phase density	ρ	lbm/ft^3	kg/m^3	16.01846
Gravitational acceleration	g	32.174 ft/s^2	9.8066352 m/s^2	0.3048
Compressibility	c	psi^{-1}	kPa^{-1}	0.1450377
Absolute temperature	T	°R	K	0.55555556
Relative permeability	k_r	fraction	fraction	1.0
Porosity	ϕ	fraction	fraction	1.0
Phase saturation	S	fraction	fraction	1.0
Compressibility factor	Z	dimensionless	dimensionless	1.0
Time	t	day	day	1.0
Angle	θ, Θ	rad	rad	1.0
Transmissibility conversion factor	β_c	1.127	86.4x10^{-6}	—
Gravity conversion factor	γ_c	0.21584x10^{-3}	10^{-3}	—
Volume conversion factor	α_c	5.614583	1	—

*Multiply customary unit by conversion factor to obtain metric unit.
**STB and scf are measured at 60°F and 14.696 psia; std m^3 is measured at 15°C and 100 kPa.

Eq. 4.29 can be written as

$$(m_i - m_o)_\theta = \alpha_c\Big[(\rho u_\theta \Delta r \Delta z)_{\theta-\Delta\theta/2} - (\rho u_\theta \Delta r \Delta z)_{\theta+\Delta\theta/2}\Big]\Delta t. \quad (4.31)$$

Flow Term for the z Direction.

$$(m_i - m_o)_z = \Big[(w)_{z-\Delta z/2}\Delta t - (w)_{z+\Delta z/2}\Delta t\Big]. \quad (4.32)$$

This time the area perpendicular to flow along the z direction is written as (see Example 4.3)

$$A_{z-\Delta z/2} = A_{z+\Delta z/2} = r\Delta r\Delta\theta. \quad (4.33)$$

Eq. 4.33 can be used to redefine Eq. 4.32 as

$$(m_i - m_o)_z = \alpha_c\Big[(\rho u_z r\Delta r\Delta\theta)_{z-\Delta z/2} - (\rho u_z r\Delta r\Delta\theta)_{z+\Delta z/2}\Big]\Delta t. \quad (4.34)$$

Mass-Accumulation Term.

$$[m_a(t+\Delta t) - m_a(t)] = V_b\Big[(\phi\rho)_{t+\Delta t} - (\phi\rho)_t\Big], \quad (4.35)$$

where the bulk volume of the element is defined as (see Example 4.3)

$$V_b = r\Delta r\Delta\theta\Delta z. \quad (4.36)$$

Now, bring all the $m_i - m_o$ and m_a terms together into a mass-balance statement,

$$-\Big[(r\rho u_r\Delta\theta\Delta z)_{r+\Delta r/2} - (r\rho u_r\Delta\theta\Delta z)_{r-\Delta r/2} + (\rho u_\theta\Delta r\Delta z)_{\theta+\Delta\theta/2} - (\rho u_\theta\Delta r\Delta z)_{\theta-\Delta\theta/2} + (\rho u_z r\Delta r\Delta\theta)_{z+\Delta z/2} - (\rho u_z r\Delta r\Delta\theta)_{z-\Delta z/2}\Big]\Delta t = \frac{1}{\alpha_c} r\Delta r\Delta\theta\Delta z \times \Big[(\phi\rho)_{t+\Delta t} - (\phi\rho)_t\Big]. \quad (4.37)$$

Dividing Eq. 4.37 by $r\Delta r\Delta\theta\Delta z\Delta t$ yields

$$-\frac{1}{r}\left[\frac{(r\rho u_r)_{r+\Delta r/2} - (r\rho u_r)_{r-\Delta r/2}}{\Delta r}\right]$$

$$-\frac{1}{r}\left[\frac{(\rho u_\theta)_{\theta+\Delta\theta/2} - (\rho u_\theta)_{\theta-\Delta\theta/2}}{\Delta\theta}\right]$$

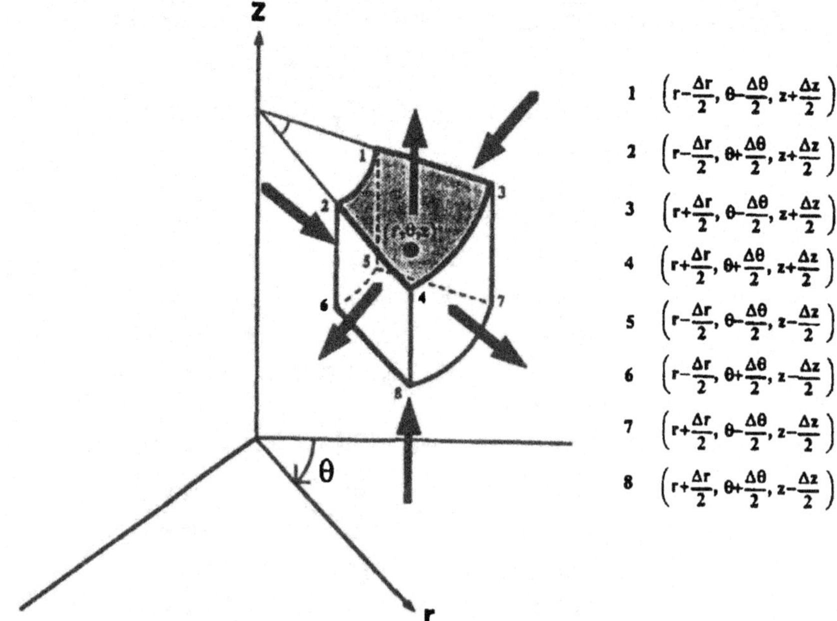

Fig. 4.8—Control volume in cylindrical coordinates.

$$-\left[\frac{(\rho u_z)_{z+\Delta z/2}-(\rho u_z)_{z-\Delta z/2}}{\Delta z}\right]$$

$$=\frac{1}{\alpha_c}\left[\frac{(\phi\rho)_{t+\Delta t}-(\phi\rho)_t}{\Delta t}\right]. \quad \text{.................. (4.38)}$$

At this stage of the development, take the simultaneous limits as Δr, $\Delta\theta$, Δz, and Δt approach zero. In other words,

$$\lim_{\substack{\Delta r\to 0\\ \Delta\theta\to 0\\ \Delta z\to 0\\ \Delta t\to 0}}\left[-\frac{1}{r}\frac{(r\rho u_r)_{r+\Delta r/2}-(r\rho u_r)_{r-\Delta r/2}}{\Delta r}\right.$$

$$-\frac{1}{r}\frac{(\rho u_\theta)_{\theta+\Delta\theta/2}-(\rho u_\theta)_{\theta-\Delta\theta/2}}{\Delta\theta}$$

$$\left.-\frac{(\rho u_z)_{z+\Delta z/2}-(\rho u_z)_{z-\Delta z/2}}{\Delta z}\right]$$

$$=\lim_{\substack{\Delta r\to 0\\ \Delta\theta\to 0\\ \Delta z\to 0\\ \Delta t\to 0}}\frac{1}{\alpha_c}\left[\frac{(\phi\rho)_{t+\Delta t}-(\phi\rho)_t}{\Delta t}\right]. \quad \text{............... (4.39)}$$

After taking the limits and applying the definition of a partial derivative, Eq. 4.39 reduces to

$$-\frac{1}{r}\frac{\partial}{\partial r}(r\rho u_r)-\frac{1}{r}\frac{\partial}{\partial\theta}(\rho u_\theta)-\frac{\partial}{\partial z}(\rho u_z)=\frac{1}{\alpha_c}\frac{\partial}{\partial t}(\phi\rho).$$

$$\text{.................... (4.40)}$$

Eq. 4.40 is the continuity equation for three-dimensional (3D) radial-cylindrical coordinates without an external source/sink term.

Darcy's law gives the superficial-velocity components in radial-cylindrical coordinates (for the θ component see Example 4.3) as

$$u_r=-\beta_c\frac{k_r}{\mu}\frac{\partial\Phi}{\partial r}, \quad \text{.......................... (4.41a)}$$

$$u_\theta=-\beta_c\frac{k_\theta}{\mu}\frac{1}{r}\frac{\partial\Phi}{\partial\theta}, \quad \text{........................ (4.41b)}$$

and $u_z=-\beta_c\dfrac{k_z}{\mu}\dfrac{\partial\Phi}{\partial z}$. .... (4.41c)

Substituting these expressions of velocity into Eq. 4.40 and setting $\rho=\rho_{sc}/B$ gives

$$\frac{1}{r}\frac{\partial}{\partial r}\left(r\beta_c\frac{k_r}{\mu B}\frac{\partial\Phi}{\partial r}\right)+\frac{1}{r^2}\frac{\partial}{\partial\theta}\left(\beta_c\frac{k_\theta}{\mu B}\frac{\partial\Phi}{\partial\theta}\right)+\frac{\partial}{\partial z}\left(\beta_c\frac{k_z}{\mu B}\frac{\partial\Phi}{\partial z}\right)$$

$$=\frac{1}{\alpha_c}\frac{\partial}{\partial t}\left(\frac{\phi}{B}\right). \quad \text{............................ (4.42)}$$

Table 4.1 gives the units for k_r, k_θ, k_z, μ, B, Φ, ϕ, r, θ, z, and t, and the values of α_c, β_c, and γ_c.

Example 4.3

1. Find the expressions that define the areas perpendicular to the flow along the r, θ, and z directions of the control volume of Fig. 4.8. Also, obtain an expression that defines the bulk volume.

2. Obtain the expression that defines the θ component of the velocity term in radial-cylindrical coordinates.

Solution.

1. Consider the plan view of the two concentric cylinders with a height of Δz, as shown in **Fig. 4.9**.

The crosshatched section in Fig. 4.9 represents the top view of the control volume of Fig. 4.8. To calculate the area of the inner boundary, $A_{r-\Delta r/2}$, it is necessary to calculate the inner surface area at radius $r-\Delta r/2$, which is $2\pi(r-\Delta r/2)\Delta z$. Because the control volume exposes only $\Delta\theta/2\pi$ fraction of this area, $A_{r-\Delta r/2}$ at radius $r-\Delta r/2$ is

$$A_{r-\Delta r/2}=2\pi(r-\Delta r/2)\Delta z\frac{\Delta\theta}{2\pi} \quad \text{.................. (4.43)}$$

or $A_{r-\Delta r/2}=(r-\Delta r/2)\Delta z\Delta\theta$. .... (4.44)

Similarly, $A_{r+\Delta r/2}$ at radius $r+\Delta r/2$ will be

$$A_{r+\Delta r/2}=(r+\Delta r/2)\Delta z\Delta\theta. \quad \text{..................... (4.45)}$$

To find the area perpendicular to the z direction, consider the ring-shaped area,

$$\pi(r+\Delta r/2)^2-\pi(r-\Delta r/2)^2=2\pi r\Delta r. \quad \text{........ (4.46)}$$

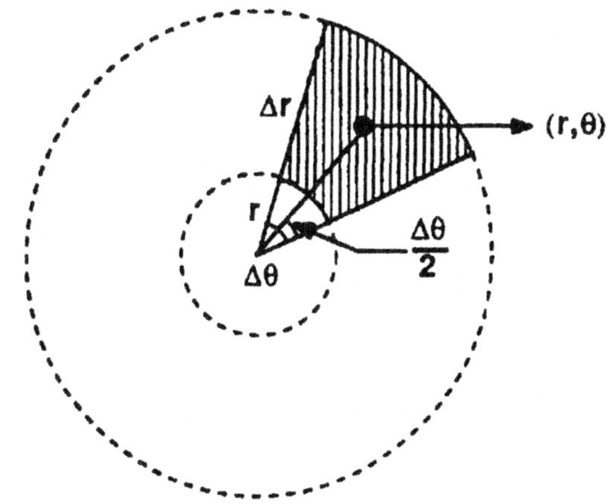

Fig. 4.9—Plan view of two concentric cylinders.

Again, only $\Delta\theta/2\pi$ fraction of this ring-shaped element appears in our control volume, so

$$A_{z-\Delta z/2}=2\pi r\Delta r\frac{\Delta\theta}{2\pi} \quad \text{(4.47)}$$

or $A_{z-\Delta z/2}=r\Delta r\Delta\theta$. .... (4.48)

Because the area along the z direction does not change,

$$A_{z+\Delta z/2}=r\Delta r\Delta\theta. \quad \text{(4.49)}$$

The area perpendicular to the θ direction is a rectangle and is simply

$$A_{\theta-\Delta\theta/2}=A_{\theta+\Delta\theta/2}=\Delta r\Delta z. \quad \text{(4.50)}$$

We can use a similar strategy to calculate the bulk volume of the control element. The total volume between the two concentric cylinders is

$$\pi(r+\Delta r/2)^2\Delta z-\pi(r-\Delta r/2)^2\Delta z=2\pi r\Delta r\Delta z. \quad \text{(4.51)}$$

The control volume represents $\Delta\theta/2\pi$ fraction of the above volume; therefore,

$$V_b=2\pi r\Delta r\Delta z\frac{\Delta\theta}{2\pi} \quad \text{(4.52a)}$$

or $V_b=r\Delta r\Delta\theta\Delta z$. .... (4.52b)

2. **Fig. 4.10** shows that u_θ is tangential to the control volume along Arc d-c, l, which passes through the center of the control volume. From Darcy's law,

$$u_\theta=-\beta_c\frac{k_\theta}{\mu}\frac{d\Phi}{l}, \quad \text{(4.53)}$$

where $l=rd\theta$, or

$$u_\theta=-\beta_c\frac{k_\theta}{\mu}\frac{1}{r}\frac{d\Phi}{d\theta}. \quad \text{(4.54)}$$

4.4 Different Forms of Flow Equations

The previous sections of this chapter developed the flow equations for a homogeneous (single-phase) fluid without specifying whether the fluid was incompressible, slightly compressible, or compressible. The following sections modify the general flow equation according to the dependency of the fluid density on pressure. We continue to consider only single-phase flow.

4.4.1 Incompressible-Fluid-Flow Equation. If the fluid is incompressible, the density is constant; in other words, B is constant. If thermal effects going up the wellbore are negligible, $B=1$; if thermal expansion is significant, the constant is something other than unity. Furthermore, for an ideal incompressible fluid, viscosity is also constant. Accordingly, Eq. 4.20 can be rewritten as

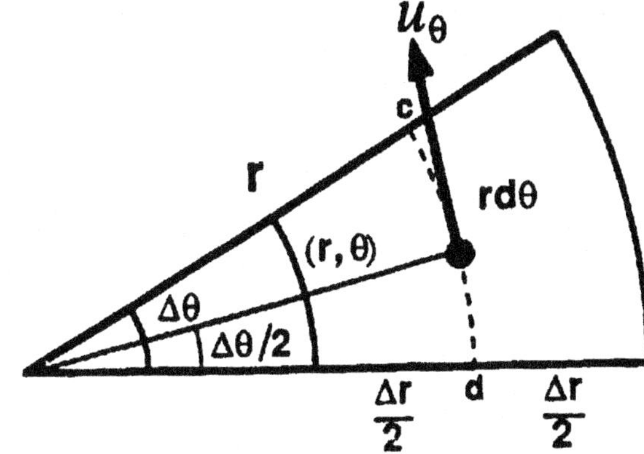

Fig. 4.10—u_θ component of the velocity.

$$\frac{\partial}{\partial x}\left(\beta_c A_x k_x\frac{\partial\Phi}{\partial x}\right)\Delta x+\frac{\partial}{\partial y}\left(\beta_c A_y k_y\frac{\partial\Phi}{\partial y}\right)\Delta y+\frac{\partial}{\partial z}\left(\beta_c A_z k_z\frac{\partial\Phi}{\partial z}\right)\Delta z+\mu q_{sc}=0. \quad \text{(4.55)}$$

It is clear that the solution of Eq. 4.55 is independent of time. The time dependency of Eq. 4.20 is removed when B is treated as constant for incompressible fluids (also porous medium is assumed to be incompressible). This indicates that Eq. 4.55 represents a steady-state-flow problem as long as the boundary conditions are independent of time. Eq. 4.55 also implies that a pressure surface (isobaric map) over the reservoir develops instantaneously and remains intact as long as the boundary conditions are not changed with time. Furthermore, Eq. 4.55 does not contain any porosity term because the reservoir rock is also treated as incompressible. This implies that incompressible-fluid flow does not allow for accumulation or depletion. In other words, whatever crosses the physical boundaries into the reservoir must displace an equivalent volume from the reservoir.

If the gravity terms are neglected, the potential gradient (Eq. 2.15) becomes equivalent to pressure gradient $\left(\vec{\nabla}\Phi=\vec{\nabla}p\right)$ and Eq. 4.55 will have pressure as the dependent variable.

$$\frac{\partial}{\partial x}\left(\beta_c A_x k_x\frac{\partial p}{\partial x}\right)\Delta x+\frac{\partial}{\partial y}\left(\beta_c A_y k_y\frac{\partial p}{\partial y}\right)\Delta y+\frac{\partial}{\partial z}\left(\beta_c A_z k_z\frac{\partial p}{\partial z}\right)\Delta z+\mu q_{sc}=0. \quad \text{(4.56)}$$

For an anisotropic ($k_x \neq k_y \neq k_z$) but homogeneous (k_x, k_y, and k_z are uniform) medium, Eq. 4.56 becomes

$$k_x\frac{\partial^2 p}{\partial x^2}+k_y\frac{\partial^2 p}{\partial y^2}+k_z\frac{\partial^2 p}{\partial z^2}+\frac{\mu q_{sc}}{\beta_c V_b}=0. \quad \text{(4.57)}$$

Note that, to arrive at Eq. 4.57, $V_b=A_x\Delta x=A_y\Delta y=A_z\Delta z$.

Furthermore, if the medium is isotropic ($k_x=k_y=k_z=k$) as well as homogeneous, we obtain

$$\frac{\partial^2 p}{\partial x^2}+\frac{\partial^2 p}{\partial y^2}+\frac{\partial^2 p}{\partial z^2}+\frac{\mu q_{sc}}{\beta_c k V_b}=0, \quad \text{(4.58)}$$

and if no well is within the domain of interest ($q_{sc}=0$), we obtain

$$\frac{\partial^2 p}{\partial x^2}+\frac{\partial^2 p}{\partial y^2}+\frac{\partial^2 p}{\partial z^2}=0. \quad \text{(4.59)}$$

Eq. 4.59 describes the pressure distribution $p=p(x,y,z)$ in the flow field of an incompressible fluid in a homogeneous and isotropic medium where there is no external source/sink term (well). Eq. 4.59 is called the Laplace equation. One interesting observation from Eq.

4.59 is that it does not contain any permeability term. This implies that the distribution of p is governed by the geometrical configuration of the reservoir and the imposed boundary conditions. The effect of k is not reflected on the pressure distribution, but only on flow rate.

Example 4.4. Show that Eq. 4.58 is dimensionally consistent.

Solution. While the differential terms $\partial^2 p/\partial x^2$, $\partial^2 p/\partial y^2$, and $\partial^2 p/\partial x^2$ have the dimensions

$$\frac{(\mathrm{m/Lt^2})}{(\mathrm{L^2})} = \left(\frac{\mathrm{m}}{\mathrm{L^3 t^2}}\right), \qquad (4.60)$$

the dimensions of the $\mu q_{sc}/\beta_c k V_b$ term are

$$\frac{(\mathrm{m/Lt})}{(\mathrm{L^2})}\frac{(\mathrm{L^3/t})}{(\mathrm{L^3})} = \left(\frac{\mathrm{m}}{\mathrm{L^3 t^2}}\right). \qquad (4.61)$$

Because Eqs. 4.60 and 4.61 have the same dimensions, Eq. 4.58 is dimensionally consistent.

Example 4.5. The following PDE describes a specific fluid-flow problem in a porous medium. After examining the given mathematical formulation, describe the flow problem to the fullest extent.

$$\frac{\partial^2 p}{\partial x^2} = C, \qquad (4.62)$$

where $C > 0$.

Solution. Obviously, $\partial^2 p/\partial x^2 = C$ represents a 1D flow problem. We can start with the most comprehensive form of the incompressible flow equation, Eq. 4.55, in one dimension and try to reduce it to the form of Eq. 4.62.

In one-dimension, Eq. 4.55 is (assuming $\vec{\nabla}\Phi = \vec{\nabla}p$)

$$\frac{\partial}{\partial x}\left(\beta_c A_x k_x \frac{\partial p}{\partial x}\right)\Delta x + \mu q_{sc} = 0; \qquad (4.63)$$

therefore, flow is through a horizontal medium. If the system is homogeneous, we have

$$\beta_c A_x k_x \frac{\partial^2 p}{\partial x^2}\Delta x + \mu q_{sc} = 0 \qquad (4.64)$$

$$\text{or } \frac{\partial^2 p}{\partial x^2} + \frac{\mu q_{sc}}{\beta_c k_x V_b} = 0, \qquad (4.65)$$

$$\text{which is } \frac{\partial^2 p}{\partial x^2} = -\frac{\mu q_{sc}}{\beta_c k_x V_b}. \qquad (4.66)$$

Comparing Eqs. 4.62 and 4.66 indicates that

$$-\frac{\mu q_{sc}}{\beta_c k_x V_b} = C, \qquad (4.67)$$

where $C > 0$. Because the entries μ, k_x, and V_b in Eq. 4.67 are all positive entries, the flow-rate entry, q_{sc}, must be a negative entry (implying production) for the equation to hold. After this analysis one can describe the flow problem as 1D incompressible-fluid flow in a horizontal, homogeneous, porous medium that has a production well producing at a rate of

$$q_{sc} = C\frac{\beta_c k_x V_b}{\mu} \text{ STB/D [std m}^3\text{/d]}. \qquad (4.68)$$

4.4.2 Slightly-Compressible-Fluid-Flow Equation. For slightly-compressible liquid flow, assume that fluid compressibility is small and remains constant within the pressure range of interest. Therefore, the FVF can be approximated as in Eq. 2.81,

$$B = B^\circ/[1 + c(p - p^\circ)], \qquad (4.69)$$

where c = fluid compressibility.

Returning to the general form of the flow equation, Eq. 4.20, substituting for B on the right side with Eq. 4.69, and assuming incompressible porous medium, yields

$$\frac{V_b}{\alpha_c}\frac{\partial}{\partial t}\left(\frac{\phi}{B}\right) = \frac{V_b\phi}{\alpha_c}\frac{\partial}{\partial t}\{[1 + c(p - p^\circ)]/B^\circ\}$$

$$= \frac{V_b\phi c}{\alpha_c B^\circ}\frac{\partial p}{\partial t}. \qquad (4.70)$$

Although this development assumes an incompressible porous medium, Chap. 8 allows for the change of porosity with pressure. The flow equation for a slightly compressible fluid then becomes

$$\frac{\partial}{\partial x}\left(\beta_c \frac{A_x k_x}{\mu B}\frac{\partial \Phi}{\partial x}\right)\Delta x + \frac{\partial}{\partial y}\left(\beta_c \frac{A_y k_y}{\mu B}\frac{\partial \Phi}{\partial y}\right)\Delta y$$

$$+ \frac{\partial}{\partial z}\left(\beta_c \frac{A_z k_z}{\mu B}\frac{\partial \Phi}{\partial z}\right)\Delta z + q_{sc} = \frac{V_b\phi c}{\alpha_c B^\circ}\frac{\partial p}{\partial t}. \qquad (4.71)$$

Again, ignoring the depth gradients $\left(\vec{\nabla}\Phi = \vec{\nabla}p\right)$ yields

$$\frac{\partial}{\partial x}\left(\beta_c \frac{A_x k_x}{\mu B}\frac{\partial p}{\partial x}\right)\Delta x + \frac{\partial}{\partial y}\left(\beta_c \frac{A_y k_y}{\mu B}\frac{\partial p}{\partial y}\right)\Delta y$$

$$+ \frac{\partial}{\partial z}\left(\beta_c \frac{A_z k_z}{\mu B}\frac{\partial p}{\partial z}\right)\Delta z + q_{sc} = \frac{V_b\phi c}{\alpha_c B^\circ}\frac{\partial p}{\partial t}. \qquad (4.72)$$

At this point, one can either keep the B terms on the left side, as shown in Eq. 4.72, or make further modification by substituting Eq. 4.69 on the left side and treating μ as a constant. Eq. 4.72 then becomes

$$\frac{\partial}{\partial x}\left\{\beta_c A_x k_x[1 + c(p - p^\circ)]\frac{\partial p}{\partial x}\right\}\Delta x$$

$$+ \frac{\partial}{\partial y}\left\{\beta_c A_y k_y[1 + c(p - p^\circ)]\frac{\partial p}{\partial y}\right\}\Delta y$$

$$+ \frac{\partial}{\partial z}\left\{\beta_c A_z k_z[1 + c(p - p^\circ)]\frac{\partial p}{\partial z}\right\}\Delta z + B^\circ\mu q_{sc}$$

$$= \frac{V_b\phi\mu c}{\alpha_c}\frac{\partial p}{\partial t}. \qquad (4.73)$$

Expanding the derivatives on the left side gives

$$[1 + c(p - p^\circ)]\frac{\partial}{\partial x}\left(\beta_c A_x k_x \frac{\partial p}{\partial x}\right)\Delta x + \beta_c A_x k_x c\left(\frac{\partial p}{\partial x}\right)^2\Delta x$$

$$+ [1 + c(p - p^\circ)]\frac{\partial}{\partial y}\left(\beta_c A_y k_y \frac{\partial p}{\partial y}\right)\Delta y + \beta_c A_y k_y c\left(\frac{\partial p}{\partial y}\right)^2\Delta y$$

$$+ [1 + c(p - p^\circ)]\frac{\partial}{\partial z}\left(\beta_c A_z k_z \frac{\partial p}{\partial z}\right)\Delta z + \beta_c A_z k_z c\left(\frac{\partial p}{\partial z}\right)^2\Delta z$$

$$+ B^\circ\mu q_{sc} = \frac{V_b\phi\mu c}{\alpha_c}\frac{\partial p}{\partial t}. \qquad (4.74)$$

In many cases, it can be safely assumed that $[1 + c(p - p^\circ)] \approx 1$ for slightly compressible fluids because c is very small. Consequently,

$$\frac{\partial}{\partial x}\left(\beta_c A_x k_x \frac{\partial p}{\partial x}\right)\Delta x + \frac{\partial}{\partial y}\left(\beta_c A_y k_y \frac{\partial p}{\partial y}\right)\Delta y + \frac{\partial}{\partial z}\left(\beta_c A_z k_z \frac{\partial p}{\partial z}\right)\Delta z$$

$$\gg c\left[\beta_c A_x k_x\left(\frac{\partial p}{\partial x}\right)^2\Delta x + \beta_c A_y k_y\left(\frac{\partial p}{\partial y}\right)^2\Delta y\right.$$

$$+\beta_c A_z k_z\left(\frac{\partial p}{\partial z}\right)^2\Delta z\Bigg]. \quad \text{(4.75)}$$

The previous assumption becomes more explicit if $\Delta x = \Delta y = \Delta z$, $k_x = k_y = k_x$, and $A_x = A_y = A_z$, resulting in

$$\frac{\partial^2 p}{\partial x^2}+\frac{\partial^2 p}{\partial y^2}+\frac{\partial^2 p}{\partial z^2} \gg c\left[\left(\frac{\partial p}{\partial x}\right)^2+\left(\frac{\partial p}{\partial y}\right)^2+\left(\frac{\partial p}{\partial z}\right)^2\right]. \quad \text{(4.76)}$$

The validity of this assumption becomes obvious when one recalls that compressibility, c, is a very small number for slightly compressible liquids and that pressure gradients are also relatively small (hence their squares become even smaller). Obviously, this is true only if $\partial p/\partial s < 1$ psi/ft [kPa/m] for $s = x,y,z$. This condition may be violated in areas of high velocities around wellbores.

Referring to Eq. 4.74, assuming that $[1+c(p-p^\circ)] \approx 1$, and neglecting the square of pressure-gradient terms yields

$$\frac{\partial}{\partial x}\left(\beta_c A_x k_x\frac{\partial p}{\partial x}\right)\Delta x+\frac{\partial}{\partial y}\left(\beta_c A_y k_y\frac{\partial p}{\partial y}\right)\Delta y+\frac{\partial}{\partial z}\left(\beta_c A_z k_z\frac{\partial p}{\partial z}\right)\Delta z$$

$$+B^\circ \mu q_{sc} = \frac{V_b\phi\mu c}{\alpha_c}\frac{\partial p}{\partial t}. \quad \text{(4.77)}$$

Eq. 4.77 represents the flow of a single-phase, slightly compressible liquid in a heterogeneous and anisotropic formation. For a homogeneous and isotropic formation, this equation can be simplified to obtain

$$\frac{\partial^2 p}{\partial x^2}+\frac{\partial^2 p}{\partial y^2}+\frac{\partial^2 p}{\partial z^2}+\frac{B^\circ\mu q_{sc}}{\beta_c k V_b} = \frac{\phi\mu c}{\beta_c\alpha_c k}\frac{\partial p}{\partial t}. \quad \text{(4.78)}$$

Furthermore, if there is no external source/sink (well) in the system, Eq. 4.78 becomes

$$\frac{\partial^2 p}{\partial x^2}+\frac{\partial^2 p}{\partial y^2}+\frac{\partial^2 p}{\partial z^2} = \frac{\phi\mu c}{\beta_c\alpha_c k}\frac{\partial p}{\partial t}. \quad \text{(4.79)}$$

Eq. 4.79 is also known as the diffusivity equation. It should be realized, however, that the flow dynamics described in Eq. 4.79 are not diffusional flow but laminar Darcy flow. Eq. 4.79 is called the diffusivity equation because of the mathematical analogy to diffusional flow. With the same analogy, the coefficient $(\phi\mu c)/(\beta_c\alpha_c k)$, that appears on the right side is often referred to as the inverse of the hydraulic diffusivity constant. A quick check on the dimensionality of this group reveals that the $(\beta_c\alpha_c k)/(\phi\mu c)$ group has the same dimensions as the diffusivity constant, as

$$\left(\frac{\beta_c\alpha_c k}{\phi\mu c}\right)\rightarrow\left[\frac{(\mathrm{L^3/L^3})(\mathrm{L^2})}{(\mathrm{m/Lt})(\mathrm{Lt^2/m})}\right] = (\mathrm{L^2/t})\rightarrow D\left(\frac{\mathrm{L^2}}{\mathrm{t}}\right). \quad \text{(4.80)}$$

In contrast to the incompressible-fluid flow equation, the slightly-compressible-flow equation describes a time-dependent problem so that the solution of Eq. 4.79 yields a pressure surface that is a function of the independent variables x, y, z, and t.

Example 4.6. Write the flow equation in 1D (r direction) radial-cylindrical coordinates for a slightly-compressible liquid in an incompressible, homogeneous, porous medium (k_r = constant).

Solution. Start by writing Eq. 4.42 in the r direction only and assuming that $\vec{\nabla}\Phi = \vec{\nabla}p$.

$$\frac{1}{r}\frac{\partial}{\partial r}\left(r\beta_c\frac{k_r}{\mu B}\frac{\partial p}{\partial r}\right) = \frac{\phi}{\alpha_c}\frac{\partial}{\partial t}\left(\frac{1}{B}\right). \quad \text{(4.81)}$$

On the left and right sides of the equality sign, substitute for $B^{-1} = [1+c(p-p^\circ)]/B^\circ$ to obtain

$$\frac{1}{r}\frac{\partial}{\partial r}\left\{r\beta_c\frac{k_r}{\mu B^\circ}[1+c(p-p^\circ)]\frac{\partial p}{\partial r}\right\}$$

$$= \frac{\phi}{\alpha_c}\frac{\partial}{\partial t}\{[1+c(p-p^\circ)]/B^\circ\}. \quad \text{(4.82)}$$

Invoke the approximation that μ is constant for a slightly compressible liquid; carry the differentiations on both sides of the equation; and treat k_r as a constant.

$$[1+c(p-p^\circ)]\frac{1}{r}\frac{\partial}{\partial r}\left(r\frac{\partial p}{\partial r}\right)+c\left(\frac{\partial p}{\partial r}\right)^2$$

$$= \frac{\phi\mu c}{\beta_c\alpha_c k}\frac{\partial p}{\partial t}. \quad \text{(4.83)}$$

Again, recalling that

$$[1+c(p-p^\circ)] \approx 1 \quad \text{(4.84)}$$

for a small compressibility, c, and realizing that

$$c\left(\frac{\partial p}{\partial r}\right)^2 \ll \frac{1}{r}\frac{\partial}{\partial r}\left(r\frac{\partial p}{\partial r}\right) \quad \text{(4.85)}$$

yields $\frac{1}{r}\frac{\partial}{\partial r}\left(r\frac{\partial p}{\partial r}\right) = \frac{\phi\mu c}{\beta_c\alpha_c k}\frac{\partial p}{\partial t}$. (4.86)

This equation forms the basis of the classic pressure-transient-analysis theory. In writing this equation we assumed that fluid properties are constant, flow is horizontal, pore compressibility is zero, pressure gradients are small, and gravitational effects are negligible.

Example 4.7. Rewrite the slightly-compressible-flow equation in 1D rectangular coordinates for situations when the pore volume varies with pressure.

Solution. When porosity becomes a function of pressure, its variation with time needs to be considered in the flow equations; therefore, we cannot bring the ϕ term out of the time derivative on the right side of the equation. Starting with the original form of the right side of Eq. 4.13, $(V_b/\alpha_c)(\partial/\partial t)(\phi\rho)$, proceed by substituting for $\rho = \rho_{sc}/B$ but do not remove ϕ to the front of the differential operator, $\partial/\partial t$. The net effect of this on the slightly-compressible-flow equation (when written only in the x direction) is

$$\frac{\partial}{\partial x}\left(\beta_c\frac{A_x k_x}{\mu B}\frac{\partial p}{\partial x}\right)\Delta x+q_{sc} = \frac{V_b}{\alpha_c}\frac{\partial}{\partial t}\left(\frac{\phi}{B}\right). \quad \text{(4.87)}$$

Substituting for $(1/B) = [1+c(p-p^\circ)]/B^\circ$ and making the necessary manipulations on the left side, Eq. 4.87 can be written as

$$\frac{\partial}{\partial x}\left(\beta_c A_x k_x\frac{\partial p}{\partial x}\right)\Delta x+B^\circ\mu q_{sc} = \frac{\mu V_b}{\alpha_c}\frac{\partial}{\partial t}\{\phi[1+c(p-p^\circ)]\}. \quad \text{(4.88)}$$

Now, we can concentrate on the right side.

$$\frac{\mu V_b}{\alpha_c}\frac{\partial}{\partial t}\{\phi[1+c(p-p^\circ)]\}$$

$$= \frac{\mu V_b}{\alpha_c}\left\{[1+c(p-p^\circ)]\frac{\partial\phi}{\partial t}+\phi c\frac{\partial p}{\partial t}\right\}. \quad \text{(4.89)}$$

With Eq. 4.89, use the chain rule to write

$$\frac{\partial\phi}{\partial t} = \frac{\partial\phi}{\partial p}\frac{\partial p}{\partial t}. \quad \text{(4.90)}$$

With Eq. 2.35 for pressure-dependent porosity,

$$\phi = \phi^{\circ}[1 + c_R(p - p^{\circ})] \quad \text{.....................} \quad (4.91)$$

yields $\dfrac{\partial \phi}{\partial p} = c_R\phi^{\circ};$ .... (4.92)

therefore, $\dfrac{\partial \phi}{\partial t} = c_R\phi^{\circ}\dfrac{\partial p}{\partial t}.$ .... (4.93)

The right side of Eq. 4.88 can now be expressed as

$$\frac{\mu V_b}{\alpha_c}\frac{\partial}{\partial t}\{\phi[1 + c(p - p^{\circ})]\}$$

$$= \frac{\mu V_b}{\alpha_c}\{[1 + c(p - p^{\circ})]c_R\phi^{\circ} + c\phi\}\frac{\partial p}{\partial t}$$

$$= \frac{\mu V_b}{\alpha_c}[c_R\phi^{\circ} + cc_R\phi^{\circ}(p - p^{\circ}) + c\phi]\frac{\partial p}{\partial t}. \quad \text{......} \quad (4.94)$$

Because both c and c_R are small terms, their product will yield a much smaller term whose contribution to the summation within the brackets will be negligible, ($cc_R \approx 0$). Therefore, the final form of the slightly compressible flow equation in 1D rectangular coordinates is

$$\frac{\partial}{\partial x}\left(\beta_c A_x k_x \frac{\partial p}{\partial x}\right)\Delta x + B^{\circ}\mu q_{sc} = \frac{V_b\phi\mu c_t}{\alpha_c}\frac{\partial p}{\partial t}, \quad \text{.......} \quad (4.95)$$

where c_t = total compressibility of the liquid and the formation,

$$c_t = c + c_R\phi^{\circ}/\phi. \quad \text{..........................} \quad (4.96)$$

In numerical reservoir simulation, the treatment of the accumulation (time-derivative) term is critical for a mass-conservative formulation. Sec. 8.5 discusses the appropriate procedures to handle the expansion of the accumulation term, resulting in a material conservative formulation.

4.4.3 Compressible-Fluid-Flow Equation. For gas flow it is impossible to assume constant compressibility and viscosity. Therefore, the real-gas law is used as an EOS to express the variation of the density of gas with pressure. Starting with Eq. 4.13, substitute for the velocity terms and use Eq. 2.191 for q_{mg} and Eq. 2.83 for B_g,

$$q_{mg} = \alpha_c q_g \rho_g \quad \text{.............................} \quad (4.97)$$

and $\rho_g = \rho_{gsc}/B_g\alpha_c,$ .... (4.98)

to obtain

$$\frac{\partial}{\partial x}\left(\beta_c \frac{\rho_{gsc}A_x k_x}{\alpha_c\mu_g B_g}\frac{\partial p}{\partial x}\right)\Delta x + \frac{\partial}{\partial y}\left(\beta_c \frac{\rho_{gsc}A_y k_y}{\alpha_c\mu_g B_g}\frac{\partial p}{\partial y}\right)\Delta y$$

$$+ \frac{\partial}{\partial z}\left(\beta_c \frac{\rho_{gsc}A_z k_z}{\alpha_c\mu_g B_g}\frac{\partial p}{\partial z}\right)\Delta z + \frac{q_{gsc}}{\alpha_c}\rho_{gsc}$$

$$= \frac{V_b}{\alpha_c}\frac{\partial}{\partial t}\left(\frac{\phi\rho_{gsc}}{\alpha_c B_g}\right). \quad \text{........................} \quad (4.99)$$

Eq. 4.99 assumed that $\vec{\nabla}\Phi = \vec{\nabla}p$. Dividing the entire equation by ϱ_{gsc}/α_c yields

$$\frac{\partial}{\partial x}\left(\beta_c \frac{A_x k_x}{\mu_g B_g}\frac{\partial p}{\partial x}\right)\Delta x + \frac{\partial}{\partial y}\left(\beta_c \frac{A_y k_y}{\mu_g B_g}\frac{\partial p}{\partial y}\right)\Delta y$$

$$+ \frac{\partial}{\partial z}\left(\beta_c \frac{A_z k_z}{\mu_g B_g}\frac{\partial p}{\partial z}\right)\Delta z + q_{gsc}$$

$$= \frac{V_b}{\alpha_c}\frac{\partial}{\partial t}\left(\frac{\phi}{B_g}\right). \quad \text{........................} \quad (4.100)$$

Assuming that porosity is independent of pressure and substituting for the gas-phase FVF (as expressed by Eq. 2.83),

$$B_g = \frac{p_{sc}TZ}{\alpha_c T_{sc}p}, \quad \text{..............................} \quad (4.101)$$

on the right side of Eq. 4.100 yields the final form of the compressible flow equation,

$$\frac{\partial}{\partial x}\left(\beta_c \frac{A_x k_x}{\mu_g B_g}\frac{\partial p}{\partial x}\right)\Delta x + \frac{\partial}{\partial y}\left(\beta_c \frac{A_y k_y}{\mu_g B_g}\frac{\partial p}{\partial y}\right)\Delta y$$

$$+ \frac{\partial}{\partial z}\left(\beta_c \frac{A_z k_z}{\mu_g B_g}\frac{\partial p}{\partial z}\right)\Delta z + q_{gsc}$$

$$= \frac{V_b\phi T_{sc}}{p_{sc}T}\frac{\partial}{\partial t}\left(\frac{p}{Z}\right), \quad \text{........................} \quad (4.102)$$

with the units as reported in Table 4.1. Eq. 4.102 is a nonlinear PDE and can only be solved numerically. The nonlinearity arises from the strong dependency of μ_g, B_g, and Z (compressibility factor) on pressure, the dependent variable.

Example 4.8. Linearization of Eq. 4.102 is possible in several ways. One option is to assume ideal-gas behavior. Simply substitute for B_g in Eq. 4.102, set $Z = 1$, and treat μ as a constant. Can you recognize the resulting equation?

Solution. To simplify the development, consider only 1D flow and substitute $B_g = p_{sc}TZ/\alpha_c T_{sc}p$ with Eq. 4.101 into Eq. 4.102.

$$\frac{\partial}{\partial x}\left(\beta_c \frac{A_x k_x}{\mu_g}\frac{\alpha_c T_{sc}p}{p_{sc}TZ}\frac{\partial p}{\partial x}\right)\Delta x + q_{gsc}$$

$$= \frac{V_b\phi T_{sc}}{p_{sc}T}\frac{\partial}{\partial t}\left(\frac{p}{Z}\right) \quad \text{........................} \quad (4.103)$$

$$\text{or } \frac{\partial}{\partial x}\left(\beta_c A_x k_x \frac{p}{\mu_g Z}\frac{\partial p}{\partial x}\right)\Delta x + q_{gsc}\frac{p_{sc}T}{\alpha_c T_{sc}}$$

$$= \frac{V_b\phi}{\alpha_c}\frac{\partial}{\partial t}\left(\frac{p}{Z}\right). \quad \text{........................} \quad (4.104)$$

For an ideal gas ($Z = 1$ and μ_g is constant), Eq. 4.104 simplifies to

$$\frac{\partial}{\partial x}\left(\beta_c A_x k_x p \frac{\partial p}{\partial x}\right)\Delta x + q_{gsc}\frac{\mu_g p_{sc}T}{\alpha_c T_{sc}}$$

$$= \frac{V_b\mu_g\phi}{\alpha_c}\frac{\partial p}{\partial t}. \quad \text{.........................} \quad (4.105)$$

Recalling that $p\partial p = \tfrac{1}{2}\partial p^2$,

$$\frac{\partial}{\partial x}\left(\beta_c A_x k_x \frac{\partial p^2}{\partial x}\right)\Delta x + q_{gsc}\frac{2\mu_g p_{sc}T}{\alpha_c T_{sc}}$$

$$= \frac{2V_b\mu_g\phi}{\alpha_c}\frac{1}{2p}\frac{\partial p^2}{\partial t}. \quad \text{......................} \quad (4.106)$$

For a homogeneous porous medium with no well,

$$\frac{\partial^2 p^2}{\partial x^2} = \frac{\phi\mu_g}{\beta_c\alpha_c k}\frac{1}{p}\frac{\partial p^2}{\partial t}. \quad \text{......................} \quad (4.107)$$

Again for an ideal gas, $c_g = 1/p$ (see Example 2.4); then

$$\frac{\partial^2 p^2}{\partial x^2} = \frac{\phi\mu_g c_g}{\beta_c\alpha_c k}\frac{\partial p^2}{\partial t}, \quad \text{......................} \quad (4.108)$$

which is the 1D form of the diffusivity equation in the pressure-squared form. This form of the compressible-flow equation has applications in low-pressure gas reservoirs (usually up to 500 psia)

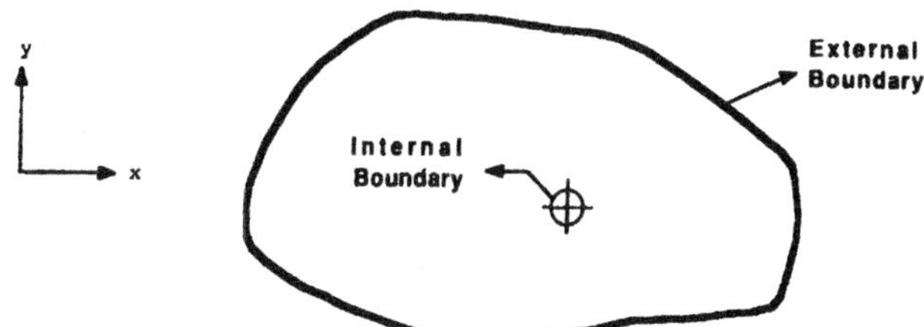

Fig. 4.11—Two-dimensional flow domain with a well.

where real-gas behavior can be approximated effectively by the ideal-gas equation.

4.5 Initial and Boundary Conditions

Sec. 3.3.3 briefly presented initial and boundary conditions with the discussion of basic differential equations. In this section, we deal with this topic in more detail, with specific application to fluid-flow problems. The equations we have studied represent specific physical problems. For example, Eq. 4.59 represents a large class of physical phenomena known as steady-state phenomena. Within the scope of this book, Eq. 4.59 represents the flow of a single-phase, incompressible liquid through an incompressible, 3D porous medium that has homogeneous and isotropic properties. For the sake of discussion, recall that

$$\frac{\partial^2 p}{\partial x^2}+\frac{\partial^2 p}{\partial y^2}+\frac{\partial^2 p}{\partial z^2}=0. \quad \text{(4.59)}$$

Eq. 4.59 has an infinite number of solutions. To choose one particular solution from the infinite set of solutions, additional conditions must be specified at the boundaries of the domain under consideration. These conditions are called boundary conditions. The problem of finding the solution to Eq. 4.59 that satisfies the imposed boundary conditions is called a boundary-value problem.

If the problem is similar to the diffusivity equation,

$$\frac{\partial^2 p}{\partial x^2}+\frac{\partial^2 p}{\partial y^2}+\frac{\partial^2 p}{\partial z^2}=\frac{\phi\mu c}{\beta_c\alpha_c k}\frac{\partial p}{\partial t}, \quad \text{(4.79)}$$

which describes a time-dependent (unsteady-state flow) phenomenon, the boundary conditions must be satisfied for all times $t \geqq 0$. In the case of Eq. 4.79, the initial conditions must also be satisfied at every point of the domain at the particular instant of time when the physical process begins, $t=0$. The problem of finding the solution of Eq. 4.79 that satisfies the specified boundary conditions and initial conditions is called an initial-boundary-value problem.

Consider the two-dimensional (2D) flow domain shown in **Fig. 4.11** for a well located in the central portion of the field. The flow domain described by Eq. 4.79 is the area between the limits of the reservoir and the wellbore. Therefore, we can group the boundaries under two general names: external, which are the physical boundaries of the flow domain, and internal, which are the wellbores. Any specification of boundary conditions for the PDE's developed in this chapter should provide a description of the geometric shape of the boundary and the locations of the wellbores. We now review the various boundary conditions that are encountered in fluid-flow problems in porous media.

4.5.1 Pressure Specified on the Boundary—Dirichlet Problem. At the internal boundaries, or wellbores, this specification implies a well producing (or injecting) at a constant sandface pressure. On the other hand, at the external boundaries, such a specification implies that the pressure on the boundary remains constant. This type of boundary condition occurs in reservoirs that are constantly charged by strong water influx so that the pressure at the interface between the hydrocarbon reservoir and the supporting aquifer remains constant. In the theory of PDE's, the problem of finding a solution for a domain with a pressure specification on its boundaries is known as the Dirichlet problem. **Fig. 4.12** shows a typical Dirichlet problem.

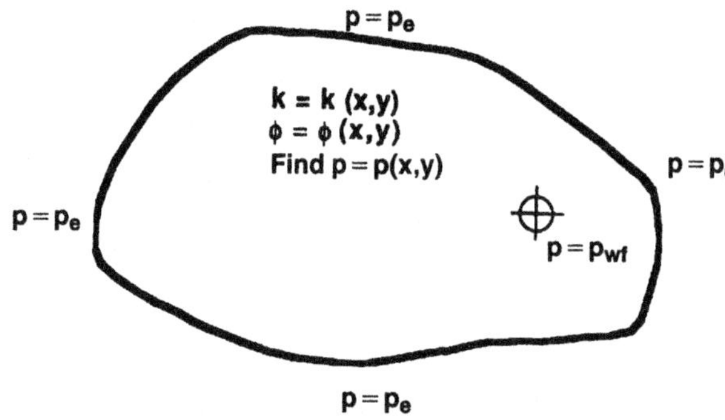

Fig. 4.12—Steady-state Dirichlet problem.

4.5.2 Pressure Gradient Specified on the Boundary—Neumann Problem. By specifying a pressure gradient normal to the boundary, the flux (or velocity) normal to the boundary is prescribed. Therefore, a constant-flow-rate specification at the wellbore is equivalent to specifying the pressure gradient at the sandface. This statement can be understood better if one considers Darcy's law written at the sandface of a well,

$$q=\frac{-2\pi\beta_c r_w kh}{\mu}\frac{dp}{dr}\Big|_{r=r_w}. \quad \text{(4.109)}$$

Eq. 4.109 can be rearranged to solve for the pressure gradient as

$$\frac{dp}{dr}\Big|_{r=r_w}=-\frac{q\mu}{2\pi\beta_c r_w kh}. \quad \text{(4.110)}$$

In Eq. 4.110, μ, r_w, k, and h are problem specific and, by specifying a constant flow rate (fixing the value of q), one simply specifies the value of $(dp/dr)|_{r=r_w}$. Note that q is the sandface rate in Eq. 4.110.

Again, the specification of the pressure gradient along an external boundary results in the specification of the flux normal to the boundary. A special case often encountered in reservoir engineering is the no-flow boundary where the flux vanishes everywhere on the boundary. Obviously, if flow across the boundary does not exist, this implies that the pressure gradient across the boundary is also zero. A volumetric reservoir with completely sealed outer boundaries is equivalent to a zero pressure gradient across its outer boundaries.

The problem of solving for the pressure distribution in a domain with a pressure-gradient specification across its boundaries is known as the Neumann problem. **Fig. 4.13** shows a typical Neumann problem schematically.

4.5.3 Pressure Gradient and Pressure Specifications on the Boundary. Sometimes both the potential and its first derivative are prescribed on different segments of the boundary. Such a condition is possible when we are dealing with a porous medium that has a semipervious (leaking) boundary. Under these conditions, the Dirichlet-type boundary condition is prescribed over a part of the boundary and the Neumann condition is prescribed over the remainder of the boundary. An oil reservoir that is partially exposed to a strong aquifer is a typical example of the mixed-boundary-condition specification (**Fig. 4.14**).

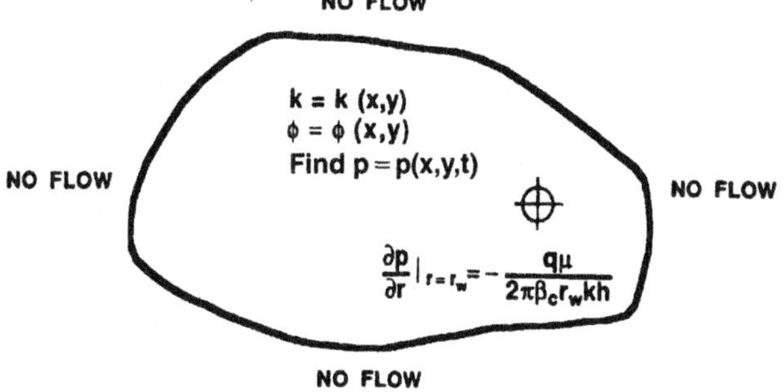

Fig. 4.13—Unsteady-state Neumann problem.

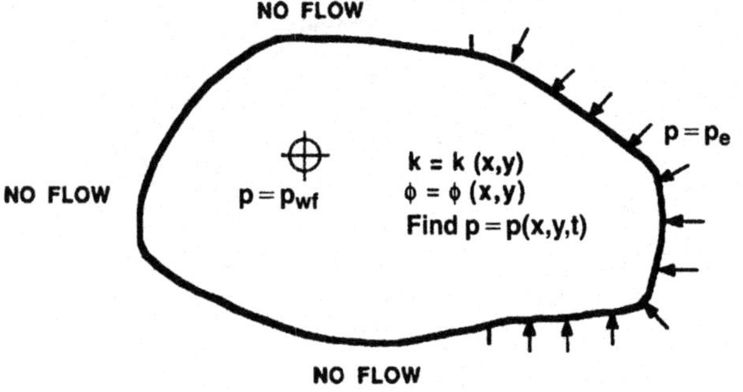

Fig. 4.14—Mixed-boundary-condition specification.

In time-dependent problems (unsteady-state flow), the boundary conditions must be specified for all $t \geqq 0$. For these problems, the boundary conditions can also become a function of time. For example, a well that was put on production at a constant rate, shut in for a period of time, and finally put on production at another rate illustrates a situation where the imposed boundary conditions are a function of time.

To complete the mathematical description of the problem, we must specify the initial condition for the time-dependent variables. This is accomplished by specifying the pressures at each point at the initial time. Generally, initial pressures are specified at a specific datum depth and the existing hydrostatic gradients are used to initialize the problem at other depths. Secs. 9.7.1 and 9.7.2 present detailed discussions of initial and boundary conditions in multiphase flow.

The nature and magnitude of the boundary and initial conditions are governed by the physical problem at hand. A PDE with proper boundary and initial conditions will define a well-posed problem if the solution exists and is unique. If the mathematical problem and its solution satisfy these requirements, then we have a properly formulated problem and we can proceed with a numerical solution. Obviously, some rigorous tests may be necessary to verify that the solution generated fulfills these necessary conditions. However, because these tests are beyond the scope of this book, we implicitly assume that we are always dealing with a well-posed problem.

Example 4.9. Consider **Fig. 4.15**, which shows 1D, single-phase, steady-state flow taking place in homogeneous, porous medium. Which of the following boundary conditions are appropriate?

1. $p=p_0$ at $x=0$; $p=p_L$ at $x=L$
2. $q=C_0$ at $x=0$; $q=C_L$ at $x=L$
3. $q=C_0$ at $x=0$; $p=p_0$ at $x=0$
4. $q=C_0$ at $x=0$; $p=p_L$ at $x=L$

Solution. To analyze this problem, it is necessary to realize that the pressure distribution $p=p(x)$ is a linear function of x. This can be verified easily by integrating $\partial^2 p/\partial x^2=0$ twice.

The first integration yields

$$\frac{\partial p}{\partial x} = m_1, \quad (4.111)$$

and the second integration yields

$$p = m_1 x + m_2, \quad (4.112)$$

where m_1 and m_2 = two integration constants to be determined from the two boundary conditions.

1. At $x=0$, $p=p_0$, implying that $p_0=m_2$; at $x=L$, $p=p_L$, implying that $p_L=m_1 L+m_2$; and $m_1=(p_L-p_0)/L$. Then, the formal solution is

$$p = \frac{(p_L - p_0)x}{L} + p_0. \quad (4.113)$$

Eq. 4.113 provides a unique solution to the problem; therefore, the conditions given in Part 1 are well posed.

2. At $x=0$, $q=C_0$, implying that

$$\frac{\partial p}{\partial x}\Big|_{x=0} = -C_0\frac{\mu}{\beta_c Ak}; \quad (4.114)$$

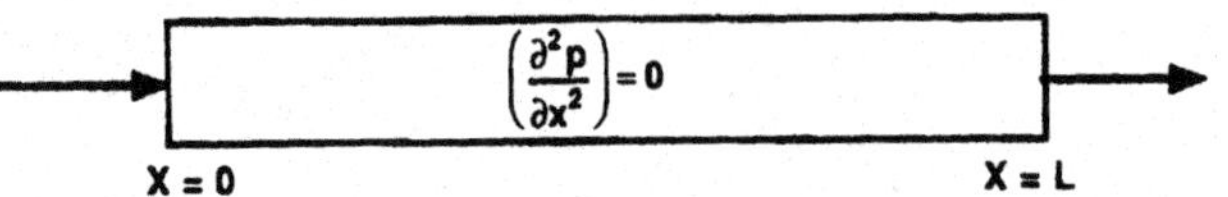

Fig. 4.15—One-dimensional steady-state flow problem.

and at $x=L$, $q=C_L$, implying that

$$\frac{\partial p}{\partial x}\Big|_{x=L} = -C_L\frac{\mu}{\beta_c Ak}. \quad (4.115)$$

Because the variation of pressure with position is a linear function of x, $(\partial p/\partial x)|_{x=0}$ must equal $(\partial p/\partial x)|_{x=L}$. If $C_0 \neq C_L$, this requirement is violated. In other words, this specification will either be inconsistent or redundant. If it is inconsistent, it is obvious that the problem is ill posed. Further analysis of the redundant case also shows that this problem is ill posed. This is because in the redundant case, we basically have only one piece of information: $C=C_0=C_L$, which implies that

$$\frac{\partial p}{\partial x}\Big|_{x=0} = \frac{\partial p}{\partial x}\Big|_{x=L} \quad (4.116a)$$

and

$$\frac{\partial p}{\partial x}\Big|_{x=0} = \frac{-C\mu}{\beta_c Ak}, \quad (4.116b)$$

or, from Eq. 4.111, that $m_1 = -C\mu/\beta_c Ak$. Now, because we have used all our information on the boundaries, we do not have any available information to evaluate m_2 in Eq. 4.112. The best we can do is

$$p = \frac{-C\mu}{\beta_c Ak}x + m_2, \quad (4.117)$$

which is nonunique because every value of the constant m_2 will result in a different solution to the problem. Because uniqueness is a property of a well-posed problem, the conditions given in Part 2 will always be ill posed.

3. At $x=0$, $q=C_0$, implying that

$$\frac{\partial p}{\partial x}\Big|_{x=0} = -C_0\frac{\mu}{\beta_c Ak}; \quad (4.118)$$

from Eq. 4.111, $m_1 = -C_0\mu/\beta_c Ak$; and at $x=0$, $p=p_0$, implying that $m_2=p_0$ (from Eq. 4.112). Then, the formal solution is

$$p = -C_0\frac{\mu}{\beta_c Ak}x + p_0. \quad (4.119)$$

Here again, the problem is well posed.

4. At $x=0$, $q=C_0$, implying that (from Eq. 4.111), $m_1 = -C_0\mu/\beta_c Ak$; and at $x=L$, $p=p_L$, implying that (from Eq. 4.112)

$$p_L = -C_0\frac{\mu}{\beta_c Ak}L + m_2 \quad (4.120)$$

or

$$m_2 = p_L + C_0\frac{\mu}{\beta_c Ak}L. \quad (4.121)$$

Then, the formal solution is

$$p = -C_0\frac{\mu}{\beta_c Ak}x + p_L + C_0\frac{\mu}{\beta_c Ak}L \quad (4.122)$$

$$= C_0\frac{\mu}{\beta_c Ak}(L - x) + p_L.$$

Here again, the problem is well posed.

4.6 Chapter Project

Initially, we consider the A-1 reservoir to be a single-phase reservoir and study the single-phase-flow problem for incompressible, slightly compressible, and compressible fluids. Chap. 9 discusses multi-

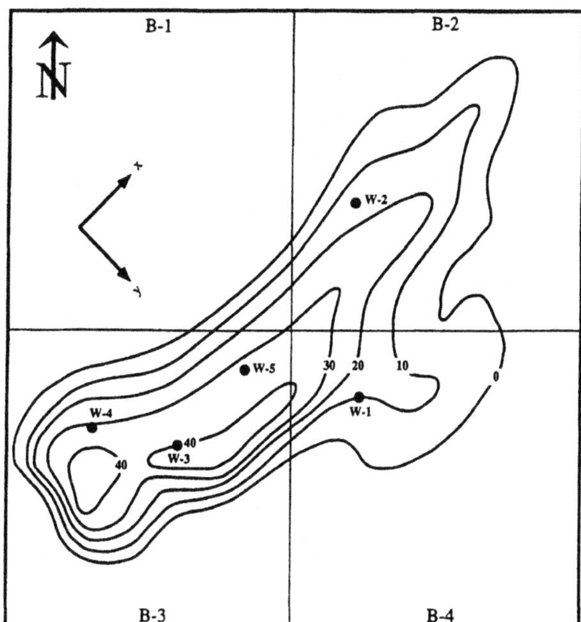

Fig. 4.16—A-1 reservoir and positioning of the axes of the coordinate system with respect to geographical directions.

phase-flow problems. As Chap. 5 shows, a 2D rectangular grid model is used to describe the A-1 reservoir.

The rectangular coordinate system is set in such a manner that the x and y directions of the coordinate system coincide with the main flow directions. Recall from Chap. 2 that the main flow directions are identified as southwest-northeast and southeast-northwest. Accordingly, the axes of the rectangular coordinate system are placed parallel to the southwest-northeast and southeast-northwest directions, respectively (**Fig. 4.16**). In this way, the four-component permeability tensor in a 2D space is approximated with a permeability vector with two entries, k_x and k_y. The two directions with the largest and smallest permeability values are identified as the x and y directions, respectively (refer to Sec. 2.6.2, where the southeast-northwest directional permeability is reported as the 80% of the southwest-northeast directional permeability).

4.6.1 Incompressible-Fluid-Flow Formulation for the A-1 Reservoir. The 2D incompressible single-phase-fluid-flow equation for the A-1 reservoir can be obtained directly from Eq. 4.55 by dropping the z-direction term. This yields

$$\frac{\partial}{\partial x}\left(A_x k_x \frac{\partial \Phi}{\partial x}\right)\Delta x + \frac{\partial}{\partial y}\left(A_y k_y \frac{\partial \Phi}{\partial y}\right)\Delta y + \frac{\mu}{\beta_c} q_{sc} = 0. \quad \text{(4.123)}$$

Because A_x, k_x, A_y, and k_y are kept within the differential operators $\partial/\partial x$ and $\partial/\partial y$, we can accommodate the heterogeneous nature of the system. Furthermore, the existing anisotropy of the system is maintained by assigning directional subscripts x and y to the area and permeability terms.

4.6.2 Slightly-Incompressible-Fluid-Flow Formulation for the A-1 Reservoir. This time, we start with the general form of the slightly-compressible-fluid equation as given by Eq. 4.71. Again, dropping the z-direction term to describe the flow problem in a 2D (x and y directions only) flow domain yields

$$\frac{\partial}{\partial x}\left(\frac{A_x k_x}{\mu B}\frac{\partial \Phi}{\partial x}\right)\Delta x + \frac{\partial}{\partial y}\left(\frac{A_y k_y}{\mu B}\frac{\partial \Phi}{\partial y}\right)\Delta y + \frac{q_{sc}}{\beta_c}$$

$$= \frac{V_b \phi c}{\beta_c \alpha_c B^\circ}\frac{\partial p}{\partial t}. \quad \text{(4.124)}$$

4.6.3 Compressible Fluid Flow Formulation for the A-1 Reservoir. For this case, the starting equation is Eq. 4.102, which, when written in two dimensions, gives

$$\frac{\partial}{\partial x}\left(\frac{A_x k_x}{\mu_g B_g}\frac{\partial p}{\partial x}\right)\Delta x + \frac{\partial}{\partial y}\left(\frac{A_y k_y}{\mu_g B_g}\frac{\partial p}{\partial y}\right)\Delta y + \frac{q_{gsc}}{\beta_c}$$

$$= \frac{V_b \phi T_{sc}}{\beta_c p_{sc} T}\frac{\partial}{\partial t}\left(\frac{p}{Z}\right). \quad \text{(4.125)}$$

Eq. 4.125 ignores the hydrostatic head of the gas column because the density of gas is low. This results in $\vec{\nabla}\Phi = \vec{\nabla}p$. Note that the nonlinearity of the PDE is retained by treating μ_g, B_g, and Z as functions of the dependent variable p.

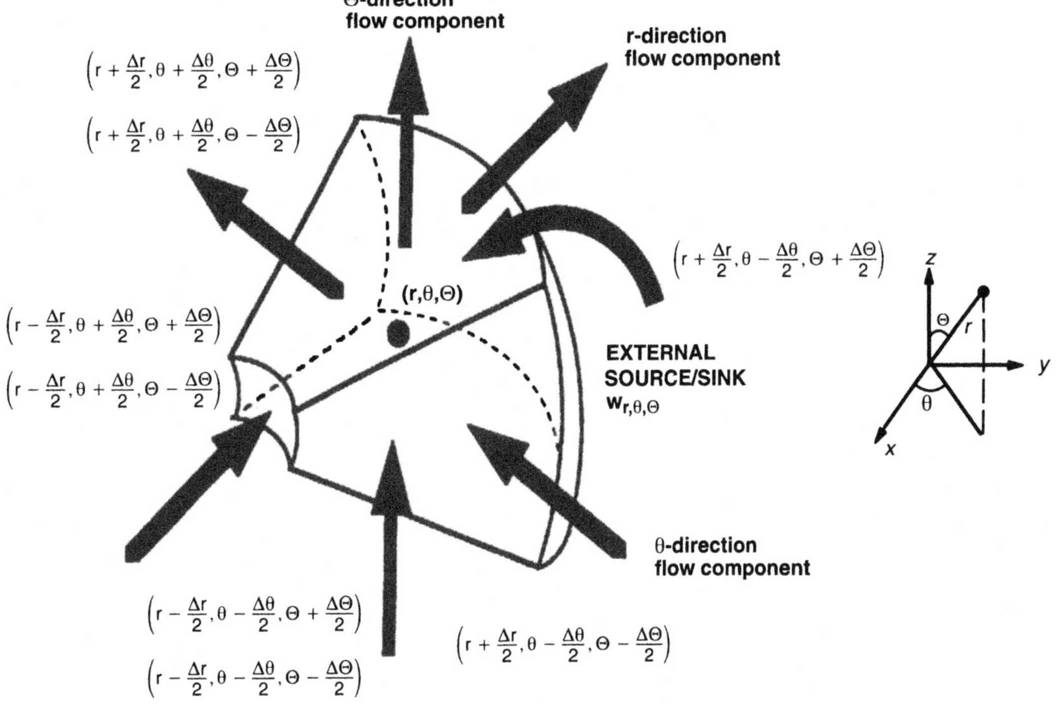

Fig. 4.17—Control volume in spherical coordinates.

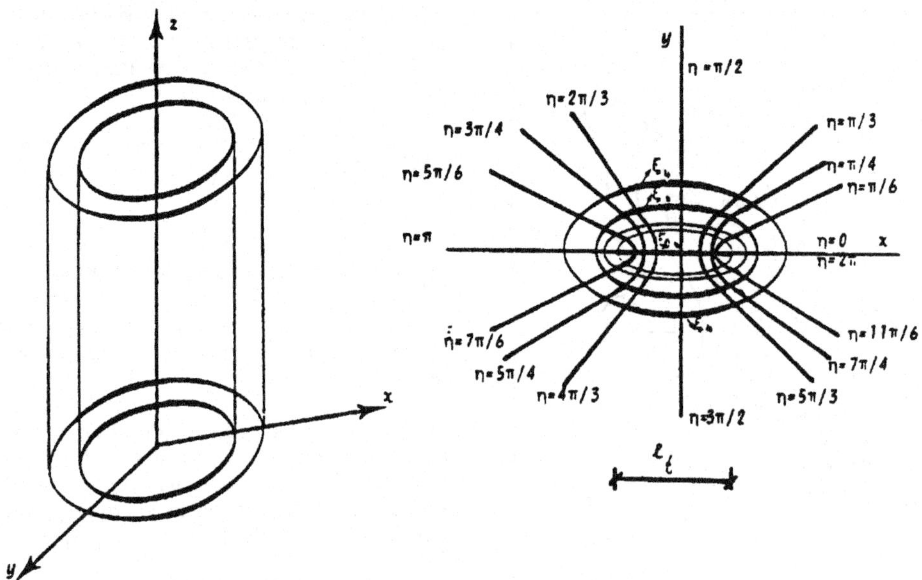

Fig. 4.18—Elliptic-cylindrical coordinates.

Exercises

4.1 Develop the single-phase-flow equation in 3D spherical coordinates. To develop the mass balance, use the elementary volume shown in **Fig. 4.17.** (Spherical-flow geometry is encountered around the perforations as well as around wells that are partially penetrating a thick formation.)

4.2 Develop the 3D Laplace equation in the elliptic-cylindrical coordinates (ξ, η, z) shown in **Fig. 4.18.** (The elliptic-cylindrical coordinate system is practical for analyzing fluid-flow dynamics in porous media with a vertical fracture plane along the well. Furthermore, in distinctly anisotropic formations, equipotential lines are developed as confocal ellipses rather than concentric circles.) Functional relationships between the rectangular and elliptical coordinate systems are $x = l_f \cosh \xi \cos \eta$, $y = l_f \sinh \xi \sin \eta$, and $z = z$, where $\xi \geqq 0$, $0 \leqq \eta \leqq 2\pi$, and $-\infty < z < +\infty$.

4.3 Derive Eq. 4.40 from Eq. 4.12 using coordinate transformation. Note that $x = r\cos\theta$, $y = r\sin\theta$, and $z = z$.

4.4 Derive Eq. 4.12 from Eq. 4.40 using coordinate transformation.

4.5 Give a complete mathematical description of the unsteady-state radial flow converging to a fully penetrating well with radius r_w producing at a constant rate q_{sc} for the following.

1. An infinitely large homogeneous reservoir.
2. A finite reservoir with constant pressure at the outer boundary.
3. A finite reservoir with no flow at the outer boundary.

4.6 Consider the following 1D, horizontal, porous medium in which steady-state flow of oil is taking place in the positive x direction. Note that there is no well in the system (**Fig. 4.19**). The permeability of the system varies according to the expression $k_x = (1{,}000) \div (980 + 0.04x)$, where x is in feet and k_x is in darcies. It is also known that at $x = 0$, $p = p_w$, and, at $x = L$, $p = p_L$ (pressures are in psia). If the viscosity of oil is μ_o cp and the dimensions of the porous medium are h, b, and L, give a complete mathematical statement for the problem and obtain an expression that describes the pressure gradient at any point in the porous medium.

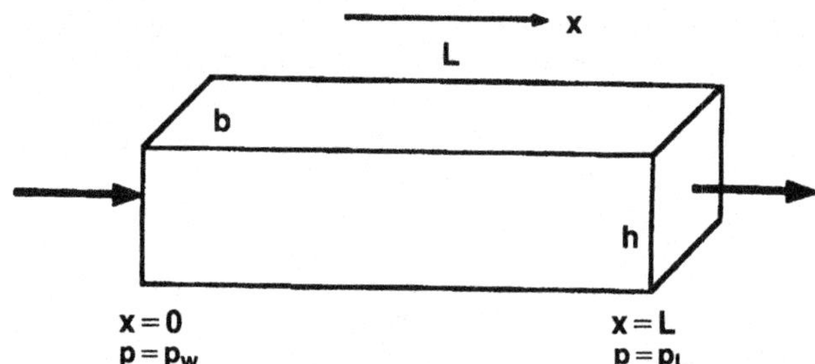

Fig. 4.19—One-dimensional reservoir in Exercise 4.6.

4.7 The PDE $\partial^2 p/\partial x^2 = 400$ describes a specific fluid-flow problem in porous media with the boundary conditions $p(x = 0) = 200$ psia and $p(x = 100) = 100$ psia. After examining the given mathematical formulation, describe the flow problem to the fullest extent.

4.8 Given $A_x = A_y = 100$ ft^2, $\Delta x = 200$ ft, $\Delta y = 100$ ft, $k_y = 100$ md, and $\mu = 1$ cp, and the PDE $(\partial^2 p/\partial x^2) + ½(\partial^2 p/\partial y^2) = 0$ that describes the fluid-flow problem in the homogeneous system, what is the permeability of the system along the x direction?

4.9 Consider the equation

$$\left(1 + \frac{a}{p}\right)\frac{\partial}{\partial x}\left(\frac{A_x}{\mu_g B_g}\frac{\partial p}{\partial x}\right)\Delta x - \frac{A_x}{\mu_g B_g}\frac{a}{p^2}\left(\frac{\partial p}{\partial x}\right)^2\Delta x$$

$$= \frac{1}{\beta_c \alpha_c}\frac{V_b}{k_\infty}\frac{\partial}{\partial t}\left(\frac{\phi}{B_g}\right).$$

Show that this PDE represents real-gas flow in a 1D porous system without wells if the permeability pressure dependence is described by the Klinkenberg equation, $k(p) = k_\infty(1 + a/p)$, where k_∞ and a are constants.

4.10 After examining the PDE $(\partial/\partial x)[k_x(\partial p/\partial x)] + \partial^2 p/\partial y^2 = -1$ and **Fig. 4.20**, describe the flow problem quantitatively and qualitatively to the fullest extent.

4.11 A fluid-flow problem in a porous medium is expressed by the PDE $(\partial/\partial x)[1.127A_x k_x(\partial p/\partial x)] - 0.0433(\partial/\partial x)(1.127A_x k_x) = 0$. If properties of the flowing fluid are $\mu = 1$ cp, $B = 1$ RB/STB, and $\rho = 62.4$ lbm/ft^3, describe the physical characteristics of the reservoir qualitatively and quantitatively.

4.12 The differential equation $(1/r)(\partial/\partial r)[r\beta_c k_r(\partial\Phi/\partial r)] = 0$ describes 1D, single-phase, incompressible flow in a circular, homogeneous reservoir.

1. For the boundary conditions shown in **Fig. 4.21**, obtain an expression that gives the potential distribution as a function of radius.
2. Using the solution to Part 1, determine the flow rate into the well.
3. What is the flow rate across the outer boundary of the system?

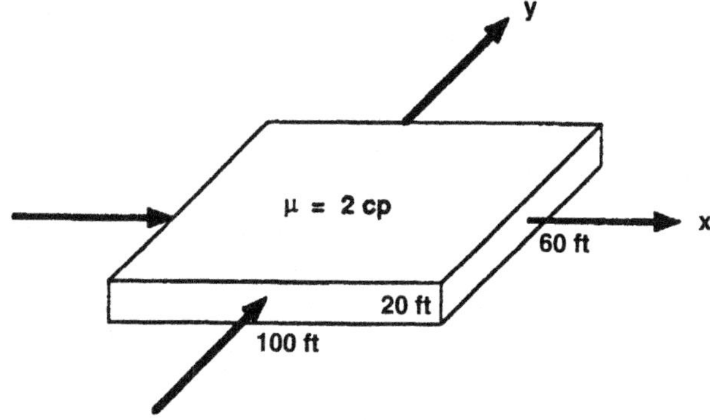

Fig. 4.20—Two-dimensional reservoir in Exercise 4.10.

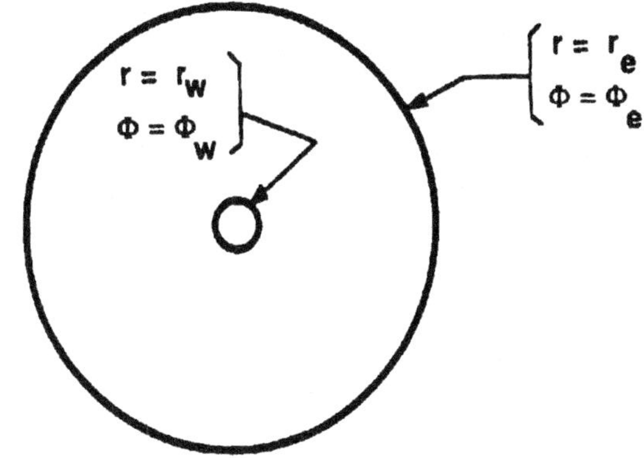

Fig. 4.21—Reservoir in Exercise 4.12.

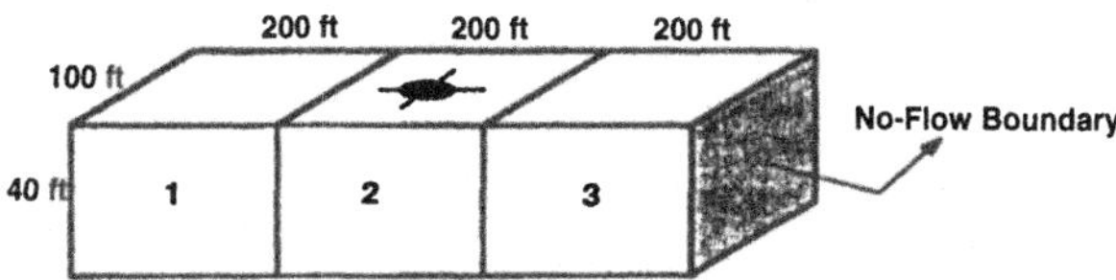

Fig. 4.22—Discretized 1D reservoir in Exercise 4.13.

4.13 Consider the incompressible-fluid-flow problem in the 1D porous body shown in **Fig. 4.22** (viscosity of the fluid is 2.0 cp).

1. If the well in Block 2 is produced at a steady flow rate of 450 STB/D and this rate creates a pressure distribution of $p_1 = 2{,}400$ psia, $p_2 = 800$ psia, and $p_3 = 800$ psia, what is the permeability of this linear, homogeneous system?

2. What kind of boundary condition would you assign to the extreme left end of the system? Quantify your answer.

3. If all the length dimensions of the Blocks 1, 2, and 3 are doubled, what would the flow rate into the well be if the same pressure distribution is assigned to the new system?

4. Assume that the viscosity of the fluid of Part 1 is 4 cp and the wellblock pressure is maintained at 800 psia. What would the well flow rate and the pressures in Blocks 1 and 3 be if the extreme ends of the system represent no-flow boundaries?

4.14 Linearize the compressible-flow equation, Eq. 4.102, by use of the transformation

$$m = \int_o^p \frac{p}{\mu Z} dp.$$

Hint: Substitute the definition of B_g into Eq. 4.102 before applying the above transformation.

4.15 Does $\partial^2 p / \partial x^2 = 0$ represent any fluid-flow problem in porous media? If it does, provide a full description of the problem.

4.16 Give the simplest form of the PDE that governs the flow of an incompressible fluid in a 2D homogeneous but anisotropic formation with no depth gradients. Assume that no well is in the reservoir.

4.17 The surface properties, such as surface tension, interfacial tension, and specific surface area, play important roles on fluid-flow dynamics in porous media. Explain why these properties do not appear in the fluid-flow equations.

4.18 Show that $-(\partial/\partial x)(\rho u_x) = \rho\phi(c + c_R)(\partial p/\partial t)$ represents the 1D form of the continuity equation for single-phase flow where porosity is treated as a function of pressure. In this equation, c and c_R represent the fluid and pore compressibilities, respectively.

Nomenclature

a = constant
A = cross-sectional area normal to flow, L^2, ft² [m²]
A_r = cross-sectional area normal to r direction, L^2, ft² [m²]
A_x = cross-sectional area normal to x direction, L^2, ft² [m²]
A_y = cross-sectional area normal to y direction, L^2, ft² [m²]
A_z = cross-sectional area normal to z direction, L^2, ft² [m²]
A_θ = cross-sectional area normal to θ direction, L^2, ft² [m²]
b = width, L, ft [m]
B = FVF, L^3/L^3, reservoir volume/volume at standard conditions
B_g = gas FVF, L^3/L^3, RB/scf [m³/std m³]
B_o = oil FVF, L^3/L^3, RB/STB [m³/std m³]
B_w = water FVF, L^3/L^3, RB/B [m³/std m³]
B° = FVF at reference pressure and reservoir temperature, L^3/L^3 RB/STB [m³/std m³]
c = compressibility, Lt^2/m, psi⁻¹ [kPa⁻¹]
c_g = gas compressibility, Lt^2/m, psi⁻¹ [kPa⁻¹]
c_R = reservoir rock compressibility, Lt^2/m, psi⁻¹ [kPa⁻¹]
C = constant
C_L, C_0 = constants in Example 4.9
D = diffusivity, L^2/t, ft²/D [m²/d]
g = acceleration of gravity, L/t^2, ft/s² [m/s²]
h = thickness, L, ft [m]
k = permeability, L^2, darcy [μm²]
k_r = permeability in the r direction, L^2, darcy [μm²]
k_x = permeability in the direction of the x axis, L^2, darcy [μm²]
k_y = permeability in the direction of the y axis, L^2, darcy [μm²]
k_z = permeability in the direction of the z axis, L^2, darcy [μm²]
k_∞ = gas permeability at infinite pressure, L^2, darcy [μm²]
k_θ = θ-direction permeability, L^2, darcy [μm²]
l_f = total fracture length (Exercise 4.2), L, ft [m]
L = distance, displacement, L, ft [m]
m = mass per unit volume of porous medium, m/L^3, lbm/ft³ [kg/m³]
m_a = mass accumulated, or mass of excess material stored in or depleted from the control volume over a time interval, m, lbm [kg]

m_i = mass in, or mass of component entering the control volume from other parts of the reservoir, m, lbm [kg]
m_o = mass out, or mass of component leaving the control volume to other parts of the reservoir, m, lbm [kg]
m_s = sink/source, or mass of component leaving or entering the control volume externally (through wells), m, lbm [kg]
$\vec{\dot{m}}$ = mass flux vector, m/L²t, lbm/(D-ft²)[kg/(d · m²)]
$\dot{m}_x$ = x component of mass flux vector, m/L²t, lbm/(D-ft²)[kg/(d · m²)]
$\dot{m}_y$ = y component of mass flux vector, m/L²t, lbm/(D-ft²)[kg/(d · m²)]
$\dot{m}_z$ = z component of mass flux vector, m/L²t, lbm/(D-ft²)[kg/(d · m²)]
p = pressure, m/Lt², psia [kPa]
p_e = pressure at external reservoir boundaries, m/Lt², psia [kPa]
p_o = reference pressure, m/Lt², psia [kPa]
p_w = pressure at $x=0$, m/Lt², psia [kPa]
p_{wf} = flowing well bottomhole pressure, m/Lt², psia [kPa]
p° = reference pressure, m/Lt², psia [kPa]
$\vec{\nabla} p$ = pressure gradient vector, m/L²t², psi/ft [kPa/m]
q = production or flow rate, L³/t, RB/D [m³/d]
q_g = gas production rate, L³/t, RB/D [m³/d]
q_{gsc} = gas production rate at standard conditions, L³/t, scf/D [std m³/d]
q_m = mass production rate, m/t, lbm/D [kg/d]
q_{mg} = mass production rate of gas, m/t, lbm/D [kg/d]
q_{osc} = oil production rate at standard conditions, L³/t, STB/D [std m³/d]
q_{sc} = production rate at standard conditions, L³/t, STB/D [std m³/d]
q_{wsc} = water flow rate at standard conditions, L³/t, B/D [std m³/d]
r = distance in radial direction in both cylindrical and spherical coordinate systems, L, ft [m]
r_e = radius of external boundary, L, ft [m]
r_w = well radius, L, ft [m]
R_s = solution-gas/oil ratio, L³/L³, scf/STB [std m³/std m³]
Δr = difference along r direction ($\Delta r = r_{i+1} - r_i$), L, ft [m]
S = saturation, fraction
t = time, t, days
Δt = time interval ($\Delta t = t^{n+1} - t^n$), t, days
T = absolute temperature, T, °R [K]
T_{sc} = standard condition temperature, T, °R [K]
u_r = superficial velocity component in r direction, L/t, RB/(D-ft²) [m³/(d · m²)]
u_x = superficial velocity component in x direction, L/t, RB/(D-ft²) [m³/(d · m²)]
u_y = superficial velocity component in y direction, L/t, RB/(D-ft²) [m³/(d · m²)]
u_z = superficial velocity component in z direction, L/t, RB/(D-ft²) [m³/(d · m²)]
u_θ = superficial velocity component in θ direction, L/t, RB/(D-ft²) [m³/(d · m²)]
V_b = bulk volume, control volume, or gridblock bulk volume, L³, ft³ [m³]
$\vec{w}$ = mass flow rate vector, m/t, lbm/D [kg/d]
w_r = mass flow rate component in r direction, m/t, lbm/D [kg/d]
w_x = mass flow rate component in x direction, m/t, lbm/D [kg/d]
w_y = mass flow rate component in y direction, m/t, lbm/D [kg/d]
w_z = mass flow rate component in z direction, m/t, lbm/D [kg/d]
x = distance in x direction in the Cartesian coordinate system, L, ft [m]
Δx = control volume dimension along the x direction ($\Delta x = x_{i+½} - x_{i-½}$), L, ft [m]
y = distance in y direction in the Cartesian coordinate system, L, ft [m]
Δy = control volume dimension along y direction ($\Delta y = y_{j+½} - y_{j-½}$), L, ft [m]
z = distance in z direction in the Cartesian coordinate system, L, ft [m]
Z = gas-compressibility factor ($Z = pM/\varrho RT$), dimensionless
Δz = control volume dimension along z direction ($\Delta z = z_{k+½} - z_{k-½}$), L, ft [m]
α_c = volume conversion factor whose numerical value is given in Table 4.1
β_c = transmissibility conversion factor whose numerical value is given in Table 4.1
γ = gravity defined by Eq. 2.2, m/L²t², psi/ft [kPa/m]
γ_c = gravity conversion factor whose numerical value is given in Table 4.1
Δ = difference, difference operator
η = the η coordinate in the elliptic-cylindrical coordinate system
θ = angle in θ direction in both cylindrical and spherical coordinate systems, rad [rad]
Θ = the Θ coordinate in the spherical coordinate system
μ = viscosity, m/Lt, cp [Pa · s]
μ_g = gas viscosity, m/Lt, cp [Pa · s]
ρ_g = gas-phase density, m/L³, lbm/ft³ [kg/m³]
ρ_{gsc} = gas-phase density at standard conditions, m/L³, lbm/ft³ [kg/m³]
ρ_{sc} = density at standard conditions, m/L³, lbm/ft³ [kg/m³]
ϕ = porosity, fraction
Φ = potential, m/Lt², psia [kPa]
Φ_e = potential at external radius, m/Lt², psia [kPa]
Φ_w = potential at well radius, m/Lt², psia [kPa]
$\vec{\nabla}\Phi$ = potential gradient vector, m/L²t², psi/ft [kPa/m]
Ψ = streamline function
ξ = the ξ coordinate in the elliptic-cylindrical coordinate system
$\vec{\nabla}$ = gradient operator

Superscripts

° = reference
→ = vector

References

1. Odeh, A.S.: "An Overview of Mathematical Modeling of the Behavior of Hydrocarbon Reservoirs," *Soc. of Industrial and Applied Mathematics Review* (1982) **24,** No. 3, 263.
2. Muskat, M.: *The Flow of Homogeneous Fluids Through Porous Media*, Intl. Human Resources Development Corp., Boston, Massachusetts (1982) 470.
3. Bear, J.: *Dynamics of Fluids in Porous Media*, Dover Publications Inc., New York City (1988) 196.

SI Metric Conversion Factors

cp	× 1.0*	E − 03 = Pa · s
ft	× 3.048*	E − 01 = m
ft²	× 9.290 304*	E − 02 = m²
md	× 9.869 233	E − 04 = μm²
psi	× 6.894 757	E + 00 = kPa

*Conversion factor is exact.

Chapter 5
Finite-Difference Approximation to Linear-Flow Equations

5.1 Introduction

Chap. 4 derived the equations for single-phase flow through porous media—partial-differential equations (PDE's) that are second order in space and first order in time. In general, these equations cannot be solved analytically (exactly) because of their nonlinear nature. Numerical (approximate) techniques must be used to solve the flow equations. The most popular numerical method currently in use in the oil industry is the finite-difference method.

The finite-difference method is implemented by superimposing a finite-difference grid over the reservoir to be modeled. The chosen grid system is then used to approximate the spatial derivatives in the continuous equations. These approximations are obtained by truncating the Taylor series expansion of the unknown variables (usually pressure for single-phase-flow problems and pressure and saturation for two-phase-flow problems) in the equations, as discussed in Sec. 3.4.2. A similar procedure is used in the time domain.

Two types of grid systems are generally used in reservoir simulation: block centered (body centered) and point distributed (mesh centered). Although these grid systems are discussed in terms of rectangular (Cartesian) coordinates, they are equally applicable in any coordinate system—cylindrical, spherical, or elliptical. Sec. 5.2 discusses these grid systems.

Implementation of finite-difference approximations result in algebraic equations called finite-difference equations. It should be emphasized that the solutions of the finite-difference equations can be obtained only at the discrete points defined by the grid system. In other words, pressures calculated from a reservoir simulator are known only at gridpoints within the reservoir. This is in contrast to the solutions of the continuous equations, which can be obtained at all points in the reservoir.

Discretization is the process of converting continuous equations into finite-difference equations. **Fig. 5.1** shows the discretization step in the development of a finite-difference simulator.

Chap. 4 derived the transport equations describing unsteady-state flow; these equations contain a second derivative of pressure with respect to space and a first derivative of pressure with respect to time. The second derivative in the flow equation is generally approximated by the central-difference approximation because of the higher-order nature of the approximation. The first derivative is generally approximated by the backward-difference approximation. These choices are dictated by the stability of the final system of equations. Stability is a property that describes the capacity of a small error to propagate and grow with subsequent calculations. The following sections discuss the discretization process and the errors introduced by the use of finite-difference approximations.

5.2 Construction and Properties of Finite-Difference Grids

Two types of finite-difference grids are used in reservoir simulation: block centered and point distributed. In a block-centered grid, gridblocks with known dimensions are superimposed over the reservoir. For a rectangular coordinate system, the gridpoints are defined as the centers of these gridblocks. In a point-distributed grid, gridpoints are distributed over the reservoir before block boundaries are defined. For a rectangular grid, a block boundary is placed halfway between two adjacent pressure points. Historically, reservoir simulators have used block-centered finite differences because the volume associated with each representative point is clearly defined.

The purpose of the grid system is to partition the reservoir into blocks to which representative rock properties can be assigned. Therefore, the grid cells should be small enough to describe the heterogeneous nature of the reservoir and to allow the averaged grid-cell properties to represent the flow behavior in the reservoir adequately. This, however, may not always be achieved because the effort required for a simulation study is directly related to the number of grid cells used in the study.

There are two methods of handling the boundary conditions as discussed in Secs. 5.2.1 and 5.2.2. The first method, with no discrete points on the boundary, is most appropriate for no-flow boundary conditions. The second method, with points on the boundary, is most applicable to situations where a dependent variable, such as pressure, is specified on the boundary.

The following sections discuss the construction of block-centered and point-distributed grid systems. Discussion of these systems considers flow in only one direction (the x direction). For flow in more than one direction, the principles discussed in this chapter can be extended easily to multiple dimensions.

5.2.1 Block-Centered Grid Systems.

For flow in the x direction, a block-centered grid system can be constructed as in **Fig. 5.2**. In this figure, a grid system consisting of n_x gridblocks is superimposed over the reservoir. These gridblocks have predetermined dimen-

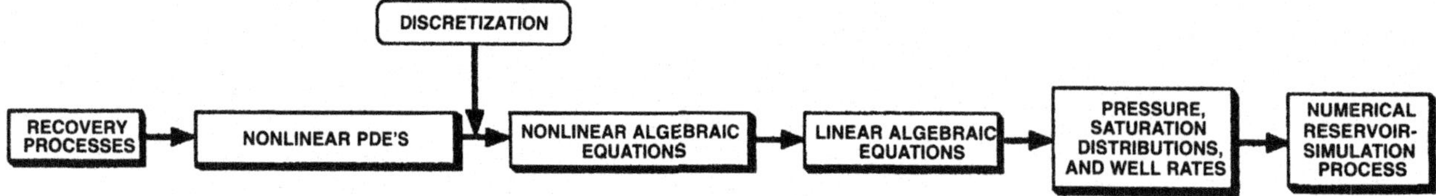

Fig. 5.1—Discretization step in the development of a reservoir simulator (redrawn from Ref. 1).

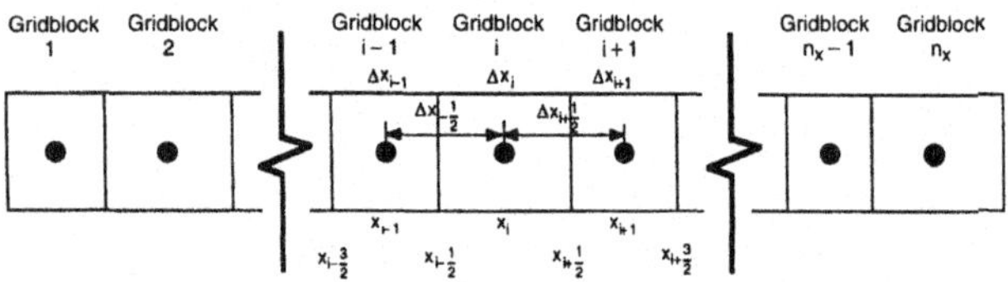

Fig. 5.2—One-dimensional, block-centered, finite-difference grid. Note that gridpoints are in the center of the gridblocks.

sions of Δx_i that are not necessarily equal. These gridblocks must satisfy the relationship

$$\sum_{i=1}^{n_x} \Delta x_i = L_x. \quad (5.1)$$

In other words, the gridblocks must span the entire length, L_x, of the reservoir in the direction of interest. This includes both the hydrocarbon-bearing rock and any associated aquifer.

Once the gridblocks are defined, the points where pressures are calculated are placed in the interior of the blocks. For rectangular grid systems, the gridpoints are placed at the center of the blocks (hence the name block centered), while the pressure points are slightly offset from the center for cylindrical grid systems. The boundaries of the ith gridblock are designated $x_{i-1/2}$ and $x_{i+1/2}$, whereas the block center is designated x_i. These gridblock properties are related through the relationships

$$x_i = \left(x_{i-1/2} + x_{i+1/2}\right)/2 \quad (5.2a)$$

$$\text{and } \Delta x_i = x_{i+1/2} - x_{i-1/2}. \quad (5.2b)$$

Fig. 5.2 illustrates the terms x_i, $x_{i-1/2}$, $x_{i+1/2}$, Δx_i, Δx_{i-1}, and Δx_{i+1}. Note that, in a block-centered grid system, the gridpoints of the first and last gridblocks lie in the interior of the reservoir. **Fig. 5.3** illustrates a nonuniform, block-centered grid system in two dimensions.

5.2.2 Point-Distributed Grid Systems. For flow in the x direction, a point-distributed grid system can be constructed as in **Fig. 5.4**. Gridpoints are placed on the boundary of the reservoir and within its interior. Note that, by placing gridpoints on the boundaries of the reservoir, a point-distributed grid will, by definition, span the entire length of the reservoir in the direction of interest.

For rectangular grids, the block boundaries are placed halfway between two adjacent gridpoints; that is,

$$x_{i\pm 1/2} = \left(x_{i\pm 1} + x_i\right)/2. \quad (5.3)$$

In a point-distributed grid, the left boundary of the first gridblock is, by definition, placed on top of the gridpoint of the block; that is,

$$x_{1/2} = x_1. \quad (5.4)$$

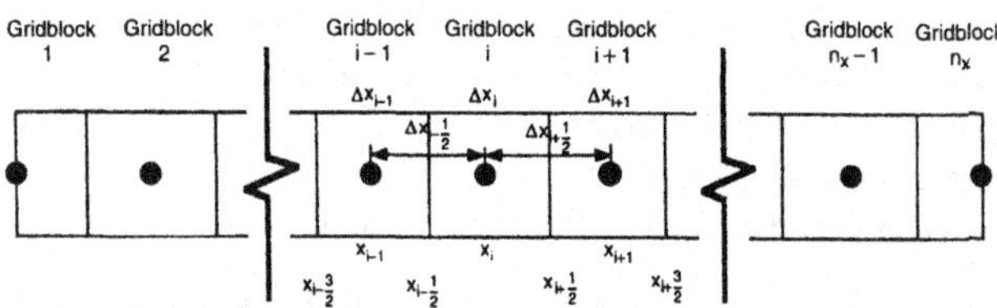

Fig. 5.4—One-dimensional, point-distributed, finite-difference grid. Note that gridpoints are offset from the gridblock centers and that gridblock boundaries lie midway between gridpoints.

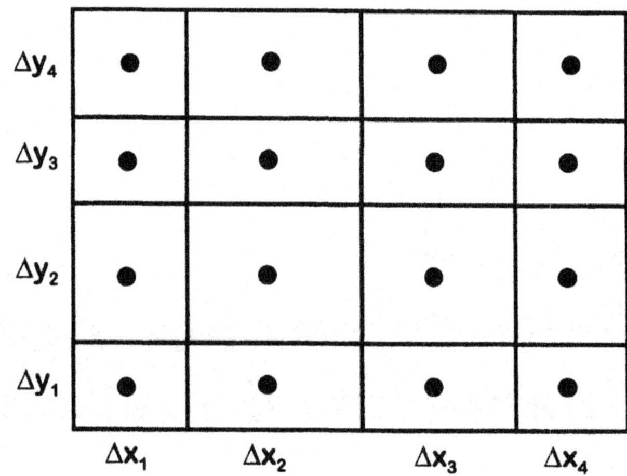

Fig. 5.3—Typical 2D, nonuniform, rectangular block-centered finite-difference grid. Note that pressure points are in the centers of the gridblocks.

If the gridblock were extended farther, the block would contain nonreservoir rock. Similarly, the right boundary of the last gridblock is placed on top of the gridpoint of the block; that is,

$$x_{n_x+1/2} = x_{n_x}. \quad (5.5)$$

The block dimensions can then be calculated from the block boundaries as

$$\Delta x_i = x_{i+1/2} - x_{i-1/2}. \quad (5.6)$$

Fig. 5.5 illustrates a point-distributed grid system in two dimensions.

In both block-centered and point-distributed grid systems, the block dimensions can vary for each gridblock. Either grid system can be used in reservoir simulation. Use of point-distributed grid systems has several advantages when implementing certain boundary conditions. In addition, point-distributed grid systems have numerical adantages when nonuniform spacing is used. In particular, a point-distributed-grid results in a consistent finite-difference operator on a nonuniform grid, while a block-centered grid does not.[2] For a defini-

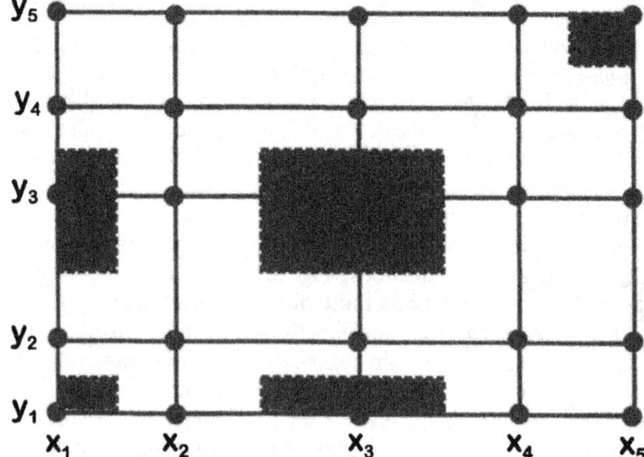

Fig. 5.5—Typical 2D, nonuniform, rectangular, point-distributed, finite-difference grid. Shaded areas reflect cell volumes associated with gridpoints. Note that the pressure points are offset from cell volume centers.

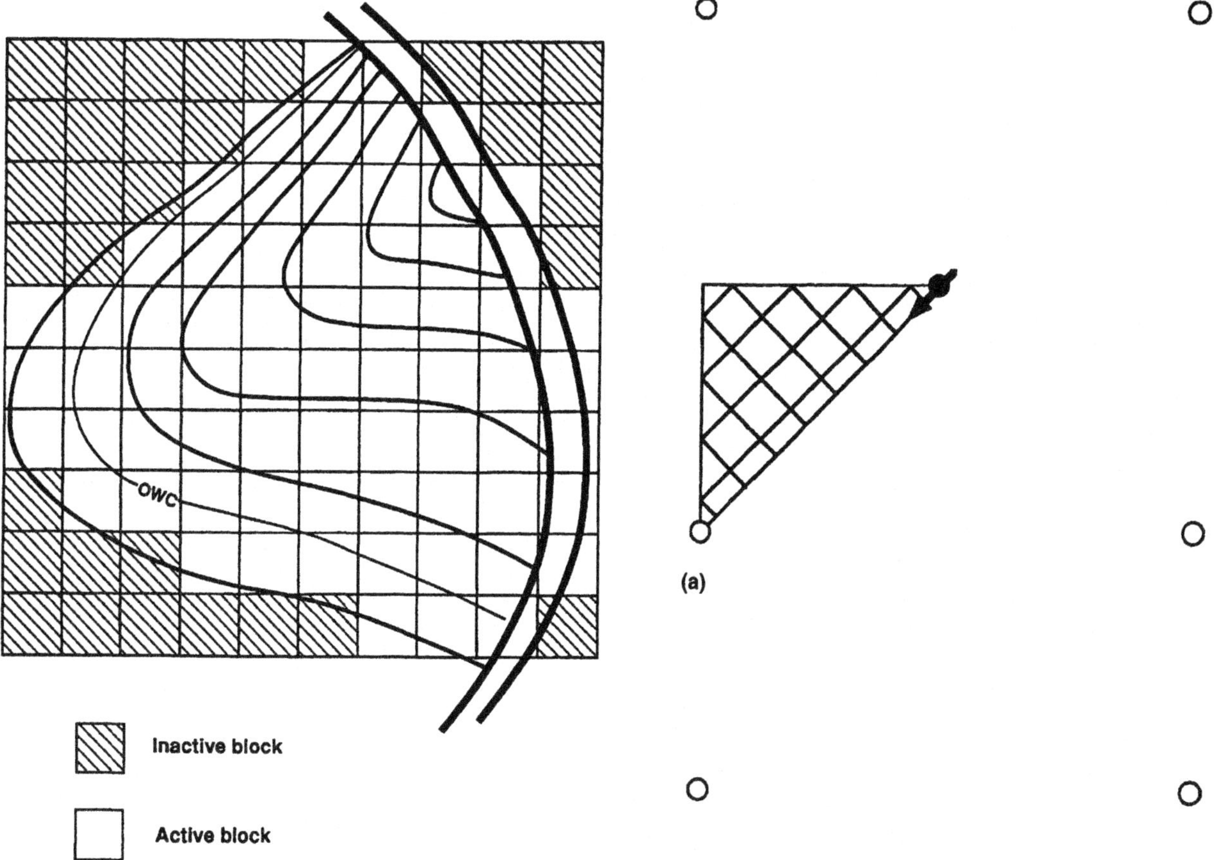

Fig. 5.6—Block-centered grid over a hydrocarbon reservoir; OWC = oil/water contact.

tion of consistency, see Consistency and Consistency Analysis in Sec. 5.6.3. Although these advantages exist for point-distributed grid systems, historically the block-centered grid system has been the most commonly used grid system in petroleum reservoir simulation. This is because the block-centered grid system adheres more closely to the material-balance concept used in reservoir engineering. Also, for reservoirs bounded with no-flow boundaries, the block-centered grid offers easy implementation of external boundary conditions (see Sec. 5.5.2).

5.2.3 Areal Grid Geometries. Although the previous sections emphasized rectangular geometry, several grid systems are commonly used in reservoir simulation when the objectives of the simulation study require the gridblocks to approximate closely, or match exactly, the geometry of the problem to be modeled. The use of the specialized geometries requires use of the corresponding form of the differential equation and its finite-difference analog in the simulation study.

Rectangular Coordinate Geometry. Rectangular coordinate geometry has many applications and is the most commonly used grid geometry in reservoir simulation. A rectangular grid can be used to answer questions regarding the full-field performance of a reservoir, the performance of individual well patterns, and the performance of interwell cross sections.

Full-field simulations are performed to determine the behavior of the entire subject reservoir. These simulations generally use a rectangular grid because rectangular grid systems are flexible enough to be fitted over any reservoir geometry. The grid spacing for full-field simulations can be nonuniform. Generally, a refined grid (small grid spacing) is used in areas of interest, such as hydrocarbon-bearing regions, while a less refined grid is used in less important areas, such as aquifers.

Fig. 5.6 shows an areal view of a grid system of an example full-field simulation and illustrates the use of inactive gridblocks. To allow the grid system to fit properly over the subject reservoir, gridblocks outside the reservoir boundaries must be inactivated. All commercial simulation software has the facility to inactivate unnecessary gridblocks.

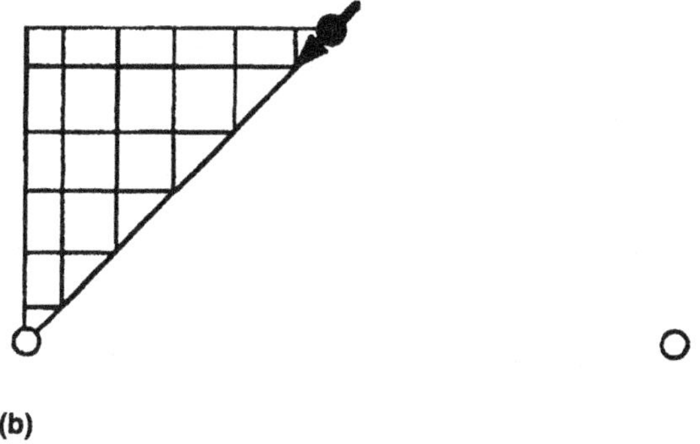

Fig. 5.7—Two rectangular grid systems for modeling an inverted five-spot pattern: (a) parallel grid and (b) diagonal grid.

Rectangular grid systems are also used to model pattern elements in pattern flood. When modeling a well pattern with reservoir simulation, symmetry is generally used to reduce the number of gridblocks required to model the displacement adequately. For example, to model an interior five-spot pattern, symmetry can be used to reduce the model to one-eighth of the pattern. Typically, uniform grid spacing is used for pattern studies. When a block-centered grid is used, the pore volumes, transmissibilities, and injection and production rates must be adjusted to account for the volume of the grid outside the pattern.[3]

Fig. 5.7 shows two grid systems that can be used when modeling an inverted five-spot pattern. In a parallel grid, the grid lines are par-

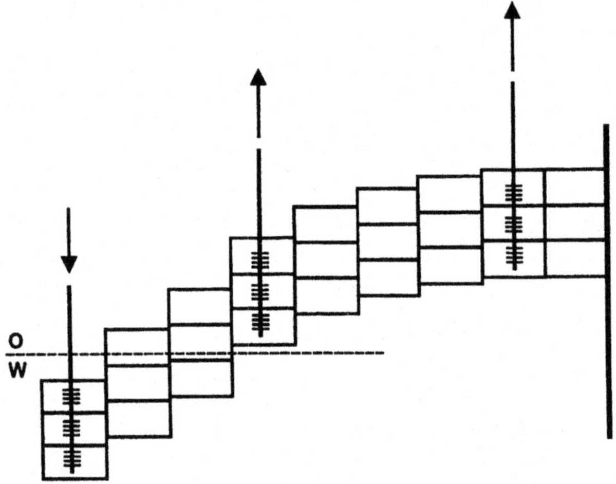

Fig. 5.8—Typical rectangular grid system used in a cross-sectional study; O = oil and W = water.

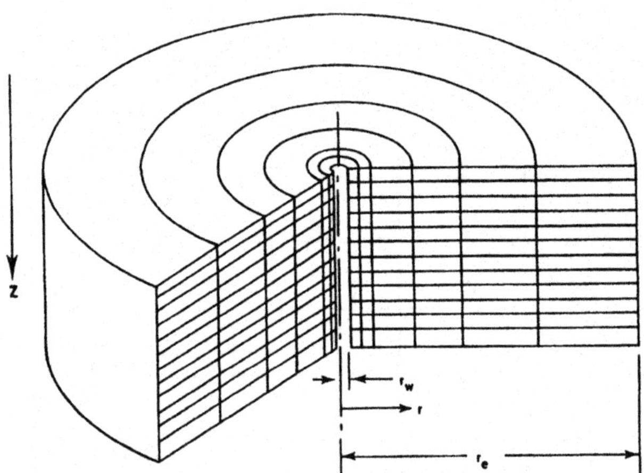

Fig. 5.9—Cylindrical grid system in the vicinity of a wellbore.

allel and are perpendicular to the line drawn from the producer to the injector. In a diagonal grid, on the other hand, the grid lines are diagonal to the line drawn through the producer/injector pair.

Rectangular grid systems are also used in cross-sectional simulation studies, which are performed to determine the interwell behavior of several wells along a given cross section. The objectives of a cross-sectional study may include determining the effect of shales on gravity override/underride in displacement processes, determining the effect of detailed reservoir geology on well performance, and aiding in the scaleup of core properties to reservoir scale (see discussion on dynamic interblock pseudofunctions in Sec. 10.4.3). **Fig. 5.8** shows a typical cross-sectional grid.

Cylindrical Grid Geometries. Cylindrical grid geometries are used for single-well simulation studies. The objectives of single-well simulation include predicting the performance of individual wells, determining the effects of completion/production strategies on gas and water coning, and optimizing perforation intervals. **Fig. 5.9** illustrates a cylindrical grid in the presence of a single well.

While the gridblock sizes are relatively arbitrary for rectangular grid systems, the construction of a cylindrical grid system follows this particular set of rules.

1. The pressure points are spaced logarithmically away from the wellbore;

$$r_{i+1} = \alpha_{lg} r_i \, , \quad (5.7)$$

where $i = 1, 2, \ldots, n_r - 1$.

2. The block boundaries for interblock flow calculations are defined by the formula

$$r_{i+½} = \frac{r_{i+1} - r_i}{\log_e(r_{i+1}/r_i)} \, , \quad (5.8)$$

where $i = 1, 2, \ldots, n_r - 1$.

3. The block boundaries for volumetric calculations are defined by the formula

$$r^2_{i+½} = \frac{r^2_{i+1} - r^2_i}{\log_e\left(r^2_{i+1}/r^2_i\right)} \, . \quad (5.9)$$

These three rules are applicable to both block-centered and point-distributed grid systems. Eq. 5.7 is used to keep pressure drops across all gridblocks approximately equal (remember that the pressure distribution around a wellbore is logarithmic). Eq. 5.8 is used to ensure that the flux from one gridblock to the next gridblock calculated by the finite-difference (discrete) equations is equal to that calculated by the continuous form of Darcy's law[2]. Finally, Eq. 5.9 is used to ensure that the volume of the discrete gridblocks is equal to the volume of the continuous gridblocks. Rules 1 and 2 are derived from steady-state theory.

Example 5.1. Show that the grid spacing defined by Eq. 5.7 will result in a constant pressure drop across all gridblocks for incompressible, steady-state flow toward a production well.

Solution. For incompressible flow, Darcy's law for a horizontal, radial system is

$$q = \frac{-2\pi\beta_c khr}{\mu} \frac{dp}{dr} \, . \quad (5.10)$$

Separating variables and integrating results in

$$\int_{r_i}^{r_{i+1}} \frac{1}{r} dr = \frac{-2\pi\beta_c kh}{q\mu} \int_{p_i}^{p_{i+1}} dp \, . \quad (5.11)$$

Performing all integrations results in

$$\log_e\left(\frac{r_{i+1}}{r_i}\right) = \frac{-2\pi\beta_c kh}{q\mu}(p_{i+1} - p_i), \quad (5.12)$$

where $i = 1, 2, \ldots, n_r - 1$. We now need to determine which radii, $r_1, r_2, r_3 \ldots r_{n_r}$, will result in uniform pressure drops across all grid cells. Define the constant pressure drop as

$$\Delta p = p_{i+1} - p_i \, , \quad (5.13)$$

where $i = 1, 2, \ldots, n_r - 1$. Substituting into Eq. 5.12 results in

$$\log_e\left(\frac{r_{i+1}}{r_i}\right) = \frac{-2\pi\beta_c kh}{q\mu}\Delta p \, , \quad (5.14)$$

where $i = 1, 2, \ldots, n_r - 1$. Because the right side of Eq. 5.14 is constant for incompressible flow, it can be rewritten (remember q is negative for production) as

$$\log_e\left(\frac{r_{i+1}}{r_i}\right) = \alpha'_{lg} \, , \quad (5.15)$$

where $i = 1, 2, \ldots, n_r - 1$. Taking the exponent of Eq. 5.15 yields

$$\frac{r_{i+1}}{r_i} = e^{\alpha'_{lg}} \quad (5.16)$$

or

$$\frac{r_{i+1}}{r_i} = \alpha_{lg} \, , \quad (5.17)$$

where $\alpha_{lg} = e^{\alpha'_{lg}}$ and $i = 1, 2, \ldots, n_r - 1$. Rearranging Eq. 5.17 results in Eq. 5.7.

$$r_{i+1} = \alpha_{lg} r_i \, , \quad (5.7)$$

where $i = 1, 2, \ldots, n_r - 1$.

Example 5.2. Show that the block boundaries defined by Eq. 5.8 ensure that the flux across the grid boundaries is identical for the continuous and discrete forms of Darcy's law.

Solution. Again, start with the radial form of Darcy's law,

$$q = \frac{-2\pi\beta_c khr}{\mu}\frac{dp}{dr}. \quad (5.18)$$

As in the previous example, Eq. 5.18 can be converted to the continuous form, Eq. 5.12.

$$\log_e\left(\frac{r_{i+1}}{r_i}\right) = \frac{-2\pi\beta_c kh}{q\mu}(p_{i+1} - p_i). \quad (5.12)$$

We can also take the central difference approximation of Eq. 5.18 about the point $r = r_{i+1/2}$, as

$$q = \frac{-2\pi\beta_c khr_{i+1/2}}{\mu}\left(\frac{p_{i+1} - p_i}{r_{i+1} - r_i}\right) \quad (5.19)$$

or $$\frac{r_{i+1} - r_i}{r_{i+1/2}} = \frac{-2\pi\beta_c kh}{q\mu}(p_{i+1} - p_i). \quad (5.20)$$

Equating Eq. 5.12 and Eq. 5.20 results in

$$\frac{r_{i+1} - r_i}{r_{i+1/2}} = \log_e\left(\frac{r_{i+1}}{r_i}\right) \quad (5.21)$$

or, finally,

$$r_{i+1/2} = \frac{r_{i+1} - r_i}{\log_e(r_{i+1}/r_i)}. \quad (5.8)$$

We can now use Eqs. 5.7 and 5.8 to develop specific grid systems for block-centered and point-distributed grid systems.

For block-centered grids,

$$\alpha_{lg} = \left(\frac{r_e}{r_w}\right)^{1/n_r} \quad (5.22)$$

and $$r_1 = \frac{r_w \log_e(\alpha_{lg})}{1 - (1/\alpha_{lg})}. \quad (5.23)$$

For point-distributed grids,

$$\alpha_{lg} = \left(\frac{r_e}{r_w}\right)^{1/(n_r - 1)} \quad (5.24)$$

and $r_1 = r_w$. (5.25)

After defining r_1, Eq. 5.7 can be used to calculate all other pressure points. Eq. 5.8 can then be used to generate the interblock boundaries for transmissibility and flux calculations. Finally, Eq. 5.9 can be used to generate the interblock boundaries for volumetric calculations, such as material-balance checks.

Example 5.3. Derive Eqs. 5.22 and 5.23 for block-centered grid systems.

Solution. For block-centered grid systems, by definition,

$$r_{o+1/2} = r_w \quad (5.26)$$

and $r_{n_r+1/2} = r_e$. (5.27)

Define an imaginary gridpoint, r_o, that is outside the grid system and inside the wellbore. That is, $r_o < r_w$. Also, define a second imaginary gridpoint, r_{n_r+1}, that is outside the grid system and beyond the external radius. That is, $r_{n_r+1} > r_e$.

From Eq. 5.7,

$$r_1 = \alpha_{lg} r_o, \quad (5.28)$$

$$r_2 = \alpha_{lg} r_1 = \alpha_{lg}(\alpha_{lg} r_o) = \alpha_{lg}^2 r_o, \quad (5.29a)$$

or recursively, $r_{n_r} = \alpha_{lg}^{n_r} r_o$. (5.29b)

Equating Eqs. 5.26 and 5.8 yields

$$r_{o+1/2} = r_w = \frac{r_1 - r_o}{\log_e(r_1/r_o)} \quad (5.30)$$

and, similarly,

$$r_{n_r+1/2} = r_e = \frac{r_{n_r+1} - r_{n_r}}{\log_e(r_{n_r+1}/r_{n_r})}. \quad (5.31)$$

From Eq. 5.7, we can substitute for r_1 in Eq. 5.30 and r_{n_r+1} in Eq. 5.31,

$$r_w = \frac{\alpha_{lg} r_o - r_o}{\log_e(\alpha_{lg})} = \frac{(\alpha_{lg} - 1)r_o}{\log_e(\alpha_{lg})} \quad (5.32)$$

and $$r_e = \frac{\alpha_{lg} r_{n_r} - r_{n_r}}{\log_e(\alpha_{lg})} = \frac{(\alpha_{lg} - 1)r_{n_r}}{\log_e(\alpha_{lg})}. \quad (5.33)$$

Dividing Eq. 5.33 by Eq. 5.32 results in

$$\frac{r_e}{r_w} = \frac{r_{n_r}}{r_o}. \quad (5.34)$$

Substituting Eq. 5.29b yields

$$\frac{r_e}{r_w} = \alpha_{lg}^{n_r} \quad (5.35)$$

or $$\alpha_{lg} = \left(\frac{r_e}{r_w}\right)^{1/n_r}. \quad (5.22)$$

We now need to derive an expression for the radius of the first grid cell, r_1. From Eq. 5.7, we can substitute for r into Eq. 5.30.

$$r_w = \frac{r_1 - r_1/\alpha_{lg}}{\log_e(\alpha_{lg})} = \frac{r_1(1 - 1/\alpha_{lg})}{\log_e(\alpha_{lg})} \quad (5.36)$$

or $$r_1 = \frac{r_w \log_e(\alpha_{lg})}{1 - (1/\alpha_{lg})}. \quad (5.23)$$

Example 5.4. Derive Eqs. 5.24 and 5.25 for point-distributed grid systems.

Solution. For point-distributed grid systems, by definition,

$$r_1 = r_w \quad (5.25)$$

and $r_{n_r} = r_e$. (5.37)

From Eq. 5.7,

$$r_2 = \alpha_{lg} r_1, \quad (5.38)$$

$$r_3 = \alpha_{lg} r_2 = \alpha_{lg}(\alpha_{lg} r_1) = \alpha_{lg}^2 r_1, \quad (5.39a)$$

or recursively, $r_{n_r} = \alpha_{lg}^{n_r - 1} r_1$. (5.39b)

Substituting Eq. 5.25 and Eq. 5.37 into Eq. 5.39b results in

$$r_e = \alpha_{lg}^{n_r - 1} r_w \quad (5.40)$$

or $$\alpha_{lg} = \left(\frac{r_e}{r_w}\right)^{1/(n_r - 1)}. \quad (5.24)$$

Corner-Point Geometry. Corner-point geometry uses polygons for grid cells, and gridblocks are defined by specifying the corners of polygons. Gridblock properties, such as grid centers, thicknesses, and transmissibilities, are then determined from the gridblock corners. **Fig. 5.10** shows a typical corner-point grid.

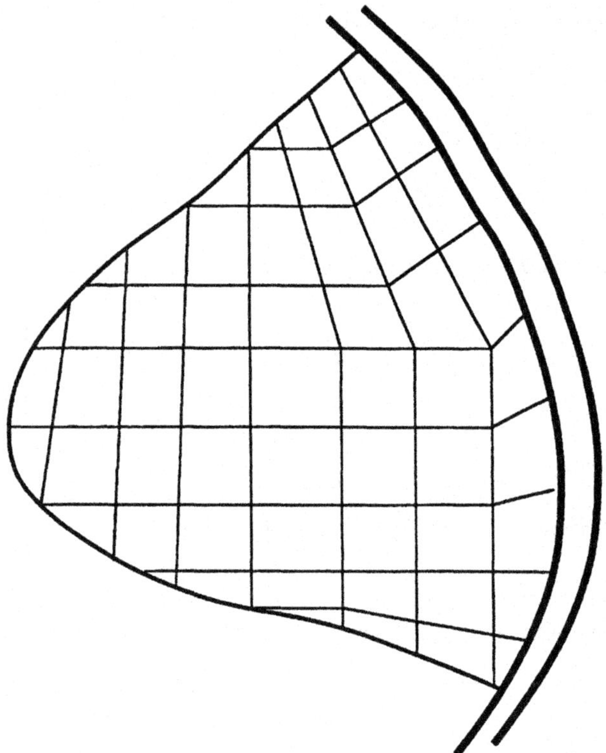

Fig. 5.10—Typical corner-point-geometry grid over a hydrocarbon reservoir.

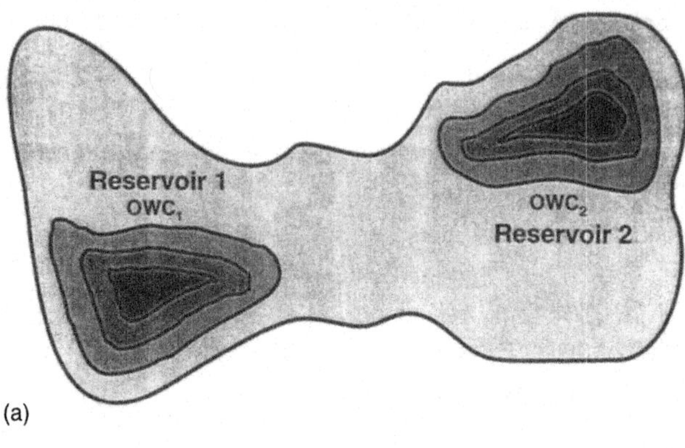

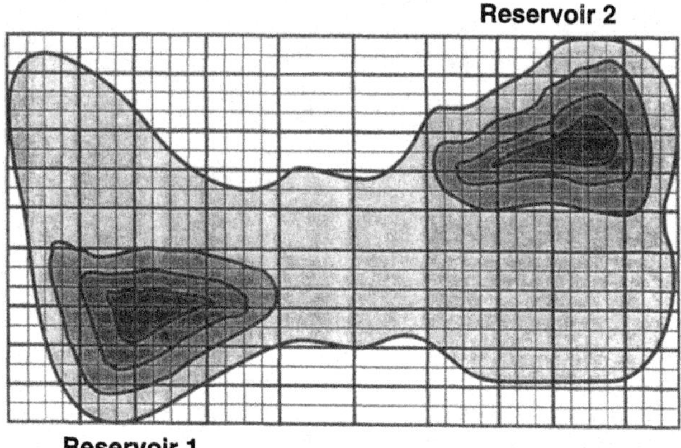

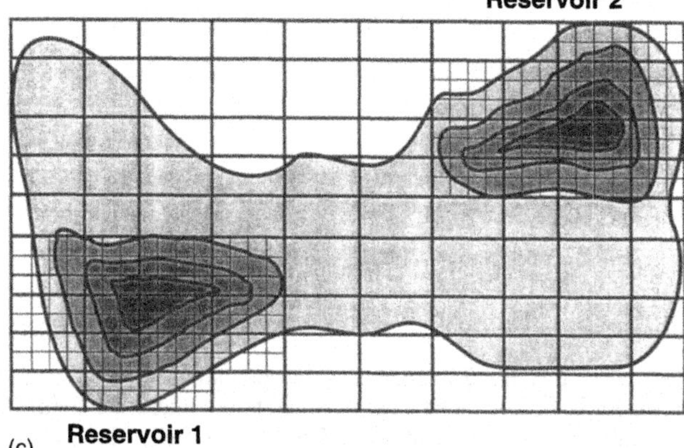

Fig. 5.11—Illustration of the use of locally refined grids. Note the reduction in number of grid cells in the areas that are not of interest. (a) Reservoirs to be modeled, (b) conventional rectangular grid, and (c) locally refined grid.

Corner-point geometry can be used for all full-field applications; however, its principal use is for highly faulted reservoirs. For these reservoirs, the edges of the polygons can be placed on the faults. The description of the faults is generally better with corner-point geometry than the description obtained from rectangular grid systems. One detrimental feature with the use of corner-point geometry is that the resulting grid system is nonorthogonal. The use of a nonorthogonal grid system with a standard seven-point finite-difference grid may result in significant errors because of the exclusion of the cross-derivative terms. This problem may be alleviated to some extent by use of higher-order finite-difference approximations, which include a full tensor representation of the permeability.

Local Grid Refinement and Hybrid Grids. Locally refined grid systems use a secondary (or fine) grid system embedded in the primary (or coarse) grid system. **Fig. 5.11** illustrates the objective of using the fine grid: to place a more refined grid in areas of interest in the hydrocarbon reservoir while maintaining a minimum number of active cells in the model.

Fig. 5.11a shows two hydrocarbon reservoirs in communication through a common aquifer. Fig. 5.11b shows a conventional grid system, while Fig. 5.11c shows a locally refined grid over the same reservoir. Because both the fine and coarse grids are rectangular, the techniques discussed earlier in this section under Rectangular Coordinate Geometry are appropriate. Special techniques are required to describe the transmissibilities and fluxes at the common boundary where the two grid systems meet.

When the fine grid uses a different geometry than the coarse grid, the resulting grid is hybrid.[4] Hybrid grid systems are generally used to provide better definition of the near-wellbore areas in full-field simulations. **Fig. 5.12** shows vertical and horizontal wells in a hybrid grid. Sec. 6.4 discusses details of the use of hybrid grids. Construction of the radial portion of the hybrid grid implements the same rules are applied to the pure radial grid.

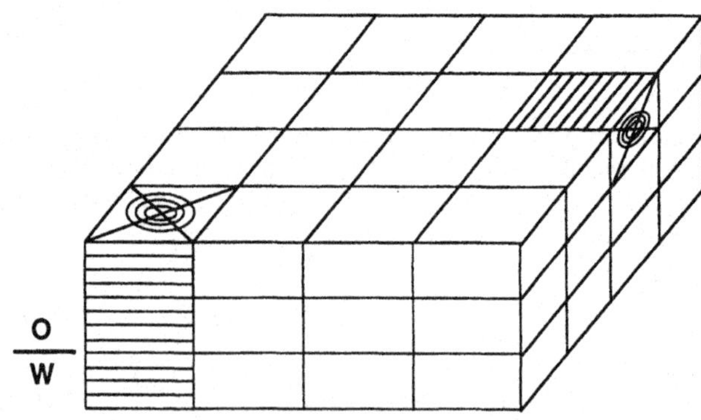

Fig. 5.12—Hybrid grid system for improving the coupling of wellbores to the reservoir model; O = oil and W = water.

5.2.4 Vertical Grid Geometry. In the previous discussions of areal grid geometries (with the exception of the rectangular cross-sectional grid) the vertical grid or layering system was not mentioned. Three types of layering systems can be used with the areal grids discussed in the previous sections[5]: stratigraphic, proportional, and tank type.

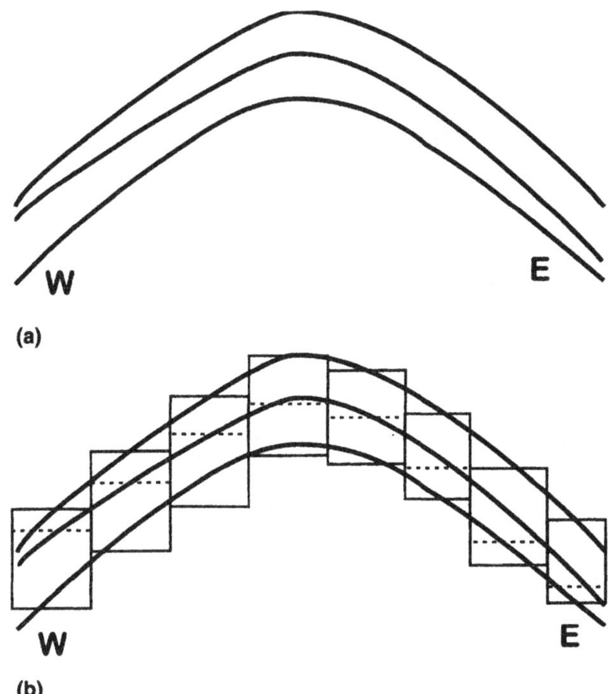

Fig. 5.13—Stratigraphic layering in reservoir simulation. (a) Reservoir to be modeled. Note the thickening of the top layer from west to east and the thinning of the bottom layer from west to east. (b) Stratigraphic grid system of reservoir under study. Note the varying proportions of the grid thicknesses from west to east.

Stratigraphic layering, as the name implies and as **Fig. 5.13** illustrates, follows the stratigraphy or natural geological layering of the reservoir. Stratigraphic layering is used to incorporate geological information into the reservoir model in a manner that is consistent with the stratigraphy of the reservoir under study. This is the most commonly used grid system in full-field reservoir simulation.

Proportional layering, as the name implies and as **Fig. 5.14** illustrates, keeps the ratios of the layer thicknesses constant between two mapped surfaces. Proportional layering is used to add definition (additional layers) to a single mapped layer.

Tank-type layering, illustrated in **Fig. 5.15,** uses a horizontal gridblock system, even in the presence of dip or structural features. Tank-type layering has limited use in full-field simulation, but may be used in single-well radial modeling or conceptual modeling.

5.3 Finite-Difference Approximation of the Spatial Derivative

The flow equations in porous media contain continuous derivatives with respect to the space and time variables. Chap. 3 discussed techniques to approximate derivatives with finite differences. The basic principle behind these techniques was to replace the partial derivatives in the flow equations with algebraic approximations.

This chapter focuses on the Taylor series method for finite differences to approximate the fluid-flow equations. These approximations are obtained by Taylor series expansion of the dependent variable in the vicinity of the gridpoints. When the approximations are applied to a single-flow equation, the PDE is replaced by a system of algebraic equations. Discretization is the process of converting the continuous PDE to a system of algebraic equations. Other equally applicable methods of discretization include the integral method for finite differences, the finite-element method, and the finite-boundary method (or boundary integral equation method).

The equation for single-phase, slightly compressible flow through porous media was derived in Chap. 4 as Eq. 4.72. For one-dimensional (1D) flow, this equation has the form

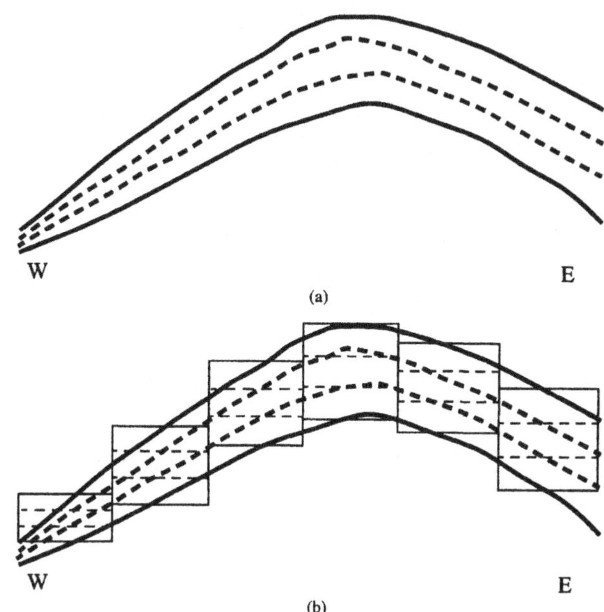

Fig. 5.14—Proportional layering in reservoir simulation: (a) top layer from reservoir in Fig. 5.13 and (b) use of proportional grid to add definition to a mapped geological layer. Note the identical proportions of the grid thickness from west to east.

$$\frac{\partial}{\partial x}\left(\beta_c \frac{A_x k_x}{\mu_l B_l}\frac{\partial p}{\partial x}\right)\Delta x + q_{lsc} = \frac{V_b \phi c_l}{\alpha_c B_l^\circ}\frac{\partial p}{\partial t}, \quad \text{.........} \quad (5.41)$$

where Subscript l refers to Phase l (o or w). Remember that Eq. 5.41 ignores the depth gradient and assumes incompressible porous media. Chap. 8 removes these assumptions from the solution of the flow equation.

5.3.1 Approximation on a Uniform Grid in One Dimension. Fig. 5.16 shows the 1D, block-centered grid used to discretize Eq. 5.41.

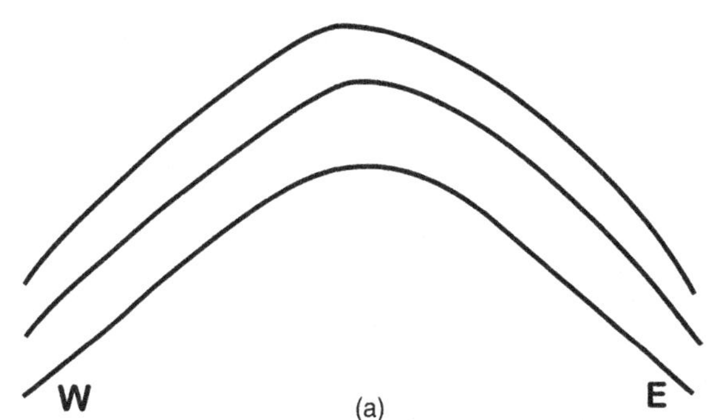

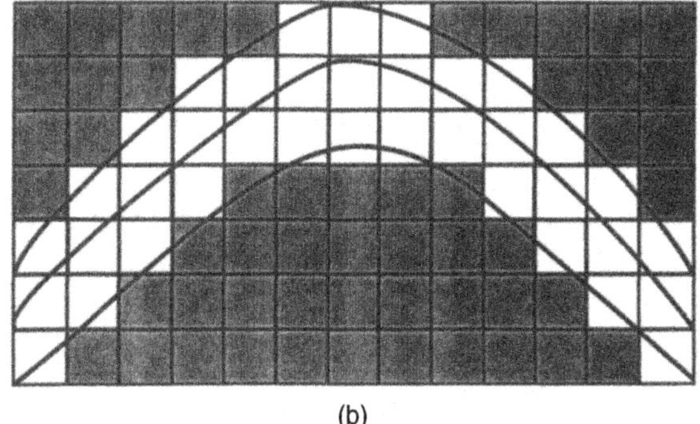

Fig. 5.15—Tank-type layering in reservoir simulation: (a) reservoir to be modeled and (b) tank-type grid system. Note that shaded areas represent inactive grid cells.

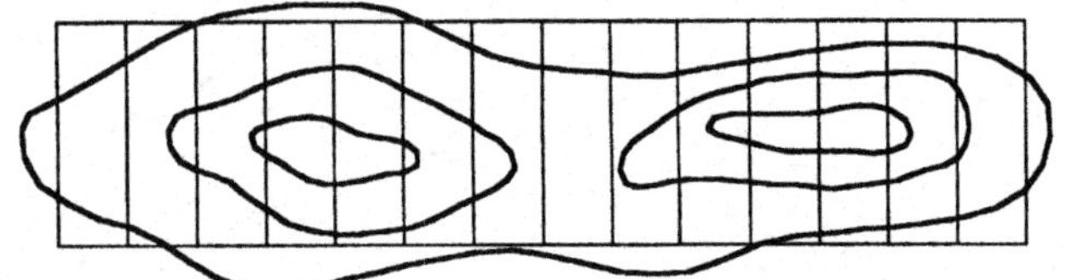

Fig. 5.16—Uniform grid used for discretization of a hydrocarbon reservoir.

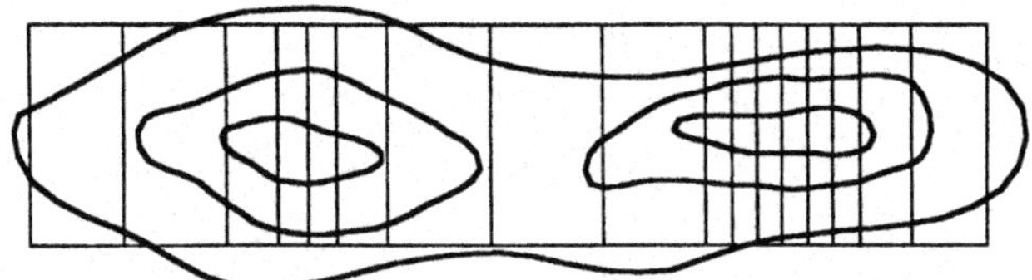

Fig. 5.17—Nonuniform grid used for discretization of a hydrocarbon reservoir. Note refined grid in the areas of interest.

Although a block-centered grid illustrates the discretization of Eq. 5.41, the procedure is identical for a point-distributed grid. This section illustrates the discretization process on a nonuniform grid. The resulting equation is then simplified to obtain the approximation for a uniform grid.

Chap. 3 defines the central-difference approximation to the first derivative as

$$\frac{\partial}{\partial x}\left(\beta_c \frac{A_x k_x}{\mu_l B_l}\frac{\partial p}{\partial x}\right)_i \approx \frac{1}{\Delta x_i}\left[\left(\beta_c \frac{A_x k_x}{\mu_l B_l}\frac{\partial p}{\partial x}\right)_{i+1/2} - \left(\beta_c \frac{A_x k_x}{\mu_l B_l}\frac{\partial p}{\partial x}\right)_{i-1/2}\right]. \quad (5.42)$$

Although the equality in Eq. 5.42 is approximate, the subsequent equations use an equal sign so the development is consistent with the computational procedures.

Using Eq. 5.42 to approximate the spatial derivative at Gridpoint i and substituting the result into the left side of Eq. 5.41 results in

$$\frac{1}{\Delta x_i}\left[\left(\beta_c \frac{A_x k_x}{\mu_l B_l}\right)_{i+1/2}\left(\frac{\partial p}{\partial x}\right)_{i+1/2} - \left(\beta_c \frac{A_x k_x}{\mu_l B_l}\right)_{i-1/2}\left(\frac{\partial p}{\partial x}\right)_{i-1/2}\right]$$

$$\times \Delta x_i + q_{lsc_i} = \left(\frac{V_b \phi c_l}{\alpha_c B_l^{\circ}}\frac{\partial p}{\partial t}\right)_i. \quad (5.43)$$

Now, use of central differences to approximate $(\partial p/\partial x)_{i+1/2}$ and $(\partial p/\partial x)_{i-1/2}$ yields

$$\left(\frac{\partial p}{\partial x}\right)_{i+1/2} = \frac{p_{i+1} - p_i}{x_{i+1} - x_i} = \frac{p_{i+1} - p_i}{\Delta x_{i+1/2}} \quad (5.44)$$

and

$$\left(\frac{\partial p}{\partial x}\right)_{i-1/2} = \frac{p_i - p_{i-1}}{x_i - x_{i-1}} = \frac{p_i - p_{i-1}}{\Delta x_{i-1/2}}. \quad (5.45)$$

Substituting Eqs. 5.44 and 5.45 into Eq. 5.43 results in

$$\left(\beta_c \frac{A_x k_x}{\mu_l B_l \Delta x}\right)_{i+1/2}(p_{i+1} - p_i) - \left(\beta_c \frac{A_x k_x}{\mu_l B_l \Delta x}\right)_{i-1/2}(p_i - p_{i-1})$$

$$+ q_{lsc_i} = \left(\frac{V_b \phi c_l}{\alpha_c B_l^{\circ}}\right)_i \frac{\partial p_i}{\partial t}. \quad (5.46)$$

or

$$T_{lx_{i+1/2}}(p_{i+1} - p_i) - T_{lx_{i-1/2}}(p_i - p_{i-1}) + q_{lsc_i}$$

$$= \left(\frac{V_b \phi c_l}{\alpha_c B_l^{\circ}}\right)_i \frac{\partial p_i}{\partial t}. \quad (5.47)$$

The coefficients $T_{lx_{i+1/2}}$ and $T_{lx_{i-1/2}}$ are referred to as the transmissibilities of the porous medium and are defined by

$$T_{lx_{i+1/2}} = \left(\beta_c \frac{A_x k_x}{\mu_l B_l \Delta x}\right)_{i+1/2} \quad (5.48)$$

and

$$T_{lx_{i-1/2}} = \left(\beta_c \frac{A_x k_x}{\mu_l B_l \Delta x}\right)_{i-1/2}. \quad (5.49)$$

The transmissibility of a porous medium is considered to be a property of the porous medium, the fluid flowing through the medium (Subscript l), the direction of flow (Subscript x), and the position in space (Subscripts $i + 1/2$ and $i - 1/2$).

For a uniform block-centered grid, the spacings between the gridpoints (or block centers) are the same and are equal to the block dimension Δx. That is,

$$\Delta x_{i-1/2} = \Delta x_{i+1/2} = \Delta x_i = \Delta x. \quad (5.50)$$

Eq. 5.46 and Eq. 5.47 show that, to solve for p_i, the pressures p_{i+1} and p_{i-1} must be known. Consequently, Eq. 5.47 must be written for each gridblock in the reservoir model. This results in a system of equations that approximates Eq. 5.41. Sec. 5.6 discusses this in more detail.

The $(i \pm 1/2)$ subscripts in the group $\{\beta_c[(A_x k_x)/(\mu_l B_l \Delta x)]\}_{i\pm 2}$ and in the transmissibilities, $T_{lx_{i\pm 1/2}}$, indicate that these properties are evaluated at the block boundaries. Because these properties are specified only at the gridblock centers, the transmissibilities must be obtained by averaging the properties of adjacent gridblocks. Secs. 8.2.2 and 8.3.1 discuss this. For the time being, assume that A_x, k_x, and Δx are constants and are the same for all gridblocks.

5.3.2 Approximation on a Nonuniform Grid in One Dimension.

The procedure for discretizing the flow equation on a nonuniform grid is identical to the procedure used on a uniform grid. In fact, Eq. 5.46 was derived for a nonuniform grid. **Fig. 5.17** shows the grid system used in the discretization. Eq. 5.46 is valid for both block-centered and point-distributed grid systems.

For a block-centered grid system, $\Delta x_{i+1/2}$ and $\Delta x_{i-1/2}$ are defined as (see Fig. 5.2)

$$\Delta x_{i+1/2} = \frac{\Delta x_{i+1} + \Delta x_i}{2} \quad (5.51a)$$

or

$$\Delta x_{i+1/2} = x_{i+1} - x_i, \quad (5.51b)$$

and, in the backward direction,

$$\Delta x_{i-1/2} = \frac{\Delta x_i + \Delta x_{i-1}}{2} \quad (5.52a)$$

or

$$\Delta x_{i-1/2} = x_i - x_{i-1}. \quad (5.52b)$$

For a point-distributed grid system, $\Delta x_{i+1/2}$ and $\Delta x_{i-1/2}$ are defined as (see Fig. 5.4)

$$\Delta x_{i+1/2} = x_{i+1} - x_i \quad (5.53)$$

and, similarly, in the backward direction,

$$\Delta x_{i-1/2} = x_i - x_{i-1}. \quad (5.54)$$

5.3.3 Approximation in Multiple Dimensions.

Previous sections discussed the discretization process for a single dimension. We can apply these same techniques to multidimensional problems. Applying the central-difference approximation to Eq. 4.72 results in

$$\left(\beta_c \frac{A_x k_x}{\mu_l B_l \Delta x}\right)_{i+1/2,j,k}(p_{i+1,j,k} - p_{i,j,k})$$

$$-\left(\beta_c\frac{A_xk_x}{\mu_l B_l\Delta x}\right)_{i-½,j,k}\left(p_{i,j,k}-p_{i-1,j,k}\right)$$

$$+\left(\beta_c\frac{A_yk_y}{\mu_l B_l\Delta y}\right)_{i,j+½,k}\left(p_{i,j+1,k}-p_{i,j,k}\right)$$

$$-\left(\beta_c\frac{A_yk_y}{\mu_l B_l\Delta y}\right)_{i,j-½,k}\left(p_{i,j,k}-p_{i,j-1,k}\right)$$

$$+\left(\beta_c\frac{A_zk_z}{\mu_l B_l\Delta z}\right)_{i,j,k+½}\left(p_{i,j,k+1}-p_{i,j,k}\right)$$

$$-\left(\beta_c\frac{A_zk_z}{\mu_l B_l\Delta z}\right)_{i,j,k-½}\left(p_{i,j,k}-p_{i,j,k-1}\right)$$

$$+q_{lsc_{i,j,k}}=\left(\frac{V_b\phi c_l}{\alpha_c B_l^\circ}\right)_{i,j,k}\frac{\partial p_{i,j,k}}{\partial t}, \quad (5.55)$$

where $l=o$ or w. In terms of transmissibilities,

$$\mathrm{T}_{lx_{i+½,j,k}}\left(p_{i+1,j,k}-p_{i,j,k}\right)-\mathrm{T}_{lx_{i-½,j,k}}\left(p_{i,j,k}-p_{i-1,j,k}\right)$$

$$+\mathrm{T}_{ly_{i,j+½,k}}\left(p_{i,j+1,k}-p_{i,j,k}\right)-\mathrm{T}_{ly_{i,j-½,k}}\left(p_{i,j,k}-p_{i,j-1,k}\right)$$

$$+\mathrm{T}_{lz_{i,j,k+½}}\left(p_{i,j,k+1}-p_{i,j,k}\right)-\mathrm{T}_{lz_{i,j,k-½}}\left(p_{i,j,k}-p_{i,j,k-1}\right)$$

$$+q_{lsc_{i,j,k}}=\left(\frac{V_b\phi c_l}{\alpha_c B_l^\circ}\right)_{i,j,k}\frac{\partial p_{i,j,k}}{\partial t}. \quad (5.56)$$

The definition of the transmissibilities in Eq. 5.56 can be written as

$$\mathrm{T}_{lx_{i\pm½,j,k}}=G_{i\pm½,j,k}\left(\frac{1}{\mu_l B_l}\right)_{i\pm½,j,k}, \quad (5.57)$$

$$\mathrm{T}_{ly_{i,j\pm½,k}}=G_{i,j\pm½,k}\left(\frac{1}{\mu_l B_l}\right)_{i,j\pm½,k}, \quad (5.58)$$

and $$\mathrm{T}_{lz_{i,j,k\pm½}}=G_{i,j,k\pm½}\left(\frac{1}{\mu_l B_l}\right)_{i,j,k\pm½}, \quad (5.59)$$

where the G terms represent the constant parts of the transmissibilities. Table 6.7 gives the definition of these terms.

This finite-difference approximation in multidimensional, radial/cylindrical flow geometry can be written in a form similar to Eq. 5.56. The only differences between the rectangular and cylindrical formulations are the definitions of G in Eqs. 5.57 through 5.59. Table 6.6 lists the definitions of G for radial/cylindrical flow geometry.

5.4 Finite-Difference Approximation of the Time Derivative

The discretization of the time derivative in Eqs. 5.46 and 5.47 is handled in the same manner as the spatial derivative. Three possible approximations can be used for the time derivative: backward difference, forward difference, and central difference.

Both the backward- and forward-difference approximations are first-order approximations, while the central-difference approximation is a second-order approximation. Although the central-difference approximation is a higher-order approximation, it generally is not used because of stability problems (see Example 5.18) and difficulties in applying the initial conditions.[2] The backward-difference approximation generally is used in reservoir simulation because its use does not restrict the size of the timestep for a stable solution.

5.4.1 Backward-Difference Approximation to the Flow Equation. Chap. 3 (Eq. 3.157) defined the backward-difference approximation to the first derivative at the base time level t^{n+1}.

$$\frac{\partial p}{\partial t}\approx\frac{p(t^{n+1})-p(t^n)}{\Delta t}. \quad (5.60)$$

With the notation

$$p^n=p(t^n), \quad (5.61)$$

$$p^{n+1}=p\left(t^{n+1}\right). \quad (5.62)$$

Eq. 5.60 written for Gridpoint i with an equal sign rather than an approximation sign becomes

$$\frac{\partial p_i}{\partial t}=\frac{p_i^{n+1}-p_i^n}{\Delta t}. \quad (5.63)$$

Substituting into Eq. 5.46 at time level t^{n+1} results in

$$\left(\beta_c\frac{A_xk_x}{\mu_l B_l\Delta x}\right)_{i+½}\left(p_{i+1}^{n+1}-p_i^{n+1}\right)$$

$$-\left(\beta_c\frac{A_xk_x}{\mu_l B_l\Delta x}\right)_{i-½}\left(p_i^{n+1}-p_{i-1}^{n+1}\right)$$

$$+q_{lsc_i}=\left(\frac{V_b\phi c_l}{\alpha_c B_l^\circ\Delta t}\right)_i\left(p_i^{n+1}-p_i^n\right), \quad (5.64)$$

or, in terms of the transmissibilities $\mathrm{T}_{lx+½}$ and $\mathrm{T}_{lx-½}$,

$$\mathrm{T}_{lx_{i+½}}\left(p_{i+1}^{n+1}-p_i^{n+1}\right)-\mathrm{T}_{lx_{i-½}}\left(p_i^{n+1}-p_{i-1}^{n+1}\right)$$

$$+q_{lsc_i}=\left(\frac{V_b\phi c_l}{\alpha_c B_l^\circ\Delta t}\right)_i\left(p_i^{n+1}-p_i^n\right). \quad (5.65)$$

Note that the pressures used in the spatial derivatives on the left side of the flow equation are assigned the base time level t^{n+1}. In other words, these equations are written at time level t^{n+1}. Eqs. 5.64 and 5.65 are known as the backward-difference approximations to the flow equation because the time difference on the right side looks backward with reference to the base time level, t^{n+1}. In these equations, all pressures assigned to the time level t^{n+1} are the unknowns. Later, this chapter discusses the procedure for advancing the simulation in time.

Eqs. 5.48 and 5.49 define the transmissibility terms in Eq. 5.65. Because of the pressure dependence of the B_l and μ_l terms, time levels must also be assigned to transmissibilities. That is, at what pressure, p^{n+1} or p^n, should we evaluate B_l and μ_l? If we choose to evaluate the transmissibility at p^{n+1}, the coefficients of the equations are functions of the unknowns, resulting in a nonlinear algebraic equation that requires additional modification before it can be solved with a suitable linear-equation solver. Linearization (discussed in Chap. 8) is the technique used to convert nonlinear algebraic equations to linear algebraic equations. These nonlinear problems arise in the single-phase flow (slightly compressible and compressible flow) and in multiphase flow.

If we evaluate the transmissibility at p^n, we can evaluate the coefficients of the equations explicitly with the known pressures. For the time being, we will use the explicit treatment of the coefficients and defer the discussion of linearization until Sec. 8.4.1. Eq. 5.65 can now be written as

$$\mathrm{T}^n_{lx_{i+½}}\left(p_{i+1}^{n+1}-p_i^{n+1}\right)-\mathrm{T}^n_{lx_{i-½}}\left(p_i^{n+1}-p_{i-1}^{n+1}\right)+q_{lsc_i}$$

$$= \left(\frac{V_b \phi c_l}{\alpha_c B_l^\circ \Delta t}\right)_i (p_i^{n+1} - p_i^n). \quad (5.66)$$

5.4.2 Forward-Difference Approximation to the Flow Equation. Similarly, if the base time level is assumed to be t^n, then the forward-difference approximation to the first derivative (see Eq. 3.154) becomes

$$\frac{\partial p_i}{\partial t} \approx \frac{p_i^{n+1} - p_i^n}{\Delta t}. \quad (5.67)$$

Although Eqs. 5.63 and 5.67 are identical, the base time levels in the two approximations are different. This will become clearer later in this discussion. Substituting Eq. 5.67 into Eq. 5.46 written at time level t^n results in

$$\left(\beta_c \frac{A_x k_x}{\mu_l B_l \Delta x}\right)_{i+\frac{1}{2}}^n (p_{i+1}^n - p_i^n) - \left(\beta_c \frac{A_x k_x}{\mu_l B_l \Delta x}\right)_{i-\frac{1}{2}}^n (p_i^n - p_{i-1}^n) + q_{lsc_i} = \left(\frac{V_b \phi c_l}{\alpha_c B_l^\circ \Delta t}\right)_i (p_i^{n+1} - p_i^n) \quad (5.68)$$

or, in terms of the transmissibilities,

$$\mathrm{T}_{lx_{i+\frac{1}{2}}}^n (p_{i+1}^n - p_i^n) - \mathrm{T}_{lx_{i-\frac{1}{2}}}^n (p_i^n - p_{i-1}^n) + q_{lsc_i} = \left(\frac{V_b \phi c_l}{\alpha_c B_l^\circ \Delta t}\right)_i (p_i^{n+1} - p_i^n). \quad (5.69)$$

Eqs. 5.68 and 5.69 are known as the forward-difference approximations to the flow equation because the time difference on the right side looks forward with reference to t^n. The difference between the backward- and forward-difference approximations (Eqs. 5.66 and 5.69, respectively) is now clear. In these equations, the pressures on the left side of the equations are evaluated at the old time level, n, for the forward-difference approximation and the new time level, $n+1$, for the backward-difference approximation.

5.4.3 Central-Difference Approximation to the Flow Equation. If the base time level is assumed to be t^n and the central difference-approximation defined by Eq. 3.161 is used,

$$\frac{\partial p_i}{\partial t} = \frac{p_i^{n+1} - p_i^{n-1}}{2\Delta t}. \quad (5.70)$$

Substituting Eq. 5.70 into Eq. 5.46 at t_n yields

$$\left(\beta_c \frac{A_x k_x}{\mu_l B_l \Delta x}\right)_{i+\frac{1}{2}}^n (p_{i+1}^n - p_i^n) - \left(\beta_c \frac{A_x k_x}{\mu_l B_l \Delta x}\right)_{i-\frac{1}{2}}^n (p_i^n - p_{i-1}^n) + q_{lsc_i} = \left(\frac{V_b \phi c_l}{2\alpha_c B_l^\circ \Delta t}\right)_i (p_i^{n+1} - p_i^{n-1}) \quad (5.71)$$

or, in terms of the transmissibility,

$$\mathrm{T}_{lx_{i+\frac{1}{2}}}^n (p_{i+1}^n - p_i^n) - \mathrm{T}_{lx_{i-\frac{1}{2}}}^n (p_i^n - p_{i-1}^n) + q_{lsc_i} = \left(\frac{V_b \phi c_l}{2\alpha_c B_l^\circ \Delta t}\right)_i (p_i^{n+1} - p_i^{n-1}). \quad (5.72)$$

The central-difference approximation, sometimes referred to as Richardson's[7] approximation, is a higher-order (second-order) approximation because it is derived by truncating the Taylor series expansion after the second term. This approximation, therefore, contains additional information not contained in either the forward- or backward-difference approximations (both of which were truncated after the first term). Although it is a higher-order approximation, it is rarely used in reservoir simulation because it is always unstable (see Example 5.18) and because it is difficult to apply the initial conditions.[2]

5.5 Implementation of Initial and Boundary Conditions

In earlier sections of this chapter, three finite-difference approximations suitable for reservoir simulation were derived: the backward-, forward-, and central-difference approximations. These approximations were made to the single-phase, PDE governing fluid flow through porous media.

Chap. 3 discussed solutions to general differential equations. These solutions were found to be families of functions that satisfy the original differential equation. To obtain the desired engineering solution to the problem at hand, the differential equation must be subjected to appropriate initial and boundary conditions. Initial and boundary conditions are used to determine which function solves the given problem uniquely. While an entire family of solutions honors the differential equation, only one unique solution honors the differential equation, the initial conditions, and the boundary conditions simultaneously. Therefore, to obtain a unique solution to the reservoir-simulation problem, initial and boundary conditions must also be approximated by finite-difference methods and be incorporated into the reservoir simulator. Sec. 4.5 discusses the initial and boundary conditions for the single-phase-flow equations that are relevant to common reservoir-engineering problems.

5.5.1 Implementing Initial Conditions. We restrict this discussion to single-phase-flow problems. The objective of reservoir simulation is to predict pressure distribution and production rates throughout time. This is accomplished by use of the finite-difference equations to advance the simulation from a known time level (the time at which all dependent variables are known, n) to an unknown time level (the time at which dependent variables are to be predicted, $n+1$).

In the finite-difference equations, the term p^n represents the pressure values of the gridpoints at the known time level. The stepwise procedure for advancing the simulation in time begins by assigning known pressure values to the n time level in the finite-difference equations. The equations can then be solved for the unknown pressures, p^{n+1}. Once determined, the values of p^{n+1} are used as the known pressures for the next timestep. To start this procedure, the known pressures used in the equations for the first timestep are the pressures at the initial conditions.

For single-phase problems, initial pressures in the reservoir can be determined by the local pressure gradient. The pressures assigned to the grid cells are initially calculated with Eq. 2.14 and setting $\Phi - \Phi^\circ = 0$ for all grid cells, giving

$$p_{i,j,k}^n = p^\circ + \gamma_l (Z_{i,j,k} - Z^\circ). \quad (5.73)$$

In Eq. 5.73, p° = pressure at the datum depth Z° and $Z_{i,j,k}$ = depth of the Cell (i,j,k) at which pressure is $p_{i,j,k}^n$. Note from Eq. 2.20 that the term γ_l contains the phase density, ρ_l, which is pressure dependent for slightly compressible and compressible fluids. Therefore, the application of Eq. 5.73 may require iteration. Chap. 9 presents a complete treatment of initial conditions in multiphase problems.

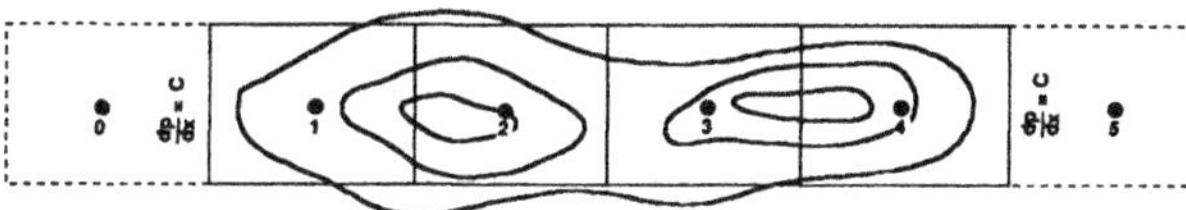

Fig. 5.18—Porous medium and block-centered finite-difference grid with specified-pressure-gradient boundaries.

5.5.2 Implementing Boundary Conditions. The boundaries in a petroleum reservoir can be extremely complicated, consisting of the external and internal boundaries that delineate the reservoir system. The external boundaries must include the limits of both the hydrocarbon-bearing reservoir and any associated aquifers. Most commercial reservoir simulators assume that the reservoir/aquifer system is bounded by a no-flow boundary at some distance from the hydrocarbon-bearing rock. Internally, petroleum reservoirs may contain several types of boundaries, including wellbores, nonreservoir rock, and sealing faults.

External Boundaries. The external boundaries of all reservoirs consist of the limits of the hydrocarbon-bearing zone and any associated aquifer. Two important types of boundaries are generally considered in reservoir simulation: specified pressure gradient (which include no-flow boundaries) and specified pressure. The implementation of boundary conditions depends on the type of boundary encountered in the field and the grid system (block centered or point distributed) used in the discretization.

Specified-Pressure-Gradient Boundaries. The equation

$$\frac{\partial p}{\partial x} = C \quad \text{(5.74)}$$

is used for a specified pressure gradient at the external boundary of the field. It is valid for all specified-pressure-gradient boundaries and can be used to model a no-flow boundary by setting $C=0$. In general, C can be a function of time. For this discussion, however, consider C to be constant. Because Eq. 5.74 encompasses no-flow type boundaries, this is the most commonly used condition for external boundaries in reservoir simulation. Eq. 5.74 must be discretized before it can be incorporated into the finite-difference reservoir simulator. This discretization is dependent on the grid system (block centered or point distributed) used by the simulator.

Fig. 5.18 shows a 1D, block-centered grid system over a porous medium. In this figure, the boundaries lie on the edges of the first and last grid cells (as well as the edges along the length of the medium). Writing the finite-difference equation (in this case the backward-difference approximation) for each cell in this grid, yields a system of four equations in six unknowns. This represents an ill-posed system of equations because there are more unknowns to be solved for than there are equations. The system of finite-difference equations that represents 1D flow for the grid system depicted in Fig. 5.18 is, for Gridblock 1,

$$\mathrm{T}^n_{lx_{1+1/2}}\left(p_2^{n+1} - p_1^{n+1}\right) - \mathrm{T}^n_{lx_{1-1/2}}\left(p_1^{n+1} - p_0^{n+1}\right) + q_{lsc_1} = \left(\frac{V_b \phi c_l}{\alpha_c B_l^\circ \Delta t}\right)_1 \left(p_1^{n+1} - p_1^n\right); \quad \text{(5.75)}$$

for Gridblock 2,

$$\mathrm{T}^n_{lx_{2+1/2}}\left(p_3^{n+1} - p_2^{n+1}\right) - \mathrm{T}^n_{lx_{2-1/2}}\left(p_2^{n+1} - p_1^{n+1}\right) + q_{lsc_2} = \left(\frac{V_b \phi c_l}{\alpha_c B_l^\circ \Delta t}\right)_2 \left(p_2^{n+1} - p_2^n\right); \quad \text{(5.76)}$$

for Gridblock 3,

$$\mathrm{T}^n_{lx_{3+1/2}}\left(p_4^{n+1} - p_3^{n+1}\right) - \mathrm{T}^n_{lx_{3-1/2}}\left(p_3^{n+1} - p_2^{n+1}\right) + q_{lsc_3} = \left(\frac{V_b \phi c_l}{\alpha_c B_l^\circ \Delta t}\right)_3 \left(p_3^{n+1} - p_3^n\right); \quad \text{(5.77)}$$

and for Gridblock 4,

$$\mathrm{T}^n_{lx_{4+1/2}}\left(p_5^{n+1} - p_4^{n+1}\right) - \mathrm{T}^n_{lx_{4-1/2}}\left(p_4^{n+1} - p_3^{n+1}\right) + q_{lsc_4} = \left(\frac{V_b \phi c_l}{\alpha_c B_l^\circ \Delta t}\right)_4 \left(p_4^{n+1} - p_4^n\right). \quad \text{(5.78)}$$

The reason that there are more unknowns than equations is that the finite-difference equations for the gridblocks on the boundaries contain pressures outside the reservoir (p_0^{n+1} and p_5^{n+1}). We can use Eq. 5.74 to complete the system of equations. The central-difference approximation of Eq. 5.74, written at the left boundary ($x=x_{1-1/2}$) in Fig. 5.18, is

$$\frac{\partial p}{\partial x} \approx \frac{p_1 - p_0}{x_1 - x_0} = C \quad \text{(5.79a)}$$

$$\text{or } p_0 = p_1 - C(x_1 - x_0). \quad \text{(5.79b)}$$

Similarly, the central-difference approximation can be used in Eq. 5.74 for the boundary on the right side ($x=x_{4+1/2}$) in Fig. 5.18 to obtain

$$p_5 = p_4 + C(x_5 - x_4). \quad \text{(5.80)}$$

These two additional equations are used to complete the system of equations in the reservoir simulator for the 1D reservoir shown in Fig. 5.18.

For a no-flow boundary ($C=0$), Eqs. 5.79b and 5.80 indicate that, for a block-centered grid, the pressures of the grid cells just outside the reservoir are equal to the pressures of the boundary grid cells just inside the reservoir. If we substitute the pressures for a no-flow boundary ($p_0=p_1$ and $p_4=p_5$) into Eqs. 5.75 and 5.78, the terms containing the boundary pressures go to zero. That is,

$$\mathrm{T}^n_{lx_{1+1/2}}\left(p_2^{n+1} - p_1^{n+1}\right) + q_{lsc_1} = \left(\frac{V_b \phi c_l}{\alpha_c B_l^\circ \Delta t}\right)_1 \left(p_1^{n+1} - p_1^n\right) \quad \text{(5.81)}$$

for Eq. 5.75, and

$$-\mathrm{T}^n_{lx_{4-1/2}}\left(p_4^{n+1} - p_3^{n+1}\right) + q_{lsc_4} = \left(\frac{V_b \phi c_l}{\alpha_c B_l^\circ \Delta t}\right)_4 \left(p_4^{n+1} - p_4^n\right) \quad \text{(5.82)}$$

for Eq. 5.78. Because zero transmissibility on the boundary would also cause this term to vanish, an alternative approach to modeling no-flow boundaries in a block-centered grid is to assign a zero value to boundary transmissibilities. That is, for no-flow boundaries in a block-centered grid,

$$\mathrm{T}^n_{lx_{1-1/2}} = 0 \quad \text{(5.83)}$$

$$\text{and } \mathrm{T}^n_{lx_{4+1/2}} = 0. \quad \text{(5.84)}$$

Example 5.5. For the block-centered grid system shown in Fig. 5.18, show that the use of Eq. 5.79a with $C=0$ is equivalent to use of Eq. 5.83 for implementing a no-flow boundary in Eq. 5.75.

Solution. Using a value of $C=0$ in Eq. 5.79a results in $p_0 = p_1$. Substituting this pressure into Eq. 5.75 results in

$$\mathrm{T}^n_{lx_{1+1/2}}\left(p_2^{n+1} - p_1^{n+1}\right) - \mathrm{T}^n_{lx_{1-1/2}}\left(p_1^{n+1} - p_1^{n+1}\right) + q_{lsc_1} = \left(\frac{V_b \phi c_l}{\alpha_c B_l^\circ \Delta t}\right)_1 \left(p_1^{n+1} - p_1^n\right) \quad \text{(5.85a)}$$

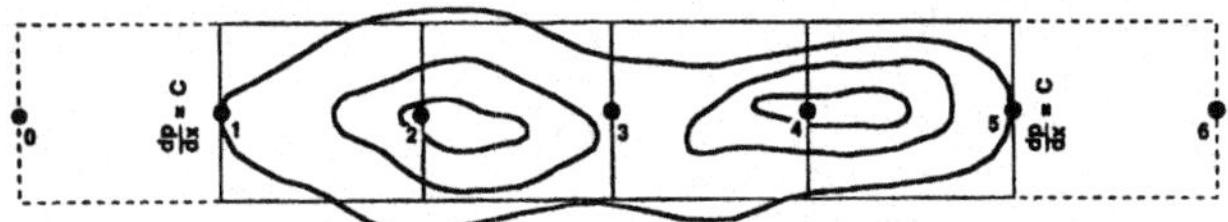

Fig. 5.19—Porous medium and point-distributed finite-difference grid with specified-pressure-gradient boundaries.

or $T^n_{lx_{1+1/2}}(p_2^{n+1} - p_1^{n+1}) + q_{lsc_1}$

$$= \left(\frac{V_b \phi c_l}{\alpha_c B_l^\circ \Delta t}\right)_1 (p_1^{n+1} - p_1^n). \quad (5.85b)$$

Similarly, substituting Eq. 5.83 into Eq. 5.75 results in Eq. 5.85b.

$$T^n_{lx_{1+1/2}}(p_2^{n+1} - p_1^{n+1}) + 0(p_1^{n+1} - p_0^{n+1}) + q_{lsc_1}$$

$$= \left(\frac{V_b \phi c_l}{\alpha_c B_l^\circ \Delta t}\right)_1 (p_1^{n+1} - p_1^n) \quad (5.86)$$

or $T^n_{lx_{1+1/2}}(p_2^{n+1} - p_1^{n+1}) + q_{lsc_1}$

$$= \left(\frac{V_b \phi c_l}{\alpha_c B_l^\circ \Delta t}\right)_1 (p_1^{n+1} - p_1^n). \quad (5.85b)$$

Fig. 5.19 shows a 1D, point-distributed grid system over the same reservoir discussed earlier. Note that, in the point-distributed grid system, the gridpoints lie on the boundaries of the reservoir. For a point-distributed grid, we can use the central-difference approximation for both boundaries. Applying the central-difference approximation to Eq. 5.74 at the left boundary (at $x = x_1$) in Fig. 5.19 results in

$$\frac{\partial p}{\partial x} \approx \frac{p_2 - p_0}{x_2 - x_0} = C \quad (5.87a)$$

or $p_0 = p_2 - C(x_2 - x_0)$. (5.87b)

Similarly, for the right boundary (at $x = x_5$) of the grid system shown in Fig. 5.19,

$$p_6 = p_4 + C(x_6 - x_4). \quad (5.88)$$

For a no-flow boundary ($C = 0$), Eqs. 5.87b and 5.88 indicate that, for a point-distributed grid, the pressures of the grid cells just outside the reservoir equal the pressures of the grid cells located one grid cell away from the boundary cells. Again, an alternative approach to modeling no-flow boundaries is to adjust values of transmissibility of appropriate terms in the finite-difference equations and to use the actual bulk volume of boundary blocks.

For no-flow boundaries ($C = 0$), Eqs. 5.87b and 5.88 become

$$p_0 = p_2 \quad (5.89)$$

and $p_6 = p_4$. (5.90)

We can also use the transmissibility terms to model no-flow boundaries. For a point-distributed grid system, we need to assign a zero value to boundary transmissibilities

$$T_{lx_{1-1/2}} = 0 \quad (5.91)$$

and $T_{lx_{5+1/2}} = 0$ (5.92)

and use the actual bulk volume and actual production (injection) rate for the boundary blocks. Example 5.6 provides the details of the development of Eq. 5.91.

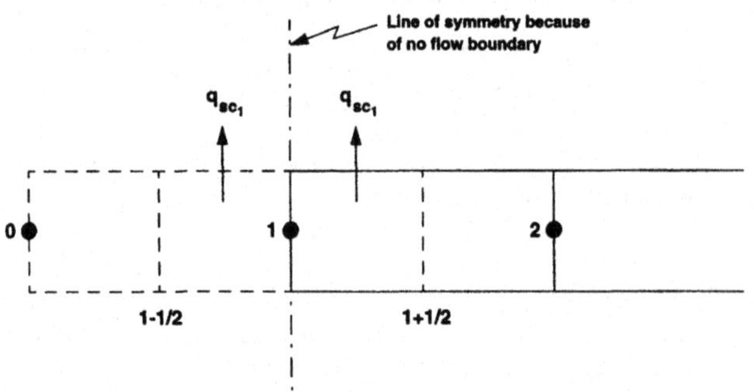

Fig. 5.20—Handling of a no-flow boundary with a point-distributed finite-difference grid (Example 5.6).

Example 5.6. For the point-distributed grid system in Fig. 5.19, show that the use of Eq. 5.89 is equivalent to the use of Eq. 5.91 for implementing a no-flow boundary in Eq. 5.75.

Solution. Eq. 5.75, written for the complete Gridblock 1, which is enclosed between boundaries 1 − ½ and 1 + ½, is the following (see **Fig. 20**):

$$T^n_{lx_{1+1/2}}(p_2^{n+1} - p_1^{n+1}) - T^n_{lx_{1-1/2}}(p_1^{n+1} - p_0^{n+1}) + q_{sc}$$

$$= \left(\frac{V_b \phi_1 c_l}{\alpha_c B_l^\circ \Delta t}\right)(p_1^{n+1} - p_1^n) \quad (5.93a)$$

where $q_{sc} = 2q_{sc1}$, (5.93b)

$$V_b = 2V_{b1}, \quad (5.93c)$$

$$T_{lx_{1-1/2}} = T_{lx_{1+1/2}}, \quad (5.93d)$$

and $p_0 = p_2$. (5.93e)

Substituting Eqs. 5.93b through e into Eq. 5.93a results in

$$T^n_{lx_{1+1/2}}(p_2^{n+1} - p_1^{n+1}) - T^n_{lx_{1+1/2}}(p_1^{n+1} - p_2^{n+1}) + 2q_{sc_1}$$

$$= \left(\frac{2V_{b_1} \phi_1 c_l}{\alpha_c B_l^\circ \Delta t}\right)(p_1^{n+1} - p_1^n). \quad (5.94a)$$

or $2T^n_{lx_{1+1/2}}(p_2^{n+1} - p_1^{n+1}) + 2q_{sc_1}$

$$= 2\left(\frac{V_b \phi c_l}{\alpha_c B_l^\circ \Delta t}\right)_1 (p_1^{n+1} - p_1^n). \quad (5.94b)$$

or after dividing through by 2, the equation for actual Gridblock 1 is

$$T^n_{lx_{1+1/2}}(p_2^{n+1} - p_1^{n+1}) + q_{sc_1}$$

$$= \left(\frac{V_b \phi c_l}{\alpha_c B_l^\circ \Delta t}\right)_1 (p_1^{n+1} - p_1^n). \quad (5.94c)$$

Eq. 5.94c also can be obtained from Eq. 5.75 by setting $T^n_{lx_{1-1/2}} = 0$ and using the actual bulk volume, V_{b1}, and production rate, q_{sc_1}, of Gridblock 1 (enclosed between x_1 and $x_{1+1/2}$).

$$T^n_{lx_{1+1/2}}(p_2^{n+1} - p_1^{n+1}) - 0(p_1^{n+1} - p_0^{n+1}) + q_{sc_1}$$

$$= \left(\frac{V_b \phi c_l}{\alpha_c B_l^\circ \Delta t}\right)_1 (p_1^{n+1} - p_1^n), \quad (5.95)$$

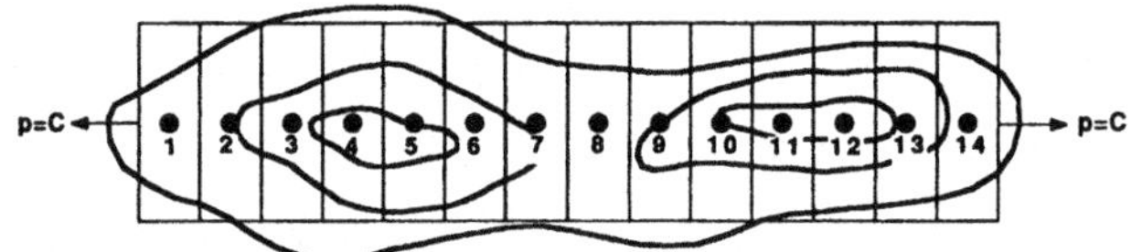

Fig. 5.21—Porous medium and block-centered, finite-difference grid with specified-pressure boundaries.

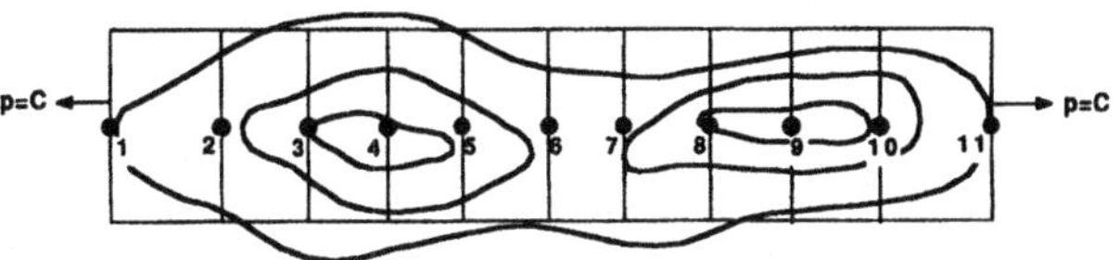

Fig. 5.22—Porous medium and point-distributed, finite-difference grid with specified-pressure boundaries.

which, after simplification, is identical to Eq. 5.94c.

Specified-Pressure Boundaries. For a specified pressure at the external boundary,

$$p_1 = C \quad \text{(5.96)}$$

is valid. Boundaries of this type are encountered in the presence of strong aquifers. Again, the value of C can be a function of time, but for the present discussion it will be assumed constant.

Fig. 5.21 shows a block-centered grid system in the presence of a specified-pressure boundary. Several methods can be used to approximate a specified-pressure boundary for a block-centered grid system. The simplest approach is to assign the specified boundary pressure to the grid cells on the boundary. The advantage of this method is that we do not have to solve any equation for grid cells on the boundary. There is one disadvantage with this treatment: for block-centered grids, the pressure point for boundary cells is not actually on the boundary but is $\Delta x/2$ away from the boundary. This problem can be somewhat alleviated by reducing the grid size along the boundary.

A second approach that can be used for block-centered grids is to extrapolate the boundary pressure, C, from the two closest pressure points to the reservoir boundary. One such approximation, written for the left boundary in Fig. 5.21, is

$$(1 + \Omega)p_1 - \Omega p_2 = C, \quad \text{(5.97a)}$$

where $\Omega = \Delta x_1/(\Delta x_2 + \Delta x_1)$. For the special case of uniform grid spacing, $\Delta x_1 = \Delta x_2$, and Eq. 5.97a becomes

$$\frac{3}{2}p_1 - \frac{1}{2}p_2 = C, \quad \text{(5.97b)}$$

Eq. 5.97 is the common form of the extrapolation approach that appears in the petroleum literature.[2]

Example 5.7. Derive Eq. 5.97 for a block–centered grid system.

Solution. For a block–centered grid system, the slope of the pressure with respect to distance, x, (the pressure gradient) is (see Fig. 5.21)

$$m = \frac{p_2 - p_1}{\frac{\Delta x_2}{2} + \frac{\Delta x_1}{2}} = \frac{2(p_2 - p_1)}{\Delta x_2 + \Delta x_1}. \quad \text{(5.98)}$$

Extrapolating the pressure from p_1 to the left boundary of the reservoir results in

$$C = p_1 - m\left(\frac{\Delta x_1}{2}\right) \quad \text{(5.99a)}$$

$$= p_1 - \frac{2(p_2 - p_1)}{\Delta x_2 + \Delta x_1}\left(\frac{\Delta x_1}{2}\right). \quad \text{(5.99b)}$$

Note that the negative sign in Eq. 5.99a is the result of the fact that we are extrapolating pressure in the negative x direction. If we were extrapolating in the positive x direction (right boundary in Fig. 5.21), then we would use a positive sign.

Setting $\Omega = \Delta x_1/(\Delta x_2 + \Delta x_1)$, results in

$$C = p_1 - \Omega(p_2 - p_1)$$

or $C = (1 + \Omega)p_1 - \Omega p_2$,

which is Eq. 5.97a. For the special case of a uniform gird, $\Delta x = \Delta x_1 = \Delta x_2$. Consequently,

$$\Omega = \frac{\Delta x}{\Delta x + \Delta x} = \frac{1}{2}.$$

Substituting into Eq. 5.97a results in

$$C = \frac{3}{2}p_1 - \frac{1}{2}p_2,$$

which is Eq. 5.97b.

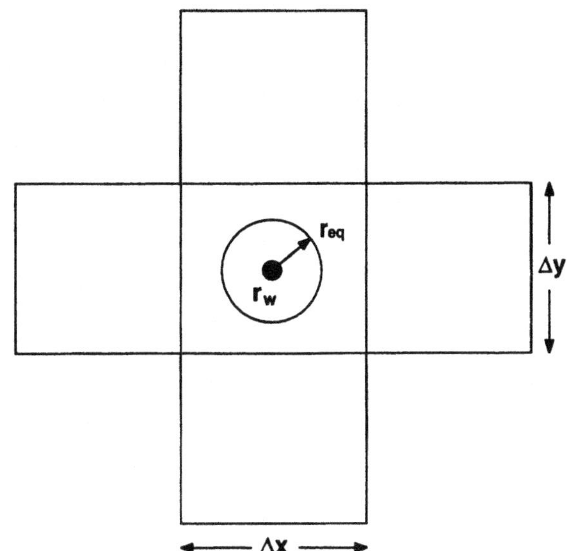

Fig. 5.23—Finite-difference gridblock containing a wellbore.

Although this approach is more rigorous, it has the disadvantage that additional equations must be solved along with the finite-difference equations. This directly corresponds to more central-processing-unit time for a simulation run.

The implementation of specified-pressure boundaries for a point-distributed grid is relatively simple; **Fig. 5.22** shows an example. Because the pressure point of the point-distributed grid lies on the boundary, the specified pressure can be applied by assigning it as the pressure of the boundary cell. No extrapolations are required for specified-pressure boundaries on a point-distributed grid.

Internal Boundaries. Internal boundaries in a hydrocarbon reservoir include wells, nonreservoir rock, and sealing faults. Each of these boundaries requires a different implementation method.

Wells. With the exception of single-well simulations in cylindrical coordinates, the dimensions of a simulation gridblock are generally much larger than the dimensions of the wellbore. For these cases, it can be assumed that the well has relatively little volume and behaves like a line source in the gridblock. For full-field models in rectangular coordinates, therefore, the boundary conditions can be approximated by a line-source/sink term. The source/sink terms are applied through the q_{lsc_i} terms in the finite-difference equations. **Fig. 5.23** shows a wellbore in a large rectangular grid system.

Expressions for the source/sink term can be obtained by use of the steady-state well theory. The flow into a wellbore can be estimated from a well model, such as

$$q_{lsc_{i,j,k}} = \frac{-2\pi\beta_c k_H h}{\left[\log_e\left(r_{eq}/r_w\right) + s\right]} \frac{1}{\mu_l B_l}\left(p_{i,j,k} - p_{wf}\right), \quad \text{(5.100)}$$

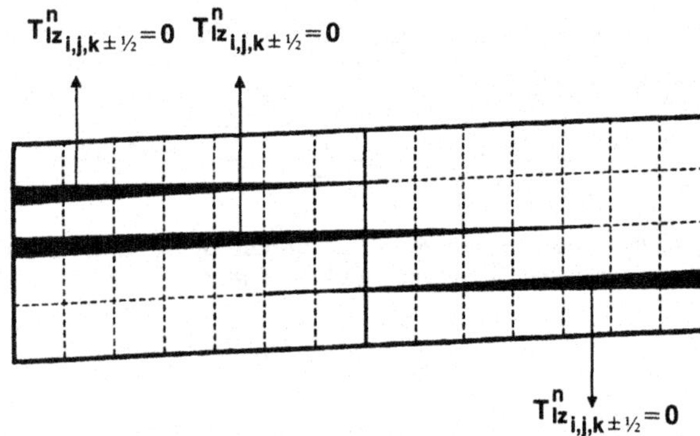

Fig. 5.24—Cross section showing vertical flow barriers.

where, for anisotropic reservoirs in rectangular grid cells, Peaceman[6] showed that the equivalent radius of a well block, r_{eq}, is

$$r_{eq} = 0.28\frac{\left[\left(k_y/k_x\right)^{1/2}(\Delta x)^2 + \left(k_x/k_y\right)^{1/2}(\Delta y)^2\right]^{1/2}}{\left(k_y/k_x\right)^{1/4} + \left(k_x/k_y\right)^{1/4}}, \quad \ldots\ (5.101)$$

and the horizontal permeability is

$$k_H = \sqrt{k_x k_y}. \quad \ldots\ (5.102)$$

Chaps. 6 and 9 discuss the details of well treatment in reservoir simulation for single-phase and multiphase flow, respectively.

Nonreservoir Rock. The presence of nonreservoir rock in a petroleum reservoir may have a significant impact on reservoir performance. The performance most significantly affected by nonreservoir rock includes the volumetrics of the in-place hydrocarbons, gas- and water-coning behavior in the presence of shales, and gravity over-/underride during displacement processes in the presence of shales. In addition, the effective vertical permeability of a gridblock also depends on the amount and continuity of any shales it contains.

Shale stringers of negligible volume that act as flow barriers can be modeled effectively by assigning zero values of vertical transmissibility to the layers bounded by the shale. The section on external boundaries discussed this approach to modeling no-flow boundaries. If the shales are more massive, it may be necessary to alter the net-/gross-thickness ratio or adjust cell tops to allow for vertical gaps between flow units. Most commercial simulators have the capability to alter these grid properties. **Fig. 5.24** shows a cross-sectional view of a finite-difference grid in the presence of vertical flow barriers.

Sealing Faults. Faults are common geologic features in petroleum reservoirs; often, they are sealing faults that act as barriers to flow. We have already seen how zero values of transmissibility can be used to model no-flow boundaries. This method can also be applied to sealing faults. **Fig. 5.25** shows a cross-sectional view of a finite-difference grid in the presence of a sealing fault.

5.6 Explicit and Implicit Finite-Difference Formulations

The problem to be solved in reservoir modeling is to advance the simulation from the initial conditions to future times. This is accomplished by stepping through the simulation with discrete time intervals called timesteps.

Earlier, this chapter derived two finite-difference approximations: the forward- and the backward-difference equations (Eqs. 5.69 and 5.66, respectively). Although they have similar forms, there is a fundamental difference between the two formulations. Because of the time levels assigned to the pressures on the left sides of the equations, the forward-difference equation results in an explicit calculation for the new-time-level pressures while the backward-difference equation results in an implicit calculation for the new-time-level pressures. This difference is the subject of this section.

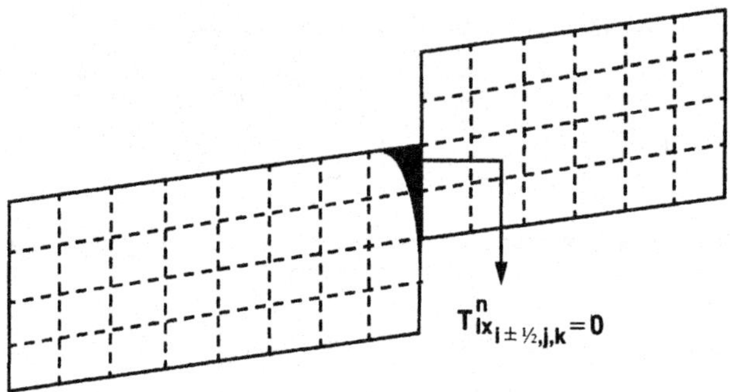

Fig. 5.25—Cross section showing a sealing fault.

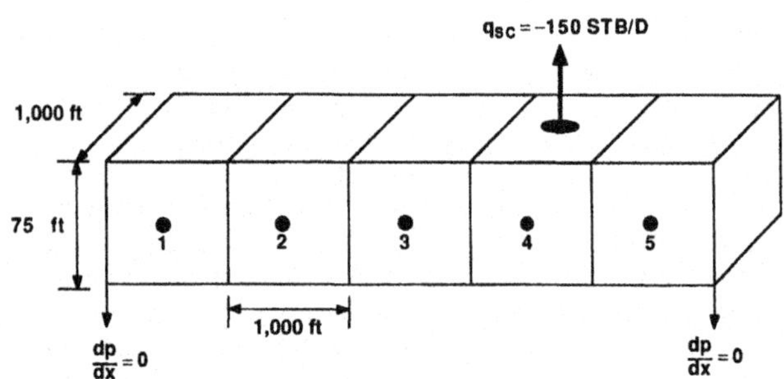

Fig. 5.26—Porous medium and block-centered grid system for Example 5.8.

5.6.1 Explicit Formulation. The forward-difference approximation to the flow equation results in an explicit calculation procedure for the new-time-level pressures (designated $n+1$ in the finite-difference equations). Solving the forward-difference equation (Eq. 5.69) for the unknown quantity, p_i^{n+1}, yields the expression

$$p_i^{n+1} = p_i^n + \left(\frac{\alpha_c B_l^\circ \Delta t}{V_b \phi c_l}\right)_i q_{lsc_i} + \left(\frac{\alpha_c B_l^\circ \Delta t}{V_b \phi c_l}\right)_i \times \left[T^n_{lx_{i+1/2}} p^n_{i+1} - \left(T^n_{lx_{i+1/2}} + T^n_{lx_{i-1/2}}\right) p_i^n + T^n_{lx_{i-1/2}} p^n_{i-1}\right]. \quad \ldots\ (5.103)$$

All terms on the right side of Eq. 5.103 are known because all pressures appearing on this side are at the known (old) time level, n. In this equation, the pressures at the new-time level can be obtained explicitly by use of these known pressures. The following examples show the explicit calculation procedure.

Example 5.8. For the 1D, block-centered grid shown in **Fig. 5.26**, determine the pressure distribution during the first year of production. The initial reservoir pressure is 6,000 psia. The rock and fluid properties for this problem are $\Delta x = 1{,}000$ ft, $\Delta y = 1{,}000$ ft, $\Delta z = 75$ ft, $B_l = 1$ RB/STB, $c_l = 3.5 \times 10^{-6}$ psi^{-1}, $k_x = 15$ md, $\phi = 0.18$, $\mu_l = 10$ cp, and $B_l^\circ = 1$ RB/STB.

Use timestep sizes of $\Delta t = 10$, 15, and 30 days. Assume B_l acts as a constant within the pressure range of interest. [This example is also presented as an exercise (Exercise 5.12) where this assumption is not used.]

Solution.

1. For $\Delta t = 10$ days.

Because this problem uses customary units, we refer to Table 4.1 to calculate the fluid and block properties as $\Delta x = 1{,}000$ ft, $A_x = \Delta y \Delta z = (1{,}000\text{ ft})(75\text{ ft}) = 75{,}000\text{ ft}^2$, $V_b = \Delta x \Delta y \Delta z = (1{,}000\text{ ft})(1{,}000\text{ ft})(75\text{ ft}) = 75 \times 10^6\text{ ft}^3$, $k_x = 0.015$ darcy, $\mu_l = 10$ cp, $B_l = 1$ RB/STB and $B_l^\circ = 1$ RB/STB, $c_l = 3.5 \times 10^{-6}$ psi^{-1}, $q_{lsc_4} = -150$ STB/D, $\phi = 0.18$, and $\Delta t = 10$ days. Therefore,

$(\alpha_c B_l^\circ \Delta t/V_b \phi c_l)_i = [(5.615)(1)(10)]/[(75\times 10^6)(0.18)(3.5\times 10^{-6})]$ $= 1.18836$; and, for uniform gridblocks,

$$T^n_{lx_{i+½}} = T^n_{lx_{i-½}} = \left(\beta_c \frac{A_x k_x}{\mu_l B_l \Delta x}\right)^n_{i-½} = \left(\beta_c \frac{A_x k_x}{\mu_l B_l \Delta x}\right)^n_{i+½}$$

$$= \beta_c \frac{A_x k_x}{\mu_l B_l \Delta x} \quad \text{(5.104)}$$

or $\{[(1.127)(75{,}000)(0.015)]/[(10)(1)(1{,}000)]\} = 0.1268$. We now apply the initial conditions at $n=0$; $p_i^n = 6{,}000$ psia for Gridblocks $i=1, 2, \ldots, 5$. For Gridblock 1, Timestep 1,

$$p_1^{n+1} = p_1^n + 1.18836[0.1268\ p_2^n - 0.126840\ p_1^n + (0)p_0]$$
$$= p_1^n + (0.1507)p_2^n - (0.1507)p_1^n + (0)p_0$$
$$= 6{,}000 + (0.1507)(6{,}000) - (0.1507)(6{,}000)$$
$$= 6{,}000 \text{ psia.}$$

For Gridblock 2, Timestep 1,

$$p_2^{n+1} = p_2^n + (0.1507)p_3^n - (0.3013)p_2^n + (0.1507)p_1^n$$
$$= 6{,}000 + (0.1507)(6{,}000)$$
$$- (0.3013)(6{,}000) + (0.1507)(6{,}000)$$
$$= 6{,}000 \text{ psia.}$$

For Gridblock 3, Timestep 1,

$$p_3^{n+1} = p_3^n + (0.1507)p_4^{n+1} - (0.3013)p_3^n + (0.1507)p_2^n$$
$$= 6{,}000 + (0.1507)(6{,}000) - (0.3013)(6{,}000)$$
$$+ (0.1507)(6{,}000)$$
$$= 6{,}000 \text{ psia.}$$

For Gridblock 4, Timestep 1,

$$p_4^{n+1} = p_4^n + (1.18836)(-150)$$
$$+ (0.1507)p_5^n - (0.3013)p_4^n + (0.1507)p_3^n$$
$$= 6{,}000 - (178.2540) + (0.1507)(6{,}000)$$
$$- (0.3013)(6{,}000) + (0.1507)(6{,}000)$$
$$= 5{,}821.75 \text{ psia.}$$

For Gridblock 5, Timestep 1,

$$p_5^{n+1} = p_5^n + (0)p_6^n - (0.1507)p_5^n + (0.1507)p_4^n$$
$$= 6{,}000 - (0.1507)(6{,}000) + (0.1507)(6{,}000)$$
$$= 6{,}000 \text{ psia.}$$

This is the end of the first timestep. Now, set $p_i^n = p_i^{n+1}$, where $i=1, 2, \ldots, 5$. That is to say, $p_1^1=6{,}000$ psia, $p_2^1=6{,}000$ psia, $p_3^1=6{,}000$ psia, $p_4^1=5{,}821.75$ psia, and $p_5^1=6{,}000$ psia at $t=10$ days. We now proceed to the next timestep.

For Gridblock 1, Timestep 2,

$$p_1^{n+1} = p_1^n + (0.1507)p_2^n - (0.1507)p_1^n + (0)p_0^n$$
$$= 6{,}000 + (0.1507)(6{,}000) - (0.1507)(6{,}000)$$
$$= 6{,}000 \text{ psia.}$$

For Gridblock 2, Timestep 2,

$$p_2^{n+1} = p_2^n + (0.1507)p_3^n - (0.3013)p_2^n + (0.1507)p_1^n$$
$$= 6{,}000 + (0.1507)(6{,}000) - (0.3013)(6{,}000)$$
$$+ (0.1507)(6{,}000)$$
$$= 6{,}000 \text{ psia.}$$

For Gridblock 3, Timestep 2,

$$p_3^{n+1} = p_3^n + (0.1507)p_4^n - (0.3013)p_3^n + (0.1507)p_2^n$$
$$= 6{,}000 + (0.1507)(5821.75) - (0.3013)(6{,}000)$$
$$+ (0.1507)(6{,}000)$$
$$= 5{,}973.14 \text{ psia.}$$

For Gridblock 4, Timestep 2,

$$p_4^{n+1} = p_4^n - (178.254) + (0.1507)p_5^n - (0.3013)p_4^n + (0.1507)p_3^n$$
$$= 5{,}821.75 - 178.254 + (0.1507)(6{,}000)$$
$$- (0.3013)(5{,}821.75) + (0.1507)(6{,}000)$$
$$= 5{,}697.21 \text{ psia.}$$

For Gridblock 5, Timestep 2,

$$p_5^{n+1} = p_5^n + (0)p_6^n - (0.1507)p_5^n + (0.1507)p_4^n$$
$$= 6{,}000 - (0.1507)(6{,}000) + (0.1507)(5{,}821.75)$$
$$= 5{,}973.14 \text{ psia.}$$

This is the end of the second timestep. This procedure is repeated until the end of the simulation. **Table 5.1** shows the results of this explicit simulation.

2. For $\Delta t = 15$ days,

$$\left(\frac{\alpha_c B_l^\circ \Delta t}{V_b \phi c_l}\right)_i = \frac{(5.615)(1)(15)}{(75\times 10^6)(0.18)(3.5\times 10^{-6})} = 1.78254$$

and $$\left(\beta_c \frac{A_x k_x}{\mu_l B_l \Delta x}\right)_{i-½} = \left(\beta_c \frac{A_x k_x}{\mu_l B_l \Delta x}\right)_{i+½} = 0.1268.$$

For Gridblock 1,

$$p_1^{n+1} = p_1^n + (0.2260)p_2^n - (0.2260)p_1^n + (0)p_0^n.$$

For Gridblock 2,

$$p_2^{n+1} = p_2^n + (0.2260)p_3^n - (0.4520)p_2^n + (0.2260)p_1^n.$$

For Gridblock 3,

$$p_3^{n+1} = p_3^n + (0.2260)p_4^n - (0.4520)p_3^n + (0.2260)p_2^n.$$

For Gridblock 4,

$$p_4^{n+1} = p_4^n + (1.78254)(-150) + (0.2260)p_5^n$$
$$- (0.4520)p_4^n + (0.2260)p_3^n.$$

For Gridblock 5,

$$p_5^{n+1} = p_5^n + (0)p_6^n - (0.2260)p_5^n + (0.2260)p_4^n.$$

Table 5.2 shows the results of this explicit simulation.

3. For $\Delta t = 30$ days,

$$\left(\frac{\alpha_c B_l^\circ \Delta t}{V_b \phi c_l}\right)_i = 3.56508$$

and $$\left(\beta_c \frac{A_x k_x}{\mu_l B_l \Delta x}\right)_{i-½} = \left(\beta_c \frac{A_x k_x}{\mu_l B_l \Delta x}\right)_{i+½} = 0.1268.$$

For Gridblock 1,

$$p_1^{n+1} = p_1^n + (0.4520)p_2^n - (0.4520)p_1^n + (0)p_0^n.$$

TABLE 5.1—EXPLICIT-SIMULATION-STUDY RESULTS OF THE PROBLEM IN FIG. 5.26 (Δt=10 days)

Time (days)	Pressure (psia) Block 1	Block 2	Block 3	Block 4	Block 5
0.0	6,000.00	6,000.00	6,000.00	6,000.00	6,000.00
10.0	6,000.00	6,000.00	6,000.00	5,821.75	6,000.00
20.0	6,000.00	6,000.00	5,973.14	5,697.21	5,973.14
30.0	6,000.00	5,995.95	5,935.61	5,602.10	5,931.57
40.0	5,999.39	5,987.47	5,894.46	5,523.74	5,881.93
50.0	5,997.59	5,975.25	5,852.61	5,455.31	5,827.96
60.0	5,994.23	5,960.14	5,811.23	5,393.06	5,771.81
70.0	5,989.09	5,942.84	5,770.66	5,334.88	5,714.75
80.0	5,982.12	5,923.87	5,730.95	5,279.52	5,657.51
90.0	5,973.35	5,903.58	5,692.00	5,226.23	5,600.56
100.0	5,962.83	5,882.21	5,653.70	5,174.55	5,544.16
110.0	5,950.69	5,859.93	5,615.94	5,124.18	5,488.47
120.0	5,937.01	5,836.84	5,578.61	5,074.91	5,433.59
130.0	5,921.92	5,813.03	5,541.62	5,026.59	5,379.54
140.0	5,905.51	5,788.54	5,504.91	4,979.11	5,326.36
150.0	5,887.89	5,763.43	5,468.43	4,932.40	5,274.04
160.0	5,869.14	5,737.73	5,432.11	4,886.38	5,222.57
170.0	5,849.34	5,711.49	5,395.94	4,841.01	5,171.92
180.0	5,828.57	5,684.71	5,359.87	4,796.22	5,122.06
190.0	5,806.89	5,657.44	5,323.89	4,751.99	5,072.96
200.0	5,784.38	5,629.70	5,287.98	4,708.26	5,024.60
210.0	5,761.07	5,601.52	5,252.12	4,665.02	4,976.94
220.0	5,737.03	5,572.92	5,216.30	4,622.22	4,929.94
230.0	5,712.30	5,543.91	5,180.52	4,579.84	4,883.58
240.0	5,686.93	5,514.53	5,144.77	4,537.85	4,837.81
250.0	5,660.96	5,484.80	5,109.04	4,496.24	4,792.62
260.0	5,634.42	5,454.72	5,073.32	4,454.97	4,747.96
270.0	5,607.34	5,424.33	5,037.62	4,414.03	4,703.82
280.0	5,579.77	5,393.64	5,001.93	4,373.39	4,660.16
290.0	5,551.72	5,362.67	4,966.25	4,333.05	4,616.95
300.0	5,523.24	5,331.42	4,930.57	4,292.97	4,574.17
310.0	5,494.34	5,299.93	4,894.90	4,253.15	4,531.81
320.0	5,465.05	5,268.19	4,859.23	4,213.58	4,489.82
330.0	5,435.39	5,236.24	4,823.57	4,174.22	4,448.20
340.0	5,405.38	5,204.07	4,787.91	4,135.09	4,406.92
350.0	5,375.05	5,171.70	4,752.25	4,096.15	4,365.96
360.0	5,344.41	5,139.14	4,716.60	4,057.40	4,325.31

For Gridblock 2,

$$p_2^{n+1} = p_2^n + (0.4520)p_3^n - (0.9040)p_2^n + (0.4520)p_1^n.$$

For Gridblock 3,

$$p_3^{n+1} = p_3^n + (0.4520)p_4^n - (0.9040)p_3^n + (0.4520)p_2^n.$$

For Gridblock 4,

$$p_4^{n+1} = p_4^n + (3.5608)(-150) + (0.4520)p_5^n - (0.9040)p_4^n + (0.4520)p_3^n.$$

For Gridblock 5,

$$p_5^{n+1} = p_5^n + (0)p_6^n - (0.4520)p_5^n + (0.4520)p_4^n.$$

TABLE 5.2—EXPLICIT-SIMULATION-STUDY RESULTS OF THE PROBLEM IN FIG. 5.26 (Δt=15 days)

Time (days)	Pressure (psia) Block 1	Block 2	Block 3	Block 4	Block 5
0.0	6,000.00	6,000.00	6,000.00	6,000.00	6,000.00
15.0	6,000.00	6,000.00	6,000.00	5,732.62	6,000.00
30.0	6,000.00	6,000.00	5,939.57	5,586.10	5,939.57
45.0	6,000.00	5,986.34	5,873.34	5,478.49	5,859.68
60.0	5,996.91	5,963.89	5,809.64	5,386.50	5,773.53
75.0	5,989.45	5,936.49	5,748.87	5,302.22	5,686.06
90.0	5,977.48	5,906.06	5,690.33	5,222.53	5,599.31
105.0	5,961.34	5,873.44	5,633.36	5,146.03	5,514.16
120.0	5,941.48	5,839.05	5,577.48	5,071.99	5,430.96
135.0	5,918.33	5,803.08	5,522.35	4,999.98	5,349.83
150.0	5,892.28	5,765.68	5,467.74	4,929.72	5,270.76
165.0	5,863.67	5,726.96	5,413.48	4,861.01	5,193.69
180.0	5,832.77	5,687.01	5,359.47	4,793.68	5,118.50
195.0	5,799.83	5,645.93	5,305.62	4,727.58	5,045.09
210.0	5,765.05	5,603.80	5,251.89	4,662.60	4,973.33
225.0	5,728.60	5,560.71	5,198.24	4,598.63	4,903.10
240.0	5,690.66	5,516.74	5,144.65	4,535.57	4,834.29
255.0	5,651.35	5,471.95	5,091.09	4,473.36	4,766.78
270.0	5,610.81	5,426.42	5,037.55	4,411.90	4,700.46
285.0	5,569.13	5,380.21	4,984.04	4,351.14	4,635.25
300.0	5,526.44	5,333.37	4,930.54	4,291.00	4,571.04
315.0	5,482.80	5,285.96	4,877.04	4,231.45	4,507.75
330.0	5,438.31	5,238.03	4,823.55	4,172.42	4,445.30
345.0	5,393.05	5,189.62	4,770.07	4,113.87	4,383.63
360.0	5,347.07	5,140.78	4,716.58	4,055.76	4,322.66

TABLE 5.3—EXPLICIT-SIMULATION-STUDY RESULTS OF THE PROBLEM IN FIG. 5.26 (Δt=30 days)

Time (days)	Pressure (psia) Block 1	Block 2	Block 3	Block 4	Block 5
0.0	6,000.00	6,000.00	6,000.00	6,000.00	6,000.00
30.0	6,000.00	6,000.00	6,000.00	5,465.24	6,000.00
60.0	6,000.00	6,000.00	5,758.28	5,413.91	5,758.28
90.0	6,000.00	5,890.74	5,711.88	5,190.47	5,602.62
120.0	5,950.61	5,859.28	5,557.04	5,077.69	5,416.33
150.0	5,909.33	5,763.95	5,476.98	4,912.67	5,263.26
180.0	5,843.62	5,699.95	5,351.62	4,791.45	5,104.79
210.0	5,778.68	5,607.44	5,255.87	4,651.52	4,963.16
240.0	5,701.28	5,525.93	5,141.61	4,530.79	4,822.29
270.0	5,622.02	5,431.47	5,039.23	4,403.89	4,690.53
300.0	5,535.89	5,340.30	4,929.35	4,285.87	4,560.97
330.0	5,447.49	5,242.96	4,824.25	4,166.31	4,436.62
360.0	5,355.04	5,146.14	4,716.11	4,051.12	4,314.44

Table 5.3 shows the results of this explicit simulation.

This example illustrates several points discussed throughout this chapter. The first point is that the no-flow boundaries can be modeled by assigning zero transmissibilities at the edges of the porous medium. The second is that the pressures calculated at identical times are different, depending on the timestep size used in the calculation. This is indicative of the approximate nature of the finite-difference technique. There is no reason why these approximations should give the

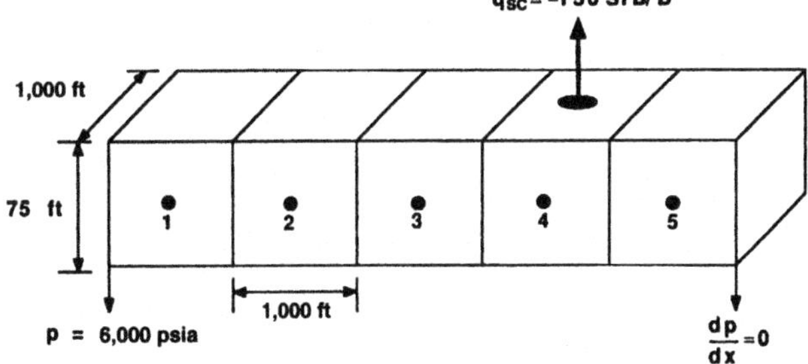

Fig. 5.27—Porous medium and block-centered grid system for Example 5.9.

same results for different timestep sizes. Because the approximation is first order, the smaller timestep sizes generally give more precise results when compared with the solution of the original PDE.

A final point illustrated by this example is that the pressure transient created by fluid withdrawal from the well in Gridblock 4 can move only one cell per timestep. This is a property of the explicit methods only. For a timestep size of 10 days, it takes the pressure transient 40 days to reach the left boundary, while for a timestep size of 30 days it takes the pressure transient 120 days to reach the boundary. That is, four timesteps are always needed for the pressure transient to reach the left boundary in this example.

Example 5.9. For the 1D, block-centered grid shown in **Fig. 5.27**, determine the pressure distribution during the first year of production. This problem is identical to Example 5.8, except that the no-flow boundary on the left side of the reservoir is replaced by a constant-pressure boundary. Use the same rock and fluid properties as in Example 5.8. Although this is a block-centered grid system, assume that the pressure in Gridblock 1 is equal to the boundary pressure. Use a timestep of 15 days.

Solution. As in Example 5.8, $\alpha_c B_l^{\circ} \Delta t / V_b \phi c_l = 1.78254$ and $\beta_c A_x k_x / \mu_l B_l \Delta x = 0.1268$ for all blocks.

For Gridblock 1, Timestep 1, $p_1^{n+1} = 6,000$ psia.

For Gridblock 2, Timestep 1,

$$p_2^{n+1} = p_2^n + 1.78254\big[0.1268\ p_3^n - (0.1268 + 0.1268)\ p_2^n + 0.1268 p_1^n\big]$$

$$= p_2^n + (0.2260)p_3^n - (0.4520)p_2^n + (0.2260)p_1^n$$

$$= 6,000 + (0.2260)(6,000) - (0.4520)(6,000) + (0.2260)(6,000)$$

$$= 6,000 \text{ psia.}$$

For Gridblock 3, Timestep 1,

$$p_3^{n+1} = p_3^n + (0.2260)p_4^n - (0.4520)p_3^n + (0.2260)p_2^n$$

$$= 6,000 + (0.2260)(6,000) - (0.4520)(6,000) + (0.2260)(6,000)$$

$$= 6,000 \text{ psia.}$$

For Gridblock 4, Timestep 1,

$$p_4^{n+1} = p_4^n + (1.78254)(-150) + (0.2260)p_5^n - (0.4520)p_4^n + (0.2260)p_3^n$$

$$= 6,000 - 267.381 + (0.2260)(6,000) - (0.4520)(6,000) + (0.2260)(6,000)$$

$$= 5,732.62 \text{ psia.}$$

TABLE 5.4—EXPLICIT-SIMULATION-STUDY RESULTS OF THE PROBLEM IN FIG. 5.27 (Δt= 15 days)

Time	Pressure (psia)				
(days)	Block 1	Block 2	Block 3	Block 4	Block 5
0.0	6,000.00	6,000.00	6,000.00	6,000.00	6,000.00
15.0	6,000.00	6,000.00	6,000.00	5,732.62	6,000.00
30.0	6,000.00	6,000.00	5,939.57	5,586.10	5,939.57
45.0	6,000.00	5,986.34	5,873.34	5,478.49	5,859.68
60.0	6,000.00	5,963.89	5,809.64	5,386.50	5,773.53
75.0	6,000.00	5,937.19	5,748.87	5,302.22	5,686.06
90.0	6,000.00	5,908.82	5,690.49	5,222.53	5,599.31
105.0	6,000.00	5,880.09	5,634.07	5,146.07	5,514.16
120.0	6,000.00	5,851.59	5,579.38	5,072.17	5,430.97
135.0	6,000.00	5,823.61	5,526.27	5,000.51	5,349.88
150.0	6,000.00	5,796.27	5,474.64	4,930.91	5,270.92
165.0	6,000.00	5,769.63	5,424.45	4,863.26	5,194.08
180.0	6,000.00	5,743.68	5,375.63	4,797.47	5,119.31
195.0	6,000.00	5,718.43	5,328.14	4,733.49	5,046.57
210.0	6,000.00	5,693.86	5,281.96	4,671.26	4,975.82
225.0	6,000.00	5,669.96	5,237.03	4,610.73	4,906.99
240.0	6,000.00	5,646.70	5,193.33	4,551.85	4,840.03
255.0	6,000.00	5,624.09	5,150.82	4,494.58	4,774.90
270.0	6,000.00	5,602.08	5,109.46	4,438.86	4,711.55
285.0	6,000.00	5,580.68	5,069.24	4,384.67	4,649.92
300.0	6,000.00	5,559.86	5,030.11	4,331.95	4,589.97
315.0	6,000.00	5,539.61	4,992.05	4,280.67	4,531.66
330.0	6,000.00	5,519.91	4,955.03	4,230.79	4,474.93
345.0	6,000.00	5,500.75	4,919.01	4,182.27	4,419.76
360.0	6,000.00	5,482.10	4,883.98	4,135.07	4,366.08

For Gridblock 5, Timestep 1,

$$p_5^{n+1} = p_5^n + (0)p_6^n - (0.2260)p_5^n + (0.2260)p_4^n$$

$$= 6,000 - (0.2260)(6,000) + (0.2260)(6,000)$$

$$= 6,000 \text{ psia.}$$

This is the end of the first timestep. Now, set $p_i^n = p_i^{n+1}$, where $i = 1, 2, \ldots, 5$, and proceed to the second timestep.

For Gridblock 1, Timestep 2, $p_1^{n+1} = 6,000$ psia.

For Gridblock 2, Timestep 2,

$$p_2^{n+1} = p_2^n + (0.2260)p_3^n - (0.4520)p_2^n + (0.2260)p_1^n$$

$$= 6,000 + (0.2260)(6,000) - (0.4520)(6,000) + (0.2260)(6,000)$$

$$= 6,000 \text{ psia.}$$

For Gridblock 3, Timestep 2,

$$p_3^{n+1} = p_3^n + (0.2260)p_4^n - (0.4520)p_3^n + (0.2260)p_2^n$$

$$= 6,000 + (0.2260)(5,732.62) - (0.4520)(6,000) + (0.2260)(6,000)$$

$$= 5,939.57 \text{ psia.}$$

For Gridblock 4, Timestep 2,

$$p_4^{n+1} = p_4^n - 267.381 + (0.2260)p_5^n - (0.4520)p_4^n + (0.2260)p_3^n$$

$$= 6,000 - 267.381 + (0.2260)(6,000)$$

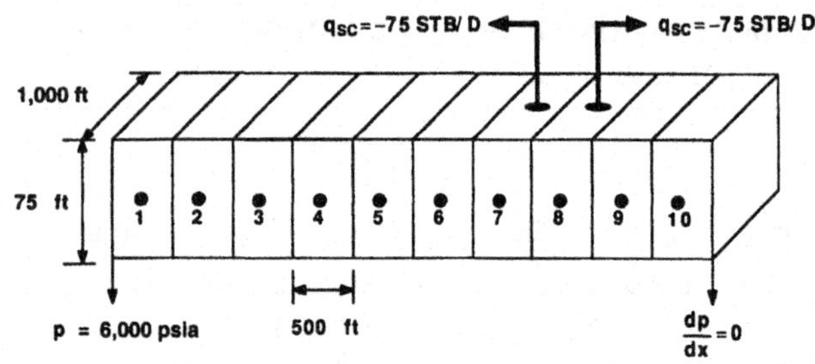

Fig. 5.28—Porous medium and block-centered grid system for Example 5.10.

$$- (0.4520)(5,732.62) + (0.2260)(6,000)$$

$$= 5,586.10 \text{ psia}.$$

For Gridblock 5, Timestep 2,

$$p_5^{n+1} = p_5^n + (0)p_6^n - (0.2260)p_5^n + (0.2260)p_4^n$$

$$= 6,000 - (0.2260)(6,000) + (0.2260)(5,732.62)$$

$$= 5,939.57 \text{ psia}.$$

This is the end of the second timestep. This procedure is continued until the end of the simulation. **Table 5.4** shows the results of this simulation.

In this example, the difference between the two types of boundary conditions is illustrated clearly. At 360 days, the pressure in the gridblock containing the well is approximately 80 psi greater in the case of pressure-specified boundary compared with the case of the no-flow boundary. This is because the pressure specified for the boundary provides pressure support to the gridblock containing the well.

The method of implementing the specified boundary pressure in Example 5.9 is the least rigorous method available for block-centered grid systems. This is because the pressure on the boundary is shifted from the gridblock edge to the block center (i.e., $\Delta x/2$ away from the reservoir boundary). Although this method is the least accurate method of implementing boundaries with specified pressure, it is the most practical method of implementation; consequently, it is the most common method of implementing boundaries with specified pressure in reservoir simulators.

One method to improve the description of a constant-pressure boundary is to use a more refined grid in the vicinity of the pressure-specified boundaries. In general, this method can improve the accuracy of modeling boundaries with specified pressure in block-centered grids. For the explicit solution techniques, however, this may lead to stability problems. Example 5.10 illustrates this.

Example 5.10. Example 5.9 used a grid spacing of $\Delta x = 1,000$ ft. Because the grid system was block centered, the specified pressure was shifted 500 ft toward the interior of the reservoir. By halving the grid spacing, this shift is reduced to 250 ft. Use the explicit forward-difference equation to simulate the problem illustrated in **Fig. 5.28** with a timestep size of $\Delta t = 15$ days. Note that this problem is identical to the problem shown in Fig. 5.27.

Solution. All gridblocks are equal; therefore, $A_{x_i} = 1,000 \times 75 = 75,000$ ft^2; $V_{b_i} = 500 \times 75 \times 1,000 = 37.5 \times 10^6$ ft^3;

$$\left(\frac{\alpha_c B_l^\circ \Delta t}{V_b \phi c_l}\right)_i = \frac{(5.615)(1)(15)}{(37.5 \times 10^6)(0.18)(3.5 \times 10^{-6})} = 3.56508;$$

and

$$\left(\beta_c \frac{A_x k_x}{\mu_l B_l \Delta x}\right)_{i-1/2} = \left(\beta_c \frac{A_x k_x}{\mu_l B_l \Delta x}\right)_{i+1/2}$$

$$= (1.127)\frac{(75,000)(0.015)}{(10)(1)(500)} = 0.25358.$$

For Gridblock 1, Timestep 1, $p_1^{n+1} = 6,000$ psia.

For Gridblock 2, Timestep 1,

$$p_2^{n+1} = p_2^n + 3.56508[0.25358\, p_3^n - (0.25358 + 0.25358)\, p_2^n + 0.25358 p_1^n]$$

$$= p_2^n + (0.9040)p_3^n - (1.808)p_2^n + (0.9040)p_1^n$$

$$= 6,000 + (0.9040)(6,000) - (1.808)(6,000) + (0.9040)(6,000)$$

$$= 6,000 \text{ psia}.$$

For Gridblock 3, Timestep 1,

$$p_3^{n+1} = p_3^n + (0.9040)p_4^n - (1.808)p_3^n + (0.9040)p_2^n$$

$$= 6,000 + (0.9040)(6,000) - (1.808)(6,000) + (0.9040)(6,000)$$

$$= 6,000 \text{ psia}.$$

For Gridblock 4, Timestep 1,

$$p_4^{n+1} = p_4^n + (0.9040)p_5^n - (1.808)p_4^n + (0.9040)p_3^n$$

$$= 6,000 + (0.9040)(6,000) - (1.808)(6,000) + (0.9040)(6,000)$$

$$= 6,000 \text{ psia}.$$

For Gridblock 5, Timestep 1,

$$p_5^{n+1} = p_5^n + (0.9040)p_6^n - (1.808)p_5^n + (0.9040)p_4^n$$

$$= 6,000 + (0.9040)(6,000) - (1.808)(6,000) + (0.9040)(6,000)$$

$$= 6,000 \text{ psia}.$$

For Gridblock 6, Timestep 1,

$$p_6^{n+1} = p_6^n + (0.9040)p_7^n - (1.808)p_6^n + (0.9040)p_5^n$$

$$= 6,000 + (0.9040)(6,000) - (1.808)(6,000) + (0.9040)(6,000)$$

$$= 6,000 \text{ psia}.$$

For Gridblock 7, Timestep 1,

$$p_7^{n+1} = p_7^n + (3.56508)(-75) + (0.9040)p_8^n - (1.808)p_7^n + (0.9040)p_6^n$$

$$= 6,000 - 267.381 + (0.9040)(6,000) - (1.808)(6,000) + (0.9040)(6,000)$$

$$= 5,732.62 \text{ psia}.$$

For Gridblock 8, Timestep 1,

$$p_8^{n+1} = p_8^n + (3.56508)(-75) + (0.9040)p_9^n - (1.808)p_8^n + (0.9040)p_7^n$$

$$= 6,000 - 267.381 + (0.9040)(6,000) - (1.808)(6,000) + (0.9040)(6,000)$$

$$= 5,732.62 \text{ psia}.$$

For Gridblock 9, Timestep 1,

$$p_9^{n+1} = p_9^n + (0.9040)p_{10}^n - (1.808)p_9^n + (0.9040)p_8^n$$

$$= 6,000 + (0.9040)(6,000) - (1.808)(6,000) + (0.9040)(6,000)$$

$$= 6,000 \text{ psia}.$$

TABLE 5.5—EXPLICIT-SIMULATION-STUDY RESULTS OF THE PROBLEM IN FIG. 5.28 (Δt= 15 days)

Time	Pressure (psia)									
(days)	Block 1	Block 2	Block 3	Block 4	Block 5	Block 6	Block 7	Block 8	Block 9	Block 10
0.0	6,000.00	6,000.00	6,000.00	6,000.00	6,000.00	6,000.00	6,000.00	6,000.00	6,000.00	6,000.00
15.0	6,000.00	6,000.00	6,000.00	6,000.00	6,000.00	6,000.00	5,732.62	5,732.62	6,000.00	6,000.00
30.0	6,000.00	6,000.00	6,000.00	6,000.00	6,000.00	5,758.28	5,706.95	5,706.95	5,758.28	6,000.00
45.0	6,000.00	6,000.00	6,000.00	6,000.00	5,781.48	5,930.40	5,485.98	5,485.98	5,930.40	5,781.48
60.0	6,000.00	6,000.00	6,000.00	5,802.46	6,113.64	5,394.02	5,620.36	5,620.36	5,394.02	5,916.10
75.0	6,000.00	6,000.00	5,821.42	6,262.36	5,181.77	6,249.19	5,148.36	5,148.36	6,070.61	5,444.13
90.0	6,000.00	5,838.56	6,381.47	4,886.88	7,123.60	4,289.06	5,876.14	5,714.70	4,670.53	6,010.48
105.0	6,000.00	6,475.30	4,539.54	8,260.04	2,539.11	8,286.27	4,028.07	4,649.32	6,825.81	4,799.15
120.0	6,000.00	4,295.66	9,652.88	−275.15	12,906.43	−758.72	8,171.78	5,787.90	3,026.10	6,631.28
135.0	6,000.00	10,679.42	−4,165.22	20,616.29	−11,363.42	19,668.09	−2,323.97	5,178.88	8,781.94	3,372.14
150.0	6,000.00	−6,970.62	31,657.41	−30,696.70	45,599.66	−28,266.00	24,072.48	1,386.04	634.18	8,262.68
165.0	6,000.00	39,675.33	−59,631.96	94,645.40	−90,149.06	85,824.44	−44,018.56	20,947.85	8,210.15	1,366.40
180.0	6,000.00	−80,542.95	169,612.37	—	235,990.59	—	131,824.68	−49,565.21	13,538.36	7,553.26
195.0	6,000.00	223,837.34	—	537,877.05	—	486,551.96	—	171,193.17	−48,918.84	12,963.88
210.0	6,000.00	—	—	—	—	—	856,091.84	—	206,008.62	−42,979.02
225.0	6,000.00	—	—	—	—	—	—	—	—	182,109.54
240.0	6,000.00	—	—	—	—	—	—	—	—	—
255.0	6,000.00	—	—	—	—	—	—	—	—	—
270.0	6,000.00	—	—	—	—	—	—	—	—	—
285.0	6,000.00	—	—	—	—	—	—	—	—	—
300.0	6,000.00	—	—	—	—	—	—	—	—	—
315.0	6,000.00	—	—	—	—	—	—	—	—	—
330.0	6,000.00	—	—	—	—	—	—	—	—	—
345.0	6,000.00	—	—	—	—	—	—	—	—	—
360.0	6,000.00	—	—	—	—	—	—	—	—	—

For Gridblock 10, Timestep 1,

$$\begin{aligned} p_{10}^{n+1} &= p_{10}^{n} + (0)p_{11}^{n} - (0.9040)p_{10}^{n} + (0.9040)p_{9}^{n} \\ &= 6,000 - (0.9040)(6,000) + (0.9040)(6,000) \\ &= 6,000 \text{ psia.} \end{aligned}$$

This is the end of the first timestep. This procedure is continued until the end of the simulation. **Table 5.5** shows the results of this explicit simulation.

The erratic behavior shown in Table 5.5 is caused by the conditionally stable nature of the explicit forward-difference formulation. The forward-difference equation is conditionally stable because under certain conditions errors in the solution tend to go to zero during the subsequent timestep calculations, while under other conditions these same errors propagate uncontrollably during subsequent timestep calculations. This is a serious limitation of the forward-difference formulation.

Examples 5.8 and 5.9 presented appropriate conditions for a stable solution, while Example 5.10 violated the conditions for a stable solution. Stability and Stability Analysis in Sec. 5.6.3 discuss stability analysis and conditions.

To summarize, the implementation of the explicit formulation technique involves pressures at the old-time-level only. At this time level, these quantities are known and can be used in an explicit calculation procedure to advance the simulation in time. **Fig. 5.29** shows the explicit calculation procedure schematically.

5.6.2 Implicit Formulation. The backward-difference approximation to the slightly compressible flow equation (Eq. 5.66) results in an implicit calculation procedure for the new-time-level pressures. Rearranging Eq. 5.66 yields

$$\mathrm{T}_{lx_{i+1/2}}^{n} p_{i+1}^{n+1} - \left[\left(\frac{V_b \phi c_l}{\alpha_c B_l^{\circ} \Delta t}\right)_i + \mathrm{T}_{lx_{i+1/2}}^{n} + \mathrm{T}_{lx_{i-1/2}}^{n}\right] p_i^{n+1} + \mathrm{T}_{lx_{i-1/2}}^{n} \times p_{i-1}^{n+1} = -\left[q_{lsc_i} + \left(\frac{V_b \phi c_l}{\alpha_c B_l^{\circ} \Delta t}\right)_i p_i^n\right], \quad \ldots\ldots\ (5.105)$$

where the quantities p_{i+1}^{n+1}, p_i^{n+1}, and p_{i-1}^{n+1} are all unknowns. Unlike the explicit formulation, Eq. 5.105 cannot be solved explicitly for p_i^{n+1} because both p_{i+1}^{n+1} and p_{i-1}^{n+1} are also unknown. Consequently, we must solve Eq. 5.105 written for all gridblocks and unknowns simultaneously. Examples 5.11 through 5.13 illustrate this procedure.

Example 5.11. Solve the problem described in Example 5.8 using the implicit backward-difference formulation. Use a timestep size of Δt = 15 days.

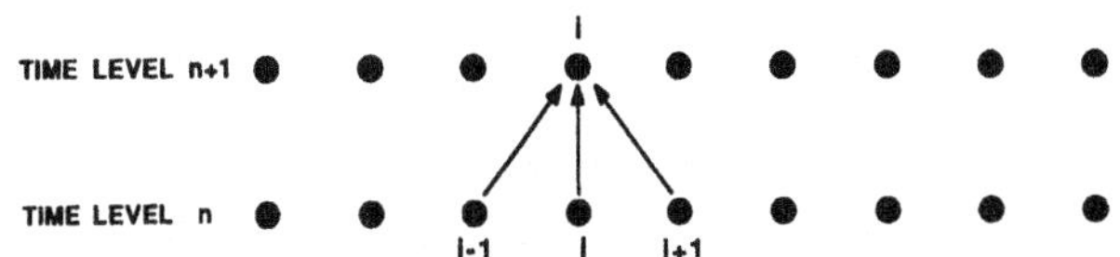

Fig. 5.29—Schematic representation of contribution of gridblocks and their time levels in the explicit equation for Gridblock *I*.

Solution. For $\Delta t = 15$ days, we calculated the following quantities in Example 5.8. $\left(V_b\phi c_l/\alpha_c B_l^{\circ}\Delta t\right)_i = 0.56100$ and

$$T^n_{lx_{i+1/2}} = T^n_{lx_{i-1/2}} = \left[\beta_c\left(\frac{A_x k_x}{\mu_l B_l \Delta x}\right)\right]^n_{i-1/2}$$

$$= \left[\beta_c\left(\frac{A_x k_x}{\mu_l B_l \Delta x}\right)\right]^n_{i+1/2} = 0.1268. \quad \ldots\ldots\ldots\ldots (5.106)$$

For Gridblock 1, Timestep 1,

$$(0.1268)p_2^{n+1} - (0.56100 + 0.1268 + 0)p_1^{n+1}$$

$$+ (0)p_0^{n+1} = -[0 + (0.56100)(6,000)],$$

where $\{\beta_c[(A_x k_x)/(\mu_l B_l \Delta x)]\}_{1/2} = 0$ for no-flow boundary condition, or

$$(0.1268)p_2^{n+1} - (0.6878)p_1^{n+1} + 0p_0^{n+1} = -3,365.98.$$

For Gridblock 2, Timestep 1,

$$(0.1268)p_3^{n+1} - (0.56100 + 0.1268 + 0.1268)p_2^{n+1}$$

$$+ 0.1268p_1^{n+1} = -[0 + (0.56100)(6,000)]$$

or $(0.1268)p_3^{n+1} - (0.8146)p_2^{n+1} + (0.1268)p_1^{n+1} = -3,365.98.$

For Gridblock 3, Timestep 1,

$$(0.1268)p_4^{n+1} - (0.56100 + 0.1268 + 0.1268)p_3^{n+1}$$

$$+ (0.1268)p_2^{n+1} = -[0 + (0.56100)(6,000)]$$

or $(0.1268)p_4^{n+1} - (0.8146)p_3^{n+1} + (0.1268)p_2^{n+1} = -3,365.98.$

For Gridblock 4, Timestep 1,

$$(0.1268)p_5^{n+1} - (0.56100 + 0.1268 + 0.1268)p_4^{n+1}$$

$$+ (0.1268)p_3^{n+1} = -[-150 + (0.56100)(6,000)]$$

or $(0.1268)p_5^{n+1} - (0.8146)p_4^{n+1} + (0.1268)p_3^{n+1} = -3,215.98.$

For Gridblock 5, Timestep 1,

$$(0)p_6^{n+1} - (0.56100 + 0 + 0.1268)p_5^{n+1}$$

$$+ (0.1268)p_4^{n+1} = -[0 + (0.56100)(6,000)],$$

where $\beta_c(A_x k_x/\mu_l B_l \Delta x)_{5+1/2} = 0$ for no-flow boundary condition, or

$$(0)p_6^{n+1} - (0.6878)p_5^{n+1} + (0.1268)p_4^{n+1} = -3,365.98.$$

Table 5.6 shows the system of equations to be solved for the first timestep.

Sec. 3.5.4 showed how systems of equations can be represented by a matrix equation. The matrix equation for this problem is

$$\begin{bmatrix} -0.6878 & +0.1268 & 0 & 0 & 0 \\ +0.1268 & -0.8146 & +0.1268 & 0 & 0 \\ 0 & +0.1268 & -0.8146 & +0.1268 & 0 \\ 0 & 0 & +0.1268 & -0.8146 & +0.1268 \\ 0 & 0 & & +0.1268 & -0.6878 \end{bmatrix} \begin{bmatrix} p_1^{n+1} \\ p_2^{n+1} \\ p_3^{n+1} \\ p_4^{n+1} \\ p_5^{n+1} \end{bmatrix}$$

$$= \begin{bmatrix} -3,365.98 \\ -3,365.98 \\ -3,365.98 \\ -3,215.98 \\ -3,365.98 \end{bmatrix}.$$

Chap. 7 discusses the solution of linear matrix equations. For the time being, any linear algebraic technique can be used to solve this system of equations. The solution that uses a direct technique gives $p_1^{n+1} = 5,999.08$ psia, $p_2^{n+1} = 5,995.02$ psia, $p_3^{n+1} = 5,968.94$ psia, $p_4^{n+1} = 5,805.44$ psia, and $p_5^{n+1} = 5,964.13$ psia.

Although direct solution techniques will not be discussed until Chap. 7, the solution in the previous paragraph can be verified easily by substituting these values into the original equations. This is the end of the first timestep. The values of p_i^n can now be updated with the known values.

Note that, in this problem, updating the pressures does not affect the coefficients on the left side of the equation, but only those on the right side. This is because we assumed that μ_l and B_l were constant. If these properties were pressure dependent, we would update the coefficients at this point. Therefore, for Gridblock 1, Timestep 2,

$$(0.1268)p_2^{n+1} - (0.6878)p_1^{n+1} = -[0 + 0.56100(5,999.08)]$$

or $(0.1268)p_2^{n+1} - (0.6878)p_1^{n+1} = -3,365.47.$

For Gridblock 2, Timestep 2,

$$(0.1268)p_3^{n+1} - (0.8146)p_2^{n+1} + (0.1268)p_1^{n+1}$$

$$= -[0 + (0.56100)(5,995.02)]$$

or $(0.1268)p_3^{n+1} - (0.8146)p_2^{n+1} + (0.1268)p_1^{n+1} = -3,363.19.$

For Gridblock 3, Timestep 2,

$$(0.1268)p_4^{n+1} - (0.8146)p_3^{n+1} + (0.1268)p_2^{n+1}$$

$$= -[0 + (0.56100)(5,968.94)]$$

or $(0.1268)p_4^{n+1} - (0.8146)p_3^{n+1} + (0.1268)p_2^{n+1} = -3,348.56.$

For Gridblock 4, Timestep 2,

$$(0.1268)p_5^{n+1} - (0.8146)p_4^{n+1} + (0.1268)p_3^{n+1}$$

$$= -[(-150) + (0.56100)(5,805.44)]$$

or $(0.1268)p_5^{n+1} - (0.8146)p_4^{n+1} + (0.1268)p_3^{n+1} = -3,106.83.$

TABLE 5.6—SYSTEM OF EQUATIONS IN EXAMPLE 5.11

$$\begin{bmatrix} -0.6878p_1^{n+1} & +0.1268p_2^{n+1} & & & \\ +0.1268p_1^{n+1} & -0.8146p_2^{n+1} & +0.1268p_3^{n+1} & & \\ & +0.1268p_2^{n+1} & -0.8146p_3^{n+1} & +0.1268p_4^{n+1} & \\ & & +0.1268p_3^{n+1} & -0.8146p_4^{n+1} & +0.1268p_5^{n+1} \\ & & & +0.1268p_4^{n+1} & -0.6878p_5^{n+1} \end{bmatrix} = \begin{bmatrix} -3,365.98 \\ -3,365.98 \\ -3,365.98 \\ -3,215.98 \\ -3,365.98 \end{bmatrix}$$

TABLE 5.7—IMPLICIT-SIMULATION-STUDY RESULTS OF THE PROBLEM IN FIG. 5.26 (Δt=15 days)

Time (days)	Pressure (psia) Block 1	Block 2	Block 3	Block 4	Block 5
0.0	6,000.00	6,000.00	6,000.00	6,000.00	6,000.00
15.0	5,999.08	5,995.02	5,968.94	5,805.44	5,964.13
30.0	5,996.29	5,983.93	5,922.46	5,655.35	5,907.21
45.0	5,990.91	5,967.09	5,868.77	5,532.88	5,838.21
60.0	5,982.51	5,945.36	5,812.08	5,427.95	5,762.58
75.0	5,970.92	5,919.63	5,754.47	5,334.42	5,683.65
90.0	5,956.12	5,890.64	5,696.92	5,248.58	5,603.45
105.0	5,938.22	5,859.01	5,639.84	5,168.07	5,523.19
120.0	5,917.38	5,825.19	5,583.33	5,091.45	5,443.60
135.0	5,893.81	5,789.52	5,527.39	5,017.75	5,365.10
150.0	5,867.72	5,752.26	5,471.95	4,946.35	5,287.91
165.0	5,839.31	5,713.62	5,416.94	4,876.82	5,212.13
180.0	5,808.79	5,673.74	5,362.26	4,808.85	5,137.79
195.0	5,776.34	5,632.76	5,307.86	4,742.22	5,064.87
210.0	5,742.13	5,590.78	5,253.66	4,676.77	4,993.32
225.0	5,706.32	5,547.88	5,199.64	4,612.35	4,923.09
240.0	5,669.06	5,504.15	5,145.74	4,548.85	4,854.11
255.0	5,630.45	5,459.65	5,091.94	4,486.19	4,786.28
270.0	5,590.63	5,414.44	5,038.22	4,424.29	4,719.55
285.0	5,549.70	5,368.58	4,984.56	4,363.08	4,653.84
300.0	5,507.75	5,322.12	4,930.94	4,302.50	4,589.07
315.0	5,464.86	5,275.11	4,877.35	4,242.49	4,525.18
330.0	5,421.13	5,227.59	4,823.79	4,183.00	4,462.11
345.0	5,376.60	5,179.60	4,770.25	4,124.00	4,399.78
360.0	5,331.36	5,131.18	4,716.73	4,065.45	4,338.15

For Gridblock 5, Timestep 2,

$$-(0.6878)p_5^{n+1}-(0.1268)p_4^{n+1}=-[0+(0.56100)(5,964.13)]$$

or $(0.6878)p_5^{n+1}-(0.1268)p_4^{n+1}=-3,345.86$.

Solving the system of updated equations results in the following pressure distribution at Day 30: $p_1^{n+1}=5{,}996.29$ psia, $p_2^{n+1}=5{,}983.93$ psia, $p_3^{n+1}=5{,}922.46$ psia, $p_4^{n+1}=5{,}655.35$ psia, and $p_5^{n+1}=5{,}907.21$ psia. This is the end of the second timestep. This procedure continues until the end of the simulation; **Table 5.7** shows the results.

Example 5.11 illustrates that the amount of computation required for the implicit solution procedure is much greater than that for the explicit solution procedure. This is because at each timestep, a system of equations must be solved for the unknowns of the problem. In general, most of the computational time used in implicit simulations is in the solution of the linear equations.

This example also illustrates that the pressure transient can move more than one block per timestep. Here, it has moved to the left boundary during the first timestep. Also, the results from the implicit backward-difference formulation and the explicit forward-difference formulation will not give identical results even when the same timestep is used. Again, this is because of the approximate nature of the finite-difference approach.

Finally, the no-flow boundary can be implemented by assigning a zero transmissibility to the boundaries. This is the same method used in earlier examples. Example 5.12 illustrates the implementation of a specified-pressure boundary.

TABLE 5.8—IMPLICIT-SIMULATION-STUDY RESULTS OF THE PROBLEM IN FIG. 5.27 (Δt=15 days)

Time (days)	Pressure (psia) Block 1	Block 2	Block 3	Block 4	Block 5
0.0	6,000.00	6,000.00	6,000.00	6,000.00	6,000.00
15.0	6,000.00	5,995.17	5,968.97	5,805.44	5,964.13
30.0	6,000.00	5,984.62	5,922.59	5,655.37	5,907.22
45.0	6,000.00	5,969.05	5,869.18	5,532.97	5,838.23
60.0	6,000.00	5,949.59	5,813.05	5,428.16	5,762.63
75.0	6,000.00	5,927.37	5,756.42	5,334.90	5,683.78
90.0	6,000.00	5,903.34	5,700.38	5,249.48	5,603.72
105.0	6,000.00	5,878.25	5,645.46	5,169.65	5,523.71
120.0	6,000.00	5,852.62	5,591.87	5,094.00	5,444.49
135.0	6,000.00	5,826.86	5,539.69	5,021.65	5,366.55
150.0	6,000.00	5,801.21	5,488.93	4,952.02	5,290.13
165.0	6,000.00	5,775.86	5,439.55	4,884.76	5,215.41
180.0	6,000.00	5,750.92	5,391.52	4,819.60	5,142.44
195.0	6,000.00	5,726.48	5,344.79	4,756.37	5,071.27
210.0	6,000.00	5,702.57	5,299.33	4,694.95	5,001.90
225.0	6,000.00	5,679.21	5,255.10	4,635.25	4,934.31
240.0	6,000.00	5,656.43	5,212.05	4,577.18	4,868.48
255.0	6,000.00	5,634.22	5,170.15	4,520.69	4,804.37
270.0	6,000.00	5,612.57	5,129.37	4,465.72	4,741.94
285.0	6,000.00	5,591.49	5,089.67	4,412.23	4,681.16
300.0	6,000.00	5,570.95	5,051.04	4,360.16	4,621.99
315.0	6,000.00	5,550.95	5,013.43	4,309.48	4,564.38
330.0	6,000.00	5,531.48	4,976.81	4,260.15	4,508.30
345.0	6,000.00	5,512.53	4,941.18	4,212.13	4,453.70
360.0	6,000.00	5,494.07	4,906.48	4,165.39	4,400.55

Example 5.12. Solve the problem described in Example 5.9 using the implicit backward-difference formulation. Use a timestep size of Δt= 15 days.

Solution. For the first timestep for Gridblock 1, $p_1^{n+1}=6{,}000$. For all other gridblocks for the first timestep, both the left and right sides of the finite-difference equations are identical to those in Example 5.11. The difference equation for Gridblock 2 can be rearranged because p_1^{n+1} is known: $(0.1268)(6,000)-(0.8146)p_2^{n+1}+(0.1268)p_3^{n+1}=3{,}365.98$ or $-(0.8146)p_2^{n+1}+0.1268p_3^{n+1}=-4,126.78$. The matrix equation for the first timestep is

$$\begin{bmatrix} -0.8146 & +0.1268 & 0 & 0 \\ +0.1268 & -0.8146 & +0.1268 & 0 \\ 0 & +0.1268 & -0.8146 & +0.1268 \\ 0 & 0 & +0.1268 & -0.6878 \end{bmatrix}\begin{bmatrix} p_2^{n+1} \\ p_3^{n+1} \\ p_4^{n+1} \\ p_5^{n+1} \end{bmatrix}$$

$$=\begin{bmatrix} -4,126.78 \\ -3,365.98 \\ -3,215.98 \\ -3,365.98 \end{bmatrix}.$$

The solution to this system of equations is $p_1^{n+1}=6{,}000$ psia (fixed), $p_2^{n+1}=5{,}995.17$ psia, $p_3^{n+1}=5{,}968.97$ psia, $p_4^{n+1}=5{,}805.44$ psia, and $p_5^{n+1}=5{,}964.13$ psia. This is the end of the first timestep. For all future timesteps, the left side of the finite-difference equations remains constant and only the right side changes. For the second timestep, the matrix equation becomes

TABLE 5.9—MATRIX EQUATION IN EXAMPLE 5.13

$$\begin{bmatrix} -0.7877 & +0.2536 & 0 & 0 & 0 & 0 & 0 & 0 & 0 \\ +0.2536 & -0.7877 & +0.2536 & 0 & 0 & 0 & 0 & 0 & 0 \\ 0 & +0.2536 & -0.7877 & +0.2536 & 0 & 0 & 0 & 0 & 0 \\ 0 & 0 & +0.2536 & -0.7877 & +0.2536 & 0 & 0 & 0 & 0 \\ 0 & 0 & 0 & +0.2536 & -0.7877 & +0.2536 & 0 & 0 & 0 \\ 0 & 0 & 0 & 0 & +0.2536 & -0.7877 & +0.2536 & 0 & 0 \\ 0 & 0 & 0 & 0 & 0 & +0.2536 & -0.7877 & +0.2536 & 0 \\ 0 & 0 & 0 & 0 & 0 & 0 & +0.2536 & -0.7877 & +0.2536 \\ 0 & 0 & 0 & 0 & 0 & 0 & 0 & +0.2536 & -0.5341 \end{bmatrix} \begin{bmatrix} p_2^{n+1} \\ p_3^{n+1} \\ p_4^{n+1} \\ p_5^{n+1} \\ p_6^{n+1} \\ p_7^{n+1} \\ p_8^{n+1} \\ p_9^{n+1} \\ p_{10}^{n+1} \end{bmatrix} = \begin{bmatrix} -3,204.59 \\ -1,682.99 \\ -1,682.99 \\ -1,682.99 \\ -1,682.99 \\ -1,607.99 \\ -1,607.99 \\ -1,682.99 \\ -1,682.99 \end{bmatrix}$$

$$\begin{bmatrix} -0.8146 & +0.1268 & 0 & 0 \\ +0.1268 & -0.8146 & +0.1268 & 0 \\ 0 & +0.1268 & -0.8146 & +0.1268 \\ 0 & 0 & +0.1268 & -0.6878 \end{bmatrix} \begin{bmatrix} p_2^{n+1} \\ p_3^{n+1} \\ p_4^{n+1} \\ p_5^{n+1} \end{bmatrix} = \begin{bmatrix} -4,124.09 \\ -3,348.56 \\ -3,106.83 \\ -3,345.86 \end{bmatrix}.$$

The solution to this system of equations is $p_1^{n+1} = 6{,}000$ psia (fixed), $p_2^{n+1} = 5{,}984.62$ psia, $p_3^{n+1} = 5{,}922.59$ psia, $p_4^{n+1} = 5{,}655.37$ psia, and $p_5^{n+1} = 5{,}907.22$ psia. This is the end of the second timestep. This procedure is continued until the end of the simulation. **Table 5.8** shows the results of this example.

As a final example, we investigate the problem defined in Fig. 5.28, which exhibited instability with the explicit formulation.

Example 5.13. Solve the problem described in Example 5.10 by use of the implicit backward-difference formulation. Use a timestep size of $\Delta t = 15$ days.

Solution. The matrix equation for the first timestep can be written following the procedure outlined in Examples 5.11 and 5.12. Because $p_1^{n+1} = 6{,}000$ psia at all times, the equation for Gridblock 1 is removed from the system and the equation for Gridblock 2 is modified by substituting for $p_1^{n+1} = 6{,}000$ psia and carrying the term involving p_1^{n+1} to the right side. **Table 5.9** shows the resulting matrix equation, and **Table 5.10** shows the results of this simulation.

Example 5.13 demonstrates that no stability problems are associated with the implicit formulation. This is because the implicit formulation is unconditionally stable. This property states that no conditions exist where the backward-difference formulation exhibits unstable behavior. Although this statement indicates that any gridblock dimension and/or timestep size can be used with no stability problems, the use of large timestep sizes and block dimensions may result in unrealistically coarse approximations. This becomes apparent in the solution as a departure from the true physics of the problem. Because of the unconditionally stable nature of the implicit formulation, the backward-difference formulation is the most commonly used formulation in petroleum reservoir simulation.

As a summary, **Fig. 5.30** is a schematic diagram of the implicit formulation. The figure illustrates the need to solve a system of equations because more than one pressure at the $n+1$ time level is required for the solution.

5.6.3 Truncation Error, Stability, and Consistency Analysis of Finite-Difference Schemes. To replace a continuous PDE with its finite-difference representation, certain aspects of the approximation have to be investigated carefully. In particular, it is important to estimate the magnitude of the error introduced when the approximation is implemented, whether errors introduced at a certain stage in the computations grow uncontrollably to dominate the solution and, finally, whether the finite-difference approximation used is compatible with the original PDE. The next three sections present analysis procedures that can be used to address these questions.

Truncation Error and Truncation-Error Analysis. As Secs. 5.3 and 5.4 discuss, the replacement of the spatial derivative and time derivative is achieved by use of a truncated Taylor series expansion. Truncation error is, therefore, a direct result of this approximation. The net result of this truncation error is the approximate nature of the solution. In other words, if a computer with the capacity to carry an infinite number of digits were used to obtain the solution to the finite-difference equations (that is, a solution with no round-off error), the solution would differ from the exact solution of the original PDE because of this truncation error. The problems we need to address are the magnitude of the truncation error and how can we increase the accuracy of an approximation by decreasing the magnitude of this error.

As mentioned previously, the deviation of the PDE from its corresponding finite-difference approximation at a given point in space and at a given instant in the time domain is called the local truncation error or local discretization error.[2] In other words, the truncation error, ε_{L_i}, can be expressed as

$$\varepsilon_{L_i}^n = \left[f_{fd}\right]_i^n - \left[f_d\right]_i^n. \quad \text{(5.107)}$$

Consider the diffusivity equation

$$\frac{\partial^2 p}{\partial x^2} = \frac{1}{D}\frac{\partial p}{\partial t} \quad \text{(5.108)}$$

and its corresponding forward difference approximation

$$\frac{p_{i-1}^n - 2p_i^n + p_{i+1}^n}{(\Delta x)^2} = \frac{1}{D_i}\frac{p_i^{n+1} - p_i^n}{\Delta t}. \quad \text{(5.109)}$$

The local truncation error at Discrete Point i and Time Level n can be defined by Eq. 5.107 as

$$\varepsilon_{L_i}^n = \left[\frac{p_{i-1}^n - 2p_i^n + p_{i+1}^n}{\left(\Delta x_i\right)^2} - \frac{1}{D_i}\frac{p_i^{n+1} - p_i^n}{\Delta t}\right] - \left(\frac{\partial^2 p}{\partial x^2} - \frac{1}{D}\frac{\partial p}{\partial t}\right)_i^n. \quad \text{(5.110)}$$

The local truncation error as described by Eq. 5.110 is not readily quantifiable because the subtraction cannot be carried out when one group of terms is in an algebraic (discrete) form and the other group is in a continuous form. Example 5.14 illustrates the procedure used to overcome this difficulty.

Example 5.14. Determine the local truncation error of the explicit finite-difference approximation to $\partial^2 p/\partial x^2 = (1/D)(\partial p/\partial t)$.

Solution. To express the terms in the first bracket of Eq. 5.110, use the Taylor series expansion to expand each entry in the finite-difference form at Point i and Time Level n.

TABLE 5.10—IMPLICIT-SIMULATION-STUDY RESULTS OF THE PROBLEM IN FIG. 5.28 (Δt=15 days)

Time	Pressure (psia)									
(days)	Block 1	Block 2	Block 3	Block 4	Block 5	Block 6	Block 7	Block 8	Block 9	Block 10
0.0	6,000.00	6,000.00	6,000.00	6,000.00	6,000.00	6,000.00	6,000.00	6,000.00	6,000.00	6,000.00
15.0	6,000.00	5,999.05	5,997.04	5,991.76	5,977.35	5,937.90	5,829.75	5,829.06	5,935.04	5,969.16
30.0	6,000.00	5,996.26	5,989.44	5,974.20	5,939.56	5,863.10	5,703.90	5,701.25	5,853.00	5,914.01
45.0	6,000.00	5,991.31	5,977.14	5,949.38	5,894.14	5,788.68	5,600.89	5,594.92	5,767.10	5,844.26
60.0	6,000.00	5,984.33	5,960.95	5,919.66	5,845.50	5,717.53	5,510.87	5,500.40	5,681.15	5,766.81
75.0	6,000.00	5,975.71	5,941.88	5,886.96	5,795.85	5,649.82	5,428.89	5,413.05	5,596.36	5,685.88
90.0	6,000.00	5,965.87	5,920.85	5,852.57	5,746.25	5,585.08	5,352.28	5,330.51	5,513.20	5,603.89
105.0	6,000.00	5,955.20	5,898.59	5,817.37	5,697.21	5,522.80	5,279.51	5,251.50	5,431.85	5,522.21
120.0	6,000.00	5,944.01	5,875.65	5,781.91	5,648.95	5,462.61	5,209.69	5,175.30	5,352.38	5,441.58
135.0	6,000.00	5,932.55	5,852.41	5,746.55	5,601.59	5,404.22	5,142.26	5,101.49	5,274.84	5,362.41
150.0	6,000.00	5,920.97	5,829.12	5,711.52	5,555.15	5,347.43	5,076.89	5,029.81	5,199.20	5,284.92
165.0	6,000.00	5,909.39	5,805.97	5,676.95	5,509.68	5,292.11	5,013.35	4,960.07	5,125.43	5,209.20
180.0	6,000.00	5,897.90	5,783.08	5,642.93	5,465.17	5,238.17	4,951.50	4,892.17	5,053.51	5,135.27
195.0	6,000.00	5,886.54	5,760.52	5,609.54	5,421.62	5,185.53	4,891.22	4,826.01	4,983.37	5,063.15
210.0	6,000.00	5,875.36	5,738.34	5,576.80	5,379.03	5,134.16	4,832.45	4,761.50	4,914.98	4,992.80
225.0	6,000.00	5,864.37	5,716.58	5,544.73	5,337.39	5,084.00	4,775.12	4,698.61	4,848.28	4,924.18
240.0	6,000.00	5,853.59	5,695.26	5,513.34	5,296.69	5,035.03	4,719.19	4,637.26	4,783.24	4,857.26
255.0	6,000.00	5,843.03	5,674.38	5,482.63	5,256.92	4,987.21	4,664.62	4,577.42	4,719.80	4,791.99
270.0	6,000.00	5,832.69	5,653.95	5,452.61	5,218.06	4,940.53	4,611.36	4,519.04	4,657.91	4,728.33
285.0	6,000.00	5,822.58	5,633.97	5,423.27	5,180.10	4,894.95	4,559.38	4,462.08	4,597.55	4,666.24
300.0	6,000.00	5,812.69	5,614.44	5,394.60	5,143.03	4,850.45	4,508.65	4,406.51	4,538.66	4,605.66
315.0	6,000.00	5,803.03	5,595.36	5,366.58	5,106.82	4,807.01	4,459.14	4,352.28	4,481.20	4,546.57
330.0	6,000.00	5,793.58	5,576.72	5,339.22	5,071.47	4,764.60	4,410.82	4,299.36	4,425.15	4,488.92
345.0	6,000.00	5,784.35	5,558.50	5,312.50	5,036.95	4,723.20	4,363.66	4,247.73	4,370.45	4,432.67
360.0	6,000.00	5,775.34	5,540.71	5,286.41	5,003.24	4,682.79	4,317.64	4,197.34	4,317.08	4,377.79

$$p_{i+1}^n = p_i^n + \Delta x \frac{\partial p}{\partial x}\bigg|_i^n + \frac{(\Delta x)^2}{2!}\frac{\partial^2 p}{\partial x^2}\bigg|_i^n + \frac{(\Delta x)^3}{3!}\frac{\partial^3 p}{\partial x^3}\bigg|_i^n$$

$$+ \frac{(\Delta x)^4}{4!}\frac{\partial^4 p}{\partial x^4}\bigg|_i^n + \ldots \qquad (5.111)$$

$$p_{i-1}^n = p_i^n - \Delta x \frac{\partial p}{\partial x}\bigg|_i^n + \frac{(\Delta x)^2}{2!}\frac{\partial^2 p}{\partial x^2}\bigg|_i^n - \frac{(\Delta x)^3}{3!}\frac{\partial^3 p}{\partial x^3}\bigg|_i^n$$

$$+ \frac{(\Delta x)^4}{4!}\frac{\partial^4 p}{\partial x^4}\bigg|_i^n + \ldots \qquad (5.112)$$

$$p_i^{n+1} = p_i^n + \Delta t \frac{\partial p}{\partial t}\bigg|_i^n + \frac{(\Delta t)^2}{2!}\frac{\partial^2 p}{\partial t^2}\bigg|_i^n + \frac{(\Delta t)^3}{3!}\frac{\partial^3 p}{\partial t^3}\bigg|_i^n$$

$$+ \frac{(\Delta t)^4}{4!}\frac{\partial^4 p}{\partial t^4}\bigg|_i^n + \ldots \qquad (5.113)$$

Substituting the expansions in Eqs. 5.111 through 5.113 into Eq. 5.110 yields

$$\varepsilon_{L_i}^n = \left\{ \frac{1}{(\Delta x)^2}\left[p_i^n - \Delta x \frac{\partial p}{\partial x}\bigg|_i^n + \frac{(\Delta x)^2}{2!}\frac{\partial^2 p}{\partial x^2}\bigg|_i^n - \frac{(\Delta x)^3}{3!}\frac{\partial^3 p}{\partial x^3}\bigg|_i^n \right.\right.$$

$$+ \frac{(\Delta x)^4}{4!}\frac{\partial^4 p}{\partial x^4}\bigg|_i^n + \ldots - 2p_i^n + p_i^n + \Delta x \frac{\partial p}{\partial x}\bigg|_i^n$$

$$\left. + \frac{(\Delta x)^2}{2!}\frac{\partial^2 p}{\partial x^2}\bigg|_i^n + \frac{(\Delta x)^3}{3!}\frac{\partial^3 p}{\partial x^3}\bigg|_i^n + \frac{(\Delta x)^4}{4!}\frac{\partial^4 p}{\partial x^4}\bigg|_i^n + \ldots \right]$$

$$- \frac{1}{D_i \Delta t}\left[p_i^n + \Delta t \frac{\partial p}{\partial t}\bigg|_i^n + \frac{(\Delta t)^2}{2!}\frac{\partial^2 p}{\partial t^2}\bigg|_i^n + \frac{(\Delta t)^3}{3!}\frac{\partial^3 p}{\partial t^3}\bigg|_i^n \right.$$

$$\left.\left. + \frac{(\Delta t)^4}{4!}\frac{\partial^4 p}{\partial t^4}\bigg|_i^n + \ldots - p_i^n \right]\right\}$$

$$- \left(\frac{\partial^2 p}{\partial x^2}\bigg|_i^n - \frac{1}{D_i}\frac{\partial p}{\partial t}\bigg|_i^n \right), \qquad (5.114)$$

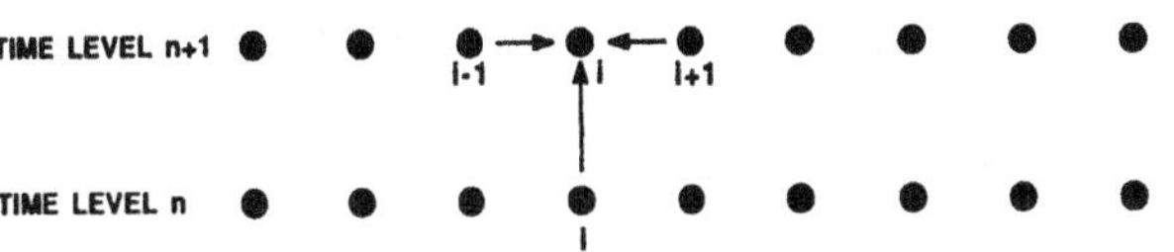

Fig. 5.30—Schematic representation of contribution of gridblocks and their time levels in the implicit equation for Gridblock *I*.

which simplifies to

$$\varepsilon^n_{L_i} = \left[\frac{(\Delta x)^2}{12}\frac{\partial^4 p}{\partial x^4}\bigg|^n_i + \frac{(\Delta x)^4}{360}\frac{\partial^6 p}{\partial x^6}\bigg|^n_i + \ldots\right.$$

$$\left. - \frac{(\Delta t)}{2D_i}\frac{\partial^2 p}{\partial t^2}\bigg|^n_i - \frac{(\Delta t)^2}{6D_i}\frac{\partial^3 p}{\partial t^3}\bigg|^n_i - \ldots\right]. \quad \ldots\ldots\ldots (5.115)$$

The principal part of the local truncation error is, then,

$$e_L = \left[\frac{(\Delta x)^2}{12}\frac{\partial^4 p}{\partial x^4}\bigg|^n_i - \frac{(\Delta t)}{2D_i}\frac{\partial^2 p}{\partial t^2}\bigg|^n_i\right]. \quad \ldots\ldots\ldots (5.116)$$

It is conventional to express the principal part of the local truncation error in terms of the order of the error, O, as

$$e_L = O\left[(\Delta x)^2\right] + O(\Delta t). \quad \ldots\ldots\ldots (5.117)$$

In Example 5.14, the notation $O[(\Delta x)^2]$ can be interpreted to mean that when Δx is small enough, the term $[(\Delta x)^2/12][(\partial^4 p)/(\partial x^4)]$ behaves essentially like a constant multiplied by $(\Delta x)^2$. This implies that as Δx decreases, the truncation error decreases (this same observation is true for Δt, as well). A decrease in Δx and/or Δt corresponds to a decrease in the mesh size and the timestep size, resulting in an increased number of discrete points or simply in an increased number of computational operations. Because every arithmetical operation introduces additional error called round-off error, the increased number of operations in the computer will increase the round-off error proportionally. This is why one may not generally conclude that decreasing the mesh size always increases accuracy. Therefore, this tradeoff between truncation error and round-off error should be scrutinized carefully.

Example 5.15 introduces a thought process through which the possibility of decreasing the truncation error of a finite-difference approximation is explored.

Example 5.15. How would you decrease the magnitude of the truncation error of the approximation used in Example 5.14?

Solution. Here, the goal is to seek a way to be able to set the principal part of the local truncation error to zero, as

$$\frac{(\Delta x)^2}{12}\frac{\partial^4 p}{\partial x^4} - \frac{\Delta t}{2D}\frac{\partial^2 p}{\partial t^2} = 0. \quad \ldots\ldots\ldots (5.118)$$

If the statement in Eq. 5.118 is achieved, the principal part of the local truncation error will be $O[(\Delta x)^4] + O[(\Delta t)^2]$. From the original differential equation we know that

$$\frac{\partial^2}{\partial x^2}(f) = \frac{1}{D}\frac{\partial}{\partial t}(f). \quad \ldots\ldots\ldots (5.119)$$

If we let $f = \partial p/\partial t$, then

$$\frac{\partial^2}{\partial x^2}\left(\frac{\partial p}{\partial t}\right) = \frac{1}{D}\frac{\partial}{\partial t}\left(\frac{\partial p}{\partial t}\right). \quad \ldots\ldots\ldots (5.120)$$

Or, substituting for $\partial p/\partial t$ on the left side of Eq. 5.120 with Eq. 5.108,

$$\frac{\partial^2}{\partial x^2}\left(D\frac{\partial^2 p}{\partial x^2}\right) = \frac{1}{D}\frac{\partial^2 p}{\partial t^2}, \quad \ldots\ldots\ldots (5.121)$$

which reduces to

$$D\frac{\partial^4 p}{\partial x^4} = \frac{1}{D}\frac{\partial^2 p}{\partial t^2}. \quad \ldots\ldots\ldots (5.122)$$

Combining Eqs. 5.118 and 5.122 by eliminating $\partial^2 p/\partial t^2$ yields

$$\frac{(\Delta x)^2}{12}\frac{\partial^4 p}{\partial x^4} - D\frac{(\Delta t)}{2}\frac{\partial^4 p}{\partial x^4} = 0 \quad \ldots\ldots\ldots (5.123)$$

$$\text{or}\ \left[\frac{(\Delta x)^2}{12} - D\frac{(\Delta t)}{2}\right]\frac{\partial^4 p}{\partial x^4} = 0. \quad \ldots\ldots\ldots (5.124)$$

Eq. 5.124 is satisfied if $\Delta t = (\Delta x)^2/(6D)$; that is, if, in the discretization process, the timestep size and the grid dimension are selected so that the relation $\Delta t = (\Delta x)^2/(6D)$ is satisfied, the finite-difference approximation has a local truncation error of $O[(\Delta x)^4] + O[(\Delta t)^2]$. Naturally, the practicality of this observation depends on the magnitude of the diffusivity constant, D. If Δt turns out to be very small for reasonable values of Δx, the computational work involved increases substantially and the dilemma of round-off error vs. truncation error arises again.

Stability and Stability Analysis. As the previous section discussed, the solution of the finite-difference (discrete) problem will not converge to the exact solution of the differential problem even if the grid dimensions are made small. The disparity in the two solutions is mainly the effect of round-off error, which may differ from one computer to another depending on the number of digits they carry during the computations and on the internal order of the computations. The resulting round-off error may soon dominate the desired solution and lead to incorrect results. A numerical scheme that cannot control the growth of this error generates an unstable solution. Example 5.10 illustrates this.

There are several procedures for analyzing the stability of a given finite-difference approximation. After performing a stability analysis on a given finite-difference approximation, one can determine the stability criteria of the proposed scheme (that is, whether the proposed scheme is unconditionally stable, conditionally stable, or unconditionally unstable).

Stability Analysis by Fourier Series Method. In this method, the initial error in the finite-difference approximation is represented by a finite Fourier series of the form

$$\sum_n A_n e^{\left(\frac{In\pi x}{l}\right)},$$

where $I = \sqrt{-1}$ and l = interval through which the function is defined. In the Fourier series method, the notation used suggests that the solution can be decomposed into a product of space- and time-dependent terms. Accordingly, discrete values of a function (e.g., p) appearing in the finite-difference approximation should be expressed as products of space- and time-dependent terms. The following are examples.

$$p^n_{i,j} = \xi^n e^{I\left(\gamma_1 x + \gamma_2 y\right)}. \quad \ldots\ldots\ldots (5.125)$$

$$p^n_{i+1,j} = \xi^n e^{I\left[\gamma_1(x+\Delta x) + \gamma_2 y\right]}. \quad \ldots\ldots\ldots (5.126)$$

$$p^n_{i,j+1} = \xi^n e^{I\left[\gamma_1 x + \gamma_2(y+\Delta y)\right]}. \quad \ldots\ldots\ldots (5.127)$$

$$p^{n+1}_{i+1,j-1} = \xi^{n+1} e^{I\left[\gamma_1(x+\Delta x) + \gamma_2(y-\Delta y)\right]}. \quad \ldots\ldots\ldots (5.128)$$

The Fourier series method states that a scheme is stable as long as the amplification factor, μ_{max}, is less than one. The amplification factor describes how an error grows with simulated time. The definition of the amplification factor is

$$\mu_{max} = \left(\frac{|\xi^{n+1}|}{|\xi^n|}\right)_{max}. \quad \ldots\ldots\ldots (5.129)$$

In other words, we want to find the conditions under which the error term at the new timestep, ξ^{n+1}, is less than the error term at the old timestep, ξ^n. If the error at the new timestep is less, we know that it will not grow as we advance the finite-difference solution in time.

The following three examples show application of the Fourier series method to analyze the stability of different finite-difference approximations.

Example 5.16. Investigate the stability of the backward finite-difference (implicit) approximation as applied to

$$\frac{\partial^2 p}{\partial x^2} = \frac{1}{D}\frac{\partial p}{\partial t}, \quad \text{(5.108)}$$

where D = a positive constant.

Solution. The backward finite-difference approximation to the given PDE is

$$\frac{p_{i+1}^{n+1} - 2p_i^{n+1} + p_{i-1}^{n+1}}{(\Delta x)^2} = \frac{1}{D}\frac{p_i^{n+1} - p_i^n}{\Delta t}. \quad \text{(5.130)}$$

Rearranging Eq. 5.130 gives

$$\frac{D\Delta t}{(\Delta x)^2}\left(p_{i+1}^{n+1} - 2p_i^{n+1} + p_{i-1}^{n+1}\right) = p_i^{n+1} - p_i^n. \quad \text{(5.131)}$$

Letting $r = (D\Delta t)/(\Delta x)^2$, noting that r is always a positive quantity, and using the Fourier series notation (Eqs. 5.125 through 5.128), Eq. 5.131 can be written

$$r\left[\xi^{n+1}e^{I\gamma_1(x+\Delta x)} - 2\xi^{n+1}e^{I\gamma_1 x} + \xi^{n+1}e^{I\gamma_1(x-\Delta x)}\right]$$

$$= \xi^{n+1}e^{I\gamma_1 x} - \xi^n e^{I\gamma_1 x}. \quad \text{(5.132)}$$

Dividing by $e^{I\gamma_1 x}$ and rearranging Eq. 5.132 gives

$$\xi^{n+1}\left[r\left(e^{I\gamma_1\Delta x} + e^{-I\gamma_1\Delta x}\right) - 2r - 1\right] = -\xi^n. \quad \text{(5.133)}$$

Applying Euler's identity, $e^{\pm I\theta} = \cos\theta \pm I\sin\theta$ where, in this case, $\theta = \gamma_1\Delta x$, yields

$$\xi^{n+1}(r\cos\gamma_1\Delta x + Ir\sin\gamma_1\Delta x + r\cos\gamma_1\Delta x$$

$$- Ir\sin\gamma_1\Delta x - 2r - 1) = -\xi^n. \quad \text{(5.134)}$$

Now, rearranging in terms of the amplification factor gives

$$\mu_{\max} = \left(\frac{|\xi^{n+1}|}{|\xi^n|}\right)_{\max} = \frac{1}{|1 + 2r(1 - \cos\gamma_1\Delta x)|}$$

$$= \frac{1}{1 + 2r(1 - \cos\gamma_1\Delta x)}. \quad \text{(5.135)}$$

For stability, any error will decrease with time. This implies that $\mu_{\max} \leqq 1$; then,

$$\frac{1}{1 + 2r(1 - \cos\gamma_1\Delta x)} \leqq 1. \quad \text{(5.136)}$$

Because r is always positive, Eq. 5.136 simplifies to

$$1 - \cos\gamma_1\Delta x \geqq 0 \quad \text{(5.137)}$$

or $\cos\gamma_1\Delta x \leqq 1, \quad \text{(5.138)}$

which is true for all values of γ_1 and Δx. In other words, the stability criterion is always satisfied regardless of the value of r, so the implicit finite-difference scheme is unconditionally stable. Example 5.13 illustrates this.

Example 5.17. Investigate the stability of the forward finite-difference (explicit) approximation as applied to

$$\frac{\partial^2 p}{\partial x^2} = \frac{1}{D}\frac{\partial p}{\partial t}, \quad \text{(5.108)}$$

where D = a positive constant.

Solution. The explicit finite-difference approximation to the diffusivity equation is

$$\frac{p_{i+1}^n - 2p_i^n + p_{i-1}^n}{(\Delta x)^2} = \frac{1}{D}\frac{p_i^{n+1} - p_i^n}{\Delta t}. \quad \text{(5.139)}$$

Letting $r = (D\Delta t)/(\Delta x)^2$ yields

$$r\left(p_{i+1}^n - 2p_i^n + p_{i-1}^n\right) = p_i^{n+1} - p_i^n. \quad \text{(5.140)}$$

Using the Fourier series notation, the above equation may be written

$$r\left[\xi^n e^{I\gamma_1(x+\Delta x)} - 2\xi^n e^{I\gamma_1 x} + \xi^n e^{I\gamma_1(x-\Delta x)}\right]$$

$$= \xi^{n+1}e^{I\gamma_1 x} - \xi^n e^{I\gamma_1 x}. \quad \text{(5.141)}$$

Following a similar development as in Example 5.16, the amplification factor can be determined as

$$\mu_{\max} = \left(\frac{|\xi^{n+1}|}{|\xi^n|}\right)_{\max} = |1 - 2r(1 - \cos\gamma_1\Delta x)|_{\max}. \quad \text{(5.142)}$$

The stability condition requires that $|1 - 2r(1 - \cos\gamma_1\Delta x)| \leqq 1$. Now consider the following three situations.

1. $\gamma_1\Delta x = 0 \rightarrow \cos\gamma_1\Delta x = 1 \rightarrow |1| \leqq 1$ which is always true but provides no useful information.
2. $\gamma_1\Delta x = \pi/2 \rightarrow \cos\gamma_1\Delta x = 0 \rightarrow |1 - 2r| \leqq 1$.
3. $\gamma_1\Delta x = \pi \rightarrow \cos\gamma_1\Delta x = -1 \rightarrow |1 - 4r| \leqq 1$.

If the last condition is satisfied, then the second condition is also satisfied. This imposes the requirement $|1 - 4r| \leqq 1$ for the stability, which gives either $4r \geqq 0$ or $4r \leqq 2$. More explicitly, $0 \leqq 4r \leqq 2$, where $r = (D\Delta t)/(\Delta x)^2$, leading to the stability condition

$$\Delta t \leqq \frac{1}{2}\frac{(\Delta x)^2}{D} \quad \text{(5.143)}$$

because Δt is always positive.

Therefore, the explicit finite-difference scheme is stable only if the requirement in Eq. 5.143 is satisfied. This leads to the conclusion that the scheme is only conditionally stable.

Example 5.18. Investigate the stability of the central finite-difference approximation (Richardson's[7] approximation) to the diffusivity equation

$$\frac{p_{i+1}^n - 2p_i^n + p_{i-1}^n}{(\Delta x)^2} = \frac{1}{D}\frac{p_i^{n+1} - p_i^{n-1}}{2\Delta t}. \quad \text{(5.144)}$$

Solution. Again, let $r = (D\Delta t)/(\Delta x)^2$. The Fourier series notation leads to

$$\xi^n\left(2re^{I\gamma_1\Delta x} - 4r + 2re^{-I\gamma_1\Delta x}\right) = \xi^{n+1} - \xi^{n-1}. \quad \text{(5.145)}$$

Dividing both sides by ξ^n gives

$$2re^{I\gamma_1\Delta x} - 4r + 2re^{-I\gamma_1\Delta x} = \mu - \frac{1}{\mu} \quad \text{(5.146a)}$$

because $\mu = \dfrac{\xi^{n+1}}{\xi^n} = \dfrac{\xi^n}{\xi^{n-1}}. \quad \text{(5.146b)}$

Substituting Euler's identity yields the quadratic equation

$$\mu^2 + 4r(1 - \cos\gamma_1\Delta x)\mu - 1 = 0. \quad \text{(5.147)}$$

Solving for the roots of Eq. 5.147 yields

$$\mu_1 = -2r(1 - \cos\gamma_1\Delta x)$$

$$- \sqrt{4r^2(1 - \cos\gamma_1\Delta x)^2 + 1} \quad \text{(5.148)}$$

and $\mu_2 = -2r(1 - \cos\gamma_1\Delta x) + \sqrt{4r^2(1 - \cos\gamma_1\Delta x)^2 + 1}$. .... (5.149)

For stability, one needs to use the larger root in absolute value (remember that $\mu_{max} \leqq 1$). Because $|\mu_1| > |\mu_2|$, the stability condition requires that

$$2r(1 - \cos\gamma_1\Delta x) + \sqrt{4r^2(1 - \cos\gamma_1\Delta x)^2 + 1} \leqq 1, \quad (5.150)$$

which can be written as

$$4r^2(1 - \cos\gamma_1\Delta x)^2 + 1 \leqq \left[1 - 2r(1 - \cos\gamma_1\Delta x)\right]^2, \quad (5.151)$$

which simplifies to

$$-4r(1 - \cos\gamma_1\Delta x) \geqq 0. \quad (5.152)$$

This condition can never be satisfied because r is always a positive constant and $(1 - \cos\gamma_1\Delta x) \geqq 0$ for all values of $\gamma_1\Delta x$. Therefore, the proposed scheme[7] is unconditionally unstable.

Stability Analysis by Matrix Method. As the previous series of examples showed, the Fourier series method ignores the effect of the boundary conditions on stability. This is why, although the conditions specified in Example 5.10 satisfy the stability criteria as prescribed by the Fourier series method, the solution is still unstable (see Table 5.5). When boundary conditions affect stability, the matrix method must be used.[8] In this method, equations are expressed in a matrix form and the eigenvalues of the resulting matrix are examined. For a stable solution method, it is necessary to show that the absolute value of the maximum eigenvalue (spectral radius) of the matrix is less than one. Because determination of the eigenvalues of a large matrix is an arduous task, the matrix method is rarely used. It is also interesting to note that in less complex cases, the amplification factor of the Fourier series method is equal to the spectral radius of the matrix in the stability analysis by matrix method.

Consistency and Consistency Analysis. The consistency (or compatibility) of a finite-difference approximation with the differential equation is another important property that must be examined carefully. Sometimes it is possible to approximate a PDE with a finite-difference equation that passes the stability test while the solution offered by the finite-difference equation may converge to the solution of another differential equation as the mesh sizes approach zero. For a consistent scheme, it is expected that the finite-difference approximation becomes identical to the original PDE as the mesh sizes tend to zero.

Example 5.19. Consider the following three-time-level finite-difference approximation to the diffusivity equation given by Eq. 5.108 with $D = 1$.

$$\frac{p^n_{i+1} - 2\left[\theta p^n_i + (1 - \theta)p^{n-1}_i\right] + p^n_{i-1}}{(\Delta x)^2} = \frac{p^{n+1}_i - p^{n-1}_i}{2\Delta t}, \quad (5.153)$$

where $0 \leqq \theta \leqq 1$. Find the value of θ that ensures the consistency of the finite-difference approximation with the diffusivity equation.

Solution. The application of truncation-error analysis (see Truncation Error and Truncation Error Analysis) leads to

$$\varepsilon^n_{L_i} = \left(\frac{\partial p}{\partial t} - \frac{\partial^2 p}{\partial x^2}\right)^n_i + \left[\frac{(\Delta t)^2}{6}\frac{\partial^3 p}{\partial t^3}\bigg|^n_i - \frac{(\Delta x)^2}{12}\frac{\partial^4 p}{\partial x^4}\bigg|^n_i + (2\theta - 1)\frac{2\Delta t}{(\Delta x)^2}\frac{\partial p}{\partial t}\bigg|^n_i + \frac{(\Delta t)^2}{(\Delta x)^2}\frac{\partial^2 p}{\partial t^2}\bigg|^n_i\right]. \quad (5.154)$$

Let us investigate the following two cases.

Case 1. $\Delta t = r\Delta x$, where r is a positive constant.

$$\varepsilon^n_{L_i} = \left(\frac{\partial p}{\partial t} - \frac{\partial^2 p}{\partial x^2}\right)^n_i + (2\theta - 1)\frac{2r\Delta x}{(\Delta x)^2}\frac{\partial p}{\partial t}\bigg|^n_i + \frac{r^2(\Delta x)^2}{(\Delta x)^2}\frac{\partial^2 p}{\partial t^2}\bigg|^n_i + \frac{r^2(\Delta x)^2}{6}\frac{\partial^3 p}{\partial t^3}\bigg|^n_i - \frac{(\Delta x)^2}{12}\frac{\partial^4 p}{\partial x^4}\bigg|^n_i. \quad (5.155)$$

As mesh length, Δx, tends to zero,

$$\varepsilon^n_{L_i} = \left(\frac{\partial p}{\partial t} - \frac{\partial^2 p}{\partial x^2}\right)^n_i + \lim_{\Delta x \to 0}(2\theta - 1)\frac{2r}{\Delta x}\frac{\partial p}{\partial t}\bigg|^n_i + r^2\frac{\partial^2 p}{\partial t^2}\bigg|^n_i. \quad (5.156)$$

Obviously when $\theta \neq ½$, the limit tends to infinity as Δx tends to zero. On the other hand, when $\theta = ½$, the value of $\varepsilon^n_{L_i}$ in the limit when Δx approaches zero is

$$\varepsilon_L = \frac{\partial p}{\partial t} - \frac{\partial^2 p}{\partial x^2} + r^2\frac{\partial^2 p}{\partial t^2} = 0. \quad (5.157)$$

In this case, the finite-difference equation is not compatible with the diffusivity equation, but it is consistent with a hyperbolic PDE. Therefore, when $\Delta t = r\Delta x$, the proposed scheme is inconsistent with the diffusivity equation for any value of θ.

Case 2. $\Delta t = r(\Delta x)^2$. This time the truncation-error term is

$$\varepsilon^n_{L_i} = \left(\frac{\partial p}{\partial t} - \frac{\partial^2 p}{\partial x^2}\right)^n_i + (2\theta - 1)\frac{2r(\Delta x)^2}{(\Delta x)^2}\frac{\partial p}{\partial t}\bigg|^n_i + \frac{r^2(\Delta x)^4}{(\Delta x)^2}\frac{\partial^2 p}{\partial t^2}\bigg|^n_i + \frac{r^2(\Delta x)^4}{6}\frac{\partial^3 p}{\partial t^3}\bigg|^n_i - \frac{(\Delta x)^2}{12}\frac{\partial^4 p}{\partial x^4}\bigg|^n_i. \quad (5.158)$$

Again, as $\Delta x \to 0$, the truncation-error term is

$$\varepsilon^n_{L_i} = \left(\frac{\partial p}{\partial t} - \frac{\partial^2 p}{\partial x^2}\right)^n_i + (2\theta - 1)2r\frac{\partial p}{\partial t}\bigg|^n_i. \quad (5.159)$$

If $\theta \neq ½$, the difference scheme is inconsistent with the original PDE because

$$\frac{\partial^2 p}{\partial x^2} = [1 + 2(2\theta - 1)r]\frac{\partial p}{\partial t}. \quad (5.160)$$

If, however, $\theta = ½$, the difference scheme is consistent with the original PDE because the local truncation error goes to zero in the limit when mesh size tends to zero

$$\left(\frac{\partial p}{\partial t} - \frac{\partial^2 p}{\partial x^2}\right)^n_i = 0. \quad (5.161)$$

Lax and Richtmeyer[9] studied the relation between consistency and stability. The major result of their study is the Lax equivalence theorem, which states that, given a properly posed linear-initial-value problem and finite-difference approximation to it that satisfies the consistency condition, stability is a necessary and sufficient condition for convergence. The proof of this theorem is beyond the scope of this book.

5.7 Chapter Project

In Sec. 5.2 construction and properties of finite-difference grids as used in reservoir simulation were presented. **Fig. 5.31** shows the two-dimensional (2D), nonuniform block-centered finite-dif-

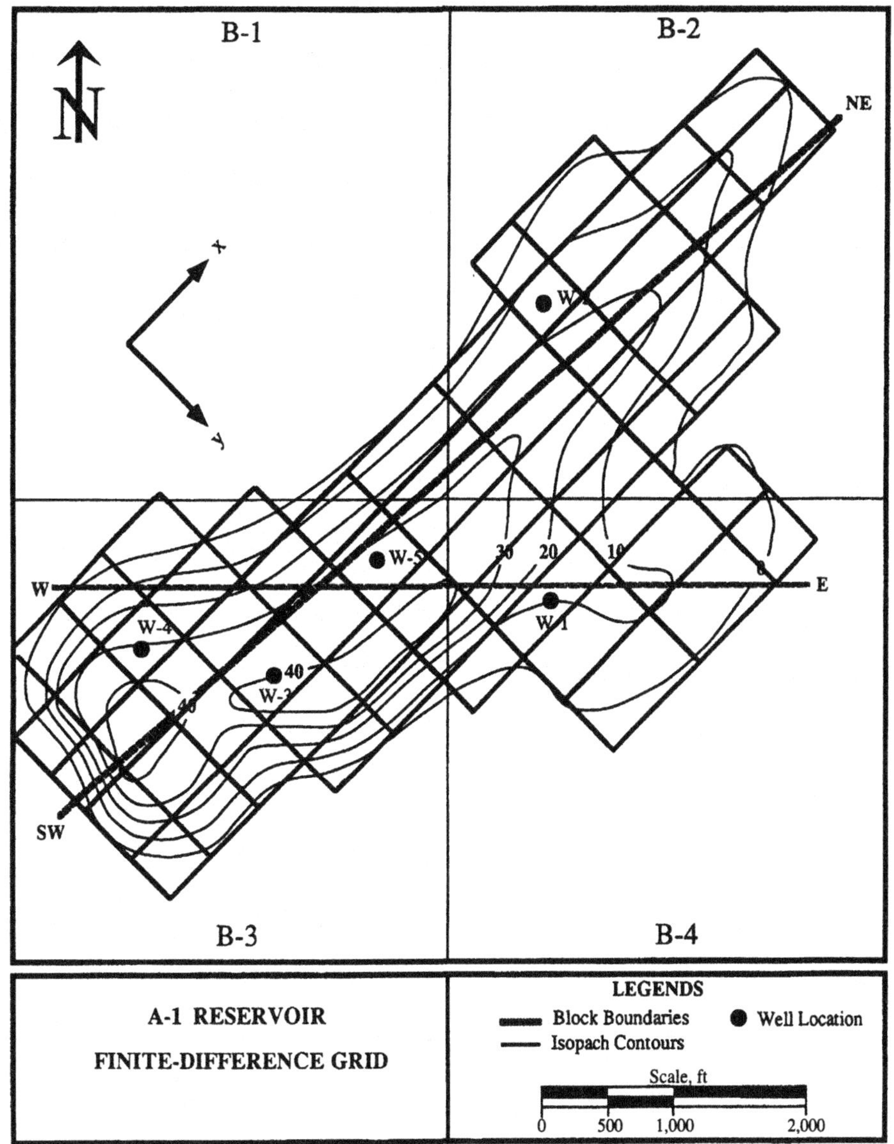

Fig. 5.31—Gridblock-centered grid layout for A-1 reservoir.

ference grid as overlaid on the A-1 reservoir. Note that, as discussed in Sec. 4.6 and indicated in Fig. 4.16, the rectangular grid system is oriented in a manner that ensures that the x and y directions of the rectangular coordinate system are parallel to the principal permeability directions of the reservoir. **Fig. 5.32** gives a three-dimensional view of the 2D rectangular grid system.

Fig. 5.33 presents the two cross sections obtained along west-east and southwest-northeast directions. They can be compared with the cross sections presented in Fig. 2.23.

Fig. 5.34 shows the numbering of the gridblocks. The gridblocks bordered by four bold lines represent the blocks that are part of the A-1 reservoir. All the remaining blocks are outside the A-1 reservoir. In this way it is possible to locate the 60 active blocks used to represent the A-1 reservoir. **Figs. 5.35 through 5.37** show reservoir properties assigned to the gridblocks.

Note that, in Fig. 5.35, Δx values along each column of blocks and Δy values along each row of blocks are kept uniform. This ensures the continuity of the major grid lines of the grid system; however, the Δx and Δy values are allowed to vary along the x and y directions, respectively (nonuniform grid spacing).

The depths to the structure top of the gridblocks as reported in Fig. 5.36 are considered as positive downward from sea level. Also note that, by combining the information presented in the depth and thickness arrays, one can easily find the depths to the base of the structure. For example, for Gridblock (1,2), the depth to the base of the formation is 9,349 ft. Similarly, along the central axis of Gridblock (9,5), the depth to the base is 9,307 ft. Accordingly, depths to the centers of Gridblocks (1,2) and (9,5) can be calculated as 9,345 and 9,299 ft, respectively.

Fig. 5.37 shows absolute permeability values (along the x and y directions) and porosity values assigned to the gridblocks of the A-1 reservoir. The y-direction permeabilities are assigned as 80% of the x-direction permeabilities, in agreement with the description in Sec. 2.6.2 that discusses the anisotropic nature of the formation permeability.

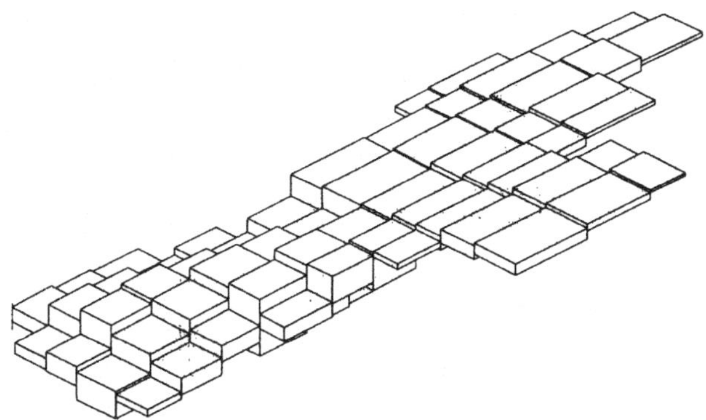

Fig. 5.32—Three-dimensional visualization of grid system proposed for A-1 reservoir.

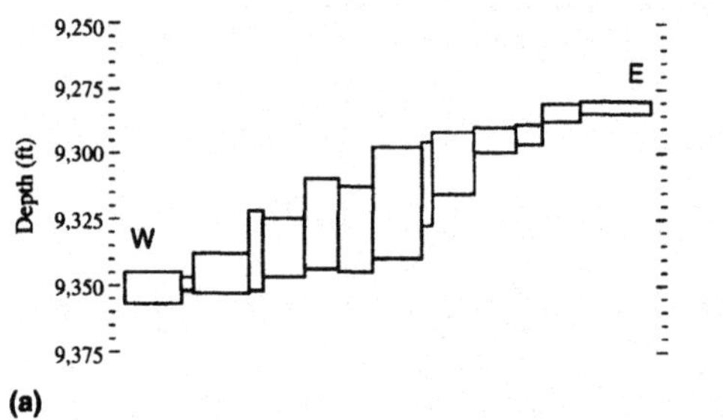

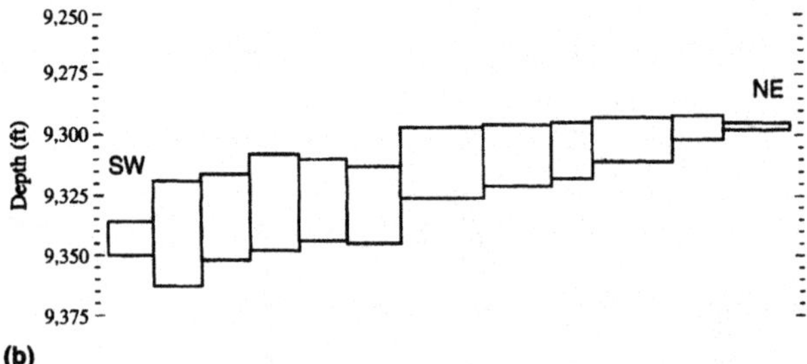

Fig. 5.33—Structural cross sections of A-1 reservoir as approximated by proposed grid layout: (a) west-east cross section and (b) southwest-northeast cross section.

Table 5.11 summarizes the A-1 reservoir parameters as approximated by the grid system presented in this section (Figs. 5.31 and 5.32).

Exercises

5.1 Which grid systems (rectangular, cylindrical, spherical, corner-point, hybrid) can be used for the following?

1. Single-well simulation
2. Full-field simulation
3. Pattern simulation
4. Cross-sectional simulation

5.2 Derive the identity $\Delta x_{i+½} = x_{i+1} - x_i = ½(\Delta x_{i+1} + \Delta x_i)$ for block-centered grids (refer to Fig. 5.2).

5.3 A 2D, slightly compressible-fluid transport equation is given as

$$\frac{\partial}{\partial x}\left(\beta_c \frac{A_x k_x}{\mu_l B_l}\frac{\partial p}{\partial x}\right)\Delta x + \frac{\partial}{\partial y}\left(\beta_c \frac{A_y k_y}{\mu_l B_l}\frac{\partial p}{\partial y}\right)\Delta y + q_{lsc} = \frac{V_b \phi c_l}{\alpha_c B_l^\circ}\frac{\partial p}{\partial t}.$$

1. Write the forward-difference approximation to this equation.
2. Write the backward-difference approximation to this equation.

(1,1)	(2,1)	(3,1)	(4,1)	(5,1)	(6,1)	(7,1)	(8,1)	(9,1)	(10,1)	(11,1)	(12,1)
(1,2)	(2,2)	(3,2)	(4,2)	(5,2)	(6,2)	(7,2)	(8,2)	(9,2)	(10,2)	(11,2)	(12,2)
(1,3)	(2,3)	(3,3)	(4,3)	(5,3)	(6,3)	(7,3)	(8,3)	(9,3)	(10,3)	(11,3)	(12,3)
(1,4)	(2,4)	(3,4)	(4,4)	(5,4)	(6,4)	(7,4)	(8,4)	(9,4)	(10,4)	(11,4)	(12,4)
(1,5)	(2,5)	(3,5)	(4,5)	(5,5)	(6,5)	(7,5)	(8,5)	(9,5)	(10,5)	(11,5)	(12,5)
(1,6)	(2,6)	(3,6)	(4,6)	(5,6)	(6,6)	(7,6)	(8,6)	(9,6)	(10,6)	(11,6)	(12,6)
(1,7)	(2,7)	(3,7)	(4,7)	(5,7)	(6,7)	(7,7)	(8,7)	(9,7)	(10,7)	(11,7)	(12,7)
(1,8)	(2,8)	(3,8)	(4,8)	(5,8)	(6,8)	(7,8)	(8,8)	(9,8)	(10,8)	(11,8)	(12,8)
(1,9)	(2,9)	(3,9)	(4,9)	(5,9)	(6,9)	(7,9)	(8,9)	(9,9)	(10,9)	(11,9)	(12,9)

Fig. 5.34—Numbering of gridblocks for A-1 reservoir.

5.4 Use the results of Exercise 5.3.

1. Write the 2D, forward-difference approximation in a format suitable for an explicit calculation method (that is, solve the equation in Part 1 of Exercise 5.3 for $p_{i,j}^{n+1}$).
2. Write the 2D, backward-difference approximation in a format suitable for an implicit calculation method (that is, write the equation in Part 2 of Exercise 5.3 with $p_{i+1,j}^{n+1}$, $p_{i,j+1}^{n+1}$, $p_{i,j}^{n+1}$, $p_{i,j-1}^{n+1}$, and $p_{i-1,j}^{n+1}$ on the left side, and $q_{sc_{i,j}}$ and $p_{i,j}^{n}$ on the right side).

5.5 Use **Fig. 5.38**, where the reservoir has no-flow boundaries, $\Delta x = 1{,}000$ ft, $\Delta y = 750$ ft, $\Delta z = 50$ ft, $k_x = 50$ md, $\phi = 0.27$, $c_l = 1.6 \times 10^{-6}$ psi^{-1}, $\mu_l = 30$ cp, $p_i = 4{,}500$ psia, $B_l \approx 1$ RB/STB, and $B_l^o = 1$ RB/STB.

1. Calculate a stable timestep size for the explicit formulation.
2. Perform the explicit calculations for several timesteps.

5.6 Use the case in Exercise 5.5.

1. Write the system of equations for the first timestep of the implicit formulation. (Do not attempt to solve this 6×6 matrix equation.) Use the same timestep size as that of stable explicit timestep size.
2. Lump the gridblocks to form three $2{,}000 \times 750 \times 50$-ft gridblocks.
3. Write the system of equations for the new grid system.
4. Solve the 3×3 matrix equation for the new grid system.

5.7 Use **Fig. 5.39** to answer the following.

1. Write the PDE that governs the incompressible-fluid-flow problem described in Fig. 5.39 and put it into its simplest form.
2. Give a finite-difference approximation of the PDE of Part 1 and put it into a characteristic form.
3. Generate the system of equations that must be solved to determine the pressure distribution in the system. (Do not solve the equations.)
4. Offer an educated guess for the expected flow rate from the well located in Gridlock 1.

```
BLOCK DIMENSION IN x DIRECTION (ft)
439.0 509.0 491.0 596.0 526.0 561.0 912.0 807.0 439.0 877.0 544.0 772.0
439.0 509.0 491.0 596.0 526.0 561.0 912.0 807.0 439.0 877.0 544.0 772.0
439.0 509.0 491.0 596.0 526.0 561.0 912.0 807.0 439.0 877.0 544.0 772.0
439.0 509.0 491.0 596.0 526.0 561.0 912.0 807.0 439.0 877.0 544.0 772.0
439.0 509.0 491.0 596.0 526.0 561.0 912.0 807.0 439.0 877.0 544.0 772.0
439.0 509.0 491.0 596.0 526.0 561.0 912.0 807.0 439.0 877.0 544.0 772.0
439.0 509.0 491.0 596.0 526.0 561.0 912.0 807.0 439.0 877.0 544.0 772.0
439.0 509.0 491.0 596.0 526.0 561.0 912.0 807.0 439.0 877.0 544.0 772.0
439.0 509.0 491.0 596.0 526.0 561.0 912.0 807.0 439.0 877.0 544.0 772.0

BLOCK DIMENSION IN y DIRECTION (ft)
474.0 474.0 474.0 474.0 474.0 474.0 474.0 474.0 474.0 474.0 474.0 474.0
404.0 404.0 404.0 404.0 404.0 404.0 404.0 404.0 404.0 404.0 404.0 404.0
386.0 386.0 386.0 386.0 386.0 386.0 386.0 386.0 386.0 386.0 386.0 386.0
491.0 491.0 491.0 491.0 491.0 491.0 491.0 491.0 491.0 491.0 491.0 491.0
404.0 404.0 404.0 404.0 404.0 404.0 404.0 404.0 404.0 404.0 404.0 404.0
316.0 316.0 316.0 316.0 316.0 316.0 316.0 316.0 316.0 316.0 316.0 316.0
316.0 316.0 316.0 316.0 316.0 316.0 316.0 316.0 316.0 316.0 316.0 316.0
421.0 421.0 421.0 421.0 421.0 421.0 421.0 421.0 421.0 421.0 421.0 421.0
526.0 526.0 526.0 526.0 526.0 526.0 526.0 526.0 526.0 526.0 526.0 526.0
```

Fig. 5.35—Nonuniform gridblock dimensions along x and y directions.

```
DEPTHS TO THE STRUCTURE TOP (ft)
******* 9342.0 9345.0 9347.0 ************************************************
9341.0 9327.0 9330.0 9338.0 9333.0 ********************** 9311.0 9310.0 *************
9336.0 9319.0 9316.0 9322.0 9325.0 9315.0 9299.0 9300.0 9299.0 9297.0 9297.0 9305.0
9340.0 9326.0 9316.0 9308.0 9310.0 9313.0 9297.0 9296.0 9295.0 9293.0 9292.0 9295.0
9342.0 9332.0 9323.0 9305.0 9298.0 9298.0 9296.0 9292.0 9291.0 9288.0 *************
********************** 9315.0 9297.0 9295.0 9292.0 9289.0 9289.0 9287.0 *************
*********************************** 9294.0 9290.0 9286.0 **************************
***************************************** 9289.0 9281.0 9282.0 *********************
***************************************** 9290.0 9280.0 9278.0 *********************

BLOCK THICKNESSES (ft)
***** 10.0 12.0  5.0 ***************************************
 8.0 35.0 30.0 15.0  6.0 ************** 4.0  5.0 *********
14.0 44.0 36.0 30.0 22.0 16.0 12.0 14.0 15.0 11.0  6.0  3.0
20.0 34.0 35.0 40.0 34.0 32.0 29.0 25.0 22.0 18.0 10.0  3.0
 5.0 12.0 12.0 40.0 44.0 42.0 32.0 20.0 16.0 10.0 *********
**************** 10.0 19.0 27.0 24.0 10.0  6.0  3.0 *********
************************* 4.0 10.0  6.0 ********************
****************************** 8.0  7.0  3.0 **************
****************************** 4.0  5.0  2.0 **************
```

Fig. 5.36—Depths to structure top of gridblocks and individual gridblock thicknesses assigned to the A-1 reservoir grid system.

```
PERMEABILITY IN x DIRECTION (md)
******  275.0  270.0  252.0  **********************************************************
 267.0  274.0  280.0  265.0  253.0  *********************  259.0  270.0  ************
 265.0  280.0  289.0  278.0  271.0  271.0  270.0  269.0  270.0  279.0  283.0  275.0
 258.0  271.0  295.0  297.0  282.0  280.0  281.0  276.0  290.0  293.0  279.0  270.0
 253.0  259.0  275.0  285.0  290.0  280.0  289.0  277.0  290.0  280.0  ************
*******************  272.0  276.0  273.0  288.0  281.0  274.0  268.0  ************
*********************************  265.0  280.0  290.0  ***************************
****************************************  270.0  280.0  270.0  *******************
****************************************  260.0  268.0  260.0  *******************
```

```
PERMEABILITY IN y DIRECTION (md)
******  220.0  216.0  201.6  **********************************************************
 213.6  219.2  224.0  212.0  202.4  *********************  207.2  216.0  *************
 212.0  224.0  231.2  222.4  216.8  216.8  216.0  215.2  216.0  223.2  226.4  220.0
 206.4  216.8  236.0  237.6  225.6  224.0  224.8  220.8  232.0  234.4  223.2  216.0
 202.4  207.2  220.0  228.0  232.0  224.0  231.2  221.6  232.0  224.0  *************
*******************  217.6  220.8  218.4  230.4  224.8  219.2  214.4  *************
*********************************  212.0  224.0  232.0  ***************************
****************************************  216.0  224.0  216.0  *******************
****************************************  208.0  214.4  208.0  *******************
```

```
POROSITY (fraction)
******  0.192  0.197  0.202  **********************************************************
 0.190  0.195  0.200  0.204  0.207  *********************  0.215  0.205  *************
 0.190  0.196  0.205  0.207  0.210  0.216  0.220  0.223  0.215  0.210  0.203  0.200
 0.185  0.195  0.205  0.213  0.216  0.221  0.225  0.226  0.220  0.215  0.207  0.200
 0.183  0.195  0.205  0.212  0.218  0.225  0.232  0.232  0.225  0.219  *************
*******************  0.210  0.219  0.226  0.235  0.230  0.220  0.216  *************
*********************************  0.225  0.235  0.230  ***************************
****************************************  0.232  0.226  0.217  *******************
****************************************  0.229  0.220  0.217  *******************
```

Fig. 5.37—A-1 reservoir-gridblock permeabilities and porosities.

5.8 Determine the truncation error involved in the following approximation of the differential equation $\partial^2 p/\partial x^2 = (1/D)(\partial p/\partial t)$.

$$\frac{p_{i+1}^n - \left(p_i^{n+1} + p_i^{n-1}\right) + p_{i-1}^n}{(\Delta x)^2} = \frac{p_i^{n+1} - p_i^{n-1}}{2D\Delta t}.$$

This three-time-level approximation is known as the DuFort-Frankel[10] approximation.

5.9 Investigate the stability of the DuFort-Frankel approximation as applied to the diffusivity equation in Exercise 5.8 using the Fourier series analysis method.

5.10 Use the Fourier stability-analysis procedure to investigate the stability of the following finite-difference scheme for the PDE $\partial^2 p/\partial x^2 = \partial p/\partial t$.

$$p_i^{n+1} = \frac{1}{6}\left(p_{i-1}^n + p_{i+1}^n\right) + \frac{2}{3}p_i^n.$$

5.11 The equation $\partial^2 p/\partial x^2 = \partial p/\partial t$ is approximated by the equation

$$\frac{p_{i-1}^n - 2p_i^n + p_{i+1}^n}{(\Delta x)^2} = 3\left(\frac{p_i^{n+1} - p_i^n}{2\Delta t}\right) - \left(\frac{p_i^n - p_i^{n-1}}{2\Delta t}\right).$$

Investigate the stability of the proposed scheme.

5.12 Rework Example 5.8 for three timesteps using $\Delta t = 30$ days and varying B_l according to the relationship $B_l = B_l^\circ/[1 + c_l(p - p^\circ)]$ where $p^\circ = 6{,}000$ psia. Compare your results with those given in Table 5.3. Hint: After each timestep, use the expression given here for B_l and recalculate the transmissibility terms, $T_{lx_{i+1/2}}$ and $T_{lx_{i-1/2}}$, before entering the new timestep calculations.

TABLE 5.11—SUMMARY OF A-1 RESERVOIR PARAMETERS CALCULATED FROM BLOCK PROPERTIES

Average* porosity, %	21.4
Average permeability, md	279.6
Total bulk volume, 10^6 ft^3	263.5
Total pore volume, 10^6 res bbl	10.1

*Volumetric average.

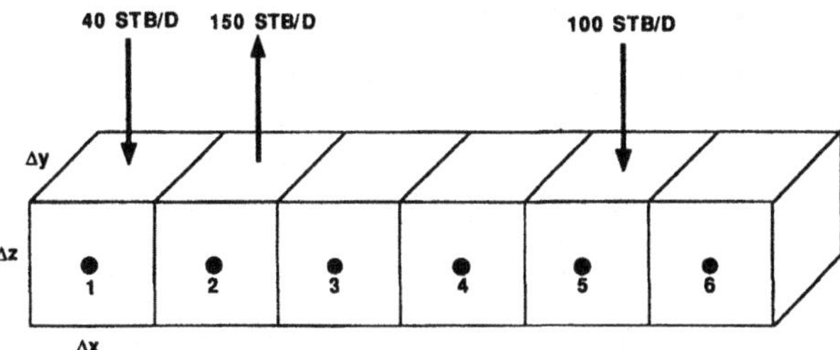

Fig. 5.38—Discretized reservoir in Exercise 5.5.

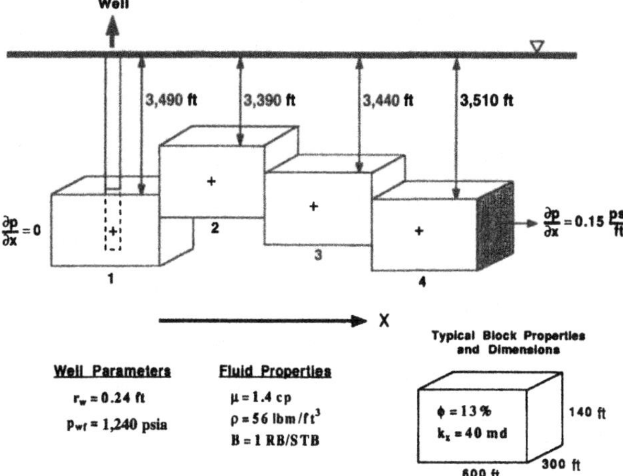

Fig. 5.39—Reservoir description in Exercise 5.7.

Nomenclature

A_n = nth coefficient of Fourier series determined from initial and boundary conditions
A_x = cross-sectional area normal to the x direction, L^2, ft^2 [m^2]
A_{x_i} = cross-sectional area normal to the x direction for Gridblock i, L^2, ft^2 [m^2]
A_y = cross-sectional area normal to the y direction, L^2, ft^2 [m^2]
B_l = formation volume factor (FVF) of Phase l, L^3/L^3, reservoir volume/volume at standard conditions
c_l = compressibility for Phase l, Lt^2/m, psi^{-1} [kPa^{-1}]
C = constant
D = diffusion coefficient, L^2/t, ft^2/D [m^2/d]
D_i = diffusion coefficient for Gridpoint i, L^2/t, ft^2/D [m^2/d]
$e^{\alpha'_{lg}}$ = exponential function of α'_{lg}
$G_{i,j,k}$ = constant part of the transmissibility
f_d = differential form of a PDE
f_{fd} = finite-difference form of a PDE
h = thickness, L, ft [m]
I = $\sqrt{-1}$
k = permeability, L^2, darcy [μm^2]
k_H = horizontal permeability, L^2, darcy [μm^2]
k_x = permeability in the direction of the x axis, L^2, darcy [μm^2]
k_y = permeability in the direction of the y axis, L^2, darcy [μm^2]
k_z = permeability in the direction of the z axis, L^2, darcy [μm^2]
L_x = total length of the reservoir along the x direction, L, ft [m]
n_r = number of gridblocks in the r direction

n_x = number of gridblocks in the x direction
O = order of error
p = pressure, m/Lt^2, psia [kPa]
p^n = pressure at old time level n, m/Lt^2, psia [kPa]
p° = reference pressure, m/Lt^2, psia [kPa]
p_i = initial pressure, m/Lt^2, psia [kPa]
$p_{i,j,k}$ = pressure of Gridblock (i,j,k), m/Lt^2, psia [kPa]
p_{wf} = flowing well bottomhole pressure, m/Lt^2, psia [kPa]
p_1 through p_5 = pressure of Gridblocks 1 through 5, m/Lt^2, psia [kPa]
Δp = pressure difference, m/Lt^2, psi [kPa]
q = production rate or flow rate, L^3/t, B/D [m^3/d]
q_{lsc} = production rate of Phase l at standard conditions, L^3/t
q_{lsc_i} = production rate of Phase l at standard conditions for Gridblock i, L^3/t
q_{sc} = production rate at standard conditions, L^3/t, STB/D [m^3/d]
r = distance in radial direction in both cylindrical and spherical coordinate systems, L, ft [m]
r_e = radius of external boundary, L, ft [m]
r_{eq} = equivalent radius of a well block, L, ft [m]
r_i = radius of Mesh Point (or Gridblock) i in radial coordinates, L, ft [m]
r_{n_r} = distance to the outermost gridblock in the r direction, L, ft [m]
r_w = well radius, L, ft [m]
t = time, t, days
t^n = old time level, t, days
Δt = timestep ($\Delta t = t^{n+1} - t^n$), t, days
V_b = bulk volume, L^3, ft^3 [m^3]
V_{b_i} = Gridblock i bulk volume, L^3, ft^3 [m^3]
x = distance in the x direction in the Cartesian coordinate system, L, ft [m]
x_i = x coordinate of Gridpoint i, L, ft [m]
Δx = difference along the x direction ($\Delta x = x_{i+1} - x_i$), L, ft [m]
Δx_i = x direction block dimension for Gridblock i, L, ft [m]
y = distance in the y direction in the Cartesian coordinate system, L, ft [m]
Δy = difference along the y direction ($\Delta y = y_{j+1} - y_j$), L, ft [m]
Δz = difference along the z direction ($\Delta z = z_{k+1} - z_k$), L, ft [m]
$Z_{i,j,k}$ = elevation of Gridblock (i,j,k) with respect to datum, L, ft [m]
α_c = volume conversion factor whose numerical value is given in Table 4.1
α_{lg} = logarithmic spacing constant, dimensionless
β_c = transmissibility conversion factor whose numerical value is given in Table 4.1
γ_l = gravity of Phase l, m/L^{2}t^2, psi/ft [kPa/m]
μ = amplification factor in Fourier series method (Sec. 5.6.3), dimensionless
μ = viscosity, m/Lt, cp [Pa·s]
μ_l = viscosity of Phase l, m/Lt, cp [Pa·s]
μ_{max} = maximum amplification factor in Fourier series method (Eq. 5.129), dimensionless
ϵ_{Li} = local truncation error for Gridblock i
T_{lx} = transmissibility of Phase l in the x direction
T_{ly} = transmissibility of Phase l in the y direction
T_{lz} = transmissibility of Phase l in the z direction
ϕ = porosity, fraction
Φ = potential, m/Lt^2, psia [kPa]
Ω = constant used in the extrapolation of block-centered pressures to boundary pressure, dimensionless

Superscripts

n = old time level
$n+1$ = current (or new) time level
$^\circ$ = reference

Subscripts

o = oil phase
w = water phase

References

1. Odeh, A.S.: "An Overview of Mathematical Modeling of the Behavior of Hydrocarbon Reservoirs," *SIAM Rev.* (July 1982), **24**, No. 3, 263.
2. Aziz, K. and Settari, A.: *Petroleum Reservoir Simulation*, Applied Science Publishers Ltd., London (1979).
3. Abou-Kassem, J.H., Ertekin, T., and Lutchmansingh, P.M.: "Three-Dimensional Modeling of One-Eighth of Confined Five- and Nine-Spot Patterns," *J. Pet. Sci. Eng.* (1991) **5**, 137.
4. Pedrosa, O.A. and Aziz, K.: "Use of Hybrid Grid in Reservoir Simulation," *SPERE* (November 1986) 611; *Trans.*, AIME, **282**.
5. Saleri, N.G. and Toronyi, D.M.: "Engineering Control in Reservoir Simulation," paper SPE 18305 presented at the 1988 SPE Annual Technical Conference and Exhibition, Houston, 2–5 October.
6. Peaceman, D.W.: "Interpretation of Wellblock Pressures in Numerical Reservoir Simulation," *SPEJ* (June 1983) 531.
7. Richardson, L.F.: "The Approximate Arithmetical Solution by Finite Differences of Physical Problems Involving Differential Equations with an Application to the Stresses in a Masonry Dam," *Trans.*, Royal Soc. London Series A (1910) **210**, 307.
8. Smith, G.D.: *Numerical Solution of Partial Differential Equations: Finite Difference Methods*, Oxford Applied Mathematics and Computing Science Series, Oxford U. Press, Oxford (1978).
9. Lax, P.D. and Richtmeyer, R.D.: "Survey of the Stability of Linear Finite Difference Equations," *Communications on Pure Applied Mathematics* (1956) **9**, 267.
10. DuFort, E.C. and Frankel, S.P.: "Stability Conditions in the Numerical Treatment of Parabolic Differential Equations," *Math Tables*, Natl. Research Council, Washington, DC (1953) **7**, 135.

SI Metric Conversion Factors

bbl	× 1.589 873	E−01	= m^3
cp	× 1.0*	E−03	= Pa·s
ft	× 3.048*	E−01	= m
ft^2	× 9.290 304*	E−02	= m^2
ft^3	× 2.831 685	E−02	= m^3
lbm	× 4.535 924	E−01	= kg
md	× 9.869 233	E−04	= μm^2
psi	× 6.894 757	E+00	= kPa
psi^{-1}	× 1.450 377	E−01	= kPa^{-1}

*Conversion factor is exact.

Chapter 6
Well Representation

6.1 Introduction

The ultimate goal of reservoir-simulation study is to forecast well flow rates and/or flowing bottomhole pressures accurately and to estimate pressure and saturation distributions. Well treatment in reservoir simulators presents difficulties that require special consideration. In general, these difficulties can be divided into three categories.

1. The block hosting the well completion is usually large compared with the size of the well, so that the pressure of the block as computed by the reservoir simulator is a poor estimate of the flowing well pressure.

2. Coupling of the complex interaction between the reservoir and the wellbore is often problematic, particularly in the case of multilayered wells.

3. Allocating phase production rates in multiphase flow when single-phase or total production rate from the well is specified.

Other problems arise when several wells are in a single gridblock and a well is not located at the center of the block. Treatment of an individual well becomes even more complicated when considering instantaneous well-inflow performance, completion details, wellbore and surface-system hydraulics, and well stimulation. This chapter investigates the treatment of source and sink terms, develops a fundamental equation for the production rate, and reviews some of the well models as they apply to single- and multilayer reservoirs. **Fig. 6.1** shows the well-representation step in the development of a reservoir simulator.

6.2 Treatment of Source/Sink Terms

Wells are considered to be internal boundaries of the reservoir system (see Fig. 4.11). As such, a boundary condition must be specified at the well to develop a properly posed problem. This internal boundary condition can be in the form of flowing sandface pressure specification (Dirichlet-type boundary condition) or in the form of flow-rate specification (Neumann-type boundary condition). The next section shows that by specifying the bottomhole flow rate (flow rate at reservoir conditions), the pressure gradient at the sandface is specified and the Neumann-type boundary condition is imposed. Except for single-well simulations in radial coordinates, the well specifications cannot be implemented as boundary conditions but require the use of an additional source/sink term.

6.2.1 Review of Inflow-Performance Relationships (IPR's). Assuming steady-state flow in the immediate vicinity of the wellbore, the radial form of Darcy's law is written as

$$q = \frac{-2\pi\beta_c khr_w}{\mu}\left.\frac{\partial p}{\partial r}\right|_{r=r_w}. \qquad (6.1a)$$

This book follows the sign convention of $q<0$ for a production well; $q=0$ for no well in a gridblock, a shut-in well, or an abandoned well; and $q>0$ for an injection well.

In Eq. 6.1a, entries, such as r_w, h, k, and μ, are problem-specific constants. Therefore, if the flow rate, q, is fixed at a specified value, q_{sp}, the pressure gradient at the wellbore is fixed. Rearranging Eq. 6.1a gives

$$\left.\frac{\partial p}{\partial r}\right|_{r=r_w} = -\frac{\mu}{2\pi\beta_c khr_w}q_{sp}, \qquad (6.1b)$$

showing that a production-rate specification for a well implies fixing the pressure gradient at the wellbore radius, r_w.

The gridblock containing a production or injection well is not different from other gridblocks in the model. To establish well performance, however, it is necessary to know the average pressure in the gridblock, $p_{i,j,k}$, the flowing sandface pressure, p_{wf}, and the production rate, q_{sp}. Because the wellblock has an additional unknown, flowing sandface pressure (if the production rate is specified) or the production rate (if flowing sandface pressure is specified), it is necessary to develop an expression relating the gridblock unknowns to the additional unknown introduced by the wellbore. In other words, an equation must couple the specified wellbore condition to the gridblock hosting the well. The basic assumption involves considering steady- or pseudosteady-state flow in the near-well region. For steady-state conditions, consider the radial flow of an incompressible fluid toward a vertical wellbore of radius r_w in a horizontal formation with uniform thickness and permeability:

$$q = \frac{-2\pi\beta_c k_H hr}{\mu}\frac{\partial p}{\partial r}. \qquad (6.2)$$

Separating variables and integrating between the wellbore radius, r_w, and an arbitrary radius, r ($r_w \leqq r \leqq r_e$), results in

$$\int_{r_w}^{r}\frac{1}{r}\partial r = \frac{-2\pi\beta_c k_H h}{q\mu}\int_{p_{wf}}^{p}\partial p, \qquad (6.3)$$

which, on integration, gives the steady-state-pressure distribution

$$p = p_{wf} - \frac{q\mu}{2\pi\beta_c k_H h}\log_e\left(\frac{r}{r_w}\right). \qquad (6.4)$$

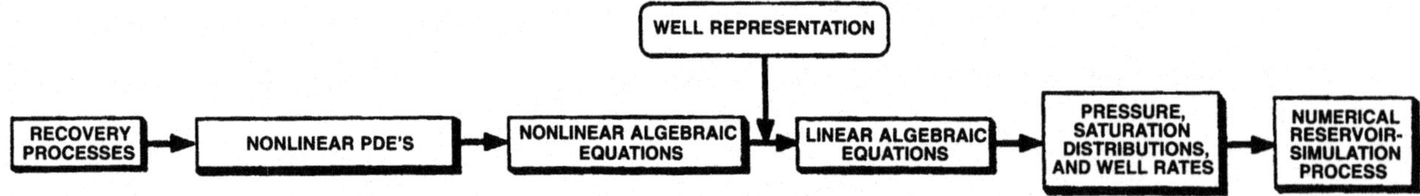

Fig. 6.1—Well-representation step in the development of a reservoir simulator (redrawn from Ref. 1).

At the external radius, r_e, where the pressure is p_e, Eq. 6.4 becomes

$$q = \frac{-2\pi\beta_c k_H h}{\mu \log_e(r_e/r_w)}(p_e - p_{wf}), \quad \text{(6.5a)}$$

which can be expressed at standard conditions as

$$q_{sc} = \frac{-2\pi\beta_c k_H h}{\mu B \log_e(r_e/r_w)}(p_e - p_{wf}). \quad \text{(6.5b)}$$

Eq. 6.5 provides the well production in terms of wellbore and external-boundary pressures. This is the final form of the IPR for an undamaged well produced under steady-state conditions.

In reservoir engineering, however, the production rate of a well at standard conditions is usually expressed in terms of average reservoir and wellbore pressures. Such an equation can be obtained following the development of van Poollen *et al.*[2] In a cylindrical reservoir system, the volumetrically averaged reservoir pressure between r_w and r_e is

$$\bar{p} = \left[\int_{r_w}^{r_e} 2\pi rhp\,dr\right] \Big/ \left[\int_{r_w}^{r_e} 2\pi rh\,dr\right] \quad \text{(6.6)}$$

$$= \frac{2}{(r_e^2 - r_w^2)}\int_{r_w}^{r_e} pr\,dr.$$

Substituting for the steady-state-pressure distribution (given by Eq. 6.4) into Eq. 6.6 yields

$$\bar{p} = \frac{2}{(r_e^2 - r_w^2)}\int_{r_w}^{r_e}\left[p_{wf} - \frac{q\mu}{2\pi\beta_c k_H h}\log_e\left(\frac{r}{r_w}\right)\right]r\,dr, \quad \text{(6.7)}$$

which, upon integration, gives

$$\bar{p} = p_{wf} - \frac{q\mu}{2\pi\beta_c k_H h(r_e^2 - r_w^2)}\left[r_e^2\log_e\left(\frac{r_e}{r_w}\right) - \tfrac{1}{2}(r_e^2 - r_w^2)\right]. \quad \text{(6.8)}$$

For $r_e \gg r_w$, Eq. 6.8 simplifies to

$$\bar{p} = p_{wf} - \frac{q\mu}{2\pi\beta_c k_H h}\left[\log_e\left(\frac{r_e}{r_w}\right) - \tfrac{1}{2}\right] \quad \text{(6.9)}$$

$$\text{or } q = \frac{-2\pi\beta_c k_H h}{\mu[\log_e(r_e/r_w) - \tfrac{1}{2}]}(\bar{p} - p_{wf}), \quad \text{(6.10a)}$$

which can be expressed at standard conditions as

$$q_{sc} = \frac{-2\pi\beta_c k_H h}{\mu B[\log_e(r_e/r_w) - \tfrac{1}{2}]}(\bar{p} - p_{wf}). \quad \text{(6.10b)}$$

Eq. 6.10 differs from Eq. 6.5 in that, in Eq. 6.10, the factor ½ appears in the denominator and $\bar{p}$ is used instead of p_e. Eq. 6.10 can be modified for skin simply by observing that the skin factor, s, is a dimensionless pressure drop. This observation yields (see Example 6.1)

$$q_{sc} = \frac{-2\pi\beta_c k_H h(\bar{p} - p_{wf})}{\mu B[\log_e(r_e/r_w) + s - \tfrac{1}{2}]}. \quad \text{(6.11)}$$

Example 6.1. Show that Eq. 6.10 can be transformed into Eq. 6.11 if the skin factor, s, (which represents near-wellbore damage or stimulation, perforation, and partial-penetration effects) is incorporated into the formulation.

Solution. Inclusion of s implies that there will be an increased pressure drop caused by well damage or a reduced pressure drop caused by stimulation. A positive skin value indicates damage in the near-wellbore region while a negative value indicates improved conditions around the wellbore. Because s is a dimensionless quantity, start with the definition of dimensionless pressure drop,

$$\Delta p_D = \frac{-2\pi\beta_c k_H h(\bar{p} - p_{wf})}{B\mu q_{sc}}. \quad \text{(6.12)}$$

Because of the sign convention we have adapted, where q_{sc} is negative for production, Δp_D as expressed by Eq. 6.12 is positive for production. Substituting Eq. 6.12 into Eq. 6.10b gives the dimensionless pressure without skin (ideal pressure drop) as

$$\Delta p_D = \left[\log_e\left(\frac{r_e}{r_w}\right) - \tfrac{1}{2}\right]. \quad \text{(6.13)}$$

Now, the dimensionless total pressure drop minus the dimensionless pressure caused by damage or stimulation equals the ideal dimensionless pressure drop:

$$\Delta p_D - s = \left[\log_e\left(\frac{r_e}{r_w}\right) - \tfrac{1}{2}\right], \quad \text{(6.14)}$$

which can be rewritten as

$$\Delta p_D = \left[\log_e\left(\frac{r_e}{r_w}\right) - \tfrac{1}{2} + s\right]. \quad \text{(6.15)}$$

Substituting for Δp_D from Eq. 6.12 into Eq. 6.15 gives

$$\frac{-2\pi\beta_c k_H h(\bar{p} - p_{wf})}{B\mu q_{sc}} = \log_e\left(\frac{r_e}{r_w}\right) - \tfrac{1}{2} + s. \quad \text{(6.16)}$$

Finally, rearranging Eq. 6.16 gives

$$q_{sc} = \frac{-2\pi\beta_c k_H h(\bar{p} - p_{wf})}{\mu B[\log_e(r_e/r_w) - \tfrac{1}{2} + s]}. \quad \text{(6.11)}$$

For unsteady-state, radial, single-phase flow in a finite, closed, cylindrical reservoir, the analytical solution for constant-production-rate specification may be expressed as[3,4]

$$\frac{\bar{p} - p_{wf}}{p_i q_D} = \log_e\left(\frac{r_D}{r_w}\right), \quad \text{(6.17)}$$

where $\log_e\left(\frac{r_D}{r_w}\right) = \tfrac{1}{2}[\log_e(t_D) + 0.809]$ (6.18a)

if $t_D \leqq \tfrac{1}{4}(r_e/r_w)^2$,

and $\log_e\left(\frac{r_D}{r_w}\right) = \log_e\left(0.472\frac{r_e}{r_w}\right)$ (6.18b)

if $t_D > \tfrac{1}{4}(r_e/r_w)^2$;

$$q_D = \frac{-\mu B q_{sc}}{2\pi\beta_c k_H h p_i} \quad \text{(6.19)}$$

for compressible fluids, where q_D is positive for negative q_{sc} (production); and

$$t_D = \alpha_c\beta_c\frac{k_H t}{\phi\mu c r_w^2}. \quad (6.20)$$

Eqs. 6.17 through 6.20 represent the final form of the unsteady-state (transient) IPR for an undamaged well.

Examination of Eqs. 6.18 and 6.20 reveals that, at sufficiently large times $\left[t = t_{pss} > (\phi\mu c r_e^2)/(4\alpha_c\beta_c k_H)\right]$, pseudosteady-state conditions prevail. For typical reservoir properties, pseudosteady-state conditions exist on the order of a few hours to a few days after production is started. Under pseudosteady-state conditions, the drainage radius becomes constant because

$$\log_e\left(\frac{r_D}{r_w}\right) = \log_e\left(0.472\frac{r_e}{r_w}\right) = \log_e\left(\frac{r_e}{r_w}\right) - 3/4. \quad (6.21)$$

Substituting Eqs. 6.19 and 6.21 into Eq. 6.17 yields

$$q_{sc} = \frac{-2\pi\beta_c k_H h}{\mu B\left[\log_e(r_e/r_w) - 3/4\right]}\left(\bar{p} - p_{wf}\right). \quad (6.22)$$

Again, incorporating the skin factor into Eq. 6.22 gives

$$q_{sc} = \frac{-2\pi\beta_c k_H h\left(\bar{p} - p_{wf}\right)}{\mu B\left[\log_e(r_e/r_w) + s - 3/4\right]}, \quad (6.23)$$

the final form of the pseudosteady-state IPR. During pseudosteady state, the reservoir pressure declines at a constant rate at all points in a finite, closed reservoir. In this case, the average reservoir pressure can be obtained from material-balance considerations:

$$q_{sc} = \frac{\pi r_e^2 h\phi c}{\alpha_c B}\frac{dp}{dt} \quad (6.24)$$

or, after separating variables and integrating,

$$\bar{p} = p_i + \frac{\alpha_c B q_{sc} t}{\pi r_e^2 h\phi c}. \quad (6.25)$$

In reservoir engineering, it is customary to write Eqs. 6.11 and 6.23 in a more compact form as

$$q_{sc} = -J_w\left(\bar{p} - p_{wf}\right), \quad (6.26)$$

where the productivity index, J_w, is

$$J_w = \frac{2\pi\beta_c k_H h}{\mu B\left[\log_e(r_e/r_w) + s - F\right]} \quad (6.27a)$$

$$\text{or } J_w = \frac{1}{\mu B}G_w, \quad (6.27b)$$

$$\text{where } G_w = \frac{2\pi\beta_c k_H h}{\log_e(r_e/r_w) + s - F}. \quad (6.28)$$

Although the productivity index, J_w, is strictly defined by Eq. 6.26, it will be used more loosely in this chapter with the meaning obtained from Eq. 6.27, where G_w = well geometric factor, which is determined from a well model. G_w depends on wellbore geometry and local reservoir properties. The factor F in Eq. 6.28 has the values of ½ for steady-state conditions and ¾ for pseudosteady-state-flow conditions.

In Eqs. 6.11 and 6.23, r_e represents the external drainage radius and $\bar{p}$ represents the average pressure in a circular area defined by r_e. Furthermore, remember that k_H represents the permeability value in the radial direction. Considering the fact that, in most reservoir grid systems, wells are located in the centers of rectangular gridblocks, the values of r_e, $\bar{p}$, and k_H in the flow-rate equations must be related to the properties of the rectangular gridblocks for simulation purposes. This is accomplished by a well model.

6.2.2 Well Models for Reservoir Simulation. In numerical reservoir simulation, it is a good practice to allow no more than one well to penetrate a gridblock. Furthermore, it is desirable to have at least one to two empty blocks between wells to model pressure-interference effects adequately. Block-centered grid systems should be designed so that the location of a well in a given block is approximately at the center of the block. In mesh-centered (point-distributed) grids, a well should coincide with the mesh point; therefore, it is necessary to place the major grid lines so they intersect at well locations. **Fig. 6.2** shows preferred locations of wells in body- and mesh-centered grids.

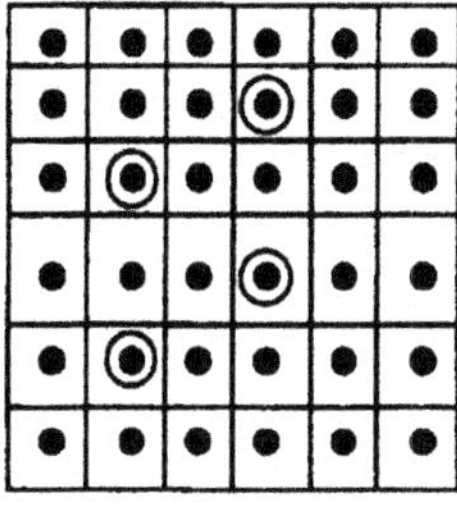

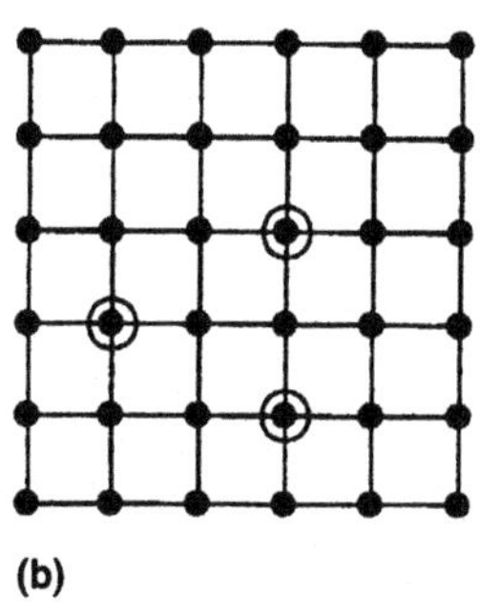

(a) (b)

Fig. 6.2—Well placement in (a) body-centered grid and (b) mesh-centered grid.

Sometimes placing all the wells at the center of gridblocks results in a grid system with a large number of blocks that are not computationally feasible or cost-effective to solve. Under these conditions, the engineer performing the study should try to design the most optimum grid network, even if it is necessary to place some wells in off-center locations in the gridblocks. This, however, is only one consideration in the overall grid design for a particular simulation study. Sometimes it is impossible to design a grid system that ensures the existence of only one well in a single gridblock. The most practical solution to this problem is to represent multiple wells in a gridblock with a single lumped source/sink term. Combining all the wells into a single hypothetical well by use of the principle of superposition gives this lumped term. Obviously, the accuracy of this representation increases if the combined wells have similar production characteristics and histories. Most commercial simulators allow data for individual wells to be read separately but internally lump the overall well contributions.

Single-Layer Well Models. This section discusses single-phase production in two dimensions (that is, a single reservoir layer). The three single-layer well models described in this book (the van Poollen *et al.*,[2] Peaceman,[5] and Abou-Kassem and Aziz[6] models) all consider a wellblock surrounded by four neighboring blocks (as in **Fig. 6.3**).

The van Poollen et al.[2] *Model.* van Poollen *et al.* made one of the earliest attempts to develop a reservoir-simulation well model. This model generally is not used today, but it is historically noteworthy. van Poollen *et al.* used the steady-state-flow equation, Eq. 6.11; in this model, the r_e term in Eq. 6.11 represents the radius of the block hosting the well. In other words, the equivalent wellblock radius, r_{eq}, is calculated from

$$\pi r_{eq}^2 = \Delta x\Delta y, \quad (6.29)$$

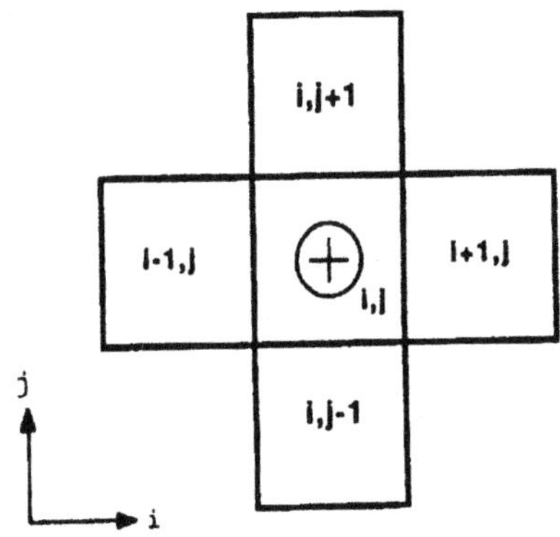

Fig. 6.3—Wellblock with four neighboring blocks in the lateral plane.

which yields

$$r_{eq} = \sqrt{\frac{\Delta x \Delta y}{\pi}}. \qquad (6.30)$$

Eq. 6.30 for a square block ($\Delta x = \Delta y$) reduces to

$$r_{eq} = 0.5642\Delta x. \qquad (6.31)$$

For the $\bar{p}$ term of Eq. 6.11, van Poollen *et al.* assumed that the well-block pressure is the same as the gridblock pressure. Eq. 6.11 then becomes

$$q_{sc} = \frac{-2\pi\beta_c k_H h\left(p_{i,j,k} - p_{wf}\right)}{\mu B\left[\log_e\left(r_{eq}/r_w\right) + s - ½\right]}, \qquad (6.32)$$

in which van Poollen *et al.*[2] assumed isotropic permeabilities in the wellblocks. For anisotropic wellblock properties, the geometric mean permeability should be used for k_H. That is,

$$k_H = (k_x k_y)^{½}. \qquad (6.33)$$

Peaceman's[5] *Model for Nonsquare Wellblocks With Anisotropic Permeability.* Peaceman, using numerical solutions for a single-phase, five-spot pattern showed that the equivalent wellblock radius, r_{eq} (at which the steady-state pressure in the reservoir is equal to the wellblock pressure, $p_{i,j,k}$), is given by

$$r_{eq} = 0.28\frac{\left\{\left[\left(k_y/k_x\right)^{½}(\Delta x)^2\right] + \left[\left(k_x/k_y\right)^{½}(\Delta y)^2\right]\right\}^{½}}{\left(k_y/k_x\right)^{¼} + \left(k_x/k_y\right)^{¼}}. \qquad (6.34)$$

For the special case of isotropic permeability in the horizontal plane, ($k_x = k_y$), the equivalent wellbore radius becomes

$$r_{eq} = 0.14\left[(\Delta x)^2 + (\Delta y)^2\right]^{½}. \qquad (6.35)$$

The exact value of the constant in Eq. 6.35 is 0.1403, which is equal to $e^{-\gamma}/4$, where $\gamma = 0.5772157$ is Euler's constant. For the special case of square gridblocks ($\Delta x = \Delta y$), the equivalent wellblock radius becomes

$$r_{eq} = 0.198\Delta x, \qquad (6.36a)$$

which, in ordinary reservoir-engineering practice, is approximated by

$$r_{eq} = 0.2\Delta x. \qquad (6.36b)$$

Note the difference in Peaceman's definition of equivalent wellblock radius, r_{eq}, (Eq. 6.36b) and van Poollen *et al.*'s[2] definition of r_{eq} (Eq. 6.31).

Peaceman's well model is based on the premise that pressure calculated for a wellblock is the same as the flowing pressure at an equivalent radius, r_{eq}. The definition of r_{eq} can be used to relate the wellbore pressure, p_{wf}, to flow rate, q_{sc}, through the gridblock pressure, $p_{i,j,k}$, in the IPR,

$$q_{sc} = \frac{-2\pi\beta_c k_H h\left(p_{i,j,k} - p_{wf}\right)}{\mu B\left[\log_e\left(r_{eq}/r_w\right) + s\right]}, \qquad (6.37)$$

or, more explicitly,

$$q_{sc} = \left[-2\pi\beta_c k_H h\left(p_{i,j,k} - p_{wf}\right)\right] \Big/ \left(\mu B\left\{\log_e\left[0.28\left\{\left[\left(k_y/k_x\right)^{½} \times (\Delta x)^2\right] + \left[\left(k_x/k_y\right)^{½}(\Delta y)^2\right]\right\}^{½} \Big/ \left[\left(k_y/k_x\right)^{¼} + \left(k_x/k_y\right)^{¼}\right]\right] - \log_e(r_w) + s\right\}\right). \qquad (6.38)$$

Again, for anisotropic properties, k_H is approximated by the geometric mean permeability described by Eq. 6.33.

The following examples, by use of the logic developed by Peaceman, show the development of the equivalent block radius, r_{eq}, for square grid cells in isotropic reservoirs (Eq. 6.36b), rectangular grid cells in isotropic reservoirs (Eq. 6.35), and rectangular grid cells in anisotropic reservoirs (Eq. 6.34).

Example 6.2. Using the finite-difference approximation of the two-dimensional (2D), single-phase flow equation as implemented at an interior wellblock, develop an approximate calculation procedure yielding Eq. 6.36b for a homogeneous, isotropic flow domain that is discretized by square grids.

Solution. The 2D partial-differential equation (PDE) describing single-phase incompressible flow in a homogeneous and isotropic reservoir can be written with Eq. 4.58 as

$$\frac{\partial^2 p}{\partial x^2} + \frac{\partial^2 p}{\partial y^2} + \frac{\mu q_{sc}}{\beta_c k_H V_b} = 0. \qquad (6.39)$$

The finite-difference approximation to Eq. 6.39 as implemented at Wellblock (i,j) is (see Fig. 6.3)

$$p_{i,j-1} + p_{i-1,j} - 4p_{i,j} + p_{i+1,j} + p_{i,j+1} + \left(\frac{\mu q_{sc}}{\beta_c k_H h}\right)_{i,j} = 0. \qquad (6.40)$$

Note that, in arriving at Eq. 6.40, we used the properties of a square grid where $(\Delta x)_{i,j} = (\Delta y)_{i,j}$. Now, regroup Eq. 6.40 as

$$\left(\frac{\beta_c k_H h}{\mu}\right)_{i,j}\left(p_{i,j-1} + p_{i-1,j} - 4p_{i,j} + p_{i+1,j} + p_{i,j+1}\right) = -q_{sc_{i,j}}. \qquad (6.41)$$

If the wellblock and surrounding blocks are assumed to be located away from the physical boundaries of the reservoir and other wells (in addition to the assumptions of a homogeneous and isotropic porous medium), it is reasonable to assume that

$$p_{i,j-1} \approx p_{i-1,j} \approx p_{i+1,j} \approx p_{i,j+1}. \qquad (6.42)$$

Combining Eqs. 6.41 and 6.42 gives

$$\left(\beta_c\frac{k_H h}{\mu}\right)_{i,j}\left(4p_{i+1,j} - 4p_{i,j}\right) = -q_{sc_{i,j}}. \qquad (6.43)$$

The steady-state-flow rate expression (Eq. 6.32) can be written with the pressures of the surrounding blocks [for example,Gridblock $(i+1,j)$] and Wellblock (i,j) and the distance between them for $s = 0$ and $B = 1$, as

$$q_{sc} = -\frac{2\pi\beta_c k_H h\left(p_{i+1,j} - p_{i,j}\right)}{\mu\left[\log_e\left(\Delta x/r_{eq}\right)\right]}. \qquad (6.44)$$

Substituting Eq. 6.44 into Eq. 6.43 yields

$$\log_e\frac{\Delta x}{r_{eq}} = \frac{\pi}{2} \qquad (6.45)$$

or $r_{eq} = e^{-\pi/2}\Delta x, \qquad (6.46)$

which is

$$r_{eq} = 0.208\Delta x. \quad \ldots\ldots (6.47)$$

Example 6.3. Use the solution procedure structured in Example 6.2 as a basis to develop a procedure to check the validity of Eq. 6.35.

Solution. This example uses the same PDE as in Example 6.2. However, the finite-difference approximation is different because here, $(\Delta x)_{i,j} \neq (\Delta y)_{i,j}$. In other words,

$$\left(\frac{\Delta y}{\Delta x}\right)_{i,j}\left(p_{i+1,j} - 2p_{i,j} + p_{i-1,j}\right) + \left(\frac{\Delta x}{\Delta y}\right)_{i,j}\left(p_{i,j+1} - 2p_{i,j} + p_{i,j-1}\right) + \left(\frac{\mu q_{sc}}{\beta_c k_H h}\right)_{i,j} = 0 \quad \ldots\ldots (6.48)$$

is the finite-difference approximation as implemented at Wellblock (i,j) with block dimensions $(\Delta y)_{i,j}$, $(\Delta x)_{i,j}$, and $h_{i,j}$.

Also, note that, this time, the following equalities hold [with symmetric axes around Wellblock (i,j)]:

$$p_{i+1,j} = p_{i-1,j} \quad \ldots\ldots (6.49)$$

and $p_{i,j+1} = p_{i,j-1}$. ...... (6.50)

Now, write two sets of steady-state-flow equations between Wellblock (i,j,k) and the surrounding blocks as

$$\left(p_{i+1,j} - p_{i,j}\right) = \left(p_{i-1,j} - p_{i,j}\right) = \frac{-q_{sc}\mu}{2\pi\beta_c k_H h}\log_e\left(\frac{\Delta x}{r_{eq}}\right)_{i,j} \quad \ldots\ldots (6.51)$$

and $\left(p_{i,j+1} - p_{i,j}\right) = \left(p_{i,j-1} - p_{i,j}\right) = \dfrac{-q_{sc}\mu}{2\pi\beta_c k_H h}\log_e\left(\dfrac{\Delta y}{r_{eq}}\right)_{i,j}$. ...... (6.52)

Eqs. 6.51 and 6.52 again assumed that Wellblock (i,j) and its four surrounding blocks are located in a central portion of the field, away from the physical boundaries and other wells.

Substituting Eqs. 6.51 and 6.52 into Eq. 6.48 gives

$$\left(\frac{\Delta y}{\Delta x}\right)_{i,j}\left[\left(\frac{-q_{sc}\mu}{\pi\beta_c k_H h}\right)_{i,j}\log_e\left(\frac{\Delta x}{r_{eq}}\right)_{i,j}\right] + \left(\frac{\Delta x}{\Delta y}\right)_{i,j}\left[\left(\frac{-q_{sc}\mu}{\pi\beta_c k_H h}\right)_{i,j}\log_e\left(\frac{\Delta y}{r_{eq}}\right)_{i,j}\right] + \left(\frac{\mu q_{sc}}{\beta_c k_H h}\right)_{i,j} = 0 \quad \ldots\ldots (6.53)$$

or $\left(\dfrac{\Delta y}{\Delta x}\right)_{i,j}\log_e\left(\dfrac{\Delta x}{r_{eq}}\right)_{i,j} + \left(\dfrac{\Delta x}{\Delta y}\right)_{i,j}\log_e\left(\dfrac{\Delta y}{r_{eq}}\right)_{i,j} = \pi$. ...... (6.54)

Defining $a_{i,j} = (\Delta y/\Delta x)_{i,j}$, where $a_{i,j}$ is known as the aspect ratio, Eq. 6.54 can be written as

$$a_{i,j}\log_e\left(\frac{\Delta x}{r_{eq}}\right)_{i,j} + \frac{1}{a_{i,j}}\log_e\left(\frac{\Delta y}{r_{eq}}\right)_{i,j} = \pi. \quad \ldots\ldots (6.55)$$

Because $(\Delta y)_{i,j} = a_{i,j}\,(\Delta x)_{i,j}$, we can rewrite Eq. 6.55 in the form

$$a_{i,j}\log_e\left(\frac{\Delta x}{r_{eq}}\right)_{i,j} + \frac{1}{a_{i,j}}\log_e\left[a_{i,j}\left(\frac{\Delta x}{r_{eq}}\right)_{i,j}\right] = \pi, \quad \ldots (6.56)$$

which can be reduced to

$$a_{i,j}^2\log_e\left(\frac{\Delta x}{r_{eq}}\right)_{i,j} + \log_e\left(\frac{\Delta x}{r_{eq}}\right)_{i,j} + \log_e\left(a_{i,j}\right) = \pi a_{i,j} \quad \ldots\ldots (6.57)$$

$$\text{or } \log_e\left(\frac{\Delta x}{r_{eq}}\right)_{i,j} = \frac{\pi a_{i,j} - \log_e\left(a_{i,j}\right)}{a_{i,j}^2 + 1}. \quad \ldots\ldots (6.58)$$

Finally, Eq. 6.58 can be solved for $r_{eq_{i,j}}$:

$$r_{eq_{i,j}} = (\Delta x)_{i,j}e^{\left[\left(\log_e a - \pi a\right)/\left(a^2+1\right)\right]_{i,j}}. \quad \ldots\ldots (6.59)$$

Table 6.1 examines the validity of Eq. 6.59 by applying some numerical entries and comparing the resulting r_{eq} values with the r_{eq} values generated from Eq. 6.35. As the last column of the table shows, the agreement between two formulations is reasonably good, especially for aspect ratios of up to 3. Also, note that, for grid cells where $\Delta x = \Delta y$ $(a = 1)$, Eq. 6.59 reduces to Eq. 6.46 in Example 6.2.

Example 6.4. Use the observations made in Examples 6.2 and 6.3 to obtain the equivalent wellblock radius for nonsquare wellblocks with anisotropic permeability (Eq. 6.34).

Solution. The 2D, single-phase, incompressible-flow equation in an anisotropic, homogeneous medium can be written as

$$k_x\frac{\partial^2 p}{\partial x^2} + k_y\frac{\partial^2 p}{\partial y^2} = 0. \quad \ldots\ldots (6.60)$$

Now examine Eq. 6.60 in a *u-v* plane where the transformations

$$u = \left(\frac{k_y}{k_x}\right)^{1/4} x \quad \ldots\ldots (6.61)$$

$$\text{and } v = \left(\frac{k_x}{k_y}\right)^{1/4} y \quad \ldots\ldots (6.62)$$

are applied (see Exercise 3.15). From Eqs. 6.61 and 6.62 it follows that

$$\frac{\partial u}{\partial x} = \left(\frac{k_y}{k_x}\right)^{1/4} \quad \ldots\ldots (6.63)$$

TABLE 6.1—COMPARISON OF EQUIVALENT WELLBLOCK RADII GENERATED BY EQS. 6.35 AND 6.59

$\Delta x_{i,j}$ (ft)	$\Delta y_{i,j}$ (ft)	$a_{i,j}$	$^* r_{eq_{i,j}}$ (ft)	$^{**} r_{eq_{i,j}}$ (ft)	$^* r_{eq_{i,j}} / ^{**} r_{eq_{i,j}}$
400	400	1	83.152	79.196	1.050
400	800	2	130.772	125.220	1.044
400	1,200	3	173.964	177.088	0.982
400	1,600	4	207.227	230.893	0.898
400	2,000	5	232.575	285.545	0.814

*As calculated from Eq. 6.59.
**As calculated from Eq. 6.35.

$$\text{and } \frac{\partial v}{\partial y} = \left(\frac{k_x}{k_y}\right)^{1/4} \quad \text{.............................. (6.64)}$$

$$\text{because } \frac{\partial^2 p}{\partial x^2} = \frac{\partial}{\partial u}\left(\frac{\partial p}{\partial u}\frac{\partial u}{\partial x}\right)\frac{\partial u}{\partial x} = \frac{\partial}{\partial u}\left[\frac{\partial p}{\partial u}\left(\frac{k_y}{k_x}\right)^{1/4}\right]\left(\frac{k_y}{k_x}\right)^{1/4} \quad \text{.................... (6.65a)}$$

$$\text{or } \frac{\partial^2 p}{\partial x^2} = \left(\frac{k_y}{k_x}\right)^{1/2}\frac{\partial^2 p}{\partial u^2} \quad \text{......................... (6.65b)}$$

$$\text{and } \frac{\partial^2 p}{\partial y^2} = \frac{\partial}{\partial v}\left(\frac{\partial p}{\partial v}\frac{\partial v}{\partial y}\right)\frac{\partial v}{\partial y} = \frac{\partial}{\partial v}\left[\frac{\partial p}{\partial v}\left(\frac{k_x}{k_y}\right)^{1/4}\right]\left(\frac{k_x}{k_y}\right)^{1/4} \quad \text{.................... (6.66a)}$$

$$\text{or } \frac{\partial^2 p}{\partial y^2} = \left(\frac{k_x}{k_y}\right)^{1/2}\frac{\partial^2 p}{\partial v^2}. \quad \text{......................... (6.66b)}$$

Substituting Eqs. 6.65b and 6.66b into Eq. 6.60 yields

$$\left(k_x k_y\right)^{1/2}\frac{\partial^2 p}{\partial u^2} + \left(k_x k_y\right)^{1/2}\frac{\partial^2 p}{\partial v^2} = 0 \quad \text{................ (6.67)}$$

$$\text{or } \frac{\partial^2 p}{\partial u^2} + \frac{\partial^2 p}{\partial v^2} = 0. \quad \text{.......................... (6.68)}$$

Eqs. 6.67 and 6.68 indicate that, with the use of the transformation functions (Eqs. 6.61 and 6.62), we can study Eq. 6.60 in the u-v plane where the porous medium becomes isotropic in permeability with $k_H = (k_x k_y)^{1/2}$. It is necessary to study and compare the equations for the well both in the x-y and u-v planes.

In the x-y plane, pressure specification at the wellbore can be expressed as

$$p = p_{wf} \quad \text{.................................... (6.69a)}$$

$$\text{at } r_w^2 = \left(x^2 + y^2\right). \quad \text{........................... (6.69b)}$$

Substituting the new variables u and v into Eq. 6.69, this specification can be written as $p = p_{wf}$ at

$$r_w^2 = \left(\frac{k_x}{k_y}\right)^{1/2} u^2 + \left(\frac{k_y}{k_x}\right)^{1/2} v^2. \quad \text{.................... (6.70)}$$

A closer look at Eq. 6.70 reveals that the circular well in the x-y plane becomes an elliptical well in the u-v plane, because

$$\frac{u^2}{r_w^2\left(k_x/k_y\right)^{-1/2}} + \frac{v^2}{r_w^2\left(k_y/k_x\right)^{-1/2}} = 1 \quad \text{................ (6.71)}$$

represents an ellipse rather than a circle. This implies that the boundary condition $p = p_{wf}$ is specified on an ellipse rather than a circle and the solution to Eq. 6.68 in the u-v plane is not radial. The equipotential contours in the u-v plane are, therefore, a family of confocal ellipses (not concentric circles), where the innermost ellipse is the well itself. However, because r_w is much smaller than the size of the reservoir, we can still assume that the equipotential contours in the u-v plane are essentially circular and that the pressure essentially satisfies the equation

$$p - p_{wf} = \frac{-q_{sc}\mu}{2\pi\beta_c\left(k_x k_y\right)^{1/2} h}\log_e\!\left(\frac{r^{uv}}{\bar{r}_w}\right), \quad \text{............ (6.72)}$$

where r^{uv} represents the radius at which pressure is p in the u-v plane and can be expressed as

$$r^{uv} = \left(u^2 + v^2\right)^{1/2}. \quad \text{.......................... (6.73)}$$

Because the major and minor axes of the elliptical well are expected to be close to each other, define an average wellbore radius by taking the arithmetic average of the major and minor axes as

$$\bar{r}_w = \frac{1}{2}(a + b), \quad \text{............................ (6.74)}$$

where the definitions of a and b are from Eq. 6.71 as

$$a = r_w\left(\frac{k_y}{k_x}\right)^{1/4} \quad \text{.............................. (6.75a)}$$

$$\text{and } b = r_w\left(\frac{k_x}{k_y}\right)^{1/4}. \quad \text{........................ (6.75b)}$$

Substituting Eq. 6.75 into Eq. 6.74 gives

$$\bar{r}_w = \tfrac{1}{2} r_w\left[\left(\frac{k_y}{k_x}\right)^{1/4} + \left(\frac{k_x}{k_y}\right)^{1/4}\right]. \quad \text{................. (6.76)}$$

The finite-difference equation for the steady-state pressure in an anisotropic medium written at the wellblock is (see Eq. 6.48)

$$\left(k_x\frac{\Delta y}{\Delta x}\right)_{i,j}\left(p_{i+1,j} - 2p_{i,j} + p_{i-1,j}\right) + \left(k_y\frac{\Delta x}{\Delta y}\right)_{i,j}\left(p_{i,j+1} - 2p_{i,j} + p_{i,j-1}\right) + \left(\frac{\mu q_{sc}}{\beta_c h}\right)_{i,j} = 0. \quad \text{......................... (6.77)}$$

With the change of variables, this transforms to

$$\left[\left(k_x k_y\right)^{1/2}\frac{\Delta v}{\Delta u}\right]_{i,j}\left(p_{i+1,j} - 2p_{i,j} + p_{i-1,j}\right) + \left[\left(k_x k_y\right)^{1/2}\frac{\Delta u}{\Delta v}\right]_{i,j}\left(p_{i,j+1} - 2p_{i,j} + p_{i,j-1}\right) + \left(\frac{\mu q_{sc}}{\beta_c h}\right)_{i,j} = 0. \quad \text{......................... (6.78)}$$

Eqs. 6.60 and 6.68 and Eqs. 6.77 and 6.78 are differential and finite-difference representations, respectively, of the same problem in the x-y and u-v planes. More importantly, we can now recognize that the differential and finite-difference representations (Eqs. 6.68 and 6.78, respectively) are essentially identical to the isotropic problem in Example 6.3. Therefore, in the u-v plane,

$$r_{eq}^{uv} = 0.14\left[\left(\Delta u^2\right) + \left(\Delta v^2\right)\right]^{1/2} \quad \text{.................. (6.79)}$$

$$\text{and } q_{sc} = \frac{-2\pi\beta_c\left(k_x k_y\right)^{1/2} h\left(p_{i,j} - p_{wf}\right)}{B\mu\left[\log_e\left(r_{eq}^{uv}/\bar{r}_w\right)\right]}, \quad \text{............ (6.80)}$$

which can be rearranged as

$$\left(p_{i,j} - p_{wf}\right) = \frac{-q_{sc}\mu B}{2\pi\beta_c\left(k_x k_y\right)^{1/2} h}\left[\log_e\left(\frac{r_{eq}^{uv}}{\bar{r}_w}\right)\right]. \quad \text{........ (6.81)}$$

The corresponding equation in the x-y plane is

$$\left(p_{i,j} - p_{wf}\right) = \frac{-q_{sc}\mu B}{2\pi\beta_c\left(k_x k_y\right)^{1/2} h}\left[\log_e\left(\frac{r_{eq}}{r_w}\right)\right]. \quad \text{........ (6.82)}$$

Dividing Eq. 6.81 by Eq. 6.82 gives

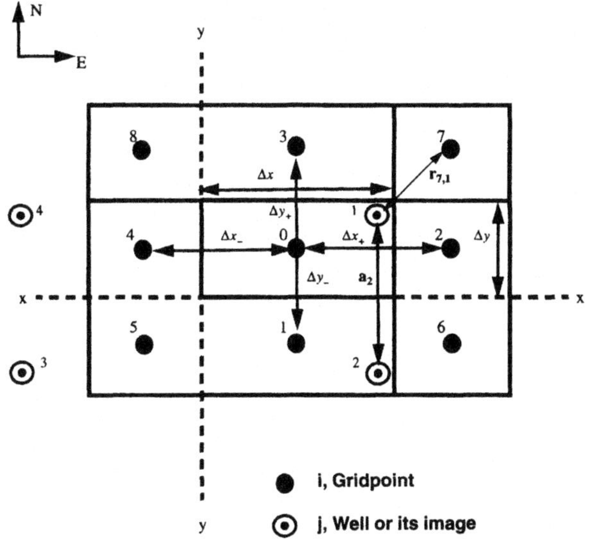

Fig. 6.4—Wellblock 0 and its surrounding gridblocks in a block-centered grid.

$$\frac{r_{eq}^{uv}}{\bar{r}_w} = \frac{r_{eq}}{r_w} \qquad (6.83)$$

$$\text{or } r_{eq} = \left(\frac{r_w}{\bar{r}_w}\right) r_{eq}^{uv}. \qquad (6.84)$$

Substituting the definitions of $\bar{r}_w$ and r_{eq}^{uv} yields

$$r_{eq} = \frac{r_w}{\frac{1}{2} r_w \left[(k_y/k_x)^{1/4} + (k_x/k_y)^{1/4} \right]} \times 0.14 \left\{ \left[\left(\frac{k_y}{k_x}\right)^{1/4} \Delta x \right]^2 + \left[\left(\frac{k_x}{k_y}\right)^{1/4} \Delta y \right]^2 \right\}^{1/2} \qquad (6.85)$$

or, finally,

$$r_{eq} = 0.28 \frac{\left[(k_y/k_x)^{1/2} (\Delta x)^2 + (k_x/k_y)^{1/2} (\Delta y)^2 \right]^{1/2}}{(k_y/k_x)^{1/4} + (k_x/k_y)^{1/4}}. \qquad (6.34)$$

The Abou-Kassem and Aziz[6] Model. Abou-Kassem and Aziz developed another equivalent-wellblock-radius equation that is applicable to wells located in off-center locations in a square or rectangular gridblock with aspect ratio $\Delta y/\Delta x$ in the range of ½ to 2. In this formulation, which uses Eq. 6.37, the equivalent wellblock radius is defined as

$$r_{eq} = \left\{ \exp(-2\pi f) \prod_i \left[r_{i,1}^{T_i} \prod_j \left(\frac{r_{i,j}}{a_j} \right)^{T_i} \right] \right\}^b ; \qquad (6.86)$$

this is better understood by reviewing **Figs. 6.4 and 6.5**. The wellblock, Gridblock 0, is referred to as an interior block if all reservoir boundaries are outside the wellblock boundaries; otherwise, it is a boundary block. Flow into interior Gridblock 0 is only from Gridblocks 1 through 4 in five-point finite-difference formulations, while all eight adjacent blocks in the *x-y* plane influence production in nine-point finite-difference formulations. If one of the reservoir

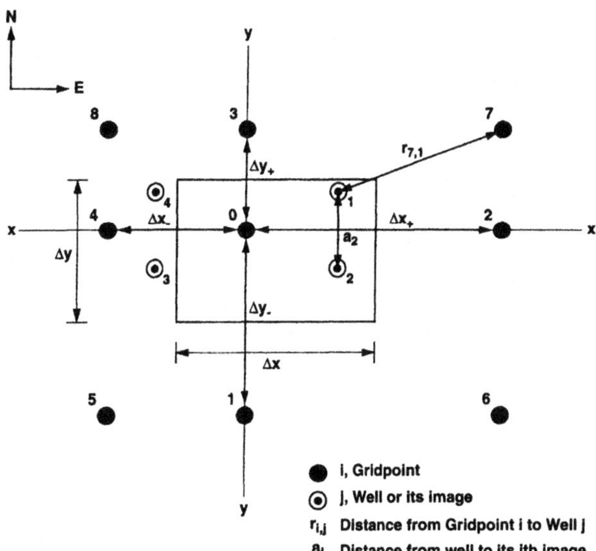

Fig. 6.5—Wellblock 0 and its surrounding gridblocks in a point-distributed grid.

boundaries falls on the southern boundary of the block and the reservoir is north of this boundary (denoted by *xx* in Fig. 6.4), Gridblocks 1, 5, and 6 do not exist. Similarly, if a reservoir boundary also falls on the western boundary of the wellblock and the reservoir is east of this boundary (denoted by *yy* in Fig. 6.4), Gridblocks 4, 5, and 8 also do not exist. The well in Gridblock 0 is labeled 1, and $r_{i,j}$ is the distance from Node *i* to Well *j*. If the wellblock is an interior block, no image wells exist. If a wellblock is a boundary block, however, one or more image wells will be present, depending on the number of reservoir boundaries of the reservoir that fall on the edges of the wellblock. The distance between Well 1 and its image well, Well *j*, is referred to as a_j. In Eq. 6.86,

$$\prod_j$$

is the product over all existing well images and

$$\prod_i$$

is the product over all existing surrounding gridpoints. The factor f = fraction of well flow from the wellblock (f = 1 for an interior well, f = ½ for a well on one boundary, and f = ¼ for a well on two boundaries). Finally, the exponent

$$b = 1/\sum_i T_i$$

includes the summation over all existing surrounding gridpoints. Fig. 6.5 shows Gridblock 0 (wellblock) and its surrounding blocks in a point-distributed grid and provides the definitions of the entries of Eq. 6.86 for point-distributed grids.

Table 6.2 summarizes the equations for the interface transmissibility factor, T_i, between a surrounding Gridblock *i* and the wellblock.

Example 6.5. Show that the equivalent-wellblock-radius formula of Abou-Kassem and Aziz[6] (Eq. 6.86) agrees closely with Peaceman's[5] model (Eq. 6.36a) when $\Delta x = \Delta y$ and the well is located at the center of a square block for a five-point finite-difference scheme (**Fig. 6.6**).

Solution. From Table 6.2, for a five-point scheme, $T_1 = T_2 = T_3 = T_4 = 1$ and $T_5 = T_6 = T_7 = T_8 = 0$. Also, for a well located at the center of block, $f = 1$,

$$r_{eq} = \left\{ \exp(-2\pi f) \prod_i \left[r_{i,1}^{T_i} \prod_j \left(\frac{r_{i,j}}{a_j} \right)^{T_i} \right] \right\}^b . \qquad (6.86)$$

TABLE 6.2—INTERFACE TRANSMISSIBILITY FACTORS BETWEEN A SURROUNDING GRIDBLOCK *i* AND THE WELLBLOCK

$$T_1 = \left(\frac{\Delta x}{\Delta y_-}\right) - (T_5 + T_6)$$

$$T_2 = \left(\frac{\Delta y}{\Delta x_+}\right) - (T_6 + T_7)$$

$$T_3 = \left(\frac{\Delta x}{\Delta y_+}\right) - (T_7 + T_8)$$

$$T_4 = \left(\frac{\Delta y}{\Delta x_-}\right) - (T_5 + T_8)$$

$$T_5 = \frac{1}{3}\left[\frac{(\Delta x_-)(\Delta y_-)}{(\Delta x_-)^2 + (\Delta y_-)^2}\right]$$

$$T_6 = \frac{1}{3}\left[\frac{(\Delta x_+)(\Delta y_-)}{(\Delta x_+)^2 + (\Delta y_-)^2}\right]$$

$$T_7 = \frac{1}{3}\left[\frac{(\Delta x_+)(\Delta y_+)}{(\Delta x_+)^2 + (\Delta y_+)^2}\right]$$

$$T_8 = \frac{1}{3}\left[\frac{(\Delta x_-)(\Delta y_+)}{(\Delta x_-)^2 + (\Delta y_+)^2}\right]$$

Note that, for a uniform square grid, $\Delta x = \Delta y$, the transmissibility factors simplify to $T_5 = T_6 = T_7 = T_8 = 0$ (for the five-point difference scheme) and $1/6$ (for the nine-point difference scheme); and $T_1 = T_2 = T_3 = T_4 = 1$ (for the five-point difference scheme) and $2/3$ (for the nine-point difference scheme).

It is possible to construct the entries in **Table 6.3** to use in Eq. 6.86 (note that for an interior block there are no image wells) with

$$b = \frac{1}{\sum_i T_i} = 1/4$$

and $f = 1$. Then, simplify the equivalent-wellblock-radius equation to

$$r_{eq} = \left[\exp(-2\pi)\prod_i \left(r_{i,1}^{T_i}\right)\right]^{1/4} \quad \text{.................... (6.87)}$$

$$= \left[\exp(-2\pi)(\Delta x)^4\right]^{1/4}$$

$$= \exp(-2\pi)^{1/4}\Delta x$$

$$= e^{(-\pi/2)}\Delta x$$

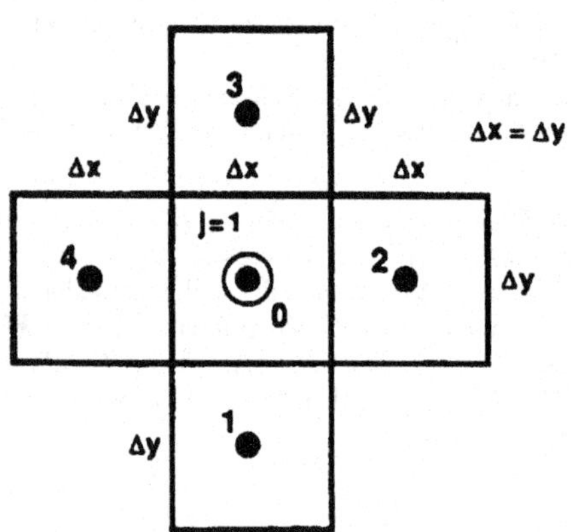

Fig. 6.6—Square Gridblock 0 with well at the center and its surrounding gridblocks (Example 6.5).

TABLE 6.3—ENTRIES FOR USE IN EQ. 6.87

i	$r_{i,1}$	T_i
1	$r_{1,1} = \Delta x$	$T_1 = 1$
2	$r_{2,1} = \Delta x$	$T_2 = 1$
3	$r_{3,1} = \Delta x$	$T_3 = 1$
4	$r_{4,1} = \Delta x$	$T_4 = 1$

TABLE 6.4—ENTRIES CALCULATED FOR EXAMPLE 6.6

i	$r_{i,1}$	T_i
1	$r_{1,1} = \Delta y$	$T_1 = \Delta x/\Delta y$
2	$r_{2,1} = \Delta x$	$T_2 = \Delta y/\Delta x$
3	$r_{3,1} = \Delta y$	$T_3 = \Delta x/\Delta y$
4	$r_{4,1} = \Delta x$	$T_4 = \Delta y/\Delta x$

or $r_{eq} = 0.2079\Delta x$, which agrees closely with Eq. 6.36a, where $r_{eq} = 0.198\Delta x$.

Example 6.6. Show that Eqs. 6.86 and 6.35 give reasonably close values of r_{eq} for a rectangular interior wellblock with a well located at its center and where the aspect ratio, α, is between ½ and 2 (**Fig. 6.7**).

Solution. **Table 6.4** gives the entries calculated for this example. Also,

$$\sum_i T_i = \frac{\Delta x}{\Delta y} + \frac{\Delta y}{\Delta x} + \frac{\Delta x}{\Delta y} + \frac{\Delta y}{\Delta x} = 2\left(\frac{\Delta x}{\Delta y} + \frac{\Delta y}{\Delta x}\right) = 2\frac{(\Delta x)^2 + (\Delta y)^2}{\Delta x \Delta y}$$

.... (6.88a)

$$\text{or } b = \frac{\Delta x \Delta y}{2\left[(\Delta x)^2 + (\Delta y)^2\right]}. \quad \text{...................... (6.88b)}$$

Again, for a wellblock surrounded by four other reservoir blocks, $f = 1$, no image wells exist, and the equivalent-wellblock-radius equation becomes ($a_j = r_{i,j} = 1$ if Image Well j does not exist)

$$r_{eq} = \left[\exp(-2\pi)\prod_i r_{i,1}^{T_i}\right]^b . \quad \text{.................. (6.89)}$$

Expanding the product explicitly yields

$$r_{eq} = \left[\exp(-2\pi)\left(r_{1,1}^{T_1} r_{2,1}^{T_2} r_{3,1}^{T_3} r_{4,1}^{T_4}\right)\right]^b , \quad \text{........... (6.90)}$$

and substituting for the $r_{i,1}$ and b terms results in

$$r_{eq} = \left\{\exp(-2\pi)\left[\Delta y^{(\Delta x/\Delta y)}\Delta x^{(\Delta y/\Delta x)}\Delta y^{(\Delta x/\Delta y)}\Delta x^{(\Delta y/\Delta x)}\right]\right\}^{\frac{\Delta x \Delta y}{2\left[(\Delta x)^2 + (\Delta y)^2\right]}}$$

$$= \left\{\exp(-2\pi)\left[\Delta y^{2(\Delta x/\Delta y)}\Delta x^{2(\Delta y/\Delta x)}\right]\right\}^{\frac{\Delta x \Delta y}{2\left[(\Delta x)^2 + (\Delta y)^2\right]}}$$

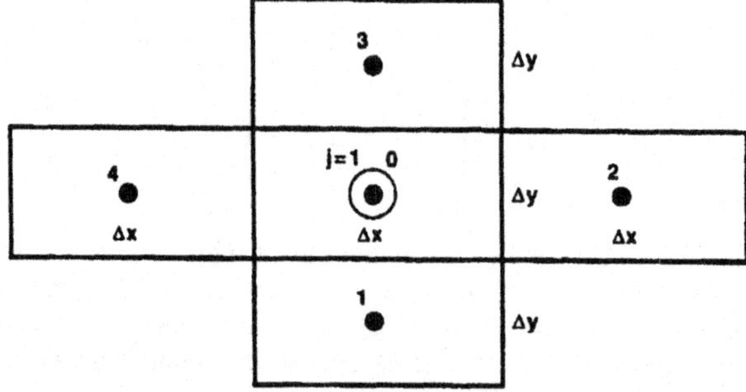

Fig. 6.7—Rectangular wellblock (Gridblock 0) with a well at the center and its surrounding gridblocks (Example 6.6).

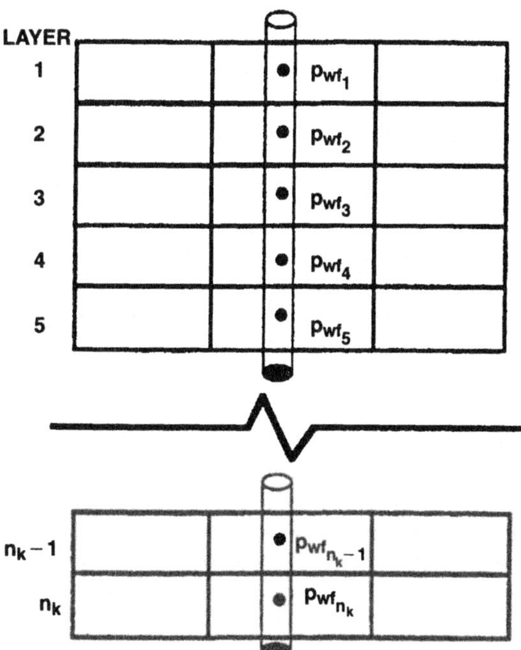

Fig. 6.8—Multilayer wellbore configuration.

$$= \left\{ \left[\exp(-2\pi) \right]^{\frac{\alpha}{2(1+\alpha^2)}} \times \alpha^{\frac{1}{(1+\alpha^2)}} \right\} \Delta x, \quad \text{.......... (6.91)}$$

where $\alpha = \Delta y / \Delta x$.

Assume that, for a given problem, $\Delta x = 400$ ft and $\Delta y = 600$ ft. Calculating r_{eq} from Eq. 6.91 yields $\alpha = 600/400 = 1.5$ and

$$r_{eq} = \left[\left[\exp(-2\pi) \right]^{\left(1.5 / \left\{ 2\left[1 + (1.5)^2 \right] \right\} \right)} \times 1.5^{\left\{ 1 / \left[1 + (1.5)^2 \right] \right\}} \right] 400$$

$= 106.30$ ft.

Applying these values to Peaceman's[5] well model,

$$r_{eq} = 0.14 \left[(\Delta x)^2 + (\Delta y)^2 \right]^{1/2}, \quad \text{.................. (6.35)}$$

which gives $r_{eq} = 0.14(160{,}000 + 360{,}000)^{1/2} = 100.96$ ft. Again, agreement between the r_{eq} values obtained from the two models is remarkably close.

Vertical, Multilayer Well Models. So far, we have not considered the case of wells penetrating multiple layers (that is, a column of vertical blocks) as shown in **Fig. 6.8**.

For Wellblock k, where $k \in \psi_w$, the flow-rate expression can be written as

$$q_{sc_k} = \frac{-2\pi\beta_c k_{Hk} h_k \left(p_k - p_{wf_k} \right)}{\mu_k B_k \left[\log_e \left(r_{eq_k} / r_w \right) + s_k \right]} \quad \text{.............. (6.92)}$$

$$\text{or } q_{sc_k} = -J_{w_k} \left(p_k - p_{wf_k} \right), \quad \text{..................... (6.93)}$$

$$\text{where } J_{w_k} = \frac{2\pi\beta_c k_{Hk} h_k}{\mu_k B_k \left[\log_e \left(r_{eq_k} / r_w \right) + s_k \right]} \quad \text{............ (6.94)}$$

$$\text{or } J_{w_k} = \frac{1}{\mu_k B_k} G_{w_k}. \quad \text{............................ (6.95)}$$

The total flow rate for the well is the sum of the rates for all perforated intervals,

$$q_{sc} = -\sum_k J_{w_k} \left(p_k - p_{wf_k} \right), \quad \text{.................. (6.96)}$$

where $k \in \psi_w$.

In Eqs. 6.92 through 6.96, Subscript k = properties associated with Wellblock k and ψ_w = the set of blocks perforated by the well. The subscript k is used in Eqs. 6.92 through 6.96 because the geometric mean permeability in the lateral direction and the thickness of the wellblock may differ from one wellblock to another. Because the p_k values represent block pressures, they are also different in each wellblock. The use of subscript k with the s factor signifies that the skin value may also differ from one wellblock to another within the wellbore. This is especially true if different perforation densities and intervals exist within each individual simulation layer. Viscosity and formation volume factors (FVF's)—and relative permeabilities for multiphase flow—also need to be calculated with the pressures of the individual wellblocks of different layers, p_k. The flowing sandface pressure, p_{wf_k}, is different from one wellblock to another, depending on the existing pressure drop within the wellbore (often approximated with the hydrostatic gradient). Finally, Subscript k in the term r_{eq_k} reflects the fact that different simulation layers can have different equivalent wellblock radii, depending on different wellblock properties (see Eq. 6.34).

As with all terms in the finite-difference equations, we must select a time level (n or $n+1$) at which to evaluate production and injection rates. We can use several techniques to evaluate these terms, including the explicit method, where $q^n_{sc_k}$ (inflow-performance parameters are evaluated at Time Level n); the simple-iteration method, where $q^{n+1}_{sc_k}$ (inflow-performance parameters are evaluated at Time Level $n+1$ but at the previous iteration level v); the linearized-implicit method, where

$$q^{n+1}_{sc_k} \approx q^n_{sc_k} + \left. \frac{\partial q_{sc_k}}{\partial S_{w_k}} \right|^n \left(S^{n+1}_{w_k} - S^n_{w_k} \right)$$

$$+ \left. \frac{\partial q_{sc_k}}{\partial S_{g_k}} \right|^n \left(S^{n+1}_{g_k} - S^n_{g_k} \right)$$

$$+ \left. \frac{\partial q_{sc_k}}{\partial p_{o_k}} \right|^n \left(p^{n+1}_{o_k} - p^n_{o_k} \right)$$

$$+ \left. \frac{\partial q_{sc_k}}{\partial p_{wf_{ref}}} \right|^n \left(p^{n+1}_{wf_{ref}} - p^n_{wf_{ref}} \right); \quad \text{................ (6.97)}$$

Nolen and Berry's[7] semi-implicit method, where

$$\overset{(v+1)}{q^{n+1}_{sc_k}} \approx q^n_{sc_k} + \left. \frac{\Delta q_{sc_k}}{\Delta S_{w_k}} \right|^n \left(\overset{(v+1)}{S^{n+1}_{w_k}} - S^n_{w_k} \right)$$

$$+ \left. \frac{\Delta q_{sc_k}}{\Delta S_{g_k}} \right|^n \left(\overset{(v+1)}{S^{n+1}_{g_k}} - S^n_{g_k} \right)$$

$$+ \left. \frac{\Delta q_{sc_k}}{\Delta p_{o_k}} \right|^n \left(\overset{(v+1)}{p^{n+1}_{o_k}} - p^n_{o_k} \right)$$

$$+ \left. \frac{\Delta q_{sc_k}}{\Delta p_{wf_{ref}}} \right|^n \left(\overset{(v+1)}{p^{n+1}_{wf_{ref}}} - p^n_{wf_{ref}} \right); \quad \text{............. (6.98)}$$

and the fully-implicit method, where

$$\overset{(v+1)}{q_{sc_k}^{n+1}} \approx \overset{(v)}{q_{sc_k}^{n+1}} + \left.\frac{\partial q_{sc_k}}{\partial S_{w_k}}\right|^{\overset{(v+1)}{n+1}} \left(\overset{(v+1)}{S_{w_k}^{n+1}} - \overset{(v)}{S_{w_k}^{n+1}} \right)$$

$$+ \left.\frac{\partial q_{sc_k}}{\partial S_{g_k}}\right|^{\overset{(v)}{n+1}} \left(\overset{(v+1)}{S_{g_k}^{n+1}} - \overset{(v)}{S_{g_k}^{n+1}} \right)$$

$$+ \left.\frac{\partial q_{sc_k}}{\partial p_{o_k}}\right|^{\overset{(v)}{n+1}} \left(\overset{(v+1)}{p_{o_k}^{n+1}} - \overset{(v)}{p_{o_k}^{n+1}} \right)$$

$$+ \left.\frac{\partial q_{sc_k}}{\partial p_{wf_{ref}}}\right|^{\overset{(v)}{n+1}} \left(\overset{(v+1)}{p_{wf_{ref}}^{n+1}} - \overset{(v)}{p_{wf_{ref}}^{n+1}} \right). \quad \text{(6.99)}$$

The next two sections discuss applying these methods for multilayer wells.

Explicit Treatment of Multilayer Wells. *Pressure-Specified Wells.* For a pressure-specified well, where $p_{wf_{ref}} = p_{wfsp}$, the wellbore pressure at the individual simulation layers can be determined by

$$p_{wf_k} = p_{wf_{ref}} + \int_{H_{ref}}^{H_k} \gamma_{wb} dH \quad \text{(6.100a)}$$

or, if an average wellbore pressure gradient is assumed,

$$p_{wf_k} = p_{wf_{ref}} + \bar{\gamma}_{wb}\left(H_k - H_{ref}\right). \quad \text{(6.100b)}$$

In Eq. 6.100, $p_{wf_{ref}}$= flowing sandface pressure at a reference depth of H_{ref} in the wellbore. In this chapter we assume that H_{ref} is the depth of the topmost perforated layer and that $p_{wf_{ref}}$ is the pressure at this depth. Eq. 6.100 assumes that frictional and inertial losses are negligible compared with the hydrostatic gradient. The hydrostatic gradient, $\bar{\gamma}_{wb}$, is defined by

$$\bar{\gamma}_{wb} = \bar{\gamma}_l = \gamma_c g \frac{\rho_{lsc}}{B_l} \quad \text{(6.101a)}$$

for single-phase flow of Phase l ($l = o$, w, or g), or

$$\bar{\gamma}_{wb} = \gamma_c g \frac{\rho_{osc} q_{osc} + \rho_{wsc} q_{wsc} + \rho_{gsc} q_{gsc}/a_c}{B_o q_{osc} + B_w q_{wsc} + B_g q_{fgsc}} \quad \text{(6.101b)}$$

for three-phase flow, where $q_{fgsc} = q_{gsc} - R_s q_{osc}$.

Note that, in Eq. 6.101, the FVF appears in the definition of $\bar{\gamma}_{wb}$. For $\bar{\gamma}_{wb}$ to be an averaged value, the FVF must be evaluated at the average wellbore pressure, $\bar{p}_{wf}$. That is,

$$B_l = B_l\left(\bar{p}_{wf}\right), \quad \text{(6.102)}$$

where $l = o$, w, or g and

$$\bar{p}_{wf} = \frac{p_{wf_{ref}} + p_{wf_{n_k}}}{2}, \quad \text{(6.103)}$$

where $p_{wf_{n_k}}$ = wellbore pressure at the lowermost perforated layer.

The following algorithm is used to estimate the average wellbore hydrostatic gradient.

1. Assume $\bar{p}_{wf} = p_{wfsp}$.
2. Evaluate B_l ($l = o$, w, or g) at $\bar{p}_{wf}$.
3. Calculate $\bar{\gamma}_{wb}$ from Eq. 6.101.
4. Calculate p_{wf_1} through $p_{wf_{n_k}}$ from Eq. 6.100.
5. Recalculate $\bar{p}_{wf}$ using Eq. 6.103.
6. Check for convergence. Go to Step 2 if necessary.

This algorithm can be improved as follows to allow for a variable pressure gradient between simulation layers.

1. Set $p_{wf_1} = p_{wfsp}$.
2. Use the previous algorithm to go from p_{wf_1} to p_{wf_2}.
3. When p_{wf_2} converges, proceed in a similar manner from p_{wf_2} to p_{wf_3}.
4. Continue with this procedure for all completed layers.

For multiphase-flow problems, the definition of the wellbore pressure gradient, Eq. 6.101b, requires the production rates for all phases. In the explicit method, for inflow performance, these rates are evaluated at the old time level, n. Once all the wellbore pressures, p_{wf_k}, are determined, they can be used in Eq. 6.93 to calculate q_{sc_k} for each simulation layer. These values of q_{sc_k} can then be substituted into the finite-difference equations of the gridblocks containing the well completions.

Rate-Specified Wells. The term q_{sc} in the finite-difference equations represents a sink for production (negative sign) and a source for injection (positive sign). For a single-block well with a rate specification, the specified production or injection rate, $q_{sc} = q_{spsc}$, is placed in the finite-difference equation with the correct sign. In the case of multiblock well completions, this procedure becomes more complicated because a specified production or injection rate for the entire well must be allocated to each perforated gridblock. There are two methods for allocating the specified rates to the individual simulation layers: the potential method and the productivity-index (PI) -weighted method.

Potential Method. In the potential method for allocating produced or injected fluids, Eqs. 6.93 and 6.96 are combined to obtain

$$q_{sc_k} = \frac{J_{w_k}\left(p_k - p_{wf_k}\right)}{\sum_m J_{w_m}\left(p_m - p_{wf_m}\right)} q_{spsc}, \quad \text{(6.104)}$$

where $m, k \in \psi_w$. The application of Eq. 6.104 presents two difficulties. First, the unknown wellbore pressures, p_{wf_k}, appear in the equation. Second, the summation in the denominator of Eq. 6.104 introduces additional gridblock unknowns into the finite-difference equations of the gridblocks hosting the wellbore. In addition to the pressures of the neighboring gridblocks caused by interblock flow ($p_{i+1,j,k}$; $p_{i,j+1,k}$; $p_{i,j,k+1}$; $p_{i,j,k}$; $p_{i,j,k-1}$; $p_{i,j-1,k}$; $p_{i-1,j,k}$), the pressures of the column of grid cells p_k, where $k \in \psi_w$, containing the well also appear in the finite-difference equations of wellblocks. Substituting Eq. 6.100b into Eq. 6.96 and solving gives (also, see Example 6.10)

$$p_{wf_{ref}} = \frac{\sum_k \left\{ J_{w_k}\left[p_k - \bar{\gamma}_{wb}\left(H_k - H_{ref}\right)\right] \right\} + q_{sc}}{\sum_k J_{w_k}}, \quad \text{(6.105)}$$

where $k \in \psi_w$.

In Eq. 6.105, $\bar{\gamma}_{wb}$ is defined by Eq. 6.101. If we substitute the specified production or injection rate, q_{spsc}, into Eq. 6.105, then we can estimate the flowing well pressure at the reference depth $p_{wf_{ref}}$. The following algorithm is used to estimate the flowing wellbore pressures required for Eq. 6.105.

1. Assume a value of $\bar{\gamma}_{wb}$ (usually the converged value from the previous timestep).
2. Calculate $p_{wf_{ref}}$ from Eq. 6.105 using q_{spsc} and the assumed value of $\bar{\gamma}_{wb}$.
3. Use $p_{wf_{ref}}$ (calculated in Step 2) and the assumed value of $\bar{\gamma}_{wb}$ to calculate the wellbore pressures at all perforated gridblocks with Eq. 6.100b.
4. Calculate the average wellbore pressure, $\bar{p}_{wf}$, with Eq. 6.103.
5. Recalculate the average pressure gradient with $\bar{p}_{wf}$ from Step 4 and Eq. 6.101a or Eq. 6.101b in consideration of whether flow in well is single phase or multiphase, respectively.
6. Check for convergence. Go to Step 2 if necessary.

For Step 5 in multiphase flow, Eq. 6.101b requires the production rates for each flowing phase. For the explicit method of allocating production, these rates are evaluated at the old time level (Time Level n). This algorithm can also be improved to allow for a variable $\bar{\gamma}_{wb}$ between simulation layers. To implement such an algorithm for multiphase flow, the rates in Eq. 6.101b are not the well rates but the summations of all upstream rates.

This algorithm provides the wellbore pressure for the flowing well pressures at each perforated wellblock. This solves the first difficulty discussed with the application of Eq. 6.103: the addition of the sandface pressures, p_{wf_k}, into the finite-difference equations. The second difficulty (the addition of the gridblock pressures p_k, where $k \in \psi_w$) is more challenging to solve because the introduction of the additional unknowns alters the structure of the coefficient matrix (discussed in Implicit Treatment of Multilayer Wells in the next section). To avoid this problem, these additional pressures are evaluated at the known time level (Time Level n).

PI-Weighted Method. The PI-weighted method of allocating specified production/injection rates assumes that a constant drawdown/buildup exists for all simulation layers. That is,

$$\Delta p = p_k - p_{wf_k}, \qquad (6.106)$$

where $k \in \psi_w$. Substituting Eq. 6.106 into Eq. 6.104 results in

$$q_{sc_k} = q_{spsc} \frac{J_{w_k} \Delta p}{\sum_m J_{w_m} \Delta p} \qquad (6.107)$$

$$\text{or } q_{sc_k} = q_{spsc} \frac{J_{w_k}}{\sum_m J_{w_m}}, \qquad (6.108)$$

where $m, k \in \psi_w$. Although it appears that Eq. 6.108 does not introduce additional unknowns into the finite-difference equation for grid cells containing wells, in reality, the summation in the denominator of Eq. 6.108 does contain the pressure-dependent terms μ and B (and saturation-dependent relative permeabilities for multiphase flow). Consequently, the use of Eq. 6.108 introduces some dependency on pressures from nonneighboring gridblocks into the finite-difference equations. In the explicit method of calculating production/injection, all pressures and saturations are evaluated at the old time level, n.

After solving for the gridblock pressures in the reservoir, Eq. 6.93 can be used to estimate the flowing sandface pressures, p_{wf_k}, at each simulation layer. Remember that the sandface pressures calculated in this manner for the PI-weighted method do not obey any pressure-gradient equation, such as Eq. 6.100 (that is, they are not compatible with the pressure drop in the tubing), but simply satisfy the relationship defined by Eq. 6.106.

In the previous discussion on the explicit method, both for pressure- and rate-specified wells, all the additional unknowns introduced into the finite-difference equations by the IPR's are evaluated at the old time level, n. For the simple-iteration method, these properties are evaluated at the new time level, $n+1$, lagged one iteration level, ν, behind the desired solution.

Implicit Treatment of Multilayer Wells. In the explicit method of calculating production/injection, all parameters used in the inflow performance were evaluated at Time Level n, while in the simple-iteration method, these parameters were evaluated at Time Level $n+1$, one iteration behind the desired solution. In some cases, these methods lead to physically unrealistic oscillations because of the nature of the evaluation of the unknowns. These oscillations occur when small changes in the inflow-performance parameters result in large changes in the resulting production/injection rate. This occurs, for example, at water or gas breakthrough during a secondary recovery project.

To improve the stability of the finite-difference formulation, we need to develop a method to evaluate the unknowns in the IPR at the new time level, $n+1$, and the current iteration level, $\nu+1$. This can be accomplished by expanding Eq. 6.93 about the current time level, $n+1$, and the previous iteration level, ν, with the Taylor series expansion

$$\overset{(\nu+1)}{q_{sc_k}^{n+1}} \approx \overset{(\nu)}{q_{sc_k}^{n+1}} + \left.\frac{\partial q_{sc_k}}{\partial S_{w_k}}\right|^{\overset{(\nu)}{n+1}} \left(\overset{(\nu+1)}{S_{w_k}^{n+1}} - \overset{(\nu)}{S_{w_k}^{n+1}} \right)$$

$$+ \left.\frac{\partial q_{sc_k}}{\partial S_{g_k}}\right|^{\overset{(\nu)}{n+1}} \left(\overset{(\nu+1)}{S_{g_k}^{n+1}} - \overset{(\nu)}{S_{g_k}^{n+1}} \right)$$

$$+ \left.\frac{\partial q_{sc_k}}{\partial p_{o_k}}\right|^{\overset{(\nu)}{n+1}} \left(\overset{(\nu+1)}{p_{o_k}^{n+1}} - \overset{(\nu)}{p_{o_k}^{n+1}} \right)$$

$$+ \left.\frac{\partial q_{sc_k}}{\partial p_{wf_{ref}}}\right|^{\overset{(\nu)}{n+1}} \left(\overset{(\nu+1)}{p_{wf_{ref}}^{n+1}} - \overset{(\nu)}{p_{wf_{ref}}^{n+1}} \right), \qquad (6.109)$$

where $k \in \psi_w$. Eq. 6.109 assumes that S_w, S_g, and p_o are the primary unknowns in the finite-difference formulation. If another set of unknowns is selected, Eq. 6.109 must be written in terms of the new unknowns. Chap. 9 discusses the selection of unknowns for multiphase-flow simulation.

In Eq. 6.109, the partial derivatives with respect to the unknowns are obtained from the IPR, Eq. 6.93,

$$\left.\frac{\partial q_{sc_k}}{\partial S_{w_k}}\right| = -\left.\frac{\partial J_{w_k}}{\partial S_{w_k}}\right|\left(p_{o_k} - p_{wf_k}\right), \qquad (6.110)$$

$$\left.\frac{\partial q_{sc_k}}{\partial S_{g_k}}\right| = -\left.\frac{\partial J_{w_k}}{\partial S_{g_k}}\right|\left(p_{o_k} - p_{wf_k}\right), \qquad (6.111)$$

$$\left.\frac{\partial q_{sc_k}}{\partial p_{o_k}}\right| = -\left.\frac{\partial J_{w_k}}{\partial p_{o_k}}\right|\left(p_{o_k} - p_{wf_k}\right) - J_{w_k}, \qquad (6.112)$$

$$\text{and } \left.\frac{\partial q_{sc_k}}{\partial p_{wf_{ref}}}\right| = J_{w_k} \frac{\partial p_{wf_k}}{\partial p_{wf_{ref}}}, \qquad (6.113)$$

where $k \in \psi_w$, and $\partial p_{wf_k} / \partial p_{wf_{ref}}$ can be obtained from Eq. 6.100, as

$$\frac{\partial p_{wf_k}}{\partial p_{wf_{ref}}} = 1 + \frac{\partial \bar{\gamma}_{wb}}{\partial p_{wf_{ref}}}\left(H_k - H_{ref}\right), \qquad (6.114)$$

where $k \in \psi_w$.

For single-phase flow problems, all of the derivatives with respect to the water and gas saturations are set equal to zero. This is also done for the pressure solution of the implicit-pressure/explicit-saturation and sequential-solution methods for multiphase flow. Chap. 9 discusses these methods.

For three-phase flow problems, Eq. 6.109 introduces seven unknowns: $q_{osc_k}^{n+1}$, $q_{wsc_k}^{n+1}$, $q_{gsc_k}^{n+1}$, $S_{w_k}^{n+1}$, $S_{g_k}^{n+1}$, $p_{o_k}^{n+1}$, and $p_{wf_{ref}}^{n+1}$. These unknowns are at the new iteration level, $\nu+1$.

To solve for these unknowns, we have only six equations: Eq. 6.93 written for the oil, water, and gas phases (three equations), and the oil-, water-, and gas-phase mass-balance equations. To solve the system of equations generated by the fully-implicit method, we must find a way to eliminate one of the unknowns. This is accomplished by implementing the well specifications.

Pressure-Specified Wells. For pressure-specified wells, the sandface pressure, $p_{wf_{ref}}$, at the end of Iteration $\nu+1$ must equal the sandface pressure at the beginning of Iteration ν. That is,

$$\overset{(\nu+1)}{p_{wf_{ref}}^{n+1}} = \overset{(\nu)}{p_{wf_{ref}}^{n+1}} = p_{wfsp}. \qquad (6.115)$$

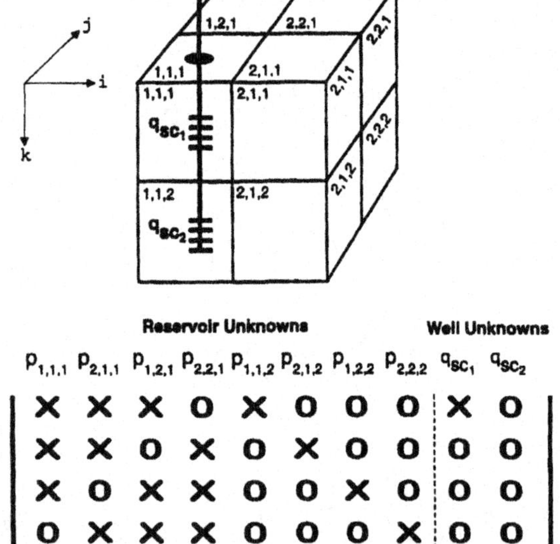

	$p_{1,1,1}$	$p_{2,1,1}$	$p_{1,2,1}$	$p_{2,2,1}$	$p_{1,1,2}$	$p_{2,1,2}$	$p_{1,2,2}$	$p_{2,2,2}$	q_{sc_1}	q_{sc_2}
Finite-Difference, Mass-Balance Equations (Discussed in Chap. 7)	X	X	X	O	X	O	O	O	X	O
	X	X	O	X	O	X	O	O	O	O
	X	O	X	X	O	O	X	O	O	O
	O	X	X	X	O	O	O	X	O	O
	X	O	O	O	X	X	X	O	O	X
	O	X	O	O	X	X	O	X	O	O
	O	O	X	O	X	O	X	X	O	O
	O	O	O	X	O	X	X	X	O	O
Well Equations (Discussed in Sec. 6.2.2)	X	O	O	O	O	O	O	O	X	O
	O	O	O	O	X	O	O	O	O	X

Fig. 6.9—Three-dimensional reservoir/wellbore system for a pressure-specified well and its corresponding finite-difference coefficient matrix.

Substituting Eq. 6.115 into Eq. 6.109 yields

$$\overset{(\nu+1)}{q_{sc_k}^{n+1}} \approx \overset{(\nu)}{q_{sc_k}^{n+1}} + \left.\frac{\partial q_{sc_k}}{\partial S_{w_k}}\right|^{\overset{(\nu)}{n+1}} \left(\overset{(\nu+1)}{S_{w_k}^{n+1}} - \overset{(\nu)}{S_{w_k}^{n+1}} \right)$$

$$+ \left.\frac{\partial q_{sc_k}}{\partial S_{g_k}}\right|^{\overset{(\nu)}{n+1}} \left(\overset{(\nu+1)}{S_{g_k}^{n+1}} - \overset{(\nu)}{S_{g_k}^{n+1}} \right)$$

$$+ \left.\frac{\partial q_{sc_k}}{\partial p_{o_k}}\right|^{\overset{(\nu)}{n+1}} \left(\overset{(\nu+1)}{p_{o_k}^{n+1}} - \overset{(\nu)}{p_{o_k}^{n+1}} \right), \quad \ldots\ldots\ldots\ldots (6.116)$$

where $k \in \psi_w$. Note that Eq. 6.116 no longer contains the unknown, $p_{wf_{ref}}^{n+1}$ at the new iteration level, $\nu+1$. Consequently, this treatment has eliminated this unknown from the equation set.

Now consider how to evaluate the unknowns appearing in Eq. 6.116. In previous methods, we were content to evaluate these unknowns at Time Level n (the explicit method) or Time Level $n+1$, Iteration Level ν (the simple-iteration method). The objective of the fully-implicit method is to improve the stability of the finite-difference formulation. To preserve the stability of the fully-implicit method, evaluate the unknowns at Time Level $n+1$ and Iteration Level $\nu+1$. To do this, include Eq. 6.116 in the matrix equation. **Fig. 6.9** shows this schematically for single-phase flow. In Fig. 6.9, × represents nonzero entries in the coefficient matrix. Chap. 7 presents a discussion of linear algebra, including the construction of the coefficient matrix.

Rate-Specified Wells. For rate-specified wells, we specify the rate for the entire well. Unfortunately, Eq. 6.109 is written for each perforated wellblock. To develop the appropriate constraint equation for the entire wellbore, we sum Eq. 6.109 over all the open perforations. That is,

$$\sum_k \overset{(\nu+1)}{q_{sc_k}^{n+1}} = \sum_k \overset{(\nu)}{q_{sc_k}^{n+1}} + \sum_k \left[\left.\frac{\partial q_{sc_k}}{\partial S_{w_k}}\right|^{\overset{(\nu)}{n+1}} \left(\overset{(\nu+1)}{S_{w_k}^{n+1}} - \overset{(\nu)}{S_{w_k}^{n+1}} \right) \right.$$

$$+ \left.\frac{\partial q_{sc_k}}{\partial S_{g_k}}\right|^{\overset{(\nu)}{n+1}} \left(\overset{(\nu+1)}{S_{g_k}^{n+1}} - \overset{(\nu)}{S_{g_k}^{n+1}} \right)$$

$$+ \left.\frac{\partial q_{sc_k}}{\partial p_{o_k}}\right|^{\overset{(\nu)}{n+1}} \left(\overset{(\nu+1)}{p_{o_k}^{n+1}} - \overset{(\nu)}{p_{o_k}^{n+1}} \right)$$

$$\left. + \left.\frac{\partial q_{sc_k}}{\partial p_{wf_{ref}}}\right|^{\overset{(\nu)}{n+1}} \left(\overset{(\nu+1)}{p_{wf_{ref}}^{n+1}} - \overset{(\nu)}{p_{wf_{ref}}^{n+1}} \right) \right], \quad \ldots\ldots\ldots (6.117)$$

where $k \in \psi_w$. For a rate-specified well, the production/injection rate at the end of Iteration $\nu+1$ must equal the rate at the beginning of Iteration ν. Therefore,

$$\sum_k \overset{(\nu+1)}{q_{sc_k}^{n+1}} = \sum_k \overset{(\nu)}{q_{sc_k}^{n+1}} = q_{spsc}, \quad \ldots\ldots\ldots\ldots\ldots\ldots\ldots (6.118)$$

where $k \in \psi_w$. Substituting Eq. 6.118 into Eq. 6.117 results in

$$\sum_k \left[\left.\frac{\partial q_{sc_k}}{\partial S_{w_k}}\right|^{\overset{(\nu)}{n+1}} \left(\overset{(\nu+1)}{S_{w_k}^{n+1}} - \overset{(\nu)}{S_{w_k}^{n+1}} \right) + \left.\frac{\partial q_{sc_k}}{\partial S_{g_k}}\right|^{\overset{(\nu)}{n+1}} \left(\overset{(\nu+1)}{S_{g_k}^{n+1}} - \overset{(\nu)}{S_{g_k}^{n+1}} \right) \right.$$

$$+ \left.\frac{\partial q_{sc_k}}{\partial p_{o_k}}\right|^{\overset{(\nu)}{n+1}} \left(\overset{(\nu+1)}{p_{o_k}^{n+1}} - \overset{(\nu)}{p_{o_k}^{n+1}} \right)$$

$$\left. + \left.\frac{\partial q_{sc_k}}{\partial p_{wf_{ref}}}\right|^{\overset{(\nu)}{n+1}} \left(\overset{(\nu+1)}{p_{wf_{ref}}^{n+1}} - \overset{(\nu)}{p_{wf_{ref}}^{n+1}} \right) \right] = 0, \quad \ldots\ldots\ldots\ldots (6.119)$$

where $k \in \psi_w$, or, after rearranging,

$$\overset{(\nu+1)}{p_{wf_{ref}}^{n+1}} = \overset{(\nu)}{p_{wf_{ref}}^{n+1}} - \sum_k \left[\left.\frac{\partial q_{sc_k}}{\partial S_{w_k}}\right|^{\overset{(\nu)}{n+1}} \left(\overset{(\nu+1)}{S_{w_k}^{n+1}} - \overset{(\nu)}{S_{w_k}^{n+1}} \right) \right.$$

$$+ \left.\frac{\partial q_{sc_k}}{\partial S_{g_k}}\right|^{\overset{(\nu)}{n+1}} \left(\overset{(\nu+1)}{S_{g_k}^{n+1}} - \overset{(\nu)}{S_{g_k}^{n+1}} \right)$$

$$\left. + \left.\frac{\partial q_{sc_k}}{\partial p_{o_k}}\right|^{\overset{(\nu)}{n+1}} \left(\overset{(\nu+1)}{p_{o_k}^{n+1}} - \overset{(\nu)}{p_{o_k}^{n+1}} \right) \right] \div \sum_k \left.\frac{\partial q_{sc_k}}{\partial p_{wf_{ref}}}\right|^{\overset{(\nu)}{n+1}},$$

$$\ldots\ldots\ldots\ldots\ldots\ldots\ldots (6.120)$$

where $k \in \psi_w$. Note that Eq. 6.120 allows the completion rates to vary from Iteration Level ν to Iteration Level $\nu+1$, but constrains the total rate of the well to q_{spsc}. **Fig. 6.10** shows the coefficient matrix generated by the fully-implicit method for a rate-specified well for single-phase-flow problem.

In the fully-implicit method, the partial derivatives with respect to the unknowns are evaluated at Time Level $n+1$ and Iteration Level ν. In the linearized-implicit method, these derivatives are evaluated once, at Time Level n and held constant during subsequent iterations

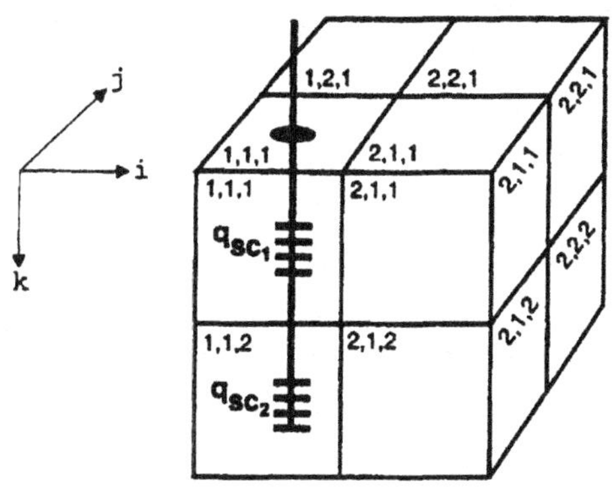

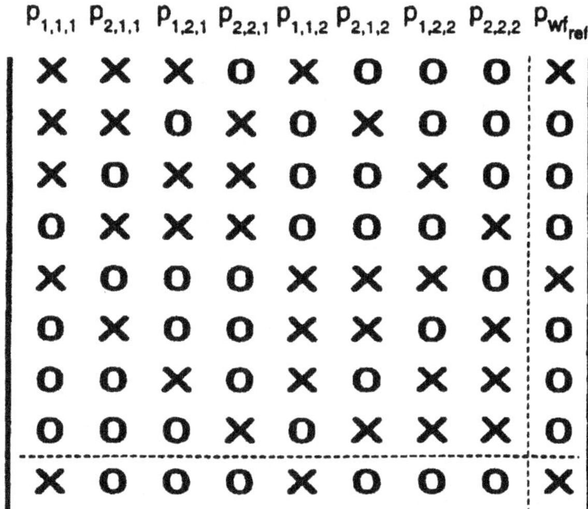

Fig. 6.10—Three-dimensional reservoir/wellbore system for a rate-specified well and its corresponding finite-difference coefficient matrix.

for Time Level $n+1$. (In this treatment, the linearized-implicit method is identical to the first iteration of the fully-implicit method.[8]) Finally, in Nolen and Berry's[7] semi-implicit method, these derivatives are approximated by chord slopes.

Horizontal-Well Models. Recently, horizontal wells have been receiving considerable attention in petroleum literature. Because of the larger contact area, horizontal wells may outperform vertical wells in draining equivalent reservoir volumes. The increased productivity is not the only reason to drill a horizontal well; the ability to orient the horizontal well to intersect higher-permeability channels and minimizing coning problems are other objectives of horizontal wells. Although the solution for the flow behavior of a horizontal well is complex for most routine applications, it can be simplified for reservoir-simulation purposes.[9]

One logical approach to reduce the complexity of the solution is to use Peaceman's[5] vertical-well model by rotating the axes of the model to account for the horizontal well. In this modification, the y and z axes are interchanged if the horizontal well is placed parallel to y direction so that Eq. 6.38 is expressed as

$$q_{sc} = -2\pi\beta_c k\Delta y\left(p_{i,j,k} - p_{wf}\right) \Big/ \left\{ \mu B \left[\log_e\left(0.28 \left\{ \left[\left(k_x/k_z\right)^{1/2}(\Delta z)^2 + \left(k_z/k_x\right)^{1/2}(\Delta x)^2 \right]^{1/2} \Big/ \left[\left(k_x/k_z\right)^{1/4} + \left(k_z/k_x\right)^{1/4} \right] \right\} \right) - \log_e(r_w) + s \right] \right\} \quad \text{(6.121)}$$

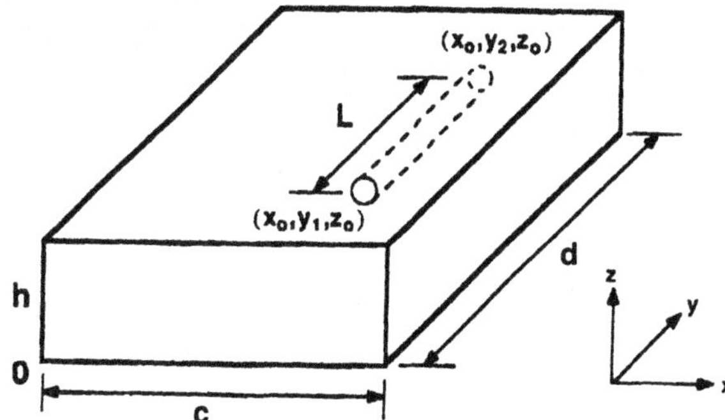

Fig. 6.11—Schematic of a horizontal well as depicted by Babu and Odeh's[9] model. Note that the well is not in the center of the wellblock and is parallel to the y direction.

(note that, if the horizontal well is placed parallel to the y direction, the y and z axes are interchanged). In Eq. 6.121, k in the numerator becomes

$$k = \left(k_x k_z\right)^{1/2}. \quad \text{(6.122)}$$

Peaceman[10] cautions users of Eq. 6.121 that successful implementation of this equation depends on the assumption that the grid spacing and permeability are uniform, the well is isolated (not located near any other well), and the well is not near any grid boundary. This last assumption can easily be violated in the simulation of a horizontal well. According to Peaceman[10] the well-location requirements are (conservatively) achieved by the following.

1. An isolated well should be at a distance greater than ten times the max $(\Delta x, \Delta z)$ from any other well.
2. The well should be no closer than $5\Delta x + 0.5(\Delta z/\Delta x)$ from a vertical grid boundary.
3. The well should be no closer than $5\Delta z + 0.5(\Delta x/\Delta z)$ from a horizontal grid boundary.

Babu and Odeh's[9] Pseudosteady-State Productivity Model. Babu and Odeh developed an equation for calculating the productivity of a horizontal well. This equation also has a form similar to the flow equation of a vertical well. **Fig. 6.11** shows the physical model on which Babu and Odeh's equation is based.

The Babu and Odeh inflow-performance equation for a horizontal well is

$$q_{sc} = \frac{-2\pi\beta_c dk\left(p_{i,j,k} - p_{wf}\right)}{\mu B\left[\log_e\left(A^{1/2}/r_w\right) + \log_e(C_H) + s - 3/4\right]}. \quad \text{(6.123)}$$

Because Eq. 6.123 is written for a horizontal well placed parallel to the y direction, Eq. 6.122 gives the definition of permeability, k.

Other entries in Eq. 6.123 are

$$d = \Delta y, \quad \text{(6.124)}$$

$$A = ch = \Delta x \Delta z, \quad \text{(6.125)}$$

and

$$\log_e(C_H) = 6.28\frac{c}{h}\sqrt{\frac{k_z}{k_x}}\left[\frac{1}{3} - \frac{X_0}{c} + \left(\frac{X_0}{c}\right)^2\right] - \log_e\left(\sin\frac{\pi Z_0}{h}\right) - 0.5\log_e\left[\left(\frac{c}{h}\right)\sqrt{\frac{k_z}{k_x}}\right] - 1.088, \quad \text{(6.126)}$$

where X_0 and Z_0 are the coordinates of the center of the well in the vertical (x-z) plane [as shown in Fig. 6.11, (X_0, y_1, Z_0) and (X_0, y_2, Z_0) represent the coordinates of the beginning and end of the well, respectively]. The accuracy of Eq. 6.126 increases when

$$c \geqq 0.75h\sqrt{\frac{k_x}{k_z}} \quad \text{(6.127)}$$

TABLE 6.5—FORMULAS TO CALCULATE FUNCTION F IN EQ. 6.132

Argument	Function F
$\frac{L}{2d}$	$-\left(\frac{L}{2d}\right)\left[0.145+\log_e\left(\frac{L}{2d}\right)-0.137\left(\frac{L}{2d}\right)^2\right]$
$\frac{4y_{mid}+L}{2d}\leqq 1$	$-\left(\frac{4y_{mid}+L}{2d}\right)\left[0.145+\log_e\left(\frac{4y_{mid}+L}{2d}\right)-0.137\left(\frac{4y_{mid}+L}{2d}\right)^2\right]$
$\frac{4y_{mid}+L}{2d}>1$	$\left(2-\frac{4y_{mid}+L}{2d}\right)\left[0.145+\log_e\left(2-\frac{4y_{mid}+L}{2d}\right)-0.137\left(2-\frac{4y_{mid}+L}{2d}\right)^2\right]$
$\frac{4y_{mid}-L}{2d}\leqq 1$	$-\left(\frac{4y_{mid}-L}{2d}\right)\left[0.145+\log_e\left(\frac{4y_{mid}-L}{2d}\right)-0.137\left(\frac{4y_{mid}-L}{2d}\right)^2\right]$
$\frac{4y_{mid}-L}{2d}>1$	$\left(2-\frac{4y_{mid}-L}{2d}\right)\left[0.145+\log_e\left(2-\frac{4y_{mid}-L}{2d}\right)-0.137\left(2-\frac{4y_{mid}-L}{2d}\right)^2\right]$

and when a minimum distance between the well and the boundaries exists. That is,

$$\min(X_0, c-X_0)\geqq 0.75h\sqrt{\frac{k_x}{k_z}}. \quad \text{(6.128)}$$

Because $h \ll c$, Eqs. 6.127 and 6.128 generally are satisfied in practice.

The skin factor, s, in Eq. 6.123 is a composite that includes both the mechanical skin, s_m, and the skin resulting from partial penetration, s_p. In other words,

$$s = s_p + s_m. \quad \text{(6.129)}$$

If the horizontal well fully penetrates the wellblock, $L=y_2-y_1=d$, then $s_p=0$. For the computation of s_p, two cases need to be considered.

Case 1. $\left(c/\sqrt{k_x}\right)\geqq 0.75\left(d/\sqrt{k_y}\right)\gg 0.75\left(h/\sqrt{k_z}\right)$, and if $L<d$,

$$s_p = P_{xyz}+P'_{xy}, \quad \text{(6.130)}$$

where
$$P_{xyz}=\left(\frac{d}{L}-1\right)\left[\log_e\left(\frac{h}{r_w}\right)+0.25\log_e\left(\frac{k_x}{k_z}\right)-\log_e\left(\sin\frac{\pi Z_0}{h}\right)-1.84\right] \quad \text{(6.131)}$$

and
$$P'_{xy}=\frac{2d^2}{Lh}\sqrt{\frac{k_z}{k_y}}\times\left\{F\left(\frac{L}{2d}\right)+0.5\left[F\left(\frac{4y_{mid}+L}{2d}\right)-F\left(\frac{4y_{mid}-L}{2d}\right)\right]\right\}, \quad \text{(6.132)}$$

where y_{mid} = midpoint coordinate of the well = 0.5 (y_1+y_2).

The function F in Eq. 6.132 describes the effects of the well location in the horizontal plane. **Table 6.5** shows the evaluation of function F for different arguments.

Case 2. $\left(d/\sqrt{k_y}\right)>1.33\left(c/\sqrt{k_x}\right)\gg\left(h/\sqrt{k_z}\right)$, and $L<d$, then,

$$s_p = P_{xyz}+P_y+P_{xy}. \quad \text{(6.133)}$$

P_{xyz} is as given by Eq. 6.131. P_y is calculated from

$$P_y=\frac{6.28d^2}{ch}\frac{\sqrt{k_xk_z}}{k_y}\left[\left(\tfrac{1}{3}-\frac{y_{mid}}{d}+\frac{y_{mid}^2}{d^2}\right)+\frac{L}{24d}\left(\frac{L}{d}-3\right)\right], \quad \text{(6.134)}$$

where, again, y_{mid} = midpoint coordinate of the well. Finally, the P_{xy} component is defined by

$$P_{xy}=\left(\frac{d}{L}-1\right)\left(\frac{6.28c}{h}\sqrt{\frac{k_z}{k_x}}\right)\left(\tfrac{1}{3}-\frac{X_0}{c}+\frac{X_0^2}{c^2}\right). \quad \text{(6.135)}$$

Example 6.7. Compare the results of Eqs. 6.121 and 6.123 in calculating the production rate of a horizontal well that fully penetrates the hosting block and whose center coincides with the center of the block. Assume zero mechanical skin, isotropic permeabilities, and $\mu=1$ cp, $B=1$ RB/STB, and $r_w=0.4$ ft.

Solution. Assuming that the horizontal well is oriented parallel to the y direction (as Fig. 6.11 shows), make the following assumptions.

1. Full penetration occurs along the y direction. $L=y_2-y_1$, with $y_1=0$ and $y_2=d$. Then, $L=d$ and $s_p=0$.
2. The well center coincides with the center of the block. $X_0=c/2$ and $Z_0=h/2$.
3. There is zero mechanical skin ($s_m=0$), so $s=s_p+s_m=0$.

When these properties are implemented, the Babu and Odeh[9] inflow-performance equation (Eq. 6.123) can be written as

$$q_{sc}=\frac{-2\pi\beta_c dk\left(p_{i,j,k}-p_{wf}\right)}{\mu B\left[\log_e(A^{1/2}/r_w)+\log_e(C_H)-\tfrac{3}{4}\right]}, \quad \text{(6.136)}$$

where $\log_e(C_H)$ entry can be simplified with $X_0=c/2$ and $Z_0=h/2$ in Eq. 6.126 as

$$\log_e(C_H)=6.28\frac{c}{h}\sqrt{\frac{k_z}{k_x}}\left[\tfrac{1}{3}-\tfrac{1}{2}+(\tfrac{1}{2})^2\right]-\log_e\left(\sin\frac{\pi}{2}\right)-0.5\log_e\left[\left(\frac{c}{h}\right)\sqrt{\frac{k_z}{k_x}}\right]-1.088 \quad \text{(6.137)}$$

$$\text{or } \log_e(C_H) = \frac{6.28}{12}\frac{c}{h}\sqrt{\frac{k_z}{k_x}} - 0.5\log_e\left[\left(\frac{c}{h}\right)\sqrt{\frac{k_z}{k_x}}\right] - 1.088. \quad (6.138)$$

Let $c=800$ ft, $d=800$ ft, and $h=40$ ft. Furthermore, assume that $k_x=k_y=100$ md and $k_z=10$ md. With these specifications, $\log_e(C_H)$ can be calculated: $\log_e(C_H)=(6.28/12)(800/40)\sqrt{10/100}-0.5\log_e[(800/40)\sqrt{10/100}]-1.088=3.310-0.922-1.088=1.300$. Also, because $k=(k_xk_z)^{½}$ and $A=ch$, $k=0.0316$ darcy and $A=32{,}000$ ft^2.

The PI of the Babu and Odeh[9] inflow-performance equation for a horizontal well can be calculated from

$$J_{B-O} = \frac{2\pi\beta_c dk}{\mu B[\log_e(A^{½}/r_w) + \log_e(C_H) + s - ¾]}. \quad (6.139)$$

Using the entries calculated earlier yields

$$J_{B-O} = \frac{(2\pi)(1.127)(800)(0.0316)}{(1)(1)[\log_e(32,000^{½}/0.4) + 1.300 - ¾]}$$

or $J_{B-O}=26.907$ STB/D-psi.

Now, calculate the PI of Peaceman's[5] equation (Eq. 6.121) from

$$J_p = 2\pi\beta_c k\Delta y \Big/ \left\{\mu B\left[\log_e\left(0.28\left\{\left[(k_x/k_z)^{½}(\Delta z)^2 + (k_z/k_x)^{½}(\Delta x)^2\right]^{½} \Big/ \left[(k_x/k_z)^{¼} + (k_z/k_x)^{¼}\right]\right\}\right) - \log_e(r_w) + s\right]\right\}, \quad (6.140)$$

which yields

$$J_p = (2\pi)(1.127)(0.0316)(800)$$

$$\div (1)(1)\left[\log_e\left(0.28\left\{\left[(100/10)^{½}(40)^2 + (10/100)^{½}(800)^2\right]^{½} \Big/ \left[(100/10)^{¼} + (10/100)^{¼}\right]\right\}\right) - \log_e 0.4\right] = 31.053 \text{ STB/D-psi.}$$

Example 6.8. How does the PI of the horizontal well in Example 6.7 change if the center of the well is located at $X_0=0.75c$ and $Z_0=h/2$.

Solution. For this case, the value of C_H must be recalculated as

$$\log_e(C_H) = 6.28\left(\frac{800}{40}\right)\sqrt{\frac{10}{100}}\left[⅓ - ¾ + (¾)^2\right] - \log_e\left(\sin\frac{\pi}{2}\right) - 0.5\log_e\left[\left(\frac{800}{40}\right)\sqrt{\frac{10}{100}}\right] - 1.088$$

or $\log_e(C_H) = 3.782$. The PI for the new configuration is

$$J_{B-O} = \frac{(2\pi)(1.127)(800)(0.0316)}{(1)(1)[\log_e(32,000^{½}/0.4) + 3.782 - ¾]},$$

or $J_{B-O}=19.596$ STB/D-psi, which indicates an approximate 27% decrease with respect to the productivity of the well in Example 6.7. Note that the use of the Peaceman[5] method does not lend itself to reorienting the position of the well within a simulation layer.

Example 6.9. Using the data of Example 6.7, compare the productivities of a vertical well drilled in the center of the block to that of a horizontal well completed in the center of the block. Assume isotropic permeabilities.

Solution. For an isotropic permeability and square gridblock, Eq. 6.36a gives the wellblock radius for a vertical well as $r_{eq}=0.198\,\Delta x$.

The PI of Peaceman's[5] vertical-well model can be extracted from Eq. 6.37 as

$$J_v = \frac{2\pi\beta_c k_H h}{\mu B[\log_e(r_{eq}/r_w) + s]}. \quad (6.141)$$

With the data from Example 6.7, the PI of a vertical well is calculated as

$$J_v = \frac{(2\pi)(1.127)(0.1)(40)}{(1)(1)(\log_e\{[(0.198)(800)]/0.4\})}$$

or $J_v=4.74$ STB/D-psi.

Comparing this PI value with the PI values calculated in Eqs. 6.139 and 6.140, we can conclude that, for the reservoir/wellbore systems under consideration, the productivity of a horizontal borehole is approximately six times greater than that of a vertical well.

Currently, for multiple-cell horizontal wells, there is no industry standard method to account for frictional losses in the wellbore. For multiple-cell vertical wells, we assumed that the frictional losses are negligible compared with the gravity head and used Eq. 6.100 to approximate the pressure drop in the wellbore. For multiple-cell horizontal wells, the gravity head is negligible and frictional losses may dominate. Nghiem *et al.*[11] discuss several industry approaches for incorporating wellbore hydraulics into the inflow-performance calculations in a reservoir simulator; however, implementation of these techniques is beyond the scope of this textbook. For multiple-cell horizontal wells, we simply assume no pressure drop in the horizontal section of the well. With this assumption, all the methods for multilayered vertical wells are applicable, provided that Eq. 6.100 is replaced with

$$p_{wf_k} = p_{wf_{ref}}, \quad (6.142)$$

where $k \in \psi_w$. The assumption of negligible pressure drop is valid if the reservoir drawdown is significantly greater than the pressure drop along the length of the horizontal well.

6.3 Single-Well Simulation

Single-well simulation studies are generally used to analyze well tests and coning problems. Conducting a simulation study for these types of problems is not different from other simulation studies with the exception that a computer model in r-θ-z coordinates is used.

As the previous chapters discuss, the use of an r-θ-z model is based on the assumption of radial flow in the lateral directions. **Fig. 6.12** shows a schematic of an r-θ-z model and the details of a typical block in that model.

Consider Eq. 4.42 written in the r-z coordinates only:

$$\frac{1}{r}\frac{\partial}{\partial r}\left(r\beta_c\frac{k_r}{\mu_l B_l}\frac{\partial p}{\partial r}\right) + \frac{\partial}{\partial z}\left(\beta_c\frac{k_z}{\mu_l B_l}\frac{\partial p}{\partial z}\right) = \frac{1}{\alpha_c}\frac{\partial}{\partial t}\left(\frac{\phi}{B_l}\right). \quad (6.143)$$

The development of a single-well model presents some challenges not encountered in rectangular coordinates. The difficulty stems from the convergent nature of the flow toward the wellbore. This convergent flow results in higher fluid velocities as the area perpendicular to the flow along the r direction becomes progressively smaller. This

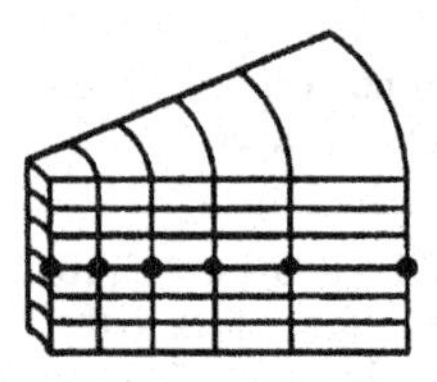

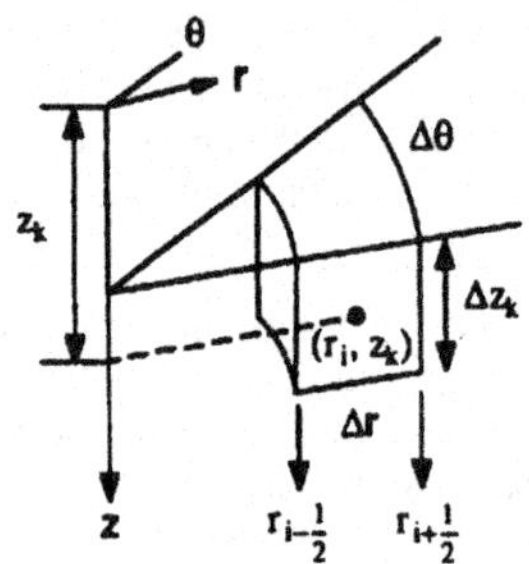

Fig. 6.12—Discretized radial-cylindrical-flow geometry and details of a typical block.

increase in fluid velocity in the near-wellbore vicinity necessitates the use of smaller timesteps to generate numerically stable results. In Fig. 6.12, the locations of the mesh points, represented by the solid dots, are spaced logarithmically between the external radius and the well radius. Logarithmic spacing results in increased density of mesh points in the high-pressure-gradient region near the wellbore.

Eq. 6.143, written only in the r direction for a slightly compressible fluid and incompressible porous medium, takes the form

$$\frac{1}{r}\frac{\partial}{\partial r}\left(r\beta_c\frac{k_r}{\mu_l B_l}\frac{\partial p}{\partial r}\right) = \frac{\phi c_l}{\alpha_c B_l^{\circ}}\frac{\partial p}{\partial t}. \quad \text{(6.144)}$$

When discretizing Eq. 6.144, the grid spacing and interblock boundaries (defined by the equations discussed in Sec. 5.2.3) are used.

The solution of Eq. 6.144 requires that an initial condition and two boundary conditions at $r=r_w$ and $r=r_e$ be specified (in the case of Eq. 6.143 two additional boundary conditions at the top and bottom surfaces of the formation also need to be specified). The initial condition is given as the pressure distribution at time zero. In the case of a newly drilled well in a previously undisturbed formation, the pressure is based on hydrostatic equilibrium. The two boundary conditions are imposed on the internal and external boundaries. At the wellbore, the inner boundary of the reservoir, either a Dirichlet-type (constant pressure) or a Neumann-type (constant flow rate) boundary condition can be specified. In a similar manner, a Dirichlet-type or a Neumann-type condition can be imposed at the external boundary. In the case of pure Dirichlet-type problem, the first and last mesh points along the r direction are not included in the unknown list. After solving the pressure values for the internal grid nodes, we calculate the pressure gradient at $r=r_w$ and the flow rate by

$$q_{sc} = \frac{-2\pi\beta_c r_w k_H h}{B\mu}\left.\frac{\partial p}{\partial r}\right|_{r=r_w}. \quad \text{(6.145)}$$

If the flow rate is specified at the wellbore, the pressure gradient at $r=r_w$ is fixed by

$$\left.\frac{\partial p}{\partial r}\right|_{r=r_w} = \frac{-q_{sc}B\mu}{2\pi\beta_c r_w k_H h}. \quad \text{(6.146)}$$

The solution to single-well problems by use of Eq. 6.144 assumes that the solution is axisymmetric. In a multilayer single-well problem, the rates are distributed between the layers according to the procedures described earlier in this chapter. The axisymmetric nature of the solution, however, is still preserved.

6.4 Use of Hybrid Grids in the Wellblocks

Pedrosa and Aziz[12] introduced the use of hybrid grids to improve the coupling of the wellbore to the reservoir. Hybrid grids insert a locally refined, cylindrical grid inside a full-field rectangular grid at the well locations. **Fig. 6.13** shows two such grid systems, one for a vertical well and one for a horizontal well.

The hybrid grid is constructed with the same logarithmic spacing for the cylindrical portion of the grid, which was discussed in Sec. 5.2.3. For the radial grid, an equivalent external radius is defined by the dimensions of the host rectangular cell. That is,

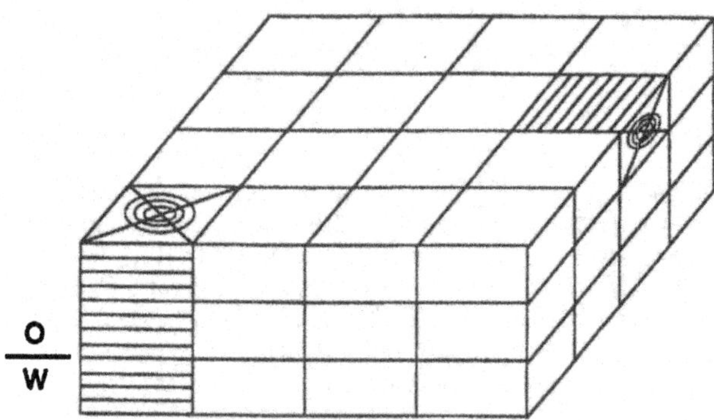

Fig. 6.13—Hybrid grid system for improving the coupling of wellbores to the reservoir model; O = oil and W = water.

$$r_e = \sqrt{\frac{\Delta x \Delta y}{\pi}} \quad \text{(6.147a)}$$

for a vertical well,

$$r_e = \sqrt{\frac{\Delta y \Delta z}{\pi}} \quad \text{(6.147b)}$$

for a horizontal well oriented parallel to the x direction, or

$$r_e = \sqrt{\frac{\Delta x \Delta z}{\pi}} \quad \text{(6.147c)}$$

for a horizontal well oriented parallel to the y direction.

The rectangular grid system is constructed in the same general manner as all rectangular grids. Note, in Fig. 6.13, that the rectangular grid was also locally refined in the direction parallel to the well. The reasons for this are discussed later. Finally, the time domain may also be refined to improve the stability of the solution of the radial-flow equations.

The transmissibilities of the rectangular and cylindrical grid sections are identical to the transmissibilities of their pure grid (nonhybrid) counterparts with the exception of the odd-shaped cells that couple the cylindrical grid to the rectangular grid. **Fig. 6.14** shows an example of this coupling cell in plan view.

The transmissibilities for these coupling cells are given by

$$T_{l_{m\pm ½}} = \left(\beta_c G\frac{k_{rl}}{B_l\mu_l}\right)_{m\pm ½}, \quad \text{(6.148)}$$

where $l=o$, w, or g.

Pedrosa and Aziz[12] provide the expressions for the geometrical factor, G, for theoretical cylindrical grid along the radial, angular, and vertical directions. Also, in the reservoir section, rectangular blocks are used with a different set of geometrical factors. **Tables 6.6 and 6.7** present definitions of geometrical factors for cylindrical and rectangular grids in three directions. Hybrid grids serve several purposes, including the following.

1. Model wells in coning situations in a full-field study.
2. Incorporate gradients into the well performance model. (Note that IPR's, such as Eq. 6.37, do not consider the pressure gradient.)

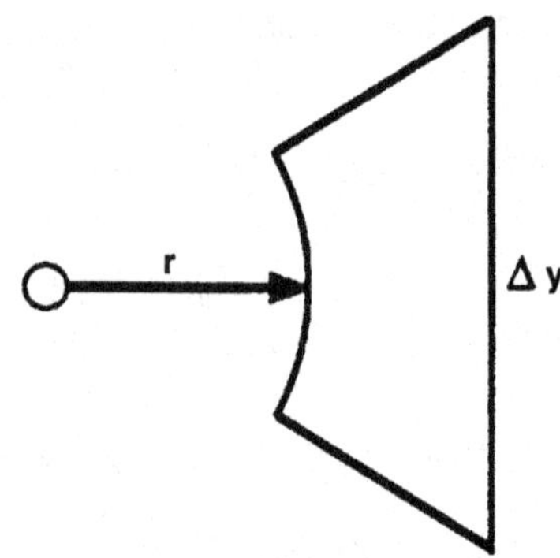

Fig. 6.14—Plan view of coupling cell in a hybrid grid system.

TABLE 6.6—FORMULAS TO CALCULATE THE GEOMETRICAL FACTOR G IN EQ. 6.148 FOR CYLINDRICAL GRIDS[12]

Direction	G
Radial	$\dfrac{\Delta\theta_j \Delta z_k}{\dfrac{1}{k_{r_{i,j,k}}}\log_e(r_{i+½}/r_i) + \dfrac{1}{k_{r_{i+1,j,k}}}\log_e(r_{i+1}/r_{i+½})}$
Angular	$\dfrac{\log_e(r_{i+½}/r_{i-½})\Delta z_k}{(\theta_{j+½}-\theta_j)/k_{\theta_{i,j,k}} + (\theta_{j+1}-\theta_{j+½})/k_{\theta_{i,j+1,k}}}$
Vertical	$\dfrac{(\Delta\theta_j/2)(r^2_{i+½}-r^2_{i-½})}{(z_{k+½}-z_k)/k_{z_{i,j,k}} + (z_{k+1}-z_{k+½})/k_{z_{i,j+1,k}}}$

TABLE 6.7—FORMULAS TO CALCULATE THE GEOMETRICAL FACTOR G IN EQ. 6.148 FOR RECTANGULAR GRIDS[12]

Direction	G
x	$\dfrac{\Delta y_j \Delta z_k}{(x_{i+½}-x_i)/k_{x_{i,j,k}} + (x_{i+1}-x_{i+½})/k_{x_{i+1,j,k}}}$
y	$\dfrac{\Delta x_i \Delta z_k}{(y_{j+½}-y_j)/k_{y_{i,j,k}} + (y_{j+1}-y_{j+½})/k_{y_{i,j+1,k}}}$
z	$\dfrac{\Delta x_i \Delta y_j}{(z_{k+½}-z_k)/k_{z_{i,j,k}} + (z_{k+1}-z_{k+½})/k_{z_{i,j,k+1}}}$

3. Add greater definition in the near-wellbore region (in the area of high velocities).

4. Incorporate well specifications as boundary conditions instead of as sources/sinks.

When hybrid grids are used to model wells in coning situations, it is always preferable to use local grid refinement in the direction parallel to the well (at least to the contacts of the coning phases) because coarse grid layers between the well perforations and the fluid contacts may lead to numerical dispersion, which could defeat the original purpose of using a hybrid grid.

6.5 Coupling Reservoir and Wellbore-Hydraulics Models

To make realistic reservoir forecasts in reservoir simulation, it is often necessary to specify the pressure of surface equipment. For example, this may occur when several wells are producing into a common manifold, flowline, or separator. When surface pressures, p_{th} or p_{sep}, are specified, they must be converted to flowing sandface pressures, p_{wf}, for inclusion in the IPR, Eq. 6.37. The procedure used to convert surface pressures to sandface pressures is identical to the procedure production engineers use to perform systems analysis.[13]

Fig. 6.15 shows a wellbore completed in a multiple-layer simulation model. Vertical, Multilayer Well Models in Sec. 6.2.2 discusses the techniques used to prorate the production rate of the well to the individually completed layers. Because it is generally assumed that p_{wf} corresponds to the first (topmost) completion, these techniques are used from the first perforation downward. The techniques discussed in Vertical, Multilayer Well Models in Sec. 6.2.2 assume that the friction loss is negligible compared with the hydrostatic head. This assumption is valid for most practical situations. Exceptions to this may include high-velocity wells, such as gas wells, commingled wells where there is a significant distance between producing horizons, or highly deviated wells. In general, however, the assumption of negligible frictional losses is not applicable from the surface to the topmost completion because these distances can be on the order of thousands of feet.

The pressure drop in a length of tubing is governed by an energy-balance equation of the form

$$\left.\frac{dp}{dl}\right|_{\text{total}} = \left.\frac{dp}{dl}\right|_{\text{gravity}} + \left.\frac{dp}{dl}\right|_{\text{friction}} + \left.\frac{dp}{dl}\right|_{\text{acceleration}}, \quad\text{..... (6.149)}$$

where $$\left.\frac{dp}{dl}\right|_{\text{gravity}} = \rho\frac{g}{g_c}\sin\theta, \quad\text{..... (6.150)}$$

$$\left.\frac{dp}{dl}\right|_{\text{friction}} = \frac{f_m \rho v^2}{2Dg_c}, \quad\text{..... (6.151)}$$

and $$\left.\frac{dp}{dl}\right|_{\text{acceleration}} = \frac{\rho v}{g_c}\frac{dv}{dl}. \quad\text{..... (6.152)}$$

Eqs. 6.149 through 6.152 assume that Direction l is positive in the downward direction. Also note that $\Delta l = \Delta z$ for true vertical wells only. For deviated or horizontal wells, $\Delta l > \Delta z$.

In most practical petroleum-engineering applications, the acceleration term can be neglected. This term is important, for example, in transmission lines going over hills and mountains or through valleys. Even when this term is neglected, the solution of Eq. 6.149 for multiphase problems is beyond the scope of this book. Brown *et al.*[13] give an excellent discussion of the solution of this equation.

Fig. 6.16 shows a partial solution for a typical multiphase-flow problem in a vertical production well. This solution is a family of curves which are dependent on the surface pressure, p_{th}; the watercut, f_w; and the gas/liquid ratio, R_{gL}, or, equivalently, the gas/oil ratio. In Fig. 6.16, only the dependence on R_{gL} is shown. In most simulation studies, the tubing performance curves are generated with stand-alone runs of a surface-facilities, or pipe-flow, simulator. These curves are then read into the reservoir simulation model in a tabular form.

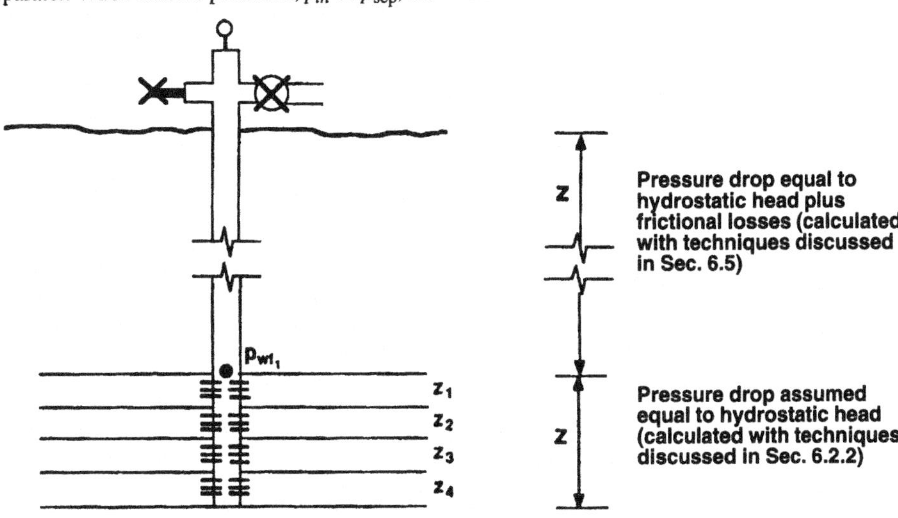

Fig. 6.15—Wellbore schematic of a well penetrating a four-layer simulation model.

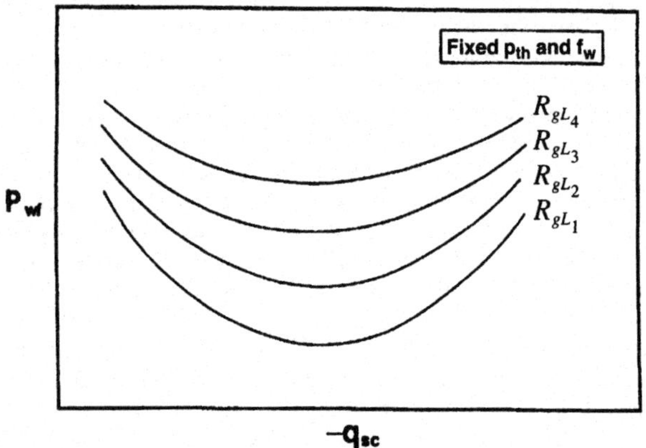

Fig. 6.16—Typical tubing performance relationships for a multiphase production well.

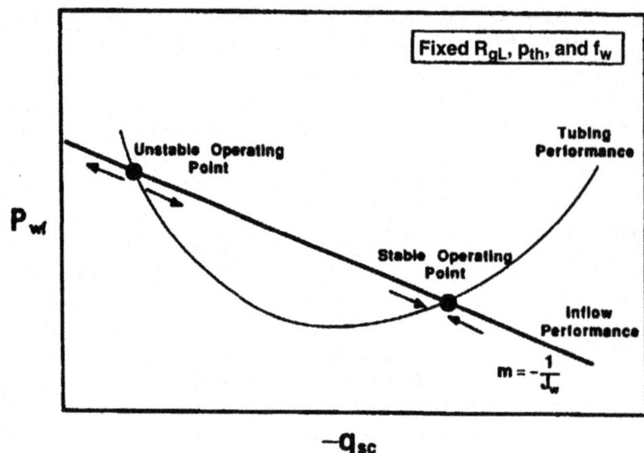

Fig. 6.17—Tubing-performance relationship and IPR for a typical production well. The intersections of these two curves are the operating points of the well.

Fig. 6.17 shows a single tubing performance curve for fixed values of p_{th}, f_w, and R_{gL}. The IPR, Eq. 6.26, can be rearranged as

$$p_{wf} = \bar{p} + \frac{q_{sc}}{J_w}, \quad \text{(6.153)}$$

which is a straight-line relationship (plotted in Fig. 6.17) between p_{wf} and q_{sc} (quadratic, Vogel[14]-type relationships can also be used).

Example 6.10. For a multilayer simulation model, what are physical and mathematical interpretations of the variables used in Eq. 6.153?

Solution. The production rate from the well equals the sum of the production rates from the individual layers. That is,

$$q_{sc} = \sum_k q_{sc_k}, \quad \text{(6.154)}$$

where $k \in \psi_w$. Substituting the IPR's for the individual layers gives

$$q_{sc} = -\sum_k J_{w_k}\left(p_k - p_{wf_k}\right), \quad \text{(6.96)}$$

where $k \in \psi_w$. The sandface pressures can be estimated with the pressure at the reference depth (depth of the top completion) and an average wellstream gradient.

$$p_{wf_k} = p_{wf_{ref}} + \bar{\gamma}_{wb}\left(H_k - H_{ref}\right), \quad \text{(6.100b)}$$

where $k \in \psi_w$, which neglects friction losses from the reference completion, H_{ref}. Substituting into the IPR yields

$$q_{sc} = -\sum_k J_{w_k}\left\{p_k - \left[p_{wf_{ref}} + \bar{\gamma}_{wb}\left(H_k - H_{ref}\right)\right]\right\}, \quad \text{(6.155)}$$

where $k \in \psi_w$, or rearranging,

$$q_{sc} = -\sum_k J_{w_k}\left[p_k - \bar{\gamma}_{wb}\left(H_k - H_{ref}\right)\right] + \sum_k J_{w_k} p_{wf_{ref}}, \quad \text{(6.156)}$$

where $k \in \psi_w$. After further rearrangement,

$$p_{wf_{ref}} = \frac{\sum_k J_{w_k}\left[p_k - \bar{\gamma}_{wb}\left(H_k - H_{ref}\right)\right] + q_{sc}}{\sum_k J_{w_k}} \quad \text{(6.105)}$$

$$\text{or } p_{wf_{ref}} = \frac{\sum_k J_{w_k}\left[p_k - \bar{\gamma}_{wb}\left(H_k - H_{ref}\right)\right] + q_{sc}}{J_w}, \quad \text{(6.157)}$$

where $J_w = \sum_k J_{w_k}$ (6.158)

and $k \in \psi_w$ in Eqs. 6.156 through 6.158. Note that

$$\hat{p}_k = p_k - \bar{\gamma}_{wb}\left(H_k - H_{ref}\right), \quad \text{(6.159)}$$

where $\hat{p}_k$ is the datum corrected pressure of p_k at Depth H_{ref} derived from the average wellstream gradient $\bar{\gamma}_{wb}$.

Substituting Eq. 6.159 into Eq. 6.157 yields

$$p_{wf_{ref}} = \frac{\sum_k J_{w_k}\hat{p}_k + q_{sc}}{J_w}, \quad \text{(6.160)}$$

where $k \in \psi_w$. Finally, note that

$$\bar{p} = \frac{\sum_k J_{w_k}\hat{p}_k}{J_w}, \quad \text{(6.161)}$$

where $k \in \psi_w$, is the PI-weighted average value of $\hat{p}_k$, which upon substitution in Eq. 6.160 gives

$$p_{wf_{ref}} = \bar{p} + \frac{q_{sc}}{J_w}. \quad \text{(6.162)}$$

Comparing Eq. 6.162 with Eq. 6.153 gives the following final results of this example.

1. $p_{wf_{ref}}$ = pressure at Reference Depth H_{ref} (topmost completion).
2. $\bar{p}$ = PI-weighted average value of the wellblock pressures (corrected to H_{ref}, with the average wellstream gradient, $\bar{\gamma}_{wb}$).
3. J_w = sum over all PI's of the open completions ($k \in \psi_w$).

Fig. 6.17 plots both the tubing-performance relationship and the IPR. Note that the slope of the IPR is the negative reciprocal of J_w. Because the well must obey both the tubing-performance relationship and the IPR, the well must operate at the intersection of these two curves.

Two operating points exist in Fig. 6.17. Further examination of these two points is required before the production rate and flowing pressure of the well can be established. Once established, these well conditions can be used to prorate production to the various simulation layers with the techniques discussed in Vertical, Multilayer Well Models in Sec. 6.2.2.

Our discussion begins with the operating point for the higher value of $-q_{sc}$ in Fig. 6.17 marked "stable operating point." Consider a slight fluctuation in the production rate:

$$q'_{sc} = q_{sc} + \varepsilon. \quad \text{(6.163)}$$

If ε is positive, the tubing exerts additional backpressure against the sandface (that is, for a positive ε, the value of p_{wf} described by the

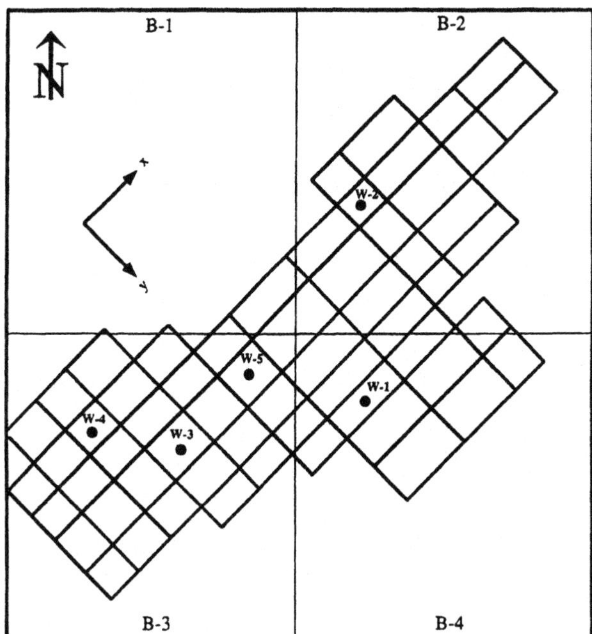

Fig. 6.18—Well locations and wellblocks in A-1 reservoir.

tubing-performance curve is greater than the value of p_{wf} described by the inflow-performance curve). Consequently, the production rate drifts back to q_{sc}. On the other hand, if ε is negative, the well will be slightly underbalanced and the production rate will again drift back to q_{sc}. Thus, the rate at the higher value of $-q_{sc}$ is referred to as a stable operating point. The arrows in Fig. 6.17 refer to the direction in which production will drift with any fluctuation in q_{sc}.

Now investigate the operating point for the lower value of $-q_{sc}$ marked "unstable operating point" in Fig. 6.17. A positive fluctuation in $-q_{sc}$ creates an underbalanced-pressure situation causing $-q_{sc}$ to increase (eventually terminating at the stable operating point). On the other hand, if ε is negative, the tubing exerts a greater backpressure and further chokes back the well. Eventually, the well loads up and ceases to flow.

Therefore, there can be two mathematically feasible operating points for a given tubing/reservoir configuration. Because all wells, in practice, exhibit fluctuations in production, physical considerations dictate that the wells produce at the stable operating point. The algorithm for converting a specified surface pressure p_{th}, to a sandface pressure, p_{wf}, and well rate, q_{sc}, can be summarized as follows.

1. Assume values of q_{osc}, q_{wsc}, and q_{gsc}. These are usually chosen to be the values at the old time level, t_n.

2. Calculate the total well productivity, J_w, as

$$J_w = \sum_k J_{w_k}, \qquad (6.158)$$

where $k \in \psi_w$.

3. Calculate the wellblock pressures corrected to the datum depth of the reference completion, H_{ref},

$$\hat{p}_k = p_k + \bar{\gamma}_{wb}\left(H_k - H_{ref}\right), \qquad (6.159)$$

where $k \in \psi_w$,

$$\bar{\gamma}_{wb} = \gamma_c g \frac{\rho_{osc} q_{osc} + \rho_{wsc} q_{wsc} + \rho_{gsc} q_{gsc}/\alpha_c}{B_o q_{osc} + B_w q_{wsc} + B_g q_{fgsc}}, \qquad (6.101b)$$

and $q_{fgsc} = q_{gsc} - R_s q_{osc}$. (6.164)

WELL NAME	WELLBLOCK	
	Location	Dimensions
• W-1	(7,7)	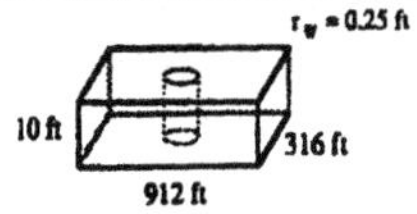 r_w = 0.25 ft; 10 ft; 316 ft; 912 ft
• W-2	(9,3)	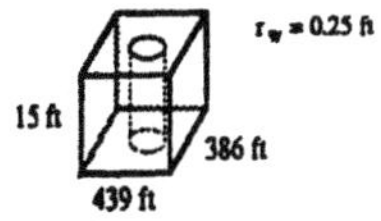 r_w = 0.25 ft; 15 ft; 386 ft; 439 ft
• W-3	(4,4)	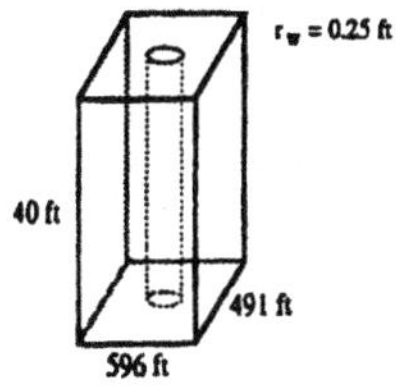 r_w = 0.25 ft; 40 ft; 491 ft; 596 ft
• W-4	(3,2)	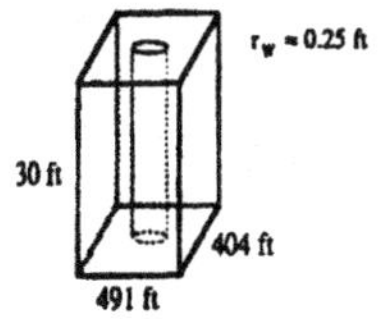 r_w = 0.25 ft; 30 ft; 404 ft; 491 ft
• W-5	(6,4)	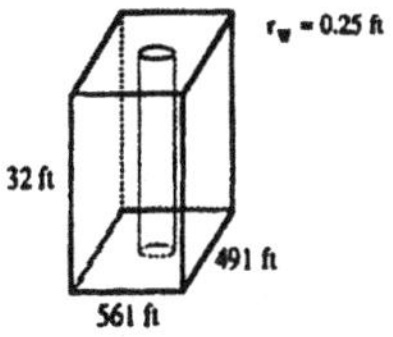 r_w = 0.25 ft; 32 ft; 491 ft; 561 ft

Fig. 6.19—Wellblock configurations for the five wells of the A-1 reservoir (note that vertical scale is magnified).

4. Calculate the PI-weighted average value of $\hat{p}_k$.

$$\bar{p} = \frac{\sum_k J_{w_k} \hat{p}_k}{J_w}, \qquad (6.161)$$

where $k \in \psi_w$.

5. Calculate the watercut, f_w, and R_{gL} at sandface conditions, from the assumed values of q_{osc}, q_{wsc}, and q_{gsc}.

$$f_w = \frac{B_w q_{wsc}}{B_o q_{osc} + B_w q_{wsc}} \qquad (6.165)$$

$$R_{gL} = \frac{B_g\left(q_{gsc} - R_s q_{osc}\right)}{B_o q_{osc} + B_w q_{wsc}}. \qquad (6.166)$$

6. Using the specified surface pressure, p_{th}, and the calculated values of f_w and R_{gL}, select the appropriate tubing-performance curve from the tables that were read for the well. (See Fig. 6.16.)

7. Estimate the intersection(s) of the tubing-performance curve (Step 6) and the IPR defined by $\bar{p}$ and J_w. Define p_{wf} and $-q_{sc}$ from the stable operating point (the intersection point with the highest value of $-q_{sc}$) in Fig. 6.17.

8. Use the techniques described in Vertical Multilayer Well Models in Sec. 6.2.2 to prorate q_{sc} to the individual wellblocks ($k \in \psi_w$).

9. Check the resulting values of q_{osc}, q_{wsc}, and q_{gsc}. If they are sufficiently close to the starting values, the solution has converged. Otherwise, update q_{osc}, q_{wsc}, and q_{gsc} and continue with Step 2.

If a sandface pressure or rate is specified, this procedure can be reversed to calculate the resulting surface pressure. Finally, a similar procedure can be used for injection wells.

TABLE 6.8—WELLBLOCK PROPERTIES AND PI VALUES

Well	Wellblock	Δx (ft)	Δy (ft)	h (ft)	k_x (darcies)	k_y (darcies)	k (darcies)	r_{eq} (ft)	*J_w (STB/D-psi)
W-1	(7,7)	912	316	10	0.280	0.224	0.250	129.3	2.833
W-2	(9,3)	439	386	15	0.270	0.216	0.242	81.4	4.438
W-3	(4,4)	596	491	40	0.297	0.238	0.266	107.1	12.432
W-4	(3,2)	491	404	30	0.280	0.224	0.250	88.2	9.054
W-5	(6,4)	561	491	32	0.280	0.224	0.250	103.8	9.396

*J_w values are calculated for $\mu=1$ cp, $B=1$ RB/STB, $s=0$, and $F=0$ with Peaceman's[5] approach.

6.6 Chapter Project

Fig. 6.18 shows five wells completed in A-1 reservoir. The grid system is designed so that not more than one well is in a gridblock and wells occupy approximately central positions in their respective blocks. Furthermore, specific attention is given to ensure that no wellblocks are next to an existing wellblock.

Fig. 6.19 provides the dimensions of the five wellblocks of A-1 reservoir. Note that all wells are assumed to be open completions and to penetrate the formation fully. In other words, the entire formation thickness of a wellblock is exposed to the well.

Table 6.8 gives a detailed description of the wellblock properties and the PI's of the wells located in A-1 reservoir.

Exercises

6.1 Compare the flow rates generated by the model of van Poollen *et al.*[2] and Peaceman's[5] model for the following data: $\Delta x=\Delta y=600$ ft; $h=40$ ft; $k_x=k_y=100$ md; $p_{wf}=350$ psia; $p_0=\bar{p}=1{,}600$ psia; $\mu=2$ cp; $B=1.1$ RB/STB; $s=0$; $r_w=0.25$ ft.

6.2 Repeat Exercise 1 for $\Delta x=\Delta y=200, 400, 800, 1{,}000$, and $1{,}200$ ft, and state your observations.

6.3 Compare and contrast the equivalent wellblock radii calculated with Eqs. 6.30 and 6.35 for different aspect ratios of $\Delta y/\Delta x$.

6.4 Calculate the equivalent wellblock radius r_{eq} with the Abou-Kassem and Aziz[6] model for a well in a corner block in a block-centered grid as shown in **Fig. 6.20**.

6.5 Calculate the equivalent wellblock radius r_{eq} with the Abou-Kassem and Aziz[6] model for a well in a corner block in a point-distributed grid as shown in **Fig. 6.21**.

6.6 Consider the multiblock well completion shown in **Fig. 6.22**. At the middle of the top layer, flowing sandface pressure is specified as 1,643 psia.

1. Assuming incompressible fluid behavior, calculate the flowing sandface pressures at the midpoints of Layers 2 through 4 (use a fluid density of 53 lbm/ft^3).

2. For the flowing sandface pressures calculated above, a numerical simulator calculates the wellblock pressures for Wellblocks 1 through 4 as 2,400, 2,443, 2,479, and 2,503 psia, respectively. First calculate the PI for each wellblock, then calculate the total flow rate out of the well. Use Peaceman's[5] equivalent-wellblock-radius concept. Assume that $\mu=1.3$ cp, $B=1.00$ RB/STB, $s_k=0$ for all wellblocks, and $r_w=0.27$ ft.

6.7 Investigate the effects of well length, L, and degree of penetration, L/d, on Eq. 6.123.

6.8 What are the effects of well location and drainage volume on the productivity of a horizontal wellbore? Use the Babu and Odeh[9] model in your investigation.

6.9 Compare and contrast the PI's of Eqs. 6.121 and 6.123 for a given anisotropic porous medium. Under what conditions do these two equations generate similar values, and when do they deviate? Note that, to make a meaningful comparison, you must write both equations for the same orientation of the horizontal well. Furthermore, assume that the horizontal well fully penetrates the wellblock (set $s=0$ for both equations).

6.10 Consider single-phase, incompressible fluid flow taking place in two identical one-dimensional (1D), homogeneous reservoirs shown in **Fig. 6.23**. As indicated in the figure, the boundary conditions imposed on both systems are identical. The only difference is the values of skin encountered at the wells. How would you compare the expected flow rates from these two wells? Explain.

6.11 Consider the body-centered grid representation of a 1D reservoir as shown in **Fig. 6.24**. The reservoir has homogeneous property distribution and is 100% saturated with water (assume zero compressibility). Gridblocks 1 and 4 are kept at 3,500 and 3,000 psia, respectively, by strong edgewater drives. The well in Gridblock 2 (with $r_w=0.5$ ft) is produced at a flowing sandface pressure of $p_{wf}=2{,}000$

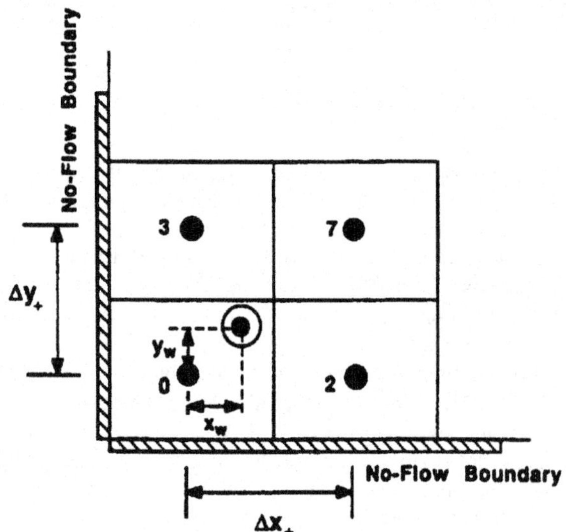

Fig. 6.20—Well in a corner block in a block-centered grid.

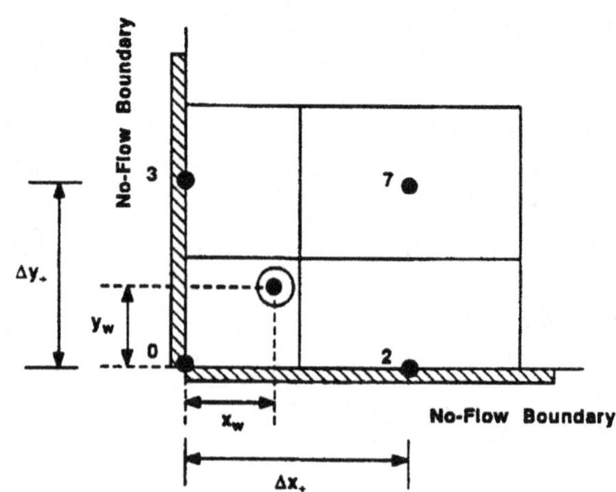

Fig. 6.21—Well in a corner block in a point-distributed grid.

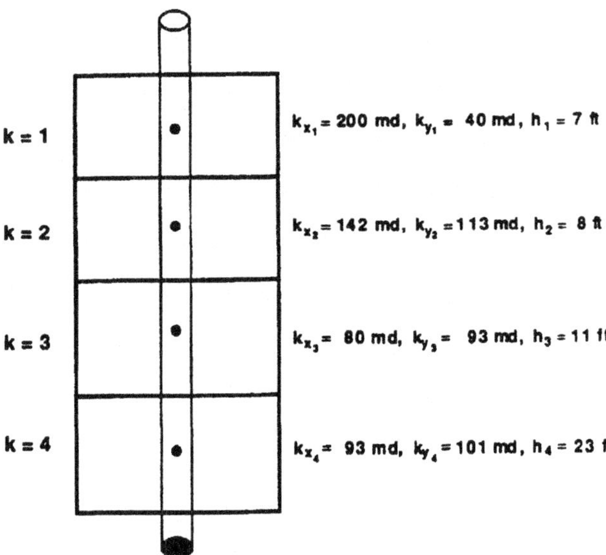

Fig. 6.22—Multiblock well completion of Exercise 6.6.

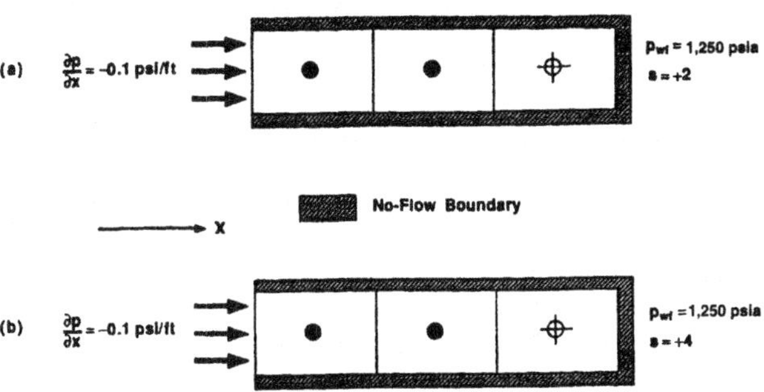

Fig. 6.23—One-dimensional reservoirs of Exercise 6.10.

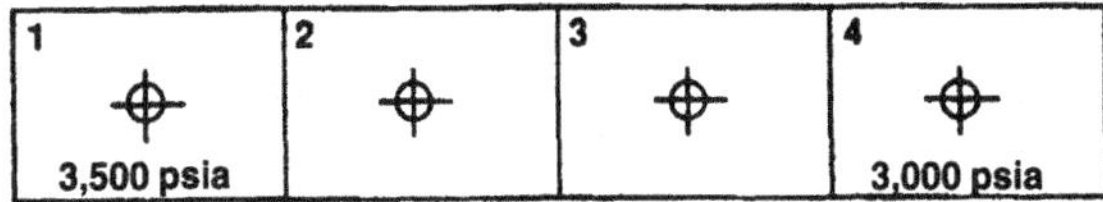

Fig. 6.24—One-dimensional reservoir of Exercise 6.11.

psia. Calculate the pressure distribution in the reservoir and the production rate from the well. Also consider the gridblock properties $h=100$ ft; $\Delta x=800$ ft; $A_x=20{,}000$ ft^2; $k_x=36$ md; $\phi=17\%$; $s=-2.0$; and fluid properties $c=0$ psi^{-1}; $B=1.0$ RB/STB; and $\mu=1.0$ cp.

6.12 Investigate the change in PI of a horizontal well as a function of the formation thickness. Use Babu and Odeh's[9] model in your analysis.

Nomenclature

a = constant
a_j = distance from well to its jth image, L, ft [m]
A = area defined by Eq. 6.125, L^2, ft^2 [m^2]
b = exponent in Eq. 6.86, $\left(b = 1/\sum_i T_i\right)$, dimensionless
B = FVF, L^3/L^3, reservoir volume/volume at standard conditions
B_g = gas FVF, L^3/L^3, RB/scf [m^3/std m^3]
B_l = FVF of Phase l, L^3/L^3, reservoir volume/volume at standard conditions
B_o = oil FVF, L^3/L^3, RB/STB [m^3/std m^3]
B_w = water FVF, L^3/L^3, RB/B [m^3/std m^3]
c = Δx = constant
c_l = compressiblity of Phase l, Lt^2/m, psi^{-1} [kPa^{-1}]
C_H = function defined by Eq. 6.126
d = Δy = constant
D = inner diameter of tubing, L, ft [m]
f = fraction of well flow associated with wellblock in Eq. 6.86, dimensionless
f_m = Moody's friction factor (Eq. 6.151)
f_w = water cut at sandface conditions, dimensionless
F = specific function defined in Table 6.5
g = acceleration of gravity, L/t^2, 32.174 ft/sec^2 [9.8066352 m/s^2]
g_c = units conversion factor in Newton's law
G_w = well geometric factor
h = thickness, L, ft [m]
$h_{i,j}$ = thickness of Gridblock (i,j), L, ft [m]
h_k = thickness of Wellblock k, L, ft [m]
H_k = depth to Wellblock k from datum, L, ft [m]
H_{ref} = depth of topmost completion, L, ft [m]
J_w = well PI or injectivity index, L^{4}t/m, STB/(D-psi) [std m^3/(d·kPa)]
J_{w_k} = well productivity assigned to Wellblock k in well
k = permeability, L^2, darcy [μm^2]
k_H = horizontal permeability, L^2, darcy [μm^2]
k_{H_k} = horizontal permeability of Wellblock k, L^2, darcy [μm^2]
k_{rl} = relative permeability to Phase l, dimensionless
k_x = permeability in the direction of the x axis, L^2, darcy [μm^2]
k_y = permeability in the direction of the y axis, L^2, darcy [μm^2]
k_z = permeability in the direction of the z axis, L^2, darcy [μm^2]
$k_{x_{i,j,k}}$ = x-direction permeability for Gridblock (i,j,k), L^2, darcy [μm^2]
$k_{y_{i,j,k}}$ = y-direction permeability for Gridblock (i,j,k), L^2, darcy [μm^2]
$k_{z_{i,j,k}}$ = z-direction permeability for Gridblock (i,j,k), L^2, darcy [μm^2]
$k_{\theta_{i,j,k}}$ = θ-direction permeability for Gridblock (i,j,k), L^2, darcy [μm^2]
l = length segment of tubing, L, ft [m]
Δl = length interval, L, ft [m]
L = well length, L, ft [m]
p = pressure, m/Lt^2, psia [kPa]
$\overline{p}$ = average reservoir pressure, m/Lt^2, psia [kPa]
Δp = pressure difference, m/Lt^2, psi [kPa]
Δp_D = dimensionless well pressure drop defined by Eq. 6.12, dimensionless
p_e = external pressure, m/Lt^2, psia [kPa]
p_i = initial pressure, m/Lt^2, psia [kPa]
$p_{i,j,k}$ = pressure for Gridblock (i,j,k), m/Lt^2, psia [kPa]
p_k = pressure for Wellblock k, m/Lt^2, psia [kPa]
$\hat{p}_k$ = datum corrected pressure of p_k at the depth of the topmost formation, m/Lt^2, psia [kPa]
p_{o_k} = pressure for Wellblock k, m/Lt^2, psia [kPa]
p_{sep} = separator pressure, m/Lt^2, psia [kPa]
p_{th} = surface pressure, m/Lt^2, psia [kPa]
p_{wf} = flowing well bottomhole pressure, m/Lt^2, psia [kPa]
p_{wf_k} = flowing well bottomhole pressure for Wellblock k, m/Lt^2, psia [kPa]
$p_{wf_{nk}}$ = flowing well bottomhole pressure for the bottommost wellblock, m/Lt^2, psia [kPa]
$p_{wf_{ref}}$ = flowing well pressure at reference elevation, m/Lt^2, psia [kPa]

$p_{wf_{sp}}$ = specified flowing bottomhole pressure, m/Lt^2, psia [kPa]
P_{xyz} = function defined by Eq. 6.131
P'_{xy} = function defined by Eq. 6.132
P_{xy} = function defined by Eq. 6.135
P_y = function defined by Eq. 6.134
q = production rate or flow rate, L^3/t, B/D [m^3/d]
q_D = dimensionless flow rate defined by Eq. 6.19
q_{fgsc} = free gas production rate at standard conditions, L^3/t, scf/D [std m^3/d]
q_{gsc} = gas production rate at standard conditions, L^3/t, scf/D [std m^3/d]
q_{osc} = oil production rate at standard conditions, L^3/t, STB/D [std m^3/d]
q_{sc} = production rate at standard conditions, L^3/t, STB/D [std m^3/d]
q'_{sc} = perturbed production rate at standard conditions, L^3/t, STB/D [std m^3/d]
$q_{sc_{i,j}}$ = Wellblock (i,j) flow rate at standard conditions, L^3/t, STB/D [std m^3/d]
q_{sc_k} = production rate from Wellblock k, L^3/t, STB/D [std m^3/d]
q_{sp} = specified production rate
q_{spsc} = specified well flow rate at standard conditions, L^3/t, STB/D [std m^3/d]
q_{wsc} = water flow rate at standard conditions, L^3/t, B/D [std m^3/d]
r = distance in radial direction in cylindrical coordinate system, L, ft [m]
r^{uv} = radius defined by Eq. 6.73
r_D = drainage radius, L, ft [m]
r_e = radius of external boundary, L, ft [m]
r_{eq} = equivalent wellblock radius, L, ft [m]
$r_{eq_{i,j}}$ = equivalent wellblock radius for Wellblock (i,j), L, ft [m]
$r^{uv}_{eq_{i,j}}$ = equivalent wellblock radius of Gridblock (i,j,k) in the u-v plane, L, ft [m]
r_{eq_k} = equivalent wellblock radius for Wellblock k, L, ft [m]
$r_{i,j}$ = distance between neighboring Gridblock i and Well j, L, ft [m]
r_w = well radius, L, ft [m]
$\bar{r}_w$ = average well radius, L, ft [m]
R_{gL} = GLR at sandface conditions, L^3/L^3, RB/RB, [m^3/m^3]
s = skin factor, dimensionless
s_k = skin factor for Wellblock k, dimensionless
s_m = mechanical skin factor, dimensionless
s_p = partial penetration skin factor, dimensionless
S_g = gas saturation, fraction
S_{g_k} = gas saturation for Wellblock k, fraction
S_w = water saturation, fraction
S_{w_k} = water saturation for Wellblock k, fraction
t = time, t, days
t_D = dimensionless time defined by Eq. 6.20
t_{pss} = time to reach pseudosteady-state conditions, t, days
T_i = interface transmissibility for flow between Gridblock i and wellblock (defined in Table 6.2), dimensionless
$T_{l_{m\pm ½}}$ = transmissibilty of coupling cell defined by Eq. 6.148
u = u coordinate in the u-v plane, L, ft [m]
Δu = corresponding dimension of Δx in the u-v plane, L, ft [m]
v = v coordinate in the u-v plane, L, ft [m]
Δv = corresponding dimension of Δy in the u-v plane, L, ft [m]
x = distance in the x direction in the Cartesian coordinate system, L, ft [m]
x_w = well coordinate in the x direction with center at wellblock gridpoint, L, ft [m]
Δx = difference along the x direction, L, ft [m]
$\Delta x_{i,j}$ = x-direction length of Gridblock (i,j), L, ft [m]
X_0 = x coordinate of the center of the horizontal well in the x-z plane (Fig. 6.11), L, ft [m]
y = distance in the y direction in the Cartesian coordinate system, L, ft [m]
y_{mid} = midpoint coordinate of well in y direction, L, ft, [m]
y_w = well coordinate in the y direction with center at wellblock gridpoint, L, ft [m]
Δy = difference along the y direction, L, ft [m]
$\Delta y_{i,j}$ = y-direction length of Gridblock (i,j), L, ft [m]
z = distance in the z direction in the Cartesian coordinate system, L, ft [m]
Δz = difference along the z direction, L, ft [m]
Δz_k = thickness of a block for the kth layer, L, ft [m]
Z_0 = z coordinate of the center of the horizontal well in the x-z plane (Fig. 6.11), L, ft [m]
α = aspect ratio $(\alpha = \Delta y/\Delta x)$, dimensionless
α_c = volume conversion factor whose numerical value is given in Table 4.1
$\alpha_{i,j}$ = aspect ratio for the lateral dimensions of Wellblock (i,j), dimensionless
β_c = transmissibility conversion factor whose numerical value is given in Table 4.1
γ = fluid gravity defined by Eq. 2.2, m/L^{2}t^2, psi/ft [kPa/m]
γ = Euler's constant, $\gamma = 0.5772157$
γ_c = gravity conversion factor whose numerical value is given in Table 4.1
$\bar{\gamma}_{wb}$ = multiphase hydrostatic wellbore pressure gradient (Eq. 6.101), m/L^{2}t^2, psi/ft [kPa/m]
ε = perturbance
$\Delta\theta_j$ = θ direction block dimension of cylindrical element, L, ft [m]
μ = viscosity, m/Lt, cp [Pa·s]
μ_k = viscosity in Wellblock k, m/Lt, cp[Pa·s]
ρ = density, m/L^3, lbm/ft^3 [kg/m^3]
ρ_{gsc} = gas-phase density at standard conditions, m/L^3, lbm/ft^3 [kg/m^3]
ρ_{lsc} = density of Phase l at standard conditions, m/L^3, lbm/ft^3 [kg/m^3]
ρ_{osc} = oil-phase density at standard conditions, m/L^3, lbm/ft^3 [kg/m^3]
ρ_{wsc} = water-phase density at standard conditions, m/L^3, lbm/ft^3 [kg/m^3]
ϕ = porosity, fraction
ψ_w = set of blocks penetrated by a well

Superscripts

n = old timestep
$n+1$ = current (or new) timestep
(v) = old iteration
$(v+1)$ = current iteration
$^\circ$ = reference
$'$ = perturbed

Subscripts

g = gas phase
k = index for block penetrated by well $(k \in \psi_w)$
l = index for oil, water, or gas
m = index for block penetrated by well $(m \in \psi_w)$
o = oil phase
w = water phase

References

1. Odeh, A.S.: "An Overview of Mathematical Modeling of the Behavior of Hydrocarbon Reservoirs," *Soc. of Industrial and Applied Mathematics Review* (July 1982) **24**, No. 3, 263.
2. van Poollen, H.K., Breitenback, E.A., and Thurnau, D.H.: "Treatment of Individual Wells and Grids in Reservoir Modeling," *SPEJ* (December 1968) 341.
3. Matthews, C.S. and Russell, D.G.: *Pressure Buildup and Flow Tests in Wells*, Monograph Series, SPE, Richardson, TX (1967) **1.**
4. *The Theory and Practice of the Testing of Gas Wells*, third edition, manual, Energy Resources Conservation Board, Calgary (1975).
5. Peaceman, D.W.: "Interpretation of Wellblock Pressures in Numerical Reservoir Simulation With Nonsquare Gridblocks and Anisotropic Permeability," *SPEJ* (June 1983) 531.
6. Abou-Kassem, J.H. and Aziz, K: "Analytical Well Models for Reservoir Simulation," *SPEJ* (August 1985) 573.
7. Nolen, J.S. and Berry, D.W.: "Tests of the Stability and Time-Step Sensitivity of Semi-Implicit Reservoir Simulation Techniques," *SPEJ* (June 1972) 253; *Trans.*, AIME, **253.**
8. Aziz, K. and Settari, A.: *Petroleum Reservoir Simulation*, Applied Science Publishers Ltd., London (1979)104-105.
9. Babu, D.K. and Odeh, A.S.: "Productivity of a Horizontal Well," *SPERE* (November 1989) 417.
10. Peaceman, D.W.: "Representation of a Horizontal Well in Numerical Reservoir Simulation," *SPE Advanced Technology Series* (April 1993) 7.
11. Nghiem, L., Collins, D.A., and Sharma, R.: "Seventh SPE Comparative Solution Project: Modeling of Horizontal Wells in Reservoir Simulation," paper SPE 21221 presented at the 1991 SPE Symposium on Reservoir Simulation, Anaheim, California, 17–20 February.
12. Pedrosa, O.A. Jr. and Aziz, K.: "Use of a Hybrid Grid in Reservoir Simulation," *SPERE* (November 1986) 611; *Trans.*, AIME (1986) **281.**
13. Brown, K.E. *et al*: *The Technology of Artificial Lift Methods*, PennWell Books, Tulsa, Oklahoma (1977) 1–2.
14. Vogel, J.V.: "Inflow Performance Relationships for Solution-Gas-Drive Wells," *JPT* (January 1968) 83; *Trans.*, AIME (1968) **243.**

SI Metric Conversion Factors

bbl	× 1.589 873	E − 01 = m^3
cp	× 1.0*	E − 03 = Pa · s
ft	× 3.048*	E − 01 = m
ft^2	× 9.290 304*	E − 02 = m^2
lbm	× 4.535 924	E − 01 = kg
md	× 9.869 233	E − 04 = μm^2
psi	× 6.894 757	E + 00 = kPa
psi^{-1}	× 1.450 377	E − 01 = kPa^{-1}

*Conversion factor is exact.

Chapter 7
Solution of Linear Difference Equations

7.1 Introduction

The solution of linear systems of equations is one of the most central-processing-unit-intensive steps in reservoir simulation. All the mathematical techniques presented in the previous chapters result in a set of algebraic equations that may be linear or nonlinear. The linear or nonlinear character of the system of equations is determined by the nature of the problem [linear or nonlinear partial-differential equations (PDE's)] and the nature of the finite-difference approximation (explicit or implicit treatment of the coefficients). Even when a nonlinear system of equations is obtained from the finite-difference approximations, these equations can be converted to linear form by use of the linearization techniques discussed in Chap. 8. **Fig. 7.1** shows the algebraic-solution step in the reservoir-simulation process.

This chapter deals with the solution of linear systems of equations of the form

$$[\mathbf{A}]\vec{x} = \vec{d}, \quad \ldots\ldots (7.1)$$

where $[\mathbf{A}]$ = square coefficient matrix, $\vec{d}$ = vectors of known values, and $\vec{x}$ = vector of unknown values. Numerous algorithms can be used to solve a given system of linear equations, each with distinct advantages and disadvantages. This chapter introduces several of these methods and identifies their inherent advantages and disadvantages. With few exceptions, most of the examples and algorithms in this chapter are based on the content of the preceding chapters.

7.2 Difference Equations in Matrix Form

Approximating the continuous differential equations that describe fluid flow in porous media by finite-differences yields linear systems of equations of the form

$$a_{11}x_1 + a_{12}x_2 + a_{13}x_3 + \ldots + a_{1n}x_n = d_1 \quad \ldots\ldots (7.2a)$$

$$a_{21}x_1 + a_{22}x_2 + a_{23}x_3 + \ldots + a_{2n}x_n = d_2 \quad \ldots\ldots (7.2b)$$

$$a_{31}x_1 + a_{32}x_2 + a_{33}x_3 + \ldots + a_{3n}x_n = d_3 \quad \ldots\ldots (7.2c)$$

through $a_{n1}x_1 + a_{n2}x_2 + a_{n3}x_3 + \ldots + a_{nn}x_n = d_n$.

$$\ldots\ldots (7.2d)$$

Therefore, we are concerned with a system of n equations relating n unknowns $(x_1, x_2, x_3, \ldots, x_n)$; $n \times n$ coefficients, a_{ij}; and n right-side members, d_i.

Before we describe the application of various algorithms to solve systems of equations, we show step by step how the finite-difference approximation of a PDE can be written in matrix form. First, we discuss one-dimensional (1D) reservoir applications, and, later, we consider two- and three-dimensional (2D and 3D) cases.

7.2.1 Difference Equations for 1D Flow Problems. ***Incompressible-Flow Equation.*** Consider the incompressible-fluid-flow equation, Eq. 4.56, as applied to a 1D horizontal reservoir $\left(\vec{\nabla}\Phi = \vec{\nabla}p\right)$.

$$\frac{\partial}{\partial x}\left(\beta_c A_x k_x \frac{\partial p}{\partial x}\right)\Delta x + \mu q_{sc} = 0. \quad \ldots\ldots (7.3)$$

Suppose we want to implement a finite-difference approximation to Eq. 7.3 over the discrete system in **Fig. 7.2**. Furthermore, for simplicity, assume that we are dealing with a homogeneous system where the permeability distribution, thickness, and width of the reservoir are uniform throughout. Because we are dealing with an incompressible system and a homogeneous reservoir with respect to every property, Eq. 7.3 can be rewritten as

$$\beta_c A_x k_x \frac{\partial p}{\partial x}\left(\frac{\partial p}{\partial x}\right)\Delta x + \mu q_{sc} = 0 \quad \ldots\ldots (7.4)$$

or $$\frac{\partial^2 p}{\partial x^2} + \frac{\mu q_{sc}}{\beta_c k_x V_b} = 0, \quad \ldots\ldots (7.5)$$

where $V_b = A_x \Delta x$.

Again, to simplify this discussion, assume that the imposed grid system consists of six uniformly spaced, block-centered gridblocks. Fig. 7.2 shows a well in Gridblock 5 producing at a rate of q_{sc}. At the extreme left of the system, the pressure of Gridblock 1 is kept constant and, at the extreme right of the system, the reservoir is completely sealed; that is, a no-flow boundary exists.

The central-difference approximation of Eq. 7.5 written for Gridblock i is

$$\frac{p_{i+1} - 2p_i + p_{i-1}}{(\Delta x)^2} + \left(\frac{\mu q_{sc}}{\beta_c k_x V_b}\right)_i = 0, \quad \ldots\ldots (7.6)$$

which can be written for the blocks where the pressure is unknown. Because we know the pressure in Gridblock 1, it is excluded from the set of unknowns. In addition, Gridblock 5 has two unknowns, the block pressure and the well sandface pressure. Writing the finite-difference approximation (Eq. 7.6) for Gridblocks $i = 2$ through 6 generates the following system of equations.

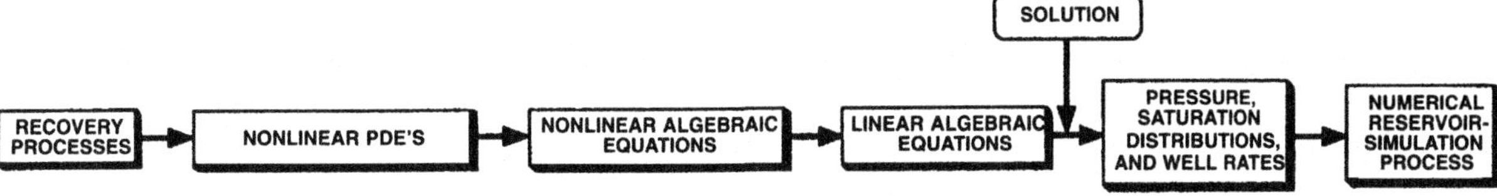

Fig. 7.1—Algebraic solution in the reservoir simulation process (redrawn from Ref. 1).

$$-2p_2 + p_3 = -p_1 \quad \text{.......... (7.7a)}$$

for $i=2$,

$$p_2 - 2p_3 + p_4 = 0 \quad \text{.......... (7.7b)}$$

for $i=3$,

$$p_3 - 2p_4 + p_5 = 0 \quad \text{.......... (7.7c)}$$

for $i=4$,

$$p_4 - 2p_5 + p_6 = -\frac{\mu q_{sc}(\Delta x)^2}{\beta_c k_x V_b} \quad \text{.......... (7.7d)}$$

for $i=5$,

and $p_5 - p_6 = 0$ .... (7.7e)

for $i=6$. Note that Eq. 7.7e implements the no-flow outer-boundary condition, and that Eq. 7.7d includes the inner-boundary condition (flow-rate specification), which is imposed on the system in the form of the sink term, q_{sc}. The linear system of equations can be written in matrix form as

$$\begin{bmatrix} -2 & 1 & 0 & 0 & 0 \\ 1 & -2 & 1 & 0 & 0 \\ 0 & 1 & -2 & 1 & 0 \\ 0 & 0 & 1 & -2 & 1 \\ 0 & 0 & 0 & 1 & -1 \end{bmatrix} \begin{bmatrix} p_2 \\ p_3 \\ p_4 \\ p_5 \\ p_6 \end{bmatrix} = \begin{bmatrix} -p_1 \\ 0 \\ 0 \\ -\dfrac{\mu q_{sc}(\Delta x)^2}{\beta_c k_x V_b} \\ 0 \end{bmatrix}. \quad \text{.......... (7.8)}$$

Eq. 7.8 illustrates that, when the finite-difference equations are written along a line, the resulting coefficient matrix always has a tridiagonal structure composed of a main diagonal, an upper codiagonal, and a lower codiagonal. Solving the system of linear equations represented by Eq. 7.8 yields the unknown block pressures for Gridlocks 2 through 6. After solving for block pressures, one of the well models in Chap. 6 can be used to obtain the flowing sandface pressure for the well located in Gridblock 5.

Slightly-Compressible-Flow Equation. If the physics of the problem dictates, we could also have started with the slightly-compressible-flow equation that describes a time-dependent problem. In this discussion, we assume that $B \approx B^{\circ}$; then the resulting PDE is

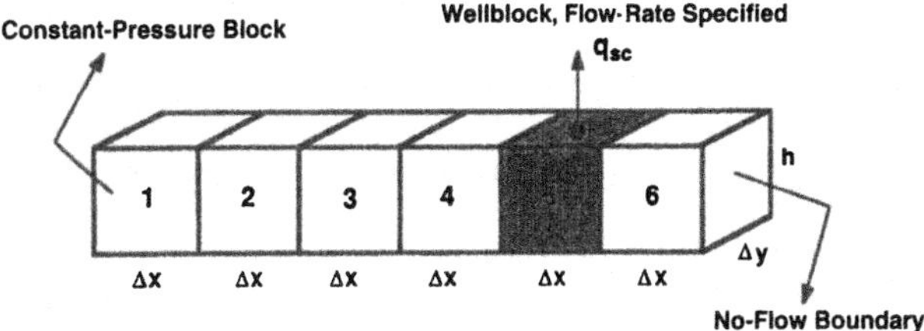

Fig. 7.2—One-dimensional discretization of a homogeneous reservoir.

$$\frac{\partial^2 p}{\partial x^2} + \frac{B^{\circ}_l \mu_l q_{lsc}}{\beta_c k_x V_b} = \frac{\phi \mu_l c_l}{\beta_c \alpha_c k_x}\frac{\partial p}{\partial t}, \quad \text{.......... (7.9)}$$

where $l=o$ or w. The finite-difference approximation to Eq. 7.9 written for Gridblock i with central-difference approximations in space and backward-difference approximation in time is

$$\frac{p_{i-1}^{n+1} - 2p_i^{n+1} + p_{i+1}^{n+1}}{(\Delta x)^2} + \left(\frac{B^{\circ}_l \mu_l q_{lsc}}{\beta_c k_x V_b}\right)_i = \left(\frac{\phi \mu_l c_l}{\beta_c \alpha_c k_x}\right)_i \left(\frac{p_i^{n+1} - p_i^n}{\Delta t}\right), \quad \text{.......... (7.10)}$$

where $l=o$ or w. In Eq. 7.10, the unknowns are the p terms at Time Level $n+1$. Collecting all the unknowns on the left side and the known terms on the right side of the equation yields

$$\frac{1}{(\Delta x)^2} p_{i-1}^{n+1} - \left[\frac{2}{(\Delta x)^2} + \left(\frac{\phi \mu_l c_l}{\beta_c \alpha_c k_x \Delta t}\right)_i\right] p_i^{n+1} + \frac{1}{(\Delta x)^2} p_{i+1}^{n+1} = -\left(\frac{B^{\circ}_l \mu_l q_{lsc}}{\beta_c k_x V_b}\right)_i - \left(\frac{\phi \mu_l c_l}{\beta_c \alpha_c k_x \Delta t}\right)_i p_i^n, \quad \text{.......... (7.11)}$$

where $l=o$ or w.

Again, writing Eq. 7.11 for every gridblock in the 1D reservoir yields a tridiagonal coefficient matrix. **Fig. 7.3** shows the resulting

$$\begin{bmatrix}
-\left[\frac{2}{(\Delta x)^2} + \frac{\phi\mu c}{\beta_c\alpha_c k_x\Delta t}\right] & \left[\frac{1}{(\Delta x)^2}\right] & 0 & 0 & 0 \\
\left[\frac{1}{(\Delta x)^2}\right] & -\left[\frac{2}{(\Delta x)^2} + \frac{\phi\mu c}{\beta_c\alpha_c k_x\Delta t}\right] & \left[\frac{1}{(\Delta x)^2}\right] & 0 & 0 \\
0 & \left[\frac{1}{(\Delta x)^2}\right] & -\left[\frac{2}{(\Delta x)^2} + \frac{\phi\mu c}{\beta_c\alpha_c k_x\Delta t}\right] & \left[\frac{1}{(\Delta x)^2}\right] & 0 \\
0 & 0 & \left[\frac{1}{(\Delta x)^2}\right] & -\left[\frac{2}{(\Delta x)^2} + \frac{\phi\mu c}{\beta_c\alpha_c k_x\Delta t}\right] & \left[\frac{1}{(\Delta x)^2}\right] \\
0 & 0 & 0 & \left[\frac{1}{(\Delta x)^2}\right] & -\left[\frac{1}{(\Delta x)^2} + \frac{\phi\mu c}{\beta_c\alpha_c k_x\Delta t}\right]
\end{bmatrix}
\begin{bmatrix} p_2^{n+1} \\ p_3^{n+1} \\ p_4^{n+1} \\ p_5^{n+1} \\ p_6^{n+1} \end{bmatrix}
=
\begin{bmatrix}
-\left[\frac{\phi\mu c}{\beta_c\alpha_c k_x\Delta t}\right] p_2^n - \left[\frac{1}{(\Delta x)^2}\right] p_1 \\
-\left[\frac{\phi\mu c}{\beta_c\alpha_c k_x\Delta t}\right] p_3^n \\
-\left[\frac{\phi\mu c}{\beta_c\alpha_c k_x\Delta t}\right] p_4^n \\
-\left[\frac{\phi\mu c}{\beta_c\alpha_c k_x\Delta t}\right] p_5^n - \left[\frac{q_{sc}\mu B^{\circ}}{\beta_c V_b k_x}\right] \\
-\left[\frac{\phi\mu c}{\beta_c\alpha_c k_x\Delta t}\right] p_6^n
\end{bmatrix}$$

Fig. 7.3—Linear system of equations resulting from the finite-difference approximation of Eq. 7.9, as applied to the 1D reservoir in Fig. 7.2.

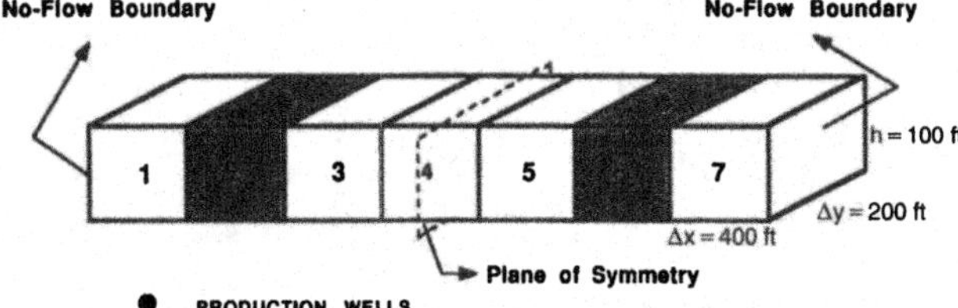

Fig. 7.4—Physical system studied in Example 7.1.

system of equations for this time-dependent problem (in matrix form) and also the tridiagonal structure of the coefficient matrix explicitly. In the case of a time-dependent problem, the resulting system of equations must be solved for multiple timesteps. For the slightly-compressible problem under consideration, the entries in the coefficient matrix do not change from one timestep to the next because μ_l and c_l are assumed to be constants and B_l was assumed to equal B_l°. This is because of the linear nature of the original PDE (Eq. 7.9). The only entries that change for each timestep computation are the p_i^n entries that appear in the right-side vector because the right-side vector is updated at the beginning of each timestep. As computations are conducted for the new timestep (Time Level $n+1$), the most recent pressure values are assigned to the old timestep (Time Level n) values. This observation is important because it implies that any computations done on the coefficient matrix to solve this particular system of equations need to be done only once at the beginning of the simulation. As we show later, this is why several of the solution procedures that use factorization techniques become attractive for the class of problems where the coefficient matrix is factored only once, at the beginning of the simulation. Improvements to Basic Direct-Solution Algorithms in Sec. 7.3.1 discusses this in detail.

Example 7.1. Consider the following 1D reservoir, where unsteady-state, single-phase oil flow is taking place.

This reservoir has the homogeneous property distributions of $\phi = 30\%$ and $k_x = 178$ md. **Fig. 7.4** shows the uniform dimensions of the finite-difference blocks. The boundary conditions at the extreme ends are specified as no-flow boundary conditions and the wells in Gridblocks 2 and 6 produce at a rate of 2,000 STB/D. Each gridblock has an initial specified pressure of 4,000 psia. Obtain the system of equations whose solution gives the pressure distribution in the reservoir at the end of 10 days. Use a timestep of 10 days to generate the system of equations, but do not attempt to solve the equations. Use the implicit, backward-difference scheme to generate the finite-difference equations. Also, note that $\mu_l = 1.0$ cp, $B_l = 1.0$ RB/STB, $c_l = 5\times10^{-6}$ psi^{-1}, and $B_l^\circ = 1.0$ RB/STB.

Solution. Eq. 4.72 gives the PDE that governs flow in this 1D system.

$$\frac{\partial}{\partial x}\left(\frac{\beta_c A_x k_x}{\mu_l B_l}\frac{\partial p}{\partial x}\right)\Delta x + q_{lsc} = \frac{V_b \phi c_l}{\alpha_c B_l^\circ}\frac{\partial p}{\partial t}, \qquad (7.12)$$

where $l = o$. This equation can be simplified (See Eq. 4.78) as

$$\frac{\partial^2 p}{\partial x^2} + \frac{B_l^\circ \mu_l q_{lsc}}{\beta_c k_x V_b} = \frac{\phi \mu_l c_l}{\beta_c \alpha_c k_x}\frac{\partial p}{\partial t}, \qquad (7.9)$$

where $l = o$, and can be expressed in the finite-difference form with the implicit backward-difference scheme (see Eq. 7.10) as

$$\frac{p_{i-1}^{n+1} - 2p_i^{n+1} + p_{i+1}^{n+1}}{(\Delta x)^2} + \left(\frac{B_l^\circ \mu_l q_{lsc}}{\beta_c k_x V_b}\right)_i = \left(\frac{\phi \mu_l c_l}{\beta_c \alpha_c k_x}\right)_i \left(\frac{p_i^{n+1} - p_i^n}{\Delta t}\right), \qquad (7.10)$$

where $l = o$. Multiplying Eq. 7.10 by $(\Delta x)^2$ yields

$$p_{i-1}^{n+1} - 2p_i^{n+1} + p_{i+1}^{n+1} + \left(\frac{B_l^\circ \mu_l q_{lsc}\Delta x}{\beta_c A_x k_x}\right)_i$$

$$= \left(\frac{\phi \mu_l c_l (\Delta x)^2}{\beta_c \alpha_c k_x \Delta t}\right)_i \left(p_i^{n+1} - p_i^n\right), \qquad (7.13)$$

where $l = o$.

$$\left(\frac{B_l^\circ \mu_l \Delta x}{\beta_c A_x k_x}\right)_i = \frac{(1)(1)(400)}{(1.127)(200\times100)(0.178)} = 0.100$$

and

$$\left(\frac{\phi \mu_l c_l (\Delta x)^2}{\beta_c \alpha_c k_x \Delta t}\right)_i = \frac{(0.30)(1)(5\times10^{-6})(400)^2}{(1.127)(5.615)(0.178)(10)} = 0.021$$

can be calculated for each block in the system. Therefore, the characteristic finite-difference equation for this problem takes the form

$$p_{i-1}^{n+1} - 2.021p_i^{n+1} + p_{i+1}^{n+1} = -0.1q_{lsc_i} - 0.021p_i^n. \qquad (7.14)$$

For the first timestep, the initial condition states that $p_i^n = 4,000$. Before writing the finite-difference equations for each unknown block, we recognize the symmetry present in the problem. The boundary conditions (inner and outer), initial conditions, reservoir geometry, and block properties are symmetric with respect to the center of Gridblock 4. In other words, $p_1 = p_7$, $p_2 = p_6$, and $p_3 = p_5$. Therefore, rather than solving for seven unknown pressures, we can solve for the pressure of the first four blocks, so it is only necessary to write the equations exclusively for Gridblocks 1 through 4. Note that $0.021\,p_i^n = 0.021(4,000) = 84$ and $q_{lsc}\left[(B_l^\circ\mu_l\Delta x)/(\beta_c A_x k_x)\right]_2 = (-2,000)(0.100) = -200$. The flow equations for the first timestep are

$$-1.021p_1^{n+1} + p_2^{n+1} = -84, \qquad (7.15a)$$

where $p_1^{n+1} = p_0^{n+1}$ for no flow boundary, for $i = 1$;

$$p_1^{n+1} - 2.021p_2^{n+1} + p_3^{n+1} = 116 \qquad (7.15b)$$

for $i = 2$;

$$p_2^{n+1} - 2.021p_3^{n+1} + p_4^{n+1} = -84 \qquad (7.15c)$$

for $i = 3$;

and

$$2p_3^{n+1} - 2.021p_4^{n+1} = -84, \qquad (7.15d)$$

where $p_5^{n+1} = p_3^{n+1}$ for symmetry, for $i = 4$.

When written in matrix form, these equations generate a tridiagonal coefficient matrix:

$$\begin{bmatrix} -1.021 & 1 & 0 & 0 \\ 1 & -2.021 & 1 & 0 \\ 0 & 1 & -2.021 & 1 \\ 0 & 0 & 2 & -2.021 \end{bmatrix}\begin{bmatrix} p_1^{n+1} \\ p_2^{n+1} \\ p_3^{n+1} \\ p_4^{n+1} \end{bmatrix} = \begin{bmatrix} -84 \\ 116 \\ -84 \\ -84 \end{bmatrix}.$$

To this point, we have dealt with the simplified case of homogeneous reservoir properties and constant fluid properties. In Sec. 5.4.1, we developed the following backward-difference approximation (Eq. 5.65) to the 1D, slightly compressible flow problem.

$$T_{lx_{i+1/2}}\left(p_{i+1}^{n+1} - p_i^{n+1}\right) - T_{lx_{i-1/2}}\left(p_i^{n+1} - p_{i-1}^{n+1}\right)$$

$$+ q_{lsc_i} = \left(\frac{V_b \phi c_l}{\alpha_c B_l^\circ \Delta t}\right)_i \left(p_i^{n+1} - p_i^n\right), \qquad (5.65)$$

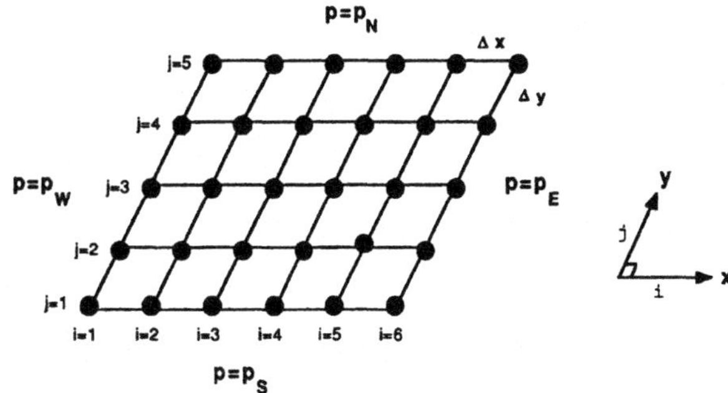

Fig. 7.5—Representation of a 2D reservoir with a mesh-centered grid.

where $l=o$ or w, which can be rearranged in the form

$$T_{lx_{i-1/2}}p_{i-1}^{n+1} - \left[T_{lx_{i-1/2}} + T_{lx_{i+1/2}} + \left(\frac{V_b\phi c_l}{\alpha_c B_l^\circ \Delta t}\right)_i\right]p_i^{n+1}$$

$$+ T_{lx_{i+1/2}}p_{i+1}^{n+1} = -\left(\frac{V_b\phi c_l}{\alpha_c B_l^\circ \Delta t}\right)_i p_i^n - q_{lsc_i}, \quad\text{(7.16a)}$$

where $l=o$ or w,

or $W_i p_{i-1}^{n+1} + C_i p_i^{n+1} + E_i p_{i+1}^{n+1} = Q_i$. .... (7.16b)

The coefficients in Eq. 7.16b are

$$W_i = T_{lx_{i-1/2}}, \quad\text{(7.17)}$$

$$C_i = -\left[T_{lx_{i-1/2}} + T_{lx_{i+1/2}} + \left(\frac{V_b\phi c_l}{\alpha_c B_l^\circ \Delta t}\right)_i\right], \quad\text{(7.18)}$$

$$E_i = T_{lx_{i+1/2}}, \quad\text{(7.19)}$$

and $$Q_i = -\left(\frac{V_b\phi c_l}{\alpha_c B_l^\circ \Delta t}\right)_i p_i^n - q_{lsc_i}. \quad\text{(7.20)}$$

Chap. 5 discussed the transmissibilities $T_{lx_{i+1/2}}$ and $T_{lx_{i-1/2}}$ (Eqs. 5.48 and 5.49, respectively).

Writing Eq. 7.16b for all the gridblocks in Fig. 7.4 yields

$$\begin{bmatrix} C_1 & E_1 & 0 & 0 & 0 & 0 & 0 \\ W_2 & C_2 & E_2 & 0 & 0 & 0 & 0 \\ 0 & W_3 & C_3 & E_3 & 0 & 0 & 0 \\ 0 & 0 & W_4 & C_4 & E_4 & 0 & 0 \\ 0 & 0 & 0 & W_5 & C_5 & E_5 & 0 \\ 0 & 0 & 0 & 0 & W_6 & C_6 & E_6 \\ 0 & 0 & 0 & 0 & 0 & W_7 & C_7 \end{bmatrix} \begin{bmatrix} p_1^{n+1} \\ p_2^{n+1} \\ p_3^{n+1} \\ p_4^{n+1} \\ p_5^{n+1} \\ p_6^{n+1} \\ p_7^{n+1} \end{bmatrix} = \begin{bmatrix} Q_1 \\ Q_2 \\ Q_3 \\ Q_4 \\ Q_5 \\ Q_6 \\ Q_7 \end{bmatrix}. \quad\text{(7.21)}$$

Sec. 7.2.2 discusses the naming convention for the coefficients W, C, and E.

7.2.2 Difference Equations for 2D Flow Problems. ***Incompressible-Flow Equation.*** The development of the finite-difference equations for 2D, horizontal reservoirs follows a process similar to that outlined in Sec. 7.2.1. Again, consider the 2D incompressible-flow equation, Eq. 4.56, or

$$\frac{\partial}{\partial x}\left(\beta_c A_x k_x \frac{\partial p}{\partial x}\right)\Delta x + \frac{\partial}{\partial y}\left(\beta_c A_y k_y \frac{\partial p}{\partial y}\right)\Delta y + \mu q_{sc} = 0. \quad\text{(7.22)}$$

Suppose we want to solve for the pressure distribution with Eq. 7.22 over the 2D reservoir surrounded by constant-pressure boundaries as **Fig. 7.5** shows. Again, for simplicity, set $\Delta y = \Delta x$ and let the reservoir have homogeneous and isotropic properties. Eq. 7.22 can be simplified to

$$\frac{\partial^2 p}{\partial x^2} + \frac{\partial^2 p}{\partial y^2} + \frac{\mu q_{sc}}{\beta_c V_b k} = 0, \quad\text{(7.23)}$$

where $k=k_x=k_y$ and $V_b = A_x\Delta x = A_y\Delta y$. Because there are no wells in the reservoir, the last term on the left side of Eq. 7.23 can be dropped, yielding

$$\frac{\partial^2 p}{\partial x^2} + \frac{\partial^2 p}{\partial y^2} = 0, \quad\text{(7.24)}$$

which is known as Laplace's equation in 2D rectangular coordinates. The finite-difference approximation of Eq. 7.24 is

$$\frac{p_{i-1,j} - 2p_{i,j} + p_{i+1,j}}{(\Delta x)^2} + \frac{p_{i,j-1} - 2p_{i,j} + p_{i,j+1}}{(\Delta y)^2} = 0 \quad\text{(7.25)}$$

or, more simply,

$$p_{i,j-1} + p_{i-1,j} - 4p_{i,j} + p_{i+1,j} + p_{i,j+1} = 0 \quad\text{(7.26)}$$

because $\Delta x = \Delta y$.

Now, the characteristic finite-difference equation can be written for each node of the grid ($i=2$ through 5, and $j=2$ through 4) for the interior 12 nodes in Fig. 7.5. The finite-difference equations for the nodes with unknown pressures are

$$-4p_{2,2} + p_{3,2} + p_{2,3} = -p_S - p_W \quad\text{(7.27a)}$$

for Node (2,2),

$$p_{2,2} - 4p_{3,2} + p_{4,2} + p_{3,3} = -p_S \quad\text{(7.27b)}$$

for Node (3,2),

$$p_{3,2} - 4p_{4,2} + p_{5,2} + p_{4,3} = -p_S \quad\text{(7.27c)}$$

for Node (4,2),

$$p_{4,2} - 4p_{5,2} + p_{5,3} = -p_S - p_E \quad\text{(7.27d)}$$

for Node (5,2),

$$p_{2,2} - 4p_{2,3} + p_{3,3} + p_{2,4} = -p_W \quad\text{(7.27e)}$$

for Node (2,3),

$$p_{3,2} + p_{2,3} - 4p_{3,3} + p_{4,3} + p_{3,4} = 0 \quad\text{(7.27f)}$$

for Node (3,3),

$$p_{4,2} + p_{3,3} - 4p_{4,3} + p_{5,3} + p_{4,4} = 0 \quad\text{(7.27g)}$$

for Node (4,3),

$$p_{5,2} + p_{4,3} - 4p_{5,3} + p_{5,4} = -p_E \quad\text{(7.27h)}$$

for Node (5,3),

$$p_{2,3} - 4p_{2,4} + p_{3,4} = -p_W - p_N \quad\text{(7.27i)}$$

for Node (2,4),

$$p_{3,3} + p_{2,4} - 4p_{3,4} + p_{4,4} = -p_N \quad\text{(7.27j)}$$

for Node (3,4),

$$p_{4,3} + p_{3,4} - 4p_{4,4} + p_{5,4} = -p_N \quad\text{(7.27k)}$$

for Node (4,4),

and $$p_{5,3} + p_{4,4} - 4p_{5,4} = -p_E - p_N \quad\text{(7.27l)}$$

for Node (5,4).

TABLE 7.1—MATRIX EQUATION REPRESENTING EQ. 7.27

$$\begin{bmatrix} -4 & 1 & 0 & 0 & 1 & 0 & 0 & 0 & 0 & 0 & 0 & 0 \\ 1 & -4 & 1 & 0 & 0 & 1 & 0 & 0 & 0 & 0 & 0 & 0 \\ 0 & 1 & -4 & 1 & 0 & 0 & 1 & 0 & 0 & 0 & 0 & 0 \\ 0 & 0 & 1 & -4 & 0 & 0 & 0 & 1 & 0 & 0 & 0 & 0 \\ 1 & 0 & 0 & 0 & -4 & 1 & 0 & 0 & 1 & 0 & 0 & 0 \\ 0 & 1 & 0 & 0 & 1 & -4 & 1 & 0 & 0 & 1 & 0 & 0 \\ 0 & 0 & 1 & 0 & 0 & 1 & -4 & 1 & 0 & 0 & 1 & 0 \\ 0 & 0 & 0 & 1 & 0 & 0 & 1 & -4 & 0 & 0 & 0 & 1 \\ 0 & 0 & 0 & 0 & 1 & 0 & 0 & 0 & -4 & 1 & 0 & 0 \\ 0 & 0 & 0 & 0 & 0 & 1 & 0 & 0 & 1 & -4 & 1 & 0 \\ 0 & 0 & 0 & 0 & 0 & 0 & 1 & 0 & 0 & 1 & -4 & 1 \\ 0 & 0 & 0 & 0 & 0 & 0 & 0 & 1 & 0 & 0 & 1 & -4 \end{bmatrix} \begin{bmatrix} p_{2,2} \\ p_{3,2} \\ p_{4,2} \\ p_{5,2} \\ p_{2,3} \\ p_{3,3} \\ p_{4,3} \\ p_{5,3} \\ p_{2,4} \\ p_{3,4} \\ p_{4,4} \\ p_{5,5} \end{bmatrix} = \begin{bmatrix} -p_S - p_W \\ -p_S \\ -p_S \\ -p_S - p_E \\ -p_W \\ 0 \\ 0 \\ -p_E \\ -p_W - p_N \\ -p_N \\ -p_N \\ -p_E - p_N \end{bmatrix}$$

Eq. 7.27 represents 12 linear equations in 12 unknowns; **Table 7.1** shows Eq. 7.27 expressed in matrix form. The system of equations has a coefficient matrix with a pentadiagonal structure.

Slightly-Compressible-Flow Equation. If the physics of the problem dictates time-dependent behavior, we can use the slightly-compressible-flow equation to describe fluid transport. Start with the 2D (horizontal) form of flow equation,

$$\frac{\partial}{\partial x}\left(\frac{\beta_c A_x k_x}{\mu_l B_l}\frac{\partial p}{\partial x}\right)\Delta x + \frac{\partial}{\partial y}\left(\frac{\beta_c A_y k_y}{\mu_l B_l}\frac{\partial p}{\partial y}\right)\Delta y$$

$$+ q_{lsc} = \frac{V_b \phi c_l}{\alpha_c B_l^\circ}\frac{\partial p}{\partial t}, \qquad (7.28)$$

where $l = o$ or w. The backward-difference approximation to Eq. 7.28 is

$$\mathrm{T}_{lx_{i+\frac{1}{2},j}}\left(p_{i+1,j}^{n+1} - p_{i,j}^{n+1}\right) - \mathrm{T}_{lx_{i-\frac{1}{2},j}}\left(p_{i,j}^{n+1} - p_{i-1,j}^{n+1}\right)$$

$$+ \mathrm{T}_{ly_{i,j+\frac{1}{2}}}\left(p_{i,j+1}^{n+1} - p_{i,j}^{n+1}\right) - \mathrm{T}_{ly_{i,j-\frac{1}{2}}}\left(p_{i,j}^{n+1} - p_{i,j-1}\right)$$

$$+ q_{lsc_{i,j}} = \left(\frac{V_b \phi c_l}{\alpha_c B_l^\circ \Delta t}\right)_{i,j}\left(p_{i,j}^{n+1} - p_{i,j}^{n}\right), \qquad (7.29a)$$

where $l = o$ or w,

$$\text{or } S_{i,j}p_{i,j-1}^{n+1} + W_{i,j}p_{i-1,j}^{n+1} + C_{i,j}p_{i,j}^{n+1}$$

$$+ E_{i,j}p_{i+1,j}^{n+1} + N_{i,j}p_{i,j+1}^{n+1} = Q_{i,j}, \qquad (7.29b)$$

where the coefficients in Eq. 7.29b are defined by

$$S_{i,j} = \mathrm{T}_{ly_{i,j-\frac{1}{2}}}, \qquad (7.30)$$

$$W_{i,j} = \mathrm{T}_{lx_{i-\frac{1}{2},j}}, \qquad (7.31)$$

$$C_{i,j} = -\left[\mathrm{T}_{ly_{i,j-\frac{1}{2}}} + \mathrm{T}_{lx_{i-\frac{1}{2},j}} + \mathrm{T}_{lx_{i+\frac{1}{2},j}}\right.$$

$$\left. + \mathrm{T}_{ly_{i,j+\frac{1}{2}}} + \left(\frac{V_b \phi c_l}{\alpha_c B_l^\circ \Delta t}\right)_{i,j}\right], \qquad (7.32)$$

$$E_{i,j} = \mathrm{T}_{lx_{i+\frac{1}{2},j}}, \qquad (7.33)$$

$$N_{i,j} = \mathrm{T}_{ly_{i,j+\frac{1}{2}}}, \qquad (7.34)$$

$$\text{and } Q_{i,j} = -\left(\frac{V_b \phi c_l}{\alpha_c B_l^\circ \Delta t}\right)_{i,j} p_{i,j}^{n} - q_{lsc_{i,j}}. \qquad (7.35)$$

Fig. 7.6 shows the matrix equation that results when Eq. 7.29b is written for each gridblock in the system.

We can now discuss the naming convention used for the coefficients in Eq. 7.16b and 7.29b. **Fig. 7.7** shows a typical gridblock in a 2D grid. For the orientation shown in this figure, the coefficients *S*, *W*, *E*, and *N* refer to the directions south, west, east, and north, respectively; the coefficient, *C*, refers to the grid cell itself (center). For 3D problems, the finite-difference approximation to the flow equation contains two additional coefficients: *A* and *B*, which refer to the directions above and below the gridblock, respectively. The remainder of this book uses the coefficients *E*, *N*, and *A* in conjunc-

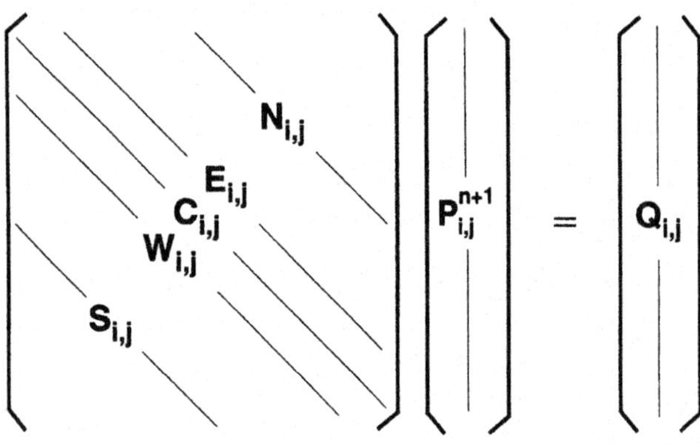

Fig. 7.6—Schematic representation of the matrix equation generated by the 2D, slightly-compressible-flow equation.

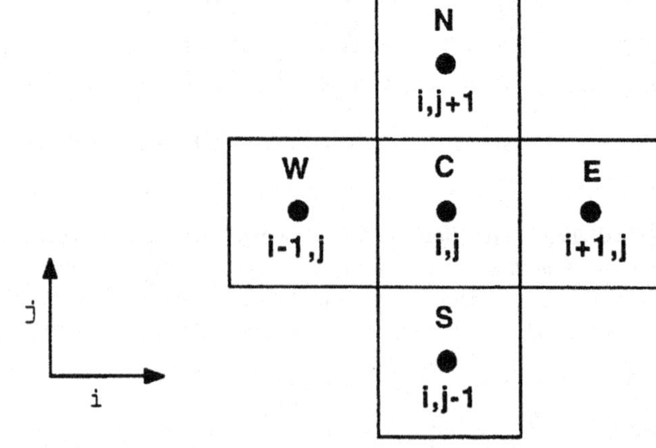

Fig. 7.7—Naming convention for the matrix coefficients, *S*, *W*, *C*, *E*, and *N*.

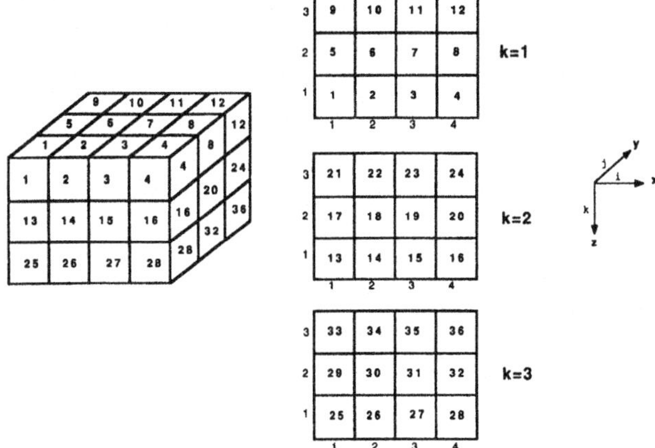

Fig. 7.8—Representation of a 3D reservoir by use of a block-centered grid and block ordering in three layers.

tion with the positive x, y, and z directions, respectively. Accordingly, the coefficients W, S, and B refer to the negative x, y, and z directions, respectively.

7.2.3 Difference Equations for 3D Flow Problems. For 3D reservoirs, the systematic procedures discussed in Secs. 7.2.1 and 7.2.2 are implemented in the same way. The presence of a third dimension results in a heptadiagonal coefficient matrix as demonstrated in the following discussion.

Incompressible-Flow Equation. Again, consider the incompressible flow equation but, this time, in three dimensions.

$$\frac{\partial}{\partial x}\left(\beta_c A_x k_x \frac{\partial p}{\partial x}\right)\Delta x + \frac{\partial}{\partial y}\left(\beta_c A_y k_y \frac{\partial p}{\partial y}\right)\Delta y + \frac{\partial}{\partial z}\left(\beta_c A_z k_z \frac{\partial p}{\partial z}\right)\Delta z + \mu q_{sc} = 0. \quad \text{.......... (4.56)}$$

For a homogeneous and isotropic porous medium, this equation can be simplified to Eq. 4.58.

$$\frac{\partial^2 p}{\partial x^2} + \frac{\partial^2 p}{\partial x^2} + \frac{\partial^2 p}{\partial y^2} + \frac{\mu q_{sc}}{(\beta_c k V_b)} = 0. \quad \text{.......... (4.58)}$$

Eq. 4.58 describes steady-state flow in a 3D reservoir (**Fig. 7.8**). The characteristic finite-difference approximation to Eq. 4.58 becomes

$$p_{i,j,k-1} + p_{i,j-1,k} + p_{i-1,j,k} - 6p_{i,j,k} + p_{i+1,j,k} + p_{i,j+1,k} + p_{i,j,k+1} = -\left(\frac{\mu q_{sc}}{\beta_c k \Delta x}\right)_{i,j,k}. \quad \text{.......... (7.36)}$$

Note that $(\Delta x)^2/V_b = 1/\Delta x$ (because $\Delta x = \Delta y = \Delta z$).

Writing Eq. 7.36 for every gridblock in the 36-block reservoir in Fig. 7.8 yields a 36×36 coefficient matrix with a heptadiagonal structure (**Fig. 7.9**).

Slightly-Compressible-Flow Equation. For slightly-compressible flow, start with the 3D form of the continuity equation

$$\frac{\partial}{\partial x}\left(\frac{\beta_c A_x k_x}{\mu_l B_l}\frac{\partial \Phi_l}{\partial x}\right)\Delta x + \frac{\partial}{\partial y}\left(\frac{\beta_c A_y k_y}{\mu_l B_l}\frac{\partial \Phi_l}{\partial y}\right)\Delta y + \frac{\partial}{\partial z}\left(\frac{\beta_c A_z k_z}{\mu_l B_l}\frac{\partial \Phi_l}{\partial z}\right)\Delta z + q_{lsc} = \frac{V_b \phi c_l}{\alpha_c B_l^\circ}\frac{\partial p}{\partial t}, \quad \text{.......... (7.37)}$$

where $l = o$ or w.

Eq. 7.37 includes the potential, Φ, in the formulation. Note that we also could have included the potential in the 1D and 2D problems for the case of dipping reservoirs. The potential gradient (see Eq. 2.15) is defined by

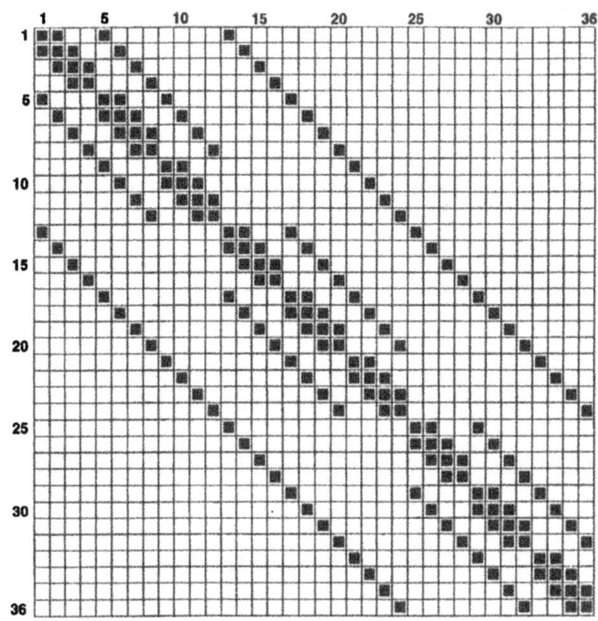

Fig. 7.9—Heptadiagonal coefficient matrix formed for a 3D reservoir whose blocks are numbered as in Fig. 7.8.

$$\vec{\nabla}\Phi_l = \vec{\nabla}p - \gamma_l \vec{\nabla}Z, \quad \text{.......... (7.38)}$$

where $l = o$ or w.

Substituting Eq. 7.38 into Eq. 7.37 and applying the backward-difference approximation result in

$$B_{i,j,k} p_{i,j,k-1}^{n+1} + S_{i,j,k} p_{i,j-1,k}^{n+1} + W_{i,j,k} p_{i-1,j,k}^{n+1} + C_{i,j,k} p_{i,j,k}^{n+1} + E_{i,j,k} p_{i+1,j,k}^{n+1} + N_{i,j,k} p_{i,j+1,k}^{n+1} + A_{i,j,k} p_{i,j,k+1}^{n+1} = Q_{i,j,k}, \quad \text{.......... (7.39)}$$

where $B_{i,j,k} = \mathrm{T}_{lz_{i,j,k-1/2}}$, ... (7.40)

$$S_{i,j,k} = \mathrm{T}_{ly_{i,j-1/2,k}}, \quad \text{.......... (7.41)}$$

$$W_{i,j,k} = \mathrm{T}_{lx_{i-1/2,j,k}}, \quad \text{.......... (7.42)}$$

$$C_{i,j,k} = -\left[\mathrm{T}_{lz_{i,j,k-1/2}} + \mathrm{T}_{ly_{i,j-1/2,k}} + \mathrm{T}_{lx_{i-1/2,j,k}} + \mathrm{T}_{lx_{i+1/2,j,k}} + \mathrm{T}_{ly_{i,j+1/2,k}} + \mathrm{T}_{lz_{i,j,k+1/2}} + \left(\frac{V_b \phi c_l}{\alpha_c B_l^\circ \Delta t}\right)_{i,j,k}\right], \quad \text{... (7.43)}$$

$$E_{i,j,k} = \mathrm{T}_{lx_{i+1/2,j,k}}, \quad \text{.......... (7.44)}$$

$$N_{i,j,k} = \mathrm{T}_{ly_{i,j+1/2,k}}, \quad \text{.......... (7.45)}$$

$$A_{i,j,k} = \mathrm{T}_{lz_{i,j,k+1/2}}, \quad \text{.......... (7.46)}$$

and $Q_{i,j,k} = -\left(\frac{V_b \phi c_l}{\alpha_c B_l^\circ \Delta t}\right)_{i,j,k} p_i^n - q_{lsc_{i,j,k}} + \mathrm{T}_{lz_{i,j,k-1/2}} \gamma_{l_{i,j,k-1/2}} \left(Z_{i,j,k-1} - Z_{i,j,k}\right)$

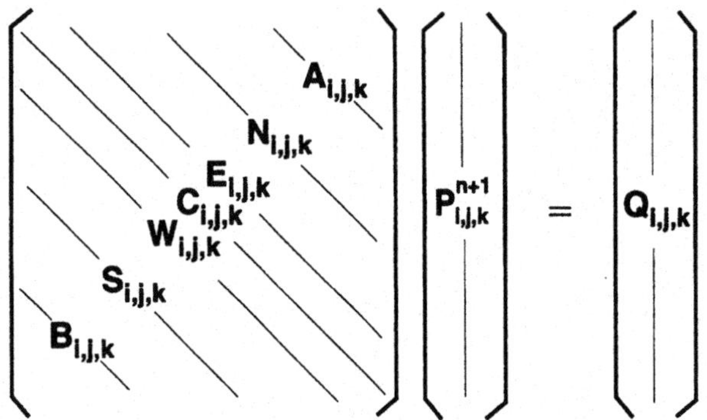

Fig. 7.10—Schematic representation of the matrix equation generated by the 3D, slightly-compressible-flow equation.

$$+ \, T_{ly_{i,j-\frac{1}{2},k}} \gamma_{l_{i,j-\frac{1}{2},k}} \left(Z_{i,j-1,k} - Z_{i,j,k} \right)$$

$$+ \, T_{lx_{i-\frac{1}{2},j,k}} \gamma_{l_{i-\frac{1}{2},j,k}} \left(Z_{i-1,j,k} - Z_{i,j,k} \right)$$

$$+ \, T_{lx_{i+\frac{1}{2},j,k}} \gamma_{l_{i+\frac{1}{2},j,k}} \left(Z_{i+1,j,k} - Z_{i,j,k} \right)$$

$$+ \, T_{ly_{i,j+\frac{1}{2},k}} \gamma_{l_{i,j+\frac{1}{2},k}} \left(Z_{i,j+1,k} - Z_{i,j,k} \right)$$

$$+ \, T_{lz_{i,j,k+\frac{1}{2}}} \gamma_{l_{i,j,k+\frac{1}{2}}} \left(Z_{i,j,k+1} - Z_{i,j,k} \right). \quad \text{........} \quad (7.47)$$

In Eq. 7.47 (in defining $Q_{i,j,k}$) the gravity-head term, $\gamma_l Z$, was introduced. Because both the transmissibility terms and the γ_l term may be pressure dependent, Eq. 7.39 may require iteration for a final solution. **Fig. 7.10** shows the matrix equation for 3D flow.

7.3 Solution Methods

Previous sections showed how finite-difference equations written for n simulation grid cells result in an $n \times n$ coefficient matrix. There are two general methods for solving the resulting matrix equation, direct and iterative.

7.3.1 Direct Methods. Fig. 7.11 shows the use of a direct linear equation solver in reservoir simulation. A direct solver has the capability to produce an exact solution after a fixed number of computations if the computer was able to carry an infinite number of digits. Because all real computers have a finite word length, the solution obtained through a direct process will have round-off errors.

Gaussian Elimination. Gaussian elimination is one of the oldest and most popular direct-solution methods and forms the basis of several other direct-solution techniques. The Gaussian elimination procedure involves two distinct stages. In the first stage, the elimination stage, unknowns are systematically removed from the rows of the matrix equation. The result of this stage is an upper triangular matrix. In the second stage, the backsubstitution stage, the unknowns are determined by substituting known quantities into the triangularized matrix equation. In the elimination stage, the first equation is divided by the coefficient of the first unknown (assuming that this coefficient is not equal to zero), then the first unknown is eliminated from the succeeding equations. Next, the modified second equation is divided by the new coefficient of the second unknown and the result is used to eliminate the second unknown from the succeeding equations. After repeating this elimination procedure n times (for a system of n equations), the forward elimination is completed and the last equation of the resulting system has only the last unknown remaining. After solving the last equation explicitly for the last unknown, the backsubstitution stage is used to solve for the remaining unknowns successively. **Fig. 7.12** illustrates the Gaussian elimination algorithm schematically.

Mathematically, the following describes the Gaussian elimination procedure.

1. Initialization stage.

For $i = 1,2 ,\ldots, n$, set

Fig. 7.11—Direct method.

$$d_i^{(o)} = d_i \quad \text{..............} \quad (7.48a)$$

and $a_{i,j}^{(o)} = a_{i,j} \quad j = 1,2 ,\ldots, n.$ .... (7.48b)

2. Elimination stage.

Set

$$d_i^{(i)} = \frac{d_i^{(i-1)}}{a_{i,i}^{(i-1)}} \quad \text{..............} \quad (7.49a)$$

for $i = 1,2 ,\ldots, n$;

$$a_{i,j}^{(i)} = \frac{a_{i,j}^{(i-1)}}{a_{i,i}^{(i-1)}} \quad \text{..............} \quad (7.49b)$$

for $j = i+1, i+2 ,\ldots, n$;

and $a_{i,i}^{(i)} = 1.0.$ .... (7.49c)

Set

$$d_k^{(i)} = d_k^{(i-1)} - d_i^{(i)} a_{k,i}^{(i-1)} \quad \text{..............} \quad (7.50a)$$

for $k = i+1, i+2 ,\ldots, n$;

$$a_{k,j}^{(i)} = a_{k,j}^{(i-1)} - a_{i,j}^{(i)} a_{k,i}^{(i-1)} \quad \text{..............} \quad (7.50b)$$

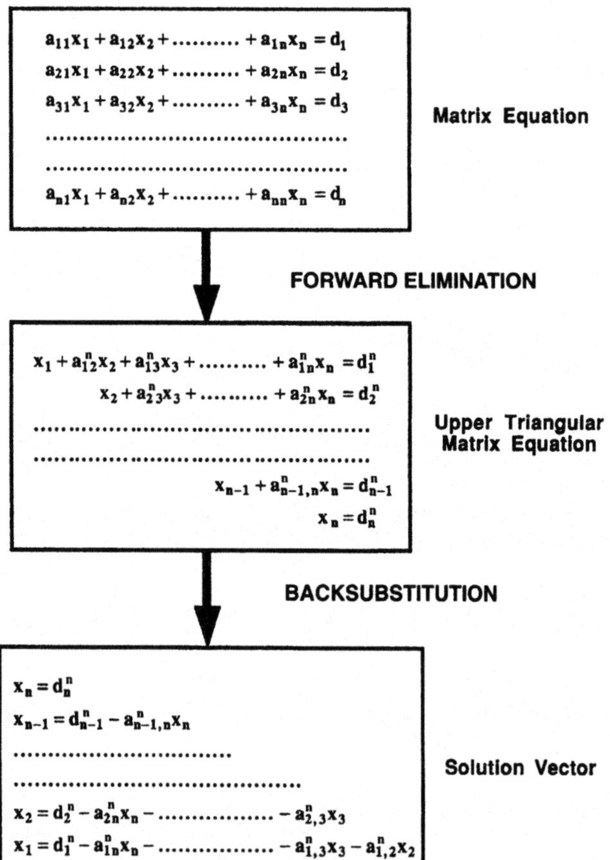

Fig. 7.12—Steps of the Gaussian elimination.

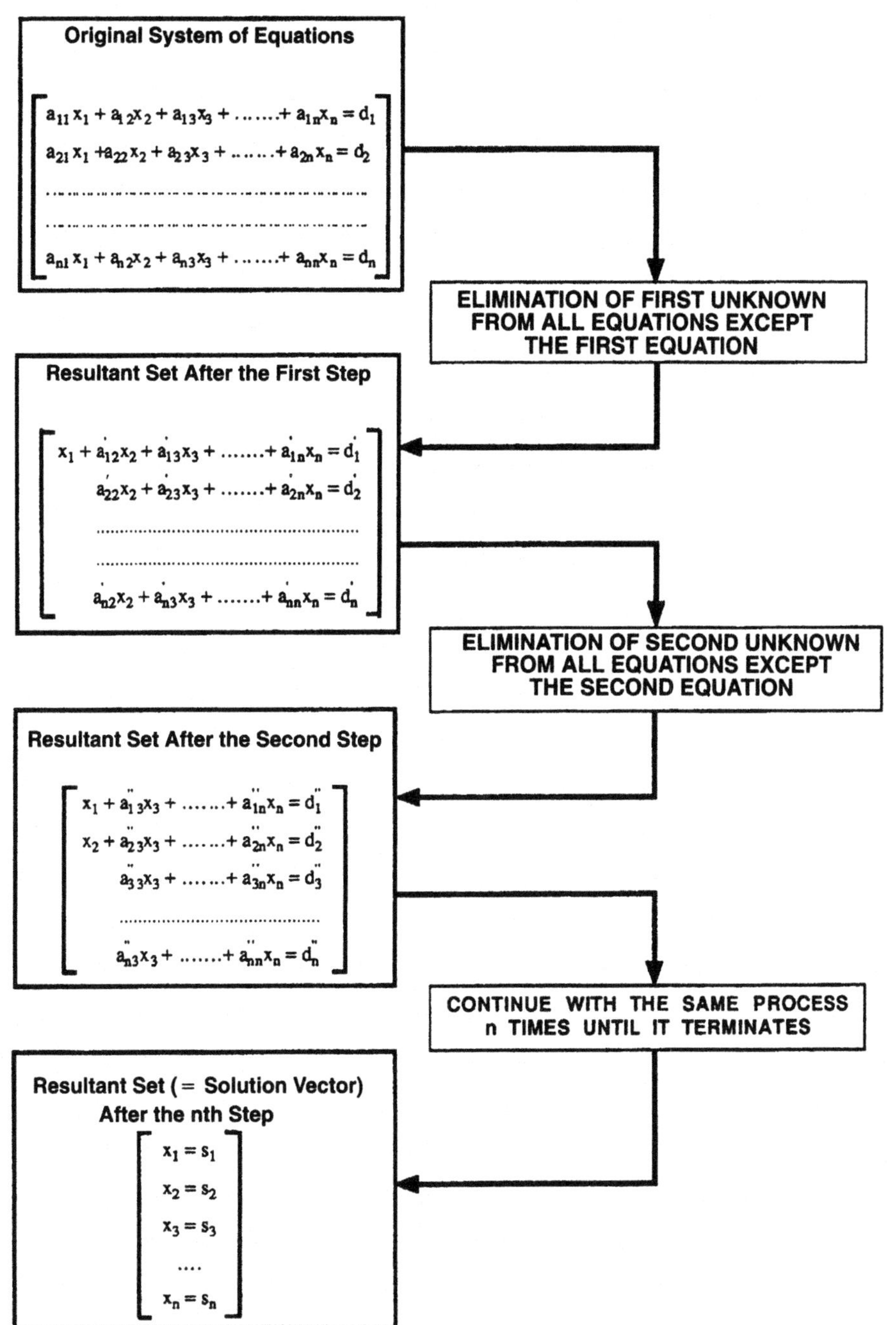

Fig. 7.13—Schematic representation of the progression of the Gauss-Jordan reduction.

for $j = i+1, i+2, \ldots, n$;

and $a_{k,i}^{(i)} = 0$. .... (7.50c)

3. Backsubstitution stage.
Set

$$x_n = d_n^{(n)}. \quad \text{(7.51)}$$

For $i = n-1, n-2, \ldots, 1$, set

$$x_i = d_i^{(n)} - \sum_{j=i+1}^{n} a_{ij}^{(n)} x_j. \quad \text{(7.52)}$$

In this procedure, it is imperative to perform all operations in the exact order shown. In addition, Eqs. 7.49a, 7.49b, and 7.50a through 7.50c are performed before i is incremented in Step 2.

Example 7.2. Solve the following system of equations with the Gaussian elimination method.

$$\begin{bmatrix} 2 & 1 & 1 \\ 1 & -2 & 2 \\ -1 & 1 & 1 \end{bmatrix} \begin{bmatrix} x_1 \\ x_2 \\ x_3 \end{bmatrix} = \begin{bmatrix} 4 \\ 1 \\ 1 \end{bmatrix}. \quad \text{(7.53)}$$

Solution. The matrix equation represents the following three equations in three unknowns.

$$2x_1 + x_2 + x_3 = 4, \quad \text{(7.54a)}$$

$$x_1 - 2x_2 + 2x_3 = 1, \quad \text{(7.54b)}$$

and $-x_1 + x_2 + x_3 = 1$. .... (7.54c)

During the first elimination step, we divide Eq. 7.54a by 2 (the coefficient of x_1) to obtain

$$x_1 + \tfrac{1}{2}x_2 + \tfrac{1}{2}x_3 = 2 \quad \text{(7.55)}$$

and Eqs. 7.54b and 7.54c.

To eliminate the first unknown, x_1, from Eqs. 7.54b and 7.54c, subtract Eq. 7.55 from Eq. 7.54b and add Eq. 7.55 to Eq. 7.54c to obtain

$$x_1 + \tfrac{1}{2}x_2 + \tfrac{1}{2}x_3 = 2, \quad \text{(7.55)}$$

$$-\tfrac{5}{2}x_2 + \tfrac{3}{2}x_3 = -1, \quad \text{(7.56a)}$$

$$\text{and } \tfrac{3}{2}x_2 + \tfrac{3}{2}x_3 = 3. \quad \text{(7.56b)}$$

Now eliminate the second unknown, x_2, from Eq. 7.56b. To achieve this, first divide Eq. 7.56a by $-5/2$ to obtain

$$x_1 + \tfrac{1}{2}x_2 + \tfrac{1}{2}x_3 = 2, \quad \text{(7.55)}$$

$$x_2 - \tfrac{3}{5}x_3 = \tfrac{2}{5}, \quad \text{(7.57)}$$

$$\text{and } \tfrac{3}{2}x_2 + \tfrac{3}{2}x_3 = 3. \quad \text{(7.56b)}$$

Then, multiply Eq. 7.57 by $3/2$ and subtract it from Eq. 7.56b. This process results in the following set of equations.

$$x_1 + \tfrac{1}{2}x_2 + \tfrac{1}{2}x_3 = 2. \quad \text{(7.55)}$$

$$x_2 - \tfrac{3}{5}x_3 = \tfrac{2}{5}. \quad \text{(7.57)}$$

$$\tfrac{12}{5}x_3 = \tfrac{12}{5}. \quad \text{(7.58)}$$

At this point, we have completed the forward-elimination stage of the algorithm. Having triangularized the original system, the unknowns x_1, x_2, and x_3 can be solved by backsubstitution. Beginning with the last equation we find, successively,

$$x_3 = \frac{d_3^{(3)}}{a_{3,3}^{(3)}} = \frac{12/5}{12/5} = 1, \quad \text{(7.59a)}$$

$$x_2 = d_2^{(3)} - a_{2,3}^{(3)}x_3 = \tfrac{2}{5} - \left[-\tfrac{3}{5}(1)\right] = 1, \quad \text{(7.59b)}$$

$$\text{and } x_1 = d_1^{(3)} - \left[a_{1,2}^{(3)}x_2 + a_{1,3}^{(3)}x_3\right] = 2 - \left[\tfrac{1}{2}(1) + \tfrac{1}{2}(1)\right] = 1. \quad \text{(7.59c)}$$

In this simple example, we were able to perform the arithmetical operations, keeping the coefficients in the form of fractions. Therefore, we did not encounter any round-off errors. In practice, it is necessary to perform the divisions and express the coefficients with a finite number of significant digits. Obviously, this results in round-off errors. The overall effect of the round-off errors on the solution depends on the size of the matrix and, in some applications of the Gaussian elimination procedure, it may become crucial. Procedures, such as pivoting and iterated improvement, can be used to reduce round-off error. These are discussed later in the chapter.

Gauss-Jordan Reduction. A modification of the Gaussian elimination procedure, known as Gauss-Jordan reduction, consists of using the ith equation at the ith step to eliminate the ith unknown, x_i, from the preceding equations as well as the succeeding ones. This method yields the solution after n elimination steps, and avoids backsubstitution. **Fig. 7.13** illustrates the Gauss-Jordan reduction algorithm schematically.

The following describe the Gauss-Jordan reduction procedure mathematically.

1. Initialization stage.
For, $i = 1,2, \ldots, n$, set

$$d_i^{(o)} = d_i \quad \text{(7.48a)}$$

$$\text{and } a_{i,j}^{(o)} = a_{i,j} \quad j = 1,2, \ldots, n. \quad \text{(7.48b)}$$

2. Gauss-Jordan reduction.
Set

$$d_i^{(i)} = \frac{d_i^{(i-1)}}{a_{i,i}^{(i-1)}} \quad \text{(7.49a)}$$

for $i = 1,2, \ldots, n$;

$$a_{i,j}^{(i)} = \frac{a_{i,j}^{(i-1)}}{a_{i,i}^{(i-1)}} \quad \text{(7.49b)}$$

for $j = i+1, i+2, \ldots, n$;

$$\text{and } a_{i,i}^{(i)} = 1.0. \quad \text{(7.49c)}$$

Set

$$d_k^{(i)} = d_k^{(i-1)} - d_i^{(i)}a_{k,i}^{(i-1)} \quad \text{(7.50a)}$$

for $k = 1,2, \ldots, n$ and $k \neq i$;

$$a_{k,j}^{(i)} = a_{k,j}^{(i-1)} - a_{i,j}^{(i)}a_{k,i}^{(i-1)} \quad \text{(7.50b)}$$

for $j = i+1, i+2, \ldots, n$;

$$\text{and } a_{k,i}^{(i)} = 0.0. \quad \text{(7.50c)}$$

3. Solution.
For $i = 1, 2, \ldots, n$, set

$$x_i = d_i^{(n)}. \quad \text{(7.60)}$$

Example 7.3. Use the Gaussian-Jordan reduction method to solve Eqs. 7.54a through 7.54c.

Solution. The first two steps are the same as in the Gaussian elimination method presented in Example 7.2, giving

$$x_1 + \tfrac{1}{2}x_2 + \tfrac{1}{2}x_3 = 2, \quad \text{(7.55)}$$

$$-\tfrac{5}{2}x_2 + \tfrac{3}{2}x_3 = -1, \quad \text{(7.56a)}$$

$$\text{and } \tfrac{3}{2}x_2 + \tfrac{3}{2}x_3 = 3. \quad \text{(7.56b)}$$

Now eliminate the second unknown from Eqs. 7.55 and 7.56b: multiply Eq. 7.56a by $1/5$ and add the resulting equation to Eq. 7.55, then multiply Eq. 7.56a by $3/5$ and add the resulting equation to Eq. 7.56b. This results in

$$x_1 + \tfrac{4}{5}x_3 = \tfrac{9}{5}, \quad \text{(7.61a)}$$

$$-\tfrac{1}{2}x_2 + \tfrac{3}{10}x_3 = -\tfrac{1}{5}, \quad \text{(7.61b)}$$

$$\text{and } x_3 = 1. \quad \text{(7.61c)}$$

During the final step of the calculations, eliminate the third unknown from Eqs. 7.61a and 7.61b. This can be achieved simply by multiplying Eq. 7.61c by $4/5$ and $3/10$, and subtracting the resulting equations from Eqs. 7.61a and 7.61b, respectively. This results in $x_1 = 1, x_2 = 1$, and $x_3 = 1$.

Comparing the number of operations performed in Examples 7.2 and 7.3 shows that the Gaussian elimination algorithm requires fewer multiplications and divisions than the Gauss-Jordan reduction algorithm. Roughly, the Gauss-Jordan reduction involves about $n^3/2$ multiplications and divisions, whereas the Gaussian elimination involves about $n^3/3$.

Crout Reduction. The Crout reduction algorithm for solving a system of linear equations, sometimes referred to as **[L][U]** factorization, is basically the same as the Gaussian elimination algorithm, except that it has the advantage of not modifying the right-side vector during the factorization process. Consequently, if the same coefficient matrix is to be used on multiple right-side vectors, the triangular matrices **[L]** and **[U]** can be stored and used as required. The following discussion provides a description and illustration of the method. Let the coefficient matrix **[A]** of $[\mathbf{A}]\vec{x} = \vec{d}$ (Eq. 7.1) be written as the product of two triangular matrices,

$$[\mathbf{L}][\mathbf{U}] = [\mathbf{A}], \quad \text{(7.62)}$$

where **[L]** and **[U]** = lower triangular and upper triangular matrices, respectively. For the case of a 3×3 matrix, Eq. 7.62 can be written as

$$\begin{bmatrix} l_{11} & 0 & 0 \\ l_{21} & l_{22} & 0 \\ l_{31} & l_{32} & l_{33} \end{bmatrix} \begin{bmatrix} u_{11} & u_{12} & u_{13} \\ 0 & u_{22} & u_{23} \\ 0 & 0 & u_{33} \end{bmatrix} = \begin{bmatrix} a_{11} & a_{12} & a_{13} \\ a_{21} & a_{22} & a_{23} \\ a_{31} & a_{32} & a_{33} \end{bmatrix}. \quad \text{. . . (7.63)}$$

Because $[\mathbf{A}]\vec{x} = \vec{d}$ and $[\mathbf{A}] = [\mathbf{L}][\mathbf{U}]$, we can write

$$[\mathbf{L}]([\mathbf{U}]\vec{x}) = \vec{d}. \quad \text{. . . . . (7.64)}$$

Then, the original problem can be solved by first solving for an intermediate vector, $\vec{y}$, such that

$$[\mathbf{L}]\vec{y} = \vec{d} \quad \text{. . . . . (7.65)}$$

and then solving for the unknown vector, $\vec{x}$, from

$$[\mathbf{U}]\vec{x} = \vec{y}. \quad \text{. . . . . (7.66)}$$

Obviously, by breaking up the original coefficient matrix **[A]** into two triangular matrices we end up solving two sets of linear algebraic equations (Eqs. 7.65 and 7.66) instead of one. However, we also realize that the solutions of Eqs. 7.65 and 7.66 are much easier because of the triangular structures of **[L]** and **[U]**. Now, the fundamental question that needs to be answered is how we can solve for **[L]** and **[U]** when **[A]** is given. To answer this question, we look at the product of **[L]** and **[U]** from Eq. 7.63,

$$\begin{bmatrix} l_{11} & 0 & 0 \\ l_{21} & l_{22} & 0 \\ l_{31} & l_{32} & l_{33} \end{bmatrix} \begin{bmatrix} u_{11} & u_{12} & u_{13} \\ 0 & u_{22} & u_{23} \\ 0 & 0 & u_{33} \end{bmatrix}$$

$$= \begin{bmatrix} l_{11}u_{11} & l_{11}u_{12} & l_{11}u_{13} \\ l_{21}u_{11} & l_{21}u_{12} + l_{22}u_{22} & l_{21}u_{13} + l_{22}u_{23} \\ l_{31}u_{11} & l_{31}u_{12} + l_{32}u_{22} & l_{31}u_{13} + l_{32}u_{23} + l_{33}u_{33} \end{bmatrix}.$$

. . . . (7.67)

Eq. 7.67 implies that

$$a_{11} = l_{11}u_{11}, \quad \text{. . . . . (7.68a)}$$

$$a_{12} = l_{11}u_{12}, \quad \text{. . . . . (7.68b)}$$

$$a_{13} = l_{11}u_{13}, \quad \text{. . . . . (7.68c)}$$

$$a_{21} = l_{21}u_{11}, \quad \text{. . . . . (7.68d)}$$

$$a_{22} = l_{21}u_{12} + l_{22}u_{22}, \quad \text{. . . . . (7.68e)}$$

$$a_{23} = l_{21}u_{13} + l_{22}u_{23}, \quad \text{. . . . . (7.68f)}$$

$$a_{31} = l_{31}u_{11}, \quad \text{. . . . . (7.68g)}$$

$$a_{32} = l_{31}u_{12} + l_{32}u_{22}, \quad \text{. . . . . (7.68h)}$$

and $a_{33} = l_{31}u_{13} + l_{32}u_{23} + l_{33}u_{33}$. . . . . (7.68i)

The set of equations in Eq. 7.68 contains Unknowns l_{ij} and u_{ij}, while the a_{ij} entries are all known because Coefficient Matrix **[A]** is given. A close examination of Eq. 7.68 reveals that there are 12 unknowns but only nine equations. Because the number of available equations is less than the number of unknowns, we must specify three unknowns arbitrarily to solve the remainder.

So far, we have used a 3 × 3 system to illustrate the problem more explicitly. We now make some generalizations. If the coefficient matrix is of order n, Eq. 7.68 can be written with the general form

$$l_{i1}u_{1j} + l_{i2}u_{2j} + \ . \ . \ . \ + l_{ii}u_{ij} = a_{ij} \quad \text{. . . . . (7.69)}$$

where $i = 1, \ldots, n$ and $j = 1, \ldots, n$.

Eq. 7.69 has a total of n^2 equations for the $n^2 + n$ unknowns of the **[L]** and **[U]** entries (by revisiting the earlier example, it is easy to see that, when $n = 3$, there are nine equations and 12 unknowns).

As discussed earlier, it is necessary to assign arbitrary values to n unknowns. Because the selection is arbitrary, set

$$l_{ii} = 1, \quad \text{. . . . . (7.70)}$$

for $i = 1, \ldots, n$.

After implementing Eq. 7.70, solve for the remaining l_{ij} and u_{ij} values.

The Crout reduction algorithm becomes very compact at this point if we reorder the equations and solutions of the unknowns in the following order.

1. Initialization. For $i = 1, 2, \ldots, n$, set

$$l_{ii} = 1 \quad \text{. . . . . (7.71)}$$

2. **[L][U]** factorization. For $j = 1, 2, \ldots, n$, perform the following two computational steps. First, for $i \leqq j$,

$$u_{ij} = a_{1j} \quad \text{. . . . . (7.72a)}$$

for $i = 1$

$$\text{and } u_{ij} = a_{ij} - \sum_{k=1}^{i-1} l_{ik}u_{kj} \quad \text{. . . . . (7.72b)}$$

for $i = 2, \ldots, j$. Second, for $i > j$,

$$l_{i1} = \frac{a_{i1}}{u_{11}} \quad \text{. . . . . (7.73a)}$$

for $j = 1$; and

$$l_{ij} = \frac{1}{u_{jj}}\left(a_{ij} - \sum_{k=1}^{j-1} l_{ik}u_{kj}\right) \quad \text{. . . . . (7.73b)}$$

for $i = j+1, j+2, \ldots, n$, and for $j \geqq 2$.

3. Forward substitution. Set

$$y_1 = d_1. \quad \text{. . . . . (7.74a)}$$

$$\text{Then } y_i = d_i - \sum_{j=1}^{i-1} l_{ij}y_j \quad \text{. . . . . (7.74b)}$$

for $i = 2, 3, \ldots, n$.

4. Backsubstitution. Set

$$x_n = \frac{y_n}{u_{nn}}. \quad \text{. . . . . (7.75a)}$$

$$\text{Then, } x_i = \frac{1}{u_{ii}}\left(y_i - \sum_{j=i+1}^{n} u_{ij}x_j\right) \quad \text{. . . . . (7.75b)}$$

for $i = n-1, n-2, \ldots, 1$.

Again, it is imperative that both of the computations of Step 2 are done before increasing the value of j. Also, note that when the upper limits of the summations are zero, the summations are set equal to zero. Now apply the procedure to the same system of equations we solved in Example 7.2.

Example 7.4. Use Crout's algorithm to solve Eqs. 7.54a through 7.54c.

Solution. The coefficient matrix **[A]** has the following entries.

$$\begin{bmatrix} 2 & 1 & 1 \\ 1 & -2 & 2 \\ -1 & 1 & 1 \end{bmatrix} = \begin{bmatrix} a_{11} & a_{12} & a_{13} \\ a_{21} & a_{22} & a_{23} \\ a_{31} & a_{32} & a_{33} \end{bmatrix}. \quad \text{. . . . . (7.76)}$$

Now perform the **[L][U]** factorization. Note that $n = 3$.

Step 1. $l_{11} = 1$, $l_{22} = 1$, and $l_{33} = 1$.

Step 2. For $j = 1$ and $i = 1$, $u_{11} = 2$.

For $j = 1$ and $i = 2$: $l_{21} = ½(1) = ½$.

For $j = 1$ and $i = 3$: $l_{31} = ½(-1 - 0) = -½$.

For $j = 2$ and $i = 1$: $u_{12} = 1$.

For $j = 2$ and $i = 2$: $u_{22} = -2 - [(½)(1)] = -{}^5/_2$.

For $j = 2$ and $i = 3$: $l_{32} = [1/(-{}^5/_2)][1 - (-½)(1)] = -{}^3/_5$.

For $j = 3$ and $i = 1$: $u_{13} = 1$.

For $j = 3$ and $i = 2$: $u_{23} = 2 - [(½)(1)] = {}^3/_2$.

For $j = 3$ and $i = 3$: $u_{33} = 1 - \left[(-½)(1) + \left(-{}^3/_5\right)\left({}^3/_2\right)\right] = {}^{12}/_5$.

At this stage we have established **[L]** and **[U]** matrices, respectively, as

$$[\mathbf{L}] = \begin{bmatrix} 1 & 0 & 0 \\ 1/2 & 1 & 0 \\ -1/2 & -3/5 & 1 \end{bmatrix} \text{ and } [\mathbf{U}] = \begin{bmatrix} 2 & 1 & 1 \\ 0 & -5/2 & 3/2 \\ 0 & 0 & 12/5 \end{bmatrix}.$$

We can easily verify that the algorithm has worked for our example problem by premultiplying **[U]** by **[L]** and comparing the resulting matrix with the original coefficient matrix. Once the **[L]** and **[U]** decomposition is obtained for **[A]**, the next steps involve the solution of Eqs. 7.65 and 7.66.

Step 3. Solve the following equation by forward substitution.

$$\begin{bmatrix} 1 & 0 & 0 \\ 1/2 & 1 & 0 \\ -1/2 & -3/5 & 1 \end{bmatrix} \begin{bmatrix} y_1 \\ y_2 \\ y_3 \end{bmatrix} = \begin{bmatrix} 4 \\ 1 \\ 1 \end{bmatrix}. \qquad (7.77)$$

This forward solution becomes $y_1 = 4$, $y_2 = -1$, and $y_3 = 12/5$.

Step 4. Solve the following equation by backsubstitution.

$$\begin{bmatrix} 2 & 1 & 1 \\ 0 & -5/2 & 3/2 \\ 0 & 0 & 12/5 \end{bmatrix} \begin{bmatrix} x_1 \\ x_2 \\ x_3 \end{bmatrix} = \begin{bmatrix} 4 \\ -1 \\ 12/5 \end{bmatrix}. \qquad (7.78)$$

The backward solution of the system of equations is $x_3 = 1$, $x_2 = 1$, and $x_1 = 1$.

Thomas' Algorithm. As shown earlier, when finite-difference equations are written along a line, a tridiagonal coefficient matrix is always generated. The general structure of a tridiagonal system has the form

$$b_1x_1 + c_1x_2 = d_1 \qquad (7.79a)$$

$$a_2x_1 + b_2x_2 + c_2x_3 = d_2 \qquad (7.79b)$$

$$a_3x_2 + b_3x_3 + c_3x_4 = d_3 \qquad (7.79c)$$

$$a_{n-1}x_{n-2} + b_{n-1}x_{n-1} + c_{n-1}x_n = d_{n-1} \qquad (7.79d)$$

through $a_nx_{n-1} + b_nx_n = d_n$, $\qquad (7.79e)$

where b_i, a_i, and c_i = coefficients of the unknowns of Gridblock i, Gridblock $i-1$, and Gridblock $i+1$, respectively. The element d_i is the right side of the equation for Gridblock i. Thomas' algorithm offers an efficient algorithm to solve systems of equations of this type. In essence, Thomas' algorithm is a special application (band algorithm) of the Crout reduction procedure. It is not necessary to store the full $n \times n$ matrix; only the entries of a_i, b_i, c_i, and d_i need to be stored as four separate vectors.

In matrix form, Eq. 7.79 can be written as

$$\begin{bmatrix} b_1 & c_1 & 0 & \cdots & \cdots & \cdots \\ a_2 & b_2 & c_2 & \cdots & \cdots & \cdots \\ \cdots & \cdots & \cdots & \cdots & \cdots & \cdots \\ \cdots & \cdots & \cdots & a_{n-1} & b_{n-1} & c_{n-1} \\ \cdots & \cdots & \cdots & 0 & a_n & b_n \end{bmatrix} \begin{bmatrix} x_1 \\ x_2 \\ \cdots \\ x_{n-1} \\ x_n \end{bmatrix} = \begin{bmatrix} d_1 \\ d_2 \\ \cdots \\ d_{n-1} \\ d_n \end{bmatrix}. \qquad (7.80)$$

Thomas' algorithm can be implemented as follows.

Forward Solution. For $i = 1$,

$$w_1 = \frac{c_1}{b_1} \qquad (7.81)$$

and $g_1 = \dfrac{d_1}{b_1}$. $\qquad (7.82)$

For $i = 2, 3, \ldots, n-1$,

$$w_i = \frac{c_i}{b_i - a_iw_{i-1}} \qquad (7.83)$$

and for $i = 2, \ldots, n$,

$$g_i = \frac{d_i - a_ig_{i-1}}{b_i - a_iw_{i-1}}. \qquad (7.84)$$

Backward Solution. For $i = n$,

$$x_n = g_n \qquad (7.85)$$

and for $i = n-1, n-2, \ldots, 3, 2, 1$,

$$x_i = g_i - w_ix_{i+1}. \qquad (7.86)$$

Now apply Thomas' algorithm to solve a simple example.

Example 7.5. Use Thomas' algorithm to solve the following system of equations.

$$4x_1 + 3x_2 = 25. \qquad (7.87a)$$

$$2x_1 + x_2 + 2x_3 = 15. \qquad (7.87b)$$

$$3x_2 + x_3 + x_4 = 12. \qquad (7.87c)$$

$$2x_3 + x_4 = 5. \qquad (7.87d)$$

Solution. The given set of equations has the tridiagonal structure as required by Thomas' algorithm,

$$\begin{bmatrix} 4 & 3 & 0 & 0 \\ 2 & 1 & 2 & 0 \\ 0 & 3 & 1 & 1 \\ 0 & 0 & 2 & 1 \end{bmatrix} \begin{bmatrix} x_1 \\ x_2 \\ x_3 \\ x_4 \end{bmatrix} = \begin{bmatrix} 25 \\ 15 \\ 12 \\ 5 \end{bmatrix}. \qquad (7.88)$$

1. Forward Solution.

For $i = 1$, $w_1 = 3/4$ and $g_1 = 25/4$.

For $i = 2$, $w_2 = \dfrac{2}{1 - (2)(3/4)} = -4$

and $g_2 = \dfrac{15 - (2)(25/4)}{1 - (2)(3/4)} = -5.$

For $i = 3$, $w_3 = \dfrac{1}{1 - (3)(-4)} = 1/13$

and $g_3 = \dfrac{12 - (3)(-5)}{1 - (3)(-4)} = 27/13.$

For $i = 4$, $g_4 = \dfrac{5 - (2)(27/13)}{1 - (2)(1/13)} = 1.$

2. Backward Solution.

For $i = 4$, $x_4 = 1$.

For $i = 3$, $x_3 = 27/13 - 1/13(1) = 2.$

For $i = 2$, $x_2 = (-5) - (-4)(2) = 3.$

For $i = 1$, $x_1 = 25/4 - 3/4(3) = 4.$

Hence, the solution vector is

$$\begin{bmatrix} x_1 \\ x_2 \\ x_3 \\ x_4 \end{bmatrix} = \begin{bmatrix} 4 \\ 3 \\ 2 \\ 1 \end{bmatrix}.$$

The efficient nature of this method, when coupled with the ease of implementation and small storage requirements, makes Thomas'

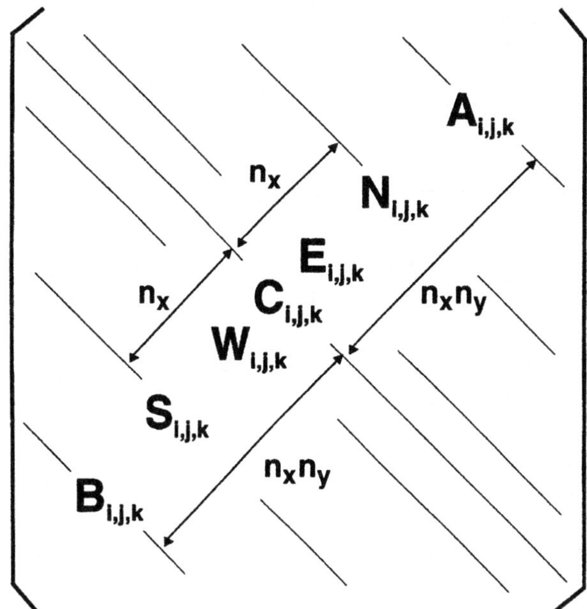

Fig. 7.14—Band structure of an $n_x \times n_y \times n_z$ grid system with unknowns ordered in the *i* direction, *j* direction, and finally the *k* direction.

algorithm a procedure that is used extensively in solving systems of equations with a tridiagonal coefficient matrix.

Improvements to Basic Direct-Solution Algorithms. The direct-solution methods described so far represent the basic algorithms for these procedures. We can incorporate additional options into these algorithms to improve various features of the procedures. This section discusses four techniques that are applicable to direct-solution methods: sparse-matrix, pivoting, multiple known vectors ($\vec{d}$), and iterated improvement.

Sparse-Matrix Techniques. All the algorithms discussed, with the exception of Thomas' algorithm, assumed that most of the entries, $a_{i,j}$, in the coefficient matrix are nonzero. As we have seen, the coefficient matrix generated by finite-difference approximations can be formulated as a banded matrix (tridiagonal, pentadiagonal, or heptadiagonal, depending on the dimensionality of the problem). These special matrices result in a structure composed of zero entries outside the outermost bands. In cases where the structure of the coefficient matrix is known *a priori* and contains many zero entries, sparse-matrix techniques can be used.

Sparse-matrix techniques improve the efficiency of a given algorithm (in terms of the number of arithmetic operations) by excluding operations on zero entries of the coefficient matrix. As we have seen, the goal of direct-solution techniques is to alter the coefficient matrix to a form that may be solved more easily with simple substitution methods (either backsubstitution or forward substitution followed by backsubstitution). The coefficient matrix was modified by use of elementary row and column operations to convert nonzero entries, $a_{i,j}$, to zero values. Because a sparse matrix already contains many zero entries, there is no need to operate on these entries. Probably the most popular sparse-matrix technique, and the one that is most applicable to numerical reservoir simulation, is the band-solution technique.

Band-solution techniques take advantage of the banded structure of the coefficient matrix. The discussion of Thomas' algorithm demonstrated the efficiency of band-solution techniques.

Sec. 7.2 shows how finite-difference approximations to the flow equation result in banded coefficient matrices. **Fig. 7.14** shows the details of the band structure of an $n_x \times n_y \times n_z$ grid system, in which the finite-difference equations are written in the *i* direction, followed by the *j* and then the *k* directions.

This figure illustrates that the finite-difference equations can be formulated in such a way that the resulting coefficient matrix contains an envelope of non-zero entries with a band width of $2b_w+1$, where $b_w = n_x \times n_y$ for 3D flow problems; $b_w = n_x$ (or n_y) for 2D flow problems, depending on the block-ordering scheme used (see Sec. 7.3.3); and $b_w = 1$ for 1D flow problems.

With this bandwidth information, the Gaussian elimination procedure can be modified to the following.

1. Initialization stage. For $i = 1, 2, \ldots, n$, set

$$d_i^{(o)} = d_i, \quad \text{(7.48a)}$$

$$j_{\min} = \max(1, i - b_w), \quad \text{(7.89a)}$$

$$j_{\max} = \min(i + b_w, n), \quad \text{(7.89b)}$$

and $a_{i,j}^{(o)} = a_{i,j} \quad j = j_{\min}, j_{\min}+1, \ldots, j_{\max}$. (7.89c)

2. Elimination stage. For $i = 1, 2, \ldots, n$, set

$$d_i^{(i)} = \frac{d_i^{(i-1)}}{a_{i,i}^{(i-1)}}, \quad \text{(7.49a)}$$

$$j_{\max} = \min(i + b_w, n), \quad \text{(7.89b)}$$

$$a_{i,j}^{(i)} = \frac{a_{i,j}^{(i-1)}}{a_{i,i}^{(i-1)}} \quad j = i, i+1, \ldots, j_{\max}. \quad \text{(7.90a)}$$

and $a_{i,i}^{(i)} = 1$. (7.90b)

For $k = i+1, i+2, \ldots, j_{\max}$, set

$$d_k^{(i)} = d_k^{(i-1)} - d_i^{(i)} a_{k,i}^{(i-1)} \quad \text{(7.91a)}$$

$$a_{k,j}^{(i)} = a_{k,j}^{(i-1)} - a_{i,j}^{(i)} a_{k,i}^{(i-1)} \quad j = i, i+1, \ldots, j_{\max}. \quad \text{(7.91b)}$$

and $a_{k,i}^{(i)} = 0$. (7.91c)

3. Backsubstitution stage. Set

$$x_n = d_n^{(n)} \quad \text{(7.51)}$$

For $i = n-1, n-2, \ldots, 1$, set

$$j_{\max} = \min(i + b_w, n) \quad \text{(7.89b)}$$

and $x_i = d_i^{(n)} - \sum_{j=i+1}^{j_{\max}} a_{i,j}^{(n)} x_j$. (7.52)

Simple implementation of the band Gaussian elimination procedure improves the efficiency of the algorithm by excluding operations on zero entries outside the band structure (envelope) of the coefficient matrix. An additional advantage of this band technique is the reduced storage requirement. This reduced storage requirement occurs because only those entries within the nonzero envelope need to be stored. Although the Gaussian elimination procedure was used to demonstrate this implementation of the band-solution technique, similar modifications can be made to the Gauss-Jordan and Crout reduction procedures. In summary, band-solution techniques improve the efficiency of direct-solution procedures by reducing the number of arithmetic operations and storage required for a solution.

Pivoting. Computations performed on computers with finite word lengths always generate round-off error in the arithmetic result. We want to formulate our direct-solution procedures to minimize the accumulation of this round-off error. Pivoting is one method used to control round-off error in direct-solution techniques.

Fig. 7.15 shows the structure of the coefficient matrix at the beginning of the *i*th elimination step of the Gaussian elimination procedure. During the *i*th elimination step, all the matrix entries in Row *i*, $a_{i,j}^{(i-1)}$, and the right-side element, $d_i^{(i-1)}$, are divided by the element $a_{i,i}^{(i-1)}$. $a_{i,i}^{(i-1)}$ is referred to as the pivot point. For the right side,

$$d_i^{(i)} = \frac{d_i^{(i-1)}}{a_{i,i}^{(i-1)}}. \quad \text{(7.49a)}$$

$$\begin{bmatrix} 1 & a_{1,2}^{(i-1)} & a_{1,3}^{(i-1)} & \cdots & a_{1,i}^{(i-1)} & a_{1,i+1}^{(i-1)} & \cdots & a_{1,n}^{(i-1)} \\ 0 & 1 & a_{2,3}^{(i-1)} & \cdots & a_{2,i}^{(i-1)} & a_{2,i+1}^{(i-1)} & \cdots & a_{2,n}^{(i-1)} \\ 0 & 0 & 1 & \cdots & a_{3,i}^{(i-1)} & a_{3,i+1}^{(i-1)} & \cdots & a_{3,n}^{(i-1)} \\ \vdots & \vdots & \vdots & \ddots & \vdots & \vdots & & \vdots \\ 0 & 0 & 0 & \cdots & a_{i,i}^{(i-1)} & a_{i,i+1}^{(i-1)} & \cdots & a_{i,n}^{(i-1)} \\ 0 & 0 & 0 & \cdots & a_{i+1,i}^{(i-1)} & a_{i+1,i+1}^{(i-1)} & \cdots & a_{i+1,n}^{(i-1)} \\ \vdots & \vdots & \vdots & & \vdots & \vdots & \ddots & \vdots \\ 0 & 0 & 0 & \cdots & a_{ni}^{(i-1)} & a_{ni+1}^{(i-1)} & \cdots & a_{nn}^{(i-1)} \end{bmatrix} \begin{bmatrix} x_1 \\ x_2 \\ x_3 \\ \vdots \\ x_i \\ x_{i+1} \\ \vdots \\ x_n \end{bmatrix} = \begin{bmatrix} d_1^{(i-1)} \\ d_2^{(i-1)} \\ d_3^{(i-1)} \\ \vdots \\ d_i^{(i-1)} \\ d_{i+1}^{(i-1)} \\ \vdots \\ d_n^{(i-1)} \end{bmatrix}$$

Fig. 7.15—Structure of the coefficient matrix at the beginning of the *i*th elimination step of the Gaussian elimination procedure.

Eq. 7.49a assumes that $a_{i,i}^{(i-1)}$ is nonzero. Because of the round-off error in $d_i^{(i-1)}$, we actually perform

$$d_i^{(i)} = \frac{\left[d_i^{(i-1)} + \varepsilon\right]}{a_{i,i}^{(i-1)}} \quad \text{(7.92a)}$$

$$\text{or } d_i^{(i)} = \frac{d_i^{(i-1)}}{a_{i,i}^{(i-1)}} + \frac{\varepsilon}{a_{i,i}^{(i-1)}}. \quad \text{(7.92b)}$$

Note that $a_{i,i}^{(i-1)}$ also contains round-off error; however, we consider only the error ε in the element $d_i^{(i-1)}$ because this directly propagates to $d_i^{(i)}$.

Comparing Eqs. 7.49a and 7.92b shows that, for a larger value of $|a_{i,i}^{(i-1)}|$, a smaller value of round-off error propagates from $d_i^{(i-1)}$ to $d_i^{(i)}$. Note that we are only interested in the absolute value of $a_{i,i}^{(i-1)}$ because we are not concerned with the sign of the error.

In the pivoting technique, selected elements of the coefficient matrix are searched to determine the maximum absolute value of the allowable possible pivot points. Rows (or rows and columns) are then switched to place the maximum value in the pivot position. Two variations of the pivoting technique are possible: partial pivoting, where only row transfers are considered, and full pivoting, where row and column transfers are considered. For diagonally dominant matrices, such as those encountered in reservoir simulation, pivoting generally is not required for a stable numerical solution.

Multiple Known Vectors. When several systems of equations with the same coefficient matrix but with different known vectors (right-side vectors) are to be solved, the direct-solution procedures can be modified to solve for all sets of equations efficiently. In the Gaussian elimination and Gauss-Jordan procedures, we performed computations on the known vector $\vec{d}$ and the coefficient matrix **[A]**, simultaneously. Consequently, improvements to these procedures for multiple known vectors can only be implemented if all right-side vectors are known *a priori*. In the Crout reduction procedure, we factored the coefficient matrix into upper and lower triangular matrices. This process did not require previous knowledge of the known vectors. Therefore, the Crout reduction procedure can be used effectively for multiple known vectors when these vectors are not known *a priori*. Sec. 7.2.2 illustrates this in the discussion of updating pressures from one timestep to the next for slightly-compressible-flow problems. This is further illustrated in the following discussion of the iterated improvement.

Iterated Improvement. The goal of the direct-solution procedure is to solve the system of equations

$$[\mathbf{A}]\vec{x} = \vec{d} \quad \text{(7.1)}$$

for the unknown vector, $\vec{x}$. In reality, however, in the presence of round-off error, we have solved for a slightly perturbed vector, $(\vec{x} + \vec{\varepsilon})$. Although we do not know either $\vec{x}$ or $\vec{\varepsilon}$ individually, we have enough information available to remove the error from our numerical solution.

Because our perturbed solution must be a solution to the problem at hand, we can post-multiply the coefficient matrix **[A]** by $(\vec{x} + \vec{\varepsilon})$ and compare the results with the known vector, $\vec{d}$. That is,

$$[\mathbf{A}](\vec{x} + \vec{\varepsilon}) = [\mathbf{A}]\vec{x} + [\mathbf{A}]\vec{\varepsilon}, \quad \text{(7.93a)}$$

which is simply a matrix/vector multiplication and not the solution of a second system of equations. We can rearrange Eq. 7.93a as

$$[\mathbf{A}]\vec{\varepsilon} = [\mathbf{A}](\vec{x} + \vec{\varepsilon}) - [\mathbf{A}]\vec{x}. \quad \text{(7.93b)}$$

Substituting Eq. 7.1 into Eq. 7.93b results in

$$[\mathbf{A}]\vec{\varepsilon} = [\mathbf{A}](\vec{x} + \vec{\varepsilon}) - \vec{d}. \quad \text{(7.94)}$$

In Eq. 7.94, all the right-side elements are known, while the left side is unknown. Consequently, Eq. 7.94 represents a system of equations for $\vec{\varepsilon}$. Once solved, $\vec{\varepsilon}$ can be subtracted from $(\vec{x} + \vec{\varepsilon})$ to improve the estimate for $\vec{x}$. Because the solution of Eq. 7.94 also contains round-off error, this procedure can be repeated several times before a final solution is obtained.

When Crout factorization is used to solve Eq. 7.1, the implementation of the iterated-improvement procedure is very efficient. This is because we have factored **[A]** into **[L]** and **[U]**. Therefore, the implementation of the iterated-improvement procedure requires one matrix/vector multiplication and one vector subtraction followed by the standard forward and backward substitutions.

7.3.2 Difference Equations for Reservoirs With Irregular Boundaries. As the previous sections show, when there are no irregularities on the outer boundaries of the reservoir, the coefficient matrix always exhibits a well-defined structure in the form of a tridiagonal, pentadiagonal, or heptadiagonal matrix for 1D, 2D, or 3D flow problems, respectively. **Fig. 7.16** shows these structures. Note that the matrix equation in Fig. 7.16 is written in increasing orders of *i*, *j*, and *k* in a nested manner, where *i* = innermost index, *j* = intermediate index, and *k* = outermost index.

Many solution methods require matrices with the structures shown in Fig. 7.16. If the subject reservoir has irregular boundaries, the structure of the coefficient matrix is not preserved and the solution techniques designed for a specific matrix structure, such as a band-solution technique, are not applicable. Therefore, it may be necessary to take some precautions to preserve the structure of the resulting coefficient matrix. To illustrate this problem, consider the 2D reservoir with irregular boundaries in **Fig. 7.17**. The overall grid

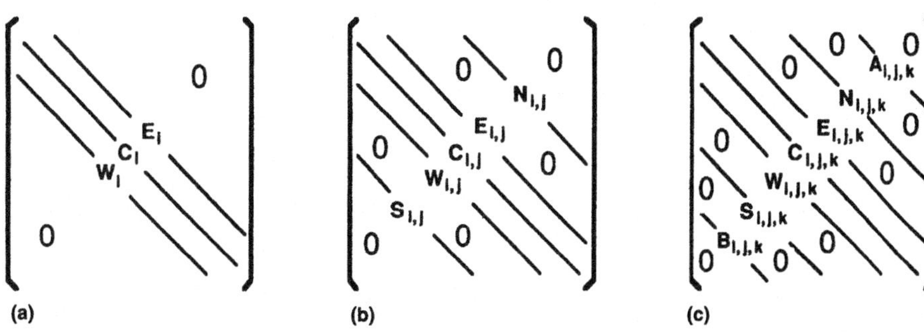

Fig. 7.16—Schematic representation of (a) tri-, (b) penta-, and (c) heptadiagonal coefficient matrices generated from reservoirs with regular boundaries.

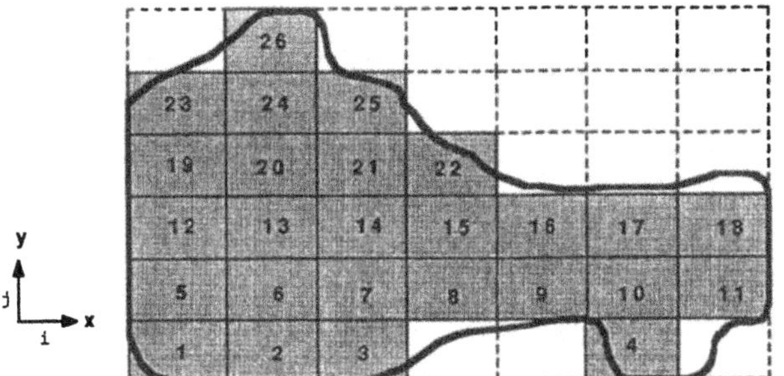

Fig. 7.17—Two-dimensional representation of a reservoir with irregular boundaries. The 26 numbered blocks are the active blocks.

in Fig. 7.17 has 42 blocks. However, as indicated in this figure, only 26 of these blocks are active. If finite-difference equations are written for only these 26 blocks, then the coefficient matrix is 26×26, and it will have a form as in **Fig. 7.18**. A closer inspection of Fig. 7.18 reveals the existence of 11 (instead of five) diagonals that are obtained from regular 2D problems. Therefore, any solver that is designed strictly for a pentadiagonal coefficient matrix cannot be used in this case. If the band structure of the coefficient matrix must be preserved because of constraints imposed by the linear equation solver, the problem must be handled in a slightly different manner to maintain the desired structure of the coefficient matrix. This can be achieved as follows. As in **Fig. 7.19**, all gridblocks (active and inactive) are numbered consecutively. Equations for the active blocks are written in the usual manner. For the inactive blocks it is necessary to write dummy equations, such as $p_4 = 10^6$, $p_5 = 10^6$, $p_{33} = 10^6$, $p_{42} = 10^6$, and so on. We call these dummy equations because they can be written in equation form. For example, the equation for Gridblock 4 becomes

$$0p_3 + 1p_4 + 0p_5 + 0p_{11} = 10^6. \qquad (7.95)$$

Because these dummy equations are not coupled to the other equations (no other unknowns appear in any of these equations), they do not affect the final solution but do help maintain the band structure for the problem. Note that preservation of the band structure of the coefficient matrix is achieved at the expense of inflating the coefficient matrix from 26×26 to 42×42. Therefore, in implementing this simple strategy, we must consider the enormous increase in the computational work and storage requirements involved. When implementing dummy equations of this type, large values (much larger than the pressures expected for the active blocks) should be assigned to the inactive blocks to ensure that, when the arrays are printed, the format used for the expected pressures does not accommodate the numbers specified and print a string of asterisks (see **Fig. 7.20**). This results in printed maps with the same shape as the reservoir (compare Fig. 7.17 with Fig. 7.20).

This method of treating irregular boundaries may not always be the optimal method for handling such cases. Other direct-solution methods that can be used to solve the matrix equation generated by irregular boundaries include sparse-matrix[2] and variable-bandwidth techniques.[3]

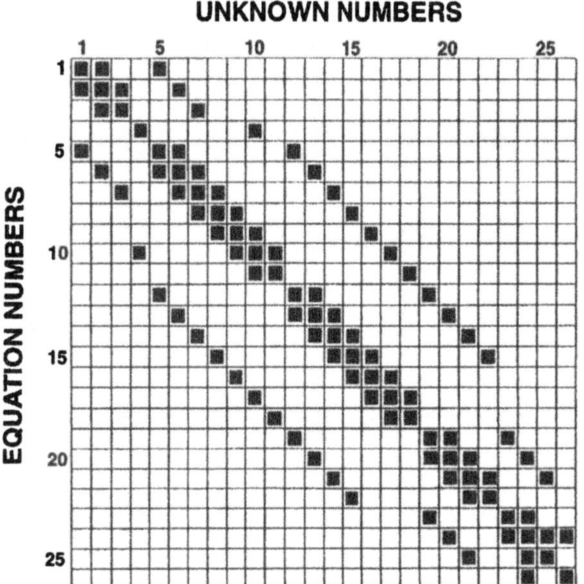

Fig. 7.18—Coefficient matrix resulting from the discretization and node numbering scheme shown in Fig. 7.17. Filled squares are nonzero entries.

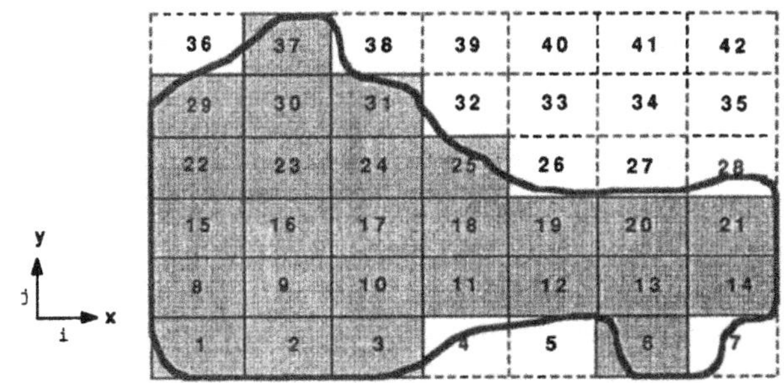

Fig. 7.19—Block ordering that includes active and inactive blocks for a 2D reservoir with irregular boundaries.

****	1648	****	****	****	****	****
1786	1812	1806	****	****	****	****
1789	1801	1792	1764	****	****	****
1763	1792	1724	1713	1701	1690	1673
1747	1754	1718	1709	1700	1690	1672
1703	1738	1707	****	****	1642	****

Fig. 7.20—Possible printout of pressure array that results from use of dummy equations such as described by Eq. 7.95 for inactive blocks.

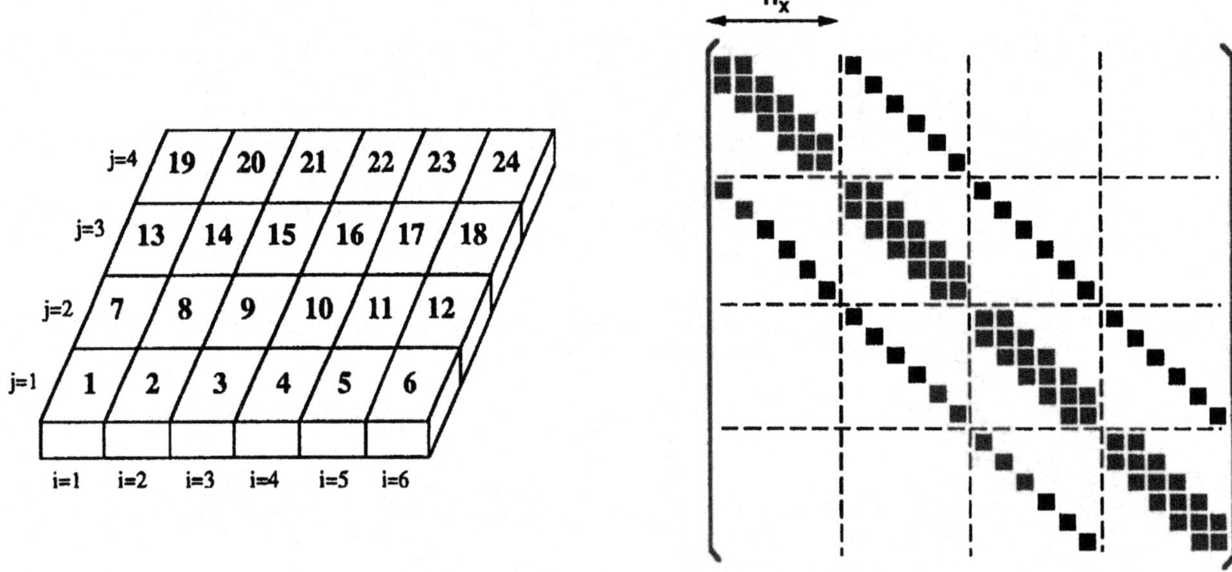

Fig. 7.21—Natural ordering by rows and resulting coefficient matrix (after Ref. 6).

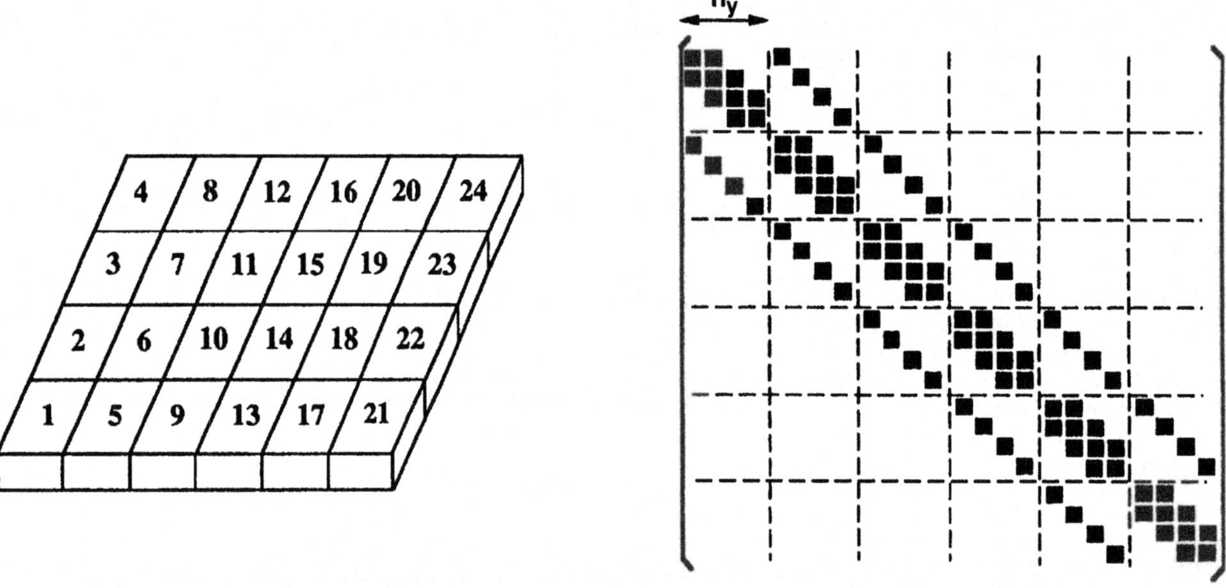

Fig. 7.22—Natural ordering by columns and resulting coefficient matrix (after Ref. 6).

As stated earlier, the use of dummy equations for irregular boundaries increases the computational work required to solve the resulting matrix equation. Although, at first glance, this may seem to degrade the efficiency of the matrix-equation solution, this is not always the case. This is because the solution of a matrix equation with a banded coefficient matrix lends itself to vector computations, while general sparse-matrix solutions may not. Because vector computations are faster than scalar computations, all the computations (including the additional computations) required by the use of dummy equations may actually be performed faster than the fewer scalar computations required by sparse-matrix techniques. Consequently, on a vector-processing computer, the use of dummy equations may be more optimal than sparse-matrix techniques. Appendix C discusses the differences between scalar- and vector-processing computers.

7.3.3 Gridblock Ordering. As Secs. 7.2.2 and 7.2.3 show, the structure of the coefficient matrix depends on the dimensions of the problem and the ordering of the gridblocks. Another general observation from the previous sections is that coefficient matrices obtained for 1D, 2D, and 3D problems have sparse structures. In other words, most of the entries of the coefficient matrices are zeros. The objective of using different gridblock-ordering schemes is to reduce the computational work involved in solving a system of finite-difference equations. This section shows how the structure of the coefficient matrix can change by use of different ordering schemes, and how this can reduce the computer time and storage requirements of a simulation run.

Natural Ordering. Consider a 2D grid with four rows and six columns. If a natural-ordering scheme by rows is implemented, the resulting coefficient matrix has a pentadiagonal structure (**Fig. 7.21**). In the resulting coefficient matrix, all nonzero entries are located between the uppermost and lowermost diagonals. If we define the bandwidth as the maximum number of elements in any row of the matrix, the coefficient matrix obtained by use of natural ordering by rows has a bandwidth of 13 (or $2 \times 6 + 1$). For natural ordering by rows, the bandwidth of a 2D problem is always $2n_x + 1$, where n_x represents the maximum number of blocks in any row.

If we reorder the gridblocks by columns to take advantage of the fact that the maximum number of blocks in any column is smaller than the number of blocks in any row (in this example, $n_x > n_y$, where $n_x = 6$ and $n_y = 4$), the bandwidth of the resulting coefficient

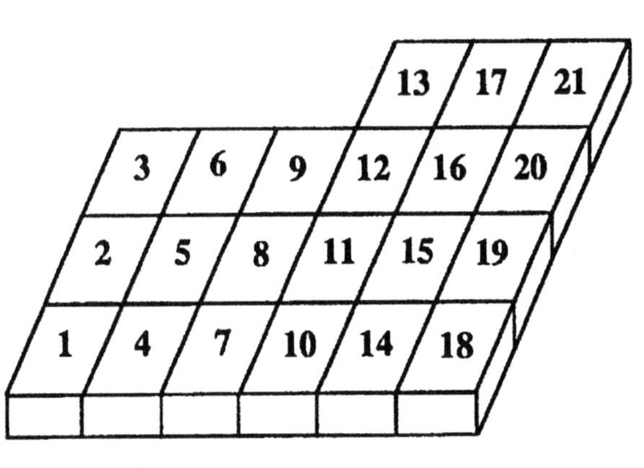

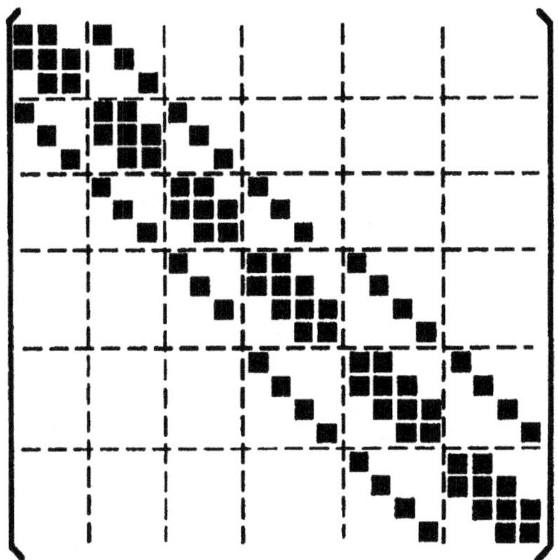

Fig. 7.23—Natural ordering of an irregular grid by columns and resulting coefficient matrix (after Ref. 6).

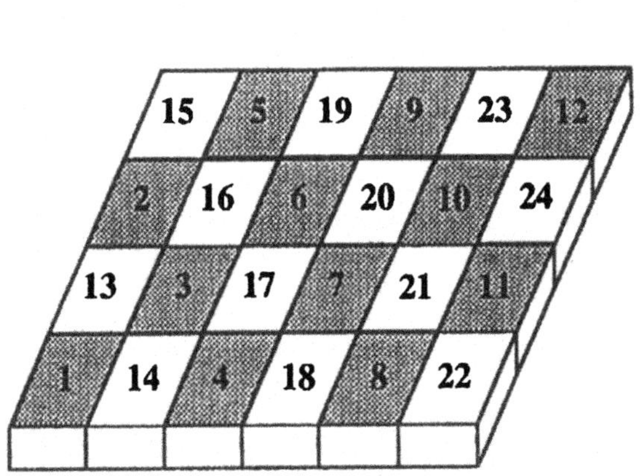

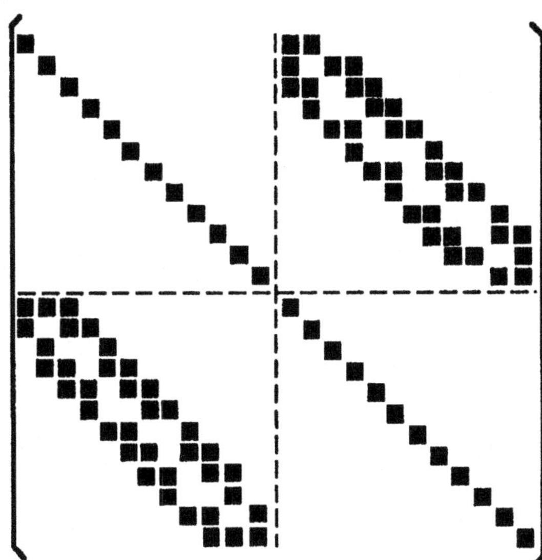

Fig. 7.24—D-4 ordering and resulting coefficient matrix.

matrix is $2n_y + 1$ or 9. The ordering scheme and the resulting coefficient matrix in **Fig. 7.22** require less computational work than those in Fig. 7.21. It is more efficient to solve problems with smaller bandwidths than problems with larger bandwidths because all computations are performed on the matrix entries within the bands. Consequently, smaller bandwidths result in fewer computations.

As Sec. 7.3.2 discusses, irregular boundaries alter the band structure of the coefficient matrix. Although the band structure is altered, the bandwidth calculation still holds. This results in a number of additional diagonals, depending on the degree of irregularity appearing in the coefficient matrix. As **Fig. 7.23** shows, the maximum bandwidth of the coefficient matrix for the associated irregular grid is still nine because the maximum $n_y = 4$. Note that, because of the appearance of extra diagonals (as shown in Fig. 7.23, where the coefficient matrix has seven diagonals instead of five), the coefficient matrix has a variable bandwidth. In summary, natural ordering (either by rows or columns) always results in a banded matrix.

D-4 Ordering. Natural ordering, either by rows or by columns, is not the only choice for ordering the grid unknowns. Other ordering techniques, such as D-4 ordering,[4] can be used to improve the efficiency of the direct-solution procedures.

In D-4 ordering, gridblocks are ordered in the form of diagonals. **Fig. 7.24** illustrates this ordering scheme. In this figure, the shaded gridblocks are the first points loaded into the coefficient matrix and the unshaded gridblocks are loaded afterward. This ordering scheme does not allow adjacent gridblocks (gridblocks that communicate) to be loaded successively into the coefficient matrix. Fig. 7.24 also shows the resulting coefficient matrix for D-4 ordering.

The structure of the coefficient matrix resulting from D-4 ordering can be partitioned into four submatrices (Fig. 7.24), consisting of two submatrices with only main diagonals and two submatrices with a general sparse structure. The benefit of the D-4-ordering technique is that the diagonal elements in the upper-left submatrix can be used to eliminate the elements in the lower-left submatrix in $n/2$ steps in the elimination process.

Fig. 7.25 shows the structure of the coefficient matrix after $n/2$ elimination steps. The squares represent locations that originally contained nonzero entries, while the circles represent locations that originally contained zero entries but that contain nonzero entries generated during the elimination process (fill locations). The system of equations defined by the lower-right matrix after $n/2$ steps (see Fig. 7.25) is referred to as the reduced system of equations. At this stage, we can use either a direct or iterative solution technique to solve the reduced system of equations. This two-step procedure results in a fully triangulated matrix suitable for backsubstitution.

Cyclic-2 (Red-Black) Ordering. In cyclic-2 ordering, gridblocks are ordered by going along a row or column and skipping every other gridblock. Again, the objective of cyclic-2 ordering is to prevent cells that are in communication from being loaded into the coefficient matrix consecutively. **Fig. 7.26** shows cyclic-2 ordering and the resulting coefficient matrix.

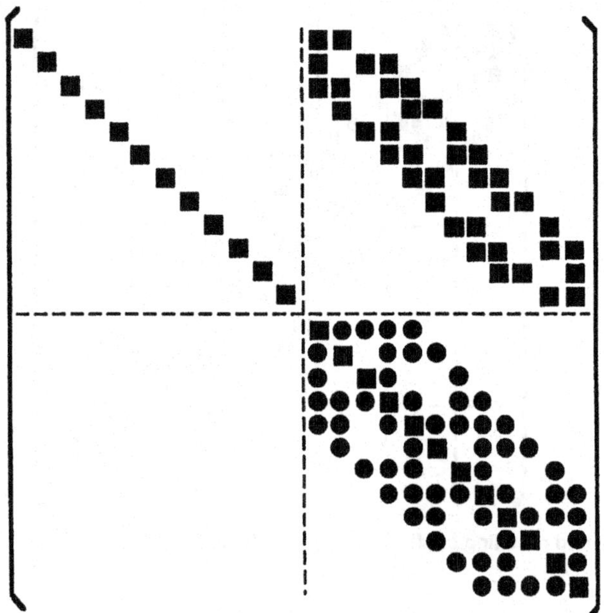

Fig. 7.25—Upper triangular matrix resulting from D-4 ordering (after Ref. 6).

The structure of the coefficient matrix resulting from cyclic-2 ordering has a structure similar to that from D-4 ordering. The only difference is the locations of the nonzero elements in the upper-right and lower-left submatrices. The procedure for solving the matrix equation formulated with cyclic-2 ordering is identical to the procedure used for D-4 ordering.

D-2 Ordering. In D-2 ordering, gridblocks are loaded into the coefficient matrix along the diagonals of the grid system. **Fig. 7.27** illustrates this ordering technique. As this figure shows, gridblocks that are in communication are allowed to be loaded into the coefficient matrix consecutively. The objective of D-2 ordering is to reduce the envelope of the nonzero elements of the coefficient matrix compared with natural ordering. As previously discussed, fewer calculations are required for smaller envelopes of nonzero entries.

7.3.4 Iterative Methods. As discussed earlier, the accuracy of a solution vector obtained through a direct process depends on the precision of the floating-point word of the computer used in the study. Round-off errors can accumulate and grow uncontrollably and may dominate the solution, especially in the case of large sets of linear equations.

Iterative methods give the solution of the system of equations as the limit of a sequence of intermediate vectors that progressively converge toward the exact solution. The process starts with an initial guess vector for the unknown vector and continues by successively improving on this guess until the final solution is obtained. For a convergent scheme, the error at the end of each iteration is reduced and the solution vector should approach the correct solution. To terminate the process, a convergence criterion is set and iterations are stopped when this criterion is met. **Fig. 7.28** shows the iterative process and the associated convergence path. As Fig. 7.28 shows, the convergence curve usually follows a monotonically decreasing path (in terms of absolute value).

One important task when an iterative equation solver is used is to establish convergence criteria for the given problem. A convergence test checks the difference between the solutions obtained at two successive iteration levels. If the absolute value of the difference becomes insignificant, this indicates small refinements to the unknowns when the solution proceeds from one iteration level to the next. It is incorrect to assume that the exact solution is within the immediate vicinity of the last iterate when the convergence criteria are met and the iteration process is terminated. **Fig. 7.29** shows this graphically; two convergence paths are shown for a given problem. As illustrated, Iteration Scheme f converges faster than Scheme s. This figure also shows that, when similar convergence criteria are used for Schemes f and s, the iteration process for Scheme s terminates at a point farther from the exact solution. This observation highlights the importance of selecting convergence criteria. Because the exact solution is not available during computations, the only comparison that can be made is on the improvement of the solution vector. The chosen convergence criteria are problem specific. Obviously, for the problem studied with Scheme s in Fig. 7.29, finer convergence criteria are desirable. Fortunately, we can decide what constitutes suitable convergence criteria for a given problem. This decision is based on material-balance checks performed after the termination of the iteration process (Secs. 8.2.7, 8.3.3, and 8.4.2). If the convergence check is satisfied but poor material-balance checks are obtained, it is advisable to make the convergence criteria tighter and to continue with additional linear iterations.

The remainder of this chapter introduces several simple iterative methods and studies various aspects of these procedures, such as convergence requirements, convergence speed, and storage needs.

Jacobi Iteration. The Jacobi iteration is one of the earliest iterative methods. Although it is rarely used in reservoir simulation because of the relatively slow convergence rate of the process, the discussion of the procedure is of historical interest because the Jacobi iteration scheme is the basis for other, more powerful iterative techniques.

Consider a system of equations of the form

$$a_{11}x_1 + a_{12}x_2 + a_{13}x_3 + a_{14}x_4 + \ldots + a_{1n}x_n = d_1 \qquad (7.2a)$$

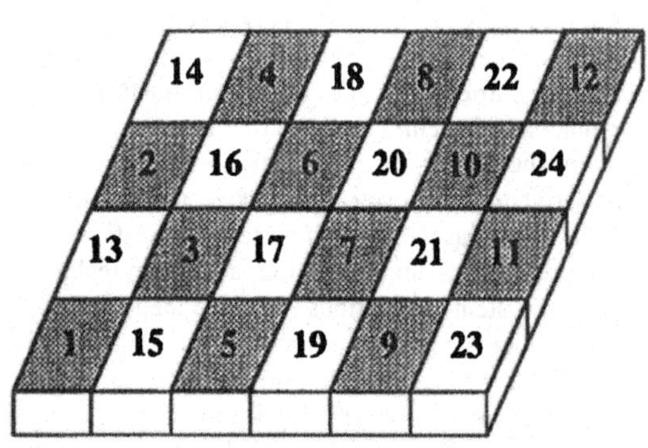

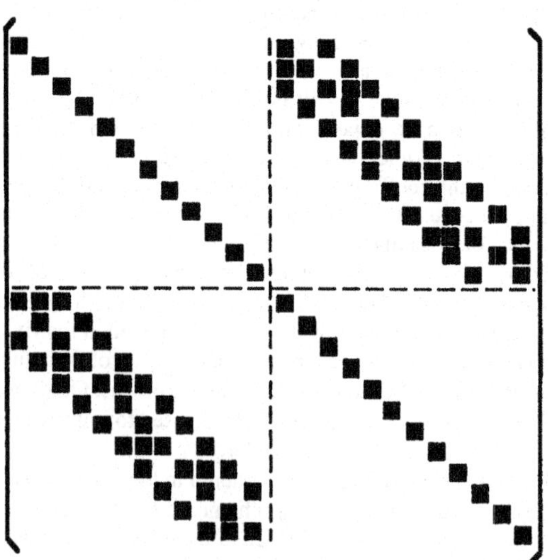

Fig. 7.26—Cyclic-2 ordering and resulting coefficient matrix (after Ref. 6).

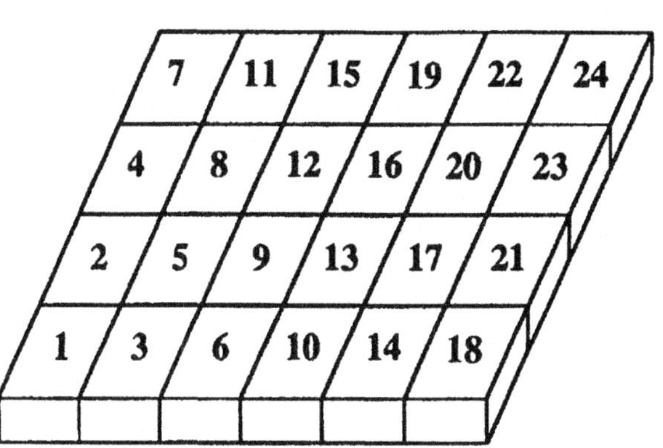

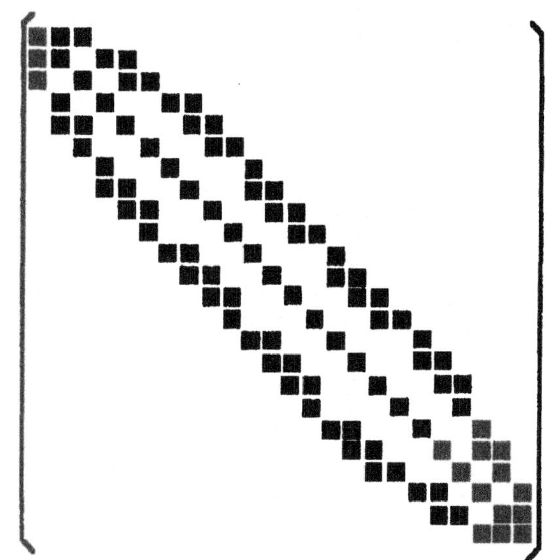

Fig. 7.27—D-2 ordering and resulting coefficient matrix (after Ref. 6).

$$a_{21}x_1 + a_{22}x_2 + a_{23}x_3 + a_{24}x_4 + \ldots + a_{2n}x_n = d_2 \quad \text{(7.2b)}$$

$$a_{31}x_1 + a_{32}x_2 + a_{33}x_3 + a_{34}x_4 + \ldots + a_{3n}x_n = d_3 \quad \text{(7.2c)}$$

through $a_{n1}x_1 + a_{n2}x_2 + a_{n3}x_3 + a_{n4}x_4 + \ldots + a_{nn}x_n = d_n$, ... (7.2d)

where $a_{ii} \neq 0$ for $i = 1,2, \ldots, n$.

The system defined by Eq. 7.2 can be rearranged to the following form by use of the equation for the ith gridblock (the first unknown from Eq. 7.2a, the second unknown from Eq. 7.2b, and so on) to solve for the ith unknown; i.e.,

$$x_1 = \frac{1}{a_{11}}(d_1 - a_{12}x_2 - a_{13}x_3 - a_{14}x_4 \ldots - a_{1n}x_n), \quad \text{(7.96a)}$$

$$x_2 = \frac{1}{a_{22}}(d_2 - a_{21}x_1 - a_{23}x_3 - a_{24}x_4 \ldots - a_{2n}x_n), \quad \text{(7.96b)}$$

$$x_3 = \frac{1}{a_{33}}(d_3 - a_{31}x_1 - a_{32}x_2 - a_{34}x_4 \ldots - a_{3n}x_n), \quad \text{(7.96c)}$$

through $x_n = \frac{1}{a_{nn}}(d_n - a_{n1}x_1 - a_{n2}x_2 - a_{n3}x_3 \ldots - a_{n,n-1}x_{n-1})$. ..... (7.96d)

An initial approximation to all the unknowns starts the iteration process. The left sides of Eqs. 7.96a through 7.96d are calculated at the new iteration level by use of the initial approximation on the right-side computations. If we denote the new iteration level with the superscript $(k+1)$ (throughout the text, a superscript within a set of parentheses indicates the iteration level) and the old iteration level with the superscript (k), Eq. 7.96 can be written as

$$x_1^{(k+1)} = \frac{1}{a_{11}}\left[d_1 - a_{12}x_2^{(k)} - a_{13}x_3^{(k)} - a_{14}x_4^{(k)} \ldots - a_{1n}x_n^{(k)}\right], \quad \text{(7.97a)}$$

$$x_2^{(k+1)} = \frac{1}{a_{22}}\left[d_2 - a_{21}x_1^{(k)} - a_{23}x_3^{(k)} - a_{24}x_4^{(k)} \ldots - a_{2n}x_n^{(k)}\right], \quad \text{(7.97b)}$$

$$x_3^{(k+1)} = \frac{1}{a_{33}}\left[d_3 - a_{31}x_1^{(k)} - a_{32}x_2^{(k)} - a_{34}x_4^{(k)} \ldots - a_{3n}x_n^{(k)}\right], \quad \text{(7.97c)}$$

through $x_n^{(k+1)} = \frac{1}{a_{nn}}\left[d_n - a_{n1}x_1^{(k)} - a_{n2}x_2^{(k)} - a_{n3}x_3^{(k)} \ldots - a_{n,n-1}x_{n-1}^{(k)}\right]$. ..... (7.97d)

During the implementation of the Jacobi iteration at each step, the values of $x_1, x_2, \ldots, x_n$ at the old iteration level, (k), are updated with the values at the new iteration level, $(k+1)$. This cyclic feedback operation is repeated until the input and output of a cycle eventually agree within a specified tolerance and the iterations are terminated. Remember that, in the implementation of the convergence test, a solution vector is not considered converged unless every single component of the unknown vector satisfies the convergence criterion.

The algorithm for the Jacobi iteration is as follows. Calculate

$$x_i^{(k+1)} = \frac{1}{a_{ii}}\left[d_i - \sum_{\substack{j=1 \\ j \neq i}}^{n} a_{ij}x_j^{(k)}\right] \quad \text{(7.98)}$$

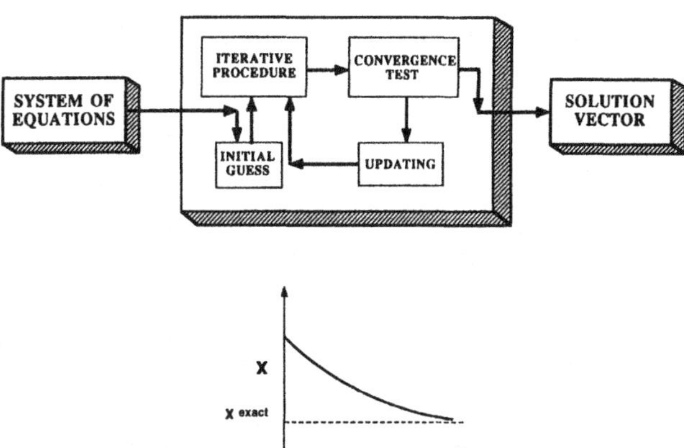

Fig. 7.28—Schematic representation of an iterative process and a convergence path.

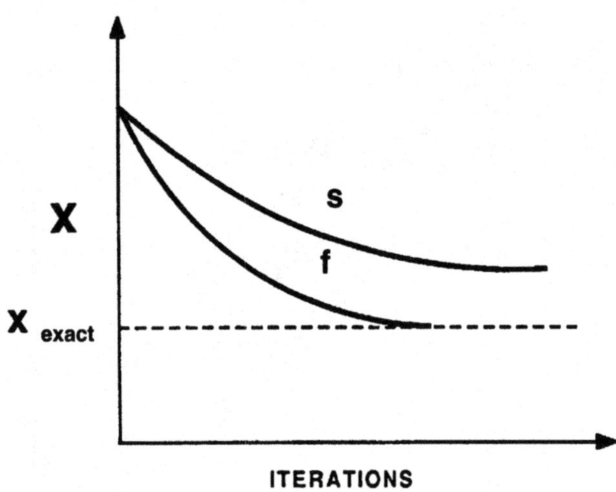

Fig. 7.29—Fast (f) and slow (s) convergence paths.

for $i = 1, 2, \ldots, n$, and check for convergence with

$$|x_i^{(k+1)} - x_i^{(k)}| \leqq \varepsilon \quad \ldots\ldots (7.99)$$

for $i = 1, 2, \ldots, n$, where ε = specified error tolerance (convergence criterion).

If the convergence test indicated by Eq. 7.99 is satisfied for each unknown, then the iterations are terminated. Otherwise the values of x_i at Iteration Level $(k+1)$ are assigned to the values at Iteration Level (k), and a new iteration is started.

Example 7.6. Use the Jacobi iteration scheme to solve the following system of equations. Use a convergence criterion of $\varepsilon = 0.5$.

$$-2p_1 + p_2 = -200. \quad \ldots\ldots (7.100a)$$

$$p_1 - 2p_2 + p_3 = 0. \quad \ldots\ldots (7.100b)$$

$$p_2 - 2p_3 = -100. \quad \ldots\ldots (7.100c)$$

Solution. The Jacobi iterative equations are

$$p_1^{(k+1)} = \tfrac{1}{2}\left[p_2^{(k)} + 200\right], \quad \ldots\ldots (7.101a)$$

$$p_2^{(k+1)} = \tfrac{1}{2}\left[p_1^{(k)} + p_3^{(k)}\right], \quad \ldots\ldots (7.101b)$$

and $p_3^{(k+1)} = \tfrac{1}{2}\left[p_2^{(k)} + 100\right]. \quad \ldots\ldots (7.101c)$

With an initial guess of 100 for all unknowns, the Jacobi iterative equations for the first iteration, $(k=0)$, predict

$$p_1^{(1)} = \tfrac{1}{2}\left[p_2^{(0)} + 200\right] = \tfrac{1}{2}(100 + 200) = 150,$$

$$p_2^{(1)} = \tfrac{1}{2}\left[p_1^{(0)} + p_3^{(0)}\right] = \tfrac{1}{2}(100 + 100) = 100,$$

and $p_3^{(1)} = \tfrac{1}{2}\left[p_2^{(0)} + 100\right] = \tfrac{1}{2}(100 + 100) = 100.$

This procedure is continued until the convergence criterion is satisfied. **Table 7.2** presents the solution within the specified tolerance obtained after 13 iterations. The exact solution to this system of equations is $p_1 = 175$, $p_2 = 150$, and $p_3 = 125$. This solution can be verified by substituting these values of p into the original set of equations.

TABLE 7.2—JACOBI ITERATION FOR EXAMPLE 7.6

$k+1$	p_1	p_2	p_3	$\max_i \lvert p_i^{(k+1)} - p_i^{(k)} \rvert$
0	100	100	100	—
1	150	100	100	50
2	150	125	100	25
3	162.5	125	112.5	12.5
4	162.5	137.5	112.5	12.5
5	168.75	137.5	118.75	6.25
6	168.75	143.75	118.75	6.25
7	171.88	143.75	121.88	3.13
8	171.88	146.88	121.88	3.13
9	173.44	146.88	123.44	1.56
10	173.44	148.44	124.44	1.56
11	174.22	148.44	124.22	0.78
12	174.22	149.22	124.22	0.78
13	174.61	149.22	124.61	0.39

Gauss-Seidel Iteration. The Gauss-Seidel iteration is a modification of the Jacobi iteration that simply uses the latest information available on the right side. In other words, each unknown on the right side is replaced by its most recently calculated approximation. The Gauss-Seidel iterative equations corresponding to those defined by Eq. 7.97 become

$$x_1^{(k+1)} = \frac{1}{a_{11}}\left[d_1 - a_{12}x_2^{(k)} - a_{13}x_3^{(k)} - a_{14}x_4^{(k)} - \ldots - a_{1n}x_n^{(k)}\right], \quad \ldots\ldots (7.102a)$$

$$x_2^{(k+1)} = \frac{1}{a_{22}}\left[d_2 - a_{21}x_1^{(k+1)} - a_{23}x_3^{(k)} - a_{24}x_4^{(k)} - \ldots - a_{2n}x_n^{(k)}\right], \quad \ldots\ldots (7.102b)$$

$$x_3^{(k+1)} = \frac{1}{a_{33}}\left[d_3 - a_{31}x_1^{(k+1)} - a_{32}x_2^{(k+1)} - a_{34}x_4^{(k)} - \ldots - a_{4n}x_n^{(k)}\right], \quad \ldots\ldots (7.102c)$$

through $x_n^{(k+1)} = \dfrac{1}{a_{nn}}\left[d_n - a_{n1}x_1^{(k+1)} - a_{n2}x_2^{(k+1)} - a_{n3}x_3^{(k+1)} - \ldots - a_{n,n-1}x_{n-1}^{(k+1)}\right]. \quad \ldots\ldots (7.102d)$

A comparison of the system of equations defined by Eqs. 7.97 and 7.102 indicates that, if unknown x_i is being calculated, the unknowns x_j for $j < i$ are evaluated at Iteration Level $(k+1)$ while the unknowns x_j for $j > i$ are evaluated at Iteration Level (k).

Because the Gauss-Seidel iteration uses the most recent information, it generally converges in fewer iterations than the Jacobi iteration (approximately half as many). In the Jacobi iteration, values of the solution vector at the old iteration level need to be stored during the new-iteration-level computations. In the Gauss-Seidel iteration, however, each entry of the solution vector at the preceding iteration level is used to calculate all succeeding entries of the solution vector. In other words, the Jacobi iteration requires that the recent iterations be kept in storage while the Gauss-Seidel iteration does not. Consequently, the Gauss-Seidel iteration is more efficient in terms of storage, as well as computer time. For the Gauss-Seidel iterative scheme to converge, the Jacobi iterative scheme must also converge for the same problem. This condition for convergence of the Gauss-Seidel scheme is necessary but not sufficient. The Gauss-Seidel iteration can be shown to converge if the coefficient matrix is strictly (row) diagonally dominant. **[A]** of Order n is strictly (row) diagonally dominant if

$$|a_{ii}| > \sum_{\substack{j=1 \\ j \neq 1}}^{n} |a_{ij}| \quad \ldots\ldots (7.103)$$

for $i = 1,2,\ldots, n$.

The algorithm for the Gauss-Seidel iteration is as follows. Calculate

$$x_i^{(k+1)} = \frac{1}{a_{ii}}\left[d_i - \sum_{j=1}^{i-1} a_{ij}x_j^{(k+1)} - \sum_{j=i+1}^{n} a_{ij}x_j^{(k)}\right] \quad \text{(7.104)}$$

for $i = 1,2,\ldots, n$, and check for convergence with

$$|x_i^{(k+1)} - x_i^{(k)}| \leqq \varepsilon \quad \text{(7.99)}$$

for $i = 1,2,\ldots, n$. Again, the convergence check needs to be satisfied for every unknown.

Example 7.7. Use the Gauss-Seidel iterative scheme to solve the system of equations of Example 7.6. Again, start with an initial guess of 100 for each unknown and use a convergence criterion of $\varepsilon = 0.5$. Compare the performance of the Gauss-Seidel iteration with that of the Jacobi iteration.

Solution. Gauss-Seidel iterative equations for the problem of Example 7.6 are

$$p_1^{(k+1)} = ½\left(p_2^{(k)} + 200\right) \quad \text{(7.105a)}$$

$$p_2^{(k+1)} = ½\left(p_1^{(k+1)} + p_3^{(k)}\right) \quad \text{(7.105b)}$$

and $p_3^{(k+1)} = ½\left(p_2^{(k+1)} + 100\right)$. (7.105c)

For an initial guess of 100 for p_1, p_2 and p_3, the Gauss-Seidel iterative equations for the first iteration, $(k=0)$, predict

$$p_1^{(1)} = ½\left[p_2^{(o)} + 200\right] = ½(100 + 200) = 150,$$

$$p_2^{(1)} = ½\left[p_1^{(1)} + p_3^{(0)}\right] = ½(150 + 100) = 125,$$

and $p_3^{(1)} = ½\left[p_2^{(1)} + 100\right] = ½(125 + 100) = 112.5.$

Table 7.3 shows the solution that satisfies the convergence criterion of $\varepsilon = 0.5$ obtained after seven iterations.

It is clear from Tables 7.2 and 7.3 that the Gauss-Seidel iterative scheme converges approximately two times faster (in terms of the number of iterations) than the Jacobi iterative scheme for the same problem and tolerance. **Fig. 7.30** shows the convergence paths followed for each member of the solution vector for the Jacobi and Gauss-Seidel iterative schemes. The figure clearly indicates that Gauss-Seidel iteration converges faster than the Jacobi iteration for each element of the solution vector.

Successive Overrelaxation (SOR) Methods. In SOR methods, the convergence rate is accelerated by modifying the values of the estimated unknowns with the objective of reducing the number of iterations required for a solution. The selection of an appropriate relaxation factor used to accelerate the Gauss-Seidel iteration is studied in detail later.

TABLE 7.3—GAUSS-SEIDEL ITERATION FOR EXAMPLE 7.7

$k+1$	p_1	p_2	p_3	$\max_i \lvert p_i^{(k+1)} - p_i^{(k)}\rvert$
0	100	100	100	—
1	150	125	112.5	50
2	162.5	137.5	118.75	12.5
3	168.75	143.75	121.88	6.25
4	171.88	146.88	123.44	3.13
5	173.44	148.44	124.22	1.56
6	174.22	149.22	124.61	0.78
7	174.61	149.61	124.81	0.39

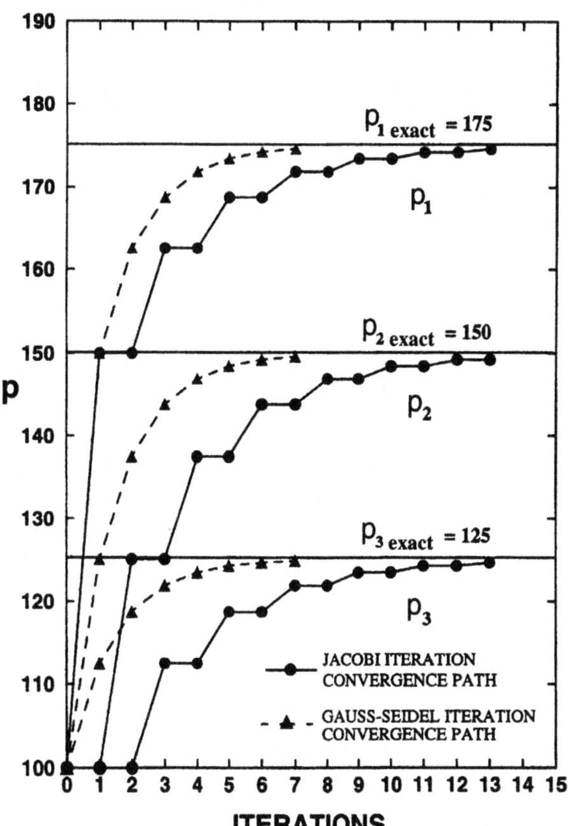

Fig. 7.30—Comparison of convergence rates of Jacobi and Gauss-Seidel iterative schemes.

Point SOR (PSOR) Method. Here, we start with the Gauss-Seidel iterative equations by writing Eq. 7.102 in a slightly different way. Adding $x_i^{(k)}$ to the right side and subtracting $x_i^{(k)}$ from the right side of equations for $i = 1,2,\ldots, n$ yields

$$x_1^{(k+1)} = x_1^{(k)} + \left\{\frac{1}{a_{11}}\left[d_1 - a_{11}x_1^{(k)} - a_{12}x_2^{(k)} - a_{13}x_3^{(k)} - a_{14}x_4^{(k)} - \ldots - a_{1n}x_n^{(k)}\right]\right\}, \quad \text{(7.106a)}$$

$$x_2^{(k+1)} = x_2^{(k)} + \left\{\frac{1}{a_{22}}\left[d_2 - a_{21}x_1^{(k+1)} - a_{22}x_2^{(k)} - a_{23}x_3^{(k)} - a_{24}x_4^{(k)} - \ldots - a_{2n}x_n^{(k)}\right]\right\}, \quad \text{(7.106b)}$$

$$x_3^{(k+1)} = x_3^{(k)} + \left\{\frac{1}{a_{33}}\left[d_3 - a_{31}x_1^{(k+1)} - a_{32}x_2^{(k+1)} - a_{33}x_3^{(k)} - a_{34}x_4^{(k)} - \ldots - a_{3n}x_n^{(k)}\right]\right\}, \quad \text{(7.106c)}$$

through $x_n^{(k+1)} = x_n^{(k)} + \left\{\frac{1}{a_{nn}}\left[d_n - a_{n1}x_1^{(k+1)} - a_{n2}x_2^{(k+1)} - a_{n3}x_3^{(k+1)} - a_{n4}x_4^{(k+1)} - \ldots - a_{n,n-1}x_n^{(k+1)} - a_{nn}x_n^{(k)}\right]\right\}.$ (7.106d)

These equations can be interpreted as $x_i^{(k+1)} = x_i^{(k)}$ + corrections made by each convergent Gauss-Seidel iteration.

We can observe that the correction term for the unknown x_i is nothing but the residual of the equation for Gridblock i divided by a_{ii} resulting from application of the Gauss-Seidel iteration. Now, we must determine whether we can improve on the Gauss-Seidel correction term by multiplying it with a constant relaxation factor. This concept forms the basis of the SOR iteration, which is defined as

$$x_1^{(k+1)} = x_1^{(k)} + \frac{\omega}{a_{11}}\Big[d_1 - a_{11}x_1^{(k)} - a_{12}x_2^{(k)} - a_{13}x_3^{(k)} - a_{14}x_4^{(k)} - \ldots - a_{1n}x_n^{(k)}\Big], \quad \ldots\ldots\ldots\ldots (7.107a)$$

$$x_2^{(k+1)} = x_2^{(k)} + \frac{\omega}{a_{22}}\Big[d_2 - a_{21}x_1^{(k+1)} - a_{22}x_2^{(k)} - a_{23}x_3^{(k)} - a_{24}x_4^{(k)} - \ldots - a_{2n}x_n^{(k)}\Big], \quad \ldots\ldots\ldots\ldots (7.107b)$$

$$x_3^{(k+1)} = x_3^{(k)} + \frac{\omega}{a_{33}}\Big[d_3 - a_{31}x_1^{(k+1)} - a_{32}x_2^{(k+1)} - a_{33}x_3^{(k)} - a_{34}x_4^{(k)} - \ldots - a_{3n}x_n^{(k)}\Big], \quad \ldots\ldots\ldots\ldots (7.107c)$$

and $$x_n^{(k+1)} = x_n^{(k)} + \frac{\omega}{a_{nn}}\Big[d_n - a_{n1}x_1^{(k+1)} - a_{n2}x_2^{(k+1)} - a_{n3}x_3^{(k+1)} - a_{n4}x_4^{(k+1)} - \ldots - a_{n,n-1}x_n^{(k+1)} - a_{nn}x_n^{(k)}\Big]. \quad \ldots\ldots\ldots\ldots (7.107d)$$

In Eq. 7.107, ω = acceleration parameter or relaxation factor that is a positive constant between 1 and 2. The specific value of ω that maximizes the rate of convergence is known as the optimum acceleration parameter, ω_{opt}, which is problem specific. Estimation of Optimum Overrelaxation Parameter later in this section presents a simple technique to estimate its value. The challenge of finding a unique ω_{opt} implies that any arbitrary value of ω between 1 and 2 does not necessarily accelerate the convergence for each element of the unknown vector. If $\omega = 1$, the iterative equations of Eq. 7.107 reduce to the form of the Gauss-Seidel iteration.

The algorithm for the PSOR iteration is as follows. Calculate

$$x_i^{(k+1)} = \frac{\omega}{a_{ii}}\left[d_i - \sum_{j=1}^{i-1} a_{ij}x_j^{(k+1)} - \sum_{j=i+1}^{n} a_{ij}x_j^{(k)}\right] - (\omega - 1)x_i^{(k)} \quad \ldots\ldots\ldots\ldots (7.108)$$

for $i = 1, 2, \ldots, n$, and check for convergence with

$$|x_i^{(k+1)} - x_i^{(k)}| \leqq \varepsilon \quad \ldots\ldots\ldots\ldots (7.99)$$

for $i = 1, 2, \ldots, n$. If the algorithm is implemented with ω_{opt}, it is possible to accelerate the convergence rate of the Gauss-Seidel iteration by a factor of approximately two.

Example 7.8. Use the PSOR iteration scheme to solve the system of equations in Example 7.6. Again, start with an initial guess of 100 for each unknown and use an acceleration parameter of $\omega = 1.1715$ (as we show later in this section, this is the optimum value of ω). Check for convergence with a convergence criterion of $\varepsilon = 0.5$.

Solution. The PSOR iterative equations are

$$p_1^{(k+1)} = \frac{\omega}{2}\Big[p_2^{(k)} + 200\Big] - (\omega - 1)p_1^{(k)}, \quad \ldots\ldots\ldots (7.109a)$$

$$p_2^{(k+1)} = \frac{\omega}{2}\Big[p_1^{(k+1)} + p_3^{(k)}\Big] - (\omega - 1)p_2^{(k)}, \quad \ldots\ldots (7.109b)$$

and $$p_3^{(k+1)} = \frac{\omega}{2}\Big[p_2^{(k+1)} + 100\Big] - (\omega - 1)p_3^{(k)}. \quad \ldots\ldots (7.109c)$$

With an initial guess of 100 for p_1, p_2, and p_3 and an acceleration parameter of $\omega = 1.1715$, the PSOR iterative equations for the first iteration, $(k=0)$, predict

TABLE 7.4—PSOR ITERATION FOR EXAMPLE 7.8

$k+1$	p_1	p_2	p_3	$\max_i \lvert p_i^{(k+1)} - p_i^{(k)} \rvert$
0	100	100	100	—
1	158.58	134.31	120.10	58.58
2	168.63	146.09	123.55	11.78
3	173.80	149.11	124.72	5.17
4	174.68	149.80	124.93	0.88
5	174.94	149.96	124.98	0.26

$$p_1^{(1)} = \frac{1.1715}{2}\Big[p_2^{(0)} + 200\Big] - (1.1715 - 1)p_1^{(0)},$$

$$= \frac{1.1715}{2}[100 + 200] - (1.1715 - 1)(100) = 158.58,$$

$$p_2^{(1)} = \frac{1.1715}{2}\Big[p_1^{(1)} + p_3^{(0)}\Big] - (1.1715 - 1)p_2^{(0)},$$

$$= \frac{1.1715}{2}[158.58 + 100] - (1.1715 - 1)(100) = 134.31,$$

and $$p_3^{(1)} = \frac{1.1715}{2}\Big[p_2^{(1)} + 100\Big] - (1.1715 - 1)p_3^{(0)}$$

$$= \frac{1.1715}{2}[134.31 + 100] - (1.1715 - 1)(100) = 120.10.$$

Note that the values for the entries of the solution vector at the end of the first iteration are much better than those obtained from the Gauss-Seidel iteration. **Table 7.4** presents the solution that satisfies the convergence criterion of $\varepsilon = 0.5$ obtained after five iterations.

Line SOR (LSOR) Method. Implementation of the SOR technique to a group of unknowns located on a line results in the LSOR method. In this method, unknowns located on the same line are solved and relaxed simultaneously. For this discussion, consider the 2D Laplace equation,

$$\frac{\partial^2 p}{\partial x^2} + \frac{\partial^2 p}{\partial y^2} = 0. \quad \ldots\ldots\ldots\ldots (7.24)$$

The finite-difference approximation of Eq. 7.24, assuming $\Delta x = \Delta y$, is given by Eq. 7.26,

$$p_{i,j-1} + p_{i-1,j} - 4p_{i,j} + p_{i+1,j} + p_{i,j+1} = 0. \quad \ldots\ldots (7.26)$$

Consider the 2D domain in **Fig. 7.31**. When Eq. 7.26 is written for each gridblock in the system, by use of natural ordering, a pentadiagonal coefficient matrix is formed. When the LSOR method is implemented, the unknowns located in the same row (or column) are solved simultaneously. Fig. 7.31 shows the positions of unknown nodes at a given iteration level for two possible sweep directions. If the system is going to be swept along the y direction, as Fig. 7.31a shows, all the nodes that share the same j subscript make the unknowns for Line j. The unknowns for the nodes located on the previous line (nodes with Subscript $j-1$) are calculated during the previous line computations, so their values are available at the current (new) iteration level. Nodes with Subscript $j+1$ are located on the next line to be solved; therefore, their values are available at the old iteration level. On the other hand, if the system is to be swept along the x direction (Fig. 7.31b), all the unknowns of Eq. 7.26 with Subscript i are treated as the unknowns of the current iteration level; those with Subscript $i-1$ are available at the new iteration level; and those with Subscript $i+1$ are available at the old iteration level. The following equations are written for the two lines in Fig. 7.31, $j=3$ and $i=3$.

For a y-direction sweep, the LSOR equation for Line $j=3$ is

$$p_{i-1,3}^{(k+1)} - 4p_{i,3}^{(k+1)} + p_{i+1,3}^{(k+1)} = -p_{i,2}^{(k+1)} - p_{i,4}^{(k)} \quad \ldots\ldots\ldots\ldots (7.110)$$

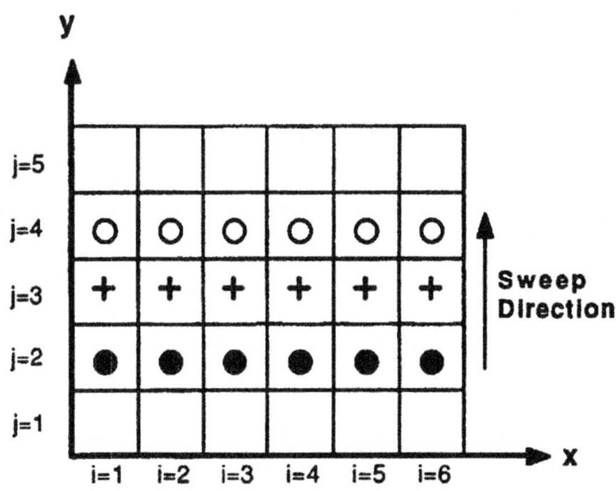

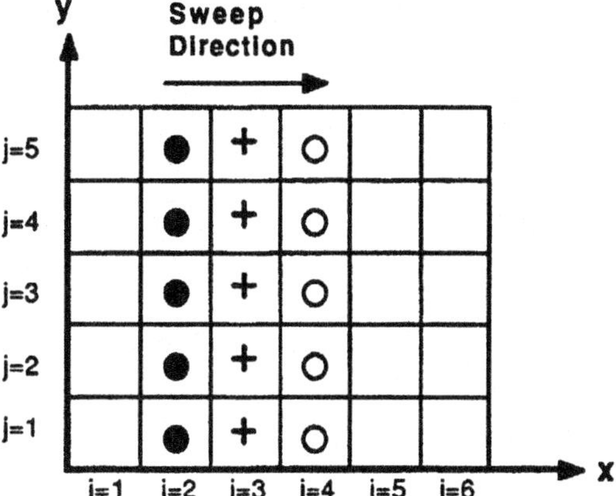

(a) Sweep direction along the y direction

(b) Sweep direction along the x direction

LEGEND: + Unknown nodes to be calculated at the current iteration level; ● Unknown nodes that are already calculated at the current iteration level; O Unknown nodes still at the old iteration level

Fig. 7.31—Arrangement of lines for the LSOR method.

for $i=1$ through 6.

For an x-direction sweep, the LSOR equation for Line $i=3$ is

$$p_{3,j-1}^{(k+1)} - 4p_{3,j}^{(k+1)} + p_{3,j+1}^{(k+1)} = -p_{2,j}^{(k+1)} - p_{4,j}^{(k)} \quad \text{.................... (7.111)}$$

for $j=1$ through 5.

A characteristic finite-difference equation for Line j for a y-direction sweep is

$$p_{i-1,j}^{*(k+1)} - 4p_{i,j}^{*(k+1)} + p_{i+1,j}^{*(k+1)} = -p_{i,j-1}^{(k+1)} - p_{i,j+1}^{(k)} \quad \text{.................... (7.112)}$$

for $i=1,2,\ldots,n_x$. Eq. 7.112 represents a tridiagonal system of equations. After this system is solved (generally with Thomas' algorithm), the unknowns on Line $j+1$ are solved in a similar fashion. After solving the equations for each line and obtaining all values of $p_{i,j}^{*(k+1)}$ for that line, the solution for that line is accelerated as

$$p_{i,j}^{(k+1)} = p_{i,j}^{(k)} + \omega\left[p_{i,j}^{*(k+1)} - p_{i,j}^{(k)}\right], \quad \text{.............. (7.113)}$$

where $p_{i,j}^{*(k+1)}$ = the unaccelerated solution at Iteration Level $(k+1)$. This solution is accelerated by use of Eq. 7.113. Therefore, $p_{i,j}^{(k+1)}$ = the accelerated solution at Iteration Level $(k+1)$.

The corresponding equation to Eq. 7.112 for Line i (if the system is swept along the x direction) is

$$p_{i,j-1}^{*(k+1)} - 4p_{i,j}^{*(k+1)} + p_{i,j+1}^{*(k+1)} = -p_{i-1,j}^{(k+1)} - p_{i+1,j}^{(k)} \quad \text{.................... (7.114)}$$

for $j=1,2,\ldots,n_y$. Eq. 7.113 is also applied.

The reason for the improvement of LSOR over PSOR is that more unknowns are evaluated at Iteration Level $(k+1)$ and, consequently, more information at the new iteration level is incorporated into the computations.

Example 7.9. Solve the following steady-state fluid-flow problem to obtain the pressure distribution in the horizontal, 2D, homogeneous, isotropic reservoir in **Fig. 7.32**. The outer boundaries of the reservoir are kept at 2,800 psia, and the production well is produced at a constant rate of 400 STB/D. In the solution of the finite-difference equations, use the LSOR method with $\omega=1$ and a pressure-convergence tolerance of 1 psi. All block properties are uniform, and $\Delta x=\Delta y=300$ ft, $h=20$ ft, $k_x=k_y=200$ md, and $\phi=16\%$. The fluid viscosity is 1 cp.

Solution. The equation describing 2D incompressible flow is

$$\frac{\partial}{\partial x}\left(\beta_c A_x k_x \frac{\partial p}{\partial x}\right)\Delta x + \frac{\partial}{\partial y}\left(\beta_c A_y k_y \frac{\partial p}{\partial y}\right)\Delta y + \mu q_{sc} = 0. \quad \text{.................... (7.22)}$$

For a homogeneous reservoir and uniform block distribution, the equation reduces to Eq. 7.23, which can be written as

$$\frac{\partial^2 p}{\partial x^2} + \frac{\partial^2 p}{\partial y^2} = -\frac{\mu q_{sc}}{\beta_c V_b k}. \quad \text{...................... (7.115)}$$

The finite-difference analog of the equation is

$$\frac{p_{i+1,j} - 2p_{i,j} + p_{i-1,j}}{(\Delta x)^2} + \frac{p_{i,j+1} - 2p_{i,j} + p_{i,j-1}}{(\Delta y)^2} = -\left(\frac{\mu q_{sc}}{\beta_c V_b k}\right)_{i,j}, \quad \text{.................... (7.116a)}$$

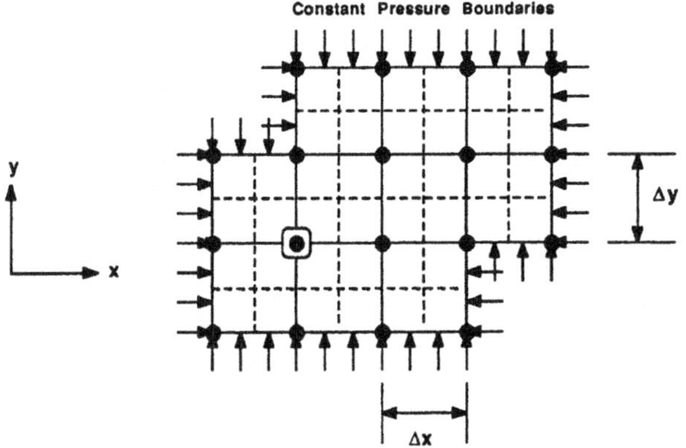

Fig. 7.32—Two-dimensional, isotropic, homogeneous reservoir of Example 7.9 (dashed lines represent block boundaries).

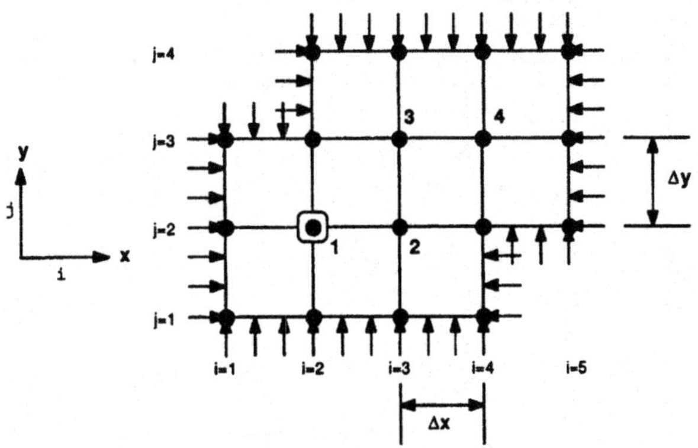

Fig. 7.33—Node numbering for the implementation of LSOR method for Example 7.9.

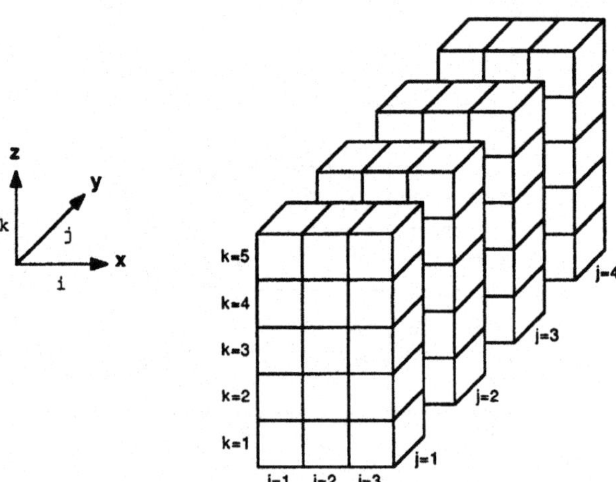

Fig. 7.34—Three-dimensional reservoir divided into four vertical planes (slices).

which can be simplified further for $\Delta x = \Delta y$ (note that $V_b = \Delta x \Delta y h$) as

$$p_{i,j-1} + p_{i-1,j} - 4p_{i,j} + p_{i+1,j} + p_{i,j+1} = -\left(\frac{\mu q_{sc}}{\beta_c hk}\right)_{i,j}. \quad (7.116b)$$

Fig. 7.33 shows the node-numbering system used in implementing the LSOR method. In the implementation of the LSOR procedure, write the line equations for $j=2$ and $j=3$ sweeping the system along the y direction. On Line $j=2$, there are two unknown nodes, numbered 1 and 2 in Fig. 7.33. Similarly, on Line $j=3$, there are two unknowns; they are numbered 3 and 4. The characteristic finite-difference equation for implementation of the LSOR method given by Eq. 7.112 is

$$p^{*(k+1)}_{i-1,j} - 4p^{*(k+1)}_{i,j} + p^{*(k+1)}_{i+1,j} = -p^{(k+1)}_{i,j-1} - p^{(k)}_{i,j+1} - \left(\frac{\mu q_{sc}}{\beta_c hk}\right)_{i,j}. \quad (7.117)$$

Now, we are ready to write the equations for the two lines that we identified. The equations for Line $j=2$, Node 1, are

$$2,800 - 4p^{*(k+1)}_1 + p^{*(k+1)}_2 = -2,800 - 2,800 - \frac{(1)(-400)}{(1.127)(20)(0.200)} \quad (7.118a)$$

or $-4p^{*(k+1)}_1 + p^{*(k+1)}_2 = -8,311.3.$ .... (7.118b)

The equations for Line $j=2$, Node 2, are

$$p^{*(k+1)}_1 - 4p^{*(k+1)}_2 + 2,800 = -2,800 - p^{(k)}_3 \quad (7.119a)$$

or $p^{*(k+1)}_1 - 4p^{*(k+1)}_2 = -5,600 - p^{(k)}_3.$ .... (7.119b)

The equations for Line $j=3$, Node 3, are

$$2,800 - 4p^{*(k+1)}_3 + p^{*(k+1)}_4 = -p^{(k+1)}_2 - 2,800 \quad (7.120a)$$

or $-4p^{*(k+1)}_3 + p^{*(k+1)}_4 = -5,600 - p^{(k+1)}_2.$ .... (7.120b)

The equations for Line $j=3$, Node 4, are

$$p^{*(k+1)}_3 - 4p^{*(k+1)}_4 + 2,800 = -2,800 - 2,800 \quad (7.121a)$$

or $p^{*(k+1)}_3 - 4p^{*(k+1)}_4 = -8,400.$ .... (7.121b)

To implement the LSOR iterations, Eqs. 7.118 and 7.119 for Line $j=2$ and Eqs. 7.120 and 7.121 for Line $j=3$ must be solved simultaneously for each line. Because, at this stage, we have not discussed how to calculate the acceleration parameter, set $\omega=1$ for simplicity, implying that solution is not going to be accelerated. Start the iterations with an initial guess of $p^{(0)}_1 = p^{(0)}_2 = p^{(0)}_3 = p^{(0)}_4 = 2,800$ psia.

The following are solutions of the line equations for first iteration ($k=0$).

For Line $j=2$,

$$-4p^{*(1)}_1 + p^{*(1)}_2 = -8,311.3 \quad (7.122a)$$

and $p^{*(1)}_1 - 4p^{*(1)}_2 = -8,400$ .... (7.122b)

for $p^{*(1)}_1 = 2,776.4$ psia and $p^{*(1)}_2 = 2,794$ psia, because $\omega=1$, $p^{(1)}_1 = 2,776.4$ psia, and $p^{(1)}_2 = 2,794$ psia.

For Line $j=3$,

$$-4p^{*(1)}_3 + p^{*(1)}_4 = -5,600 - 2,794 \quad (7.123a)$$

and $p^{*(1)}_3 - 4p^{*(1)}_4 = -8,400$ .... (7.123b)

for $p^{*(1)}_3 = 2,798.4$ psia and $p^{*(1)}_4 = 2,799.6$ psia, because $\omega=1$, $p^{(1)}_3 = 2,798.4$ psia, and $p^{(1)}_4 = 2,799.6$ psia.

Following are solutions of the line equations for the second iteration ($k=1$).

For Line $j=2$,

$$-4p^{*(2)}_1 + p^{*(2)}_2 = -8,311.3 \quad (7.124a)$$

and $p^{*(2)}_1 - 4p^{*(2)}_2 = -5,600 - 2,798.4$ .... (7.124b)

for $p^{*(2)}_1 = 2,776.2$ psia and $p^{*(2)}_2 = 2,793.7$ psia, because $\omega=1$, $p^{(2)}_1 = 2,776.2$ psia, and $p^{(2)}_2 = 2,793.7$ psia.

For Line $j=3$,

$$-4p^{*(2)}_3 + p^{*(2)}_4 = -5,600 - 2,793.7 \quad (7.125a)$$

and $p^{*(2)}_3 - 4p^{*(2)}_4 = -8,400$ .... (7.125b)

for $p^{*(2)}_3 = 2,798.3$ psia and $p^{*(2)}_4 = 2,799.6$ psia, because $\omega=1$, $p^{(2)}_3 = 2,798.3$ psia, and $p^{(2)}_4 = 2,799.6$ psia. The improvement on every node between Iteration Levels 1 and 2 is less than the specified convergence criterion ($\varepsilon = 1$ psi); therefore, the iteration process is terminated after the second iteration.

Block SOR (BSOR) Method. The BSOR method, where unknowns located on more than one line are solved simultaneously, is an extension of the LSOR technique. Again, the objective for solving for more unknowns simultaneously is to incorporate as much information as possible at Iteration Level $(k+1)$ into the iteration process. One option in implementation of the BSOR method in 3D problems is to solve for all unknowns located on the same plane simultaneously. This version of BSOR is also known as plane or slice SOR. As

Fig. 7.34 shows, at a given iteration level, equations are solved for each slice (vertical plane) of the 3D reservoir. In writing the system of equations for a plane, unknowns located on the planes solved earlier are kept at the new iteration level, while unknowns located on the planes to be solved are evaluated at the old iteration level.

Consider Laplace's 3D equation,

$$\frac{\partial^2 p}{\partial x^2} + \frac{\partial^2 p}{\partial y^2} + \frac{\partial^2 p}{\partial z^2} = 0. \quad \text{(7.126)}$$

The seven-point finite-difference approximation to Eq. 7.126 (for $\Delta x = \Delta y = \Delta z$) is obtained from Eq. 7.36,

$$p_{i,j,k-1} + p_{i,j-1,k} + p_{i-1,j,k} - 6p_{i,j,k} + p_{i+1,j,k} + p_{i,j+1,k} + p_{i,j,k+1} = 0. \quad \text{(7.127)}$$

If Eq. 7.127 is to be solved with the slice SOR method for the slices shown in Fig. 7.34, the characteristic slice equation (for Slice j) becomes

$$p^{*(k+1)}_{i,j,k-1} + p^{*(k+1)}_{i-1,j,k} - 6p^{*(k+1)}_{i,j,k} + p^{*(k+1)}_{i+1,j,k} + p^{*(k+1)}_{i,j,k+1}$$

$$= -p^{(k+1)}_{i,j-1,k} - p^{(k)}_{i,j+1,k}. \quad \text{(7.128)}$$

When Eq. 7.128 is written for every node located on Slice j, a pentadiagonal coefficient matrix is generated. This matrix equation can be solved by use of one of the techniques discussed earlier in this chapter for each slice. After solving the equation for each slice, an overrelaxation parameter, ω, is applied to the solution vector of that slice to accelerate convergence. An equation similar to Eq. 7.113, with Subscripts (i,j,k) replacing Subscripts (i,j), is used for acceleration. After each BSOR iteration is completed, a convergence check is made to see whether the preassigned convergence tolerance is satisfied. In the case of the 3D reservoir in Fig. 7.34, slice equations are solved four times during each BSOR iteration (for Slices $j=1$, $j=2$, $j=3$, and $j=4$). Obviously, if the slices were taken along the i and k directions, the number of slice equations to be solved at each iteration level would be three (for Slices $i=1$ through 3) and five (for Planes $k=1$ through 5), respectively.

Estimation of Optimum Overrelaxation Parameter. One of the most crucial steps in implementing the SOR methods is the determination of the optimum acceleration parameter, ω_{opt}. It can be shown that all the systematic iterative methods discussed in this chapter converge if the absolute value of the spectral radius (maximum eigenvalue) of the iteration matrix associated with the iterative method is less than one.

Consider a linear system of equations, such as

$$[\mathbf{A}]\vec{x} = \vec{d}, \quad \text{(7.1)}$$

where $[\mathbf{A}] = [\mathbf{D}] - [\mathbf{L}] - [\mathbf{U}]$. (7.129)

In Eq. 7.129, $[\mathbf{D}]$ = diagonal entries of $[\mathbf{A}]$ (all nondiagonal entries of $[\mathbf{D}]$ are zero), $[\mathbf{U}]$ = upper triangular elements of $[\mathbf{A}]$ (all diagonal and lower diagonal entries of $[\mathbf{U}]$ are zero), and $[\mathbf{L}]$ = lower triangular elements of $[\mathbf{A}]$ (all diagonal and upper diagonal entries of $[\mathbf{L}]$ are zero). The iteration matrix for the Jacobi iteration is

$$[\mathbf{G}]_J = [\mathbf{I}] - [\mathbf{D}]^{-1}[\mathbf{A}], \quad \text{(7.130)}$$

where $[\mathbf{I}]$ = identity matrix.

The iteration matrices for the Gauss-Seidel and PSOR iterative procedures are

$$[\mathbf{G}]_{GS} = ([\mathbf{D}] - [\mathbf{L}])^{-1}[\mathbf{U}] \quad \text{(7.131)}$$

and $$[\mathbf{G}]_{SOR} = ([\mathbf{D}] - \omega[\mathbf{L}])^{-1}\{\omega[\mathbf{U}] - (\omega - 1)[\mathbf{D}]\}, \quad \text{(7.132)}$$

respectively.

As discussed earlier, a sufficient condition for these systematic iterative procedures to converge is that the spectral radius (maximum eigenvalue), ρ_J, of $[\mathbf{G}]_J$ is less than one in absolute value. It can also be shown that the rate of convergence for a given problem depends on the magnitude of the spectral radius. As the spectral radius becomes smaller, the rate of convergence increases. Indeed, $-\log_{10} \rho_G$ gives an indication of the number of decimal digits by which the solution is improved by each convergent iteration.

The spectral radii of the Jacobi, Gauss-Seidel, and SOR iteration matrices are related to each other. The relationship between the spectral radii of the SOR iteration matrix and the Jacobi iteration matrix is[5]

$$\rho_{SOR}^{1/2} = \tfrac{1}{2}\omega\rho_J + \tfrac{1}{2}\left[\omega^2\rho_J^2 - 4(\omega - 1)\right]^{1/2}. \quad \text{(7.133)}$$

When $\omega = 1$, PSOR reduces to the Gauss-Seidel iteration and Eq. 7.133 reduces to the relationship between the spectral radii of the Gauss-Seidel and Jacobi iteration matrices.

$$\rho_{GS}^{1/2} = \rho_J. \quad \text{(7.134)}$$

Because the logarithm of the spectral radius gives an indication of the rate of convergence, one can deduce from Eq. 7.134 that the Gauss-Seidel iteration converges two times faster than the Jacobi iteration simply because

$$\log_{10}\rho_{GS} = 2\log_{10}\rho_J. \quad \text{(7.135)}$$

Close examination of Eq. 7.133 reveals that no value of ω makes $\rho_{SOR} < 1$ if $|\rho_J| > 1$. Therefore, the SOR iteration diverges if the Jacobi iteration diverges. This is why the SOR iteration helps to accelerate only the convergence of an already convergent iteration, but cannot make a divergent scheme convergent.

Ideally, we would like to find an optimum value for ω that minimizes the right side of Eq. 7.133 to yield a minimum ρ_{SOR}. It can be shown that a minimum value of ρ_{SOR} is obtained when

$$\omega^2\rho_J^2 - 4(\omega - 1) = 0. \quad \text{(7.136)}$$

From Eq. 7.136, the value of the ω_{opt} is

$$\omega_{opt} = \frac{2}{\left(1 + \sqrt{1 - \rho_J^2}\right)} \quad \text{(7.137)}$$

or, substituting for ρ_J by use of Eq. 7.134,

$$\omega_{opt} = \frac{2}{\left(1 + \sqrt{1 - \rho_{GS}}\right)}. \quad \text{(7.138)}$$

Calculation of the optimum acceleration parameter from Eqs. 7.137 and 7.138 is straightforward if either ρ_J or ρ_{GS} is obtained from its respective iteration matrix. However, calculating eigenvalues for large systems is as arduous a task as solving the original system of equations. In practice, the spectral radius of a given iteration matrix can be determined from a single test calculation with $\omega = 1$ by use of the decrease in the difference between successive approximations. The ratio of the maximum differences (improvements) of successive iterations satisfies

$$\frac{|d^{(k+1)}|}{|d^{(k)}|} \approx \rho_{GS} = \rho_J^2 \quad \text{(7.139)}$$

for sufficiently large values of k. Once the quotient of Eq. 7.139 converges to a constant value, it is used as ρ_{GS} in Eq. 7.138 to calculate ω_{opt}, and iterations can be continued with the optimum acceleration parameter from that point on.

As discussed earlier, ω_{opt} lies between 1 and 2. For a given problem, it is possible to obtain a solution to the system of equations several times with different values of ω (between 1 and 2). Because different ω values result in different ρ_{SOR} values, the number of iterations to obtain convergence also varies. Therefore, for purely academic purposes, it is possible to conduct a series of numerical exercises in which a set of linear equations is solved with ω values between 1 and 2. **Fig. 7.35** shows the qualitative nature of the relationship between the number of iterations needed for convergence and the value of ω. The shape of the curve in Fig. 7.35, where the portion of the curve for values smaller than ω_{opt} has a much steeper slope

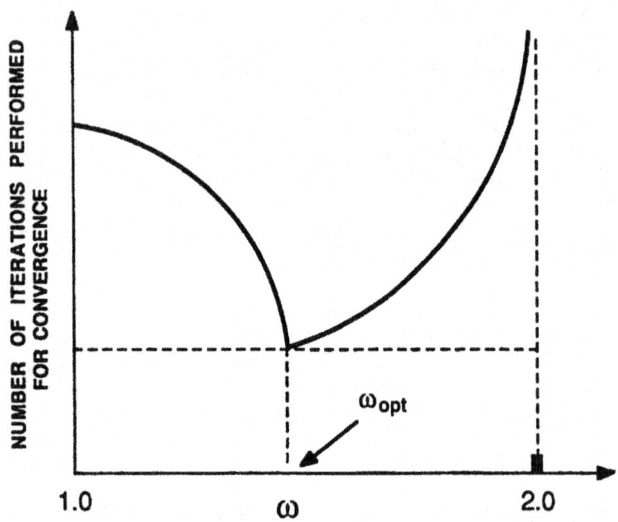

Fig. 7.35—Relationship between number of iterations performed for convergence and value of ω.

than that for values greater than ω_{opt}, is typical. This simply implies that a slightly overestimated value of ω_{opt} is not as bad as a slightly underestimated value of ω_{opt}.

Example 7.10. Find the value of ω_{opt} for the system of equations in Example 7.6.

Solution. The system of equations introduced in Example 7.6 is

$$-2p_1 + p_2 = -200, \quad \text{(7.100a)}$$

$$p_1 - 2p_2 + p_3 = 0, \quad \text{(7.100b)}$$

and $p_2 - 2p_3 = -100. \quad \text{(7.100c)}$

The PSOR iterative equations for this system (See Example 7.8) are

$$p_1^{(k+1)} = \frac{\omega_{opt}}{2}\left[p_2^{(k)} + 200\right] - (\omega_{opt} - 1)p_1^{(k)}, \quad \text{(7.140a)}$$

$$p_2^{(k+1)} = \frac{\omega_{opt}}{2}\left[p_1^{(k+1)} + p_3^{(k)}\right] - (\omega_{opt} - 1)p_2^{(k)}, \quad \text{(7.140b)}$$

and $p_3^{(k+1)} = \frac{\omega_{opt}}{2}\left[p_2^{(k+1)} + 100\right] - (\omega_{opt} - 1)p_3^{(k)}. \quad \text{(7.140c)}$

With an initial guess of 100 for the unknowns $p_1, p_2,$ and p_3, start the iterations with $\omega_{opt} = 1$ (Gauss-Seidel iteration) and check the maximum differences of successive iterations in **Table 7.5.** Table 7.5 shows that the spectral radius converges to 0.50 at the completion of the third and fourth iterations. Because ρ_{GS} is determined to be 0.50, we can estimate ω_{opt} from Eq. 7.138 as

$$\omega_{opt} = \frac{2}{\left(1 + \sqrt{1 - 0.50}\right)} = 1.1715.$$

Continuing the solution process with the SOR procedure, we use 1.1715 for the value of ω_{opt} starting with the fifth iteration, as shown in **Table 7.6.**

A comparison of Table 7.6 with Table 7.3 shows that the Gauss-Seidel and PSOR iterations took the same number of iterations to converge within the same tolerance. This is because of the relatively small number of iterations required for convergence for this specific example. This simply indicates that the relatively short convergence path experienced in this example masks the superiority of the PSOR iteration over the Gauss-Seidel iteration, especially considering that four of the seven iterations were used to calculate ω_{opt}.

Iterative Alternating-Direction Implicit Procedure (ADIP). The objective of the ADIP (sometimes referred to as operator splitting) is to separate the 3D finite-difference operator into three 1D operators. Once separated, the 1D operators can be solved with efficient, tridiagonal, linear matrix techniques (Thomas' algorithm). As Sec. 7.2.3 discusses, the finite-difference approximation to 3D reservoir flow problems results in an algebraic equation of the form

$$B_{i,j,k}x_{i,j,k-1} + S_{i,j,k}x_{i,j-1,k} + W_{i,j,k}x_{i-1,j,k} + C_{i,j,k}x_{i,j,k} + E_{i,j,k}x_{i+1,j,k} + N_{i,j,k}x_{i,j+1,k} + A_{i,j,k}x_{i,j,k+1} = Q_{i,j,k}, \quad \text{(7.141)}$$

where, for slightly-compressible-flow problems, the unknown x = pressures at the new time level; the coefficients $B, S, W, E, N,$ and A = transmissibilities in the appropriate flow directions; the coefficient C = summation of the transmissibilities plus contributions from the accumulation term; and the right side Q = summation of the gravity-head terms plus contributions from the accumulation term plus the source/sink term.

Eq. 7.141 can be approximated by separating it into the directions of flow:

$$W_{i,j,k}x^*_{i-1,j,k} + C^*_{i,j,k}x^*_{i,j,k} + E_{i,j,k}x^*_{i+1,j,k} = Q^*_{i,j,k}, \quad \text{(7.142)}$$

$$S_{i,j,k}x^{**}_{i,j-1,k} + C^{**}_{i,j,k}x^{**}_{i,j,k} + N_{i,j,k}x^{**}_{i,j+1,k} = Q^{**}_{i,j,k}, \quad \text{(7.143)}$$

and $B_{i,j,k}x^{(k+1)}_{i,j,k-1} + C^{***}_{i,j,k}x^{(k+1)}_{i,j,k} + A_{i,j,k}x^{(k+1)}_{i,j,k+1} = Q^{***}_{i,j,k}, \quad \text{(7.144)}$

TABLE 7.5—DETERMINATION OF SPECTRAL RADIUS FOR EXAMPLE 7.10

$k+1$	ω_{opt}	p_1	p_2	p_3	$\max_i \lvert p_i^{(k+1)} - p_i^{(k)} \rvert$	$\lvert d^{(k+1)}/d^{(k)} \rvert$
0	—	100	100	100	—	—
1	1	150	125	112.5	50	—
2	1	162.5	137.5	118.75	12.5	0.25
3	1	168.75	143.75	121.88	6.25	0.50
4	1	171.88	146.88	123.44	3.13	0.50

TABLE 7.6—CONTINUATION OF ITERATIONS FOR EXAMPLE 7.10 WITH ω_{opt}

$k+1$	ω_{opt}	p_1	p_2	p_3	$\max_i \lvert p_i^{(k+1)} - p_i^{(k)} \rvert$
5	1.1715	173.71	148.86	124.60	1.98
6	1.1715	174.55	149.70	124.89	0.84
7	1.1715	174.90	149.93	124.98	0.35

where, for the slightly-compressible-flow problem,

$$C^*_{i,j,k} = -\left[\mathrm{T}_{lx_{i-1/2,j,k}} + \mathrm{T}_{lx_{i+1/2,j,k}} + 1/3\left(\frac{V_b\phi c}{\alpha_c B^\circ_l \Delta t}\right)_{i,j,k} + \omega^{(k)}\Sigma \mathrm{T}_l\right], \quad \text{(7.145)}$$

$$Q^*_{i,j,k} = Q_{i,j,k} + \left[2/3\left(\frac{V_b\phi c}{\alpha_c B^\circ_l \Delta t}\right)_{i,j,k} + \omega^{(k)}\Sigma \mathrm{T}_l\right]x^{(k)}_{i,j,k} - B_{i,j,k}x^{(k)}_{i,j,k-1} - S_{i,j,k}x^{(k)}_{i,j-1,k} - N_{i,j,k}x^{(k)}_{i,j+1,k} - A_{i,j,k}x^{(k)}_{i,j,k+1}, \quad \text{(7.146)}$$

$$C^{**}_{i,j,k} = -\left[\mathrm{T}_{ly_{i,j-1/2,k}} + \mathrm{T}_{ly_{i,j+1/2,k}} + 1/3\left(\frac{V_b\phi c}{\alpha_c B^\circ_l \Delta t}\right)_{i,j,k} + \omega^{(k)}\Sigma \mathrm{T}_l\right], \quad \text{(7.147)}$$

$$Q^{**}_{i,j,k} = Q_{i,j,k} + \left[2/3\left(\frac{V_b\phi c}{\alpha_c B^\circ_l \Delta t}\right)_{i,j,k} + \omega^{(k)}\Sigma \mathrm{T}_l\right]x^*_{i,j,k} - B_{i,j,k}x^*_{i,j,k-1} - W_{i,j,k}x^*_{i-1,j,k} - E_{i,j,k}x^*_{i+1,j,k} - A_{i,j,k}x^*_{i,j,k+1}, \quad \text{(7.148)}$$

$$C^{***}_{i,j,k} = -\left[\mathrm{T}_{lz_{i,j,k-1/2}} + \mathrm{T}_{lz_{i,j,k+1/2}} + 1/3\left(\frac{V_b\phi c}{\alpha_c B^\circ_l \Delta t}\right)_{i,j,k} + \omega^{(k)}\Sigma \mathrm{T}_l\right], \quad \text{(7.149)}$$

$$Q^{***}_{i,j,k} = Q_{i,j,k} + \left[2/3\left(\frac{V_b\phi c}{\alpha_c B^\circ_l \Delta t}\right)_{i,j,k} + \omega^{(k)}\Sigma \mathrm{T}_l\right]x^{**}_{i,j,k} - S_{i,j,k}x^{**}_{i,j-1,k} - W_{i,j,k}x^{**}_{i-1,j,k} - E_{i,j,k}x^{**}_{i+1,j,k} - N_{i,j,k}x^{**}_{i,j+1,k}, \quad \text{(7.150)}$$

and

$$\Sigma \mathrm{T}_l = \mathrm{T}_{lz_{i,j,k-1/2}} + \mathrm{T}_{ly_{i,j-1/2,k}} + \mathrm{T}_{lx_{i-1/2,j,k}} + \mathrm{T}_{lx_{i+1/2,j,k}} + \mathrm{T}_{ly_{i,j+1/2,k}} + T_{lz_{i,j,k+1/2}}. \quad \text{(7.151)}$$

For 2D problems, the factors 1/3 and 2/3 in Eqs. 7.145 through 7.150 should be replaced by the factor of ½ and the appropriate directional equations should be removed from the equation set.

In Eqs. 7.145 through 7.150, $\omega^{(k)}$ is an iteration parameter. Unlike the SOR methods, $\omega^{(k)}$ is not a constant, but varies from iteration to iteration. Empirical evidence indicates that the iterative ADIP technique exhibits the best convergence behavior when $\omega^{(k)}$ is cycled through n_k values spaced geometrically between $\omega_{\min}$ and $\omega_{\max}$. The value of $\omega_{\min}$ can be determined by[6]

$$\omega_{\min} = \min_{i,j,k}\left[\frac{\pi^2}{2(n_x)^2(1+\lambda_x)}, \frac{\pi^2}{2(n_y)^2(1+\lambda_y)}, \frac{\pi^2}{2(n_z)^2(1+\lambda_z)}\right], \quad \text{(7.152)}$$

where

$$\lambda_x = \frac{\mathrm{T}_{ly_{i,j+1/2,k}}}{\mathrm{T}_{lx_{i+1/2,j,k}}} + \frac{\mathrm{T}_{lz_{i,j,k+1/2}}}{\mathrm{T}_{lx_{i+1/2,j,k}}}, \quad \text{(7.153)}$$

$$\lambda_y = \frac{\mathrm{T}_{lx_{i+1/2,j,k}}}{\mathrm{T}_{ly_{i,j+1/2,k}}} + \frac{\mathrm{T}_{lz_{i,j,k+1/2}}}{\mathrm{T}_{ly_{i,j+1/2,k}}}, \quad \text{(7.154)}$$

and

$$\lambda_z = \frac{\mathrm{T}_{lx_{i+1/2,j,k}}}{\mathrm{T}_{lz_{i,j,k+1/2}}} + \frac{\mathrm{T}_{ly_{i,j+1/2,k}}}{\mathrm{T}_{lz_{i,j,k+1/2}}}. \quad \text{(7.155)}$$

In Eqs. 7.153 through 7.155, the entire grid system is swept to determine the minimum value defined by Eq. 7.152. In these equations, values of $\lambda = 0$ and $\lambda = \infty$ should be excluded from the search.

The value of $\omega_{\max}$ can be determined by[6] $\omega_{\max} = 1$ for 3D and 2D areal problems (x–y), and $\omega_{\max} = 2$ for 2D cross-sectional problems (x–z).

The optimum number of parameters to cycle through, n_k, can be estimated as the smallest integer that satisfies

$$(0.172)^{n_k - 1} \leqq \frac{\omega_{\min}}{\omega_{\max}}. \quad \text{(7.156)}$$

Once $\omega_{\min}$, $\omega_{\max}$, and n_k are determined, all the iteration parameters can be calculated from

$$\omega^{(k)} = \omega_{\min}, \quad \text{(7.157)}$$

for $k = 1$, and

$$\omega^{(k)} = \left(\frac{\omega_{\max}}{\omega_{\min}}\right)^{\frac{1}{n_k - 1}} \omega^{(k-1)}, \quad \text{(7.158)}$$

for $k = 2, 3, \ldots, n_k$. The iterative ADIP technique can now be described by the following algorithm.

1. Estimate all iteration parameters with Eqs. 7.152 through 7.158.
2. Make an initial estimate for all unknowns, $x^{(0)}_{i,j,k}$.
3. Calculate $C^*_{i,j,k}$ and $Q^*_{i,j,k}$ with Eqs. 7.145 and 7.146, respectively.
4. Solve Eq. 7.142 for $x^*_{i,j,k}$ with Thomas' algorithm (Sec. 7.3.1) for every i-direction line in the system.
5. Calculate $C^{**}_{i,j,k}$ and $Q^{**}_{i,j,k}$ with Eqs. 7.147 and 7.148, respectively.
6. Solve Eq. 7.143 for $x^{**}_{i,j,k}$ with Thomas' algorithm for every j-direction line in the system.
7. Calculate $C^{***}_{i,j,k}$ and $Q^{***}_{i,j,k}$ with Eqs. 7.149 and 7.150, respectively.
8. Solve Eq. 7.144 for $x^{(k+1)}_{i,j,k}$ with Thomas' algorithm for every k-direction line in the system.
9. Check for convergence with

$$\left|x^{(k+1)}_{i,j,k} - x^{(k)}_{i,j,k}\right| < \varepsilon \quad \text{(7.99)}$$

for all i, j, k.

10. If the system has converged, $x^{(k+1)}_{i,j,k}$ represents the final solution of $[\mathbf{A}]\vec{x} = \vec{d}$; otherwise, update the unknowns and go to Step 3.

In the previous algorithm, if the number of iterations required for convergence is greater than the number of iteration parameters, n_k, then on Iteration Level $(n_k + 1)$, $\omega^{(1)}$ is used and the cycle is repeated for subsequent iterations.

The iterative ADIP technique was popular for reservoir simulation in the 1960's and 1970's. It is not used in most modern reservoir simulators because more powerful linear-solution techniques, such as conjugate-gradient-like (CGL) techniques, have been developed.

Approximate Factorization Techniques. The objective of approximate factorization techniques is to replace the original coefficient matrix, **[A]**, with an approximate coefficient matrix, **[A′]**, which is similar to the original coefficient matrix but is easier to factor into **[L′]** and **[U′]** components. Approximate factorization tech-

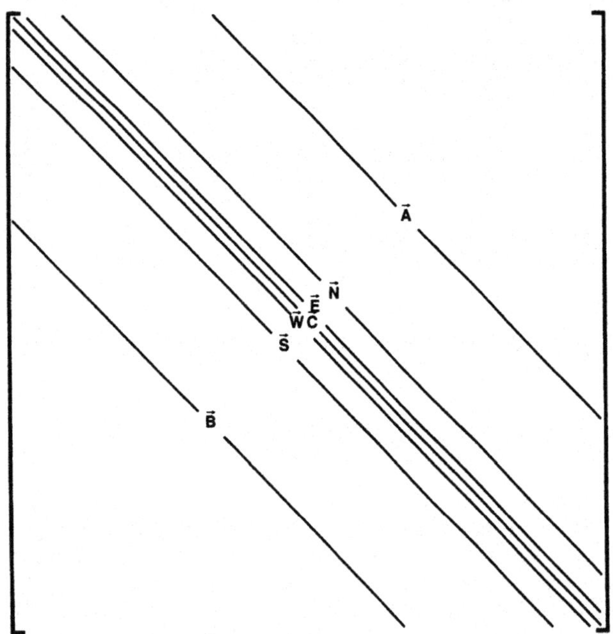

Fig. 7.36—Typical coefficient matrix, [A], for a 3D simulation problem.

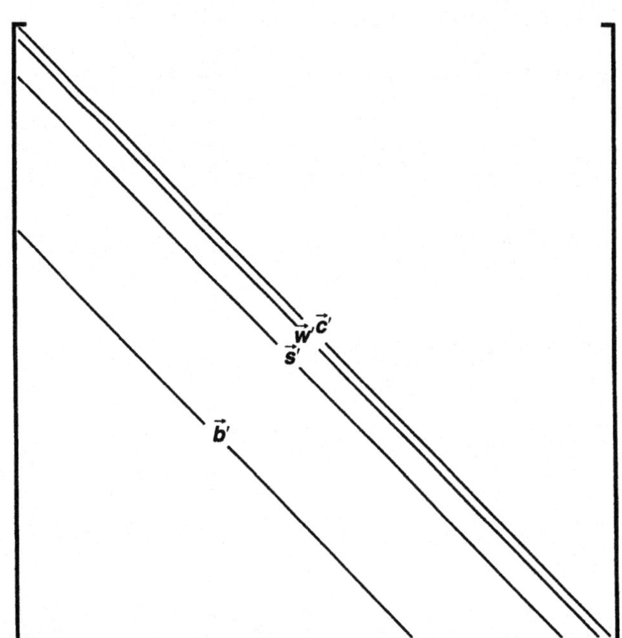

Fig. 7.37—Approximate lower triangular matrix, [L'], used in the approximate factorization technique.

niques, particularly the strongly implicit procedure (SIP), have the capacity to solve matrix equations for practical simulation problems where heterogeneity is an important consideration and for cases where the SOR or ADIP technique fails to converge.

Approximate factorization techniques are not commonly used in modern reservoir simulation because of the development of more powerful techniques. A discussion of approximate factorization is important for historical purposes; however, because they form the basis for several matrix preconditioning techniques.

Reservoir simulation attempts to solve a matrix equation of the form

$$[\mathbf{A}]\vec{x} = \vec{d}. \qquad (7.1)$$

We can define the residual of an iterative procedure as

$$\vec{r}^{(k)} = \vec{d} - [\mathbf{A}]\vec{x}^{(k)}. \qquad (7.159)$$

Now define the improvement vector, $\delta\vec{x}^{(k+1)}$, from one iteration level to the next. That is,

$$\vec{x}^{(k+1)} = \vec{x}^{(k)} + \delta\vec{x}^{(k+1)}. \qquad (7.160)$$

Substituting Eq. 7.160 into Eq. 7.1 results in

$$[\mathbf{A}]\vec{x}^{(k+1)} = [\mathbf{A}]\left[\vec{x}^{(k)} + \delta\vec{x}^{(k+1)}\right] = \vec{d}, \qquad (7.161)$$

or rearranging and substituting Eq. 7.159 results in

$$[\mathbf{A}]\delta\vec{x}^{(k+1)} \approx \vec{r}^{(k)}. \qquad (7.162a)$$

For approximate factorization techniques, we substitute an approximate coefficient matrix, **[A']**, for the coefficient matrix, **[A]**, in Eq. 7.162a to obtain

$$[\mathbf{A}']\delta\vec{x}^{(k+1)} = \vec{r}^{(k)} \qquad (7.162b)$$

or, after substituting the **[L']** and **[U']** components of **[A']**,

$$[\mathbf{L}']\left[[\mathbf{U}']\delta\vec{x}^{(k+1)}\right] = \vec{r}^{(k)}. \qquad (7.162c)$$

When going from Eq. 7.162b to Eq. 7.162c, we have replaced the approximation sign with an equal sign.

In our discussion on Crout reduction (Sec. 7.3.1), we described an intermediate vector used to expedite calculations. We can use a similar procedure for approximate factorization. Define $\delta\vec{y}^{(k+1)}$ so that

$$[\mathbf{L}']\delta\vec{y}^{(k+1)} = \vec{r}^{(k)}, \qquad (7.163)$$

where $[\mathbf{U}']\delta\vec{x}^{(k+1)} = \delta\vec{y}^{(k+1)}. \qquad (7.164)$

The use of the intermediate vector, $\delta\vec{y}^{(k+1)}$, allows us to solve for $\delta\vec{x}^{(k+1)}$ in a two-stage procedure: a forward-substitution process followed by a back-substitution process. In the forward-substitution process, Eq. 7.163 is solved for $\delta\vec{y}^{(k+1)}$ by sweeping the finite-difference grid from Gridblock (1,1,1) with increasing i, j, and k indices. In the back-substitution process, Eq. 7.164 is solved for $\delta\vec{x}^{(k+1)}$ by sweeping the finite-difference grid from Gridblock (n_x, n_y, n_z) with decreasing i, j, and k indices.

We now need to define matrix **[A']**, which approximates the original coefficient matrix, **[A]**. To achieve this, consider the coefficient matrix in **Fig. 7.36**, which illustrates the heptadiagonal band structure discussed earlier in this chapter. To obtain the approximate coefficient matrix, **[A']**, we assign the same band structure found in the original coefficient matrix, **[A]** (Fig. 7.36), to the lower diagonal matrix, **[L']** (**Fig. 7.37**), and to the upper diagonal matrix, **[U']** (**Fig. 7.38**). We can now generate **[A']** by multiplying **[L']** and **[U']**. **Fig. 7.39** shows the resulting matrix, **[A']**.

If we compare the original coefficient matrix, **[A]**, in Fig. 7.36 with the approximate coefficient matrix, **[A']**, in Fig. 7.39, we see that the two matrices have similar structures (with identical band widths) but that **[A']** has six additional bands: F', G', H', I', J' and K'.

The general equation that corresponds to coefficient matrix **[A']** is

$$\begin{aligned} &B'_{i,j,k}\delta x^{(k+1)}_{i,j,k-1} + F'_{i,j,k}\delta x^{(k+1)}_{i+1,j,k-1} + G'_{i,j,k}\delta x^{(k+1)}_{i,j+1,k-1} \\ &+ S'_{i,j,k}\delta x^{(k+1)}_{i,j-1,k} + H'_{i,j,k}\delta x^{(k+1)}_{i+1,j-1,k} + W'_{i,j,k}\delta x^{(k+1)}_{i-1,j,k} \\ &+ C'_{i,j,k}\delta x^{(k+1)}_{i,j,k} + E'_{i,j,k}\delta x^{(k+1)}_{i+1,j,k} + I'_{i,j,k}\delta x^{(k+1)}_{i-1,j+1,k} \\ &+ N'_{i,j,k}\delta x^{(k+1)}_{i,j+1,k} + J'_{i,j,k}\delta x^{(k+1)}_{i,j-1,k+1} + K'_{i,j,k}\delta x^{(k+1)}_{i-1,j,k+1} \\ &+ A'_{i,j,k}\delta x^{(k+1)}_{i,j,k+1} = r^{(k)}_{i,j,k}, \qquad (7.165) \end{aligned}$$

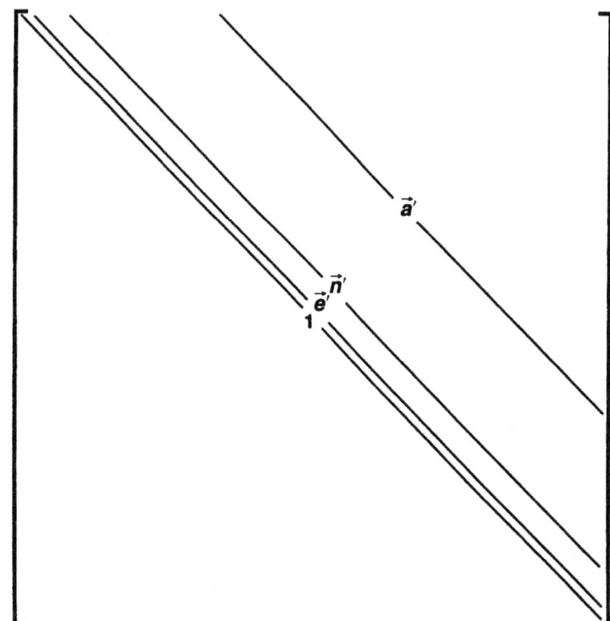

Fig. 7.38—Approximate upper triangular matrix, [U′], used in the approximate factorization technique.

where Coefficients B', F', G', S', H', W', C', E', I', N', J', K', and A' are defined in the key in Fig. 7.39. In Eq. 7.165, the nonstandard terms $F'_{i,j,k}\delta x^{(k+1)}_{i+1,j,k-1}$, $G'_{i,j,k}\delta x^{(k+1)}_{i,j+1,k-1}$, $H'_{i,j,k}\delta x^{(k+1)}_{i+1,j-1,k}$, $I'_{i,j,k}\delta x^{(k+1)}_{i-1,j+1,k}$, $J'_{i,j,k}\delta x^{(k+1)}_{i,j-1,k+1}$, and $K'_{i,j,k}\delta x^{(k+1)}_{i-1,j,k+1}$ are a direct result of the six additional bands in Fig. 7.39.

It is necessary to develop definitions for the entries of **[L′]** (b', s', w', and c' in Fig. 7.37) and the entries of **[U′]** (e', n', and a' in Fig. 7.38) in terms of the entries of the original coefficient matrix, **[A]**. We are now in a position to discuss three methods for defining these required coefficients.

Simple Coefficient Method. In the simple coefficient method, we compare Eq. 7.165 with Eq. 7.39 to obtain the following definitions for the coefficients in Eq. 7.165.

$$B'_{i,j,k} = B_{i,j,k}, \quad \text{(7.166)}$$

$$S'_{i,j,k} = S_{i,j,k}, \quad \text{(7.167)}$$

$$W'_{i,j,k} = W_{i,j,k}, \quad \text{(7.168)}$$

$$C'_{i,j,k} = C_{i,j,k}, \quad \text{(7.169)}$$

$$E'_{i,j,k} = E_{i,j,k}, \quad \text{(7.170)}$$

$$N'_{i,j,k} = N_{i,j,k}, \quad \text{(7.171)}$$

and $$A'_{i,j,k} = A_{i,j,k}. \quad \text{(7.172)}$$

In Eqs. 7.166 through 7.172, the coefficients on the left sides are the entries of the approximate coefficient matrix, **[A′]**, while those on the right sides are the entries of the original coefficient matrix, **[A]**. Combining Eqs. 7.166 through 7.172 with the relationships shown in the key in Fig. 7.39 results in the following definitions for the entries of **[L′]** and **[U′]**.

$$b'_{i,j,k} = B_{i,j,k}, \quad \text{(7.173)}$$

$$s'_{i,j,k} = S_{i,j,k}, \quad \text{(7.174)}$$

$$w'_{i,j,k} = W_{i,j,k}, \quad \text{(7.175)}$$

$$c'_{i,j,k} = C_{i,j,k} - w'_{i,j,k}e'_{i-1,j,k} - s'_{i,j,k}n'_{i,j-1,k} - b'_{i,j,k}a'_{i,j,k-1}, \quad \text{(7.176)}$$

$$e'_{i,j,k} = \frac{E_{i,j,k}}{c'_{i,j,k}}, \quad \text{(7.177)}$$

$$n'_{i,j,k} = \frac{N_{i,j,k}}{c'_{i,j,k}}, \quad \text{(7.178)}$$

and $$a'_{i,j,k} = \frac{A_{i,j,k}}{c'_{i,j,k}}. \quad \text{(7.179)}$$

In Eq. 7.176, the terms $e'_{i-1,j,k}$, $n'_{i,j-1,k}$, and $a'_{i,j,k-1}$ are removed from the equation when i, j, or $k=1$, (that is, when $i-1=0$, $j-1=0$, or $k-1=0$), respectively. Mathematically,

$$e'_{0,j,k} = n'_{i,0,k} = a'_{i,j,0} = 0. \quad \text{(7.180)}$$

The simple coefficient method tends to converge slowly because no effort has been made to minimize the effects of the nonstandard

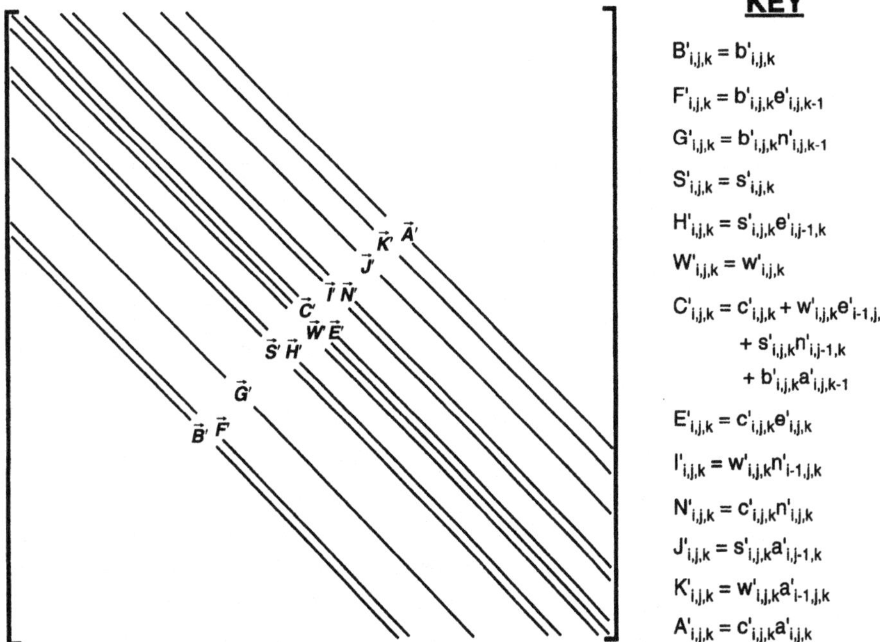

Fig. 7.39—Approximate coefficient matrix, [A′], obtained by multiplying the lower triangular matrix, [L′], and the upper triangular matrix, [U′]—i.e. the [L′][U′] product. The relationships in the key are obtained by matrix multiplication.

terms in Eq. 7.165.[5] The next two methods for selecting coefficients differ in the manner in which the effects of the nonstandard terms are reduced.

Dupont et al.[7] *Method.* To some extent, we can reduce the effects of the nonstandard terms in the finite-difference equation if we assume that the nonstandard unknowns are approximately equal to $\delta x^{(k+1)}_{i,j,k}$.[7] That is,

$$\delta x^{(k+1)}_{i+1,j,k-1} \approx \delta x^{(k+1)}_{i,j+1,k-1} \approx \delta x^{(k+1)}_{i+1,j-1,k} \approx \delta x^{(k+1)}_{i-1,j+1,k}$$

$$\approx \delta x^{(k+1)}_{i,j-1,k+1} \approx \delta x^{(k+1)}_{i-1,j,k+1} \approx \delta x^{(k+1)}_{i,j,k}. \quad \text{...................... (7.181)}$$

With this assumption, we can modify Eq. 7.169 to

$$C'_{i,j,k} = C_{i,j,k} - F'_{i,j,k} - G'_{i,j,k} - H'_{i,j,k} - I'_{i,j,k} - J'_{i,j,k} - K'_{i,j,k} + \omega^{(k)}. \quad \text{...................... (7.182)}$$

In Eq. 7.182, $\omega^{(k)}$ is an iteration parameter associated with Iteration Level (k). Note that, if we use Eq. 7.182 along with Eqs. 7.166 through 7.168 and 7.170 through 7.172, the effect of the nonstandard terms is reduced. That is, if we substitute the Dupont *et al.*[7] coefficients into Eq. 7.165, we obtain

$$B_{i,j,k}\delta x^{(k+1)}_{i,j,k-1} + F'_{i,j,k}\left[\delta x^{(k+1)}_{x+1,j,k-1} - \delta x^{(k+1)}_{i,j,k}\right]$$

$$+ G'_{i,j,k}\left[\delta x^{(k+1)}_{i,j+1,k-1} - \delta x^{(k+1)}_{i,j,k}\right] + S_{i,j,k}\delta x^{(k+1)}_{i,j-1,k}$$

$$+ H'_{i,j,k}\left[\delta x^{(k+1)}_{i+1,j-1,k} - \delta x^{(k+1)}_{i,j,k}\right] + W_{i,j,k}\delta x^{(k+1)}_{i-1,j,k}$$

$$+ \left[C_{i,j,k} + \omega^{(k)}\right]\delta x^{(k+1)}_{i,j,k} + E_{i,j,k}\delta x^{(k+1)}_{i+1,j,k}$$

$$+ I'_{i,j,k}\left[\delta x^{(k+1)}_{i-1,j+1,k} - \delta x^{(k+1)}_{i,j,k}\right] + N_{i,j,k}\delta x^{(k+1)}_{i,j,k}$$

$$+ J'_{i,j,k}\left[\delta x^{(k+1)}_{i,j-1,k+1} - \delta x^{(k+1)}_{i,j,k}\right] + K'_{i,j,k}\left[\delta x^{(k+1)}_{i-1,j,k+1}\right.$$

$$\left. - \delta x^{(k+1)}_{i,j,k}\right] + A_{i,j,k}\delta x^{(k+1)}_{i,j,k+1} = r^{(k)}_{i,j,k}. \quad \text{............ (7.183)}$$

If the assumptions stated in Eq. 7.181 are valid, then the nonstandard terms in Eq. 7.183 vanish and Eq. 7.183 becomes similar in form to the original finite-difference equation, differing only with the inclusion of $\omega^{(k)}$.

Setting Eq. 7.182 equal to the relationship for $C'_{i,j,k}$ in Fig. 7.39 results in

$$c'_{i,j,k} = C_{i,j,k} - w'_{i,j,k}e'_{i-1,j,k} - s'_{i,j,k}n'_{i,j-1,k} - b'_{i,j,k}a'_{i,j,k-1}$$

$$- F'_{i,j,k} - G'_{i,j,k} - H'_{i,j,k} - I'_{i,j,k} - J'_{i,j,k} - K'_{i,j,k} + \omega^{(k)}, \quad \text{...................... (7.184)}$$

or substituting the definitions of F', G', H', I', J', and K' from Fig. 7.39 results in

$$c'_{i,j,k} = C_{i,j,k} - w'_{i,j,k}\left(e'_{i-1,j,k} + n'_{i-1,j,k} + a'_{i-1,j,k}\right)$$

$$- s'_{i,j,k}\left(e'_{i,j-1,k} + n'_{i,j-1,k} + a'_{i,j-1,k}\right)$$

$$- b'_{i,j,k}\left(e'_{i,j,k-1} + n'_{i,j,k-1} + a'_{i,j,k-1}\right) + \omega^{(k)}. \quad \text{... (7.185)}$$

Now, if we sweep the finite-difference grid in order of increasing i, j, and k indices, we can calculate the entries in **[L′]** and **[U′]** by the following method.

1. Use Eqs. 7.173 through 7.175 to calculate $b'_{i,j,k}$, $s'_{i,j,k}$, and $w'_{i,j,k}$.
2. Use Eq. 7.185 to calculate $c'_{i,j,k}$.

In Eq. 7.185,

$$e'_{0,j,k} = e'_{i,0,k} = e'_{i,j,0} = 0, \quad \text{...................... (7.186a)}$$

$$n'_{0,j,k} = n'_{i,0,k} = n'_{i,j,0} = 0, \quad \text{...................... (7.186b)}$$

$$\text{and } a'_{0,j,k} = a'_{i,0,k} = a'_{i,j,0} = 0. \quad \text{...................... (7.186c)}$$

Because we are sweeping the finite-difference grid with increasing i, j, and k indices, the coefficients in Eq. 7.185 are either zero [if the i, j, or k indices are equal to one (and, therefore $i-1=0$, $j-1=0$, or $k-1=0$)] or are known at the time of computation.

3. Use Eqs. 7.177 through 7.179 to calculate $e'_{i,j,k}$, $n'_{i,j,k}$, and $a'_{i,j,k}$.

SIP. Stone's[8] SIP attempts to minimize the effects of the nonstandard terms in Eq. 7.165 by assuming that, for smooth distributions of the unknowns, the following relationships are valid. (Note that Stone[8] originally developed the SIP for 2D problems. The 3D formulation presented in this book was developed by Weinstein *et al.*[9])

$$\delta x^{(k+1)}_{i+1,j,k-1} \approx \delta x^{(k+1)}_{i+1,j,k} + \delta x^{(k+1)}_{i,j,k-1} - \delta x^{(k+1)}_{i,j,k}, \quad \text{...... (7.187)}$$

$$\delta x^{(k+1)}_{i,j+1,k-1} \approx \delta x^{(k+1)}_{i,j+1,k} + \delta x^{(k+1)}_{i,j,k-1} - \delta x^{(k+1)}_{i,j,k}, \quad \text{...... (7.188)}$$

$$\delta x^{(k+1)}_{i+1,j-1,k} \approx \delta x^{(k+1)}_{i+1,j,k} + \delta x^{(k+1)}_{i,j-1,k} - \delta x^{(k+1)}_{i,j,k}, \quad \text{...... (7.189)}$$

$$\delta x^{(k+1)}_{i-1,j+1,k} \approx \delta x^{(k+1)}_{i-1,j,k} + \delta x^{(k+1)}_{i,j+1,k} - \delta x^{(k+1)}_{i,j,k}, \quad \text{...... (7.190)}$$

$$\delta x^{(k+1)}_{i,j-1,k+1} \approx \delta x^{(k+1)}_{i,j-1,k} + \delta x^{(k+1)}_{i,j,k+1} - \delta x^{(k+1)}_{i,j,k}, \quad \text{...... (7.191)}$$

$$\text{and } \delta x^{(k+1)}_{i-1,j,k+1} \approx \delta x^{(k+1)}_{i-1,j,k} + \delta x^{(k+1)}_{i,j,k+1} - \delta x^{(k+1)}_{i,j,k}. \quad \text{..... (7.192)}$$

To implement the assumptions in Eqs. 7.187 through 7.192, the following definitions are used to relate the entries of the original coefficient matrix, **[A]**, to those in the approximate coefficient matrix, **[A′]**.

$$B'_{i,j,k} = B_{i,j,k} - \omega^{(k)}\left(F'_{i,j,k} + G'_{i,j,k}\right), \quad \text{.............. (7.193)}$$

$$S'_{i,j,k} = S_{i,j,k} - \omega^{(k)}\left(H'_{i,j,k} + J'_{i,j,k}\right), \quad \text{.............. (7.194)}$$

$$W'_{i,j,k} = W_{i,j,k} - \omega^{(k)}\left(I'_{i,j,k} + K'_{i,j,k}\right), \quad \text{.............. (7.195)}$$

$$C'_{i,j,k} = C_{i,j,k} - \omega^{(k)}$$

$$\times\left(F'_{i,j,k} + G'_{i,j,k} + H'_{i,j,k} + I'_{i,j,k} + J'_{i,j,k} + K'_{i,j,k}\right), \quad \text{...................... (7.196)}$$

$$E'_{i,j,k} = E_{i,j,k} - \omega^{(k)}\left(F'_{i,j,k} + H'_{i,j,k}\right), \quad \text{.............. (7.197)}$$

$$N'_{i,j,k} = N_{i,j,k} - \omega^{(k)}\left(G'_{i,j,k} + I'_{i,j,k}\right), \quad \text{.............. (7.198)}$$

$$\text{and } A'_{i,j,k} = A_{i,j,k} - \omega^{(k)}\left(J'_{i,j,k} + K'_{i,j,k}\right). \quad \text{.............. (7.199)}$$

To obtain the definitions of the entries in **[L′]** and **[U′]**, equate Eqs. 7.193 through 7.199 to the relationships in the key in Fig. 7.39. This results in

$$b'_{i,j,k} = \frac{B_{i,j,k}}{\left[1 + \omega^{(k)}\left(e'_{i,j,k-1} + n'_{i,j,k-1}\right)\right]}, \quad \text{........... (7.200)}$$

$$s'_{i,j,k} = \frac{S_{i,j,k}}{\left[1 + \omega^{(k)}\left(e'_{i,j-1,k} + a'_{i,j-1,k}\right)\right]}, \quad \text{............ (7.201)}$$

$$w'_{i,j,k} = \frac{W_{i,j,k}}{\left[1 + \omega^{(k)}\left(n'_{i-1,j,k} + a'_{i-1,j,k}\right)\right]}, \quad \text{........... (7.202)}$$

$$c'_{i,j,k} = C_{i,j,k} - w'_{i,j,k}\left[e'_{i-1,j,k} + \omega^{(k)}\left(n'_{i-1,j,k} + a'_{i-1,j,k}\right)\right]$$
$$- s'_{i,j,k}\left[n'_{i,j-1,k} + \omega^{(k)}\left(e'_{i,j-1,k} + a'_{i,j-1,k}\right)\right]$$
$$- b'_{i,j,k}\left[a'_{i,j,k-1} + \omega^{(k)}\left(e'_{i,j,k-1} + n'_{i,j,k-1}\right)\right], \quad \text{..... (7.203)}$$

$$e'_{i,j,k} = \frac{\left[E_{i,j,k} - \omega^{(k)}\left(b'_{i,j,k}e'_{i,j,k-1} + s'_{i,j,k}e'_{i,j-1,k}\right)\right]}{c'_{i,j,k}}, \quad \text{... (7.204)}$$

$$n'_{i,j,k} = \frac{\left[N_{i,j,k} - \omega^{(k)}\left(b'_{i,j,k}n'_{i,j,k-1} + w'_{i,j,k}n'_{i-1,j,k}\right)\right]}{c'_{i,j,k}},$$
$$\text{.................. (7.205)}$$

and $$a'_{i,j,k} = \frac{\left[A_{i,j,k} - \omega^{(k)}\left(s'_{i,j,k}a'_{i,j-1,k} + w'_{i,j,k}a'_{i-1,j,k}\right)\right]}{c'_{i,j,k}}.$$
$$\text{.................. (7.206)}$$

Again, these coefficients must be calculated in order of increasing i, j, and k indices.

The maximum value for the iteration parameter in Eqs. 7.200 through 7.206, ω_{max}, can be calculated by

$$1-\omega_{max} = \min_{i,j,k}\left[\frac{\pi^2}{2(n_x)^2(1+\lambda_x)}, \frac{\pi^2}{2(n_y)^2(1+\lambda_y)}, \frac{\pi^2}{2(n_z)^2(1+\lambda_z)}\right],$$
$$\text{.................. (7.207)}$$

where λ_x, λ_y, and λ_z are defined by Eqs. 7.153 through 7.155. With these definitions of λ, the right side of Eq. 7.207 is identical to the right side of Eq. 7.152. The iteration parameters, $\omega^{(k)}$, are obtained by cycling between zero and ω_{max} geometrically. That is,

$$1 - \omega^{(k)} = (1 - \omega_{max})^{\frac{k-1}{n_k-1}}, \quad \text{................. (7.208)}$$

for $k = 1,2,\ldots, n_k$.

In Eq. 7.208, n_k = number of iteration parameters. Stone[8] recommends a minimum of four iteration parameters ($n_k \geqq 4$). As with the iterative ADIP, if the number of iterations required for convergence is greater than n_k, the cycle is repeated.

The approximate factorization techniques can now be implemented as follows.

1. Use Eqs. 7.40 through 7.46 to calculate the entries of the original coefficient matrix **[A]** (B, S, W, C, E, N, A), and use Eq. 7.47 to calculate the the right side, Q.

2. Use Eqs. 7.207 and 7.208 to estimate all iteration parameters.

3. Make an initial estimate for all unknowns, $x^{(0)}_{i,j,k}$.

4. Use the iteration parameter calculated in Step 2 and one of the procedures discussed in this section: the simple coefficient method, the Dupont *et al.*[7] method, or the SIP to calculate the entries of **[L′]** and **[U′]** (b', s', w', c', e', n', and a').

5. Calculate the residual of the finite-difference equation (Eq. 7.39).

$$r^{(k)}_{i,j,k} = Q_{i,j,k} - B_{i,j,k}x^{(k)}_{i,j,k-1} - S_{i,j,k}x^{(k)}_{i,j-1,k} - W_{i,j,k}x^{(k)}_{i-1,j,k}$$
$$- C_{i,j,k}x^{(k)}_{i,j,k} - E_{i,j,k}x^{(k)}_{i+1,j,k} - N_{i,j,k}x^{(k)}_{i,j+1,k}$$
$$- A_{i,j,k}x^{(k)}_{i,j,k+1}. \quad \text{........................ (7.209)}$$

6. Solve Eq. 7.163 for $\delta\vec{y}^{(k+1)}$. Use a forward-substitution process by sweeping the finite-difference grid in the order of increasing i, j, and k indices. That is,

$$\delta y^{(k+1)}_{i,j,k} = \frac{\left\{r^{(k)}_{i,j,k} - \left[b'_{i,j,k}\delta y^{(k+1)}_{i,j,k-1} + s'_{i,j,k}\delta y^{(k+1)}_{i,j-1,k} + w'_{i,j,k}\delta y^{(k+1)}_{i-1,j,k}\right]\right\}}{c'_{i,j,k}}$$
$$\text{.................. (7.210)}$$

for $i = 1,2,\ldots, n_x$; $j = 1,2,\ldots, n_y$; and $k = 1,2,\ldots, n_z$.

7. Solve Eq. 7.164 for $\delta\vec{x}^{(k+1)}$. Use a backsubstitution process by sweeping the finite-difference grid in the order of decreasing i, j, and k indices. That is,

$$\delta x^{(k+1)}_{i,j,k} = \delta y^{(k+1)}_{i,j,k} - \left[e'_{i,j,k}\delta x^{(k+1)}_{i+1,j,k} + n'_{i,j,k}\delta x^{(k+1)}_{i,j+1,k}\right.$$
$$\left. + a'_{i,j,k}\delta x^{(k+1)}_{i,j,k+1}\right] \quad \text{........................ (7.211)}$$

for $i = n_x, n_x - 1,\ldots, 1$; $j = n_y, n_y - 1,\ldots, 1$; and $k = n_z, n_z - 1,\ldots, 1$.

8. Update the unknowns with

$$x^{(k+1)}_{i,j,k} = x^{(k)}_{i,j,k} + \delta x^{(k+1)}_{i,j,k} \quad \text{..................... (7.212)}$$

for all i, j, k.

9. Check for convergence with

$$\left|\delta x^{(k+1)}_{i,j,k}\right| \leqq \varepsilon \quad \text{.............................. (7.213)}$$

for all i, j, k.

10. If the system has converged, $x^{(k+1)}_{i,j,k}$ represents the final solution of Eq. 7.1, $[\mathbf{A}]\vec{x} = \vec{d}$; otherwise go back to Step 4.

It is also worth mentioning that changing the order of calculations in subsequent iterations can significantly improve the speed of convergence.[5] With this approach, the order in which the i, j, k indices are increased (i first, j second, k third; j first, k second, i third; and all other permutations) in Step 6 and decreased in Step 7 is changed from one iteration to the next. This produces the net effect of bringing other diagonal entries into the calculations and having no single set of nonstandard diagonals dominating the solution. Again, this technique is used to minimize the effects of nonstandard diagonals in the coefficient matrix.

Conjugate-Gradient Method. Hestenes and Stiefel[10] first introduced the method of conjugate gradients for solving systems of linear equations. The conjugate-gradient method is an iterative algorithm for solving a system of n linear equations in n unknowns. The exact solution is obtained in n iterations (assuming no round-off error); however, an approximate solution is obtained in less than n iterations. The following are some of the attractive features of the conjugate-gradient method.

1. Similar to the Gaussian elimination method, the conjugate-gradient method provides the exact solution in n steps (if no round-off error occurs) for a system of n equations in n unknowns. Consequently, if n iterations are performed, the conjugate-gradient method can be used as a direct-solution procedure. In practice, fewer than n iterations can be performed. This results in an approximate solution.

2. The conjugate-gradient method is simple to code and requires little storage memory.

3. The original coefficient matrix is unaltered during the computations. The sparse matrix structure arising from the finite-difference approximation of the flow equations is preserved.

The objective of the conjugate-gradient method is to minimize a function that is related to Eq. 7.1, $[\mathbf{A}]\vec{x} = \vec{d}$. This function has the form[11]

$$F(\vec{x}) = \frac{1}{2}\left(\vec{r} \cdot [\mathbf{A}]^{-1}\vec{r}\right). \quad \text{...................... (7.214a)}$$

where $\vec{r}$ = the residual vector defined by Eq. 7.159, $\vec{r} = \vec{d} - [\mathbf{A}]\vec{x}$. Equivalently, Eq. 7.214a can be expressed as[11]

$$F(\vec{x}) = \frac{1}{2}\left(\vec{x} \cdot [\mathbf{A}]\vec{x} - 2\vec{d} \cdot \vec{x} + \vec{d} \cdot [\mathbf{A}]^{-1}\vec{d}\right). \quad \text{.... (7.214b)}$$

To arrive at Eq. 7.214b from Eq. 7.214a, we use the identity $([\mathbf{A}]\vec{x}) \cdot ([\mathbf{A}]^{-1}\vec{d}) = \vec{d} \cdot \vec{x}$, which is valid only for symmetric matrices containing all real elements. Such matrices are called self-adjoint matrices.[11]

Eq. 7.214b has two important properties that make it suitable for solving Eq. 7.1. The first property of $F(\vec{x})$ is that the gradient $\vec{\nabla}F(\vec{x})$ is the negative of the residual of the original system of equations.[11] That is

$$\vec{\nabla}F(\vec{x}) = -\vec{r} \quad \text{(7.215a)}$$

and $$\vec{\nabla}F(\vec{x}) = [\mathbf{A}]\vec{x} - \vec{d}. \quad \text{(7.215b)}$$

While the proof of Eq. 7.215 is cumbersome in matrix form, the concept is easy to visualize by use of the scalar analogs to Eqs. 7.214b and 7.215b. The scalar analog of Eq. 7.214b is $f(x) = \frac{1}{2}(ax^2 - 2dx + d^2/a)$ and the scalar analog of Eq. 7.215b is $df/dx = ax - d$. Ref. 11 provides a rigorous proof of Eq. 7.215.

The second property of $F(\vec{x})$ that makes it suitable for solving Eq. 7.1 is that the vector $\vec{x}$ that is the solution vector, $\vec{x}^*$, to the system of equations $[\mathbf{A}]\vec{x}^* = \vec{d}$ results in a zero gradient. That is, $\vec{\nabla}F(\vec{x}^*) = \vec{0}$. This implies that $F(\vec{x})$ is either at a minimum or maximum value when evaluated at the solution vector $\vec{x}^*$. For a symmetric, positive definite coefficient matrix $[\mathbf{A}]$, we can show that $\vec{x}^*$ results in a minimum value of $F(\vec{x})$.[11] Therefore any search algorithm that identifies the vector $\vec{x}$ that minimizes Eq. 7.214 can be used to find the solution, $\vec{x}^*$, to Eq. 7.1.

In the conjugate-gradient method, a sequence of approximate solution vectors $\vec{x}^{(1)}, \vec{x}^{(2)}, \ldots, \vec{x}^{(k+1)}$ for $k+1 \leqq n$ is generated. In this inequality, n = the number of equations to be solved. This is accomplished with an initial estimate of $\vec{x}^{(0)}$ and

$$\vec{x}^{(k+1)} = \vec{x}^{(k)} + a^{(k)}\vec{p}^{(k)}, \quad \text{(7.216)}$$

where $a^{(k)}$ = a scalar variable and $\vec{p}^{(k)}$ = a direction vector. The value of $a^{(k)}$ is selected to minimize $F(\vec{x})$ along the path defined by Eq. 7.216. In other words, $a^{(k)}$ is selected to minimize $F(\vec{x}^{(k)} + a^{(k)}\vec{p}^{(k)})$. Substituting Eq. 7.216 into Eq. 7.214b gives

$$F\left(\vec{x}^{(k)} + a^{(k)}\vec{p}^{(k)}\right) = \frac{1}{2}\left\{\left(\vec{x}^{(k)} + a^{(k)}\vec{p}^{(k)}\right) \cdot [\mathbf{A}]\left(\vec{x}^{(k)} + a^{(k)}\vec{p}^{(k)}\right) - 2\vec{d} \cdot \left(\vec{x}^{(k)} + a^{(k)}\vec{p}^{(k)}\right) + \vec{d} \cdot [\mathbf{A}]^{-1}\vec{d}\right\}. \quad \text{(7.217a)}$$

After some algebraic manipulations and grouping of like terms, Eq. 7.217a becomes

$$F\left(\vec{x}^{(k)} + a^{(k)}\vec{p}^{(k)}\right) = \frac{1}{2}\left\{\vec{x}^{(k)} \cdot [\mathbf{A}]\vec{x}^{(k)} - 2\vec{d} \cdot \vec{x}^{(k)} + \vec{d} \cdot [\mathbf{A}]^{-1}\vec{d} + a^{(k)}\left(2\vec{p}^{(k)} \cdot [\mathbf{A}]\vec{x} - 2\vec{p}^{(k)} \cdot \vec{d}\right) + \left[a^{(k)}\right]^2 \vec{p}^{(k)} \cdot [\mathbf{A}]\vec{p}^{(k)}\right\}. \quad \text{(7.217b)}$$

To arrive at Eq. 7.217b, we use the identities $\vec{d} \cdot \vec{p}^{(k)} = \vec{p}^{(k)} \cdot \vec{d}$, which is valid for all vectors, and $\vec{p} \cdot [\mathbf{A}]\vec{x} = \vec{x} \cdot [\mathbf{A}]\vec{p}$, which is valid for symmetric matrices only. To minimize Eq. 7.217, we take the derivative of $F(\vec{x}^{(k)} + a^{(k)}\vec{p}^{(k)})$ with respect to $a^{(k)}$ and set the resulting expression to zero. That is

$$dF/da^{(k)} = \left(\vec{p}^{(k)} \cdot [\mathbf{A}]\vec{x} - \vec{p}^{(k)} \cdot \vec{d}\right) + a^{(k)}\vec{p}^{(k)} \cdot [\mathbf{A}]\vec{p}^{(k)} = 0. \quad \text{(7.218)}$$

Solving for $a^{(k)}$ gives

$$a^{(k)} = -\frac{\left\{\vec{p}^{(k)} \cdot [\mathbf{A}]\vec{x}^{(k)} - \vec{p}^{(k)} \cdot \vec{d}\right\}}{\vec{p}^{(k)} \cdot [\mathbf{A}]\vec{p}^{(k)}}, \quad \text{(7.219a)}$$

or $$a^{(k)} = \frac{\vec{p}^{(k)} \cdot \vec{r}^{(k)}}{\vec{p}^{(k)} \cdot [\mathbf{A}]\vec{p}^{(k)}}, \quad \text{(7.219b)}$$

after factoring the $\vec{p}^{(k)}$ term in the numerator and applying the definition of the residual. We can show that $a^{(k)}$ is a minimizer of Eq. 7.217b for a positive definite matrix.[11] For efficient implementation of the conjugate-gradient method, the definition of $a^{(k)}$ requires additional manipulation. Here, however, we discuss the direction vectors, $\vec{p}$. In the conjugate-gradient method, the direction vector at the $(k+1)$ iteration level, $\vec{p}^{(k+1)}$, is obtained with

$$\vec{p}^{(k+1)} = \vec{r}^{(k+1)} + b^{(k+1)}\vec{p}^{(k)} \quad \text{(7.220)}$$

where $b^{(k+1)}$ = a scalar value. (If we let $b^{(k+1)}$ in Eq. 7.220 equal zero, this discussion and the following algorithm result in the Steepest Decent Method.)

The direction vectors, $\vec{p}$, are also chosen to be mutually A-orthogonal (or conjugate with respect to $[\mathbf{A}]$). The definition of A-orthogonality is

$$\vec{p}^{(k)} \cdot [\mathbf{A}]\vec{p}^{(j)} = 0, \quad \text{(7.221)}$$

for $k \neq j$. Post-multiplying Eq. 7.220 by $[\mathbf{A}]\vec{p}^{(k)}$ results in

$$\vec{p}^{(k+1)} \cdot [\mathbf{A}]\vec{p}^{(k)} = \vec{r}^{(k+1)} \cdot [\mathbf{A}]\vec{p}^{(k)} + b^{(k+1)}\vec{p}^{(k)} \cdot [\mathbf{A}]\vec{p}^{(k)}. \quad \text{(7.222)}$$

Applying the definition of A-orthogonality (Eq. 7.221) to Eq. 7.222 results in

$$0 = \vec{r}^{(k+1)} \cdot [\mathbf{A}]\vec{p}^{(k)} + b^{(k+1)}\vec{p}^{(k)} \cdot [\mathbf{A}]\vec{p}^{(k)}. \quad \text{(7.223)}$$

Solving for $b^{(k+1)}$ gives

$$b^{(k+1)} = -\frac{\vec{r}^{(k+1)} \cdot [\mathbf{A}]\vec{p}^{(k)}}{\vec{p}^{(k)} \cdot [\mathbf{A}]\vec{p}^{(k)}}. \quad \text{(7.224)}$$

While Eqs. 7.219b and 7.224 can be used in their current forms, a more efficient algorithm can be developed with additional algebraic manipulation. Start with the definition of the residual $\vec{r} = \vec{d} - [\mathbf{A}]\vec{x}$ evaluated at Iteration Level $(k+1)$.

$$\vec{r}^{(k+1)} = \vec{d} - [\mathbf{A}]\vec{x}^{(k+1)}. \quad \text{(7.225)}$$

Substituting Eq. 7.216 into Eq. 7.225 gives

$$\vec{r}^{(k+1)} = \vec{d} - [\mathbf{A}]\vec{x}^{(k)} - a^{(k)}[\mathbf{A}]\vec{p}^{(k)} \quad \text{(7.226a)}$$

or $$\vec{r}^{(k+1)} = \vec{r}^{(k)} - a^{(k)}[\mathbf{A}]\vec{p}^{(k)} \quad \text{(7.226b)}$$

when the definition of r evaluated at Iteration Level (k) is applied. Premultiplying Eq. 7.226b by $\vec{p}^{(k)}$ results in

$$\vec{p}^{(k)} \cdot \vec{r}^{(k+1)} = \vec{p}^{(k)} \cdot \vec{r}^{(k)} - a^{(k)}\vec{p}^{(k)} \cdot [\mathbf{A}]\vec{p}^{(k)}. \quad \text{(7.227)}$$

From Eq. 7.219b, we have

$$a^{(k)}\vec{p}^{(k)} \cdot [\mathbf{A}]\vec{p}^{(k)} = \vec{p}^{(k)} \cdot \vec{r}^{(k)}. \quad \text{(7.228)}$$

Substituting Eq. 7.228 into Eq. 7.227 results in the relationship

$$\vec{p}^{(k)} \cdot \vec{r}^{(k+1)} = 0. \quad \text{(7.229)}$$

Eq. 7.229 states that use of $\vec{x}^{(k+1)}$ defined by Eq. 7.216 results in a residual $\vec{r}^{(k+1)}$ that is orthogonal to the previous direction vector, $\vec{p}^{(k)}$. If the procedure is initialized so that $\vec{p}^{(0)} = \vec{r}^{(0)}$, then $\vec{r}^{(0)} \cdot \vec{r}^{(1)} = 0$ from Eq. 7.229. It can be shown recursively that the resulting sequence of residuals $\vec{r}^{(k)}$ for $k = 1,2,3, \ldots \leqq n$ is mutually orthogonal.[11] That is,

$$\vec{r}^{(k)} \cdot \vec{r}^{(j)} = 0 \quad \text{(7.230)}$$

for $k \neq j$.

This is a property of the conjugate-gradient iteration; the direction vectors, $\vec{p}$, are mutually A-orthogonal (in accordance with Eq. 7.221), while the residuals, $\vec{r}$, are mutually orthogonal (in accordance with Eq. 7.230).

Eq. 7.220 evaluated at Iteration Level (k) implies that

$$\vec{p}^{(k)} = \vec{r}^{(k)} + b^{(k)}\vec{p}^{(k-1)}. \quad \ldots\ldots\ldots\ldots\ldots\ldots\ldots (7.231)$$

Post-multiplying Eq. 7.231 by $\vec{r}^{(k)}$ gives

$$\vec{p}^{(k)} \cdot \vec{r}^{(k)} = \vec{r}^{(k)} \cdot \vec{r}^{(k)} + b^{(k)}\vec{p}^{(k-1)} \cdot \vec{r}^{(k)}. \quad \ldots\ldots\ldots (7.232)$$

Substituting Eq. 7.229 into Eq. 7.232 results in the following identity.

$$\vec{p}^{(k)} \cdot \vec{r}^{(k)} = \vec{r}^{(k)} \cdot \vec{r}^{(k)}. \quad \ldots\ldots\ldots\ldots\ldots\ldots\ldots (7.233)$$

Substituting Eq. 7.233 into Eq. 7.219b results in the final definition of $a^{(k)}$.

$$a^{(k)} = \frac{\vec{r}^{(k)} \cdot \vec{r}^{(k)}}{\vec{p}^{(k)} \cdot [\mathbf{A}]\vec{p}^{(k)}}. \quad \ldots\ldots\ldots\ldots\ldots\ldots\ldots (7.234)$$

To obtain the final definition of $b^{(k+1)}$, start with Eq. 7.226b. Solving for $[\mathbf{A}]\vec{p}^{(k)}$ results in

$$[\mathbf{A}]\vec{p}^{(k)} = \left[\vec{r}^{(k)} - \vec{r}^{(k+1)}\right]/a^{(k)}. \quad \ldots\ldots\ldots\ldots\ldots (7.235)$$

Premultiplying Eq. 7.235 by $\vec{p}^{(k)}$ results in

$$\vec{p}^{(k)} \cdot [\mathbf{A}]\vec{p}^{(k)} = \vec{p}^{(k)} \cdot \left[\vec{r}^{(k)} - \vec{r}^{(k+1)}\right]/a^{(k)}, \quad \ldots\ldots (7.236a)$$

$$\vec{p}^{(k)} \cdot [\mathbf{A}]\vec{p}^{(k)} = \left[\vec{p}^{(k)} \cdot \vec{r}^{(k)} - \vec{p}^{(k)} \cdot \vec{r}^{(k+1)}\right]/a^{(k)},$$

$$\ldots\ldots\ldots\ldots\ldots\ldots (7.236b)$$

or $\vec{p}^{(k)} \cdot [\mathbf{A}]\vec{p}^{(k)} = \vec{p}^{(k)} \cdot \vec{r}^{(k)}/a^{(k)}, \quad \ldots\ldots\ldots\ldots\ldots (7.236c)$

after substituting Eq. 7.229. Substituting Eq. 7.236c into the denominator of Eq. 7.224 gives

$$b^{(k+1)} = -\frac{a^{(k)}\vec{r}^{(k+1)} \cdot [\mathbf{A}]\vec{p}^{(k)}}{\vec{p}^{(k)} \cdot \vec{r}^{(k)}}. \quad \ldots\ldots\ldots\ldots\ldots (7.237)$$

Now, substituting Eq. 7.233 into Eq. 7.237 results in

$$b^{(k+1)} = -\frac{a^{(k)}\vec{r}^{(k+1)} \cdot [\mathbf{A}]\vec{p}^{(k)}}{\vec{r}^{(k)} \cdot \vec{r}^{(k)}}. \quad \ldots\ldots\ldots\ldots\ldots (7.238)$$

We then manipulate the numerator of Eq. 7.238. Premultiplying Eq. 7.226b by $\vec{r}^{(k+1)}$ gives

$$\vec{r}^{(k+1)} \cdot \vec{r}^{(k+1)} = \vec{r}^{(k+1)} \cdot \vec{r}^{(k)} - a^{(k)}\vec{r}^{(k+1)} \cdot [\mathbf{A}]\vec{p}^{(k)}.$$

$$\ldots\ldots\ldots\ldots\ldots\ldots (7.239)$$

Applying the orthogonality relationship for residuals (Eq. 7.230) results in the identity

$$\vec{r}^{(k+1)} \cdot \vec{r}^{(k+1)} = -a^{(k)}\vec{r}^{(k+1)} \cdot [\mathbf{A}]\vec{p}^{(k)}. \quad \ldots\ldots\ldots (7.240)$$

Substituting Eq. 7.240 into the numerator of Eq. 7.238 gives the final definition of $b^{(k+1)}$.

$$b^{(k+1)} = \frac{\vec{r}^{(k+1)} \cdot \vec{r}^{(k+1)}}{\vec{r}^{(k)} \cdot \vec{r}^{(k)}}. \quad \ldots\ldots\ldots\ldots\ldots\ldots (7.241)$$

In this discussion, we used the symmetric, positive definite structure of the coefficient matrix, **[A]**, in the development of many of the equations. Therefore, implementation of this version of the conjugate-gradient method is valid for systems of equations with symmetric, positive definite coefficient matrices. The following algorithms show the implementation of such systems.

Algorithm 1—Conjugate-Gradient Method for Symmetric Coefficient Matrices. Select an estimate of $\vec{x}^{(0)}$ (arbitrary). Set $\vec{r}^{(0)} = \vec{d} - [\mathbf{A}]\vec{x}^{(0)}$ and $\vec{p}^{(0)} = \vec{r}^{(0)}$. Perform the following computations sequentially for $k = 0,1,2, \ldots,$ until convergence.

$$\vec{g}^{(k)} = [\mathbf{A}]\vec{p}^{(k)}, \quad \ldots\ldots\ldots\ldots\ldots\ldots\ldots\ldots (7.242)$$

$$a^{(k)} = \frac{\vec{r}^{(k)} \cdot \vec{r}^{(k)}}{\vec{p}^{(k)} \cdot \vec{g}^{(k)}}, \quad \ldots\ldots\ldots\ldots\ldots\ldots\ldots (7.234)$$

$$\vec{x}^{(k+1)} = \vec{x}^{(k)} + a^{(k)}\vec{p}^{(k)}, \quad \ldots\ldots\ldots\ldots\ldots\ldots (7.216)$$

$$\vec{r}^{(k+1)} = \vec{r}^{(k)} - a^{(k)}\vec{g}^{(k)}, \quad \ldots\ldots\ldots\ldots\ldots\ldots (7.226b)$$

$$b^{(k+1)} = \frac{\vec{r}^{(k+1)} \cdot \vec{r}^{(k+1)}}{\vec{r}^{(k)} \cdot \vec{r}^{(k)}}, \quad \ldots\ldots\ldots\ldots\ldots\ldots (7.241)$$

and $\vec{p}^{(k+1)} = \vec{r}^{(k+1)} + b^{(k+1)}\vec{p}^{(k)}. \quad \ldots\ldots\ldots\ldots\ldots (7.220)$

In this algorithm, $b^{(k)}$ and $a^{(k)}$ = scalar quantities; $\vec{x}$, $\vec{r}$, $\vec{p}$, and $\vec{g}$ = vector quantities; and **[A]** = original coefficient matrix.

Note that there are several possibilities where convergence checks can be made in the conjugate-gradient algorithm. If a check is to be made on the maximum change in $\vec{x}$, then, from Eq. 7.216,

$$\max\left|\vec{x}^{(k+1)} - \vec{x}^{(k)}\right| = \max\left|a^{(k)}\vec{p}^{(k)}\right| \leqq \varepsilon_x, \quad \ldots\ldots\ldots (7.243a)$$

where max = the maximum element in the vector and $|\cdot|$ = the absolute value. Eq. 7.243a can be rearranged to

$$\max\left|\left[\vec{x}^{(k+1)} - \vec{x}^{(k)}\right]/a^{(k)}\right| = \max\left|\vec{p}^{(k)}\right| \leqq |\varepsilon_x/a^{(k)}|.$$

$$\ldots\ldots\ldots\ldots\ldots\ldots (7.243b)$$

A convergence check can also be made on the residual with

$$\max\left|\vec{r}^{(k+1)}\right| \leqq \varepsilon_r. \quad \ldots\ldots\ldots\ldots\ldots\ldots\ldots\ldots (7.244)$$

To this point, we have emphasized the mechanics of the conjugate-gradient method. The method has several theoretical and computational features that are beyond the scope of this book but are important to mention. These include the following.

1. Like other direct-solution methods (such as Gaussian elimination, Gauss-Jordan reduction, and Crout reduction) the conjugate-gradient method yields the exact solution after a fixed number of calculations when no round-off error is present. It can be shown that the method converges to the exact solution in, at most, n iterations (in the absence of round-off error), where n = the number of equations. In fact, for an arbitrary initial estimate, $\vec{x}^{(0)}$, the method converges to the exact solution in, at most, n_e iterations (in the absence of round-off error), where n_e = the number of distinct eigenvalues of the coefficient matrix **[A]** and $n_e \leqq n$.[12]

2. Unlike other direct-solution methods, reasonable approximations to the exact solution are achieved in fewer than n iterations. Therefore, the method can be used as an iterative-solution method. For reasonably low values of the condition number (approximately one), acceptable convergence is achieved in far fewer than n iterations. The condition number is defined as the maximum/minimum eigenvalue ratio.

3. A condition number equal to one implies that the maximum eigenvalue equals the minimum eigenvalue and, therefore, must be equal to all intermediate eigenvalues (i.e., one distinct eigenvalue). From Point 1, this implies that the conjugate-gradient method will converge after one iteration for matrices with a condition number of one.

4. With proper matrix preconditioning (discussed later), the condition number of the preconditioned system of equations can be greatly reduced, thus improving the rate of convergence of the method.

5. The method does not contain any iteration parameters.

6. For sparse systems of equations, efficient coding can greatly reduce both computational effort and storage requirements. For example, for the heptadiagonal coefficient matrices encountered in

reservoir simulation, a matrix/vector multiplication across one row of the matrix requires only seven multiplications and six additions regardless of the size of the matrix and vector.

7. The original coefficient matrix is unaltered during the computational process.

The following example from Hestenes and Stiefel[10] is reworked with the algorithm notation used in this book. The objective of this example is to illustrate the use of the conjugate-gradient method as a direct-solution procedure.

Example 7.11. Use the conjugate-gradient method to solve the following system of equations.

$$\begin{bmatrix} 1 & 2 & -1 & 1 \\ 2 & 5 & 0 & 2 \\ -1 & 0 & 6 & 0 \\ 1 & 2 & 0 & 3 \end{bmatrix} \begin{bmatrix} x_1 \\ x_2 \\ x_3 \\ x_4 \end{bmatrix} = \begin{bmatrix} 0 \\ 2 \\ -1 \\ 1 \end{bmatrix}.$$

Solution. Note that the coefficient matrix is symmetrical in structure. The application of Algorithm 1 is as follows. For this example,

$$[\mathbf{A}] = \begin{bmatrix} 1 & 2 & -1 & 1 \\ 2 & 5 & 0 & 2 \\ -1 & 0 & 6 & 0 \\ 1 & 2 & 0 & 3 \end{bmatrix}$$

and $\vec{d} = \begin{bmatrix} 0 \\ 2 \\ -1 \\ 1 \end{bmatrix}.$

1. Initial estimate. Begin with an initial estimate of

$$\begin{bmatrix} x_1 \\ x_2 \\ x_3 \\ x_4 \end{bmatrix}^{(0)} = \begin{bmatrix} 1 \\ 0 \\ 0 \\ 0 \end{bmatrix}.$$

Then,

$$\begin{bmatrix} p_1 \\ p_2 \\ p_3 \\ p_4 \end{bmatrix}^{(0)} = \begin{bmatrix} r_1 \\ r_2 \\ r_3 \\ r_4 \end{bmatrix}^{(0)} = \begin{bmatrix} 0 \\ 2 \\ -1 \\ 1 \end{bmatrix} - \begin{bmatrix} 1 & 2 & -1 & 1 \\ 2 & 5 & 0 & 2 \\ -1 & 0 & 6 & 0 \\ 1 & 2 & 0 & 3 \end{bmatrix} \begin{bmatrix} 1 \\ 0 \\ 0 \\ 0 \end{bmatrix} = \begin{bmatrix} -1 \\ 0 \\ 0 \\ 0 \end{bmatrix}.$$

2. First iteration calculations, $(k=0)$.

$$\begin{bmatrix} g_1 \\ g_2 \\ g_3 \\ g_4 \end{bmatrix}^{(0)} = \begin{bmatrix} 1 & 2 & -1 & 1 \\ 2 & 5 & 0 & 2 \\ -1 & 0 & 6 & 0 \\ 1 & 2 & 0 & 3 \end{bmatrix} \begin{bmatrix} -1 \\ 0 \\ 0 \\ 0 \end{bmatrix} = \begin{bmatrix} -1 \\ -2 \\ 1 \\ -1 \end{bmatrix}.$$

$$a^{(0)} = \frac{\begin{bmatrix} -1 \\ 0 \\ 0 \\ 0 \end{bmatrix} \cdot \begin{bmatrix} -1 \\ 0 \\ 0 \\ 0 \end{bmatrix}}{\begin{bmatrix} -1 \\ 0 \\ 0 \\ 0 \end{bmatrix} \cdot \begin{bmatrix} -1 \\ -2 \\ 1 \\ -1 \end{bmatrix}} = \frac{1+0+0+0}{1+0+0+0} = 1.$$

$$\begin{bmatrix} x_1 \\ x_2 \\ x_3 \\ x_4 \end{bmatrix}^{(1)} = \begin{bmatrix} 1 \\ 0 \\ 0 \\ 0 \end{bmatrix} + 1 \begin{bmatrix} -1 \\ 0 \\ 0 \\ 0 \end{bmatrix} = \begin{bmatrix} 0 \\ 0 \\ 0 \\ 0 \end{bmatrix}.$$

$$\begin{bmatrix} r_1 \\ r_2 \\ r_3 \\ r_4 \end{bmatrix}^{(1)} = \begin{bmatrix} -1 \\ 0 \\ 0 \\ 0 \end{bmatrix} - 1 \begin{bmatrix} -1 \\ -2 \\ 1 \\ -1 \end{bmatrix} = \begin{bmatrix} 0 \\ 2 \\ -1 \\ 1 \end{bmatrix}.$$

$$b^{(1)} = \frac{\begin{bmatrix} 0 \\ 2 \\ -1 \\ 1 \end{bmatrix} \cdot \begin{bmatrix} 0 \\ 2 \\ -1 \\ 1 \end{bmatrix}}{\begin{bmatrix} -1 \\ 0 \\ 0 \\ 0 \end{bmatrix} \cdot \begin{bmatrix} -1 \\ 0 \\ 0 \\ 0 \end{bmatrix}} = \frac{0+4+1+1}{1+0+0+0} = 6.$$

$$\begin{bmatrix} p_1 \\ p_2 \\ p_3 \\ p_4 \end{bmatrix}^{(1)} = \begin{bmatrix} 0 \\ 2 \\ -1 \\ 1 \end{bmatrix} + 6 \begin{bmatrix} -1 \\ 0 \\ 0 \\ 0 \end{bmatrix} = \begin{bmatrix} -6 \\ 2 \\ -1 \\ 1 \end{bmatrix}.$$

3. Second iteration calculations $(k=1)$.

$$\begin{bmatrix} g_1 \\ g_2 \\ g_3 \\ g_4 \end{bmatrix}^{(1)} = \begin{bmatrix} 1 & 2 & -1 & 1 \\ 2 & 5 & 0 & 2 \\ -1 & 0 & 6 & 0 \\ 1 & 2 & 0 & 3 \end{bmatrix} \begin{bmatrix} -6 \\ 2 \\ -1 \\ 1 \end{bmatrix} = \begin{bmatrix} 0 \\ 0 \\ 0 \\ 1 \end{bmatrix}.$$

$$a^{(1)} = \frac{\begin{bmatrix} 0 \\ 2 \\ -1 \\ 1 \end{bmatrix} \cdot \begin{bmatrix} 0 \\ 2 \\ -1 \\ 1 \end{bmatrix}}{\begin{bmatrix} -6 \\ 2 \\ -1 \\ 1 \end{bmatrix} \cdot \begin{bmatrix} 0 \\ 0 \\ 0 \\ 1 \end{bmatrix}} = \frac{0+4+1+1}{0+0+0+1} = 6.$$

$$\begin{bmatrix} x_1 \\ x_2 \\ x_3 \\ x_4 \end{bmatrix}^{(2)} = \begin{bmatrix} 0 \\ 0 \\ 0 \\ 0 \end{bmatrix} + 6 \begin{bmatrix} -6 \\ 2 \\ -1 \\ 1 \end{bmatrix} = \begin{bmatrix} -36 \\ 12 \\ -6 \\ 6 \end{bmatrix}.$$

TABLE 7.7—SYSTEM OF EQUATIONS FOR EXAMPLE 7.12

$$\begin{bmatrix} 100 & 2 & 1 & 0 & 0 & 1 & 2 & 0 & 0 & 0 \\ 2 & 80 & 3 & 1 & 0 & 0 & 1 & 1 & 0 & 0 \\ 1 & 3 & 125 & 1 & 2 & 0 & 0 & 1 & 0 & 0 \\ 0 & 1 & 1 & 160 & 2 & 2 & 0 & 0 & 2 & 1 \\ 0 & 0 & 2 & 2 & 200 & 1 & 1 & 0 & 0 & 1 \\ 1 & 0 & 0 & 2 & 1 & 100 & 3 & 2 & 0 & 0 \\ 2 & 1 & 0 & 0 & 1 & 3 & 80 & 2 & 1 & 0 \\ 0 & 1 & 1 & 0 & 0 & 2 & 2 & 250 & 1 & 0 \\ 0 & 0 & 0 & 2 & 0 & 0 & 1 & 1 & 125 & 1 \\ 0 & 0 & 0 & 1 & 1 & 0 & 0 & 0 & 1 & 200 \end{bmatrix} \begin{bmatrix} x_1 \\ x_2 \\ x_3 \\ x_4 \\ x_5 \\ x_6 \\ x_7 \\ x_8 \\ x_9 \\ x_{10} \end{bmatrix} = \begin{bmatrix} 206 \\ 88 \\ 13 \\ 175 \\ 606 \\ 15 \\ 173 \\ 258 \\ 382 \\ 407 \end{bmatrix}$$

$$\begin{bmatrix} r_1 \\ r_2 \\ r_3 \\ r_4 \end{bmatrix}^{(2)} = \begin{bmatrix} 0 \\ 2 \\ -1 \\ 1 \end{bmatrix} - 6\begin{bmatrix} 0 \\ 0 \\ 0 \\ 1 \end{bmatrix} = \begin{bmatrix} 0 \\ 2 \\ -1 \\ -5 \end{bmatrix}.$$

$$b^{(2)} = \frac{\begin{bmatrix} 0 \\ 2 \\ -1 \\ -5 \end{bmatrix} \cdot \begin{bmatrix} 0 \\ 2 \\ -1 \\ -5 \end{bmatrix}}{\begin{bmatrix} 0 \\ 2 \\ -1 \\ 1 \end{bmatrix} \cdot \begin{bmatrix} 0 \\ 2 \\ -1 \\ 1 \end{bmatrix}} = \frac{0+4+1+25}{0+4+1+1} = 5.$$

$$\begin{bmatrix} p_1 \\ p_2 \\ p_3 \\ p_4 \end{bmatrix}^{(2)} = \begin{bmatrix} 0 \\ 2 \\ -1 \\ -5 \end{bmatrix} + 5\begin{bmatrix} -6 \\ 2 \\ -1 \\ 1 \end{bmatrix} = \begin{bmatrix} -30 \\ 12 \\ -6 \\ 0 \end{bmatrix}.$$

4. Third iteration calculations ($k=2$).

$$\begin{bmatrix} g_1 \\ g_2 \\ g_3 \\ g_4 \end{bmatrix}^{(2)} = \begin{bmatrix} 1 & 2 & -1 & 1 \\ 2 & 5 & 0 & 2 \\ -1 & 0 & 6 & 0 \\ 1 & 2 & 0 & 3 \end{bmatrix} \begin{bmatrix} -30 \\ 12 \\ -6 \\ 0 \end{bmatrix} = \begin{bmatrix} 0 \\ 0 \\ -6 \\ -6 \end{bmatrix}.$$

$$a^{(2)} = \frac{\begin{bmatrix} 0 \\ 2 \\ -1 \\ -5 \end{bmatrix} \cdot \begin{bmatrix} 0 \\ 2 \\ -1 \\ -5 \end{bmatrix}}{\begin{bmatrix} -30 \\ 12 \\ -6 \\ 0 \end{bmatrix} \cdot \begin{bmatrix} 0 \\ 0 \\ -6 \\ -6 \end{bmatrix}} = \frac{0+4+1+25}{0+0+36+0} = \frac{5}{6}.$$

$$\begin{bmatrix} x_1 \\ x_2 \\ x_3 \\ x_4 \end{bmatrix}^{(3)} = \begin{bmatrix} -36 \\ 12 \\ -6 \\ 6 \end{bmatrix} + {}^5/_6\begin{bmatrix} -30 \\ 12 \\ -6 \\ 0 \end{bmatrix} = \begin{bmatrix} -61 \\ 22 \\ -11 \\ 6 \end{bmatrix}.$$

$$\begin{bmatrix} r_1 \\ r_2 \\ r_3 \\ r_4 \end{bmatrix}^{(3)} = \begin{bmatrix} 0 \\ 2 \\ -1 \\ -5 \end{bmatrix} - {}^5/_6\begin{bmatrix} 0 \\ 0 \\ -6 \\ -6 \end{bmatrix} = \begin{bmatrix} 0 \\ 2 \\ 4 \\ 0 \end{bmatrix}.$$

$$b^{(3)} = \frac{\begin{bmatrix} 0 \\ 2 \\ 4 \\ 0 \end{bmatrix} \cdot \begin{bmatrix} 0 \\ 2 \\ 4 \\ 0 \end{bmatrix}}{\begin{bmatrix} 0 \\ 2 \\ -1 \\ -5 \end{bmatrix} \cdot \begin{bmatrix} 0 \\ 2 \\ -1 \\ -5 \end{bmatrix}} = \frac{0+4+16+0}{0+4+1+25} = \frac{2}{3}.$$

$$\begin{bmatrix} p_1 \\ p_2 \\ p_3 \\ p_4 \end{bmatrix}^{(3)} = \begin{bmatrix} 0 \\ 2 \\ 4 \\ 0 \end{bmatrix} + {}^2/_3\begin{bmatrix} -30 \\ 12 \\ -6 \\ 0 \end{bmatrix} = \begin{bmatrix} -20 \\ 10 \\ 0 \\ 0 \end{bmatrix}.$$

5. Fourth iteration calculations ($k=3$).

$$\begin{bmatrix} g_1 \\ g_2 \\ g_3 \\ g_4 \end{bmatrix}^{(3)} = \begin{bmatrix} 1 & 2 & -1 & 1 \\ 2 & 5 & 0 & 2 \\ -1 & 0 & 6 & 0 \\ 1 & 2 & 0 & 3 \end{bmatrix} \begin{bmatrix} -20 \\ 10 \\ 0 \\ 0 \end{bmatrix} = \begin{bmatrix} 0 \\ 10 \\ 20 \\ 0 \end{bmatrix}.$$

$$a^{(3)} = \frac{\begin{bmatrix} 0 \\ 2 \\ 4 \\ 0 \end{bmatrix} \cdot \begin{bmatrix} 0 \\ 2 \\ 4 \\ 0 \end{bmatrix}}{\begin{bmatrix} -20 \\ 10 \\ 0 \\ 0 \end{bmatrix} \cdot \begin{bmatrix} 0 \\ 10 \\ 20 \\ 0 \end{bmatrix}} = \frac{0+4+16+0}{0+100+0+0} = \frac{1}{5}.$$

$$\begin{bmatrix} x_1 \\ x_2 \\ x_3 \\ x_4 \end{bmatrix}^{(4)} = \begin{bmatrix} -61 \\ 22 \\ -11 \\ 6 \end{bmatrix} + {}^1/_5\begin{bmatrix} -20 \\ 10 \\ 0 \\ 0 \end{bmatrix} = \begin{bmatrix} -65 \\ 24 \\ -11 \\ 6 \end{bmatrix}.$$

$$\begin{bmatrix} r_1 \\ r_2 \\ r_3 \\ r_4 \end{bmatrix}^{(4)} = \begin{bmatrix} 0 \\ 2 \\ 4 \\ 0 \end{bmatrix} - {}^1/_5\begin{bmatrix} 0 \\ 10 \\ 20 \\ 0 \end{bmatrix} = \begin{bmatrix} 0 \\ 0 \\ 0 \\ 0 \end{bmatrix}.$$

The iteration terminates because the residual vector, $\vec{r}$, is the zero vector; therefore, $\vec{x}^{(4)}$ is the converged solution. Because no round-off error is encountered in the computations, the exact solution is obtained in four iterations. Note that the solution of the third iteration, $\vec{x}^{(3)}$, can be considered to be reasonably close to the exact solution obtained at the fourth iteration, $\vec{x}^{(4)}$. If a coarser tolerance had been used in this example, the procedure could have been terminated after the third iteration. This example shows both the iterative nature of the procedure and the direct-solution nature of the conjugate-gradient technique.

Example 7.12 illustrates use of the conjugate-gradient method as an iterative-solution procedure.

Example 7.12. Use the conjugate-gradient method to solve the system of equations in **Table 7.7.** The objective is to demonstrate that the method can be used as an iterative-solution procedure. Use an initial estimate of $x_i = 0$ for all i. We present only the results of the iterations here instead of the entire calculation of this problem. The conjugate-gradient solution for this example is

$$\vec{x}^{(k)} = \begin{bmatrix} 0.0000\\0.0000\\0.0000\\0.0000\\0.0000\\0.0000\\0.0000\\0.0000\\0.0000\\0.0000 \end{bmatrix}^{(0)} \rightarrow \begin{bmatrix} 1.1277\\0.4817\\0.0712\\0.9580\\3.3174\\0.0821\\0.9471\\1.4124\\2.0912\\2.2280 \end{bmatrix}^{(1)} \rightarrow \begin{bmatrix} 1.8628\\0.8330\\0.0221\\1.0846\\3.1009\\0.0501\\1.6387\\0.7906\\3.0687\\2.0623 \end{bmatrix}^{(2)}$$

$$\rightarrow \begin{bmatrix} 2.0023\\0.9381\\0.0061\\1.0187\\2.9732\\0.0276\\1.8555\\1.0313\\3.1019\\1.9794 \end{bmatrix}^{(3)} \rightarrow \begin{bmatrix} 2.0227\\0.9955\\-0.0010\\0.9830\\3.0022\\0.0040\\1.9826\\0.9991\\2.9985\\2.0024 \end{bmatrix}^{(4)} \rightarrow \begin{bmatrix} 2.0055\\1.0001\\-0.0002\\1.0036\\3.0000\\0.0005\\1.9974\\1.0001\\2.9971\\1.9994 \end{bmatrix}^{(5)}$$

$$\rightarrow \begin{bmatrix} 2.0000\\1.0002\\0.0000\\1.0000\\2.9999\\-0.0001\\1.9999\\1.0000\\3.0000\\2.0002 \end{bmatrix}^{(6)} \rightarrow \begin{bmatrix} 2.0000\\1.0001\\0.0000\\1.0000\\3.0000\\-0.0001\\1.9999\\1.0000\\3.0000\\2.0000 \end{bmatrix}^{(7)} \rightarrow \begin{bmatrix} 2.0000\\1.0000\\0.0000\\1.0000\\3.0000\\0.0000\\2.0000\\1.0000\\3.0000\\2.0000 \end{bmatrix}^{(8)}$$

$$\rightarrow \begin{bmatrix} 2.0000\\1.0000\\0.0000\\1.0000\\3.0000\\0.0000\\2.0000\\1.0000\\3.0000\\2.0000 \end{bmatrix}^{(9)} \rightarrow \begin{bmatrix} 2.0000\\1.0000\\0.0000\\1.0000\\3.0000\\0.0000\\2.0000\\1.0000\\3.0000\\2.0000 \end{bmatrix}^{(10)}.$$

This example illustrates both the direct- and iterative-solution characteristics of the conjugate-gradient method. If a tolerance of 0.0001 is used between successive iterates to terminate the process, it stops after the seventh iteration.

A serious shortcoming of the conjugate-gradient method is the requirement for a symmetric, positive definite coefficient matrix. Symmetric problems are encountered in many reservoir simulation applications; however, an important exception occurs when the fully implicit (Newton-Raphson) method of linearization is used for problems where upstream weighting on one component of the transmissibility is used (for example, relative permeability). when this occurs, the resulting Jacobian matrix is not symmetric. For cases with nonsymmetric coefficient matrices, the following variation of the conjugate-gradient method can be used.

Algorithm 2—Conjugate-Gradient Method for Nonsymmetric Coefficient Matrices. Select an estimate of $\vec{x}^{(0)}$ (arbitrary). Set $\vec{r}^{(0)} = \vec{d} - [\mathbf{A}]\vec{x}^{(0)}$, $\vec{p}^{(0)} = [\mathbf{A}]^T\vec{r}^{(0)}$, and $\vec{h}^{(0)} = \vec{p}^{(0)}$. Perform the following computations sequentially for $k=0,1,2,\ldots,$ until convergence.

$$\vec{g}^{(k)} = [\mathbf{A}]\vec{p}^{(k)}, \quad \ldots\ldots (7.242)$$

$$a^{(k)} = \frac{\vec{h}^{(k)} \cdot \vec{h}^{(k)}}{\vec{g}^{(k)} \cdot \vec{g}^{(k)}}, \quad \ldots\ldots (7.245)$$

$$\vec{x}^{(k+1)} = \vec{x}^{(k)} + a^{(k)}\vec{p}^{(k)}, \quad \ldots\ldots (7.216)$$

$$\vec{r}^{(k+1)} = \vec{r}^{(k)} - a^{(k)}\vec{g}^{(k)}, \quad \ldots\ldots (7.226b)$$

$$\vec{h}^{(k+1)} = [\mathbf{A}]^T\vec{r}^{(k+1)}, \quad \ldots\ldots (7.246)$$

$$b^{(k+1)} = \frac{\vec{h}^{(k+1)} \cdot \vec{h}^{(k+1)}}{\vec{h}^{(k)} \cdot \vec{h}^{(k)}}, \quad \ldots\ldots (7.247)$$

and $$\vec{p}^{(k+1)} = \vec{h}^{(k+1)} + b^{(k+1)}\vec{p}^{(k)}. \quad \ldots\ldots (7.248)$$

In this algorithm, $[\mathbf{A}]^T$ is the transpose of Matrix **[A]**; that is, the elements $a_{i,j}$ of **[A]** become the elements $a_{j,i}$ in $[\mathbf{A}]^T$. Example 7.13 illustrates how the algorithm is applied to solve a system of equations with a nonsymmetric coefficient matrix.

Example 7.13. Use the conjugate-gradient method to solve the following nonsymmetric system of equations.

$$\begin{bmatrix} 1 & -1 & 0\\ 0 & 2 & 1\\ 1 & 0 & -3 \end{bmatrix}\begin{bmatrix} x_1\\x_2\\x_3 \end{bmatrix} = \begin{bmatrix} 0\\3\\-2 \end{bmatrix}.$$

Solution. This example deals with a nonsymmetric coefficient matrix, so we use Algorithm 2. Note that, for this example,

$$[\mathbf{A}] = \begin{bmatrix} 1 & -1 & 0\\ 0 & 2 & 1\\ 1 & 0 & -3 \end{bmatrix},$$

$$[\mathbf{A}]^T = \begin{bmatrix} 1 & 0 & 1\\ -1 & 2 & 0\\ 0 & 1 & -3 \end{bmatrix},$$

and $$\vec{d} = \begin{bmatrix} 0\\3\\-2 \end{bmatrix}.$$

1. Initial estimate calculations. Begin with an arbitrary initial guess of

$$\begin{bmatrix} x_1 \\ x_2 \\ x_3 \end{bmatrix}^{(0)} = \begin{bmatrix} 0 \\ 0 \\ 0 \end{bmatrix}.$$

$$\begin{bmatrix} r_1 \\ r_2 \\ r_3 \end{bmatrix}^{(0)} = \begin{bmatrix} 0 \\ 3 \\ -2 \end{bmatrix} - \begin{bmatrix} 1 & -1 & 0 \\ 0 & 2 & 1 \\ 1 & 0 & -3 \end{bmatrix} \begin{bmatrix} 0 \\ 0 \\ 0 \end{bmatrix} = \begin{bmatrix} 0 \\ 3 \\ -2 \end{bmatrix}.$$

$$\begin{bmatrix} p_1 \\ p_2 \\ p_3 \end{bmatrix}^{(0)} = \begin{bmatrix} 1 & 0 & 1 \\ -1 & 2 & 0 \\ 0 & 1 & -3 \end{bmatrix} \begin{bmatrix} 0 \\ 3 \\ -2 \end{bmatrix} = \begin{bmatrix} -2 \\ 6 \\ 9 \end{bmatrix}.$$

$$\begin{bmatrix} h_1 \\ h_2 \\ h_3 \end{bmatrix}^{(0)} = \begin{bmatrix} -2 \\ 6 \\ 9 \end{bmatrix}.$$

2. First iteration calculations ($k = 0$).

$$\begin{bmatrix} g_1 \\ g_2 \\ g_3 \end{bmatrix}^{(0)} = \begin{bmatrix} 1 & -1 & 0 \\ 0 & 2 & 1 \\ 1 & 0 & -3 \end{bmatrix} \begin{bmatrix} -2 \\ 6 \\ 9 \end{bmatrix} = \begin{bmatrix} -8 \\ 21 \\ -29 \end{bmatrix}.$$

$$a^{(0)} = \frac{\begin{bmatrix} -2 \\ 6 \\ 9 \end{bmatrix} \cdot \begin{bmatrix} -2 \\ 6 \\ 9 \end{bmatrix}}{\begin{bmatrix} -8 \\ 21 \\ -29 \end{bmatrix} \cdot \begin{bmatrix} -8 \\ 21 \\ -29 \end{bmatrix}} = \frac{121}{1,346} = 0.0899.$$

$$\begin{bmatrix} x_1 \\ x_2 \\ x_3 \end{bmatrix}^{(1)} = \begin{bmatrix} 0 \\ 0 \\ 0 \end{bmatrix} + 0.0899 \begin{bmatrix} -2 \\ 6 \\ 9 \end{bmatrix} = \begin{bmatrix} -0.1798 \\ 0.5394 \\ 0.8091 \end{bmatrix}.$$

$$\begin{bmatrix} r_1 \\ r_2 \\ r_3 \end{bmatrix}^{(1)} = \begin{bmatrix} 0 \\ 3 \\ -2 \end{bmatrix} - 0.0899 \begin{bmatrix} -8 \\ 21 \\ -29 \end{bmatrix} = \begin{bmatrix} 0.7192 \\ 1.1121 \\ 0.6071 \end{bmatrix}.$$

$$\begin{bmatrix} h_1 \\ h_2 \\ h_3 \end{bmatrix}^{(1)} = \begin{bmatrix} 1 & 0 & 1 \\ -1 & 2 & 0 \\ 0 & 1 & -3 \end{bmatrix} \begin{bmatrix} 0.7192 \\ 1.1121 \\ 0.6071 \end{bmatrix} = \begin{bmatrix} 1.3263 \\ 1.5050 \\ -0.7092 \end{bmatrix}.$$

$$b^{(1)} = \frac{\begin{bmatrix} 1.3263 \\ 1.5050 \\ 0.7092 \end{bmatrix} \cdot \begin{bmatrix} 1.3263 \\ 1.5050 \\ -0.7092 \end{bmatrix}}{\begin{bmatrix} -2 \\ 6 \\ 9 \end{bmatrix} \cdot \begin{bmatrix} -2 \\ 6 \\ 9 \end{bmatrix}} = \frac{4.5271}{121} = 0.0374.$$

$$\begin{bmatrix} p_1 \\ p_2 \\ p_3 \end{bmatrix}^{(1)} = \begin{bmatrix} 1.3263 \\ 1.5050 \\ -0.7092 \end{bmatrix} + 0.0374 \begin{bmatrix} -2 \\ 6 \\ 9 \end{bmatrix} = \begin{bmatrix} 1.2515 \\ 1.7294 \\ -0.3726 \end{bmatrix}.$$

3. Second iteration calculations ($k = 1$).

$$\begin{bmatrix} g_1 \\ g_2 \\ g_3 \end{bmatrix}^{(1)} = \begin{bmatrix} 1 & -1 & 0 \\ 0 & 2 & 1 \\ 1 & 0 & -3 \end{bmatrix} \begin{bmatrix} 1.2515 \\ 1.7294 \\ -0.3726 \end{bmatrix} = \begin{bmatrix} -0.4779 \\ 3.0862 \\ 2.3693 \end{bmatrix}.$$

$$a^{(1)} = \frac{\begin{bmatrix} 1.3263 \\ 1.5050 \\ -0.7092 \end{bmatrix} \cdot \begin{bmatrix} 1.3263 \\ 1.5050 \\ -0.7092 \end{bmatrix}}{\begin{bmatrix} -0.4779 \\ 3.0862 \\ 2.3693 \end{bmatrix} \cdot \begin{bmatrix} -0.4779 \\ 3.0862 \\ 2.3693 \end{bmatrix}} = \frac{4.5274}{15.3666} = 0.2946.$$

$$\begin{bmatrix} x_1 \\ x_2 \\ x_3 \end{bmatrix}^{(2)} = \begin{bmatrix} -0.1798 \\ 0.5394 \\ 0.8091 \end{bmatrix} + 0.2946 \begin{bmatrix} 1.2515 \\ 1.7294 \\ -0.3726 \end{bmatrix} = \begin{bmatrix} 0.1889 \\ 1.0489 \\ 0.6993 \end{bmatrix}.$$

$$\begin{bmatrix} r_1 \\ r_2 \\ r_3 \end{bmatrix}^{(2)} = \begin{bmatrix} 0.7192 \\ 1.1121 \\ 0.6071 \end{bmatrix} - 0.2946 \begin{bmatrix} -0.4779 \\ 3.0862 \\ 2.3693 \end{bmatrix} = \begin{bmatrix} 0.8600 \\ 0.2029 \\ -0.0909 \end{bmatrix}.$$

$$\begin{bmatrix} h_1 \\ h_2 \\ h_3 \end{bmatrix}^{(2)} = \begin{bmatrix} 1 & 0 & 1 \\ -1 & 2 & 0 \\ 0 & 1 & -3 \end{bmatrix} \begin{bmatrix} 0.8600 \\ 0.2029 \\ -0.0909 \end{bmatrix} = \begin{bmatrix} 0.7691 \\ -0.4542 \\ 0.4756 \end{bmatrix}.$$

$$b^{(2)} = \frac{\begin{bmatrix} 0.7691 \\ -0.4542 \\ 0.4756 \end{bmatrix} \cdot \begin{bmatrix} 0.7691 \\ -0.4542 \\ 0.4756 \end{bmatrix}}{\begin{bmatrix} 1.3263 \\ 1.5050 \\ -0.7092 \end{bmatrix} \cdot \begin{bmatrix} 1.3263 \\ 1.5050 \\ -0.7092 \end{bmatrix}} = \frac{1.0239}{4.5271} = 0.2262.$$

$$\begin{bmatrix} p_1 \\ p_2 \\ p_3 \end{bmatrix}^{(2)} = \begin{bmatrix} 0.7691 \\ -0.4542 \\ 0.4756 \end{bmatrix} + 0.2262 \begin{bmatrix} 1.2515 \\ 1.7294 \\ -0.3726 \end{bmatrix}$$

$$= \begin{bmatrix} 1.0522 \\ -0.0630 \\ -0.3913 \end{bmatrix}.$$

4. Third iteration calculations ($k = 2$).

$$\begin{bmatrix} g_1 \\ g_2 \\ g_3 \end{bmatrix}^{(2)} = \begin{bmatrix} 1 & -1 & 0 \\ 0 & 2 & 1 \\ 1 & 0 & -3 \end{bmatrix} \begin{bmatrix} 1.0522 \\ -0.0630 \\ 0.3913 \end{bmatrix} = \begin{bmatrix} 1.1152 \\ 0.2653 \\ -0.1217 \end{bmatrix}.$$

$$a^{(2)} = \frac{\begin{bmatrix} 0.7691 \\ -0.4542 \\ 0.4756 \end{bmatrix} \cdot \begin{bmatrix} 0.7691 \\ -0.4542 \\ 0.4756 \end{bmatrix}}{\begin{bmatrix} 1.1152 \\ 0.2653 \\ -0.1217 \end{bmatrix} \cdot \begin{bmatrix} 1.1152 \\ 0.2653 \\ -0.1217 \end{bmatrix}} = \frac{1.0240}{1.3289} = 0.7706.$$

$$\begin{bmatrix} x_1 \\ x_2 \\ x_3 \end{bmatrix}^{(3)} = \begin{bmatrix} 0.1889 \\ 1.0489 \\ 0.6993 \end{bmatrix} + 0.7706 \begin{bmatrix} 1.0522 \\ -0.0630 \\ 0.3913 \end{bmatrix} = \begin{bmatrix} 0.9997 \\ 1.0004 \\ 1.0008 \end{bmatrix}.$$

$$\begin{bmatrix} r_1 \\ r_2 \\ r_3 \end{bmatrix}^{(3)} = \begin{bmatrix} 0.8600 \\ 0.2029 \\ -0.0909 \end{bmatrix} - 0.7706 \begin{bmatrix} 1.1152 \\ 0.2653 \\ -0.1217 \end{bmatrix} = \begin{bmatrix} 0.0006 \\ -0.0015 \\ 0.0029 \end{bmatrix}.$$

Because the $\vec{r}^{(3)}$ entries are close to zero, vector $\vec{x}^{(3)}$ represents the solution to the problem. Note that the exact solution to the problem is $x_1 = 1$, $x_2 = 1$, and $x_3 = 1$.

Other conjugate-gradient methods suitable for problems with nonsymmetric coefficient matrices include the Lanczos[13] biorthogonal vector algorithm,[11] the biconjugate-gradient method,[11,12,14] and the biconjugate-gradient stabilized method.[12,14]

Generalized Conjugate-Gradient-Like (CGL) Methods. The conjugate-gradient algorithm is not the most efficient algorithm in terms of computational effort for problems with nonsymmetric coefficient matrices because of the convergence rate of the algorithm. In Algorithm 2, we multiply the matrix **[A]** by its transpose $[\mathbf{A}]^T$. Essentially, we are using the matrix $[\mathbf{A}]^T$ as a preconditioning matrix to create a symmetric matrix from the original nonsymmetric coefficient matrix (matrix preconditioning is discussed later). Unfortunately, when we do this, we are working with the condition number squared of **[A]** rather than the condition number of **[A]**.[14,15] Other generalized CGL algorithms are available for problems with nonsymmetric matrices that work directly on the original coefficient matrix. These methods use the condition number of the original coefficient matrix and consequently possess superior convergence properties. These CGL methods differ from the conjugate-gradient method by the definition of the objective function [$F(\vec{x})$] to be minimized and by the definition of the direction vectors. A popular class of generalized CGL algorithms used in reservoir simulation is referred to collectively as minimum-residual methods.

Minimum-Residual Methods. The objective of minimum-residual methods is to minimize the residual r as measured by the Euclidean norm, $\|\cdot\|_2$,[11] which is defined by

$$\|\vec{r}\|_2 = (\vec{r}\cdot\vec{r})^{1/2}. \quad \text{(7.249)}$$

In actuality, we minimize the residual in the Euclidean norm squared; i.e.,

$$\left(\|\vec{r}\|_2\right)^2 = (\vec{r}\cdot\vec{r}). \quad \text{(7.250a)}$$

Eq. 7.250a is the objective function, comparable with Eq. 7.214a in the conjugate-gradient method, that is minimized during the minimum-residual iteration.

$$F(\vec{x}) = \left(\|\vec{r}\|_2\right)^2 = (\vec{r}\cdot\vec{r}). \quad \text{(7.250b)}$$

Like Eq. 7.214a, Eq. 7.250b has two important properties that make it suitable for solving Eq. 7.1.[15] The first property of $F(\vec{x})$ is that squaring the $\|\cdot\|_2$ ensures that $F(\vec{x})$ is always nonnegative for vectors containing real-valued elements (i.e., no imaginary elements). The second property is that the vector $\vec{x}$ that is the solution vector, $\vec{x}_*$, to the system of equations $[\mathbf{A}]\vec{x}_* = \vec{d}$ results in a zero value of $F(\vec{x})$. This implies that $F(\vec{x})$ is at a minimum [equal to $F(\vec{x}) = 0$] when evaluated at $\vec{x}_*$. Again, any search algorithm that identifies the vector $\vec{x}$ that minimizes Eq. 7.250b can be used to find the solution, $\vec{x}_*$, to Eq. 7.1. Note that, just as for the conjugate gradient method, we have come to a conclusion concerning the minimization properties of $F(\vec{x})$ without relying on the symmetry of the coefficient matrix **[A]**. The only assumption used is that the residual is composed of real-valued elements.

Orthomin Method.[16] The Orthomin method is one example of a minimum-residual method used in reservoir simulation. In the Orthomin iteration, we again generate a series of vectors for $\vec{x}^{(1)}, \vec{x}^{(2)}, \ldots, \vec{x}^{(k+1)}$ for $k+1 \leqq n$ starting from an initial estimate of $\vec{x}^{(0)}$ using Eq. 7.216. From Eq. 7.216 and the definition of the residual

$$\vec{r}^{(k+1)} = \vec{r}^{(k)} - a^{(k)}[\mathbf{A}]\vec{p}^{(k)}. \quad \text{(7.226b)}$$

Substituting Eq. 7.226b into Eq. 7.250b gives

$$F\left[\vec{x}^{(k+1)}\right] = \left(\vec{r}^{(k+1)}\cdot\vec{r}^{(k+1)}\right), \quad \text{(7.251a)}$$

$$F\left[\vec{x}^{(k+1)}\right] = \left\{\vec{r}^{(k)} - a^{(k)}[\mathbf{A}]\vec{p}^{(k)}\right\}\cdot\left\{\vec{r}^{(k)} - a^{(k)}[\mathbf{A}]\vec{p}^{(k)}\right\}, \quad \text{(7.251b)}$$

$$\text{or } F\left[\vec{x}^{(k+1)}\right] = \left\{\vec{r}^{(k)}\cdot\vec{r}^{(k)} - 2a^{(k)}\vec{r}^{(k)}\cdot[\mathbf{A}]\vec{p}^{(k)} + \left[a^{(k)}\right]^2[\mathbf{A}]\vec{p}^{(k)}\cdot[\mathbf{A}]\vec{p}^{(k)}\right\}. \quad \text{(7.251c)}$$

As with the conjugate-gradient method, to minimize $F(\vec{x})$, we take the derivative of Eq. 7.251 with respect to $a^{(k)}$ and set the resulting expression to zero, which results in

$$a^{(k)} = \frac{\vec{r}^{(k)}\cdot[\mathbf{A}]\vec{p}^{(k)}}{[\mathbf{A}]\vec{p}^{(k)}\cdot[\mathbf{A}]\vec{p}^{(k)}}. \quad \text{(7.252)}$$

In the Orthomin iteration,[16] the direction vector for Iteration Level $(k+1)$ is determined from $\vec{r}^{(k+1)}$ and a linear combination of all previous direction vectors.

$$\vec{p}^{(k+1)} = \vec{r}^{(k+1)} + \sum_{j=0}^{k} b_k^{(j)}\vec{p}^{(j)} \quad \text{(7.253a)}$$

$$\text{or } \vec{p}^{(k+1)} = \vec{r}^{(k+1)} + b_k^{(0)}\vec{p}^{(0)} + b_k^{(1)}\vec{p}^{(1)} + \ldots + b_k^{(j)}\vec{p}^{(j)} + \ldots + b_k^{(k-1)}\vec{p}^{(k-1)} + b_k^{(k)}\vec{p}^{(k)}. \quad \text{(7.253b)}$$

The subscript k in the b_k coefficients implies that the value of $b_k^{(j)}$ that multiplies the direction vector $\vec{p}^{(j)}$ changes from one iteration to the next. In addition, the vectors $[\mathbf{A}]\vec{p}$ must be mutually orthogonal; that is,

$$[\mathbf{A}]\vec{p}^{(k)}\cdot[\mathbf{A}]\vec{p}^{(j)} = 0 \quad \text{(7.254)}$$

for $k \neq j$. Premultiplying Eq. 7.253b by **[A]** and post-multiplying the resulting equation by $[\mathbf{A}]\vec{p}^{(j)}$ results in

$$\begin{aligned}[\mathbf{A}]\vec{p}^{(k+1)}\cdot[\mathbf{A}]\vec{p}^{(j)} &= [\mathbf{A}]\vec{r}^{(k+1)}\cdot[\mathbf{A}]\vec{p}^{(j)} \\ &+ b_k^{(0)}[\mathbf{A}]\vec{p}^{(0)}\cdot[\mathbf{A}]\vec{p}^{(j)} \\ &+ b_k^{(1)}[\mathbf{A}]\vec{p}^{(1)}\cdot[\mathbf{A}]\vec{p}^{(j)} \\ &+ \ldots + b_k^{(j)}[\mathbf{A}]\vec{p}^{(j)}\cdot[\mathbf{A}]\vec{p}^{(j)} \\ &+ \ldots + b_k^{(k-1)}[\mathbf{A}]\vec{p}^{(k-1)}\cdot[\mathbf{A}]\vec{p}^{(j)} \\ &+ b_k^{(k)}[\mathbf{A}]\vec{p}^{(k)}\cdot[\mathbf{A}]\vec{p}^{(j)}. \end{aligned} \quad \text{(7.255)}$$

Applying the orthogonality condition, Eq. 7.254, results in

$$0 = [\mathbf{A}]\vec{r}^{(k+1)}\cdot[\mathbf{A}]\vec{p}^{(j)} + b_k^{(j)}[\mathbf{A}]\vec{p}^{(j)}\cdot[\mathbf{A}]\vec{p}^{(j)}. \quad \text{(7.256)}$$

Finally, solving for $b_k^{(j)}$,

$$b_k^{(j)} = -\frac{[\mathbf{A}]\vec{r}^{(k+1)}\cdot[\mathbf{A}]\vec{p}^{(j)}}{[\mathbf{A}]\vec{p}^{(j)}\cdot[\mathbf{A}]\vec{p}^{(j)}}. \quad \text{(7.257)}$$

The following algorithm shows implementation of the Orthomin iteration.

Algorithm 3—The Orthomin Method. Select an estimate of $\vec{x}^{(0)}$ (arbitrary). Set $\vec{r}^{(0)} = \vec{d} - [\mathbf{A}]\vec{x}^{(0)}$ and $\vec{p}^{(0)} = \vec{r}^{(0)}$. Perform the following computations sequentially for $k = 0, 1, 2, \ldots$, until convergence.

$$\vec{g}^{(k)} = [\mathbf{A}]\vec{p}^{(k)}; \quad \text{(7.242)}$$

$$\delta^{(k)} = \vec{g}^{(k)}\cdot\vec{g}^{(k)}; \quad \text{(7.258)}$$

$$a^{(k)} = \frac{\vec{r}^{(k)} \cdot \vec{g}^{(k)}}{\delta^{(k)}}; \quad \ldots\ldots\ldots\ldots\ldots\ldots\ldots\ldots \quad (7.259)$$

$$\vec{x}^{(k+1)} = \vec{x}^{(k)} + a^{(k)}\vec{p}^{(k)}; \quad \ldots\ldots\ldots\ldots\ldots\ldots\ldots \quad (7.216)$$

$$\vec{r}^{(k+1)} = \vec{r}^{(k)} - a^{(k)}\vec{g}^{(k)}; \quad \ldots\ldots\ldots\ldots\ldots\ldots\ldots \quad (7.226b)$$

and for $j = 0, 1, \ldots, k$,

$$b_k^{(j)} = -\frac{\left\{[\mathbf{A}]\vec{r}^{(k+1)}\right\} \cdot \vec{g}^{(j)}}{\delta^{(j)}}. \quad \ldots\ldots\ldots\ldots\ldots\ldots \quad (7.260)$$

Then,

$$\vec{p}^{(k+1)} = \vec{r}^{(k+1)} + \sum_{j=0}^{k} b_k^{(j)}\vec{p}^{(j)}. \quad \ldots\ldots\ldots\ldots\ldots\ldots \quad (7.253a)$$

In the Orthomin algorithm,[16] $a^{(k)}$, $b_k^{(j)}$, and $\delta^{(k)}$ are scalar quantities, $\vec{x}$, $\vec{r}$, $\vec{p}$, and $\vec{g}$ are vector quantities, and **[A]** is the original coefficient matrix.

Examples 7.14 and 7.15 illustrate application of the Orthomin algorithm to solve systems of linear equations with a nonsymmetric coefficient matrix.

Example 7.14. Use the Orthomin method to solve the nonsymmetric system of equations considered in Example 7.13.

Solution.

$$[\mathbf{A}] = \begin{bmatrix} 1 & -1 & 0 \\ 0 & 2 & 1 \\ 1 & 0 & -3 \end{bmatrix}$$

and $\vec{d} = \begin{bmatrix} 0 \\ 3 \\ -2 \end{bmatrix}$.

1. Initialize the solution. First try an initial estimate of $\vec{x}^{(0)}$, like in Example 7.13.

$$\vec{x}^{(0)} = \begin{bmatrix} 0 \\ 0 \\ 0 \end{bmatrix}.$$

$$\vec{r}^{(0)} = \begin{bmatrix} 0 \\ 3 \\ -2 \end{bmatrix} - \begin{bmatrix} 1 & -1 & 0 \\ 0 & 2 & 1 \\ 1 & 0 & -3 \end{bmatrix}\begin{bmatrix} 0 \\ 0 \\ 0 \end{bmatrix} = \begin{bmatrix} 0 \\ 3 \\ -2 \end{bmatrix}.$$

$$\vec{p}^{(0)} = \begin{bmatrix} p_1 \\ p_2 \\ p_3 \end{bmatrix}^{(0)} = \begin{bmatrix} r_1 \\ r_2 \\ r_3 \end{bmatrix}^{(0)} = \begin{bmatrix} 0 \\ 3 \\ -2 \end{bmatrix}.$$

2. First iteration calculations, $k = 0$.

$$\vec{g}^{(0)} = \begin{bmatrix} g_1 \\ g_2 \\ g_3 \end{bmatrix}^{(0)} = \begin{bmatrix} 1 & -1 & 0 \\ 0 & 2 & 1 \\ 1 & 0 & -3 \end{bmatrix}\begin{bmatrix} 0 \\ 3 \\ -2 \end{bmatrix} = \begin{bmatrix} -3 \\ 4 \\ 6 \end{bmatrix}.$$

$$\delta^{(0)} = \begin{bmatrix} -3 \\ 4 \\ 6 \end{bmatrix} \cdot \begin{bmatrix} -3 \\ 4 \\ 6 \end{bmatrix} = 61.$$

$$a^{(0)} = \frac{\begin{bmatrix} 0 \\ 3 \\ -2 \end{bmatrix} \cdot \begin{bmatrix} -3 \\ 4 \\ 6 \end{bmatrix}}{61} = \frac{0}{61} = 0.$$

$$\vec{x}^{(1)} = \begin{bmatrix} x_1 \\ x_2 \\ x_3 \end{bmatrix}^{(1)} = \begin{bmatrix} 0 \\ 0 \\ 0 \end{bmatrix} + 0\begin{bmatrix} 0 \\ 3 \\ -2 \end{bmatrix} = \begin{bmatrix} 0 \\ 0 \\ 0 \end{bmatrix}.$$

At this point, it is obvious that the method has broken down because it continually results in solution vectors with only elements of zero. Therefore, we can never proceed beyond the initial estimate because of the initial estimate is used. Inspection of the procedure at this point shows that, for this particular coefficient matrix, any initial estimate that contains identical elements results in a value of $a^{(0)} = 0$. Therefore, reinitialize the process with a different initial estimate $\vec{x}^{(0)}$.

1. Initialize the solution. First, try an initial estimate of $\vec{x}^{(0)}$.

$$\vec{x}^{(0)} = \begin{bmatrix} -1 \\ 0 \\ 0 \end{bmatrix}.$$

$$\vec{r}^{(0)} = \begin{bmatrix} 0 \\ 3 \\ -2 \end{bmatrix} - \begin{bmatrix} 1 & -1 & 0 \\ 0 & 2 & 1 \\ 1 & 0 & -3 \end{bmatrix}\begin{bmatrix} -1 \\ 0 \\ 0 \end{bmatrix} = \begin{bmatrix} 1 \\ 3 \\ -1 \end{bmatrix}.$$

$$\vec{p}^{(0)} = \begin{bmatrix} p_1 \\ p_2 \\ p_3 \end{bmatrix}^{(0)} = \begin{bmatrix} r_1 \\ r_2 \\ r_3 \end{bmatrix}^{(0)} = \begin{bmatrix} 1 \\ 3 \\ -1 \end{bmatrix}.$$

2. First iteration calculations, $k = 0$.

$$\vec{g}^{(0)} = \begin{bmatrix} g_1 \\ g_2 \\ g_3 \end{bmatrix}^{(0)} = \begin{bmatrix} 1 & -1 & 0 \\ 0 & 2 & 1 \\ 1 & 0 & -3 \end{bmatrix}\begin{bmatrix} 1 \\ 3 \\ -1 \end{bmatrix} = \begin{bmatrix} -2 \\ 5 \\ 4 \end{bmatrix}.$$

$$\delta^{(0)} = \begin{bmatrix} -2 \\ 5 \\ 4 \end{bmatrix} \cdot \begin{bmatrix} -2 \\ 5 \\ 4 \end{bmatrix} = 45.$$

$$a^{(0)} = \frac{\begin{bmatrix} 1 \\ 3 \\ -1 \end{bmatrix} \cdot \begin{bmatrix} -2 \\ 5 \\ 4 \end{bmatrix}}{45} = \frac{-2 + 15 - 4}{45} = 0.2.$$

$$\vec{x}^{(1)} = \begin{bmatrix} x_1 \\ x_2 \\ x_3 \end{bmatrix}^{(1)} = \begin{bmatrix} -1 \\ 0 \\ 0 \end{bmatrix} + 0.2\begin{bmatrix} 1 \\ 3 \\ -1 \end{bmatrix} = \begin{bmatrix} -0.8 \\ 0.6 \\ -0.2 \end{bmatrix}.$$

$$\vec{r}^{(1)} = \begin{bmatrix} r_1 \\ r_2 \\ r_3 \end{bmatrix}^{(1)} = \begin{bmatrix} 1 \\ 3 \\ -1 \end{bmatrix} - 0.2\begin{bmatrix} -2 \\ 5 \\ 4 \end{bmatrix} = \begin{bmatrix} 1.4 \\ 2.0 \\ -1.8 \end{bmatrix}.$$

$$b_0^{(0)} = -\frac{\left(\begin{bmatrix} 1 & -1 & 0 \\ 0 & 2 & 1 \\ 1 & 0 & -3 \end{bmatrix}\begin{bmatrix} 1.4 \\ 2.0 \\ -1.8 \end{bmatrix}\right) \cdot \begin{bmatrix} -2 \\ 5 \\ 4 \end{bmatrix}}{45}$$

$$= -\frac{\begin{bmatrix} -0.6 \\ 2.2 \\ 6.8 \end{bmatrix} \cdot \begin{bmatrix} -2 \\ 5 \\ 4 \end{bmatrix}}{45} = -0.8756.$$

$$\vec{p}^{(1)} = \begin{bmatrix} p_1 \\ p_2 \\ p_3 \end{bmatrix}^{(1)} = \begin{bmatrix} 1.4 \\ 2.0 \\ -1.8 \end{bmatrix} - 0.8756 \begin{bmatrix} 1 \\ 3 \\ -1 \end{bmatrix}$$

$$= \begin{bmatrix} 0.5244 \\ -0.6267 \\ -0.9244 \end{bmatrix}.$$

3. Second iteration calculations, $k=1$.

$$\vec{g}^{(1)} = \begin{bmatrix} g_1 \\ g_2 \\ g_3 \end{bmatrix}^{(1)} = \begin{bmatrix} 1 & -1 & 0 \\ 0 & 2 & 1 \\ 1 & 0 & -3 \end{bmatrix} \begin{bmatrix} 0.5244 \\ -0.6267 \\ -0.9244 \end{bmatrix}$$

$$= \begin{bmatrix} 1.1511 \\ -2.1778 \\ 3.2978 \end{bmatrix}.$$

$$\delta^{(1)} = \begin{bmatrix} 1.1511 \\ -2.1778 \\ 3.2978 \end{bmatrix} \cdot \begin{bmatrix} 1.1511 \\ -2.1778 \\ 3.2978 \end{bmatrix} = 16.9431.$$

$$a^{(1)} = \frac{\begin{bmatrix} 1.4 \\ 2.0 \\ -1.8 \end{bmatrix} \cdot \begin{bmatrix} 1.1511 \\ -2.1778 \\ 3.2978 \end{bmatrix}}{16.9431} = -0.5123.$$

$$\vec{x}^{(2)} = \begin{bmatrix} x_1 \\ x_2 \\ x_3 \end{bmatrix}^{(2)} = \begin{bmatrix} -0.8 \\ 0.6 \\ -0.2 \end{bmatrix} -0.5123 \begin{bmatrix} 0.5244 \\ -0.6267 \\ -0.9244 \end{bmatrix}$$

$$= \begin{bmatrix} -1.0687 \\ 0.9210 \\ 0.2736 \end{bmatrix}.$$

$$\vec{r}^{(2)} = \begin{bmatrix} r_1 \\ r_2 \\ r_3 \end{bmatrix}^{(2)} = \begin{bmatrix} 1.4 \\ 2.0 \\ -1.8 \end{bmatrix} + 0.5123 \begin{bmatrix} 1.1511 \\ -2.1778 \\ 3.2978 \end{bmatrix}$$

$$= \begin{bmatrix} 1.9897 \\ 0.8843 \\ -0.1105 \end{bmatrix}.$$

$$b_1^{(0)} = -\frac{\left(\begin{bmatrix} 1 & -1 & 0 \\ 0 & 2 & 1 \\ 1 & 0 & -3 \end{bmatrix} \begin{bmatrix} 1.9897 \\ 0.8843 \\ -0.1105 \end{bmatrix} \right) \cdot \begin{bmatrix} -2 \\ 5 \\ 4 \end{bmatrix}}{45}$$

$$= -\frac{\begin{bmatrix} 1.1054 \\ 1.6581 \\ 2.3213 \end{bmatrix} \cdot \begin{bmatrix} -2 \\ 5 \\ 4 \end{bmatrix}}{45} = -0.3414.$$

$$b_1^{(1)} = -\frac{\left(\begin{bmatrix} 1 & -1 & 0 \\ 0 & 2 & 1 \\ 1 & 0 & -3 \end{bmatrix} \begin{bmatrix} 1.9897 \\ 0.8843 \\ -0.1105 \end{bmatrix} \right) \cdot \begin{bmatrix} 1.1511 \\ -2.1778 \\ 3.2978 \end{bmatrix}}{16.9431}$$

$$= -\frac{\begin{bmatrix} 1.1054 \\ 1.6581 \\ 2.3213 \end{bmatrix} \cdot \begin{bmatrix} 1.1511 \\ -2.1778 \\ 3.2978 \end{bmatrix}}{16.9431} = -0.3138.$$

$$\vec{p}^{(2)} = \begin{bmatrix} p_1 \\ p_2 \\ p_3 \end{bmatrix}^{(2)} = \begin{bmatrix} 1.9897 \\ 0.8843 \\ -0.1105 \end{bmatrix} - 0.3414 \begin{bmatrix} 1 \\ 3 \\ -1 \end{bmatrix}$$

$$- 0.3138 \begin{bmatrix} 0.5244 \\ -0.6267 \\ -0.9244 \end{bmatrix} = \begin{bmatrix} 1.4837 \\ 0.0566 \\ 0.5210 \end{bmatrix}.$$

4. Third iteration calculations, $k=2$.

$$\vec{g}^{(2)} = \begin{bmatrix} g_1 \\ g_2 \\ g_3 \end{bmatrix}^{(2)} = \begin{bmatrix} 1 & -1 & 0 \\ 0 & 2 & 1 \\ 1 & 0 & -3 \end{bmatrix} \begin{bmatrix} 1.4837 \\ 0.0566 \\ 0.5210 \end{bmatrix}$$

$$= \begin{bmatrix} 1.4271 \\ 0.6342 \\ -0.0793 \end{bmatrix}.$$

$$\delta^{(2)} = \begin{bmatrix} 1.4271 \\ 0.6342 \\ -0.0793 \end{bmatrix} \cdot \begin{bmatrix} 1.4271 \\ 0.6342 \\ -0.0793 \end{bmatrix} = 2.4451.$$

$$a^{(2)} = \frac{\begin{bmatrix} 1.9897 \\ 0.8843 \\ -0.1105 \end{bmatrix} \cdot \begin{bmatrix} 1.4271 \\ 0.6342 \\ -0.0793 \end{bmatrix}}{2.4451} = 1.3943.$$

$$\vec{x}^{(3)} = \begin{bmatrix} x_1 \\ x_2 \\ x_3 \end{bmatrix}^{(3)} = \begin{bmatrix} -1.0687 \\ 0.9210 \\ 0.2736 \end{bmatrix} + 1.3943 \begin{bmatrix} 1.4837 \\ 0.0566 \\ 0.5210 \end{bmatrix}$$

$$= \begin{bmatrix} 1.0000 \\ 1.0000 \\ 1.0000 \end{bmatrix}.$$

$$\vec{r}^{(3)} = \begin{bmatrix} r_1 \\ r_2 \\ r_3 \end{bmatrix}^{(3)} = \begin{bmatrix} 1.9897 \\ 0.8843 \\ -0.1105 \end{bmatrix} - 1.3943 \begin{bmatrix} 1.4271 \\ 0.6342 \\ -0.0793 \end{bmatrix}$$

$$= \begin{bmatrix} 0.0000 \\ 0.0000 \\ 0.0000 \end{bmatrix}.$$

Example 7.15. Use the Orthomin method to solve the symmetric system of equations considered in Example 7.12. Use an initial estimate of $x_i = 0$ for all i. The Orthomin solution for this problem is

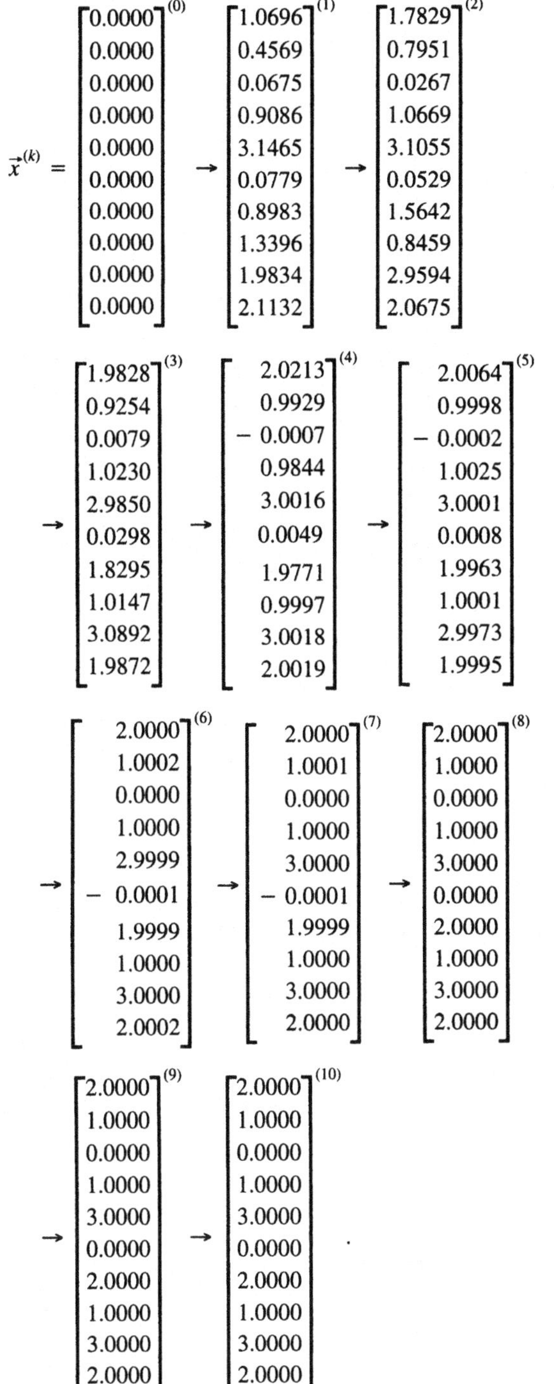

$$\vec{x}^{(k)} = \begin{bmatrix}0.0000\\0.0000\\0.0000\\0.0000\\0.0000\\0.0000\\0.0000\\0.0000\\0.0000\\0.0000\end{bmatrix}^{(0)} \rightarrow \begin{bmatrix}1.0696\\0.4569\\0.0675\\0.9086\\3.1465\\0.0779\\0.8983\\1.3396\\1.9834\\2.1132\end{bmatrix}^{(1)} \rightarrow \begin{bmatrix}1.7829\\0.7951\\0.0267\\1.0669\\3.1055\\0.0529\\1.5642\\0.8459\\2.9594\\2.0675\end{bmatrix}^{(2)}$$

$$\rightarrow \begin{bmatrix}1.9828\\0.9254\\0.0079\\1.0230\\2.9850\\0.0298\\1.8295\\1.0147\\3.0892\\1.9872\end{bmatrix}^{(3)} \rightarrow \begin{bmatrix}2.0213\\0.9929\\-0.0007\\0.9844\\3.0016\\0.0049\\1.9771\\0.9997\\3.0018\\2.0019\end{bmatrix}^{(4)} \rightarrow \begin{bmatrix}2.0064\\0.9998\\-0.0002\\1.0025\\3.0001\\0.0008\\1.9963\\1.0001\\2.9973\\1.9995\end{bmatrix}^{(5)}$$

$$\rightarrow \begin{bmatrix}2.0000\\1.0002\\0.0000\\1.0000\\2.9999\\-0.0001\\1.9999\\1.0000\\3.0000\\2.0002\end{bmatrix}^{(6)} \rightarrow \begin{bmatrix}2.0000\\1.0001\\0.0000\\1.0000\\3.0000\\-0.0001\\1.9999\\1.0000\\3.0000\\2.0000\end{bmatrix}^{(7)} \rightarrow \begin{bmatrix}2.0000\\1.0000\\0.0000\\1.0000\\3.0000\\0.0000\\2.0000\\1.0000\\3.0000\\2.0000\end{bmatrix}^{(8)}$$

$$\rightarrow \begin{bmatrix}2.0000\\1.0000\\0.0000\\1.0000\\3.0000\\0.0000\\2.0000\\1.0000\\3.0000\\2.0000\end{bmatrix}^{(9)} \rightarrow \begin{bmatrix}2.0000\\1.0000\\0.0000\\1.0000\\3.0000\\0.0000\\2.0000\\1.0000\\3.0000\\2.0000\end{bmatrix}^{(10)} .$$

This example illustrates both the direct- and iterative-solution characteristics of the Orthomin method. If a tolerance of 0.0001 is used between successive iterates to terminate the process, it stops after the seventh iteration.

The Orthomin iteration requires that all values of $\delta^{(k)}$ and all the vectors $\vec{g}^{(k)}$ be stored for use in calculating the coefficients $b_k^{(j)}$. In addition, the inner product—$\{[\mathbf{A}]\vec{r}^{(k+1)}\} \cdot \vec{g}^{(j)}$, for all j, $j \leqq k$—must be performed at each Iteration Level k for use in calculating these coefficients. Therefore, as Iteration Level k increases, both the storage and the number of computations per iteration increase dramatically.

To reduce the amount of storage and work involved in the Orthomin iteration, the "restart" process is often used. This process involves performing a fixed number of iterations, K, of the iteration; stopping the process before convergence; and restarting the process at Iteration Level (K). To initialize the restart process, $\vec{x}^{(0)} = \vec{x}^{(K)}$, $\vec{r}^{(0)} = \vec{r}^{(K)}$, and $\vec{p}^{(0)} = \vec{r}^{(0)} = \vec{r}^{(K)}$. The process can be repeated until convergence is achieved. When the restart process is applied to the Orthomin iteration after K iterations, the procedure is called the Orthomin(K) iteration.[16]

Once the iteration has been restarted, all theoretical analyses concerning the convergence properties of the iteration are no longer applicable because all the information contained in the earlier direction vectors is lost to the iterations in the current restart cycle. In other words, Vectors $[\mathbf{A}]\vec{p}$ are orthogonal only within the current restart cycle, not to all previous Vectors $[\mathbf{A}]\vec{p}$. The restart cycle tends to reduce the convergence rate of the iteration[11]; however, it is often necessary for large problems. In practice, a value of $10 \leqq K \leqq 20$ is adequate for most reservoir-simulation problems.

Other minimum-residual methods used in reservoir simulation include the generalized minimum-residual (GMR) method,[17] the generalized conjugate-residual (GCR) method,[18] and others.[19] The GMR method is the iterative-solution method most commonly used in reservoir simulation because it can be performed with approximately half the storage and approximately one-third of the work than other generalized CGL methods and is also more robust.

Matrix Preconditioning. As discussed in Items 2 through 4 in the list of theoretical and computational features of the conjugate-gradient method, the convergence rate of the conjugate-gradient and other generalized CGL methods can be greatly improved by reducing the condition number of the coefficient matrix to a value close to one. The condition number is the ratio of the maximum eigenvalue of the coefficient matrix to the minimum eigenvalue. Matrix preconditioning is one way to reduce the condition number. The objective of matrix preconditioning is to alter the original system of equations in a way that clusters the eigenvalues of the modified coefficient matrix more tightly. In general, the conjugate-gradient and generalized CGL methods are always used with matrix preconditioning.

There are two common preconditioning methods: left preconditioning and right preconditioning. In left preconditioning, the system of equations $[\mathbf{A}]\vec{x} = \vec{d}$ is premultiplied by a preconditioning matrix, $[\mathbf{P}]$, to form the preconditioned system of equations.

$$[\mathbf{P}][\mathbf{A}]\vec{x} = [\mathbf{P}]\vec{d} \quad \text{.......................... (7.261a)}$$

$$\text{and } [\mathbf{A}_p]\vec{x} = \vec{d}_p. \quad \text{.......................... (7.261b)}$$

In Eq. 7.261b, $[\mathbf{A}_p] = [\mathbf{P}][\mathbf{A}]$ and $\vec{d}_p = [\mathbf{P}]\vec{d}$. In left preconditioning, we are working with pseudoresiduals, because, from Eq. 7.261b,

$$\vec{r}_p = \vec{d}_p - [\mathbf{A}_p]\vec{x}, \quad \text{.......................... (7.262a)}$$

which implies that

$$\vec{r}_p = [\mathbf{P}]\vec{r}. \quad \text{.......................... (7.262b)}$$

In right preconditioning, the system of equations $[\mathbf{A}]\vec{x} = \vec{d}$ is modified in the following manner.

$$[\mathbf{A}][\mathbf{P}]^{-1}[\mathbf{P}]\vec{x} = \vec{d} \quad \text{.......................... (7.263a)}$$

$$\text{or } [\mathbf{A}_p]\vec{y} = \vec{d}. \quad \text{.......................... (7.263b)}$$

In Eq. 7.263b, $[\mathbf{A}_p] = [\mathbf{A}][\mathbf{P}]^{-1}$ and $\vec{y} = [\mathbf{P}]\vec{x}$. In right preconditioning, we are working with actual residuals, because, from Eq. 7.263b[20]

$$\vec{r}_p = \vec{d} - [\mathbf{A}_p]\vec{y}, \quad \text{.......................... (7.264a)}$$

$$\vec{r}_p = \vec{d} - [\mathbf{A}][\mathbf{P}]^{-1}[\mathbf{P}]\vec{x}, \quad \text{.......................... (7.264b)}$$

$$\text{or } \vec{r}_p = \vec{d} - [\mathbf{A}]\vec{x} = \vec{r}, \quad \text{.......................... (7.264c)}$$

This property of right preconditioning as indicated by Eq. 7.264c is a consequence of "altering" the original system of equations by only the identity matrix $[\mathbf{I}]$; that is, $[\mathbf{P}]^{-1}[\mathbf{P}] = [\mathbf{I}]$. Because of this property, we use right preconditioning throughout the remainder of this section.

In right preconditioning, the preconditioning matrix $[\mathbf{P}]$ is selected (1) to be a close approximation of $[\mathbf{A}]$ and (2) to take less computational effort to invert than it takes to invert $[\mathbf{A}]$. These two properties generally conflict with each other, and a good preconditioning matrix tends to be a compromise between the two. The need for this compromise can be visualized through two extremes of the preconditioning matrix.[21] If the preconditioning matrix is set equal to the identity matrix, **[P]** = **[I]** and calculating $\mathbf{[P]}^{-1}$ requires no additional computational effort. Unfortunately, this choice of **[P]** does not improve the condition number of the preconditioned system of equations. The other extreme occurs if the preconditioning matrix is set equal to the original coefficient matrix. In this case, **[P]** = **[A]** and a condition number of one is ensured. Unfortunately, this choice of **[P]** does not change the computational effort required to solve the original system of equations because $\mathbf{[A]}^{-1}$ must still be computed. Note from the definition of $[\mathbf{A}_p]$ that, if the first property (i.e., $\mathbf{[A]} \approx \mathbf{[P]}$) can be achieved, $[\mathbf{A}_p] = \mathbf{[A][P]}^{-1} \approx \mathbf{[I]}$ and the resulting eigenvalues of the preconditioned coefficient matrix all cluster around one. This results in a condition number for the preconditioned system of equations that is approximately equal to one. Implementation of right preconditioning is relatively straightforward and is a direct result of substituting the preconditioned system of equations into the solution algorithms.

Algorithm 4—Preconditioned Conjugate-Gradient Method for Symmetric Coefficient Matrices. Select an estimate of $\vec{x}^{(0)}$ (arbitrary). Set $\vec{r}^{(0)} = \vec{d} - \mathbf{[A]}\vec{x}^{(0)}$ and solve $\mathbf{[P]}\vec{h}^{(0)} = \vec{r}^{(0)}$ and $\vec{p}^{(0)} = \vec{h}^{(0)}$. Perform the following computations sequentially for $k=0,1,2,\ldots,$ until convergence.

$$\vec{g}^{(k)} = \mathbf{[A]}\vec{p}^{(k)}, \qquad (7.242)$$

$$a^{(k)} = \frac{\vec{r}^{(k)} \cdot \vec{h}^{(k)}}{\vec{p}^{(k)} \cdot \vec{g}^{(k)}}, \qquad (7.265)$$

$$\vec{x}^{(k+1)} = \vec{x}^{(k)} + a^{(k)}\vec{p}^{(k)}, \qquad (7.216)$$

and $\vec{r}^{(k+1)} = \vec{r}^{(k)} - a^{(k)}\vec{g}^{(k)}$. (7.226b)

Solve

$$\mathbf{[P]}\vec{h}^{(k+1)} = \vec{r}^{(k+1)}, \qquad (7.266)$$

$$b^{(k+1)} = \frac{\vec{r}^{(k+1)} \cdot \vec{h}^{(k+1)}}{\vec{r}^{(k)} \cdot \vec{h}^{(k)}}, \qquad (7.267)$$

and $\vec{p}^{(k+1)} = \vec{h}^{(k+1)} + b^{(k+1)}\vec{p}^{(k)}$. (7.248)

This algorithm is verified easily by replacing **[P]** with **[I]** and noting that the resulting algorithm is identical to the original conjugate-gradient algorithm. It is important to note that the preconditioned conjugate-gradient method has the same requirements as the standard conjugate-gradient method. That is, the coefficient matrices of both the original and the preconditioned systems of equations must be symmetric and positive definite.

Algorithm 5—Preconditioned Orthomin(K) Method. Select an estimate of $\vec{x}^{(0)}$ (arbitrary). Set $\vec{r}^{(0)} = \vec{d} - \mathbf{[A]}\vec{x}^{(0)}$ and solve $\mathbf{[P]}\vec{p}^{(0)} = \vec{r}^{(0)}$. Perform the following computations sequentially for $k=0,1,2,\ldots,$ until convergence.

$$\vec{g}^{(k)} = \mathbf{[A]}\vec{p}^{(k)}, \qquad (7.242)$$

$$\delta^{(k)} = \vec{g}^{(k)} \cdot \vec{g}^{(k)}, \qquad (7.258)$$

$$a^{(k)} = \frac{\vec{r}^{(k)} \cdot \vec{g}^{(k)}}{\delta^{(k)}}, \qquad (7.259)$$

$$\vec{x}^{(k+1)} = \vec{x}^{(k)} + a^{(k)}\vec{p}^{(k)}, \qquad (7.216)$$

and $\vec{r}^{(k+1)} = \vec{r}^{(k)} - a^{(k)}\vec{g}^{(k)}$. (7.226b)

If $k+1 < K$, solve $\mathbf{[P]}\vec{h}^{(k+1)} = \vec{r}^{(k+1)}$. For $j = 0,1,\ldots,k$,

$$b_k^{(j)} = -\frac{\left\{\mathbf{[A]}\vec{h}^{(k+1)}\right\} \cdot \vec{g}^{(j)}}{\delta^{(j)}}. \qquad (7.268)$$

Then,

$$\vec{p}^{(k+1)} = \vec{h}^{(k+1)} + \sum_{j=0}^{k} b_k^{(j)}\vec{p}^{(j)}. \qquad (7.269)$$

If $k+1 = K$, set $k = 0$, $\vec{r}^{(0)} = \vec{r}^{(K)}$ and $\vec{x}^{(0)} = \vec{x}^{(K)}$. Solve for $\mathbf{[P]}\vec{p}^{(0)} = \vec{r}^{(0)}$. Proceed with computations.

We now can discuss methods of constructing **[P]**. While many methods are available for constructing this matrix, we limit our discussion to two methods frequently used in reservoir simulation: diagonal preconditioning and incomplete-LU-factorization (ILUF) or modified ILUF (MILUF) preconditioning.

Diagonal Preconditioning (or Diagonal Scaling or Point Jacobi Preconditioning). In diagonal preconditioning, the preconditioning matrix **[P]** is constructed by setting the diagonal elements $p_{i,i}$ equal to the diagonal elements of **[A]**, $a_{i,i}$. All off-diagonal elements are then set to zero. This is the simplest preconditioning matrix to construct. The work required to construct **[P]** in diagonal preconditioning is the same, regardless of the band structure or sparsity of the original coefficient matrix. This makes diagonal preconditioning attractive when D-4 ordering or cyclic-2 (red/black) ordering is used to order the finite-difference equations of the system of equations and a generalized CGL method is used to solve the reduced system (see Sec. 7.3.3).

When diagonal preconditioning is used in the conjugate-gradient or generalized CGL methods, the Solve steps in the preconditioned algorithms are performed by inverting **[P]**. That is, the matrix $\mathbf{[P]}^{-1}$, which is also a diagonal matrix, is constructed by setting the elements of $\mathbf{[P]}^{-1}$ equal to $1/p_{i,i}$, where $p_{i,i}$ are the elements of the preconditioning matrix **[P]**. For example, in the preconditioned conjugate-gradient algorithm, the Solve step simply becomes $h_i = r_i/p_{i,i}$ for $i=1,2,\ldots,n$, or equivalently $h_i = r_i/a_{i,i}$ for $i=1,2,\ldots,n$.

Example 7.16. Use the preconditioned conjugate-gradient method to solve the symmetric system of equations considered in Example 7.12. Use diagonal preconditioning to aid in the solution. Use an initial estimate of $x_i = 0$ for all i.

Solution. For diagonal preconditioning, the preconditioning matrix **[P]** for this problem is

$$\mathbf{[P]} = \begin{bmatrix} 100 & 0 & 0 & 0 & 0 & 0 & 0 & 0 & 0 & 0 \\ 0 & 80 & 0 & 0 & 0 & 0 & 0 & 0 & 0 & 0 \\ 0 & 0 & 125 & 0 & 0 & 0 & 0 & 0 & 0 & 0 \\ 0 & 0 & 0 & 160 & 0 & 0 & 0 & 0 & 0 & 0 \\ 0 & 0 & 0 & 0 & 200 & 0 & 0 & 0 & 0 & 0 \\ 0 & 0 & 0 & 0 & 0 & 100 & 0 & 0 & 0 & 0 \\ 0 & 0 & 0 & 0 & 0 & 0 & 80 & 0 & 0 & 0 \\ 0 & 0 & 0 & 0 & 0 & 0 & 0 & 250 & 0 & 0 \\ 0 & 0 & 0 & 0 & 0 & 0 & 0 & 0 & 125 & 0 \\ 0 & 0 & 0 & 0 & 0 & 0 & 0 & 0 & 0 & 200 \end{bmatrix}.$$

The preconditioned-conjugate-gradient solution for this problem is

$$\vec{x}^{(k)} = \begin{bmatrix} 0.0000 \\ 0.0000 \\ 0.0000 \\ 0.0000 \\ 0.0000 \\ 0.0000 \\ 0.0000 \\ 0.0000 \\ 0.0000 \\ 0.0000 \end{bmatrix}^{(0)} \rightarrow \begin{bmatrix} 2.0054 \\ 1.0708 \\ 0.1012 \\ 1.0648 \\ 2.9497 \\ 0.1460 \\ 2.1052 \\ 1.0046 \\ 2.9750 \\ 1.9811 \end{bmatrix}^{(1)} \rightarrow \begin{bmatrix} 1.9968 \\ 0.9973 \\ 0.0014 \\ 1.0013 \\ 2.9995 \\ 0.0001 \\ 1.9999 \\ 0.9988 \\ 3.0013 \\ 2.0020 \end{bmatrix}^{(2)}$$

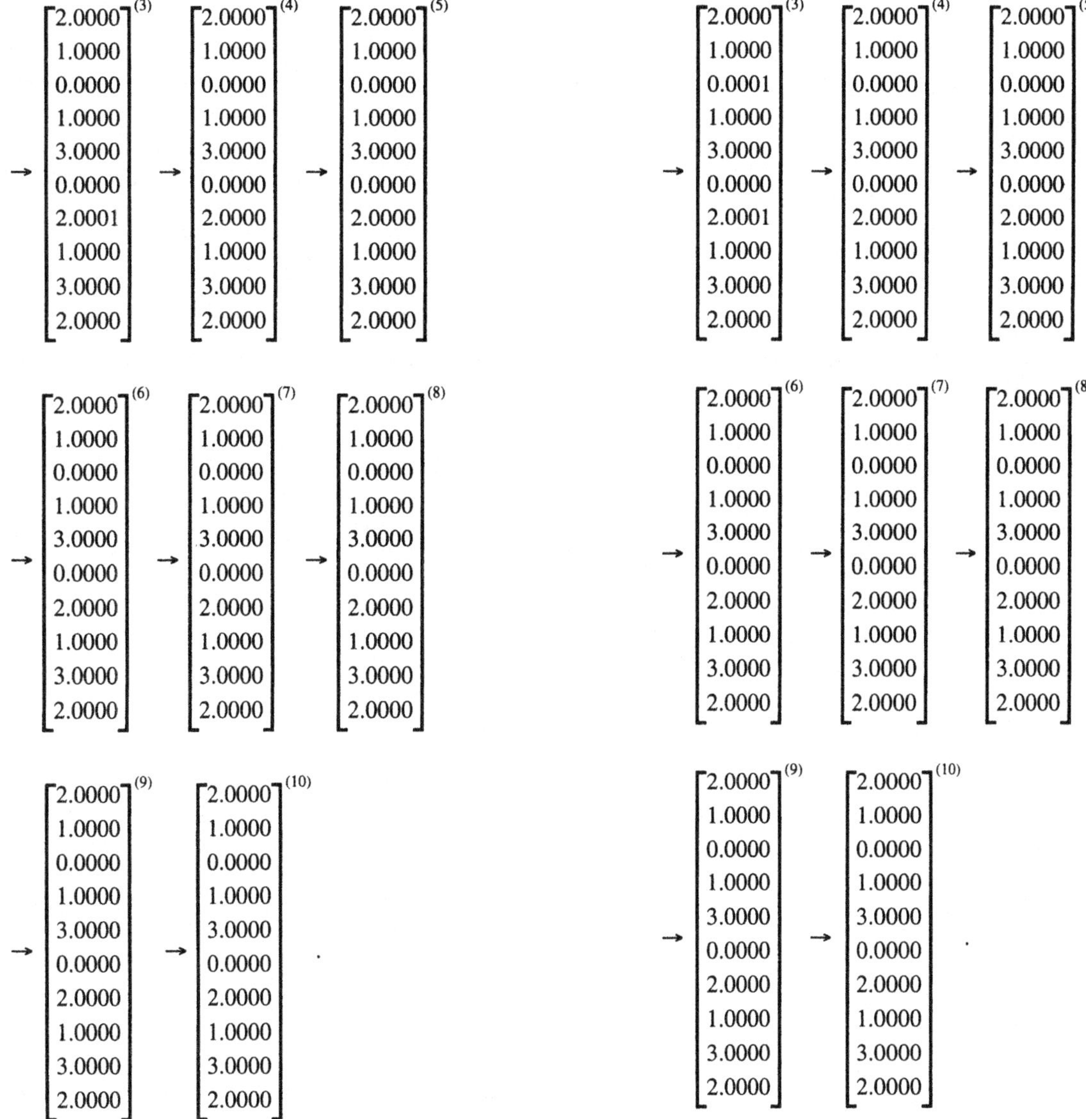

This example illustrates the power of matrix preconditioning. If a tolerance of 0.0001 is used between successive iterations to terminate the process, it stops after the third iteration, in contrast to seven iterations required to meet the same tolerance for the conjugate-gradient solution with no matrix preconditioning (Example 7.12).

Example 7.17. Use the preconditioned Orthomin method to solve the symmetric system of equations considered in Example 7.12. Use diagonal preconditioning to aid the solution.

Solution. The preconditioning matrix **[P]** is identical to that in Example 7.16. The preconditioned Orthomin solution for this problem is

$$\vec{x}^{(k)} = \begin{bmatrix} 0.0000 \\ 0.0000 \\ 0.0000 \\ 0.0000 \\ 0.0000 \\ 0.0000 \\ 0.0000 \\ 0.0000 \\ 0.0000 \\ 0.0000 \end{bmatrix}^{(0)} \rightarrow \begin{bmatrix} 2.0116 \\ 1.0742 \\ 0.1016 \\ 1.0681 \\ 2.9588 \\ 0.1465 \\ 2.1117 \\ 1.0078 \\ 2.9842 \\ 1.9872 \end{bmatrix}^{(1)} \rightarrow \begin{bmatrix} 1.9967 \\ 0.9972 \\ 0.0013 \\ 1.0012 \\ 2.9994 \\ 0.0000 \\ 1.9997 \\ 0.9988 \\ 3.0011 \\ 2.0019 \end{bmatrix}^{(2)}$$

This example illustrates the power of matrix preconditioning. If a tolerance of 0.0001 is used between successive iterations to terminate the process, it stops after the third iteration, in contrast to seven iterations required to meet the same tolerance for the Orthomin solution with no matrix preconditioning (Example 7.15).

ILUF Preconditioning. The ILUF preconditioning procedure is identical to the approximate factorization technique discussed earlier. If the simple coefficient method (Eqs. 7.173 through 7.180) is used as a preconditioning procedure, the resulting process is the ILUF preconditioning method.

A second ILUF preconditioning procedure, the MILUF preconditioning method, adjusts the diagonal terms of the preconditioning matrix **[P]** to force the sum of the elements across all rows of **[P]** to equal the sum of the elements across the corresponding rows of **[A]**; this is called the ROWSUM property of the MILUF preconditioning matrix.

The Dupont *et al.*[7] method (Eqs. 7.173 through 7.175, 7.177 through 7.179, and 7.185) also results in an MILUF preconditioning procedure because, if the assumptions stated in Eq. 7.181 are valid, the ROWSUM of the matrix/vector multiplication of $[\mathbf{P}]\vec{x}$ is equal to the ROWSUM of $[\mathbf{A}]\vec{x}$. Use of the Dupont *et al.*[7] method as a preconditioner is called DKR preconditioning.[16,22] Towler and Killough[22] also investigated the use of SIP as a matrix preconditioning method.

The approximate factoring techniques, as developed earlier in this chapter, considered only the original band structure of the coefficient matrix. If **[A]** were factored exactly, the resulting **[L]** and **[U]** matrices would have contained many additional fill locations other than those assumed in Figs. 7.37 and 7.38. Because we assumed that the approximate matrices, **[L′]** and **[U′]**, contained the same structure as the original coeffiecient matrix, we ignored the impact of these additional fill locations on the factorization process. Therefore, the resulting preconditioning methods are called the ILUF(0) and the MILFU(0) preconditioners, where the zero refers to the fill level. If we perform a symbolic factorization of the original coefficient matrix to determine the elimination step at which each fill location becomes nonzero, we can develop approximate factorization and matrix preconditioning methods based on matrix structures containing these higher fill levels. For example, if symbolic elimination is performed to determine the fill locations that become nonzero during the first elimination step and these locations are included in the approximate factorization process, the resulting preconditioning method is referred to as ILUF(1) and MILUF(1).

The objective of including the higher fill levels is to achieve a better approximation to the original coefficient matrix, **[A]**, which may result in faster convergence rates. This is achieved, however, at the expense of additional computational effort. Generally, fill levels greater than one are not used in commercial reservoir simulators.

Implementation of ILUF and MILUF preconditioning is identical to implementation of approximate factorization. When used as a preconditioner, the iteration parameter $\omega^{(k)}$ in Eq. 7.182 usually is not used.[22] This allows the matrices **[L′]** and **[U′]** to be constructed once before the iteration process starts and be kept fixed through all iterations. When ILUF or MILUF preconditioning is used in the conjugate-gradient or generalized CGL methods, the Solve steps in the preconditioned algorithms are performed with a forward-substitution step followed by a backward-substitution step.

Most modern reservoir-simulation programs have an option for a CGL linear-equation solver. The difference in these CGL techniques is the method used to minimize Eq. 7.214. Modern CGL techniques, such as Orthomin, with optimized matrix preconditioning (similar to approximate factorization techniques) and acceleration have the capacity to solve systems of 100,000 equations in 100,000 unknowns in fewer than 50 iterations.

7.3.5 Comparison of Direct and Iterative Solvers. The discretization of PDE's by use of the finite-difference method eventually leads to systems of algebraic equations. The need to use powerful linear-equation solvers becomes obvious when we are faced with the problem of solving systems with tens to hundreds of thousands of equations.

Iterative methods, in general, are used more widely to solve large systems of equations. Their application becomes more attractive when the coefficient matrix has a sparse structure, containing a large number of zero entries. Because only nonzero matrix elements are used in iterative methods, these methods require relatively little storage memory. The structure of the coefficient matrix (whether banded or not) plays no role in most iterative methods, so the problem of optimal ordering of nodes does not arise. One notable exception is the approximate factorization techniques, where the band structure of the coefficient matrix forms the basis of the procedure. Direct-solution techniques depend on the systematic elimination of unknowns from the matrix equation. In the application of the direct methods, it is necessary to store both the coefficient matrix and the right vector throughout the solution process. Unless virtual memory is used, the size of the main storage of the computer defines the upper limit on the number of equations that can be solved by use of direct procedures. On the other hand, in the case of iterative procedures, reduction of the storage requirement is often achieved at the expense of increasing the amount of required computational work. However, for small computers with no virtual-memory capacity or with slow transfer capabilities between the main storage and virtual memory, iterative methods become the preferred linear-solution technique. An important advantage of direct procedures becomes apparent when several systems of equations with the same coefficient matrix but different right-side vectors are to be solved. In implementing direct solvers to this category of problems, factorization of the coefficient matrix is done only once at the beginning of the simulation during the first timestep computations. In subsequent timesteps, it is necessary to conduct only the forward- and backward-substitution processes. In summary, the choice of a direct or iterative method depends on the the problem to be solved, the choice of solution method (single or multiple unknowns per gridblock), and the available computer.

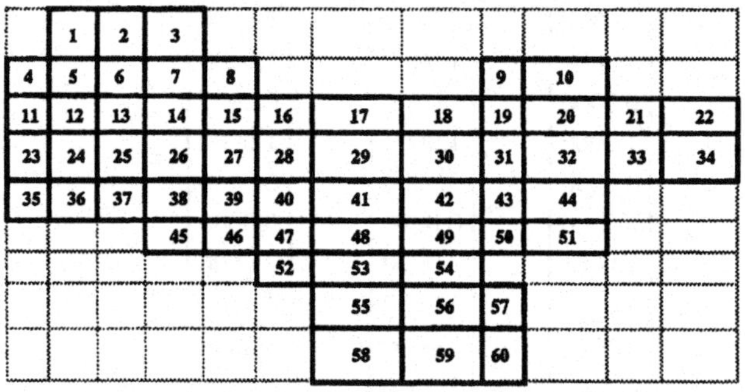

	1	2	3								
4	5	6	7	8				9	10		
11	12	13	14	15	16	17	18	19	20	21	22
23	24	25	26	27	28	29	30	31	32	33	34
35	36	37	38	39	40	41	42	43	44		
			45	46	47	48	49	50	51		
					52	53	54				
						55	56	57			
						58	59	60			

Fig. 7.40—Standard ordering of active reservoir blocks of the A-1 reservoir by rows.

In general, an equation solver should possess a few important features.

1. The solver should be simple and easy to code, requiring minimum storage memory.
2. The solver should be stable with respect to round-off errors.
3. The solver should be easily transportable from one computer to another.

7.4 Chapter Project

This chapter discusses solving the system of linear equations generated from the difference equations. The structure of the coefficient matrix developed depends on both the irregular nature of the grid system and the sequential manner in which gridblocks are numbered and equations generated. This section presents two possible standard ordering schemes applicable to the A-1 reservoir, then displays the resulting structures for the coefficient matrices.

Standard Ordering by Rows. Fig. 7.40 shows standard ordering by rows in which only the active 60 gridblocks in the A-1 reservoir are numbered in sequence by row; **Fig. 7.41** shows the resulting coefficient matrix if the A-1 reservoir gridblocks are ordered as shown in Fig. 7.40. The nonzero elements of the coefficient matrix are indicated by filled squares, and a position where a zero element exists is left blank. The size of the coefficient matrix is 60×60 (there are 60 reservoir blocks). It has a banded structure with a maximum bandwidth of 25 ($= 12 \times 2 + 1$). Because of the irregular nature of the boundaries, it has a number of diagonals. Although the coefficient matrix is sparse, the existence of a large number of diagonals increases the level of difficulty involved in handling this matrix.

Standard Ordering by Columns. Fig. 7.42 shows the standard ordering by columns for the A-1 reservoir. This ordering scheme is preferable for the A-1 reservoir because the bandwidth of the resulting coefficient matrix is 17 ($= 8 \times 2 + 1$) (**Fig. 7.43**). The more compact nature of the coefficient matrix of Fig. 7.43 leads to less computational work. Also, note that irregular structures of the coefficient matrices in Figs. 7.41 and 7.43 prohibit the use of certain solvers that are developed for systems with a fixed number of diagonal coefficient matrices such as tridiagonal, pentadiagonal, or heptadiagonal.

Exercises

7.1 Fig. 7.44 shows a 2D reservoir with regular boundaries that is discretized into 30 blocks.

1. Use the following schemes to order the reservoir gridblocks: (1) standard ordering by rows, (2) standard ordering by columns, (3) D-2 (diagonal) ordering, (4) cyclic-2 ordering, and (5) D-4 (alternating diagonal) ordering.
2. On engineering paper, show the structure of the resulting coefficient matrix (mark nonzero entries) for each ordering scheme.

1 5 10 15 20 25 30 35 40 45 50 55 60
1 5 10 15 20 25 30 35 40 45 50 55 60

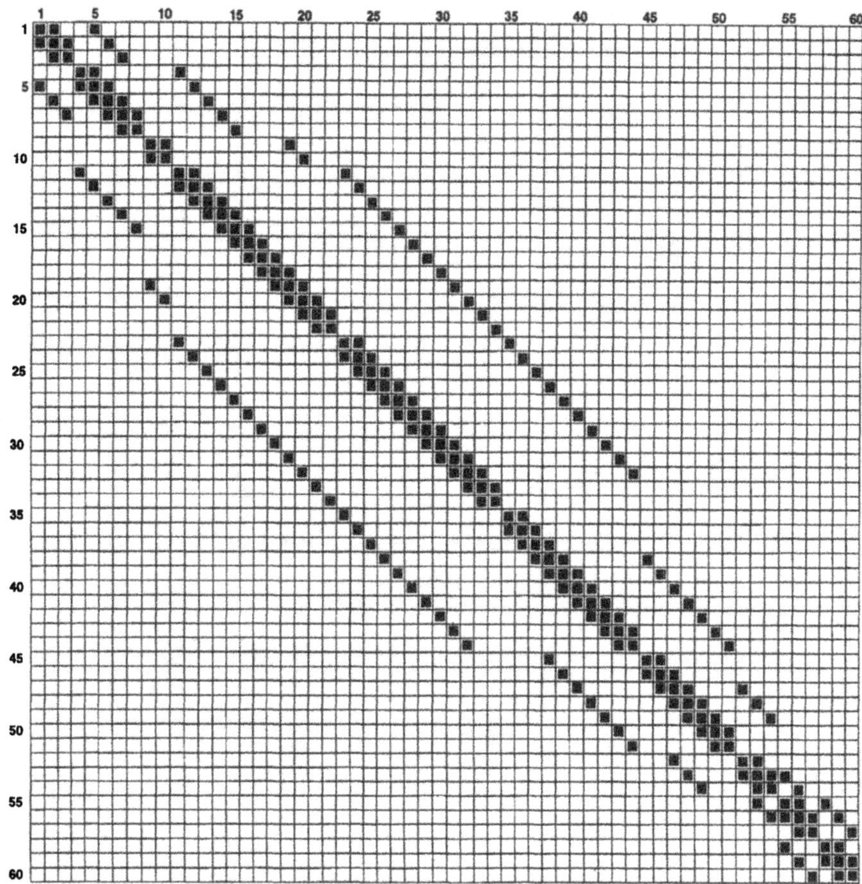

Fig. 7.41—Coefficient matrix resulting from standard ordering of the active reservoir blocks of the A-1 reservoir by rows.

7.2 Answer all questions in Exercise 7.1 as if the reservoir in Exercise 7.1 has irregular boundaries as shown in **Fig. 7.45**. Number active blocks only.

7.3 Use (1) Jacobi's algorithm and (2) Gauss-Seidel's algorithm to solve the following system of equations.

$$5x_1 + 3x_2 + 4x_3 = 12.$$

$$3x_1 + 6x_2 + 4x_3 = 13.$$

$$4x_1 + 4x_2 + 5x_3 = 13.$$

Use an initial guess of zero for all unknowns. Comment on the results.

7.4 Use the conjugate-gradient method to solve the system of equations obtained in Example 7.1. Start with an initial guess of 4,000 psia.

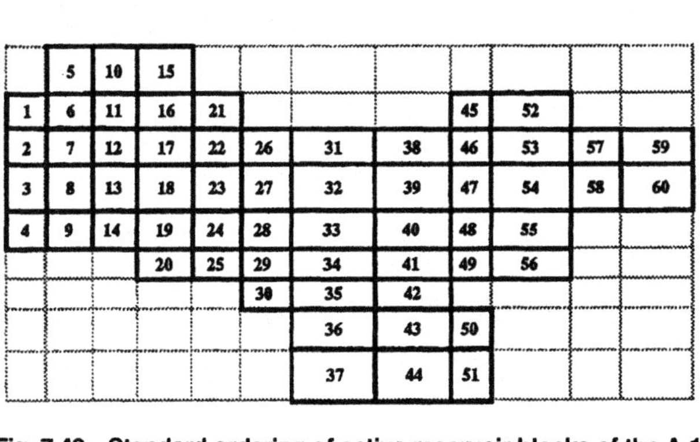

5 10 15
1 6 11 16 21 45 52
2 7 12 17 22 26 31 38 46 53 57 59
3 8 13 18 23 27 32 39 47 54 58 60
4 9 14 19 24 28 33 40 48 55
20 25 29 34 41 49 56
30 35 42
36 43 50
37 44 51

Fig. 7.42—Standard ordering of active reservoir blocks of the A-1 reservoir by columns.

7.5 Use (1) Jacobi's iteration, (2) the Gauss-Seidel iteration, and (3) the PSOR iteration with ω_{opt} to solve the system of equations obtained in Example 7.1. Begin with an initial guess of 1,200 psia for all unknowns and use a convergence tolerance of 0.5 psi.

7.6 Use (1) the Gaussian elimination method, (2) Thomas' algorithm, and (3) the Crout reduction algorithm to solve the system of equations obtained in Example 7.1.

7.7 Consider the following three equations in three unknowns.

$$3.1249x_1 + 1.0139x_2 - 0.8124x_3 = 3.0778.$$

$$1.0139x_1 + 2.0611x_2 + 0.4054x_3 = 2.7350.$$

$$0.8124x_1 + 0.4054x_2 + 2.8143x_3 = 1.3113.$$

Use (1) the Gaussian elimination method, (2) the Gauss-Jordan reduction algorithm, and (3) the Crout reduction algorithm to solve this system of equations. Compare the computational time requirements for the three algorithms.

7.8 Use (1) Jacobi's iteration, (2) Gauss-Seidel's iteration, (3) PSOR method, and (4) conjugate-gradient method to solve the following system.

$$\begin{bmatrix} 6 & -4 & 1 & 0 & 0 \\ -4 & 6 & -4 & 1 & 0 \\ 1 & -4 & 6 & -4 & 1 \\ 0 & 1 & -4 & 6 & -4 \\ 0 & 0 & 1 & -4 & 6 \end{bmatrix} \begin{bmatrix} x_1 \\ x_2 \\ x_3 \\ x_4 \\ x_5 \end{bmatrix} = \begin{bmatrix} 0 \\ 0 \\ 0 \\ 0 \\ 1 \end{bmatrix}.$$

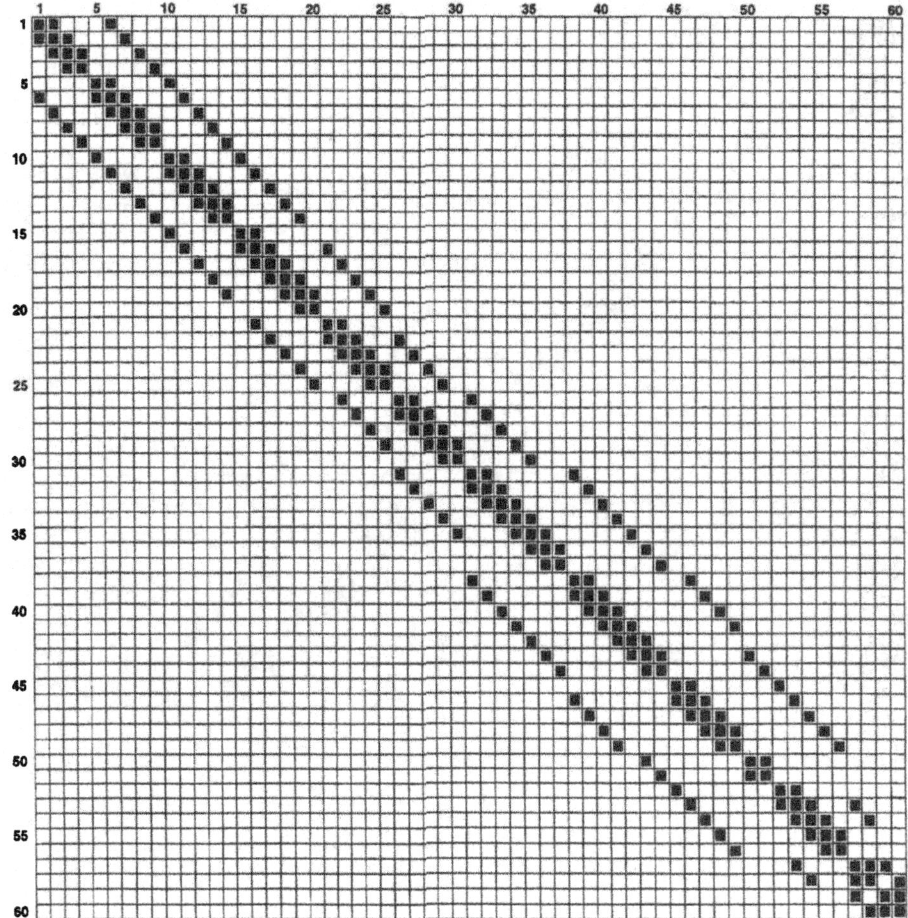

Fig. 7.43—Coefficient matrix resulting from standard ordering of the active reservoir blocks of the A-1 reservoir by columns.

7.9 Consider the following three equations.

$$-8x_1 + 8x_2 = -1.$$

$$2x_1 - 8x_2 + 4x_3 = -1.$$

$$4x_2 - 8x_3 = -1.$$

Use the Gauss-Seidel iterative technique to solve this system of equations. Start with an initial guess of $x_1^{(0)} = x_2^{(0)} = x_3^{(0)} = 1.0000$ and use a tolerance of 0.001 for convergence check.

7.10 Consider 2D, steady-state flow of water in a porous medium with the associated boundary conditions shown in **Fig. 7.46**. Generate the LSOR equations by sweeping the system parallel to the *i* direction. Express each line equations in a matrix form so that Thomas' algorithm is readily applicable.

7.11 Consider the single-phase, steady-state flow of oil in the horizontal, 2D, isotropic system in **Fig. 7.47**. Observe that there is a well in the system. Apply the LSOR method to solve for the pressure distribution in the system. Write the equations along the *j* direction to obtain the iterative equations of Iteration Level $(k + 1)$ for the unknown blocks in the system. (Assume $\omega = 1.0$ and remember to sweep the system parallel to the *j* direction.)

7.12 Consider the 3D, homogeneous finite-difference body in **Fig. 7.48**. A production well at (3,3,3) is completed and kept at a constant pressure. On the outer surfaces of the system, a uniform Dirichlet-type boundary condition is specified. Ignoring gravitational effects, answer the following questions.

1. What is the total number of unknowns (pressures)?

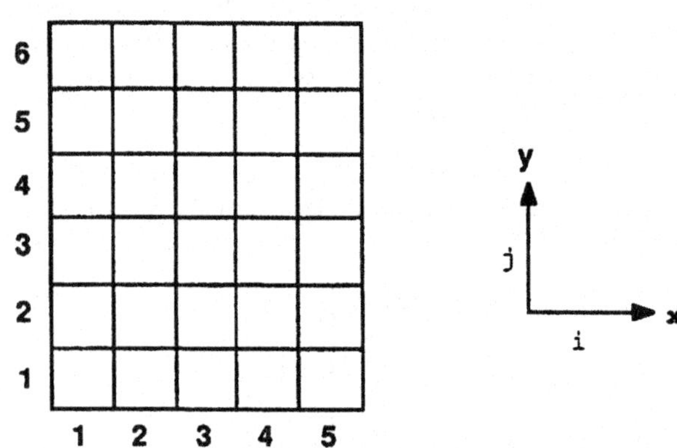

Fig. 7.44—Regular boundaries of reservoir of Exercise 7.1.

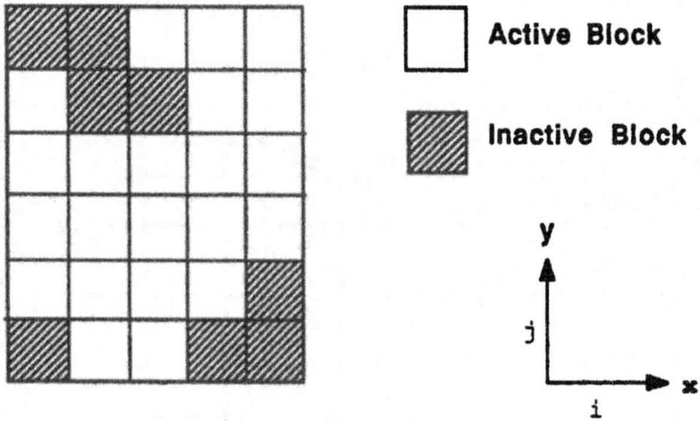

Fig. 7.45—Irregular boundaries of reservoir of Exercise 7.2.

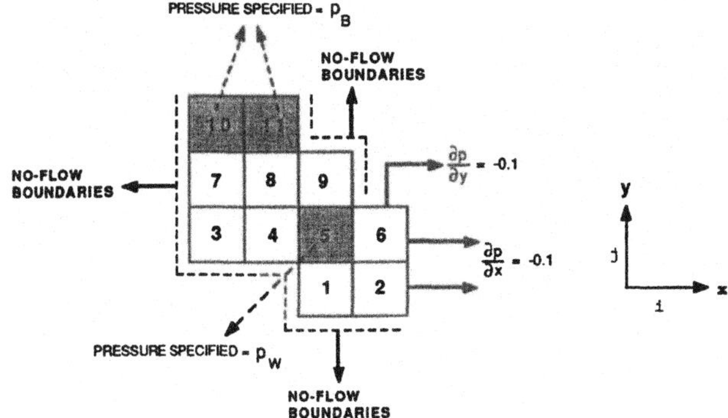

Fig. 7.46—Reservoir described in Exercise 7.10.

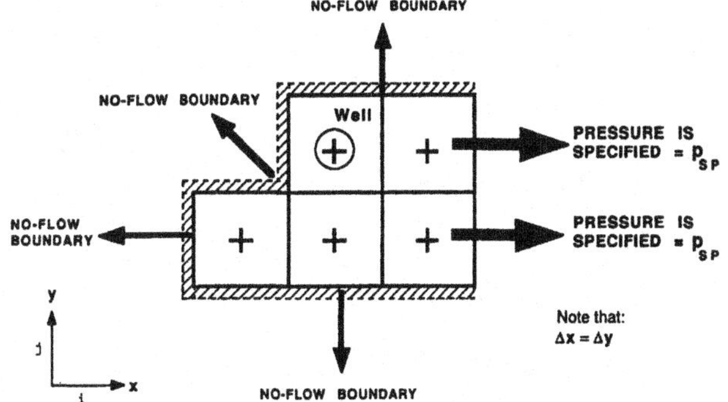

Fig. 7.47—Reservoir described in Exercise 7.11.

2. Considering the symmetry, what is the minimum number of equations you need to solve for the pressures? Indicate the nodes (in triple index notation as suggested in the figure) that you will write equations for.

3. If $k_x = k_y \neq k_z$, how many unknowns would the system have? What is the minimum number of equations you need to solve for the unknowns of the system?

4. If the same nonzero Neumann-type boundary condition is specified on $y = 0$ and $x = 0$ surfaces and if all the other surfaces of the system are represented by the no-flow boundary conditions, how many unknowns does the system have? What is the minimum number of equations you need to consider to solve for the unknowns of this problem if $k_x = k_y = k_z$?

5. If entire surfaces of the body except the lowermost plane ($z = 0$) are closed to flow and the nodes on the lowermost plane are kept at a constant pressure, how many unknowns does the system have? What is the minimum number of equations you must consider to solve for the unknowns of this problem if $k_x = k_y = k_z$?

7.13 Determine the steady-state temperature distribution in the 3D structure in **Fig. 7.49**, which is obtained by the intersection of three finite slabs. Assume homogeneous and isotropic property distribution. The lowermost plane ($z = 0$) is kept at 100°C, and the uppermost plane ($z = 120$) is kept at 0°C. All the other outer surfaces of the structure are completely insulated.

Use conventional seven-point, finite-difference approximation to solve the problem. In solving finite-difference equations, use the LSOR algorithm with optimum acceleration parameter. For the solution of line equations have PSOR (with optimum acceleration parameter) and Thomas' algorithms available.

Note: Do not use the rules of symmetry to solve this problem; instead, use them to check the validity of your solution.

7.14 Solve the equation $\partial^2 u/\partial x^2 + \partial^2 u/\partial y^2 = 0$ for the plane region shown in **Fig. 7.50** with the indicated boundary conditions for u. Use Gaussian elimination and the Crout reduction algorithms. Compare the computational time required for both algorithms.

7.15 Solve approximately Laplace's 3D equation, given by

$$\frac{\partial^2 u}{\partial x^2} + \frac{\partial^2 u}{\partial y^2} + \frac{\partial^2 u}{\partial z^2} = 0,$$

inside a cube whose edge is of unit length if $u = u(x,y,z) = 1$ on one face and 0 on the remaining faces. Use $\Delta x = \Delta y = \Delta z = 0.1$ with a mesh-centered grid. Use the Gauss-Seidel algorithm. (Hint: Use the rules of symmetry to reduce the size of the problem.)

7.16 Poisson's equation is $\partial^2 u/\partial x^2 + \partial^2 u/\partial y^2 = \rho(x,y)$, where $\rho(x,y)$ is some given function of x and y. Solve this equation approximately for the case where $\rho(x,y) = 100/(1 + x^2 + y^2)$ if the region and boundary conditions are the same as those of Exercise 7.14. Use the Crout reduction algorithm.

7.17 Obtain the steady-state temperature distribution in a square slab having the dimensions of unity aligned with x and y axes. The boundaries $x = 1, y = 0, y = 1$ are kept at zero temperature, while the boundary $x = 0$ is kept at a temperature of 100°C.

1. Solve the problem using conventional five-point, finite-difference approximation, letting $\Delta x = \Delta y = 0.05$.

2. Re-solve the same problem using the higher-accuracy nine-point, finite-difference approximation,

$$\left[\frac{\partial^2 u}{\partial x^2} + \frac{\partial^2 u}{\partial y^2}\right]_{i,j} = \frac{1}{6h^2}\Big[u_{i+1,j+1} + 4u_{i,j+1} + u_{i-1,j+1} + 4u_{i+1,j} - 20u_{i,j} + 4u_{i-1,j} + u_{i+1,j-1} + 4u_{i,j-1} + u_{i-1,j-1}\Big] + 0(h^4),$$

where $h = \Delta x = \Delta y$.

3. Compare your results with the exact solution provided here. Also, compare the computation time, storage requirements, and number of iterations. Tabulate your results. The analytical solution is

$$T(x,y) = \sum_{n=1}^{\infty} E_n T_n(x,y),$$

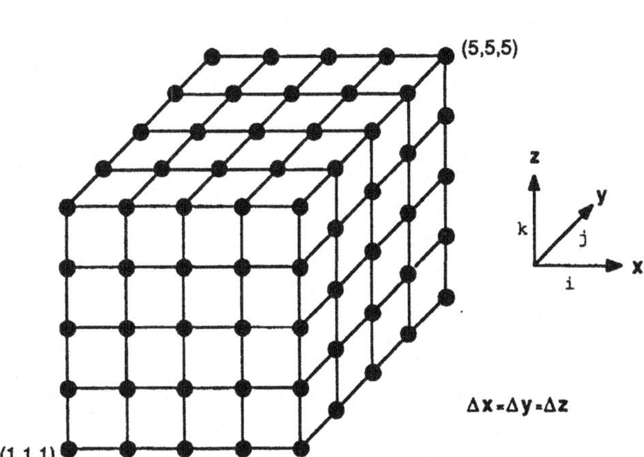

Fig. 7.48—Nodes used to describe reservoir in Exercise 7.12.

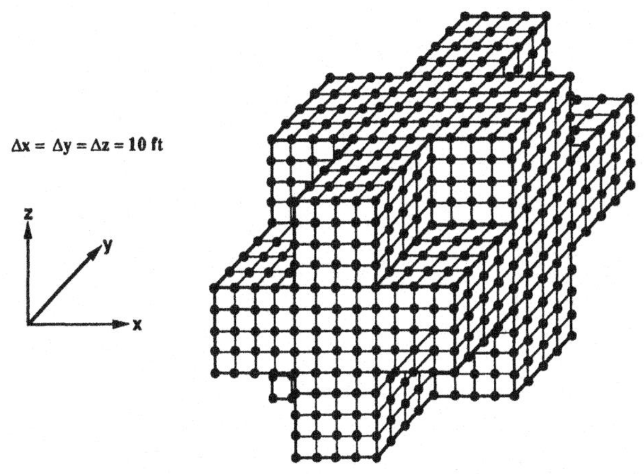

Fig. 7.49—Three-dimensional reservoir of Exercise 7.13.

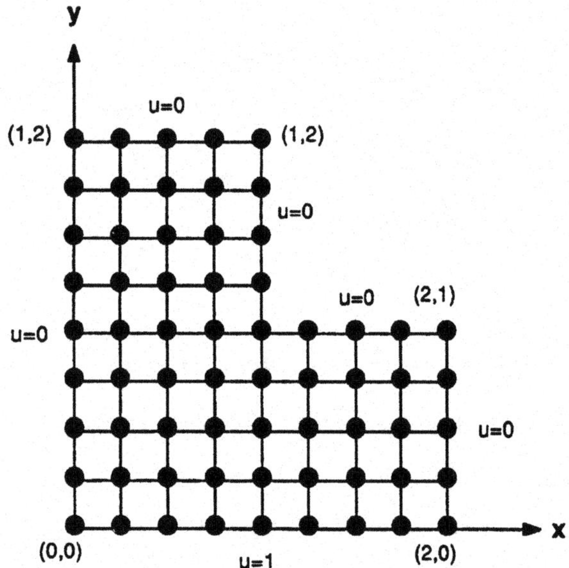

Fig. 7.50—Nodes used to describe the space domain of Exercise 7.14.

where $T_n(x,y) = E_n \sin(n\pi y)[\sinh(n\pi x) - \tanh(n\pi)\cosh(n\pi x)]$

and $E_n = -\dfrac{2}{\tanh(n\pi)}\displaystyle\int_0^1 100\sin(n\pi y)dy.$

7.18 Obtain the steady-state temperature distribution in a cube with the dimensions of unity aligned with *x*, *y*, and *z* axes. The surfaces $x=0, x=1, y=0, y=1$, and $z=0$ are kept at 0°C, while the surface $z=1$ is kept at 100°C.

1. Solve the problem using the conventional seven-point, finite-difference approximation and the LSOR algorithm, with $\omega = 1.0$. In the solution of line equations use the PSOR algorithm with ω_{opt}. (Let $\Delta x = \Delta y = \Delta z = 0.1$.)

2. Develop an algorithm for plane successive overrelaxation. Test your algorithm by resolving the problem with $\omega = 1.0$. In the solution of plane equations use LSOR with $\omega = 1.0$. In the solution of line equations of LSOR use PSOR with ω_{opt}.

3. Compare your results with the exact solution provided here. Also, compare the computation time, storage requirements, and number of iterations. Tabulate your results. The analytical solution is

$$T(x,y,z) = 400\sum_{m=1}^{\infty}\sum_{n=1}^{\infty} d_{mn}\frac{\sinh \alpha_{mn}z}{\sinh \alpha_{mn}}\sin(m\pi x)\sin(n\pi y),$$

where $\alpha_{mn} = \pi(m^2+n^2)^{1/2}$ and $d_{mn} = \displaystyle\int_0^1\int_0^1 \sin(m\pi x)\sin(n\pi y)dxdy.$

7.19 Obtain the steady-state temperature distribution in a hollow finite cylinder of length 100 ft, with outside and inside radii of 10 ft and 1 ft, respectively. The cylinder is kept at 0°C on the surfaces $r=1$ ft, $r=10$ ft, and $z=0$ ft, while the surface $z=100$ ft is kept at a temperature of 100°C.

Note that the 3D, steady-state heat flow equation in cylindrical coordinates is given as

$$\frac{\partial^2 T}{\partial r^2} + \frac{1}{r}\frac{\partial T}{\partial r} + \frac{1}{r^2}\frac{\partial^2 T}{\partial \theta^2} + \frac{\partial^2 T}{\partial z^2} = 0.$$

Use equal Δr and $\Delta\theta$ spacings in *r* and θ directions. To solve finite-difference equations, use the PSOR algorithm with optimum acceleration parameter. Check the convergence rate of PSOR against that of Gauss-Seidel.

Fig. 7.51—Semi-infinite domain described in Exercise 7.20.

7.20 Find the steady-state temperature over a set of discrete points of the semi-infinite region that is shaded in **Fig. 7.51** if the temperatures are maintained as indicated.

Note that, in polar coordinates, the analytical solution is

$$T(r,\theta) = \frac{60}{\pi}\tan^{-1}\left[\frac{(r^2-1)\sin\theta}{(r^2+1)\cos\theta - 2r}\right]$$

$$-\frac{60}{\pi}\tan^{-1}\left[\frac{(r^2-1)\sin\theta}{(r^2+1)\cos\theta + 2r}\right].$$

Use equal $\Delta\theta$ spacing and variable Δr spacing by increasing Δr as you move away from the physical boundaries. By a trial-and-error procedure, determine the number of nodes you would need in the *r* direction to place a hypothetical boundary at a certain *r* distance, while you ensure that the approximate solution is within ±5% of the exact solution. Use the Gauss-Seidel algorithm to solve finite-difference equations.

7.21 An infinite wedge-shaped region ABDE (**Fig. 7.52**) of angle $\pi/4$ has one of its sides (AB) maintained at a constant temperature, T_1. The other side, BDE, has part BD (of unit length) insulated while the remaining part, DE, is maintained at a constant temperature, T_2. Find the temperature distribution over a set of discrete points. In polar coordinates, the analytical solution is

$$T = T_1 + \frac{2(T_2 - T_1)}{\pi}$$

$$\times \sin^{-1}\left[\tfrac{1}{2}\left(r^4 + 2r^2\cos 2\theta + 1\right)^{1/2}\right.$$

$$\left. - \tfrac{1}{2}\left(r^4 - 2r^2\cos 2\theta + 1\right)^{1/2}\right].$$

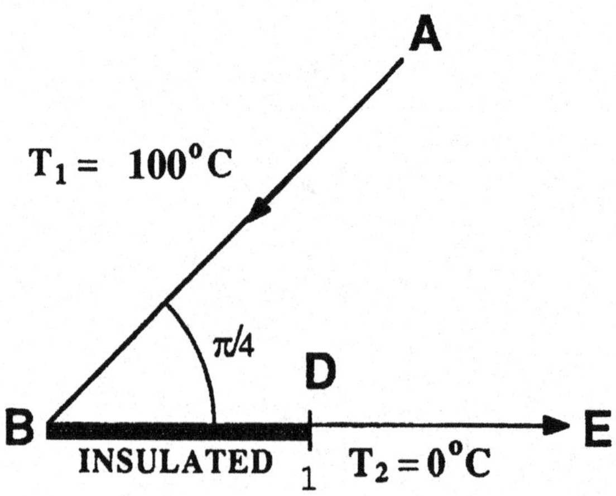

Fig. 7.52—Wedge-shaped region described in Exercise 7.21.

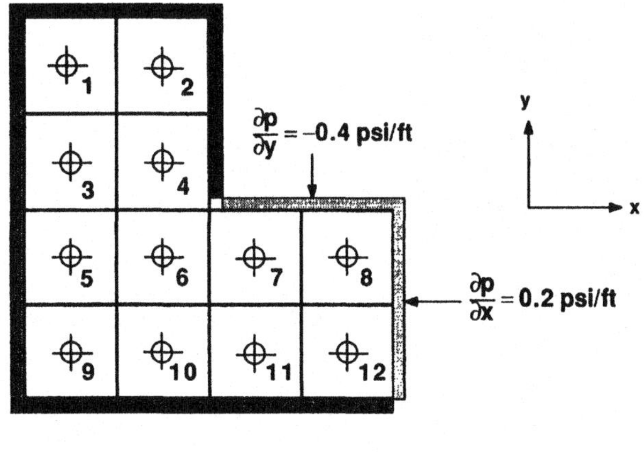

Fig. 7.54—Two-dimensional reservoir of Exercise 7.24.

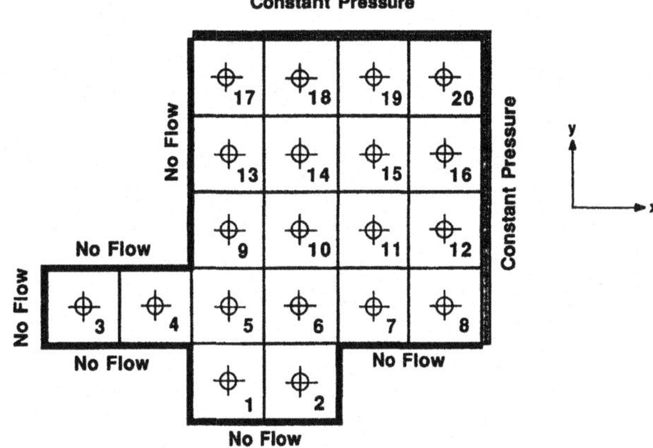

Fig. 7.55—Two-dimensional reservoir of Exercise 7.25.

Compare the accuracy of the numerical solution with the exact solution. Hint: the 2D, steady-state, heat flow equation in radial coordinates is

$$\frac{1}{r}\frac{\partial}{\partial r}\left(r\frac{\partial T}{\partial r}\right)+\frac{1}{r^2}\frac{\partial^2 T}{\partial \theta^2}=0.$$

Use equal Δr and $\Delta\theta$ spacings in the r and θ directions, respectively. By trial and error, find out the number of nodes you need to approximate the exact solution within $\pm 1\%$.

Use the PSOR algorithm with ω_{opt}. Repeat with the Gauss-Seidel algorithm.

7.22 Show that the SIP coefficients defined by Eqs. 7.193 through 7.199 remove the effects of the nonstandard terms in Eq. 7.165 when the assumptions stated in Eqs. 7.187 through 7.192 are valid and $\omega^{(k)}=1$.

7.23 Consider **Fig. 7.53**, which represents a portion of a larger grid system with the two prescribed boundary conditions. Furthermore, consider that $\Delta x = 800$ ft, $\Delta y = 200$ ft, $h = 100$ ft, and $k_x = k_y = 36$ md.

Assume that you are dealing with an incompressible liquid so that $B = 1$ RB/STB and $\mu = 1$ cp. The final form of the finite-difference equation for Meshpoint 4 is

$$Ap_4 + Bp_5 + Cp_7 = D.$$

Determine the coefficients A, B, and C, and the right-side entry, D, for this system.

7.24 Consider the 2D, body-centered grid with the boundary conditions shown in **Fig. 7.54**. Show all reflection nodes and the respective equations you need to write to solve this problem.

7.25 Construct the coefficient matrix, the unknown vector, and the right-side vector for the 2D, homogeneous, isotropic reservoir in **Fig. 7.55**. (Assume that you are solving for all unknowns simultaneously.)

7.26 Consider the slightly compressible fluid flow through the 2D porous medium as shown in **Fig. 7.56**. The porous medium has homogeneous and isotropic property distribution, and all the external boundaries are no-flow boundaries. The well is produced at a constant flow rate of q_{sc} STB/D.

Use the implicit finite-difference approximation and the LSOR procedure to solve for pressure distribution. While sweeping the system parallel to the x direction, use Thomas' algorithm to solve the line equations.

1. Construct the coefficient matrix for Line $j = 1$ equations in the $(k+1)$ LSOR iteration level.
2. In completing one LSOR iteration over the entire reservoir, how many times does one need to call Thomas' algorithm?
3. Can the answer to Part 2 be six? Why? Justify your answer explicitly by constructing a coefficient matrix.
4. Write the algorithm equation you would use to solve the line equations by use of Jacobi's procedure but not Thomas' algorithm.

7.27 The coefficient matrix in **Fig. 7.57A** was constructed to solve for the pressure distribution for the single-phase fluid-flow problem in the system in **Fig. 7.57B**. Solve for the pressure values and place them into the grid. However, the numbering scheme used for this reservoir is not given. This should not cause a problem; it requires only 15 minutes of extra work. Determine the numbering of the gridblocks that generates the given coefficient matrix.

Nomenclature

a_i = coefficient of the $i-1$ unknown in the equation of the ith gridblock in Thomas' algorithm
$a_{i,i}$ = diagonal entries in a square matrix
a_{ii} = diagonal entry in a square matrix
a_{ij} = (i, j) element of **[A]**
$a_{i,j,k}$ = element that corresponds to Gridblock (i, j, k) in the uppermost diagonal of **[U′]** in SIP iteration
a_{nn} = last diagonal entry in a square matrix

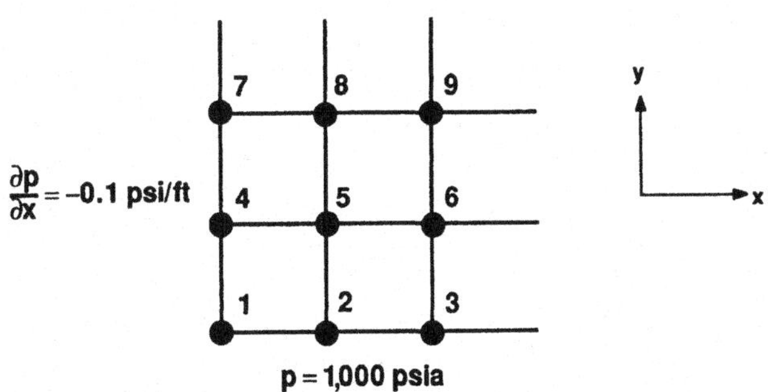

Fig. 7.53—Portion of reservoir of Exercise 7.23

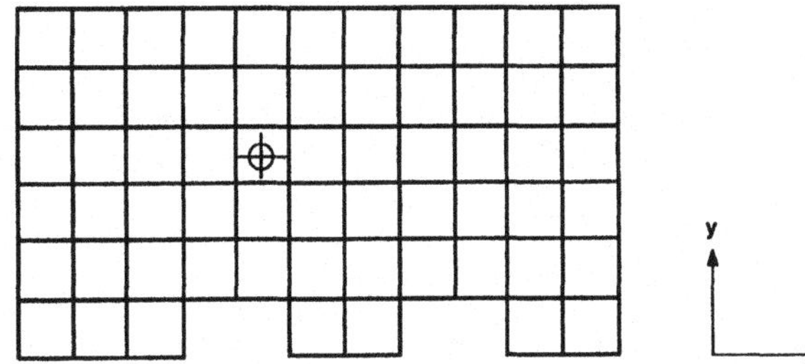

Fig. 7.56—Two-dimensional reservoir of Exercise 7.26.

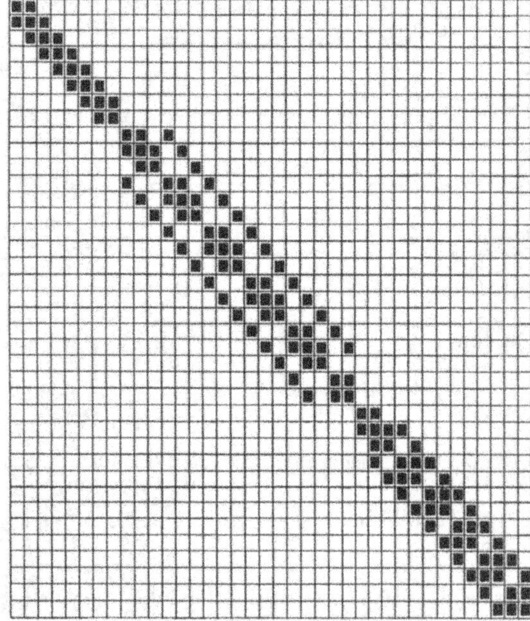

Fig. 7.57A—Coefficient matrix in Exercise 7.27

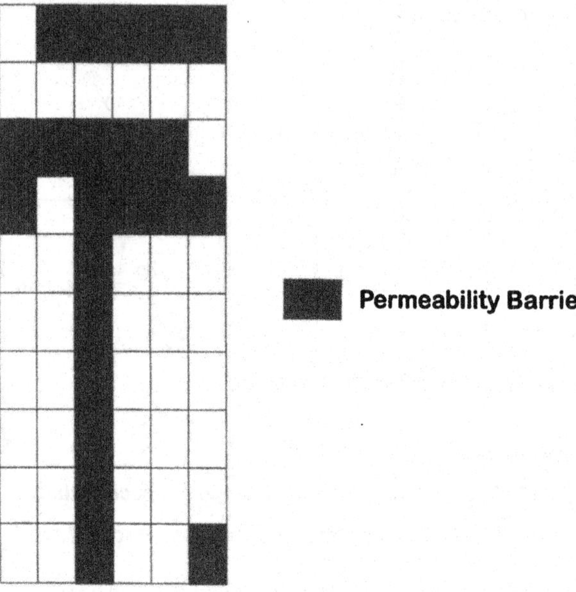

Fig. 7.57B—Reservoir described in Exercise 7.27.

$a^{(k)}$ = scalar variable to minimize the function $F(\vec{x})$ at the kth iteration of the conjugate-gradient method
$\vec{a}'$ = vector defined in Fig. 7.38
$A_{i,j,k}$ = transmissibility coefficient of $p_{i,j,k+1}$ in the matrix notation, L^4t/m, STB/(D-psi) [std m³/(d·kPa)]
A_x = cross-sectional area normal to x direction, L^2, ft² [m²]
A_y = cross-sectional area normal to y direction, L^2, ft² [m²]
A_z = cross-sectional area normal to z direction, L^2, ft² [m²]
$\vec{A}$ = vector defined in Fig. 7.36
$\vec{A}'$ = vector defined in Fig. 7.39
[A] = coefficient matrix in a matrix equation
[A′] = approximation to, but easier than, **[A]** to factor into **[L′][U′]**
$[\mathbf{A}]^T$ = transpose of **[A]**
b_i = coefficient of the i unknown in the equation of the ith gridblock in Thomas' algorithm
$b'_{i,j,k}$ = element that corresponds to Gridblock (i, j, k) in the lowermost diagonal of **[L′]** in SIP iteration
b_w = half bandwidth of a matrix
$b^{(k+1)}$ = coefficient of the direction vector $\vec{p}$ of the conjugate-gradient method between the k and $k+1$ iterations
$\vec{b}'$ = vector defined in Fig. 7.37
$B_{i,j,k}$ = transmissibility coefficient of $p_{i,j,k-1}$ in matrix notation, L^4t/m, STB/(D-psi) [std m³/(d·kPa)]
B_l = formation volume factor (FVF) of a liquid, reservoir volume/volume at standard conditions, L^3/L^3
B_l° = FVF for a liquid phase at reference pressure and reservoir temperature, L^3/L^3, RB/STB [m³/std m³]
$\vec{B}$ = vector defined in Fig. 7.36
$\vec{B}'$ = vector defined in Fig. 7.39
c = compressibility, Lt^2/m, psi^{-1} [kPa^{-1}]
c_i = coefficient of the $i+1$ unknown in the equation of the ith gridblock in Thomas' algorithm
c_l = compressibility of a liquid phase, Lt^2/m, psi^{-1} [kPa^{-1}]
$c'_{i,j,k}$ = element that corresponds to Gridblock (i, j, k) in main diagonal of **[L′]** in SIP iteration
$\vec{c}'$ = vector defined in Fig. 7.37
C = center
$C_{i,j,k}$ = transmissibility coefficient of $p_{i,j,k}$ in matrix notation, L^4t/m, STB/(D-psi) [std m³/(d·kPa)]
$\vec{C}$ = vector defined in Fig. 7.36
$\vec{C}'$ = vector defined in Fig. 7.39
d_i = right side of equation for Gridblock i in Thomas' algorithm, ith element of $\vec{d}$
d_{mn} = function defined in Exercise 7.18
$d_n^{(n)}$ = the nth element of $\vec{d}$ after the nth Gaussian elimination step
$d_k^{(i)}$ = the kth element of $\vec{d}$ after the ith Gaussian elimination step
$d^{(k)}$ = maximum deviation of unknowns between the k iteration and the $k+1$ iteration
$\vec{d}$ = right-side vector in a matrix equation
[D] = diagonal matrix
$e'_{i,j,k}$ = element that corresponds to Gridblock (i, j, k) in upper codiagonal of **[U′]** in SIP iteration
$\vec{e}'$ = vector defined in Fig. 7.38
E = east
$E_{i,j,k}$ = transmissibility coefficient of $p_{i+1,j,k}$ in matrix notation, L^4t/m, STB/(D-psi) [std m³/(d·kPa)]
E_n = function defined in Exercise 7.17
$\vec{E}$ = vector defined in Fig. 7.36
$\vec{E}'$ = vector defined in Fig. 7.39
$\vec{F}'$ = vector defined in Fig. 7.39
g_i = ith element of $\vec{g}$ defined by Eq. 7.84
g_n = nth element of $\vec{g}$
$\vec{g}^{(k)}$ = an intermediate vector at kth iteration in conjugate-gradient method
$\vec{G}'$ = vector defined in Fig. 7.39
$[\mathbf{G}]_J$ = Jacobi's iteration matrix defined by Eq. 7.130
$[\mathbf{G}]_{SOR}$ = successive overrelaxation iteration matrix defined by Eq. 7.132
h = thickness, L, ft [m]
$\vec{h}^{(k)}$ = intermediate vector at kth iteration in conjugate-gradient method
$\vec{H}'$ = vector defined in Fig. 7.39
i = dummy index, Row i, Gridblock i
$\vec{I}'$ = vector defined in Fig. 7.39

j = dummy index, Column j
j_{max} = integer defined by Eq. 7.89b
j_{min} = integer defined by Eq. 7.89a
$\vec{J}'$ = vector defined in Fig. 7.39
k = permeability, L^2, darcy [μm^2]
k_x = permeability in the x direction, L^2, darcy [μm^2]
k_y = permeability in the y direction, L^2, darcy [μm^2]
k_z = permeability in the z direction, L^2, darcy [μm^2]
$\vec{K}'$ = vector defined in Fig. 7.39
l_{ii} = ith diagonal element of [L] in Crout reduction
l_{ik} = (i,k) element of [L] in Crout reduction
[L] = lower triangular matrix
[L′] = lower triangular matrix resulting from factorizing **[A′]** in SIP iteration
n = number of equations or number of unknowns in a matrix equation
n_k = number of iteration parameters used per cycle in ADIP and SIP iterations
n_x = number of gridblocks in x direction
n_y = number of gridblocks in y direction
n_z = number of gridblocks in z direction
$n'_{i,j,k}$ = element that corresponds to Gridblock (i, j, k) in upper diagonal of **[U′]** in SIP iteration
$\vec{n}'$ = vector defined in Fig. 7.38
N = north
$N_{i,j,k}$ = transmissibility coefficient of $p_{i,j+1,k}$ in matrix notation, L^4t/m, STB/(D-psi) [std $m^3/(d \cdot kPa)$]
$\vec{N}$ = vector defined in Fig. 7.36
$\vec{N}'$ = vector defined in Fig. 7.39
p = pressure, m/Lt^2, psia [kPa]
p_1 through p_3 = pressure unknowns 1 through 3
p_B = specified pressure value, m/Lt^2
p_E = specified pressure at east boundary, m/Lt^2
p_i = pressure of Gridblock i, m/Lt^2, psia [kPa]
$p_{i,exact}$ = exact value of p_i
$p_{i,j}$ = pressure of Gridblock (i,j), m/Lt^2, psia [kPa]
p_N = specified pressure at north boundary
p_{sp} = specified pressure value, m/Lt^2
p_S = specified pressure at south boundary, m/Lt^2
p_W = specified pressure at west boundary, m/Lt^2
$\hat{p}_{i,j,k}$ = datum corrected pressure of $p_{i,j,k}$ at depth of topmost perforation, m/Lt^2, psia [kPa]
$\vec{p}^{(k)}$ = intermediate vector at kth iteration in conjugate-gradient method
[P] = preconditioning matrix
q_{lsc} = production rate of Phase l at standard conditions, L^3/t, STB/D [std m^3/d]
q_{lsc_i} = flow rate of liquid Phase l at standard conditions (well is located in Gridblock i), L^3/t, STB/D [std m^3/d]
$q_{lsc_{i,j}}$ = q_{lsc} [well is located in Gridblock (i,j,k)]
q_{sc} = production rate at standard conditions, L^3/t, STB/D [std m^3/d]
Q = right side defined by Eq. 7.47
Q_i = right-side entry for Gridblock i
$Q_{i,j,k}$ = known right side of the flow equation for Gridblock (i, j, k) in the matrix notation, L^3/t, STB/D [std m^3/d]
Δr = spacing in r direction, ft [m]
$\vec{r}$ = residual vector
$s'_{i,j,k}$ = element that corresponds to Gridblock (i,j,k) in lower diagonal of **[L′]** in SIP iteration
$\vec{s}'$ = vector defined in Fig. 7.37
S = south
$S_{i,j,k}$ = transmissibility coefficient of $p_{i,j-1,k}$ in matrix notation, L^4t/m, STB/(D-psi) [std $m^3/(d \cdot kPa)$]
$\vec{S}$ = vector defined in Fig. 7.36
$\vec{S}'$ = vector defined in Fig. 7.39
Δt = timestep ($\Delta t = t^{n+1} - t^n$), t, days
T = temperature, T, °C
T_n = function defined in Exercise 7.17
u = unknown variable
u_{ii} = ith diagonal element of **[U]** in Crout reduction
u_{ij} = the (i,j) element of **[U]** in Crout reduction
u_{kj} = the (k,j) element of **[U]** in Crout reduction
u_{nn} = the (n,n) element of **[U]** in Crout reduction
[U] = upper triangular matrix resulting from factorizing **[A]**
[U′] = upper triangular matrix resulting from factorizing **[A′]** in SIP iteration
V_b = gridblock volume, L^3, ft^3 [m^3]
w_i = element defined by Eq. 7.83
$w'_{i,j,k}$ = element that corresponds to Gridblock (i,j,k) in lower codiagonal of **[L′]** in SIP iteration
$\vec{w}'$ = vector defined in Fig. 7.37
W = west
W_i = transmissibility coefficient of p_{i-1} in matrix notation, L^4t/m, STB/(D-psi) [std $m^3/(d \cdot kPa)$]
$W_{i,j,k}$ = transmissibility coefficient of $p_{i-1,j,k}$ in matrix notation, L^4t/m, STB/(D-psi) [std $m^3/(d \cdot kPa)$]
$\vec{W}$ = vector defined by Fig. 7.36
$\vec{W}'$ = vector defined in Fig. 7.39
x = distance in the x direction in Cartesian coordinate system, L, ft [m]
x_{exact} = exact solution for an unknown entry
x_i = ith element of unknown vector $\vec{x}$
x_n = last entry of unknown vector $\vec{x}$
Δx = block size in x direction, L, ft [m]
$\vec{x}$ = unknown vector
y = distance in y direction in Cartesian coordinate system, L, ft [m]
Δy = block size in y direction, L, ft [m]
$\vec{y}$ = immediate solution vector of forward substitution defined by Eq. 7.65
z = distance in z direction in Cartesian coordinate system, L, ft [m]
Δz = block size in z direction, ft [m]
Z = elevation referred to datum (positive downward), L, ft [m]
$Z_{i,j,k}$ = elevation of center of Gridblock (i,j,k), L, ft [m]
α_c = volume conversion factor whose numerical value is given in Table 4.1
α_{mn} = function defined in Exercise 7.18
β_c = transmissibility conversion factor whose numerical value is given in Table 4.1
γ_l = gravity of Phase l, m/L^2t^2, psi/ft [kPa/m]
$\gamma_{l_{i,j,k}}$ = gravity of Phase l in Gridblock (i,j,k), m/L^2t^2, psi/ft [kPa/m]
ε = tolerance
θ = variable in θ direction in cylindrical coordinate system, rad [rad]
$\Delta\theta$ = spacing in θ direction, rad
λ_x = function defined by Eq. 7.153
λ_y = function defined by Eq. 7.154
λ_z = function defined by Eq. 7.155
μ = viscosity, m/Lt, cp [Pa · s]
μ_l = viscosity of Phase l, m/Lt, cp [Pa · s]
ϱ_{GS} = spectral radius of Gauss-Seidel iteration matrix
ϱ_J = spectral radius of Jacobi iteration matrix
ϱ_{SOR} = spectral radius of SOR iteration matrix
$T_{lx_{i\pm1/2,j,k}}$ = Phase l transmissibility along the x direction between Gridblock (i,j,k) and Gridblock $(i \pm 1, j, k)$
$T_{ly_{i,j\pm1/2,k}}$ = Phase l transmissibility along the y direction between Gridblock (i,j,k) and Gridblock $(i, j \pm 1, k)$
$T_{lz_{i,j,k\pm1/2}}$ = Phase l transmissibility along the z direction between Gridblock (i,j,k) and Gridblock $(i, j, k \pm 1)$
ϕ = porosity, fraction

Φ_l = potential of Phase l, m/Lt^2, psia [kPa]
$\omega^{(k)}$ = kth iteration parameter in ADIP and SIP iterations
ω = overrelaxation parameter
ω_{max} = maximum iteration parameter of an iterative procedure
ω_{min} = minimum iteration parameter of an iterative procedure
ω_{opt} = optimum overrelaxation parameter

Subscripts

l = phase
o = oil phase
p = premultiplied by a preconditioning matrix **[P]**
w = water phase

Superscripts

(i) = ith step in Gaussian elimination
(j) = iterations levels before the kth iteration
(k) = old iteration
n = old timestep
(n) = nth step in Gaussian elimination
$n+1$ = current (or new) timestep
$(k+1)$ = current iteration
T = transpose of
$°$ = reference
$*$ = intermediate value before acceleration in SOR or ADIP method

References

1. Odeh, A.S.: "An Overview of Mathematical Modeling of the Behavior of Hydrocarbon Reservoirs," *SIAM Review* (July 1982) 263.
2. Rose, D.J. and Willoughby, R.A.: *Sparse Matrices and Their Applications,* Plenum Press, New York City (1972).
3. Abou-Kassem, J.H. and Ertekin, T.: "An Efficient Algorithm for Removal of Inactive Blocks in Reservoir Simulation," *J. Cdn. Pet. Tech.* (February 1992) 25.
4. Price, H.S. and Coats, K.H.: "Direct Methods in Reservoir Simulation," *Trans.,* AIME (1974) **257,** 295.
5. Peaceman, D.W.: *Fundamentals of Numerical Reservoir Simulation. Developments in Petroleum Science,* Elsevier Scientific Publishing Co., New York City (1977) **6.**
6. Aziz, K. and Settari, A.: *Petroleum Reservoir Simulation,* Applied Sciences Publishers Ltd., London (1979).
7. Dupont, T., Kendal, R.P., and Rachford, H.H. Jr.: "An Approximate Factorization Procedure for Solving Self-Adjoint Elliptic Difference Equations," *SIAM J. Numerical Analysis* (1968) **5,** 559.
8. Stone, H.L.: "Iterative Solution of Implicit Approximations of Multidimensional Partial Differential Equations," *SIAM J. Numerical Analysis* (1968) **5,** 530.
9. Weinstein, H.G., Stone, H.L., and Kwan, T.V.: "Iterative Procedure for Solution of Parabolic and Elliptic Equations in Three Dimensions," *Ind. Eng. Chem. Fund.* (1969) **8,** 281.
10. Hestenes, M.R. and Stiefel, E.: "Method of Conjugate Gradients for Solving Linear Systems," *J. Res. Natl. Bureau Standards* (1952) **49,** 409.
11. Axelsson, O.: *Iterative Solution Methods,* Cambridge U. Press, Cambridge, U.K. (1996) 449–503.
12. Kelley, C.T.: *Iterative Methods for Linear and Nonlinear Equations,* Frontiers in Mathematics Series, SIAM, Philadelphia, Pennsylvania (1995) 11–31.
13. Lanczos, C.: "Solutions of Systems of Linear Equations by Minimized Iterations," *J. Res. Natl. Bureau Standards* (July 1952) **49,** No. 1, 33.
14. Barrett, R. *et al.*: *Templates for the Solution of Linear Systems: Building Blocks for Iterative Methods,* SIAM, Philadelphia, Pennsylvania (1994).
15. Press, W.H. *et al.*: *Numerical Recipes: The Art of Scientific Computing,* Cambridge U. Press, Cambridge, U.K. (1986) 70–73.
16. Vinsome, P.K.W.: "Orthomin, an Iterative Method for Solving Sparse Banded Sets of Simultaneous Linear Equations," paper SPE 5729 presented at the 1976 SPE Symposium on Numerical Simulation of Reservoir Performance, Los Angeles, 19–20 February.
17. Saad, Y. and Schultz, M.H.: "GMRES: A Generalized Minimum Residual Method for Solving Nonsymmetric Linear Systems,"*SIAM J. Sci. Stat. Comp.* (July 1986) **7,** No. 3, 856.
18. Eisenstat, S.C., Elman, H.C., and Schultz, M.H.: "Variational Iterative Methods for Nonsymmetric Systems of Linear Equations," *SIAM J. Numerical Analysis* (April 1983) **20,** No. 2, 345.
19. Jae, K.C. and Young, D.M.: "Generalized Conjugate Gradient Acceleration of Nonsymmetric Iterative Methods," *Linear Algebra & Its Applications* (December 1980) **34,** 159.
20. Simon, H.D.: "Incomplete LU Preconditioners for Conjugate-Gradient-Type Iterative Methods," paper SPE 13533 presented at the 1985 SPE Symposium on Reservoir Simulation, Dallas, 10–13 February.
21. Behie, A.: "Comparison of Nested Factorization, Constrained Pressure Residual, and Incomplete Factorization Preconditionings," paper SPE 15351 presented at the 1985 SPE Symposium on Reservoir Simulation, Dallas, 10–13 February.
22. Towler, B.F. and Killough, J.E.: "Comparison of Preconditioners for the Conjugate Gradient Method in Reservoir Simulation," paper SPE 10490 presented at the 1982 SPE Symposium on Reservoir Simulation, New Orleans, 10–13 February.

Chapter 8
Numerical Solution of Single-Phase-Flow Equations

8.1 Introduction

In Chap. 4, we developed the partial-differential equation (PDE) governing single-phase flow in an anisotropic and heterogeneous porous medium. In Chap. 5, the corresponding finite-difference approximations to the PDE were developed. This chapter studies the numerical solution of the single-phase-flow equations for incompressible, slightly compressible, and compressible fluids.

Although the algebraic forms of the finite-difference approximation to the flow equations for incompressible, slightly compressible, and compressible fluids are similar, the solution methods required to achieve a numerical solution differ. This is because the accumulation term and transmissibility terms differ in the magnitude of response caused by changes in pressure. For incompressible-flow problems, the accumulation term is removed from the flow equations and steady-state conditions prevail. In contrast, for slightly-compressible- and compressible-flow problems, the accumulation of fluid changes with pressure and unsteady-state conditions prevail.

The transmissibility terms, $T_{lx_{i\pm 1/2}}$ in the finite-difference equations are defined in Sec. 5.3 (Eqs. 5.48 and 5.49). Two difficulties arise in the calculation of the transmissibility terms in the flow equations. The first difficulty is that the transmissibilities are evaluated at the boundaries of the grid cells, while the rock properties, k_H and h, and the pressure-dependent fluid properties, μ_l and B_l, are known only at the cell centers. This is also true for multiphase-flow problems where the relative permeabilities are required at the gridblock boundaries but the saturations and, consequently, the relative permeabilities are known only in the interior of the cell.

The second difficulty with the evaluation of the transmissibility terms for the finite-difference equations is the dependence of the transmissibilities on pressure for single-phase-flow problems (and on pressure and saturation for multiphase-flow problems). The dependence of the transmissibilities on the unknowns results in a system of nonlinear algebraic equations. The equation solvers discussed in Chap. 7 are appropriate only for linear equations; therefore, the nonlinear equations must be linearized before they can be solved. **Fig. 8.1** shows the linearization step in the reservoir-simulation process.

8.2 Single-Phase Incompressible-Flow Problem

The single-phase-flow equation is derived by use of a mass-balance equation combined with an equation of state and Darcy's law (see Eq. 4.20). In its most general form, this flow equation is expressed as

$$\frac{\partial}{\partial x}\left[\beta_c\frac{A_xk_x}{\mu_lB_l}\left(\frac{\partial p}{\partial x}-\gamma_l\frac{\partial Z}{\partial x}\right)\right]\Delta x+\frac{\partial}{\partial y}\left[\beta_c\frac{A_yk_y}{\mu_lB_l}\left(\frac{\partial p}{\partial y}-\gamma_l\frac{\partial Z}{\partial y}\right)\right]\Delta y$$

$$+\frac{\partial}{\partial z}\left[\beta_c\frac{A_zk_z}{\mu_lB_l}\left(\frac{\partial p}{\partial z}-\gamma_l\frac{\partial Z}{\partial z}\right)\right]\Delta z+q_{lsc}$$

$$=\frac{V_b}{\alpha_c}\frac{\partial}{\partial t}\left(\frac{\phi}{B_l}\right), \quad\quad (8.1)$$

where $l = o, w,$ or g.

Eq. 8.1 can be simplified to describe single-phase, incompressible-fluid flow in a heterogeneous and anisotropic formation by use of the following observations.

- The density of an incompressible fluid is constant, which implies that μ_l and B_l are constants ($B_l = 1$ for isothermal conditions).
- The porous medium is incompressible, which implies that ϕ is constant.

These assumptions indicate that the right side of Eq. 8.1 contains only constant terms; therefore, $(\partial/\partial t)(\phi/B_l) = 0$. Setting the partial derivative with respect to time equal to zero implies that steady-state conditions exist. Consequently, for incompressible-flow problems, the pressure distribution will be constant with time. Although a few further simplifications on the left side of Eq. 8.1 are possible, these simplifications will not be implemented at this stage. The resulting equation is

$$\frac{\partial}{\partial x}\left[\beta_c\frac{A_xk_x}{\mu_lB_l}\left(\frac{\partial p}{\partial x}-\gamma_l\frac{\partial Z}{\partial x}\right)\right]\Delta x+\frac{\partial}{\partial y}\left[\beta_c\frac{A_yk_y}{\mu_lB_l}\left(\frac{\partial p}{\partial y}-\gamma_l\frac{\partial Z}{\partial y}\right)\right]\Delta y$$

$$+\frac{\partial}{\partial z}\left[\beta_c\frac{A_zk_z}{\mu_lB_l}\left(\frac{\partial p}{\partial z}-\gamma_l\frac{\partial Z}{\partial z}\right)\right]\Delta z+q_{lsc}=0. \quad\quad (8.2)$$

For a horizontal reservoir with negligible fluid gravity, this equation can be written as

$$\frac{\partial}{\partial x}\left(\beta_c\frac{A_xk_x}{\mu_lB_l}\frac{\partial p}{\partial x}\right)\Delta x+\frac{\partial}{\partial y}\left(\beta_c\frac{A_yk_y}{\mu_lB_l}\frac{\partial p}{\partial y}\right)\Delta y$$

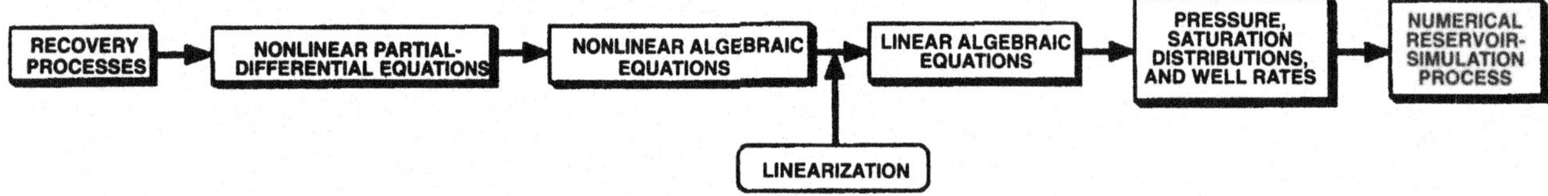

Fig. 8.1—The linearization step in reservoir simulation (redrawn from Ref. 1).

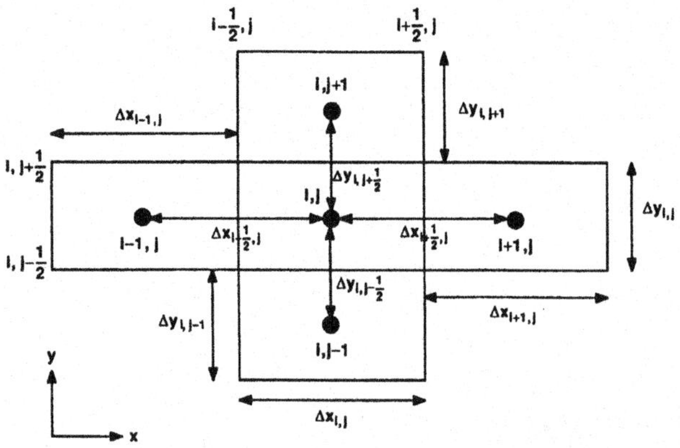

Fig. 8.2—Labeling of gridblocks in *x-y* plane.

$$+\frac{\partial}{\partial z}\left(\beta_c \frac{A_z k_z}{\mu_l B_l}\frac{\partial p}{\partial z}\right)\Delta z + q_{lsc} = 0. \quad \text{.............} \quad (8.3)$$

Table 4.1 gives the units of the variables in Eqs. 8.1, 8.2, and 8.3.

8.2.1 Finite-Difference Approximation of the Incompressible-Fluid-Flow Equation. As discussed in Chap. 5, the first step in the solution process is to replace Eq. 8.3 with its finite-difference approximation. Because the approximation of each partial derivative in Eq. 8.3 is analogous to that given on the left side of Eq. 5.46, we can write the finite-difference approximation to Eq. 8.3 as

$$\left(\beta_c \frac{A_x k_x}{\mu_l B_l \Delta x}\right)_{i+½,j,k}\left(p_{i+1,j,k}-p_{i,j,k}\right)$$

$$-\left(\beta_c \frac{A_x k_x}{\mu_l B_l \Delta x}\right)_{i-½,j,k}\left(p_{i,j,k}-p_{i-1,j,k}\right)$$

$$+\left(\beta_c \frac{A_y k_y}{\mu_l B_l \Delta y}\right)_{i,j+½,k}\left(p_{i,j+1,k}-p_{i,j,k}\right)$$

$$-\left(\beta_c \frac{A_y k_y}{\mu_l B_l \Delta y}\right)_{i,j-½,k}\left(p_{i,j,k}-p_{i,j-1,k}\right)$$

$$+\left(\beta_c \frac{A_z k_z}{\mu_l B_l \Delta z}\right)_{i,j,k+½}\left(p_{i,j,k+1}-p_{i,j,k}\right)$$

$$-\left(\beta_c \frac{A_z k_z}{\mu_l B_l \Delta z}\right)_{i,j,k-½}\left(p_{i,j,k}-p_{i,j,k-1}\right)+q_{lsc_{i,j,k}}$$

$$= 0. \quad \text{..................................} \quad (8.4)$$

The coefficients $[\beta_c(A_x k_x/\mu_l B_l \Delta x)]_{i\pm½,j,k}$ (and similarly in the y and z directions) are the transmissibilities, $T_{lx_{i\pm½,j,k}}$, and are required at the gridblock boundaries (as indicated by the $i \pm ½, j \pm ½, k \pm ½$ subscripts). **Fig. 8.2** shows the gridblock dimensions and gridblock labeling in the 2D x-y plane.

8.2.2 Calculation of Transmissibilities for the Incompressible-Flow Equation. As Fig. 8.2 shows, the gridblock dimensions along the x and y directions can vary as one moves from one gridblock to another. Similarly, other properties assigned to the gridblocks may differ, depending on the degree of heterogeneity and anisotropy existing in the system. For example, the five gridblocks shown in Fig. 8.2 may have different formation thicknesses, permeabilities, and porosities. In addition, the x-direction permeability may differ from the y-direction permeability. The transmissibility terms are calculated at the gridblock boundaries, but the rock and fluid properties are known only at the cell centers. Eqs. 8.5 through 8.8 show the techniques available to estimate property averages between two adjacent gridblocks.

Arithmetic Averaging.

$$\overline{A} = \frac{a_1 + a_2 + a_3 + \ldots + a_n}{n}. \quad \text{................} \quad (8.5)$$

Weighted Averaging.

$$\overline{W} = \frac{w_1 a_1 + w_2 a_2 + w_3 a_3 + \ldots + w_n a_n}{\sum_{i=1}^{n} w_i}. \quad \text{.......} \quad (8.6)$$

Geometric Averaging.

$$\overline{G} = \sqrt[n]{a_1 a_2 a_3 \ldots a_n}. \quad \text{.......................} \quad (8.7)$$

Harmonic Averaging.

$$\frac{1}{\overline{H}} = \frac{1}{n}\left(\frac{1}{a_1} + \frac{1}{a_2} + \frac{1}{a_3} + \ldots + \frac{1}{a_n}\right), \quad \text{............} \quad (8.8)$$

where $\overline{H} \leqq \overline{G} \leqq \overline{A}$. These averages are equal when $a_1 = a_2 = a_3 = \ldots a_n$.

The transmissibilities in Eq. 8.4 have two distinct groups of terms. $(1/\mu_l B_l)$ represents the fluid properties that stay constant for incompressible-fluid-flow problems; therefore, the question of averaging is applicable only to $(A_x k_x/\Delta x)$, which represents grid-related properties.

When averaging $(A_x k_x/\Delta x)$ between two adjacent gridblocks, the harmonic average is used because serial flow occurs between adjacent grid cells. Following the definition of harmonic averaging given by Eq. 8.8, $(A_x k_x/\Delta x)_{i+½,j}$ can be calculated for a block-centered grid as follows.

Let $\overline{H} = \left(\frac{A_x k_x}{\Delta x}\right)_{i\pm½,j}$.

It follows from Eq. 8.8 that

$$\frac{1}{\overline{H}} = \frac{1}{2}\left[\left(\frac{\Delta x}{A_x k_x}\right)_{i,j} + \left(\frac{\Delta x}{A_x k_x}\right)_{i\pm1,j}\right] \quad \text{..............} \quad (8.9a)$$

$$\text{or } \frac{1}{\overline{H}} = \frac{1}{2}\left[\frac{\Delta x_{i\pm1,j}\left(A_{x_{i,j}} k_{x_{i,j}}\right) + \Delta x_{i,j}\left(A_{x_{i\pm1,j}} k_{x_{i\pm1,j}}\right)}{A_{x_{i,j}} A_{x_{i\pm1,j}} k_{x_{i,j}} k_{x_{i\pm1,j}}}\right]. \quad \text{....................} \quad (8.9b)$$

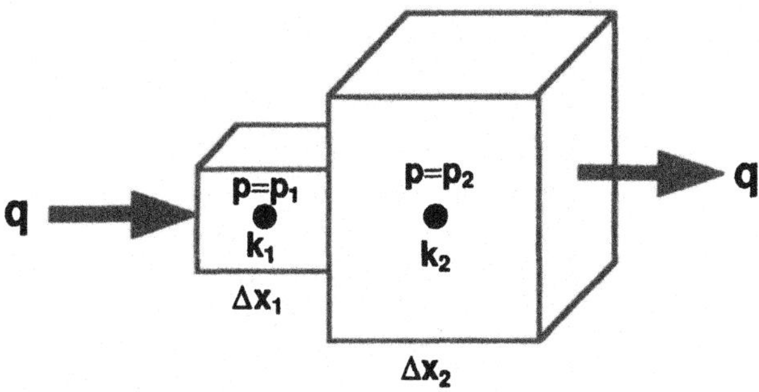

Fig. 8.3—Use of the harmonic average between two adjacent gridblocks.

Solving for $\overline{H}$,

$$\overline{H} = \left(\frac{A_x k_x}{\Delta x}\right)_{i \pm 1/2, j} = \frac{2A_{x_{i,j}} A_{x_{i \pm 1,j}} k_{x_{i,j}} k_{x_{i \pm 1,j}}}{A_{x_{i,j}} k_{x_{i,j}} \Delta x_{i \pm 1,j} + A_{x_{i \pm 1,j}} k_{x_{i \pm 1,j}} \Delta x_{i,j}}. \quad \text{(8.9c)}$$

Finally, the entire transmissibility term $[\beta_c(A_x k_x/\mu_l B_l \Delta x)]_{i \pm 1/2, j}$ can be written as

$$\left(\beta_c \frac{A_x k_x}{\mu_l B_l \Delta x}\right)_{i \pm 1/2, j} = \beta_c \frac{2A_{x_{i,j}} A_{x_{i \pm 1,j}} k_{x_{i,j}} k_{x_{i \pm 1,j}}}{A_{x_{i,j}} k_{x_{i,j}} \Delta x_{i \pm 1,j} + A_{x_{i \pm 1,j}} k_{x_{i \pm 1,j}} \Delta x_{i,j}} \times \frac{1}{\mu_l B_l}. \quad \text{(8.10)}$$

It should be emphasized that the term $(1/\mu_l B_l)$ is excluded from the averaging process because it is constant under the assumption of incompressible flow. For the slightly-compressible- and compressible-flow cases, it must be included in the averaging process. Similarly, transmissibility terms in the y direction can be written as

$$\left(\beta_c \frac{A_y k_y}{\mu_l B_l \Delta y}\right)_{i, j \pm 1/2} = \beta_c \frac{2A_{y_{i,j}} A_{y_{i,j \pm 1}} k_{y_{i,j}} k_{y_{i,j \pm 1}}}{A_{y_{i,j}} k_{y_{i,j}} \Delta y_{i,j \pm 1} + A_{y_{i,j \pm 1}} k_{y_{i,j \pm 1}} \Delta y_{i,j}} \times \frac{1}{\mu_l B_l}. \quad \text{(8.11)}$$

The choice of harmonic average for serial flow is obtained through Darcy's law as shown in Example 8.1.

Example 8.1. Obtain the expression for transmissibility for linear flow between two adjacent gridblocks with the dimensions and permeabilities shown in **Fig. 8.3**. Note that pressures p_1 and p_2 are measured at the gridblock centers.

Solution. Because we are dealing with steady-state incompressible flow, neither fluid depletion nor accumulation occurs within the gridblocks. Therefore, the amount of fluid entering Gridblock 2 must be equal to the amount of fluid leaving Gridblock 1. The linear form of Darcy's law is $q_l = \beta_c(A_x k_x \Delta p/\mu_l L)$. This expression cannot be used easily in this problem because the values of A_x and k_x change along the flow direction. The value of pressure at the interface of these two gridblocks is $p_{1+1/2}$.

$$\Delta p = p_1 - p_2 = \left(p_1 - p_{1+1/2}\right) + \left(p_{1+1/2} - p_2\right). \quad \text{(8.12)}$$

Now, we can write

$$q_l = \frac{\beta_c A_{x_1} k_{x_1}}{\mu_l (\Delta x_1/2)}\left(p_1 - p_{1+1/2}\right), \quad \text{(8.13)}$$

$$q_l = \frac{\beta_c A_{x_2} k_{x_2}}{\mu_l (\Delta x_2/2)}\left(p_{1+1/2} - p_2\right), \quad \text{(8.14)}$$

and $$q_l = \frac{\beta_c}{\mu_l}\left(\frac{A_x k_x}{\Delta x}\right)_{avg}(p_1 - p_2). \quad \text{(8.15)}$$

The factor ½ in Eqs. 8.13 and 8.14, which multiplies Δx_1 and Δx_2, arises because, for block-centered grid systems, flow from adjacent gridblocks occurs from cell center to cell center. (For point-distributed grid systems, this development will be slightly different. See Example 9.15 for these grid systems.) Solving for the pressure drops and substituting into Eq. 8.12 results in

$$\Delta p = \frac{q_l \mu_l}{\beta_c}\left(\frac{\Delta x}{A_x k_x}\right)_{avg} = \frac{q_l(\Delta x_1/2)\mu_l}{\beta_c A_{x_1} k_{x_1}} + \frac{q_l(\Delta x_2/2)\mu_l}{\beta_c A_{x_2} k_{x_2}} \quad \text{(8.16)}$$

or $$\left(\frac{\Delta x}{A_x k_x}\right)_{avg} = \frac{\Delta x_1/2}{A_{x_1} k_{x_1}} + \frac{\Delta x_2/2}{A_{x_2} k_{x_2}}, \quad \text{(8.17)}$$

which is the definition of the harmonic average.

8.2.3 Implementation of Matrix Notation for the Incompressible-Flow Equation. If we denote the transmissibilities in Eq. 8.4 as $T_{lx_{i+1/2,j,k}}$, $T_{lx_{i-1/2,j,k}}$, $T_{ly_{i,j+1/2,k}}$, $T_{ly_{i,j-1/2,k}}$, $T_{lz_{i,j,k+1/2}}$, and $T_{lz_{i,j,k-1/2}}$, the equation can be written as

$$T_{lx_{i+1/2,j,k}}\left(p_{i+1,j,k} - p_{i,j,k}\right) - T_{lx_{i-1/2,j,k}}\left(p_{i,j,k} - p_{i-1,j,k}\right)$$
$$+ T_{ly_{i,j+1/2,k}}\left(p_{i,j+1,k} - p_{i,j,k}\right) - T_{ly_{i,j-1/2,k}}\left(p_{i,j,k} - p_{i,j-1,k}\right)$$
$$+ T_{lz_{i,j,k+1/2}}\left(p_{i,j,k+1} - p_{i,j,k}\right) - T_{lz_{i,j,k-1/2}}\left(p_{i,j,k} - p_{i,j,k-1}\right)$$
$$+ q_{lsc_{i,j,k}} = 0. \quad \text{(8.18)}$$

Eq. 8.18 can be rearranged as

$$T_{lz_{i,j,k-1/2}} p_{i,j,k-1} + T_{ly_{i,j-1/2,k}} p_{i,j-1,k} + T_{lx_{i-1/2,j,k}} p_{i-1,j,k}$$
$$- \left(T_{lz_{i,j,k-1/2}} + T_{ly_{i,j-1/2,k}} + T_{lx_{i-1/2,j,k}} + T_{lx_{i+1/2,j,k}} + T_{ly_{i,j+1/2,k}} + T_{lz_{i,j,k+1/2}}\right) p_{i,j,k}$$
$$+ T_{lx_{i+1/2,j,k}} p_{i+1,j,k} + T_{ly_{i,j+1/2,k}} p_{i,j+1,k} + T_{lz_{i,j,k+1/2}} p_{i,j,k+1}$$
$$= - q_{lsc_{i,j,k}}. \quad \text{(8.19)}$$

With the matrix notation discussed in Sec. 7.2, Eq. 8.19 can be written as

$$B_{i,j,k} p_{i,j,k-1} + S_{i,j,k} p_{i,j-1,k} + W_{i,j,k} p_{i-1,j,k} + C_{i,j,k} p_{i,j,k}$$
$$+ E_{i,j,k} p_{i+1,j,k} + N_{i,j,k} p_{i,j+1,k} + A_{i,j,k} p_{i,j,k+1} = Q_{i,j,k}, \quad \text{(8.20)}$$

where

$$B_{i,j,k} = T_{lz_{i,j,k-1/2}} = \left(\beta_c \frac{A_z k_z}{\mu_l B_l \Delta z}\right)_{i,j,k-1/2}, \quad \text{(8.21)}$$

$$S_{i,j,k} = T_{ly_{i,j-1/2,k}} = \left(\beta_c \frac{A_y k_y}{\mu_l B_l \Delta y}\right)_{i,j-1/2,k}, \quad \text{(8.22)}$$

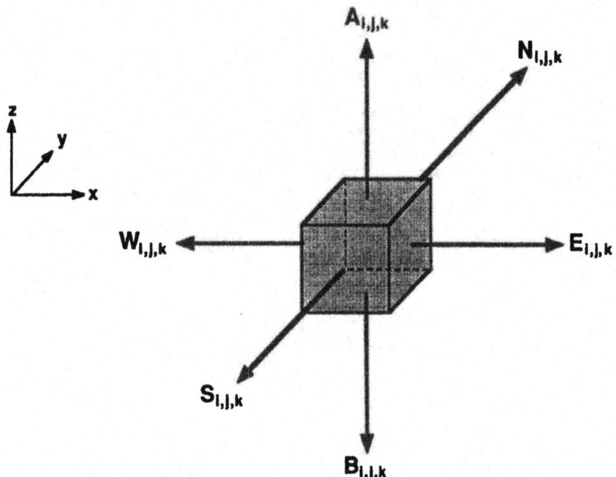

Fig. 8.4—Matrix coefficients.

$$W_{i,j,k} = \mathrm{T}_{lx_{i-½,j,k}} = \left(\beta_c \frac{A_x k_x}{\mu_l B_l \Delta x}\right)_{i-½,j,k}, \quad \text{(8.23)}$$

$$E_{i,j,k} = \mathrm{T}_{lx_{i+½,j,k}} = \left(\beta_c \frac{A_x k_x}{\mu_l B_l \Delta x}\right)_{i+½,j,k}, \quad \text{(8.24)}$$

$$N_{i,j,k} = \mathrm{T}_{ly_{i,j+½,k}} = \left(\beta_c \frac{A_y k_y}{\mu_l B_l \Delta y}\right)_{i,j+½,k}, \quad \text{(8.25)}$$

$$A_{i,j,k} = \mathrm{T}_{lz_{i,j,k+½}} = \left(\beta_c \frac{A_z k_z}{\mu_l B_l \Delta z}\right)_{i,j,k+½}, \quad \text{(8.26)}$$

$$C_{i,j,k} = -\left(B_{i,j,k} + S_{i,j,k} + W_{i,j,k} + E_{i,j,k} + N_{i,j,k} + A_{i,j,k}\right), \quad \text{(8.27)}$$

and $Q_{i,j,k} = -q_{lsc_{i,j,k}}$. .... (8.28)

As **Fig. 8.4** shows, the matrix coefficients describe the interaction of the central gridblock (i,j,k) with its six surrounding gridblocks in 3D flow geometry. Because μ_l and B_l are constants for incompressible flow, no pressure or time level needs to be assigned to the transmissibilities or matrix coefficients. Consequently, Eq. 8.20 is a linear equation and no further linearization is required for the incompressible-flow problem.

It is important to note that the definitions of $C_{i,j,k}$ and $Q_{i,j,k}$ as given by Eqs. 8.27 and 8.28 are valid for gridblocks containing rate-specified wells and for gridblocks with no wells. For gridblocks containing pressure-specified wells, $q_{lsc_{i,j,k}}$ is unknown; therefore, these definitions of $C_{i,j,k}$ and $Q_{i,j,k}$ will apply only if $q_{lsc_{i,j,k}}$ is evaluated iteratively. An alternative approach, which does not require iteration, is to substitute the inflow-performance relationship, Eq. 6.93, into Eq. 8.18 for the $q_{lsc_{i,j,k}}$ entry. This results in the following definitions of $C_{i,j,k}$ and $Q_{i,j,k}$.

$$C_{i,j,k} = -\left(B_{i,j,k} + S_{i,j,k} + W_{i,j,k} + E_{i,j,k} + N_{i,j,k} + A_{i,j,k} + J_{w_{i,j,k}}\right) \quad \text{(8.29)}$$

and $Q_{i,j,k} = -J_{w_{i,j,k}} p_{wf_{i,j,k}}$. .... (8.30)

For layered systems, calculation of $p_{wf_{i,j,k}}$ is described in Chap. 6.

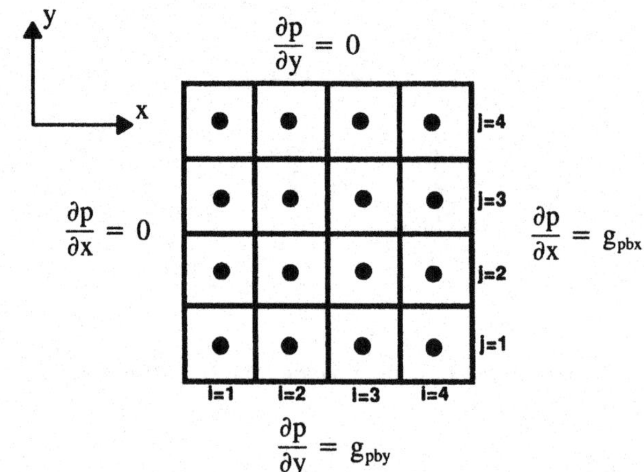

Fig. 8.5—Implementation of Neumann-type boundary condition.

The matrix notation defined by Eqs. 8.21 through 8.30 offers flexibility in writing Eq. 8.20 for multidimensional systems and in handling no-flow boundary conditions. For example, to express Eq. 8.20 in two dimensions (x and y directions), we set $B_{i,j,k}$ and $A_{i,j,k}$ coefficients equal to zero and drop the subscript k because there is no flow in the z direction. Thus, the 2D form of the equation becomes

$$S_{i,j}p_{i,j-1} + W_{i,j}p_{i-1,j} + C_{i,j}p_{i,j} + E_{i,j}p_{i+1,j} + N_{i,j}p_{i,j+1} = Q_{i,j}. \quad \text{(8.31)}$$

Similarly, Eq. 8.31 can be reduced to 1D form (x direction) by setting $S_{i,j}$ and $N_{i,j}$ coefficients to zero and dropping subscript j, which yields

$$W_i p_{i-1} + C_i p_i + E_i p_{i+1} = Q_i. \quad \text{(8.32)}$$

When we assign zero coefficients to reduce the dimensionality of a flow problem, we assign no-flow boundaries in the directions where flow does not occur.

As discussed in Chap. 7, Eq. 8.20 has seven unknowns and, when written for the entire grid system with natural ordering, generates a heptadiagonal coefficient matrix (Fig. 7.16c). Eqs. 8.31 and 8.32 have five and three unknowns, respectively, and will generate pentadiagonal (Fig. 7.16b) and tridiagonal (Fig. 7.16a) coefficient matrices.

8.2.4 Handling Boundary Conditions With Matrix Notation. If a Dirichlet-type boundary condition (constant pressure) is specified on the external boundaries of the system, gridpoints located on the boundaries are not unknowns. Therefore, after the proper transmissibility terms are calculated, they are carried to the right side of the characteristic finite-difference equation.

If a Neumann-type boundary condition (constant rate) is specified across the external boundaries of the reservoir, matrix notation facilitates the implementation of the boundary condition in the characteristic finite-difference equation. The 2D problem in **Fig. 8.5** illustrates this.

In this example, fluid can enter or leave the system across the lower and right boundaries of the system. The upper and left boundaries of the system are no-flow boundaries.

Eq. 8.31 gives the characteristic finite-difference equation for this system. For the gridblocks located on $i=1$, the W coefficient can be set equal to zero. When the W coefficient is set equal to zero in Eq. 8.31, W must also be set equal to zero in Eq. 8.27. This is handled implicitly if the transmissibility, $\mathrm{T}_{lx_{i-½,j}}$, is set equal to zero as in Example 5.5. Thus,

$$W_{1,j} = 0 \quad \text{(8.33)}$$

for $j=1$ through 4. Similarly, the N coefficient for the gridblocks located on $j=4$ will be zero; that is,

$$N_{i,4} = 0 \quad \text{(8.34)}$$

for $i=1$ through 4.

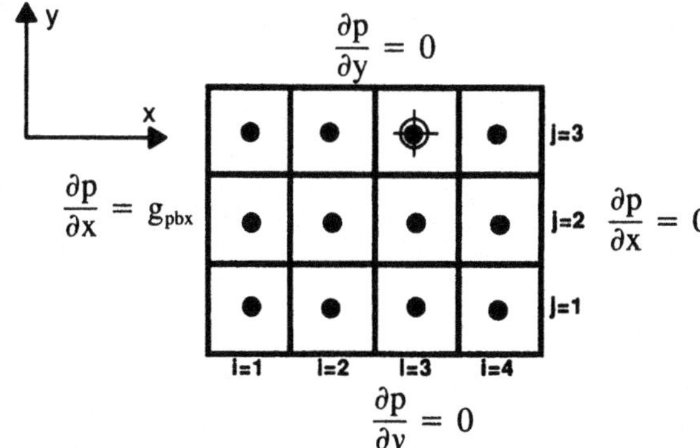

Fig. 8.6—Two-dimensional incompressible-flow problem.

For the lower and right boundaries, we use the reflection gridblocks as discussed in Sec. 5.5.2. For example,

$$\frac{p_{1,1} - p_{1,0}}{\Delta y} = g_{pby} \quad \text{.......................... (8.35)}$$

or $p_{1,0} = p_{1,1} - g_{pby}\Delta y$. Gridblock (1,0) is a reflection block adjacent to Gridblock (1,1). Similarly,

$$\frac{p_{5,4} - p_{4,4}}{\Delta x} = g_{pbx} \quad \text{.......................... (8.36)}$$

or $p_{5,4} = p_{4,4} + g_{pbx}\Delta x$. Gridblock (5,4) is a reflection gridblock adjacent to Gridblock (4,4).

The finite-difference equation for Gridblock (1,1) can be written as

$$S_{1,1}p_{1,0} + C_{1,1}p_{1,1} + E_{1,1}p_{2,1} + N_{1,1}p_{1,2} = Q_{1,1} \quad \text{... (8.37)}$$

$$\text{or } S_{1,1}\left(p_{1,1} - g_{pby}\Delta y\right) + C_{1,1}p_{1,1} + E_{1,1}p_{2,1} + N_{1,1}p_{1,2} = Q_{1,1}. \quad \text{.................... (8.38)}$$

It follows that

$$\left(C_{1,1} + S_{1,1}\right)p_{1,1} + E_{1,1}p_{2,1} + N_{1,1}p_{1,2} = Q_{1,1} + S_{1,1}g_{pby}\Delta y. \quad \text{.................... (8.39)}$$

Similarly, the finite-difference equation for Gridblock (4,4) is obtained as

$$S_{4,4}p_{4,3} + W_{4,4}p_{3,4} + \left(C_{4,4} + E_{4,4}\right)p_{4,4} = Q_{4,4} - E_{4,4}g_{pbx}\Delta x. \quad \text{.................... (8.40)}$$

8.2.5 Solution of the Finite-Difference Equations for Incompressible Flow. In this section, we present solution techniques for the finite-difference equations for the incompressible-flow problem. As discussed earlier, the finite-difference approximation of the incompressible-flow equation results in a system of linear equations. Chap. 7 discusses a number of approaches for the solution of systems of linear equations.

Consider a horizontal, 2D, incompressible-flow problem as shown in **Fig. 8.6**. The system has three external boundaries closed to flow and a pressure gradient specified on the fourth boundary. Furthermore, a well is located in Gridblock (3,3) with a specified production rate of q_{spsc}.

To find the pressure distribution within the system, we need to write Eq. 8.31 for every unknown gridblock. As discussed previously, the boundary conditions imposed on the system are taken into consideration when the characteristic equation is written for those gridblocks located on the boundaries of the system. Because there are 12 unknowns in the system, 12 equations are required to solve for the pressure distribution.

For Gridblock (1,1),

$$\left(C_{1,1} + W_{1,1}\right)p_{1,1} + E_{1,1}p_{2,1} + N_{1,1}p_{1,2} = g_{pbx}W_{1,1}\Delta x. \quad \text{.................... (8.41)}$$

For Gridblock (2,1),

$$W_{2,1}p_{1,1} + C_{2,1}p_{2,1} + E_{2,1}p_{3,1} + N_{2,1}p_{2,2} = 0. \quad \text{... (8.42)}$$

For Gridblock (3,1),

$$W_{3,1}p_{2,1} + C_{3,1}p_{3,1} + E_{3,1}p_{4,1} + N_{3,1}p_{3,2} = 0. \quad \text{.... (8.43)}$$

For Gridblock (4,1),

$$W_{4,1}p_{3,1} + C_{4,1}p_{4,1} + N_{4,1}p_{4,2} = 0. \quad \text{............. (8.44)}$$

For Gridblock (1,2),

$$S_{1,2}p_{1,1} + \left(C_{1,2} + W_{1,2}\right)p_{1,2} + E_{1,2}p_{2,2} + N_{1,2}p_{1,3} = g_{pbx}W_{1,2}\Delta x. \quad \text{........................... (8.45)}$$

For Gridblock (2,2),

$$S_{2,2}p_{2,1} + W_{2,2}p_{1,2} + C_{2,2}p_{2,2} + E_{2,2}p_{3,2} + N_{2,2}p_{2,3} = 0. \quad \text{.................... (8.46)}$$

For Gridblock (3,2),

$$S_{3,2}p_{3,1} + W_{3,2}p_{2,2} + C_{3,2}p_{3,2} + E_{3,2}p_{4,2} + N_{3,2}p_{3,3} = 0. \quad \text{.................... (8.47)}$$

For Gridblock (4,2),

$$S_{4,2}p_{4,1} + W_{4,2}p_{3,2} + C_{4,2}p_{4,2} + N_{4,2}p_{4,3} = 0. \quad \text{.... (8.48)}$$

For Gridblock (1,3),

$$S_{1,3}p_{1,2} + \left(C_{1,3} + W_{1,3}\right)p_{1,3} + E_{1,3}p_{2,3} = g_{pbx}W_{1,3}\Delta x. \quad \text{.................... (8.49)}$$

For Gridblock (2,3),

$$S_{2,3}p_{2,2} + W_{2,3}p_{1,3} + C_{2,3}p_{2,3} + E_{2,3}p_{3,3} = 0. \quad \text{.. (8.50)}$$

For Gridblock (3,3),

$$S_{3,3}p_{3,2} + W_{3,3}p_{2,3} + C_{3,3}p_{3,3} + E_{3,3}p_{4,3} = -q_{spsc}. \quad \text{.................... (8.51)}$$

For Gridblock (4,3),

$$S_{4,3}p_{4,2} + W_{4,3}p_{3,3} + C_{4,3}p_{4,3} = 0. \quad \text{............. (8.52)}$$

Fig. 8.7 shows Eqs. 8.41 through 8.52 in 12 unknowns in matrix form.

The external-boundary conditions are introduced into the finite-difference equations through the boundary-block equations. For example, the finite-difference equations for Gridblocks (1,1), (2,1), (3,1), and (4,1)—Eqs. 8.41 through 8.44—do not have S coefficients because a no-flow condition is specified along the lower boundary of the system. For the same reason, Eqs. 8.44, 8.48, and 8.52 for Gridblocks (4,1), (4,2), and (4,3) do not have any E coefficients, and Eqs. 8.49 through 8.52 for Gridblocks (1,3), (2,3), (3,3), and (4,3) do not have N coefficients. The $\partial p/\partial x = g_{pbx}$ condition imposed on the left boundary of the system is implemented when the finite-difference equations for Gridblocks (1,1), (1,2), and (1,3)—Eqs. 8.41, 8.45, and 8.49—are written. In these equations, the W coefficients are combined with the C coefficients and nonzero entries appear on the right side. The internal-boundary condition created by the well in Gridblock (3,3) is taken into consideration by

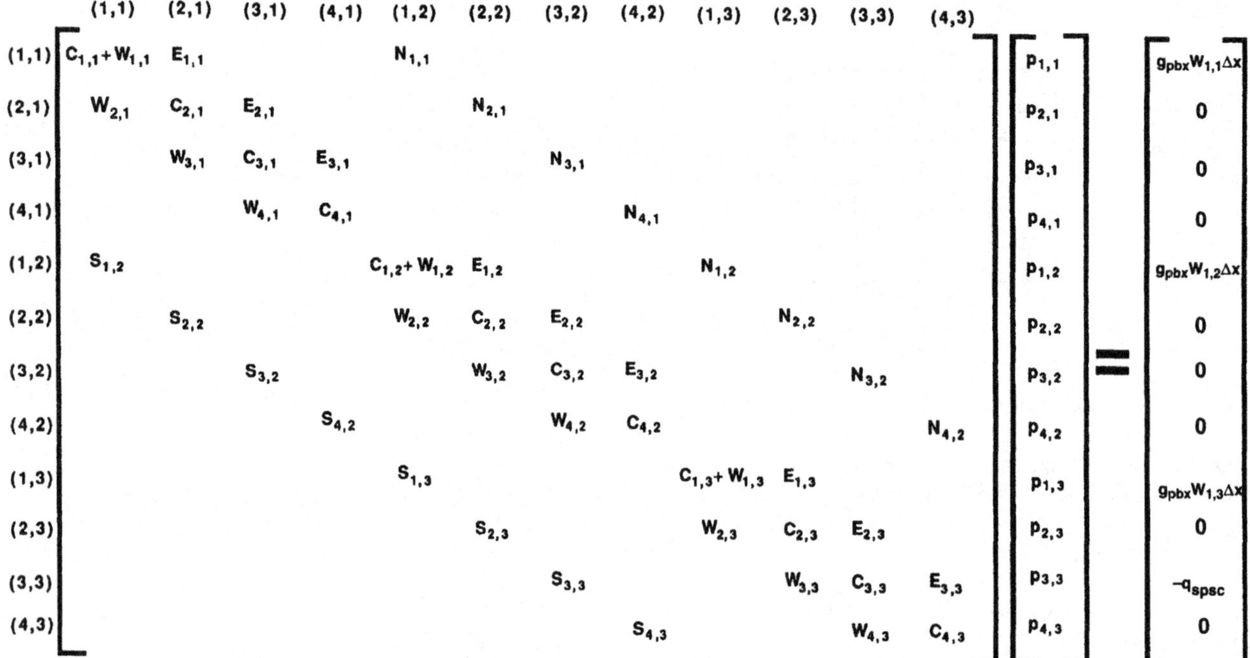

Fig. 8.7—Matrix representation of the 2D incompressible-flow problem in Fig. 8.6.

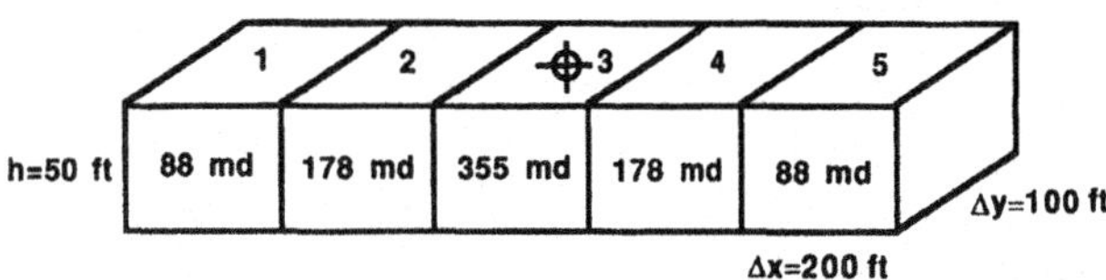

Fig. 8.8—Schematic representation of the reservoir described in Example 8.2.

entering the specified flow rate on the right side of Eq. 8.51. The matrix equation shown in Fig. 8.7 now can be solved with one of the direct or iterative methods discussed in Chap. 7. This process is illustrated further for simple 1D problems in Examples 8.2 and 8.3.

Example 8.2. Consider the 1D, single-phase, incompressible-fluid flow in the horizontal reservoir shown in **Fig. 8.8**. Gridblocks 1 and 5 are located at the boundaries of the reservoir and maintained at 3,000 psia. A production well is located in the center of Gridblock 3 and produced at a rate of 2,000 STB/D. As Fig. 8.8 shows, all gridblocks have uniform dimensions. The permeability distribution in the reservoir has a symmetry variation of $k_{x_1}=88$ md, $k_{x_2}=178$ md, $k_{x_3}=355$ md, $k_{x_4}=178$ md, and $k_{x_5}=88$ md.

With the appropriate PDE and the corresponding finite-difference approximation, calculate the pressure distribution in the system. Devise a procedure to check your solution. The fluid viscosity is 1 cp.

Solution. In this problem, the gridblock dimensions, permeability distribution, and assigned boundary conditions are all symmetrical with respect to the center of Gridblock 3. Therefore, the pressure in Gridblock 2 is expected to be equal to the pressure of Gridblock 4. Thus, Gridblocks 2 and 3 are the only unknowns of the problem. We start with the 1D, single-phase, incompressible-flow equation obtained from Eq. 8.3,

$$\frac{\partial}{\partial x}\left(\beta_c \frac{A_x k_x}{\mu_l B_l}\frac{\partial p}{\partial x}\right)\Delta x + q_{lsc} = 0. \quad \ldots\ldots\ldots\ldots\ldots\ldots (8.53)$$

The finite-difference approximation for this equation can be obtained from Eq. 8.19 as

$$\mathrm{T}_{lx_{i-½}}p_{i-1} - \left(\mathrm{T}_{lx_{i-½}} + \mathrm{T}_{lx_{i+½}}\right)p_i + \mathrm{T}_{lx_{i+½}}p_{i+1} = -\,q_{lsc_i} \quad \ldots\ldots\ldots\ldots\ldots\ldots (8.54)$$

or, in matrix notation,

$$W_i p_{i-1} + C_i p_i + E_i p_{i+1} = Q_i, \quad \ldots\ldots\ldots\ldots\ldots\ldots (8.55)$$

$$\text{where } \mathrm{T}_{lx_{i\pm½}} = \left(\beta_c \frac{A_x k_x}{\mu_l B_l \Delta x}\right)_{i\pm½}. \quad \ldots\ldots\ldots\ldots\ldots\ldots (8.56)$$

$A_x/(\mu_l B_l \Delta x)$ is constant for the entire grid system; therefore,

$$\mathrm{T}_{lx_{i\pm½}} = \left(\beta_c \frac{A_x}{\mu_l B_l \Delta x}\right)\left(k_{x_{i\pm½}}\right). \quad \ldots\ldots\ldots\ldots\ldots\ldots (8.57)$$

Now, we can calculate $k_{x_{i+½}}$ for $i=1, 2$ with the harmonic averaging technique (see Example 8.1 and Example 9.16, Part 4).

For $i=1$,

$$\frac{1}{k_{x_{1+½}}} = \frac{1}{2}\left(\frac{1}{0.088} + \frac{1}{0.178}\right)$$

or $k_{x_{1+½}} = 0.118$ darcy.

With the units in Table 4.1, applying Eq. 8.57 for $i=1$ gives (recall that $B_l=1$ for the isothermal incompressible-flow problem)

$$\mathrm{T}_{lx_{1+½}} = 1.127\left[\frac{100\times 50}{(1)(1)(200)}\right](0.118) = 3.32 \text{ STB/D-psi}.$$

Similarly, for $i=2$,

$$\frac{1}{k_{x_{2+½}}} = \frac{1}{2}\left(\frac{1}{0.178} + \frac{1}{0.355}\right)$$

or $k_{x_{2+½}} = 0.237$ darcy.

Again, with the units in Table 4.1, applying Eq. 8.57 for $i=2$ gives

$$\mathrm{T}_{lx_{2+½}} = 1.127\left[\frac{100\times 50}{(1)(1)(200)}\right](0.237) = 6.68 \text{ STB/D-psi}.$$

We can write the characteristic finite-difference equation, Eq. 8.54, for $i=2$ as

$$\mathrm{T}_{lx_{1+½}}p_1 - \left(\mathrm{T}_{lx_{1+½}} + \mathrm{T}_{lx_{2+½}}\right)p_2 + \mathrm{T}_{lx_{2+½}}p_3 = -\,q_{lsc_2}, \quad \ldots\ldots\ldots\ldots\ldots\ldots (8.58)$$

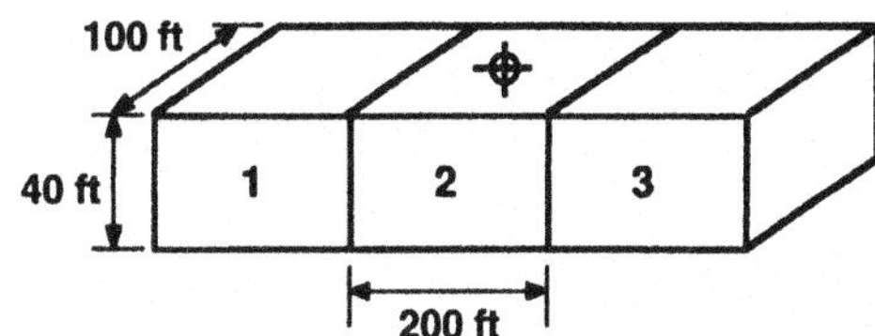

Fig. 8.9—Physical system described in Example 8.3.

which yields $3.32 \times 3,000 - (3.32 + 6.68)p_2 + 6.68p_3 = 0$ or $-10.00p_2 + 6.68p_3 = -9,960$.
For $i=3$,

$$\mathrm{T}_{lx_{2+½}}p_2 - \left(\mathrm{T}_{lx_{2+½}} + \mathrm{T}_{lx_{3+½}}\right)p_3 + \mathrm{T}_{lx_{3+½}}p_4 = -q_{lsc_3}. \quad \ldots\ldots\ldots\ldots (8.59)$$

Because of symmetry, $p_4=p_2$ and $\mathrm{T}_{lx_{3+½}} = \mathrm{T}_{lx_{2+½}}=6.68$, which results in $6.68p_2 - (6.68 + 6.68)p_3 + 6.68p_2 = -(-2,000)$ or $13.36p_2 - 13.36p_3 = 2,000$. At this point, all the necessary equations are generated.

$$-10.00p_2 + 6.68p_3 = -9,960$$

and $13.36p_2 - 13.36p_3 = 2,000$.

Solving the two equations simultaneously, we obtain $p_2 = 2,698.8$ psia (remember $p_2 = p_4$) and $p_3=2,549.1$ psia.

A material-balance check on the system can be conducted as follows. Because flow is incompressible, the total amount of fluid supplied by Gridblocks 1 and 5 to Gridblocks 2 and 4, respectively, should be equal to the fluid produced at the wellbore (in a single-phase incompressible-flow system, no fluid accumulation is possible). With the linear form of Darcy's law between Gridblocks 1 and 2, the flow rate entering the system from Gridblock 1 can be calculated as

$$q_{lsc} = \beta_c \frac{A_x k_{x_{1+½}}}{\mu_l B_l} \frac{(p_1 - p_2)}{\Delta x} = T_{lx_{1+½}}(p_1 - p_2) \quad \ldots\ldots (8.60)$$

$$= 3.32(3,000 - 2,698.8) = 999.98 \text{ STB/D}.$$

This flow rate represents one-half the total fluid entering the system. Because of symmetry, a similar volume of fluid will be supplied to the system by Gridblock 5. Therefore, the total amount of fluid entering the system is 1,999.96 STB/D, which agrees very closely with the specified production rate of 2,000 STB/D. The small discrepancy of -0.04 STB/D is caused by the cumulative roundoff error encountered in the computations. This results in an error of

$$\frac{2,000 - 1,999.96}{2,000} \times 100 = 0.002\%.$$

The calculated error is the material-balance error because it is a measure of the mass conserved during the computations. This topic is discussed in Sec. 8.2.7 and Example 8.5.

Example 8.3. Consider the incompressible-fluid flow in the 1D, homogeneous, horizontal porous medium shown in **Fig. 8.9**. The fluid viscosity is 2 cp. Answer the following questions.

1. If the well in Gridblock 2 is produced at a constant rate of 450 STB/D, which creates a pressure distribution of $p_1=2,400$ psia, $p_2=800$ psia, and $p_3=1,600$ psia, and if the boundary conditions at both extremes of the system are unknown, what is the permeability of the system?
2. What kind of boundary condition would you assign to the extreme left of the system if the right boundary is closed to flow?
3. If the dimensions of all gridblocks are doubled, what is the flow rate into the well if the same pressure distribution is assigned to the system as in Part 1?
4. Assume that the viscosity of the fluid is 4 cp and the wellblock is kept at 800 psia. Further assume that the extreme ends of the system represent no-flow boundaries. Under these conditions, what is the flow rate into the well and the pressures of Gridblocks 1 and 2?

Solution.

1. The PDE that describes this problem is obtained from Eq. 8.3 as

$$\frac{\partial}{\partial x}\left(\beta_c \frac{A_x k_x}{\mu_l B_l}\frac{\partial p}{\partial x}\right)\Delta x + q_{lsc} = 0. \quad \ldots\ldots\ldots\ldots (8.53)$$

The finite-difference equation, which corresponds to Eq. 8.53, may be obtained from Eq. 8.19 as

$$\mathrm{T}_{lx_{i-½}}p_{i-1} - \left(\mathrm{T}_{lx_{i-½}} + \mathrm{T}_{lx_{i+½}}\right)p_i + \mathrm{T}_{lx_{i+½}}p_{i+1} = -q_{lsc_i} \quad \ldots\ldots\ldots\ldots (8.54)$$

or, in matrix notation, as

$$W_i p_{i-1} + C_i p_i + E_i p_{i+1} = Q_i, \quad \ldots\ldots\ldots\ldots (8.55)$$

$$\text{where } \mathrm{T}_{lx_{i\pm½}} = \left(\beta_c \frac{A_x k_x}{\mu_l B_l \Delta x}\right)_{i\pm½} = \beta_c \frac{A_x k_x}{\mu_l B_l \Delta x} \quad \ldots\ldots (8.56)$$

for all values of $i=1,2,3$ because A_x, k_x, Δx, μ_l, and B_l are constant.

$$\mathrm{T}_{lx_{i\pm½}} = 1.127\left[\frac{(100 \times 40)(k_x)}{(2)(1)(200)}\right] = 11.27k_x, \quad \ldots\ldots (8.61)$$

where k_x is in darcies.

Substituting Eq. 8.61 into Eq. 8.54 for Gridblock 2 gives

$$(11.27k_x)p_1 - (2 \times 11.27k_x)p_2 + (11.27k_x)p_3 = -(-450). \quad \ldots\ldots\ldots\ldots (8.62)$$

For the given pressure distribution, this equation becomes $(11.27k_x)(2,400) - (2\times 11.27k_x)(800) + (11.27k_x)(1,600) = 450$, which can be solved for $k_x=0.016637$ darcy.

2. Because the well is produced at a rate of 450 STB/D and the right side of the system is closed to flow, 450 STB/D of fluid enters through the left boundary of the system. A pressure gradient must exist across the extreme left boundary for this to occur. This gradient can be quantified as

$$q_{lsc} = -\left(\beta_c \frac{A_x k_x}{\mu_l B_l}\right)\frac{\partial p}{\partial x}, \quad \ldots\ldots\ldots\ldots (8.63)$$

which may also be obtained from

$$q_{lsc} = -\mathrm{T}_{lx_{0+½}}\Delta x \frac{\partial p}{\partial x}\Big|_{x=0} \quad \ldots\ldots\ldots\ldots (8.64)$$

$$\text{or } q_{lsc} = -\mathrm{T}_{lx_{0+½}}\Delta x \frac{(p_1 - p_0)}{\Delta x}, \quad \ldots\ldots\ldots\ldots (8.65)$$

where $\mathrm{T}_{lx_{0+½}} = 11.27k_x = 11.27 \times 0.016637 = 0.1875$ STB/D-psi. Now, $450 = -(0.1875)(200)(\partial p/\partial x)|_{x=0}$, which gives $(\partial p/\partial x)|_{x=0} = -12.0$ psi/ft.

3. Examination of Eq. 8.54 for a fixed-pressure distribution reveals that q_{lsc_i} is proportional to the transmissibility given by Eq. 8.56 for this system. We observe that if the gridblock dimensions are doubled, A_x will quadruple and Δx will double. Because $\mathrm{T}_{lx_{i\pm½}} = \beta_c(A_x k_x/\mu_l B_l \Delta x)$, $\mathrm{T}_{lx_{i\pm½}}$ will only double, which will double q_{lsc_i} on the right side of Eq. 8.54. In other words, $q_{lsc_2} = -2 \times 450 = -900$ STB/D or, more explicitly,

$$\mathrm{T}_{lx_{i\pm½}} = 1.127\frac{(200 \times 80)(0.016637)}{(2)(1)(400)} = 0.375 \text{ STB/D-psi},$$

which, when substituted into Eq. 8.54, gives $(0.375)(2,400) - (2\times 0.375)(800) + (0.375)(1,600) = -q_{lsc_2}$ or $q_{lsc_2} = -900$ STB/D. Therefore, the production rate doubles to 900 STB/D.

4. Because both boundaries of the system are closed to flow, no fluid will enter the system and the flow rate from the well will be zero. This indicates that there is no pressure gradient in the system. In other words, $p_1=p_2=p_3=800$ psia.

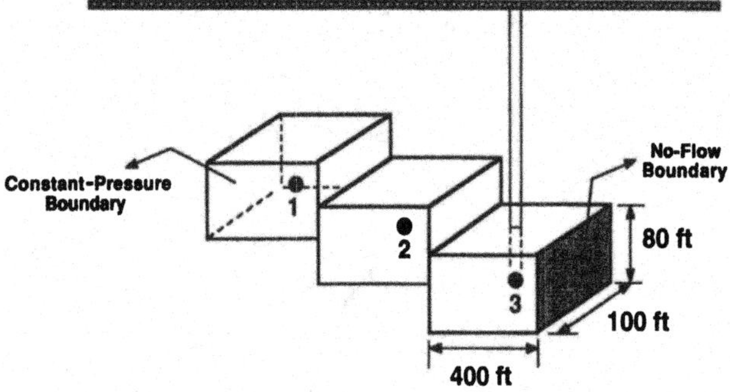

Fig. 8.10—Inclined reservoir described in Example 8.4.

8.2.6 Incompressible-Flow Equation in the Presence of Depth Gradients. To this point, we have assumed that the pressure gradient and potential gradient were the same; that is, the effects of fluid gravity and reservoir depths in Eq. 8.1 were neglected. In this section the importance of potential gradients is highlighted. The relationship between potential and pressure from Eq. 2.14 is

$$\Phi_l - \Phi_l^\circ = p - p^\circ - \gamma_l Z, \quad\text{.................... (8.66)}$$

and the relationship between the potential and pressure gradient given from Eq. 2.15 is

$$\vec{\nabla}\Phi_l = \vec{\nabla}p - \gamma_l\vec{\nabla}Z. \quad\text{.......................... (8.67)}$$

Eq. 8.2,

$$\frac{\partial}{\partial x}\left[\beta_c\frac{A_x k_x}{\mu_l B_l}\left(\frac{\partial p}{\partial x} - \gamma_l\frac{\partial Z}{\partial x}\right)\right]\Delta x + \frac{\partial}{\partial y}\left[\beta_c\frac{A_y k_y}{\mu_l B_l}\left(\frac{\partial p}{\partial y} - \gamma_l\frac{\partial Z}{\partial y}\right)\right]\Delta y$$

$$+ \frac{\partial}{\partial z}\left[\beta_c\frac{A_z k_z}{\mu_l B_l}\left(\frac{\partial p}{\partial z} - \gamma_l\frac{\partial Z}{\partial z}\right)\right]\Delta z + q_{lsc} = 0, \quad\text{..... (8.2)}$$

can be rearranged by moving the gravity-head terms to the right side.

$$\frac{\partial}{\partial x}\left(\beta_c\frac{A_x k_x}{\mu_l B_l}\frac{\partial p}{\partial x}\right)\Delta x + \frac{\partial}{\partial y}\left(\beta_c\frac{A_y k_y}{\mu_l B_l}\frac{\partial p}{\partial y}\right)\Delta y$$

$$+ \frac{\partial}{\partial z}\left(\beta_c\frac{A_z k_z}{\mu_l B_l}\frac{\partial p}{\partial z}\right)\Delta z + q_{lsc}$$

$$= \frac{\partial}{\partial x}\left(\beta_c\frac{A_x k_x}{\mu_l B_l}\gamma_l\frac{\partial Z}{\partial x}\right)\Delta x + \frac{\partial}{\partial y}\left(\beta_c\frac{A_y k_y}{\mu_l B_l}\gamma_l\frac{\partial Z}{\partial y}\right)\Delta y$$

$$+ \frac{\partial}{\partial z}\left(\beta_c\frac{A_z k_z}{\mu_l B_l}\gamma_l\frac{\partial Z}{\partial z}\right)\Delta z. \quad\text{.................... (8.68)}$$

Now we can proceed with the finite-difference representation of Eq. 8.68. The left side of the equation can be written in matrix notation as in Eq. 8.20. In other words, with the exception of the $Q_{i,j,k}$ term, it is possible to use the same definitions for the remaining matrix coefficients as follows.

$$B_{i,j,k}p_{i,j,k-1} + S_{i,j,k}p_{,i,j-1,k} + W_{i,j,k}p_{i-1,j,k} + C_{i,j,k}p_{i,j,k}$$

$$+ E_{i,j,k}p_{i+1,j,k} + N_{i,j,k}p_{i,j+1,k} + A_{i,j,k}p_{i,j,k+1}$$

$$= -q_{lsc_{i,j,k}} + \left(\beta_c\frac{A_x k_x}{\mu_l B_l \Delta x}\gamma_l\right)_{i+½,j,k}\left(Z_{i+1,j,k} - Z_{i,j,k}\right)$$

$$-\left(\beta_c\frac{A_x k_x}{\mu_l B_l \Delta x}\gamma_l\right)_{i-½,j,k}\left(Z_{i,j,k} - Z_{i-1,j,k}\right)$$

$$+\left(\beta_c\frac{A_y k_y}{\mu_l B_l \Delta y}\gamma_l\right)_{i,j+½,k}\left(Z_{i,j+1,k} - Z_{i,j,k}\right)$$

$$-\left(\beta_c\frac{A_y k_y}{\mu_l B_l \Delta y}\gamma_l\right)_{i,j-½,k}\left(Z_{i,j,k} - Z_{i,j-1,k}\right)$$

$$+\left(\beta_c\frac{A_z k_z}{\mu_l B_l \Delta z}\gamma_l\right)_{i,j,k+½}\left(Z_{i,j,k+1} - Z_{i,j,k}\right)$$

$$-\left(\beta_c\frac{A_z k_z}{\mu_l B_l \Delta z}\gamma_l\right)_{i,j,k-½}\left(Z_{i,j,k} - Z_{i,j,k-1}\right), \quad\text{........ (8.69)}$$

or we can develop a new definition of the coefficient $Q_{G_{i,j,k}}$.

$$Q_{G_{i,j,k}} = B_{G_{i,j,k}}Z_{i,j,k-1} + S_{G_{i,j,k}}Z_{i,j-1,k} + W_{G_{i,j,k}}Z_{i-1,j,k}$$

$$+ C_{G_{i,j,k}}Z_{i,j,k} + E_{G_{i,j,k}}Z_{i+1,j,k} + N_{G_{i,j,k}}Z_{i,j+1,k}$$

$$+ A_{G_{i,j,k}}Z_{i,j,k+1} \quad\text{........................ (8.70)}$$

and $Q_{i,j,k} = -q_{lsc_{i,j,k}} + Q_{G_{i,j,k}}$, ... (8.71)

where

$$B_{G_{i,j,k}} = \gamma_{l_{i,j,k-½}}B_{i,j,k}, \quad\text{........................ (8.72)}$$

$$S_{G_{i,j,k}} = \gamma_{l_{i,j-½,k}}S_{i,j,k}, \quad\text{........................ (8.73)}$$

$$W_{G_{i,j,k}} = \gamma_{l_{i-½,j,k}}W_{i,j,k}, \quad\text{........................ (8.74)}$$

$$E_{G_{i,j,k}} = \gamma_{l_{i+½,j,k}}E_{i,j,k}, \quad\text{........................ (8.75)}$$

$$N_{G_{i,j,k}} = \gamma_{l_{i,j+½,k}}N_{i,j,k}, \quad\text{........................ (8.76)}$$

$$A_{G_{i,j,k}} = \gamma_{l_{i,j,k+½}}A_{i,j,k}, \quad\text{........................ (8.77)}$$

and $C_{G_{i,j,k}} = -\left(B_{G_{i,j,k}} + S_{G_{i,j,k}} + W_{G_{i,j,k}} + E_{G_{i,j,k}}\right.$

$$\left. + N_{G_{i,j,k}} + A_{G_{i,j,k}}\right). \quad\text{.................... (8.78)}$$

Now Eq. 8.69 can be written with matrix notation as

$$B_{i,j,k}p_{i,j,k-1} + S_{i,j,k}p_{i,j-1,k} + W_{i,j,k}p_{i-1,j,k} + C_{i,j,k}p_{i,j,k}$$

$$+ E_{i,j,k}p_{i+1,j,k} + N_{i,j,k}p_{i,j+1,k} + A_{i,j,k}p_{i,j,k+1} = Q_{i,j,k}. \quad\text{.................... (8.79)}$$

In summary, the only difference between Eqs. 8.20 and 8.79 is the definition of the respective right sides. This development assumes rate specification at the wells. For pressure-specified wells, the inflow-performance relationship should be used to modify the definitions of $C_{i,j,k}$ and $Q_{i,j,k}$. Example 8.4 illustrates the importance of elevation gradients when they exist.

Example 8.4. Consider the 1D, inclined reservoir shown in **Fig. 8.10**. In this simplified system, Gridblock 1 represents a constant-pressure boundary and a production well is located in Gridblock 3. The depths to the centers of Gridblocks 1 through 3 are 2,480 ft,

2,540 ft, and 2,580 ft, respectively. A no-flow boundary is on the extreme right side of the system and the pressure of Gridblock 1 is maintained at 2,000 psia by a strong waterdrive. The dimensions of all gridblocks are $\Delta x = 400$ ft, $w = 100$ ft, and $h = 80$ ft. Permeability in the x direction is constant and equals 60 md. The well in Gridblock 3 is produced at a rate of 200 STB/D, and the fluid properties are $\mu_l = 1$ cp, $B_l = 1$ RB/STB, $\rho_l = 62.4$ lbm/ft^3, and $c_l = 0$ psi^{-1}.

Find the pressure distribution in the system by use of the point successive overrelaxation (PSOR) method with ω_{opt}. Use a tolerance of 0.01 to stabilize the spectral radius and a pressure tolerance of 1 psi as the convergence criterion. Include the effects of the elevation gradient in the calculations.

Solution. The 1D form of the incompressible-flow equation is

$$\frac{\partial}{\partial x}\left[\beta_c \frac{A_x k_x}{\mu_l B_l}\left(\frac{\partial p}{\partial x} - \gamma_l \frac{\partial Z}{\partial x}\right)\right]\Delta x + q_{lsc} = 0. \quad \text{.......... (8.80)}$$

The finite-difference approximation to this equation with matrix notation is obtained from Eq. 8.79 as

$$W_i p_{i-1} + C_i p_i + E_i p_{i+1} = Q_i, \quad \text{................ (8.55)}$$

$$\text{where } Q_i = -q_{lsc_i} + W_{G_i} Z_{i-1} + C_{G_i} Z_i + E_{G_i} Z_{i+1}. \quad \text{.................... (8.81)}$$

We now calculate Q_i and the coefficients W, C, and E as defined earlier with the units in Table 4.1. Because A_x, k_x, Δx, μ_l, and B_l are constant,

$$W_i = \left(\beta_c \frac{A_x k_x}{\mu_l B_l \Delta x}\right)_{i-½} \quad \text{...................... (8.82)}$$

$$= 1.127 \frac{(100)(80)(0.06)}{(1)(1)(400)} = 1.352,$$

for $i = 1,2,3$. Also, $E_i = 1.352$ for Gridblocks $i = 1,2$ and $E_i = 0$ for Gridblock $i = 3$. Because $C_i = -(W_i + E_i)$, $C_2 = -2.704$ and $C_3 = -1.352$. We now calculate W_G, E_G, C_G, and the right side of the equation, the Q term. First calculate γ_l using Eq. 2.20 and Table 4.1.

$$\gamma_l = \left(0.21584 \times 10^{-3}\right)(62.4)(32.17) = 0.4333 \text{ psi/ft}.$$

$$W_{G_2} = \gamma_l W_2 \quad \text{.............................. (8.83)}$$

$$= (0.4333)(1.352) = 0.586.$$

$$W_{G_3} = \gamma_l W_3 \quad \text{.............................. (8.84)}$$

$$= (0.4333)(1.352) = 0.586.$$

Similarly, $E_{G2} = 0.586$ and $E_{G3} = 0$. Because $C_{G_i} = -(W_{G_i} + E_{G_i})$, $C_{G_2} = -1.172$ and $C_{G_3} = -0.586$.

Now, we can write the finite-difference equation for Gridblocks 2 and 3 because p_2 and p_3 are the unknowns of the problem. The matrix coefficients for Gridblock 2 are $W_2 = 1.352, W_{G_2} = 0.586$, $C_2 = -2.704$, $C_{G_2} = -1.172$, $E_2 = 1.352$, and $E_{G_2} = 0.586$. With the application of Eq. 8.81, Gridblock $i = 2$ gives

$$Q_2 = -0 + (0.586)(2,480) - (1.172)(2,540)$$

$$+ (0.586)(2,580)$$

$$= -11.720.$$

The matrix coefficients for Gridblock 3 are $W_3 = 1.352$, $W_{G_3} = 0.586$, $C_3 = -1.352$, $C_{G_3} = -0.586$, $E_3 = 0$, and $E_{G_3} = 0$. With the application of Eq. 8.81, Gridblock $i = 3$ gives

$$Q_3 = -(-200) + (0.586)(2,540) - (0.586)(2,580) + 0$$

$$= 176.56.$$

Finally, the two equations, in two unknowns, for Gridblocks 2 and 3 can be obtained by writing Eq. 8.55 for Gridblocks $i = 2,3$ as

$$(1.352)(2,000) - (2.704)p_2 + (1.352)p_3 = -11.720$$

$$\text{and } (1.352)p_2 - (1.352)p_3 = 176.56.$$

These two equations can be simplified to

$$-2p_2 + p_3 = -2,008.67$$

$$\text{and } p_2 - p_3 = 130.59.$$

The PSOR iterative equations (see Eq. 7.108) for this system of equations are

$$p_2^{(k+1)} = \frac{\omega_{opt}}{2}\left[\left(2,008.67 + p_3^{(k)}\right)\right] + \left(1 - \omega_{opt}\right)p_2^{(k)} \quad \text{.................... (8.85)}$$

$$\text{and } p_3^{(k+1)} = \frac{\omega_{opt}}{1}\left[130.59 + p_2^{(k+1)}\right] + \left(1 - \omega_{opt}\right)p_3^{(k)}. \quad \text{.................... (8.86)}$$

We start the calculations with an initial guess of 1,600 psia for the pressure of both gridblocks. **Table 8.1** summarizes the results at the end of each iteration and shows that the stabilized value for the spectral radius is obtained after the fourth iteration.

The spectral radius is approximated by use of Eq. 7.139 with $\rho_{GS} = 0.50$, and ω_{opt} is calculated with Eq. 7.138.

$$\rho_{GS} = \left|\frac{d^{(k+1)}}{d^{(k)}}\right|. \quad \text{............................ (7.139)}$$

$$\omega_{opt} = \frac{2}{1 + \sqrt{1 - \rho_{GS}}} \quad \text{...................... (7.138)}$$

$$= \frac{2}{1 + \sqrt{1 - 0.50}} = 1.172.$$

The pressure distribution for this problem is $p_1 = 2,000$ psia, $p_2 = 1,877.8$ psia, and $p_3 = 1,747.3$ psia.

8.2.7 Material-Balance Check for the Incompressible-Flow Problem. To check the validity of the final solution, the calculated pressures usually are checked to ensure that they satisfy material balance. Material balance is an engineering expression for the conservation of mass over a fixed control volume. In our case, the fixed control volume is the hydrocarbon reservoir. The material-balance check is the ratio of accumulation of mass to the net mass entering and leaving the boundaries of the reservoir. In the case of incompressible flow, this check becomes trivial because no fluid depletion or accumulation occurs within the reservoir. We simply need to compare the values of the total volume of fluid entering the reservoir

TABLE 8.1—SOLUTION FOR EXAMPLE 8.4

k	ω	p_2	p_3	$\lvert d^{(k)}\rvert$	ρ_{GS}
0	—	1,600.0	1,600.0	—	—
1	1	1,804.3	1,673.7	204.3	—
2	1	1,841.2	1,710.6	36.9	0.18
3	1	1,859.6	1,729.0	18.4	0.50
4	1	1,868.8	1,738.2	9.2	0.50
5	1.171	1,874.2	1,744.5	6.3	—
6	1.171	1,877.0	1,746.7	2.8	—
7	1.171	1,877.8	1,747.3	0.8	—

with the total volume of fluid leaving the reservoir. In other words, for a perfect material balance, the ratio of mass entering the reservoir to the mass leaving the reservoir is equal to unity. Because we use approximations in the solution process and because the computer carries only a finite number of digits, a perfect material balance can never be achieved.

Example 8.5. Conduct a material-balance check on the results of Example 8.4.

Solution. The amount of fluid leaving the reservoir is specified through the well-production rate in Gridblock 3 as 200 STB/D. The extreme right side of the system is closed to flow. The 200-STB/D fluid withdrawal from the reservoir must be replenished by fluid flow from Gridblock 1 to Gridblock 2. Therefore, by use of the calculated pressure of Gridblock 2 and specified pressure of Gridblock 1, the amount of fluid entering the reservoir can be calculated. Because $p_1 = 2{,}000$ psia and $p_2 = 1{,}877.8$ psia, the potential gradient between Gridblocks 1 and 2 can be calculated as

$$\frac{d\Phi_l}{dx} = (1{,}877.8 - 2{,}000)/400$$

$$- (0.4333)(2{,}540 - 2{,}480)/400$$

$$= -0.3705 \text{ psi/ft}.$$

With the linear form of Darcy's law, the rate of fluid flow from Gridblock 1 into Gridblock 2 can be calculated as

$$q_l = -\beta_c \frac{A_x k_x}{\mu_l B_l} \frac{d\Phi_l}{dx} \quad \text{.......... (8.87)}$$

$$= -1.127\frac{(100)(80)(0.06)}{(1)(1)}(-0.3705)$$

$$= 200.43 \text{ STB/D}.$$

The ratio of mass entering the reservoir to the mass leaving the reservoir is $200.43/200 = 1.0022$.

This material-balance check indicates that the pressure-convergence tolerance of 1 psi results in a material-balance error of 0.22% on the overall computations.

8.3 Single-Phase Slightly-Compressible-Flow Problem

The general flow equation Eq. 8.1 can be simplified to describe the flow of a slightly compressible fluid in a heterogeneous and anisotropic formation. This is accomplished by observing that the fluid density and formation volume factor (FVF) can be described by Eqs. 2.94 and 2.81. That is,

$$\rho_l = \rho_l^\circ\left[1 + c_l(p - p^\circ)\right] \quad \text{.......... (8.88)}$$

$$\text{and } B_l = \frac{B_l^\circ}{\left[1 + c_l(p - p^\circ)\right]}, \quad \text{.......... (8.89)}$$

where $l = o$ or w. We also will assume that the porosity varies with pressure according to

$$\phi = \phi^\circ\left[1 + c_\phi(p - p^\circ)\right]. \quad \text{.......... (8.90)}$$

8.3.1 Finite-Difference Approximation of the Slightly-Compressible-Fluid-Flow Problem.

Finite-Difference Approximation of the Time Derivative. The expansion of the right side of Eq. 8.1 must be handled carefully to preserve the material balance of the problem. This is discussed in detail in Sec. 8.5 for single-phase flow and in Example 9.9 for multiphase flow. For an expansion of the time derivative to be materially conservative, the relationship in Eq. 8.91 must hold for every Gridblock (i,j,k).

$$\left[\frac{V_b}{\alpha_c}\frac{\partial}{\partial t}\left(\frac{\phi}{B_l}\right)\right]_{i,j,k} \approx \left\{\frac{V_b}{\alpha_c \Delta t}\left[\left(\frac{\phi}{B_l}\right)^{n+1} - \left(\frac{\phi}{B_l}\right)^{n}\right]\right\}_{i,j,k}. \quad \text{.......... (8.91)}$$

To put this approximation in terms of pressure, we add and subtract $(V_b/\alpha_c\Delta t)(\phi^n/B_l^{n+1})$ to the right side of Eq. 8.91.[2]

$$\left[\frac{V_b}{\alpha_c}\frac{\partial}{\partial t}\left(\frac{\phi}{B_l}\right)\right]_{i,j,k} \approx \left\{\frac{V_b}{\alpha_c \Delta t}\left[\frac{\phi^{n+1} - \phi^n}{B_l^{n+1}} + \left(\frac{1}{B_l^{n+1}} - \frac{1}{B_l^n}\right)\phi^n\right]\right\}_{i,j,k}. \quad \text{.......... (8.92)}$$

Applying Eqs. 8.89 and 8.90 to Eq. 8.92 and rearranging results in

$$\left[\frac{V_b}{\alpha_c}\frac{\partial}{\partial t}\left(\frac{\phi}{B_l}\right)\right]_{i,j,k} \approx \left[\frac{V_b}{\alpha_c \Delta t}\left(\frac{\phi^\circ c_\phi}{B_l^{n+1}} + \frac{\phi^n c_l}{B_l^\circ}\right)\right]_{i,j,k}\left(p_{i,j,k}^{n+1} - p_{i,j,k}^n\right) \quad \text{.......... (8.93a)}$$

or $$\left[\frac{V_b}{\alpha_c}\frac{\partial}{\partial t}\left(\frac{\phi}{B_l}\right)\right]_{i,j,k} \approx \frac{\Gamma_{l_{i,j,k}}^{n+1}}{\Delta t}\left(p_{i,j,k}^{n+1} - p_{i,j,k}^n\right), \quad \text{.......... (8.93b)}$$

$$\text{where } \Gamma_{l_{i,j,k}}^{n+1} = \left[\frac{V_b}{\alpha_c}\left(\frac{\phi^\circ c_\phi}{B_l^{n+1}} + \frac{\phi^n c_l}{B_l^\circ}\right)\right]_{i,j,k}. \quad \text{.......... (8.94)}$$

Eq. 8.93b represents the final form of the finite-difference approximation to the time derivative term in Eq. 8.1. We could have developed an equally valid definition of $\Gamma_{l_{i,j,k}}$ by adding and subtracting $(V_b/\alpha_c\Delta t)(\phi^{n+1}/B_l^n)$ (see Example 8.10).

Finite-Difference Approximation of the Spatial Derivative. The treatment of the finite-difference approximation of the spatial derivatives in the slightly-compressible-flow problem is similar to the treatment used for the incompressible-flow problem. With the approximation of the time derivative discussed in the previous section, the finite-difference approximation to Eq. 8.1 becomes

$$\mathrm{T}_{lx_{i+1/2,j,k}}\left(p_{i+1,j,k} - p_{i,j,k}\right) - \mathrm{T}_{lx_{i-1/2,j,k}}\left(p_{i,j,k} - p_{i-1,j,k}\right)$$

$$+ \mathrm{T}_{ly_{i,j+1/2,k}}\left(p_{i,j+1,k} - p_{i,j,k}\right) - \mathrm{T}_{ly_{i,j-1/2,k}}\left(p_{i,j,k} - p_{i,j-1,k}\right)$$

$$+ \mathrm{T}_{lz_{i,j,k+1/2}}\left(p_{i,j,k+1} - p_{i,j,k}\right) - \mathrm{T}_{lz_{i,j,k-1/2}}\left(p_{i,j,k} - p_{i,j,k-1}\right)$$

$$+ q_{lsc_{i,j,k}} = \frac{\Gamma_{l_{i,j,k}}^{n+1}}{\Delta t}\left(p_{i,j,k}^{n+1} - p_{i,j,k}^n\right)$$

$$+ \left[(\mathrm{T}_{lx}\gamma_l)_{i+1/2,j,k}\left(Z_{i+1,j,k} - Z_{i,j,k}\right)\right.$$

$$- (\mathrm{T}_{lx}\gamma_l)_{i-1/2,j,k}\left(Z_{i,j,k} - Z_{i-1,j,k}\right)$$

$$+ (\mathrm{T}_{ly}\gamma_l)_{i,j+1/2,k}\left(Z_{i,j+1,k} - Z_{i,j,k}\right)$$

$$- \left(\mathrm{T}_{ly}\gamma_l\right)_{i,j-½,k}\left(Z_{i,j,k} - Z_{i,j-1,k}\right)$$

$$+ \left(\mathrm{T}_{lz}\gamma_l\right)_{i,j,k+½}\left(Z_{i,j,k+1} - Z_{i,j,k}\right)$$

$$- \left(\mathrm{T}_{lz}\gamma_l\right)_{i,j,k-½}\left(Z_{i,j,k} - Z_{i,j,k-1}\right)\Big]. \quad \text{.............} \quad (8.95)$$

There is one major difference between the finite-difference approximation of the spatial derivatives for the slightly-compressible-flow problem and the incompressible-flow problem. This difference is the dependence of the transmissibility terms on pressure. The definition of transmissibility is

$$\mathrm{T}_{lx_{i\pm½,j,k}} = \left(\beta_c \frac{A_x k_x}{\mu_l B_l \Delta x}\right)_{i\pm½,j,k}. \quad \text{.................} \quad (8.96)$$

For the incompressible-flow problem, μ_l and B_l were assumed to be constant and the remaining grid property terms, $(A_x k_x)/\Delta x$, were harmonically averaged. For the slightly-compressible-flow problem, we continue to use the harmonic average for the grid property terms but must assign a time level to the pressure-dependent properties and average these properties between adjacent gridblocks.

For the slightly-compressible-flow problem, the pressure-dependent fluid properties, μ_l and B_l, represent weak nonlinearities and can be evaluated at the old time level, n. In Sec. 8.4.1 we discuss other linearization techniques that can be applied to the slightly-compressible-flow problem.

Because the fluid properties in the transmissibility term are evaluated at the gridblock boundaries, μ_l and B_l need to be averaged between adjacent gridblocks. Several methods can be used in this averaging process. Two of the more common methods are reviewed here; Sec. 9.5.2 discusses additional methods. In the first method, the pressures are averaged before the properties are evaluated. That is,

$$p_{i\pm½,j,k} = \Omega p_{i,j,k} + (1 - \Omega)p_{i\pm1,j,k}, \quad \text{.............} \quad (8.97)$$

with the fluid properties evaluated by

$$\mu_{l_{i\pm½,j,k}} = \mu_l\left(p_{i\pm½,j,k}\right) \quad \text{........................} \quad (8.98)$$

$$\text{and } B_{l_{i\pm½,j,k}} = B_l\left(p_{i\pm½,j,k}\right). \quad \text{......................} \quad (8.99)$$

In the second method, the fluid properties are evaluated with the cell-center pressures and then averaged. That is,

$$\mu_{l_{i\pm½,j,k}} = \Omega\mu_l\left(p_{i,j,k}\right) + (1 - \Omega)\mu_l\left(p_{i\pm1,j,k}\right) \quad \text{.......} \quad (8.100)$$

$$\text{and } B_{l_{i\pm½,j,k}} = \Omega B_l\left(p_{i,j,k}\right) + (1 - \Omega)B_l\left(p_{i\pm1,j,k}\right). \quad \text{.....} \quad (8.101)$$

In Eqs. 8.97 through 8.101, Ω is a weighting factor with a value of either ½ for arithmetic averaging or the fraction of the pore volumes for pore-volume weighted averaging. Although we did not assign a time level to the pressures in Eqs. 8.97 through 8.101, for this discussion of the slightly-compressible-flow problem we use the pressures at Time Level n. Eq. 8.95 can now be written with matrix notation as

$$B_{i,j,k}\left(p_{i,j,k-1} - p_{i,j,k}\right) + S_{i,j,k}\left(p_{i,j-1,k} - p_{i,j,k}\right)$$

$$+ W_{i,j,k}\left(p_{i-1,j,k} - p_{i,j,k}\right) + E_{i,j,k}\left(p_{i+1,j,k} - p_{i,j,k}\right)$$

$$+ N_{i,j,k}\left(p_{i,j+1,k} - p_{i,j,k}\right) + A_{i,j,k}\left(p_{i,j,k+1} - p_{i,j,k}\right)$$

$$= \frac{\Gamma^{n+1}_{l_{i,j,k}}}{\Delta t}\left(p^{n+1}_{i,j,k} - p^n_{i,j,k}\right) - q_{lsc_{i,j,k}} + Q_{G_{i,j,k}}. \quad \text{......} \quad (8.102)$$

In Eq.8.102, the coefficients are defined by Eqs. 8.21 through 8.26, $\Gamma^{n+1}_{l_{i,j,k}}$ is defined by Eq. 8.94, and $Q_{G_{i,j,k}}$ is defined by Eq. 8.70.

Eq. 8.102 can be written for each Gridblock (i,j,k) including boundary gridblocks in a 3D reservoir. The boundary conditions are handled as discussed in Sec. 8.2.4. Although we are evaluating the coefficients at Time Level n, we have not yet defined the time level of the unknown pressures on the left side of Eq. 8.102. The selection of the time level is related to the explicit or implicit finite-difference formulation discussed in Sec. 5.6. For the slightly-compressible-flow problem, Sec. 8.3.2 discusses selection of the timestep level.

8.3.2 Advancing the Pressure Solution in Time. Unlike the incompressible-flow problem, the pressure in the slightly-compressible-flow problem is time dependent. To obtain the pressure at a given time, t, the pressure solution must be advanced from initial conditions at $t=0$ to $t_1=\Delta t_1$. The pressure solution is then advanced from t_1 to $t_2=t_1+\Delta t_2$ and so on, to the desired time. In other words, the pressure solution is advanced progressively in time until the desired final time is reached. Advancing the pressure solution from the old time level, n, to the new time level, $n+1$, can be achieved with either the explicit or the implicit formulation methods discussed in Secs. 5.6.1 and 5.6.2.

Explicit Formulation of the Flow Equation. In the explicit formulation, which is also known as the forward-difference formulation, interblock-flow terms are evaluated at Time Level n. In other words, the pressures appearing on the left side of Eq. 8.102 are evaluated at Time Level n. Therefore Eq. 8.102 becomes

$$B^n_{i,j,k}\left(p^n_{i,j,k-1} - p^n_{i,j,k}\right) + S^n_{i,j,k}\left(p^n_{i,j-1,k} - p^n_{i,j,k}\right)$$

$$+ W^n_{i,j,k}\left(p^n_{i-1,j,k} - p^n_{i,j,k}\right) + E^n_{i,j,k}\left(p^n_{i+1,j,k} - p^n_{i,j,k}\right)$$

$$+ N^n_{i,j,k}\left(p^n_{i,j+1,k} - p^n_{i,j,k}\right) + A^n_{i,j,k}\left(p^n_{i,j,k+1} - p^n_{i,j,k}\right)$$

$$= \frac{\Gamma^{n+1}_{l_{i,j,k}}}{\Delta t}\left(p^{n+1}_{i,j,k} - p^n_{i,j,k}\right) - q^n_{lsc_{i,j,k}} + Q^n_{G_{i,j,k}}, \quad \text{......} \quad (8.103)$$

which, when solved explicitly for $p^{n+1}_{i,j,k}$, gives

$$\overset{(\nu+1)}{p^{n+1}_{i,j,k}} = p^n_{i,j,k} + \frac{\Delta t}{\underset{(\nu)}{\Gamma^{n+1}_{l_{i,j,k}}}}\Big[q^n_{lsc_{i,j,k}} - Q^n_{G_{i,j,k}} + B^n_{i,j,k}\left(p^n_{i,j,k-1} - p^n_{i,j,k}\right)$$

$$+ S^n_{i,j,k}\left(p^n_{i,j-1,k} - p^n_{i,j,k}\right) + W^n_{i,j,k}\left(p^n_{i-1,j,k} - p^n_{i,j,k}\right)$$

$$+ E^n_{i,j,k}\left(p^n_{i+1,j,k} - p^n_{i,j,k}\right) + N^n_{i,j,k}\left(p^n_{i,j+1,k} - p^n_{i,j,k}\right)$$

$$+ A^n_{i,j,k}\left(p^n_{i,j,k+1} - p^n_{i,j,k}\right)\Big], \quad \text{................} \quad (8.104)$$

where (ν) and $(\nu+1)$ represent old and new iteration levels, respectively. All terms on the right side of Eq. 8.104 are expressed at the known time level, n, and each gridblock (i,j,k) contributes only one equation in one unknown, namely $p^{n+1}_{i,j,k}$. Advancing the pressure solution from Time Level n to Time Level $n+1$ is accomplished by moving through all gridblocks (i,j,k) in a systematic manner and solving for $p^{n+1}_{i,j,k}$ for each gridblock with Eq. 8.104. In the definition of $\Gamma_{l_{i,j,k}}$, B^{n+1}_l is evaluated at Time Level $n+1$. To preserve material balance, some iteration may be required to solve Eq. 8.104. For slightly compressible flow, this iteration may not be required for most practical purposes. In other words, $\Gamma_{i,j,k}$ can be evaluated at Time Level n and Eq. 8.104 can be solved in a noniterative fashion.

As discussed in Sec. 5.6.3 (Example 5.17), the explicit formulation is conditionally stable. The timestep Δt, which ensures stability, can be expressed with matrix notation as

$$\Delta t \leq \min_{i,j,k}\left(\frac{\Gamma_{l_{i,j,k}}}{B_{i,j,k} + S_{i,j,k} + W_{i,j,k} + E_{i,j,k} + N_{i,j,k} + A_{i,j,k}}\right),$$

$$\text{...................} \quad (8.105)$$

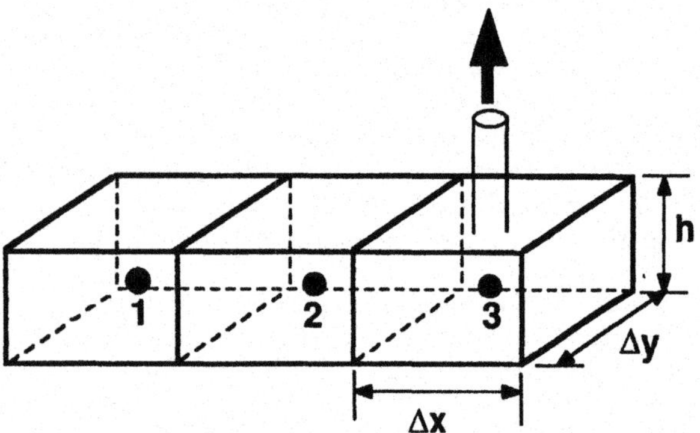

Fig. 8.11—Reservoir representation for Example 8.6.

where the minimum is over all gridblocks. Example 8.6 illustrates the timestep stability criterion of the explicit formulation.

Example 8.6. A slightly compressible oil is flowing in a volumetric, homogeneous linear reservoir. The oil has a viscosity of 2 cp, compressibility of 5×10^{-5} psi^{-1}, and FVF of approximately 1 RB/STB. The reservoir is represented by the three-gridblock system shown in **Fig. 8.11.**

The dimensions and properties of all gridblocks are $\Delta x = 200$ ft, $h = 20$ ft, $\Delta y = 100$ ft, $k_x = 100$ md, and $\phi = 0.20$. The initial reservoir pressure is 3,000 psia. The well in Gridblock 3 is produced so that the wellblock pressure is maintained at 1,500 psia for all times $t > 0$. Find the maximum timestep size that ensures the stability of the explicit formulation for the problem.

Solution. For a 1D reservoir,

$$A_i = S_i = N_i = B_i = 0; \quad \text{(8.106)}$$

therefore, Eq. 8.105 reduces to

$$\Delta t \leqq \min_i \left(\frac{\Gamma_{o_i}^{n+1}}{W_i + E_i} \right). \quad \text{(8.107)}$$

The volumetric reservoir implies no-flow boundaries; that is, $W_1 = 0$ and $E_3 = 0$.

For Gridblock 1, because all gridblocks have the same dimensions and properties, the expression for E_1 can be simplified to give

$$E_1 = \beta_c \frac{A_x k_x}{\Delta x} \frac{1}{\mu_o B_o}. \quad \text{(8.108)}$$

Substituting for numerical values, we obtain

$$E_1 = 1.127 \frac{100 \times 20 \times 0.100}{(200)} \frac{1}{(2)(1)} = 0.5635 \text{ STB/D-psi.}$$

We also have

$$\Gamma_{o_1}^{n+1} = \left(\frac{V_b \phi c_o}{\alpha_c B_o^\circ} \right)_1, \quad \text{(8.109)}$$

where $B_o^\circ = B_o = 1$ RB/STB.

Therefore,

$$\Gamma_{o_1}^{n+1} = \frac{V_{b_1} \phi_1 c_o}{\alpha_c \; B_o^\circ} \quad \text{(8.110)}$$

$$= \frac{100 \times 20 \times 200}{(5.615)} \frac{0.20 \times (5 \times 10^{-5})}{(1)}$$

$$= 0.71238 \text{ STB/psi}$$

$$\text{and } \Delta t_1 = \frac{\Gamma_{o_1}^{n+1}}{W_1 + E_1} \quad \text{(8.111a)}$$

$$= \frac{0.71238}{0 + 0.5635} = 1.26 \text{ days.}$$

For Gridblock 2,

$$W_2 = E_2 = E_1 = 0.5635 \text{ STB/D-psi,}$$

$$\Gamma_{o_2}^{n+1} = \Gamma_{o_1}^{n+1} = 0.71238 \text{ STB/psi,}$$

$$\text{and } \Delta t_2 = \frac{\Gamma_{o_2}^{n+1}}{W_2 + E_2} \quad \text{(8.111b)}$$

$$= \frac{0.71238}{0.5635 + 0.5635} = 0.63 \text{ day.}$$

For Gridblock 3,

$$W_3 = 0.5635 \text{ STB/D-psi,}$$

$$E_3 = 0,$$

$$\Gamma_{o_3}^{n+1} = \Gamma_{o_1}^{n+1} = 0.71238 \text{ STB/psi,}$$

$$\text{and } \Delta t_3 = \frac{\Gamma_{o_3}^{n+1}}{W_3 + E_3} \quad \text{(8.111c)}$$

$$= \frac{0.71238}{0.5635 + 0} = 1.26 \text{ days.}$$

The maximum stable timestep = min (1.26, 0.63, 1.26) = 0.63 day.

In advancing the pressure from initial conditions, the maximum timestep that can be used with the explicit formulation cannot exceed 0.63 day.

Implicit Formulation of the Flow Equation. The explicit formulation of the flow equation suffers from severe restrictions on the timestep size because of the conditional stability of the procedure. As a result, it is generally not used in reservoir simulation. In contrast, the implicit formulation of the flow equation is unconditionally stable and, hence, imposes no upper limit on timestep size (see Sec. 5.6.3 and Example 5.16).

In the implicit formulation, the interblock-flow terms are evaluated at Time Level $n+1$ and the time derivative is discretized with a backward-difference approximation. Eq. 8.102 becomes

$$B_{i,j,k}^n \left(p_{i,j,k-1}^{n+1} - p_{i,j,k}^{n+1} \right) + S_{i,j,k}^n \left(p_{i,j-1,k}^{n+1} - p_{i,j,k}^{n+1} \right)$$

$$+ W_{i,j,k}^n \left(p_{i-1,j,k}^{n+1} - p_{i,j,k}^{n+1} \right) + E_{i,j,k}^n \left(p_{i+1,j,k}^{n+1} - p_{i,j,k}^{n+1} \right)$$

$$+ N_{i,j,k}^n \left(p_{i,j+1,k}^{n+1} - p_{i,j,k}^{n+1} \right) + A_{i,j,k}^n \left(p_{i,j,k+1}^{n+1} - p_{i,j,k}^{n+1} \right)$$

$$= \frac{\Gamma_{l_{i,j,k}}^{n+1}}{\Delta t} \left(p_{i,j,k}^{n+1} - p_{i,j,k}^n \right) - q_{lsc_{i,j,k}}^{n+1} + Q_{G_{i,j,k}}^n, \quad \text{(8.112)}$$

which can be rearranged and rewritten with matrix notation in the form of the characteristic finite-difference equation

$$B_{i,j,k}^n \overset{(\nu+1)}{p_{i,j,k-1}^{n+1}} + S_{i,j,k}^n \overset{(\nu+1)}{p_{i,j-1,k}^{n+1}} + W_{i,j,k}^n \overset{(\nu+1)}{p_{i-1,j,k}^{n+1}}$$

$$+ \overset{(\nu)}{C_{i,j,k}^{n+1}} \overset{(\nu+1)}{p_{i,j,k}^{n+1}} + E_{i,j,k}^n \overset{(\nu+1)}{p_{i+1,j,k}^{n+1}} + N_{i,j,k}^n \overset{(\nu+1)}{p_{i,j+1,k}^{n+1}} + A_{i,j,k}^n \overset{(\nu+1)}{p_{i,j,k+1}^{n+1}}$$

$$= Q_{i,j,k}^{(\nu)}, \quad \text{(8.113)}$$

where the coefficients $B^n_{i,j,k}$, $S^n_{i,j,k}$, $W^n_{i,j,k}$, $E^n_{i,j,k}$, $N^n_{i,j,k}$, and $A^n_{i,j,k}$, are defined as before. For gridblocks without wells and for gridblocks hosting rate-specified wells,

$$\overset{(\nu)}{C^{n+1}_{i,j,k}} = -\left[B^n_{i,j,k} + S^n_{i,j,k} + W^n_{i,j,k} + E^n_{i,j,k} + N^n_{i,j,k} + A^n_{i,j,k} + \frac{\overset{(\nu)}{\Gamma^{n+1}_{l_{i,j,k}}}}{\Delta t}\right] \quad \text{(8.114)}$$

$$\text{and } Q^{(\nu)}_{i,j,k} = -\left(\frac{\overset{(\nu)}{\Gamma^{n+1}_{l_{i,j,k}}}}{\Delta t}p^n_{i,j,k} + q^{n+1}_{lsc_{i,j,k}} - Q^n_{G_{i,j,k}}\right). \quad \text{(8.115)}$$

For gridblocks hosting pressure-specified wells,

$$\overset{(\nu)}{C^{n+1}_{i,j,k}} = -\left[B^n_{i,j,k} + S^n_{i,j,k} + W^n_{i,j,k} + E^n_{i,j,k} + N^n_{i,j,k} + A^n_{i,j,k} + \frac{\overset{(\nu)}{\Gamma^{n+1}_{l_{i,j,k}}}}{\Delta t} + J^n_{w_{i,j,k}}\right] \quad \text{(8.116)}$$

$$\text{and } Q^{(\nu)}_{i,j,k} = -\left[\frac{\overset{(\nu)}{\Gamma^{n+1}_{l_{i,j,k}}}}{\Delta t}p^n_{i,j,k} + J^n_{w_{i,j,k}}p_{wf_{i,j,k}} - Q^n_{G_{i,j,k}}\right]. \quad \text{(8.117)}$$

In Eq. 8.113, we assigned Iteration Levels $(\nu+1)$ and (ν) to the left side and right side, respectively. This is done because the right side of Eq. 8.113 contains the B^{n+1}_l term in the definition of $\Gamma^{n+1}_{l_{i,j,k}}$. The assignment of the $n+1$ time level is required to meet the material-balance condition stated in Eq. 8.91. Again, for slightly-compressible-flow problems, this iteration may not be necessary for most practical situations. Example 8.7 illustrates this.

Example 8.7. Consider Example 8.6. Find the pressure of Gridblocks 1 and 2 at $t=10$ days and $t=20$ days with the implicit-formulation method.

Solution. For the 1D reservoir, Eq. 8.113 reduces to

$$W^n_i p^{n+1}_{i-1} + C^{n+1}_i p^{n+1}_i + E^n_i p^{n+1}_{i+1} = Q_i, \quad \text{(8.118)}$$

$$\text{where } C^{n+1}_i = -\left(W^n_i + E^n_i + \frac{\Gamma^{n+1}_{o_i}}{\Delta t}\right) \quad \text{(8.119)}$$

$$\text{and } Q_i = -\frac{\Gamma^{n+1}_{o_i}}{\Delta t}p^n_i - q_{osc_i}. \quad \text{(8.120)}$$

At $t=10$ Days. The solution is advanced from $t=0$ to $t=10$ days; therefore,

$$\Delta t = t^{n+1} - t^n \quad \text{(8.121)}$$

$$= 10 - 0 = 10 \text{ days},$$

$$p^n_1 = p^n_2 = p^n_3 = 3{,}000 \text{ psia},$$

and $p^{n+1}_3 = 1{,}500$ psia.

For Gridblock 1,

$W_1 = 0$ and $q_{lsc_1} = 0$,

$E_1 = 0.5635$ STB/D-psi,

$\Gamma^{n+1}_{o_1} = 0.71238$ STB/psi,

and $p^n_1 = 3{,}000$ psia.

Eq. 8.118 becomes

$$-\left(0 + 0.5635 + \frac{0.71238}{10}\right)p^{n+1}_1 + 0.5635p^{n+1}_2$$

$$= -\frac{0.71238}{10}(3{,}000) - 0 \quad \text{(8.122a)}$$

$$\text{or } -0.63474p^{n+1}_1 + 0.5635p^{n+1}_2 = -213.71. \quad \text{(8.122b)}$$

For Gridblock 2,

$W_2 = E_2 = 0.5635$ STB/D-psi,

$\Gamma^{n+1}_{o_2} = 0.71238$ STB/psi,

and $p^n_2 = 3{,}000$ psia.

Eq. 8.118 becomes

$$0.5635p^{n+1}_1 - \left(0.5635 + 0.5635 + \frac{0.71238}{10}\right)p^{n+1}_2$$

$$+ 0.5635 \times 1{,}500 = -\frac{0.71238}{10}(3{,}000) - 0 \quad \text{(8.123a)}$$

$$\text{or } 0.5635p^{n+1}_1 - 1.19824p^{n+1}_2 = -1{,}058.96. \quad \text{(8.123b)}$$

Solving Eqs. 8.122b and 8.123b simultaneously gives

$p^{n+1}_1 = 1{,}924.9$ psia

and $p^{n+1}_2 = 1{,}789.0$ psia.

At $t=20$ Days. The solution is advanced from $t=10$ to $t=20$ days; therefore,

$$\Delta t = t^{n+1} - t^n \quad \text{(8.121)}$$

$$= 20 - 10 = 10 \text{ days},$$

$p^n_1 = 1{,}924.9$ psia,

$p^n_2 = 1{,}789.0$ psia,

$p^n_3 = 1{,}500$ psia,

and $p^{n+1}_3 = 1{,}500$ psia.

For Gridblock 1,

$$-\left(0 + 0.5635 + \frac{0.71238}{10}\right)p^{n+1}_1 + 0.5635p^{n+1}_2$$

$$= -\frac{0.71238}{10}(1{,}924.9) - 0 \quad \text{(8.124a)}$$

or $-0.6347p_1^{n+1} + 0.5635p_2^{n+1} = -137.13.$ .... (8.124b)

For Gridblock 2,

$$0.5635p_1^{n+1} - \left(0.5635 + 0.5635 + \frac{0.71238}{10}\right)p_2^{n+1}$$

$$+ 0.5635 \times 1,500 = -\frac{0.71238}{10}(1,789.0) - 0 \quad \text{(8.125a)}$$

or $0.5635p_1^{n+1} - 1.19824p_2^{n+1} = -972.70.$ ...... (8.125b)

Solving Eqs. 8.124b and 8.125b simultaneously gives

$$p_1^{n+1} = 1,608.1 \text{ psia}$$

and $p_2^{n+1} = 1,568.0$ psia.

In Example 8.7, we have a simple system of two equations in two unknowns. For larger systems of equations, any of the methods discussed in Chap. 7 can be used to solve the simultaneous equations resulting from the implicit finite-difference formulations.

8.3.3 Material-Balance Check for the Slightly-Compressible-Flow Problem. As mentioned in Sec. 8.2.7, the material-balance check is the ratio of accumulation of mass to the net mass entering and leaving the boundaries of the reservoir. The material-balance check performed over a timestep is known as the incremental material balance, I_{MB}, and is expressed as

$$I_{MB} = \frac{\sum_{i=1}^{n_x}\sum_{j=1}^{n_y}\sum_{k=1}^{n_z}\frac{V_{b_{i,j,k}}}{\alpha_c}\left(\frac{\phi^{n+1}}{B_l^{n+1}} - \frac{\phi^n}{B_l^n}\right)_{i,j,k}}{\Delta t\sum_{i=1}^{n_x}\sum_{j=1}^{n_y}\sum_{k=1}^{n_z} q_{lsc_{i,j,k}}^{n+1}}. \quad \text{(8.126)}$$

The material-balance check also can be performed over the entire time period. This is known as the cumulative material balance, C_{MB}, and is expressed as

$$C_{MB} = \frac{\sum_{i=1}^{n_x}\sum_{j=1}^{n_y}\sum_{k=1}^{n_z}\frac{V_{b_{i,j,k}}}{\alpha_c}\left(\frac{\phi^{n+1}}{B_l^{n+1}} - \frac{\phi^0}{B_l^0}\right)_{i,j,k}}{\sum_{m=1}^{n+1}\Delta t^m\sum_{i=1}^{n_x}\sum_{j=1}^{n_y}\sum_{k=1}^{n_z} q_{lsc_{i,j,k}}^{m}}, \quad \text{(8.127)}$$

where ϕ^0 and B^0 represent these properties at the initial pressure and not the reference value as in Eqs. 8.89 and 8.90. Furthermore, Eqs. 8.126 and 8.127 are valid strictly for closed reservoirs. If the external-boundary conditions specify mass transport across the external boundaries, these equations need to be modified to account for these fluxes.

Both checks can be performed at every timestep. The C_{MB} tends to smooth errors occurring over the various timesteps; therefore, it is a less accurate check than the I_{MB}. The material-balance checks as expressed in Eqs. 8.126 and 8.127 must be close to unity to achieve an acceptable solution.

8.4 Single-Phase Compressible-Flow Problem

The single-phase compressible-flow equation, although similar in form to the slightly-compressible-flow equation, is generally a more difficult equation to solve numerically. The additional difficulty arises because the transmissibility of a porous medium to gas is much more sensitive to pressure changes than is the transmissibility of a porous medium to liquid. This is illustrated in Example 8.8.

Example 8.8. Given the following rock and fluid data, determine the change in transmissibility to gas with 0.61 gravity and to oil when pressure declines from 2,014.7 to 1,614.7 psia. **Table 8.2** gives the gas properties. Oil properties and gridblock dimensions are $\Delta x = \Delta y = 100$ ft, $\Delta z = 10$ ft, $k_x = 4.2$ md, $\mu_o = 3.0$ cp, $c_o = 1.6 \times 10^{-6}$ psi^{-1}, $T = 580$°R, $p_{sc} = 14.7$ psia, $T_{sc} = 520$°R, and $B_o^{\circ} = 1.22$ RB/STB, where B_o° is reported at 1,014.7 psia and reservoir temperature.

TABLE 8.2—PRESSURE/VOLUME/TEMPERATURE PROPERTIES FOR A 0.61-GRAVITY GAS (AIR GRAVITY = 1)[3]

p (psia)	μ_g (cp)	z
14.7	0.0113	1.0000
414.7	0.0118	0.9550
814.7	0.0125	0.9140
1,214.7	0.0134	0.8790
1,614.7	0.0145	0.8530
2,014.7	0.0156	0.8380

Solution. The transmissibility and properties can be estimated as follows. For the case of a real gas, the definition of transmissibility to gas is

$$T_{gx} = \beta_c \frac{A_x k_x}{\mu_g B_g \Delta x}. \quad \text{(8.128)}$$

1. Transmissibility to gas at 2,014.7 psia. The gas FVF can be estimated with Eq. 2.83.

$$B_g = \frac{p_{sc} T z}{\alpha_c T_{sc} p} \quad \text{(8.129)}$$

$$= \frac{(14.7)(580)(0.838)}{(5.615)(520)(2,014.7)} = 1.215 \times 10^{-3} \text{ RB/scf}$$

and $T_{gx} = \dfrac{(1.127)(100 \times 10)(0.0042)}{(0.0156)(1.215 \times 10^{-3})(100)} = 2,497.3$ scf/D-psi.

2. The transmissibility to gas at 1,614.7 psia is calculated as

$$B_g = \frac{(14.7)(580)(0.853)}{(5.615)(520)(1,614.7)} = 1.543 \times 10^{-3} \text{ RB/scf}$$

and $T_{gx} = \dfrac{(1.127)(100 \times 10)(0.0042)}{(0.0145)(1.543 \times 10^{-3})(100)} = 2,115.6$ scf/D-psi.

3. Change in transmissibility to gas is

$$\delta T_{gx} = \frac{2,497.3 - 2,115.6}{2,497.3} \times 100 = 15.3\%.$$

In the case of oil, the definition of transmissibility to liquid is

$$T_{ox} = \beta_c \frac{A_x k_x}{\mu_o B_o \Delta x}. \quad \text{(8.130)}$$

1. Transmissibility at 2,014.7 psia. With Eq. 2.81, B_o at 2,014.7 psia can be calculated as

$$B_o = \frac{1.22}{[1 + 1.6 \times 10^{-6}(2,014.7 - 1014.7)]} = 1.218 \text{ RB/STB}$$

and $T_{ox} = \dfrac{(1.127)(100 \times 10)(0.0042)}{(3.0)(1.218)(100)}$

$$= 1.2954 \times 10^{-2} \text{ STB/D-psi.}$$

2. Transmissibility at 1,614.7 psia. With Eq. 2.81, B_o at 1,614.7 is estimated as

$$B_o = \frac{1.22}{[1 + 1.6 \times 10^{-6}(1,614.7 - 1,014.7)]} = 1.219 \text{ RB/STB}$$

$$\text{and } T_{ox} = \frac{(1.127)(100 \times 10)(0.0042)}{(3.0)(1.219)(100)}$$

$$= 1.2943 \times 10^{-2} \text{ STB/D-psi.}$$

3. Change in liquid transmissibility.

$$\delta T_{ox} = \frac{1.2954 \times 10^{-2} - 1.2943 \times 10^{-2}}{1.2954 \times 10^{-2}} \times 100 = 0.085\%.$$

The change of transmissibility to gas is 15.3% compared with a change of transmissibility to oil of 0.085% for the same pressure change.

Example 8.8 illustrates why the transmissibilities can be evaluated at the old time level for slightly compressible fluids and why special linearization techniques are required for compressible fluids. Because the transmissibilities to liquids change very slowly during pressure decline (or buildup during repressurization), they can be approximated accurately with values at the beginning of timestep. This is not true for compressible fluids, where the change in transmissibility must be considered during the course of the pressure solution.

Although we assume a constant transmissibility for slightly compressible flow, it actually is pressure dependent (0.085% change in Example 8.8). Consequently, the linearization methods discussed in Sec. 8.4.1 also can be applied to slightly-compressible-flow problems. In addition, because of the inclusion of relative permeability and capillary pressures in the transmissibility terms for multiphase flow, these linearization techniques are required for slightly compressible fluids in multiphase-flow situations.

8.4.1 Linearization of the Flow Problem. The solution techniques discussed in Chap. 7 are appropriate only for systems of linear equations. That is, these methods are appropriate only for equations where the coefficients are constant. As we have already seen, the transmissibilities in the finite-difference equations are pressure dependent and, hence, are functions of the unknowns of the problem. To use the techniques described in Chap. 7, we must linearize the finite-difference equations. We discuss four methods for linearizing the finite-difference equations: explicit treatment of the transmissibility terms, extrapolation of the transmissibility terms, simple iteration of the transmissibility terms, and fully implicit treatment of the transmissibility terms. We discuss these methods as they apply to the single-phase compressible-flow equation. In Sec. 9.5.2, we discuss how these methods apply to multiphase-flow situations.

Explicit Treatment of the Transmissibility Terms. The simplest treatment of the transmissibility terms is the explicit treatment. This treatment is used in Sec. 8.3 for the slightly-compressible-flow equation. As the name implies, the transmissibility terms are evaluated at the old time level in the explicit treatment. That is,

$$T^{n+1}_{gx_{i\pm 1/2,j,k}} \cong T^{n}_{gx_{i\pm 1/2,j,k}} = \left(\beta_c \frac{A_x k_x}{\mu^n_g B^n_g \Delta x}\right)_{i\pm 1/2,j,k} \quad \ldots\ldots\ (8.131a)$$

$$\text{or } T^{n+1}_{gx_{i\pm 1/2,j,k}} \cong T_{gx_{i\pm 1/2,j,k}} = \left(\beta_c \frac{A_x k_x}{\Delta x}\right)_{i\pm 1/2,j,k} \left(\frac{1}{\mu_g B_g}\right)^n_{i\pm 1/2,j,k}, \quad \ldots\ldots\ (8.131b)$$

where the pressure-dependent properties μ_g and B_g are evaluated at p^n. In Eq. 8.131b, the grid-dependent term $[\beta_c(A_x k_x)/\Delta x]_{i\pm 1/2,j,k}$ is averaged between gridblocks by use of the harmonic average, as discussed in Sec. 8.2.2, and the gas-property term $(1/\mu_g B_g)^n{}_{i\pm 1/2,j,k}$ is averaged between gridblocks with one of the methods discussed in Sec. 8.3.1. Because the term $[\beta_c(A_x k_x/\Delta x)]_{i\pm 1/2,j,k}$ is constant with time, it needs to be calculated only at the beginning of the simulation; however, the gas-property term $(1/\mu_g B_g)^n{}_{i\pm 1/2,j,k}$ must be updated at the beginning of each timestep.

In this approach, the implicit finite-difference approximation to Eq. 8.102 with explicit transmissibilities becomes

$$T^n_{gx_{i+1/2,j,k}}\left(\overset{(\nu+1)}{p^{n+1}_{i+1,j,k}} - \overset{(\nu+1)}{p^{n+1}_{i,j,k}}\right) - T^n_{gx_{i-1/2,j,k}}\left(\overset{(\nu+1)}{p^{n+1}_{i,j,k}} - \overset{(\nu+1)}{p^{n+1}_{i-1,j,k}}\right)$$

$$+ T^n_{gy_{i,j+1/2,k}}\left(\overset{(\nu+1)}{p^{n+1}_{i,j+1,k}} - \overset{(\nu+1)}{p^{n+1}_{i,j,k}}\right) - T^n_{gy_{i,j-1/2,k}}\left(\overset{(\nu+1)}{p^{n+1}_{i,j,k}} - \overset{(\nu+1)}{p^{n+1}_{i,j-1,k}}\right)$$

$$+ T^n_{gz_{i,j,k+1/2}}\left(\overset{(\nu+1)}{p^{n+1}_{i,j,k+1}} - \overset{(\nu+1)}{p^{n+1}_{i,j,k}}\right) - T^n_{gz_{i,j,k-1/2}}\left(\overset{(\nu+1)}{p^{n+1}_{i,j,k}} - \overset{(\nu+1)}{p^{n+1}_{i,j,k-1}}\right)$$

$$= \frac{\overset{(\nu)}{\Gamma^{n+1}_{g_{i,j,k}}}}{\Delta t}\left(\overset{(\nu+1)}{p^{n+1}_{i,j,k}} - p^n_{i,j,k}\right) - q^{n+1}_{gsc_{i,j,k}} + Q^n_{G_{i,j,k}}, \quad \ldots\ldots\ (8.132)$$

where $\Gamma^{n+1}_{g_{i,j,k}}$ is obtained from the expansion of the time derivative term for a materially conservative scheme as

$$\Gamma^{n+1}_{g_{i,j,k}} = \frac{V_{b_{i,j,k}}}{\alpha_c}\left[\frac{\phi^\circ c_\phi}{B^{n+1}_g} + \frac{\phi^n}{B^n_g}(B^n_g/B^{n+1}_g - 1)/(p^{n+1} - p^n)\right]_{i,j,k} \quad \ldots\ldots\ (8.133)$$

and B_g is given by Eq. 2.83 as $B_g = [p_{sc}/(\alpha_c T_{sc})](Tz/p)$. While Eq. 8.94 applies to slightly compressible liquids, Eq. 8.133 applies to gas. In fact, the term $(B^n_g/B^{n+1}_g - 1)/(p^{n+1} - p^n)$ is an average gas compressibility between p^n and p^{n+1}.

Eq. 8.132 can be rewritten in terms of matrix notation as

$$B^n_{i,j,k}\overset{(\nu+1)}{p^{n+1}_{i,j,k-1}} + S^n_{i,j,k}\overset{(\nu+1)}{p^{n+1}_{i,j-1,k}} + W^n_{i,j,k}\overset{(\nu+1)}{p^{n+1}_{i-1,j,k}}$$

$$+ \overset{(\nu)}{C^{n+1}_{i,j,k}}\overset{(\nu+1)}{p^{n+1}_{i,j,k}} + E^n_{i,j,k}\overset{(\nu+1)}{p^{n+1}_{i+1,j,k}} + N^n_{i,j,k}\overset{(\nu+1)}{p^{n+1}_{i,j+1,k}} + A^n_{i,j,k}\overset{(\nu+1)}{p^{n+1}_{i,j,k+1}}$$

$$= Q^{(\nu)}_{i,j,k}. \quad \ldots\ldots\ (8.134)$$

In Eq. 8.132, Iteration Level $(\nu+1)$ is assigned to the unknown pressures and Iteration Level (ν) to $\Gamma^{n+1}_{g_{i,j,k}}$. This is required because of the B^{n+1}_g term in the definition of $\Gamma^{n+1}_{g_{i,j,k}}$. This treatment is required to preserve the material balance of the problem. This approach results in the iteration levels assigned to the terms $C^{n+1}_{i,j,k}$ and $Q_{i,j,k}$, both at Iteration Level (ν), in Eq. 8.134. The definitions of these terms become

$$\overset{(\nu)}{C^{n+1}_{i,j,k}} = -\left[B^n_{i,j,k} + S^n_{i,j,k} + W^n_{i,j,k} + E^n_{i,j,k} + N^n_{i,j,k} + A^n_{i,j,k} + \frac{\overset{(\nu)}{\Gamma^{n+1}_{g_{i,j,k}}}}{\Delta t}\right] \quad \ldots\ldots\ (8.135)$$

for gridblocks with rate-specified wells and for gridblocks with no wells,

$$\overset{(\nu)}{C^{n+1}_{i,j,k}} = -\left[B^n_{i,j,k} + S^n_{i,j,k} + W^n_{i,j,k} + E^n_{i,j,k} + N^n_{i,j,k} + A^n_{i,j,k} + \frac{\overset{(\nu)}{\Gamma^{n+1}_{g_{i,j,k}}}}{\Delta t} + J^n_{w_{i,j,k}}\right] \quad \ldots\ldots\ (8.136)$$

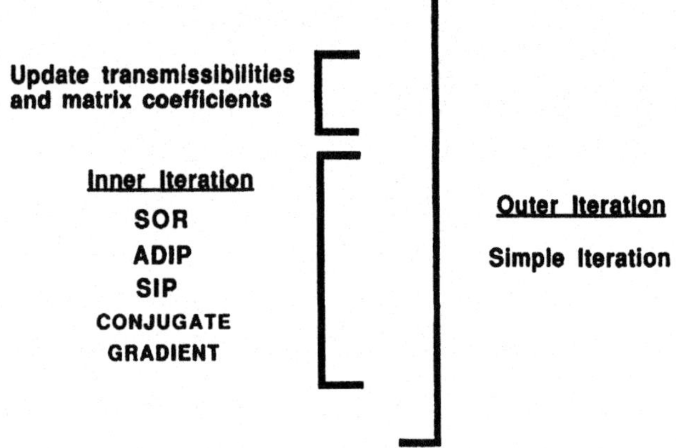

Fig. 8.12—Nesting of iterations in solving Eq. 8.134.

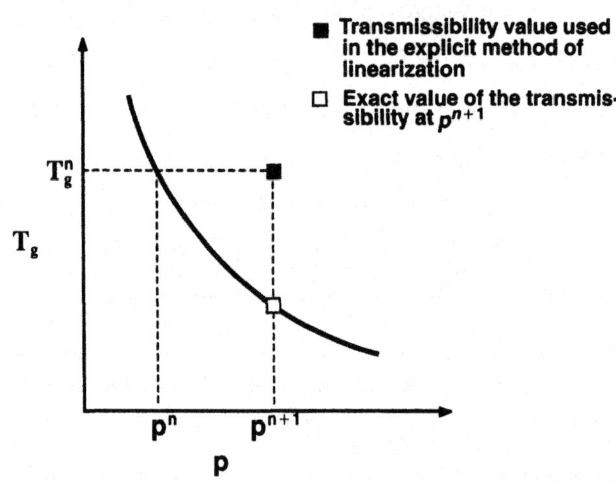

Fig. 8.13—T_g^n value used in the explicit method of linearization.

for gridblocks with pressure–specified wells,

$$Q^{(\nu)}_{i,j,k} = -\left[\frac{\overset{(\nu)}{\Gamma^{n+1}_{g_{i,j,k}}}}{\Delta t} p^n_{i,j,k} + q_{gsc_{i,j,k}} - Q^n_{G_{i,j,k}}\right] \quad \text{........ (8.137)}$$

for gridblocks with rate-specified wells and for gridblocks with no wells, and

$$Q^{(\nu)}_{i,j,k} = -\left[\frac{\overset{(\nu)}{\Gamma^{n+1}_{g_{i,j,k}}}}{\Delta t} p^n_{i,j,k} + J^n_{w_{i,j,k}} p_{wf_{i,j,k}} - Q^n_{G_{i,j,k}}\right] \quad \text{..... (8.138)}$$

for gridblocks with pressure-specified wells. In Eqs. 8.137 and 8.138, Q^n_G is defined by Eq. 8.70 with the transmissibility terms and gravity-head terms evaluated at Time Level n.

When the system of equations generated by Eq. 8.134 is solved with one of the iterative techniques discussed in Chap. 7 [successive-overrelaxation (SOR), alternating-direction implicit procedure (ADIP), strongly implicit procedure (SIP), or the conjugate gradient method], a nested iteration procedure results. **Fig. 8.12** shows this procedure schematically.

If an alternative definition of $\Gamma^{n+1}_{g_{i,j,k}}$ is used for incompressible reservoirs, $c_\phi = 0$ (see Exercise 8.21), a noniterative solution procedure for Eq. 8.134 can be developed. Often, for single-phase gas flow, it is appropriate to assume that the rock compressibility is negligible compared with the gas compressibility. **Fig. 8.13** shows the value of transmissibility used in the explicit method of linearization.

Extrapolation of the Transmissibility Terms. The explicit treatment of the transmissibility terms can result in stability problems, particularly for multiphase-flow problems.[2] These stability problems can be alleviated by evaluating the transmissibilities at Time Level $n+1$. This treatment presents one difficulty, however, because the pressures (and saturations for multiphase-flow problems) are unknown at this time level and, consequently, are unavailable to evaluate the transmissibilities.

One method used to circumvent this difficulty is to use extrapolated pressures to evaluate the transmissibilities. In this approach, the results from the last two timesteps are used to extrapolate the pressures to the new time level. That is,

$$p^{\overset{*}{n+1}}_{i,j,k} = p^n_{i,j,k} + \frac{\Delta t^{n+1}}{\Delta t^n}\left(p^n_{i,j,k} - p^{n-1}_{i,j,k}\right) \quad \text{............ (8.139a)}$$

$$\text{or } p^{\overset{*}{n+1}}_{i,j,k} = p^n_{i,j,k} + \frac{(t^{n+1} - t^n)}{(t^n - t^{n-1})}\left(p^n_{i,j,k} - p^{n-1}_{i,j,k}\right). \quad \text{...... (8.139b)}$$

With this approach, the transmissibilities are evaluated by

$$T^{n+1}_{gx_{i\pm1/2,j,k}} \cong T^{\overset{*}{n+1}}_{gx_{i\pm1/2,j,k}} = \left(\beta_c \frac{A_x k_x}{\mu_g^{\overset{*}{n+1}} B_g^{\overset{*}{n+1}} \Delta x}\right)_{i\pm1/2,j,k} \quad \text{.... (8.140a)}$$

$$\text{or } T^{n+1}_{gx_{i\pm1/2,j,k}} = T^{\overset{*}{n+1}}_{gx_{i\pm1/2,j,k}} = \left(\beta_c \frac{A_x k_x}{\Delta x}\right)_{i\pm1/2,j,k} \left(\frac{1}{\mu_g B_g}\right)^{\overset{*}{n+1}}_{i\pm1/2,j,k}. \quad \text{.................. (8.140b)}$$

The implicit finite-difference approximation to Eq. 8.102 with extrapolated transmissibilities becomes

$$\begin{aligned}
&T^{\overset{*}{n+1}}_{gx_{i+1/2,j,k}}\left(\overset{(\nu+1)}{p^{n+1}_{i+1,j,k}} - \overset{(\nu+1)}{p^{n+1}_{i,j,k}}\right) - T^{\overset{*}{n+1}}_{gx_{i-1/2,j,k}}\left(\overset{(\nu+1)}{p^{n+1}_{i,j,k}} - \overset{(\nu+1)}{p^{n+1}_{i-1,j,k}}\right)\\
&+ T^{\overset{*}{n+1}}_{gy_{i,j+1/2,k}}\left(\overset{(\nu+1)}{p^{n+1}_{i,j+1,k}} - \overset{(\nu+1)}{p^{n+1}_{i,j,k}}\right) - T^{\overset{*}{n+1}}_{gy_{i,j-1/2,k}}\left(\overset{(\nu+1)}{p^{n+1}_{i,j,k}} - \overset{(\nu+1)}{p^{n+1}_{i,j-1,k}}\right)\\
&+ T^{\overset{*}{n+1}}_{gz_{i,j,k+1/2}}\left(\overset{(\nu+1)}{p^{n+1}_{i,j,k+1}} - \overset{(\nu+1)}{p^{n+1}_{i,j,k}}\right) - T^{\overset{*}{n+1}}_{gz_{i,j,k-1/2}}\left(\overset{(\nu+1)}{p^{n+1}_{i,j,k}} - \overset{(\nu+1)}{p^{n+1}_{i,j,k-1}}\right)\\
&= \frac{\overset{(\nu)}{\Gamma^{n+1}_{g_{i,j,k}}}}{\Delta t}\left(\overset{(\nu+1)}{p^{n+1}_{i,j,k}} - p^n_{i,j,k}\right) - q^{n+1}_{gsc_{i,j,k}} + Q^{\overset{*}{n+1}}_{G_{i,j,k}} \quad \text{.... (8.141)}
\end{aligned}$$

or, in matrix notation,

$$\begin{aligned}
&A^{\overset{*}{n+1}}_{i,j,k}\overset{(\nu+1)}{p^{n+1}_{i,j,k-1}} + S^{\overset{*}{n+1}}_{i,j,k}\overset{(\nu+1)}{p^{n+1}_{i,j-1,k}} + W^{\overset{*}{n+1}}_{i,j,k}\overset{(\nu+1)}{p^{n+1}_{i-1,j,k}}\\
&+ \overset{(\nu)}{C^{\overset{*}{n+1}}_{i,j,k}}\overset{(\nu+1)}{p^{n+1}_{i,j,k}} + E^{\overset{*}{n+1}}_{i,j,k}\overset{(\nu+1)}{p^{n+1}_{i+1,j,k}} + N^{\overset{*}{n+1}}_{i,j,k}\overset{(\nu+1)}{p^{n+1}_{i,j+1,k}} + B^{\overset{*}{n+1}}_{i,j,k}\overset{(\nu+1)}{p^{n+1}_{i,j,k+1}}\\
&= \overset{(\nu)}{Q^{\overset{*}{n+1}}_{i,j,k}}. \quad \text{............................... (8.142)}
\end{aligned}$$

In Eqs. 8.141 and 8.142, Iteration Level $(\nu+1)$ is associated with the unknown pressures $p^{n+1}_{i,j,k}$ and Iteration Level (ν) is associated with $\Gamma^{n+1}_{g_{i,j,k}}$. Although the extrapolated value $B_g^{\overset{*}{n+1}}$ is evaluated at the new time level, Γ_g^{n+1}, at the old iteration, may need to be updated with an iterative process to meet the condition of mass conservation (Eq. 8.91).

Fig. 8.14 shows the pressure value used to evaluate the transmissibilities with the extrapolation method of linearization. This figure

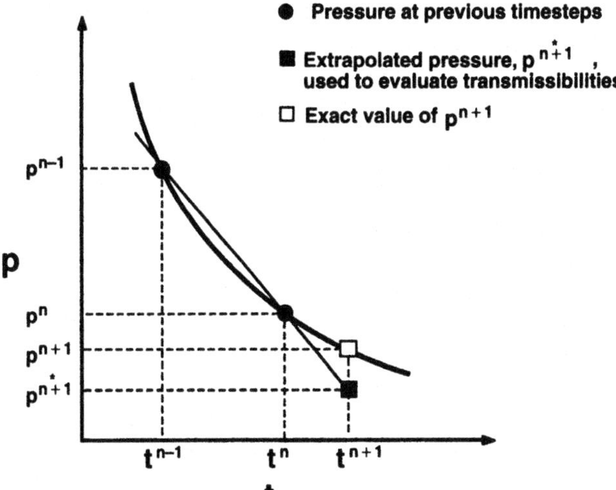

Fig. 8.14—Extrapolated pressure, $\overset{*}{p}^{n+1}$, used for the evaluation of transmissibilities in the extrapolation method of linearization.

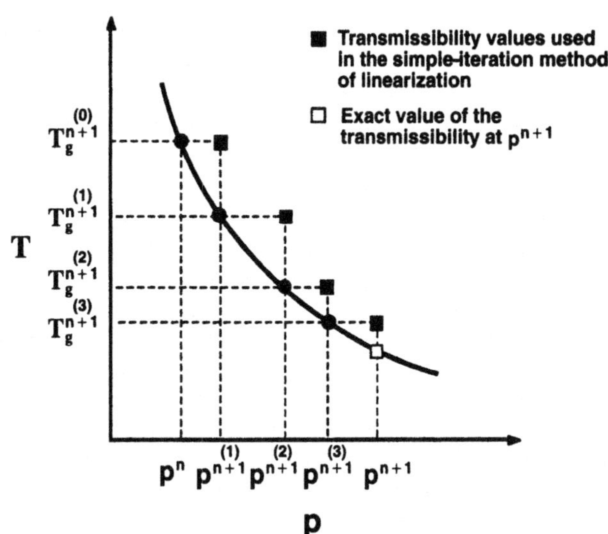

Fig. 8.15—Convergence behavior of the simple-iteration method of linearization.

indicates that the closer the actual pressure depletion is to linear behavior, the better the approximation of $\overset{*}{p}{}^{n+1}$, is to p^{n+1}. In addition, the extrapolation method does not properly account for changes in production and injection specifications with time.

Simple Iteration of the Transmissibility Terms. In the simple-iteration method, the transmissibility terms are evaluated one iteration behind the pressure solution. That is,

$$T^{n+1}_{gx_{i\pm½,j,k}} \cong \overset{(\nu)}{T}{}^{n+1}_{gx_{i\pm½,j,k}} = \left[\beta_c \frac{A_x k_x}{\overset{(\nu)}{\mu}{}_g^{n+1} \overset{(\nu)}{B}{}_g^{n+1} \Delta x}\right]_{i\pm½,j,k} \quad \ldots\ldots (8.143a)$$

$$\text{or } T^{n+1}_{gx_{i\pm½,j,k}} \cong \overset{(\nu)}{T}{}^{n+1}_{gx_{i\pm½,j,k}} = \left(\beta_c \frac{A_x k_x}{\Delta x}\right)_{i\pm½,j,k} \left(\frac{1}{\mu_g B_g}\right)^{\overset{(\nu)}{n+1}}_{i\pm½,j,k}. \quad \ldots\ldots (8.143b)$$

With this definition of transmissibility, the implicit finite-difference approximation to Eq. 8.102 becomes

$$\overset{(\nu)}{T}{}^{n+1}_{gx_{i+½,j,k}}\left(\overset{(\nu+1)}{p}{}^{n+1}_{i+1,j,k} - \overset{(\nu+1)}{p}{}^{n+1}_{i,j,k}\right) - \overset{(\nu)}{T}{}^{n+1}_{gx_{i-½,j,k}}\left(\overset{(\nu+1)}{p}{}^{n+1}_{i,j,k} - \overset{(\nu+1)}{p}{}^{n+1}_{i-1,j,k}\right)$$

$$+ \overset{(\nu)}{T}{}^{n+1}_{gy_{i,j+½,k}}\left(\overset{(\nu+1)}{p}{}^{n+1}_{i,j+1,k} - \overset{(\nu+1)}{p}{}^{n+1}_{i,j,k}\right) - \overset{(\nu)}{T}{}^{n+1}_{gy_{i,j-½,k}}\left(\overset{(\nu+1)}{p}{}^{n+1}_{i,j,k} - \overset{(\nu+1)}{p}{}^{n+1}_{i,j-1,k}\right)$$

$$+ \overset{(\nu)}{T}{}^{n+1}_{gz_{i,j,k+½}}\left(\overset{(\nu+1)}{p}{}^{n+1}_{i,j,k+1} - \overset{(\nu+1)}{p}{}^{n+1}_{i,j,k}\right) - \overset{(\nu)}{T}{}^{n+1}_{gz_{i,j,k-½}}\left(\overset{(\nu+1)}{p}{}^{n+1}_{i,j,k} - \overset{(\nu+1)}{p}{}^{n+1}_{i,j,k-1}\right)$$

$$= \frac{\overset{(\nu)}{\Gamma}{}^{n+1}_{g_{i,j,k}}}{\Delta t}\left(\overset{(\nu+1)}{p}{}^{n+1}_{i,j,k} - p^n_{i,j,k}\right) - q^{n+1}_{gsc_{i,j,k}} + \overset{(\nu)}{Q}{}^{n+1}_{G_{i,j,k}} \quad \ldots\ldots (8.144)$$

or, in matrix notation,

$$\overset{(\nu)}{B}{}^{n+1}_{i,j,k}\overset{(\nu+1)}{p}{}^{n+1}_{i,j,k-1} + \overset{(\nu)}{S}{}^{n+1}_{i,j,k}\overset{(\nu+1)}{p}{}^{n+1}_{i,j-1,k} + \overset{(\nu)}{W}{}^{n+1}_{i,j,k}\overset{(\nu+1)}{p}{}^{n+1}_{i-1,j,k}$$

$$+ \overset{(\nu)}{C}{}^{n+1}_{i,j,k}\overset{(\nu)}{p}{}^{n+1}_{i,j,k} + \overset{(\nu)}{E}{}^{n+1}_{i,j,k}\overset{(\nu+1)}{p}{}^{n+1}_{i+1,j,k} + \overset{(\nu)}{N}{}^{n+1}_{i,j,k}\overset{(\nu+1)}{p}{}^{n+1}_{i,j+1,k} + \overset{(\nu)}{A}{}^{n+1}_{i,j,k}\overset{(\nu+1)}{p}{}^{n+1}_{i,j,k+1}$$

$$= \overset{(\nu)}{Q}{}^{n+1}_{i,j,k}. \quad \ldots\ldots (8.145)$$

One difference between the simple-iteration method and the previously discussed methods is the updating of the transmissibilities during the iteration process. In the explicit and the extrapolated methods of evaluating transmissibilities, the grid-dependent terms $[\beta_c(A_x k_x/\Delta x)]_{i\pm½,j,k}$ are evaluated once at the beginning of the simulation, while the pressure-dependent terms $(1/\mu_g B_g)_{i\pm½,j,k}$ are evaluated at the beginning of each timestep. Even when an iterative procedure is used because of the $\Gamma_{g_{i,j,k}}$ term, the pressure-dependent groups appearing in the transmissibility terms are not re-evaluated. In the simple-iteration method, the pressure-dependent groups are re-evaluated at every iteration. **Fig. 8.15** shows the convergence behavior of the simple-iteration method.

Fully Implicit Method. In the previously discussed methods, we estimated the values of the nonlinear terms T_g^{n+1}, Γ_g^{n+1}, and Q_G^{n+1} with the values of pressure at various times and iteration levels. The resulting iteration processes from these methods tend to converge slowly. This is because of the poor approximation of the nonlinear terms during the iteration process compared with their actual values. Figs. 8.13 through 8.15 show these approximations; however, we have additional information that can be used to improve the approximations of these nonlinear terms. This additional information is in the form of the derivatives of T_g, Γ_g, and Q_G.

To facilitate this discussion, we consider the 1D, nonlinear, finite-difference approximation to the compressible-flow equation

$$T^{n+1}_{gx_{i+½}}\left(p^{n+1}_{i+1} - p^{n+1}_i\right) - T^{n+1}_{gx_{i-½}}\left(p^{n+1}_i - p^{n+1}_{i-1}\right)$$

$$= \frac{\Gamma^{n+1}_{g_i}}{\Delta t}\left(p^{n+1}_i - p^n_i\right) - q^{n+1}_{gsc_i} + Q^{n+1}_{G_i}. \quad \ldots\ldots (8.146)$$

In Eq. 8.146, all coefficients and variables are evaluated at Time Level $n+1$ except the p_i^n value in the approximation of the time derivative. We can develop an iterative procedure by approximating every $n+1$ variable in Eq. 8.146 by a Taylor-series expansion about Iteration Level (ν). That is,

$$T^{n+1}_{gx_{i\pm½}} \approx \overset{(\nu+1)}{T}{}^{n+1}_{gx_{i\pm½}} \approx \overset{(\nu)}{T}{}^{n+1}_{gx_{i\pm½}} + \left.\frac{\partial T_{gx_{i\pm½}}}{\partial p_{i\pm1}}\right|^{\overset{(\nu)}{n+1}}$$

$$\times\, \delta\overset{(\nu+1)}{p}{}^{n+1}_{i\pm1} + \left.\frac{\partial T_{gx_{i\pm½}}}{\partial p_i}\right|^{\overset{(\nu)}{n+1}} \delta\overset{(\nu+1)}{p}{}^{n+1}_i, \quad \ldots\ldots (8.147)$$

$$\overset{(\nu+1)}{p}{}^{n+1}_{i\pm1} \approx \overset{(\nu)}{p}{}^{n+1}_{i\pm1} + \left.\frac{\partial p_{i\pm1}}{\partial p_{i\pm1}}\right|^{\overset{(\nu)}{n+1}} \delta\overset{(\nu+1)}{p}{}^{n+1}_{i\pm1} \quad \ldots\ldots (8.148a)$$

$$\approx \overset{(\nu)}{p}{}_{i\pm1}^{n+1} + \delta \overset{(\nu+1)}{p}{}_{i\pm1}^{n+1}, \quad \text{(8.148b)}$$

$$\overset{(\nu+1)}{p}{}_{i}^{n+1} \approx \overset{(\nu)}{p}{}_{i}^{n+1} + \left.\frac{\partial p_i}{\partial p_i}\right|^{\overset{(\nu)}{n+1}} \delta \overset{(\nu+1)}{p}{}_{i}^{n+1} \quad \text{(8.149a)}$$

$$\approx \overset{(\nu)}{p}{}_{i}^{n+1} + \delta \overset{(\nu+1)}{p}{}_{i}^{n+1}, \quad \text{(8.149b)}$$

$$\overset{(\nu+1)}{\Gamma}{}_{g_i}^{n+1} \approx \overset{(\nu)}{\Gamma}{}_{g_i}^{n+1} + \left.\frac{\partial \Gamma_{g_i}}{\partial p_i}\right|^{\overset{(\nu)}{n+1}} \delta \overset{(\nu+1)}{p}{}_{i}^{n+1}, \quad \text{(8.150)}$$

$$\overset{(\nu+1)}{Q}{}_{G_i}^{n+1} \approx \overset{(\nu)}{Q}{}_{G_i}^{n+1} + \left.\frac{\partial Q_{G_i}}{\partial p_{i+1}}\right|^{\overset{(\nu)}{n+1}} \delta \overset{(\nu+1)}{p}{}_{i+1}^{n+1} + \left.\frac{\partial Q_{G_i}}{\partial p_i}\right|^{\overset{(\nu)}{n+1}} \delta \overset{(\nu+1)}{p}{}_{i}^{n+1}$$

$$+ \left.\frac{\partial Q_{G_i}}{\partial p_{i-1}}\right|^{\overset{(\nu)}{n+1}} \delta \overset{(\nu+1)}{p}{}_{i-1}^{n+1}, \quad \text{(8.151)}$$

$$\text{and } \overset{(\nu+1)}{q}{}_{gsc_i}^{n+1} \approx \overset{(\nu)}{q}{}_{gsc_i}^{n+1} + \left.\frac{\partial q_{gsc}}{\partial p_i}\right|^{\overset{(\nu)}{n+1}} \delta \overset{(\nu+1)}{p}{}_{i}^{n+1}, \quad \text{(8.152)}$$

$$\text{where } \delta \overset{(\nu+1)}{p}{}_{i\pm1}^{n+1} = \overset{(\nu+1)}{p}{}_{i\pm1}^{n+1} - \overset{(\nu)}{p}{}_{i\pm1}^{n+1} \quad \text{(8.153)}$$

$$\text{and } \delta \overset{(\nu+1)}{p}{}_{i}^{n+1} = \overset{(\nu+1)}{p}{}_{i}^{n+1} - \overset{(\nu)}{p}{}_{i}^{n+1}. \quad \text{(8.154)}$$

In Eqs. 8.147 through 8.152, we retain only the first-order terms in the expansions. Because $T_{gx_{i\pm1/2}}$ and Q_{G_i} are functions of multiple pressures, multiple-derivative terms are required in the expansions. Substituting Eqs. 8.147 through 8.154 into Eq. 8.146 results in

$$\left[\overset{(\nu)}{T}{}_{gx_{i+1/2}}^{n+1} + \left.\frac{\partial T_{gx_{i+1/2}}}{\partial p_i}\right|^{\overset{(\nu)}{n+1}} \delta \overset{(\nu+1)}{p}{}_{i}^{n+1} + \left.\frac{\partial T_{gx_{i+1/2}}}{\partial p_{i+1}}\right|^{\overset{(\nu)}{n+1}} \delta \overset{(\nu+1)}{p}{}_{i+1}^{n+1}\right]$$

$$\times \left\{\left[\overset{(\nu)}{p}{}_{i+1}^{n+1} + \delta \overset{(\nu+1)}{p}{}_{i+1}^{n+1}\right] - \left[\overset{(\nu)}{p}{}_{i}^{n+1} + \delta \overset{(\nu+1)}{p}{}_{i}^{n+1}\right]\right\}$$

$$- \left[\overset{(\nu)}{T}{}_{gx_{i-1/2}}^{n+1} + \left.\frac{\partial T_{gx_{i-1/2}}}{\partial p_i}\right|^{\overset{(\nu)}{n+1}} \delta \overset{(\nu+1)}{p}{}_{i}^{n+1} + \left.\frac{\partial T_{gx_{i-1/2}}}{\partial p_{i-1}}\right|^{\overset{(\nu)}{n+1}} \delta \overset{(\nu+1)}{p}{}_{i-1}^{n+1}\right]$$

$$\times \left\{\left[\overset{(\nu)}{p}{}_{i}^{n+1} + \delta \overset{(\nu+1)}{p}{}_{i}^{n+1}\right] - \left[\overset{(\nu)}{p}{}_{i-1}^{n+1} + \delta \overset{(\nu+1)}{p}{}_{i-1}^{n+1}\right]\right\}$$

$$= \frac{1}{\Delta t}\left[\overset{(\nu)}{\Gamma}{}_{g_i}^{n+1} + \left.\frac{\partial \Gamma_{g_i}}{\partial p_i}\right|^{\overset{(\nu)}{n+1}} \delta \overset{(\nu+1)}{p}{}_{i}^{n+1}\right]$$

$$\times \left\{\left[\overset{(\nu)}{p}{}_{i}^{n+1} + \delta \overset{(\nu+1)}{p}{}_{i}^{n+1}\right] - p_i^n\right\}$$

$$- \left[\overset{(\nu)}{q}{}_{gsc_i}^{n+1} + \left.\frac{\partial q_{gsc_i}}{\partial p_i}\right|^{\overset{(\nu)}{n+1}} \delta \overset{(\nu+1)}{p}{}_{i}^{n+1}\right]$$

$$+ \left[\overset{(\nu)}{Q}{}_{G_i}^{n+1} + \left.\frac{\partial Q_{G_i}}{\partial p_{i+1}}\right|^{\overset{(\nu)}{n+1}} \delta \overset{(\nu+1)}{p}{}_{i+1}^{n+1} + \left.\frac{\partial Q_{G_i}}{\partial p_i}\right|^{\overset{(\nu)}{n+1}} \delta \overset{(\nu+1)}{p}{}_{i}^{n+1}\right.$$

$$\left. + \left.\frac{\partial Q_{G_i}}{\partial p_{i-1}}\right|^{\overset{(\nu)}{n+1}} \delta \overset{(\nu+1)}{p}{}_{i-1}^{n+1}\right]. \quad \text{(8.155)}$$

Performing all the multiplications in Eq. 8.155 results in

$$\overset{(\nu)}{T}{}_{gx_{i+1/2}}^{n+1} \overset{(\nu)}{p}{}_{i+1}^{n+1} + \overset{(\nu)}{p}{}_{i+1}^{n+1} \left.\frac{\partial T_{gx_{i+1/2}}}{\partial p_i}\right|^{\overset{(\nu)}{n+1}} \delta \overset{(\nu+1)}{p}{}_{i}^{n+1}$$

$$+ \overset{(\nu)}{p}{}_{i+1}^{n+1} \left.\frac{\partial T_{gx_{i+1/2}}}{\partial p_{i+1}}\right|^{\overset{(\nu)}{n+1}} \delta \overset{(\nu+1)}{p}{}_{i+1}^{n+1}$$

$$+ \overset{(\nu)}{T}{}_{gx_{i+1/2}}^{n+1} \delta \overset{(\nu+1)}{p}{}_{i+1}^{n+1} - \left[\overset{(\nu)}{T}{}_{gx_{i+1/2}}^{n+1} \overset{(\nu)}{p}{}_{i}^{n+1} + \overset{(\nu)}{p}{}_{i}^{n+1} \left.\frac{\partial T_{gx_{i+1/2}}}{\partial p_i}\right|^{\overset{(\nu)}{n+1}} \delta \overset{(\nu+1)}{p}{}_{i}^{n+1}\right.$$

$$\left. + \overset{(\nu)}{p}{}_{i}^{n+1} \left.\frac{\partial T_{gx_{i+1/2}}}{\partial p_{i+1}}\right|^{\overset{(\nu)}{n+1}} \delta \overset{(\nu+1)}{p}{}_{i+1}^{n+1} + \overset{(\nu)}{T}{}_{gx_{i+1/2}}^{n+1} \delta \overset{(\nu+1)}{p}{}_{i}^{n+1}\right]$$

$$- \left[\overset{(\nu)}{T}{}_{gx_{i-1/2}}^{n+1} \overset{(\nu)}{p}{}_{i}^{n+1} + \overset{(\nu)}{p}{}_{i}^{n+1} \left.\frac{\partial T_{gx_{i-1/2}}}{\partial p_i}\right|^{\overset{(\nu)}{n+1}} \delta \overset{(\nu+1)}{p}{}_{i}^{n+1}\right.$$

$$\left. + \overset{(\nu)}{p}{}_{i}^{n+1} \left.\frac{\partial T_{gx_{i-1/2}}}{\partial p_{i-1}}\right|^{\overset{(\nu)}{n+1}} \delta \overset{(\nu+1)}{p}{}_{i-1}^{n+1} + \overset{(\nu)}{T}{}_{gx_{i-1/2}}^{n+1} \delta \overset{(\nu+1)}{p}{}_{i}^{n+1}\right]$$

$$+ \overset{(\nu)}{T}{}_{gx_{i-1/2}}^{n+1} \overset{(\nu)}{p}{}_{i-1}^{n+1} + \overset{(\nu)}{p}{}_{i-1}^{n+1} \left.\frac{\partial T_{gx_{i-1/2}}}{\partial p_i}\right|^{\overset{(\nu)}{n+1}} \delta \overset{(\nu+1)}{p}{}_{i}^{n+1}$$

$$+ \overset{(\nu)}{p}{}_{i-1}^{n+1} \left.\frac{\partial T_{gx_{i-1/2}}}{\partial p_{i-1}}\right|^{\overset{(\nu)}{n+1}} \delta \overset{(\nu+1)}{p}{}_{i-1}^{n+1} + \overset{(\nu)}{T}{}_{gx_{i-1/2}}^{n+1} \delta \overset{(\nu+1)}{p}{}_{i-1}^{n+1}$$

$$= \frac{1}{\Delta t}\left[\overset{(\nu)}{\Gamma}{}_{g_i}^{n+1} \overset{(\nu)}{p}{}_{i}^{n+1} + \overset{(\nu)}{p}{}_{i}^{n+1} \left.\frac{\partial \Gamma_{g_i}}{\partial p_i}\right|^{\overset{(\nu)}{n+1}} \delta \overset{(\nu+1)}{p}{}_{i}^{n+1} + \overset{(\nu)}{\Gamma}{}_{g_i}^{n+1} \delta \overset{(\nu+1)}{p}{}_{i}^{n+1}\right.$$

$$\left. - \overset{(\nu)}{\Gamma}{}_{g_i}^{n+1} p_i^n - p_i^n \left.\frac{\partial \Gamma_{g_i}}{\partial p_i}\right|^{\overset{(\nu)}{n+1}} \delta \overset{(\nu+1)}{p}{}_{i}^{n+1}\right]$$

$$-\left[\overset{(\nu)}{q}{}^{n+1}_{gsc_i}+\left.\frac{\partial q_{gsc_i}}{\partial p_i}\right|^{\overset{(\nu)}{n+1}}\overset{(\nu+1)}{\delta p}{}^{n+1}_{i}\right]$$

$$+\left[\overset{(\nu)}{Q}{}^{n+1}_{G_i}+\left.\frac{\partial Q_{G_i}}{\partial p_{i+1}}\right|^{\overset{(\nu)}{n+1}}\overset{(\nu+1)}{\delta p}{}^{n+1}_{i+1}+\left.\frac{\partial Q_{G_i}}{\partial p_i}\right|^{\overset{(\nu)}{n+1}}\overset{(\nu+1)}{\delta p}{}^{n+1}_{i}\right.$$

$$\left.+\left.\frac{\partial Q_{G_i}}{\partial p_{i-1}}\right|^{\overset{(\nu)}{n+1}}\overset{(\nu+1)}{\delta p}{}^{n+1}_{i-1}\right]. \qquad (8.156)$$

In Eq. 8.156, all $\delta p_{i+1}\delta p_i$, $\delta p_i\delta p_{i-1}$, $(\delta p_{i+1})^2$, $(\delta p_i)^2$, and $(\delta p_{i-1})^2$ terms are dropped. This approximation is appropriate because for convergent iteration processes, as the iterations continue, the differences between two iterations, the δ terms, become small. Therefore, when these small numbers are multiplied together, the result is a much smaller number.

Collecting like terms in Eq. 8.156 results in

$$-\left\{\overset{(\nu)}{T}{}^{n+1}_{gx_{i+1/2}}+\left.\frac{\partial T_{gx_{i+1/2}}}{\partial p_{i+1}}\right|^{\overset{(\nu)}{n+1}}\left[\overset{(\nu)}{p}{}^{n+1}_{i+1}-\overset{(\nu)}{p}{}^{n+1}_{i}\right]-\left.\frac{\partial Q_{G_i}}{\partial p_{i+1}}\right|^{\overset{(\nu)}{n+1}}\right\}$$

$$\times\,\overset{(\nu+1)}{\delta p}{}^{n+1}_{i+1}+\left[\overset{(\nu)}{T}{}^{n+1}_{gx_{i+1/2}}-\left.\frac{\partial T_{gx_{i+1/2}}}{\partial p_i}\right|^{\overset{(\nu)}{n+1}}\left[\overset{(\nu)}{p}{}^{n+1}_{i+1}-\overset{(\nu)}{p}{}^{n+1}_{i}\right]\right.$$

$$+\overset{(\nu)}{T}{}^{n+1}_{gx_{i-1/2}}+\left.\frac{\partial T_{gx_{i-1/2}}}{\partial p_i}\right|^{\overset{(\nu)}{n+1}}\left[\overset{(\nu)}{p}{}^{n+1}_{i}-\overset{(\nu)}{p}{}^{n+1}_{i-1}\right]$$

$$+\frac{1}{\Delta t}\left\{\overset{(\nu)}{\Gamma}{}^{n+1}_{g_i}+\left.\frac{\partial \Gamma_{g_i}}{\partial p_i}\right|^{\overset{(\nu)}{n+1}}\left[\overset{(\nu)}{p}{}^{n+1}_{i}-p^n_i\right]\right\}$$

$$\left.-\left.\frac{\partial q_{gsc_i}}{\partial p_i}\right|^{\overset{(\nu)}{n+1}}+\left.\frac{\partial Q_{G_i}}{\partial p_i}\right|^{\overset{(\nu)}{n+1}}\right]\overset{(\nu+1)}{\delta p}{}^{n+1}_{i}$$

$$-\left\{\overset{(\nu)}{T}{}^{n+1}_{gx_{i-1/2}}-\left.\frac{\partial T_{gx_{i-1/2}}}{\partial p_{i-1}}\right|^{\overset{(\nu)}{n+1}}\left[\overset{(\nu)}{p}{}^{n+1}_{i}-\overset{(\nu)}{p}{}^{n+1}_{i-1}\right]\right.$$

$$\left.-\left.\frac{\partial Q_{G_i}}{\partial p_{i-1}}\right|^{\overset{(\nu)}{n+1}}\right\}\overset{(\nu+1)}{\delta p}{}^{n+1}_{i-1}$$

$$=-\left(-\left\{\overset{(\nu)}{T}{}^{n+1}_{gx_{i+1/2}}\left[\overset{(\nu)}{p}{}^{n+1}_{i+1}-\overset{(\nu)}{p}{}^{n+1}_{i}\right]\right.\right.$$

$$\left.-\overset{(\nu)}{T}{}^{n+1}_{gx_{i-1/2}}\left[\overset{(\nu)}{p}{}^{n+1}_{i}-\overset{(\nu)}{p}{}^{n+1}_{i-1}\right]\right\}$$

$$\left.+\frac{\overset{(\nu)}{\Gamma}{}^{n+1}_{g_i}}{\Delta t}\left[\overset{(\nu)}{p}{}^{n+1}_{i}-p^n_i\right]-\overset{(\nu)}{q}{}^{n+1}_{gsc_i}+\overset{(\nu)}{Q}{}^{n+1}_{G_i}\right). \qquad (8.157)$$

Inspection of the right side of Eq. 8.157 reveals that it is the negative of the residual of the original finite-difference equation, Eq. 8.146 evaluated at (ν) iteration. That is,

$$\overset{(\nu)}{r}{}^{n+1}_{i}=-\left\{\overset{(\nu)}{T}{}^{n+1}_{gx_{i+1/2}}\left[\overset{(\nu)}{p}{}^{n+1}_{i+1}-\overset{(\nu)}{p}{}^{n+1}_{i}\right]\right.$$

$$\left.-\overset{(\nu)}{T}{}^{n+1}_{gx_{i-1/2}}\left[\overset{(\nu)}{p}{}^{n+1}_{i}-\overset{(\nu)}{p}{}^{n+1}_{i-1}\right]\right\}$$

$$+\frac{\overset{(\nu)}{\Gamma}{}^{n+1}_{g_i}}{\Delta t}\left[\overset{(\nu)}{p}{}^{n+1}_{i}-p^n_i\right]-\overset{(\nu)}{q}{}^{n+1}_{gsc_i}+\overset{(\nu)}{Q}{}^{n+1}_{G_i}\,. \qquad (8.158)$$

Further inspection of Eq. 8.157 indicates that the coefficients of δp_{i+1}, δp_i, and δp_{i-1} are $\partial r_i/\partial p_{i+1}$, $\partial r_i/\partial p_i$, and $\partial r_i/\partial p_{i-1}$, respectively. In other words, we can rewrite Eq. 8.157 as

$$\left.\frac{\partial r_i}{\partial p_{i+1}}\right|^{\overset{(\nu)}{n+1}}\overset{(\nu+1)}{\delta p}{}^{n+1}_{i+1}+\left.\frac{\partial r_i}{\partial p_i}\right|^{\overset{(\nu)}{n+1}}\overset{(\nu+1)}{\delta p}{}^{n+1}_{i}$$

$$+\left.\frac{\partial r_i}{\partial p_{i-1}}\right|^{\overset{(\nu)}{n+1}}\overset{(\nu+1)}{\delta p}{}^{n+1}_{i-1}=-\overset{(\nu)}{r}{}^{n+1}_{i}. \qquad (8.159)$$

When Eq. 8.159 is written for each gridblock in the system, Eq. 8.160 is obtained.

$$\overset{(\nu)}{[\mathbf{J}]}{}^{n+1}\overset{(\nu+1)}{\delta\vec{p}}{}^{n+1}=-\overset{(\nu)}{\vec{r}}{}^{n+1}. \qquad (8.160)$$

Eq. 8.160 represents the basis of the classic Newton-Raphson iteration. In this equation, $[\mathbf{J}]$ = the Jacobian matrix, $\delta\vec{p}$ = vector of change in pressure from one iteration to the next, and $\vec{r}$ = residual vector of the original equation. We can write a 3D version of Eq. 8.159 with matrix notation as

$$\overset{(\nu)}{B}{}^{n+1}_{J_{i,j,k}}\overset{(\nu)}{\delta p}{}^{n+1}_{i,j,k-1}+\overset{(\nu)}{S}{}^{n+1}_{J_{i,j,k}}\overset{(\nu)}{\delta p}{}^{n+1}_{i,j-1,k}+\overset{(\nu)}{W}{}^{n+1}_{J_{i,j,k}}\overset{(\nu)}{\delta p}{}^{n+1}_{i-1,j,k}+\overset{(\nu)}{C}{}^{n+1}_{J_{i,j,k}}\overset{(\nu)}{\delta p}{}^{n+1}_{i,j,k}$$

$$+\overset{(\nu)}{E}{}^{n+1}_{J_{i,j,k}}\overset{(\nu)}{\delta p}{}^{n+1}_{i+1,j,k}+\overset{(\nu)}{N}{}^{n+1}_{J_{i,j,k}}\overset{(\nu)}{\delta p}{}^{n+1}_{i,j+1,k}+\overset{(\nu)}{A}{}^{n+1}_{J_{i,j,k}}\overset{(\nu)}{\delta p}{}^{n+1}_{i,j,k+1}$$

$$=-\overset{(\nu)}{r}{}^{n+1}_{i,j,k}, \qquad (8.161)$$

where

$$\overset{(\nu)}{r}{}^{n+1}_{i,j,k}=\overset{(\nu)}{Q}{}^{n+1}_{i,j,k}-\overset{(\nu)}{B}{}^{n+1}_{i,j,k}\overset{(\nu)}{p}{}^{n+1}_{i,j,k-1}-\overset{(\nu)}{S}{}^{n+1}_{i,j,k}\overset{(\nu)}{p}{}^{n+1}_{i,j-1,k}-\overset{(\nu)}{W}{}^{n+1}_{i,j,k}\overset{(\nu)}{p}{}^{n+1}_{i-1,j,k}$$

$$-\overset{(\nu)}{C}{}^{n+1}_{i,j,k}\overset{(\nu)}{p}{}^{n+1}_{i,j,k}-\overset{(\nu)}{E}{}^{n+1}_{i,j,k}\overset{(\nu)}{p}{}^{n+1}_{i+1,j,k}$$

$$-\overset{(\nu)}{N}{}^{n+1}_{i,j,k}\overset{(\nu)}{p}{}^{n+1}_{i,j+1,k}-\overset{(\nu)}{A}{}^{n+1}_{i,j,k}\overset{(\nu)}{p}{}^{n+1}_{i,j,k+1}, \qquad (8.162)$$

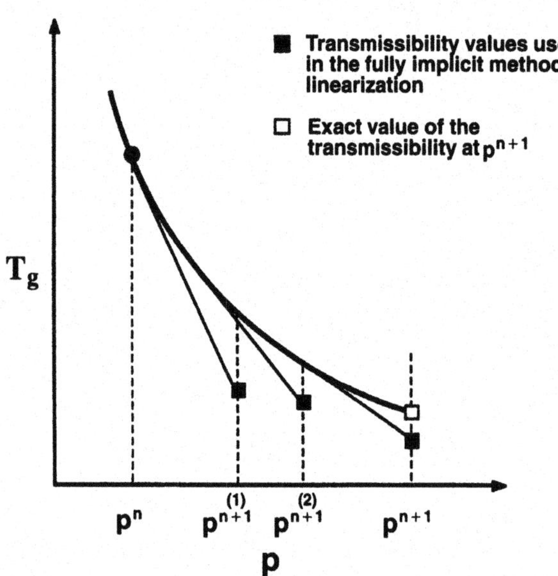

Fig. 8.16—Convergence behavior of the fully implicit method (generalized Newton-Raphson procedure) of linearization.

$$B_{J_{i,j,k}} = \frac{\partial r_{i,j,k}}{\partial p_{i,j,k-1}}, \quad \text{(8.163)}$$

$$S_{J_{i,j,k}} = \frac{\partial r_{i,j,k}}{\partial p_{i,j-1,k}}, \quad \text{(8.164)}$$

$$W_{J_{i,j,k}} = \frac{\partial r_{i,j,k}}{\partial p_{i-1,j,k}}, \quad \text{(8.165)}$$

$$C_{J_{i,j,k}} = \frac{\partial r_{i,j,k}}{\partial p_{i,j,k}}, \quad \text{(8.166)}$$

$$E_{J_{i,j,k}} = \frac{\partial r_{i,j,k}}{\partial p_{i+1,j,k}}, \quad \text{(8.167)}$$

$$N_{J_{i,j,k}} = \frac{\partial r_{i,j,k}}{\partial p_{i,j+1,k}}, \quad \text{(8.168)}$$

and $$A_{J_{i,j,k}} = \frac{\partial r_{i,j,k}}{\partial p_{i,j,k+1}}. \quad \text{(8.169)}$$

In Eqs. 8.157 and 8.163 through 8.169, the derivatives of the T_g, Γ_g, and Q_G terms with respect to pressure are required. These derivatives can be evaluated either analytically, as in Example 3.7, or numerically. If these derivatives are evaluated numerically, Eq. 8.170 is used.

$$\frac{\partial T_{gx}}{\partial p} \approx \frac{T_{gx}(p+\varepsilon) - T_{gx}(p)}{\varepsilon}. \quad \text{(8.170)}$$

ε is selected so that it is small enough that a reasonable approximation to the derivative is obtained but large enough that machine roundoff error does not dominate the approximation. The numerical differentiation scheme used in Eq. 8.170 is a forward-difference approximation. We also could have used a central-difference approximation defined by

$$\frac{\partial T_{gx}}{\partial p} \approx \frac{T_{gx}(p+\varepsilon) - T_{gx}(p-\varepsilon)}{2\varepsilon}. \quad \text{(8.171)}$$

Although the central-difference approximation is a higher-order approximation, Eq. 8.170 is used more commonly in practice. This is because $T_{gx}(p)$ is already available in the computational procedure. In addition, because the value of ε is chosen to be small enough to obtain a reasonable approximation to the derivative, the reduction in the accuracy of Eq. 8.170 is not significant. **Fig. 8.16** shows the convergence behavior of the fully implicit method of linearization.

8.4.2 Material-Balance Check for the Compressible-Flow Problem. For compressible fluids, the I_{MB} is expressed as

$$I_{MB} = \frac{\sum_{i=1}^{n_x}\sum_{j=1}^{n_y}\sum_{k=1}^{n_z} \frac{V_{b_{i,j,k}}}{\alpha_c}\left(\frac{\phi^{n+1}}{B_g^{n+1}} - \frac{\phi^n}{B_g^n}\right)_{i,j,k}}{\Delta t \sum_{i=1}^{n_x}\sum_{j=1}^{n_y}\sum_{k=1}^{n_z} q_{gsc_{i,j,k}}^{n+1}} \quad \text{(8.172)}$$

and the C_{MB} is expressed as

$$C_{MB} = \frac{\sum_{i=1}^{n_x}\sum_{j=1}^{n_y}\sum_{k=1}^{n_z} \frac{V_{b_{i,j,k}}}{\alpha_c}\left(\frac{\phi^{n+1}}{B_g^{n+1}} - \frac{\phi^0}{B_g^0}\right)_{i,j,k}}{\sum_{m=1}^{n+1} \Delta t^m \sum_{i=1}^{n_x}\sum_{j=1}^{n_y}\sum_{k=1}^{n_z} q_{gsc_{i,j,k}}^m}. \quad \text{(8.173)}$$

As in the case of slightly compressible fluids, both I_{MB} and C_{MB} checks should be in the range of 0.995 to 1.005.

8.5 Analysis of the Material-Balance Calculation Used in Reservoir Simulation

In Secs. 8.2.7, 8.3.3, and 8.4.2, we discussed the material-balance calculations for incompressible-, slightly-compressible-, and compressible-flow systems, respectively. In this section, we analyze these calculations to determine the properties of the finite-difference operators that result in a material-conservative formulation.

During the expansion of the accumulation term discussed in Sec. 8.3.1, we converted the finite-difference approximation from

$$T_{lx_{i+1/2}}(p_{i+1} - p_i) - T_{lx_{i-1/2}}(p_i - p_{i-1}) + q_{lsc_i}$$

$$= \frac{V_{b_i}}{\alpha_c \Delta t}\left(\frac{\phi^{n+1}}{B_l^{n+1}} - \frac{\phi^n}{B_l^n}\right)_i \quad \text{(8.174)}$$

to $T_{lx_{i+1/2}}(p_{i+1} - p_i) - T_{lx_{i-1/2}}(p_i - p_{i-1}) + q_{lsc_i}$

$$= \frac{\Gamma_{l_i}^{n+1}}{\Delta t}(p_i^{n+1} - p_i^n). \quad \text{(8.175)}$$

The expansion of the accumulation term is required to write the right side of Eq. 8.174 in terms of the unknown, p_i ($i = 1,2, \ldots n_x$). Because Eq. 8.174 is the direct result of the discretization of the PDE developed in Chap. 4 and Eq. 8.175 is the equation solved in numerical reservoir simulation, we need to analyze both equations to determine the requirements for a material-conservative finite-difference formulation. In Eqs. 8.174 and 8.175, we assumed 1D, horizontal flow. In addition, we have not assigned time levels to the unknowns, p_i ($i = 1,2, \ldots, n_x$), on the left side of Eqs. 8.174 and 8.175 (the explicit or implicit formulation); time levels to the source/sink term, q_{lsc_i} (explicit or implicit injection/production); or time and iteration levels to the transmissibility terms, $T_{lx_{i\pm1/2}}$ (the method of linearization). Therefore, the following analysis is sufficiently general to accommodate all the numerical approximations discussed for single-phase flow.

Eq. 8.174 is written for each gridblock in an n_x grid system. For Gridblock 1,

$$T_{lx_{1+1/2}}(p_2 - p_1) - T_{lx_{1-1/2}}(p_1 - p_0) + q_{lsc_1}$$

$$= \frac{V_{b_1}}{\alpha_c \Delta t}\left(\frac{\phi^{n+1}}{B_l^{n+1}} - \frac{\phi^n}{B_l^n}\right)_1. \quad \text{(8.176a)}$$

For Gridblock 2,

$$T_{lx_{2+1/2}}(p_3 - p_2) - T_{lx_{2-1/2}}(p_2 - p_1) + q_{lsc_2}$$

$$= \frac{V_{b_2}}{\alpha_c \Delta t}\left(\frac{\phi^{n+1}}{B_l^{n+1}} - \frac{\phi^n}{B_l^n}\right)_2 . \qquad (8.176b)$$

For Gridblock 3,

$$T_{lx_{3+1/2}}(p_4 - p_3) - T_{lx_{3-1/2}}(p_3 - p_2) + q_{lsc_3}$$

$$= \frac{V_{b_3}}{\alpha_c \Delta t}\left(\frac{\phi^{n+1}}{B_l^{n+1}} - \frac{\phi^n}{B_l^n}\right)_3 . \qquad (8.176c)$$

For Gridblock n_x,

$$T_{lx_{n_x+1/2}}(p_{n_x+1} - p_{n_x}) - T_{lx_{n_x-1/2}}(p_{n_x} - p_{n_x-1}) + q_{lsc_{n_x}}$$

$$= \frac{V_{b_{n_x}}}{\alpha_c \Delta t}\left(\frac{\phi^{n+1}}{B_l^{n+1}} - \frac{\phi^n}{B_l^n}\right)_{n_x} . \qquad (8.176d)$$

A similar system of equations is generated when Eq. 8.175 is written for each gridblock in an n_x grid system. Eq. 8.177 is obtained by adding Eqs. 8.176a through 8.176d.

$$\sum_{i=1}^{n_x} T_{lx_{i+1/2}}(p_{i+1} - p_i) - \sum_{i=1}^{n_x} T_{lx_{i-1/2}}(p_i - p_{i-1}) + \sum_{i=1}^{n_x} q_{lsc_i}$$

$$= \frac{1}{\alpha_c \Delta t}\sum_{i=1}^{n_x}\left[V_{b_i}\left(\frac{\phi^{n+1}}{B_l^{n+1}} - \frac{\phi^n}{B_l^n}\right)_i\right]. \qquad (8.177)$$

$T_{lx_{i+1/2}}(p_{i+1} - p_i)$, the first term in Eq. 8.177, is the approximation to the flow rate in STB/D [std m^3/d] across the $i + 1/2$ boundary of Gridblock i by use of the forward-difference approximation. $T_{lx_{i-1/2}}(p_i - p_{i-1})$, the second term in Eq. 177, is the approximation to the flow rate in STB/D [std m^3/d] across the $i - 1/2$ boundary of Gridblock i by use of the backward-difference approximation.

At any interior gridblock boundary, the flow rate across the boundary is calculated twice, once for each adjacent gridblock that shares the boundary. For example, in the system of linear equations listed, the equation for Gridblock 2 has the term $T_{lx_{2+1/2}}(p_3 - p_2)$, which is the forward-difference approximation of the flow rate across the gridblock boundary, while the equation for Gridblock 3 has the term, $T_{lx_{3-1/2}}(p_3 - p_2)$, which is the backward-difference approximation of the flow rate across the gridblock boundary.

Eq. 8.177 can be rewritten as

$$- T_{lx_{1-1/2}}(p_1 - p_0) + \sum_{i=1}^{n_x-1} T_{lx_{i+1/2}}(p_{i+1} - p_i)$$

$$- \sum_{i=2}^{n_x} T_{lx_{i-1/2}}(p_i - p_{i-1})$$

$$+ T_{lx_{n_x+1/2}}(p_{n_x+1} - p_{n_x}) + \sum_{i=1}^{n_x} q_{lsc_i}$$

$$= \frac{1}{\alpha_c \Delta t}\sum_{i=1}^{n_x}\left[V_{b_i}\left(\frac{\phi^{n+1}}{B_l^{n+1}} - \frac{\phi^n}{B_l^n}\right)_i\right]. \qquad (8.178)$$

The physical interpretations of the terms in Eq. 8.178 follow.

$$T_{lx_{1-1/2}}(p_1 - p_0)$$

is the backward-difference approximation of the flow rate across the external boundary at $x_{1-1/2}$ (the sign of this term refers to fluid entering or leaving the grid system).

$$\sum_{i=1}^{n_x-1} T_{lx_{i+1/2}}(p_{i+1} - p_i)$$

is the summation of the forward-difference approximations of the flow rates across interior-gridblock boundaries at $x_{i+1/2}$ (in the positive i direction).

$$\sum_{i=2}^{n_x} T_{lx_{i-1/2}}(p_i - p_{i-1})$$

is the summation of the backward-difference approximations of the flow rates across interior gridblock boundaries at $x_{i-1/2}$ (in the negative i direction).

$$T_{lx_{n_x+1/2}}(p_{n_x+1} - p_{n_x})$$

is the forward-difference approximation of the flow rate across the external boundary at $x_{n_x+1/2}$ (the sign of this term refers to fluid entering or leaving the grid system).

$$\sum_{i=1}^{n_x} q_{lsc_i}$$

is the summation of all production rates from (or injection rates into) the grid system, which is the total production/injection rate imposed on the system.

$$\frac{1}{\alpha_c \Delta t}\sum_{i=1}^{n_x}\left[V_{b_i}\left(\frac{\phi^{n+1}}{B_l^{n+1}} - \frac{\phi^n}{B_l^n}\right)_i\right]$$

is the summation of the rate of change of the fluid in place during the time interval Δt.

Because our material-balance checks, I_{MB} (Eqs. 8.126 and 8.172) and C_{MB} (Eqs. 8.127 and 8.173), are written for no-flow boundaries, we remove the flow terms across the external boundaries by setting the appropriate transmissibilities to zero. That is,

$$T_{lx_{1-1/2}} = T_{lx_{n_x+1/2}} = 0. \qquad (8.179)$$

Substituting Eq. 8.179 into Eq. 8.178 results in

$$\sum_{i=1}^{n_x-1}\left[T_{lx_{i+1/2}}(p_{i+1} - p_i)\right] - \sum_{i=2}^{n_x}\left[T_{lx_{i-1/2}}(p_i - p_{i-1})\right] + \sum_{i=1}^{n_x} q_{lsc_i}$$

$$= \frac{1}{\alpha_c \Delta t}\sum_{i=1}^{n_x}\left[V_{b_i}\left(\frac{\phi^{n+1}}{B_l^{n+1}} - \frac{\phi^n}{B_l^n}\right)_i\right]. \qquad (8.180)$$

Manipulating the indices in the first summation of Eq. 8.180 results in

$$\sum_{i=2}^{n_x}\left\{\left[T_{lx_{(i-1)+1/2}} - T_{lx_{i-1/2}}\right](p_i - p_{i-1})\right\} + \sum_{i=1}^{n_x} q_{lsc_i}$$

$$= \frac{1}{\alpha_c \Delta t}\sum_{i=1}^{n_x}\left[V_{b_i}\left(\frac{\phi^{n+1}}{B_l^{n+1}} - \frac{\phi^n}{B_l^n}\right)_i\right]. \qquad (8.181)$$

The comparable equation for Eq. 8.175 can be developed in a similar manner and has the form

$$\sum_{i=2}^{n_x}\left\{\left[T_{lx_{(i-1)+1/2}} - T_{lx_{i-1/2}}\right](p_i - p_{i-1})\right\} + \sum_{i=1}^{n_x} q_{lsc_i}$$

$$= \frac{1}{\Delta t}\sum_{i=1}^{n_x}\left[\Gamma_{l_i}^{n+1}(p_i^{n+1} - p_i^n)\right]. \qquad (8.182)$$

Eq. 8.181 is the final form of the summation of the finite-difference equations (Eq. 8.174) for the entire grid system. Because Eq. 8.174 represents the mass-balance equation for the individual gridblocks, Eq. 8.181 is the summation of these mass-balance equations and represents the mass-balance equation for the grid system in its entirety.

We could have developed a mass-balance equation for the entire grid system directly. For no-flow boundary conditions, the expression of mass balance for the entire system simply implies that the change in mass caused by production/injection must equal the change in mass stored in the system. With the terminology listed, the mass balance for the entire grid system can be written as

$$\rho_{lsc}\Delta t\sum_{i=1}^{n_x} q_{lsc_i} = \rho_{lsc}\sum_{i=1}^{n_x}\left[V_{b_i}\left(\frac{\phi^{n+1}}{B_l^{n+1}}-\frac{\phi^n}{B_l^n}\right)_i\right] \quad \ldots\ldots (8.183)$$

or, after dividing by $\rho_{lsc}\Delta t$, as

$$\sum_{i=1}^{n_x} q_{lsc_i} = \frac{1}{\alpha_c\Delta t}\sum_{i=1}^{n_x}\left[V_{b_i}\left(\frac{\phi^{n+1}}{B_l^{n+1}}-\frac{\phi^n}{B_l^n}\right)_i\right]. \quad \ldots\ldots (8.184)$$

Comparison of Eqs. 8.181 and 8.184 indicates that for the summation of the mass-balance equations of the individual gridblocks to equal the mass balance of the grid system in its entirety, the first term in Eq. 8.181 must equal zero. That is,

$$\sum_{i=2}^{n_x}\left\{\left[T_{lx_{(i-1)+1/2}} - T_{lx_{i-1/2}}\right](p_i - p_{i-1})\right\} = 0. \quad \ldots\ldots (8.185)$$

In the presence of a pressure gradient ($p_i \neq p_{i-1}$; $i=2,3,\ldots,n_x$), the condition specified by Eq. 8.185 can be guaranteed only if

$$T_{lx_{(i-1)+1/2}} = T_{lx_{i-1/2}} \quad \ldots\ldots (8.186)$$

for $i=2,3,\ldots,n_x$. The physical interpretation of Eq. 8.185 is that the flow rate across any internal gridblock boundary calculated in the positive i direction of one gridblock must equal the flow rate across the boundary calculated in the negative i direction of the adjacent gridblock. Although this conclusion is based on 1D analysis, it also holds true in multiple dimensions. For incompressible-flow systems, ϕ^{n+1}/B_l^{n+1} must equal ϕ^n/B_l^n. Consequently, for incompressible systems with no-flow boundaries, the expression for mass balance becomes

$$\sum_{i=1}^{n_x} q_{lsc_i} = 0. \quad \ldots\ldots (8.187)$$

(Recall the sign convention of negative for production and positive for injection.)

The mathematical interpretation of Eq. 8.185 is that, for a material-conservative solution to the system of linear equations generated by Eq. 8.174, the coefficient matrix to the system of equations must be symmetrical. For 3D systems, this requires that

$$W_{i,j,k} = E_{i-1,j,k}, \quad \ldots\ldots (8.188)$$

$$S_{i,j,k} = N_{i,j-1,k}, \quad \ldots\ldots (8.189)$$

and $B_{i,j,k} = A_{i,j,k-1}$. $\quad \ldots\ldots (8.190)$

To this point, we have analyzed the properties of the system of equations resulting from Eq. 8.174 that yield a material-conservative formulation. In reservoir simulation, however, we are solving the system of equations resulting from Eq. 8.175. Because Eq. 8.174 is a direct result of the discretization of the PDE's describing flow through porous media (which was derived by use of mass-conservation principles), we now must determine any material-balance error introduced when going from Eq. 8.174 to Eq. 8.175.

Because the left sides of Eqs. 8.181 and 8.182 are identical, we can equate these two equations to obtain

$$\frac{1}{\Delta t}\sum_{i=1}^{n_x}\left[\Gamma_{l_i}^{n+1}(p_i^{n+1}-p_i^n)\right] = \frac{1}{\alpha_c\Delta t}\sum_{i=1}^{n_x}\left[V_{b_i}\left(\frac{\phi^{n+1}}{B_l^{n+1}}-\frac{\phi^n}{B_l^n}\right)_i\right]. \quad \ldots\ldots (8.191)$$

If we equate the groups in the summation signs term by term, we obtain

$$\Gamma_{l_i}^{n+1}(p_i^{n+1}-p_i^n) = \frac{V_{b_i}}{\alpha_c}\left(\frac{\phi^{n+1}}{B_l^{n+1}}-\frac{\phi^n}{B_l^n}\right)_i \quad \ldots\ldots (8.192)$$

for $i=2,3,\ldots,n_x$. Eq. 8.192 is the definition of a material-conservative expansion of the accumulation term for single-phase flow. Additional information is provided for multiphase-flow problems in Sec. 9.5.1.

Example 8.9. Show that the definition of $\Gamma_{l_i}^{n+1}$ in Eq. 8.94,

$$\Gamma_{l_i}^{n+1} = \frac{V_{b_i}}{\alpha_c}\left(\frac{c_\phi\phi^\circ}{B_l^{n+1}}+\frac{\phi^n c_l}{B_l^\circ}\right)_i,$$

is a material-conservative expansion of the accumulation term. What is the advantage of this definition of $\Gamma_{l_i}^{n+1}$?

Solution. Starting with Eq. 8.192, the definition of a material-conservative expansion of the accumulation term, and adding and subtracting ϕ^n/B_l^{n+1} inside the parentheses on the right side results in

$$\Gamma_{l_i}^{n+1}(p_i^{n+1}-p_i^n) = \frac{V_{b_i}}{\alpha_c}\left(\frac{\phi^{n+1}}{B_l^{n+1}}-\frac{\phi^n}{B_l^{n+1}}+\frac{\phi^n}{B_l^{n+1}}-\frac{\phi^n}{B_l^n}\right)_i \quad \ldots\ldots (8.193a)$$

$$\text{or } \Gamma_{l_i}^{n+1}(p_i^{n+1}-p_i^n) = \frac{V_{b_i}}{\alpha_c}\left[\frac{\phi^{n+1}-\phi^n}{B_l^{n+1}}+\phi^n\left(\frac{1}{B_l^{n+1}}-\frac{1}{B_l^n}\right)\right]_i. \quad \ldots\ldots (8.193b)$$

By use of the definition of a compressible porous medium,

$$\phi = \phi^\circ\left[1 + c_\phi(p-p^\circ)\right], \quad \ldots\ldots (8.90)$$

we can develop the equation

$$\phi^{n+1}-\phi^n = c_\phi\phi^\circ\left[(p^{n+1}-p^n)\right]. \quad \ldots\ldots (8.194)$$

Similarly, by use of the definition of a slightly compressible fluid,

$$B_l = \frac{B_l^\circ}{\left[1+c_l(p-p^\circ)\right]}, \quad \ldots\ldots (8.89)$$

we can develop the equation

$$\frac{1}{B_l^{n+1}}-\frac{1}{B_l^n} = \frac{c_l}{B_l^\circ}(p^{n+1}-p^n). \quad \ldots\ldots (8.195)$$

Substituting Eqs. 8.194 and 8.195 into Eq. 8.193b results in

$$\Gamma_{l_i}^{n+1}(p_i^{n+1}-p_i^n) = \frac{V_{b_i}}{\alpha_c}\left(\frac{c_\phi\phi^\circ}{B_l^{n+1}}+\frac{\phi^n c_l}{B_l^\circ}\right)_i(p_i^{n+1}-p_i^n) \quad \ldots\ldots (8.196a)$$

$$\text{or } \Gamma_{l_i}^{n+1} = \frac{V_{b_i}}{\alpha_c}\left(\frac{c_\phi\phi^\circ}{B_l^{n+1}}+\frac{\phi^n c_l}{B_l^\circ}\right)_i, \quad \ldots\ldots (8.196b)$$

which is the desired solution.

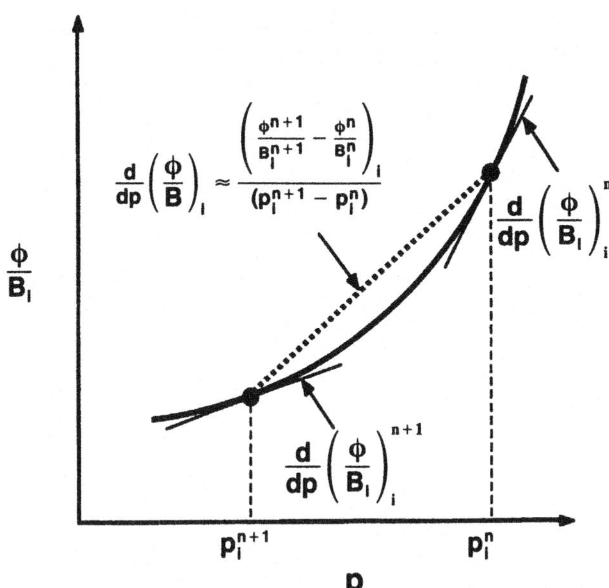

Fig. 8.17—Tangent slopes and chord slope of ϕ/B_l in the vicinity of p^{n+1} and p^n. For a depletion case, $p^{n+1} < p^n$.

The advantage of this definition of $\Gamma_{l_i}^{n+1}$ is that for an incompressible porous medium, $c_\phi = 0$ and $\Gamma_{l_i}^{n+1}$ becomes

$$\Gamma_{l_i}^{n+1} = \frac{V_{b_i}}{\alpha_c}\left(\frac{\phi^n c_l}{B_l^\circ}\right)_i. \quad (8.197)$$

This definition of $\Gamma_{l_i}^{n+1}$ does not contain any parameter evaluated at Time Level $n+1$. Consequently, the use of this definition of $\Gamma_{l_i}^{n+1}$ for slightly compressible liquids does not require any iteration for the solution of Eq. 8.104.

Example 8.10. What is the definition of $\Gamma_{l_i}^{n+1}$ when the expression ϕ^{n+1}/B_l^n is used in the expansion of the accumulation term? What is the advantage of the resulting definition of $\Gamma_{l_i}^{n+1}$?

Solution. Starting with Eq. 8.192, the definition of a material-conservative expansion of the accumulation term, and adding and subtracting ϕ^{n+1}/B_l^n inside the parentheses on the right side results in

$$\Gamma_{l_i}^{n+1}\left(p_i^{n+1} - p_i^n\right) = \frac{V_{b_i}}{\alpha_c}\left(\frac{\phi^{n+1}}{B_l^{n+1}} - \frac{\phi^{n+1}}{B_l^n} + \frac{\phi^{n+1}}{B_l^n} - \frac{\phi^n}{B_l^n}\right)_i \quad (8.198a)$$

or $\Gamma_{l_i}^{n+1}\left(p_i^{n+1} - p_i^n\right)$

$$= \frac{V_{b_i}}{\alpha_c}\left[\phi^{n+1}\left(\frac{1}{B_l^{n+1}} - \frac{1}{B_l^n}\right) + \frac{\phi^{n+1} - \phi^n}{B_l^n}\right]_i. \quad (8.198b)$$

Substituting Eqs. 8.194 and 8.195 from Example 8.9 into Eq. 8.198b results in

$$\Gamma_{l_i}^{n+1}\left(p_i^{n+1} - p_i^n\right) = \frac{V_{b_i}}{\alpha_c}\left(\frac{\phi^{n+1}c_l}{B_l^\circ} + \frac{c_\phi\phi^\circ}{B_l^n}\right)_i \times \left(p_i^{n+1} - p_i^n\right) \quad (8.199a)$$

$$\text{or} \quad \Gamma_{l_i}^{n+1} = \frac{V_{b_i}}{\alpha_c}\left(\frac{\phi^{n+1}c_l}{B_l^\circ} + \frac{c_\phi\phi^\circ}{B_l^n}\right)_i. \quad (8.199b)$$

The advantage of this $\Gamma_{l_i}^{n+1}$ definition is that for incompressible fluids, $c_l = 0$ and $\Gamma_{l_i}^{n+1}$ becomes

$$\Gamma_{l_i}^{n+1} = \frac{V_{b_i}}{\alpha_c}\left(\frac{c_\phi\phi^\circ}{B_l^n}\right)_i. \quad (8.200)$$

This definition of $\Gamma_{l_i}^{n+1}$ does not contain any parameter evaluated at Time Level $n+1$. Consequently, the use of this definition of $\Gamma_{l_i}^{n+1}$ for slightly compressible liquids does not require any iteration for the solution of Eq. 8.104 or 8.113.

Example 8.11. After discretizing the spatial derivatives in the PDE describing fluid flow through porous media, we obtain the equation

$$T_{lx_{i+1/2}}(p_{i+1} - p_i) - T_{lx_{i-1/2}}(p_i - p_{i-1}) + q_{lsc_i} = \frac{V_{b_i}}{\alpha_c}\frac{d}{dt}\left(\frac{\phi}{B_l}\right)_i. \quad (8.201)$$

We can expand the time derivative $(d/dt)(\phi/B_l)$ by use of the chain rule to obtain

$$T_{lx_{i+1/2}}(p_{i+1} - p_i) - T_{lx_{i-1/2}}(p_i - p_{i-1}) + q_{lsc_i} = \frac{V_{b_i}}{\alpha_c}\frac{d}{dp}\left(\frac{\phi}{B_l}\right)_i\frac{dp_i}{dt}. \quad (8.202)$$

Applying the backward-difference approximation to the derivative of pressure with respect to time results in

$$T_{lx_{i+1/2}}(p_{i+1}^{n+1} - p_i^{n+1}) - T_{lx_{i-1/2}}(p_i^{n+1} - p_{i-1}^{n+1}) + q_{lsc_i} = \frac{V_{b_i}}{\alpha_c\Delta t}\frac{d}{dp}\left(\frac{\phi}{B_l}\right)_i\left(p_i^{n+1} - p_i^n\right). \quad (8.203)$$

How is the term $(d/dp)(\phi/B_l)$ evaluated to conserve mass?

Solution. Inspection of the right side of Eq. 8.203 indicates that it is already in the form $\Gamma_{l_i}^{n+1}(p_i^{n+1} - p_i^n)$, where

$$\Gamma_{l_i}^{n+1} = \frac{V_{b_i}}{\alpha_c}\frac{d}{dp}\left(\frac{\phi}{B_l}\right)_i. \quad (8.204)$$

Starting with the definition of a material-conservative expansion of the accumulation term,

$$\Gamma_{l_i}^{n+1}\left(p_i^{n+1} - p_i^n\right) = \frac{V_{b_i}}{\alpha_c}\left(\frac{\phi^{n+1}}{B_l^{n+1}} - \frac{\phi^n}{B_l^n}\right)_i, \quad (8.205)$$

and substituting Eq. 8.205 into the right side of Eq. 8.203 results in

$$\frac{V_{b_i}}{\alpha_c}\frac{d}{dp}\left(\frac{\phi}{B_l}\right)_i\left(p_i^{n+1} - p_i^n\right) = \frac{V_{b_i}}{\alpha_c}\left(\frac{\phi^{n+1}}{B_l^{n+1}} - \frac{\phi^n}{B_l^n}\right)_i \quad (8.206a)$$

$$\text{or} \quad \frac{d}{dp}\left(\frac{\phi}{B_l}\right)_i \approx \frac{\left[(\phi^{n+1}/B_l^{n+1}) - (\phi^n/B_l^n)\right]_i}{\left(p_i^{n+1} - p_i^n\right)}. \quad (8.206b)$$

In Eq. 8.206b, we have replaced the equal sign with an approximation sign because the right side of this expression represents the chord slope between ϕ^{n+1}/B_l^{n+1} and ϕ^n/B_l^n, not the tangent slope. **Fig. 8.17** illustrates this.

Fig. 8.17 shows the chord slope defined by Eq. 8.206b and the tangent slopes (derivatives) evaluated at p_i^n and p_i^{n+1}. The results from this example indicate that the approximate derivative (chord slope defined by Eq. 8.206b) yields a material-conservative finite-difference formulation, while the exact derivative (tangent slope)

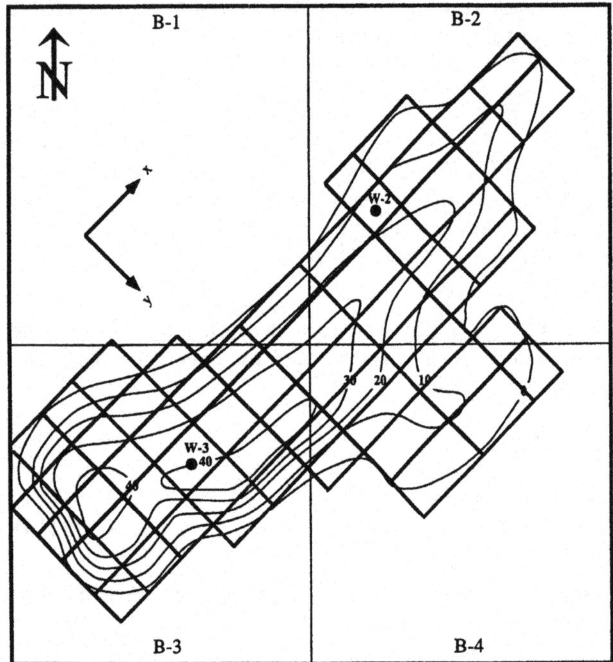

Fig. 8.18—A-1 reservoir studied as a single-phase reservoir with only two wells.

evaluated at either p_i^n or p_i^{n+1} does not yield a material-conservative finite-difference formulation. In general, this is because

$$\frac{\mathrm{d}}{\mathrm{d}p}\left(\frac{\phi}{B_l}\right)_i^n \neq \frac{\mathrm{d}}{\mathrm{d}p}\left(\frac{\phi}{B_l}\right)_i^{n+1} \neq \frac{[(\phi^{n+1}/B_l^{n+1}) - (\phi^n/B_l^n)]_i}{\left(p_i^{n+1} - p_i^n\right)}. \quad \text{(8.207)}$$

One exception to this inequality is when ϕ/B_l is linear in pressure. This would occur, for example, in an incompressible porous medium containing a slightly compressible fluid. In this case,

$$\frac{\phi}{B_l} = \frac{\phi}{B_l^\circ}\left[1 + c_l(p - p^\circ)\right], \quad \text{(8.208)}$$

TABLE 8.3—WELL INFORMATION FOR INCOMPRESSIBLE-FLUID-FLOW EXERCISE

Well	Block	Type	Radius (ft)	Specification
W-2	(9,3)	Producer	0.25	p_{wf} = 5,600.0 psia
W-3	(4,4)	Injector	0.25	q_{sc} = 2,600.0 STB/D

which is the equation of a straight line (ϕ is constant). The condition of linearity would also hold for a compressible porous medium containing an incompressible fluid. In this case,

$$\frac{\phi}{B_l} = \frac{\phi^\circ}{B_l}\left[1 + c_\phi(p - p^\circ)\right]. \quad \text{(8.209)}$$

8.6 Chapter Project

This chapter examines the numerical solution of the single-phase-flow equations for incompressible, slightly compressible, and compressible fluids. In this section, the A-1 reservoir is studied as a single-phase reservoir. First, an incompressible liquid is considered in the A-1 reservoir and a numerical solution for the pressure distribution is obtained. The system is perturbed by two wells (W-2 and W-3) through flow-rate and sandface-pressure specifications at the well locations shown in **Fig. 8.18**. As a second problem, the A-1 reservoir is studied by considering a slightly compressible liquid. The final exercise for the A-1 reservoir in this chapter involves the treatment of the system as a single-phase real-gas (compressible fluid) reservoir.

Single-Phase Incompressible Flow. Consider the A-1 reservoir with the two wells shown in Fig. 8.18. Assume the entire reservoir is 100% filled with an incompressible liquid (presumably water). The viscosity of the liquid is 1.0 cp and FVF is 1 RB/STB. The outer boundaries of the reservoir are completely sealed. **Fig. 8.19** gives the constant part of the transmissibility terms $\beta_c(A_x k_x/\Delta x)$ and $\beta_c(A_y k_y/\Delta y)$. Note the zero entries on the extreme right and on the extreme bottom of the x- and y-direction transmissibility arrays, respectively, which signify the existence of no-flow boundaries.

Table 8.3 shows the well specifications for this exercise. The injected- and produced-fluid properties are assumed to be the same. **Fig. 8.20** gives the steady-state pressure distribution as calculated with an iterative solver with a pressure convergence criterion of 1×10^{-5} psi.

X-DIRECTION TRANSMISSIBILITIES (CONSTANT PART)

```
*******  3.174  1.711  0.000 ************************************************************
 3.521  8.165  4.370  1.834  0.000 ******************** 0.848  0.000 *************
 5.450  9.830  7.332  5.448  3.998  2.118  1.755  2.696  2.207  1.435  0.693  0.000
 7.887 10.766 11.325 10.537  9.421  6.341  4.836  5.958  4.707  3.063  0.964  0.000
 1.783  2.913  4.529  9.739 10.240  6.223  3.728  3.790  2.233  0.000 ************
********************  2.230  4.037  3.423  1.699  1.285  0.525  0.000 ************
************************************ 0.833  0.902  0.000 **************************
****************************************** 1.138  0.995  0.000 *******************
****************************************** 0.802  0.820  0.000 *******************
```

Y-DIRECTION TRANSMISSIBILITIES (CONSTANT PART)

```
******  4.279  4.555  2.249 ***********************************************************
 2.700 12.495 10.392  7.266  2.867 ********************* 1.631  3.721 *************
 3.974 10.847 10.459 12.267  8.180  7.034  9.167  8.380  4.595  7.225  2.432  1.296
 1.910  5.008  5.209 13.999 11.445 11.347 15.822 10.100  4.826  6.662  0.000  0.000
 0.000  0.000  0.000  7.088 10.318 13.099 18.395  7.850  2.834  2.943 ************
*********************  0.000  0.000  2.967 10.371  4.949  0.000  0.000 ************
*********************************** 0.000  5.343  3.671 **************************
***************************************** 2.347  2.396  0.517 *******************
***************************************** 0.000  0.000  0.000 *******************
```

Fig. 8.19—Constant parts of the *x*- and *y*-direction transmissibilities for the A-1 reservoir gridblocks. Transmissibilities are reported for the positive *x* and *y* directions only.

STEADY-STATE PRESSURE DISTRIBUTION, psia

```
******* 7177.9 7178.0 7173.0 ***************************************************************
 7178.9 7178.1 7176.5 7168.1 7122.4 *********************** 6237.1 6329.9 *************
 7179.0 7178.1 7175.1 7169.5 7095.4 6987.2 6811.5 6548.4 6186.4 6347.5 6373.4 6375.8
 7182.4 7180.7 7181.6 7197.6 7084.2 6981.4 6825.3 6610.1 6444.6 6402.5 6388.1 6388.0
 7178.9 7174.8 7163.5 7137.9 7057.1 6970.6 6837.5 6653.1 6524.3 6436.3 *************
*********************** 7113.3 7036.0 6955.3 6837.4 6684.3 6558.9 6453.2 *************
************************************** 6923.3 6825.2 6717.6 ******************************
********************************************** 6809.7 6737.4 6737.0 **********************
********************************************** 6809.4 6736.7 6735.4 **********************
```

Fig. 8.20—Steady-state pressure distribution in the A-1 reservoir.

TABLE 8.4—SUMMARY OF WELL RESULTS FOR INCOMPRESSIBLE-FLOW EXERCISE

Well	Type	Wellblock Pressure (psia)	Productivity Index* (STB/D-psi)	Flow Rate (STB/D)	Sandface Pressure (psia)
W-2	Producer	6,186.4	4.434	−2,600.0044**	5,600.0†
W-3	Injector	7,197.6	12.416	2,600.0000†	7,406.9**

* $F = 1/2$ and $s = 0$

**Calculated

†Specified

TABLE 8.5—WELL INFORMATION FOR SLIGHTLY-COMPRESSIBLE-FLUID-FLOW EXERCISE

Well	Block	Type	Radius (ft)	Specification
W-2	(9,3)	Producer	0.25	$q_{sc} = -650.0$ STB/D
W-3	(4,4)	Producer	0.25	$p_{wf} = 5{,}600.0$ psia

As Fig. 8.20 shows, the left side of the A-1 reservoir is at a higher pressure than the right side of the reservoir. This is to be expected because the injection well is providing pressure support to the production well. This is highlighted with a pressure of 7,197.6 psia in the injection gridblock and a pressure of 6,186.4 psia in the production gridblock. In calculating this pressure distribution, the hydrostatic head caused by the depth gradients is taken into consideration.

In addition to the pressure distribution in the reservoir, there is one unknown to be determined at each well location. Because the Well W-2 flowing sandface pressure ($p_{wf} = 5{,}600$ psia) is specified (**Table 8.4**), the production rate from Well W-2 needs to be determined. Similarly, an injection rate of 2,600 STB/D is specified at Well W-3; therefore, the well sandface injection pressure becomes the unknown. Table 8.4 summarizes these results and provides other relevant information.

Because the fluid is treated as an incompressible liquid and the reservoir is completely sealed, similar injection and production rates are expected to be calculated. In fact, this is exactly what is reported in Table 8.4. The calculated production rate is only 4.4×10^{-3} STB/D different from the specified injection rate of 2,600.0 STB/D. The material-balance error is 0.00017%. This high-accuracy check results from the very fine convergence criterion used within the equation solver. At the injection well, a sandface pressure of 7,406.9 psia is calculated.

TABLE 8.6—SLIGHTLY-COMPRESSIBLE-FLUID PROPERTIES (UNDERSATURATED CONDITIONS)

c_o, psi^{-1}	9.0×10^{-6}
ϱ_o, lbm/ft³	52.4
B_o, RB/STB	$1/[1 + 9.0 \times 10^{-6}(p - 14.7)]$

Oil Viscosity Data

Pressure (psia)	Viscosity (cp)
4,500	0.9180
5,000	0.9200
5,500	0.9243
6,000	0.9372
6,500	0.9494
7,000	0.9650
7,500	0.9812
8,000	1.0019

Single-Phase Slightly Compressible Flow. In this exercise, the A-1 reservoir is treated as a single-phase slightly-compressible-liquid reservoir. This corresponds to an oil reservoir at undersaturated conditions. Again, only two active wells are considered (W-2 and W-3). **Table 8.5** gives the well information for this exercise.

The initial pressure distribution at $t = 0$ is 7,750 psia. This condition is enforced by assuming that all gridblocks initially are at this pressure irrespective of their elevations with respect to a datum plane. **Table 8.6** gives the fluid properties for the undersaturated conditions.

The simulation study was conducted with a timestep size of 1 day for a total of 60 days. Within the iterative solver a convergence crite-

PRESSURE DISTRIBUTION AT 60 DAYS, psia

```
******* 5479.5 5480.2 5477.9 ***************************************************************
 5478.8 5478.1 5476.9 5473.9 5465.1 *********************** 5312.0 5335.0 *************
 5477.7 5476.2 5471.6 5468.3 5460.7 5444.7 5415.8 5370.5 5296.6 5335.6 5343.3 5348.4
 5479.8 5476.2 5469.9 5463.0 5455.4 5446.1 5420.7 5384.0 5352.5 5347.2 5345.4 5347.6
 5477.4 5473.7 5466.6 5459.8 5451.5 5442.4 5423.8 5391.1 5367.3 5351.4 **************
*********************** 5456.6 5445.4 5437.8 5422.4 5395.4 5372.3 5353.5 **************
************************************** 5430.7 5419.4 5401.8 *******************************
********************************************** 5418.9 5406.5 5408.3 **********************
********************************************** 5420.4 5407.7 5408.7 **********************
```

Fig. 8.21—Pressure distribution in the A-1 reservoir (slightly-compressible-fluid study).

TABLE 8.7—WELL-REPORT OUTPUT FOR SLIGHTLY-COMPRESSIBLE-FLOW EXERCISE

Time (days)	Productivity Index (STB/D-psi) W-2	Productivity Index (STB/D-psi) W-3	Wellblock Pressure (psia) (9,3)	Wellblock Pressure (psia) (4,4)	Sandface Pressure (psia) W-2	Sandface Pressure (psia) W-3	Flow Rate (STB/D) W-2	Flow Rate (STB/D) W-3	Cumulative Production (STB) Field
1	4.783	13.393	7,641.23	7,012.80	7,505.33	5,600.00	650.00	18,921.70	19,571.70
2	4.800	13.670	7,559.01	6,771.14	7,423.60	5,600.00	650.00	16,009.89	36,231.59
3	4.813	13.750	7,462.67	6,615.36	7,327.63	5,600.00	650.00	13,961.21	50,842.80
4	4.827	13.802	7,354.77	6,494.22	7,220.12	5,600.00	650.00	12,341.84	63,834.64
5	4.840	13.842	7,240.56	6,394.68	7,106.27	5,600.00	650.00	10,999.98	75,484.62
6	4.854	13.866	7,124.24	6,310.95	6,990.33	5,600.00	650.00	9,857.81	85,992.44
7	4.868	13.886	7,008.78	6,239.15	6,875.25	5,600.00	650.00	8,875.14	95,517.58
8	4.882	13.903	6,896.21	6,176.79	6,763.08	5,600.00	650.00	8,019.17	104,186.75
9	4.895	13.918	6,787.88	6,122.03	6,655.10	5,600.00	650.00	7,265.69	112,102.44
10	4.908	13.931	6,684.61	6,073.48	6,552.18	5,600.00	650.00	6,596.29	119,248.73
11	4.920	13.943	6,586.88	6,030.11	6,454.77	5,600.00	650.00	5,997.06	125,995.78
12	4.932	13.954	6,494.89	5,991.09	6,363.10	5,600.00	650.00	5,457.13	132,102.91
13	4.943	13.963	6,408.69	5,955.79	6,277.19	5,600.00	650.00	4,968.12	137,721.03
14	4.950	13.973	6,328.15	5,923.73	6,196.85	5,600.00	650.00	4,523.40	142,894.44
15	4.957	13.981	6,253.09	5,894.49	6,121.97	5,600.00	650.00	4,117.43	147,661.88
16	4.964	13.989	6,183.28	5,867.77	6,052.33	5,600.00	650.00	3,745.82	152,057.70
17	4.970	13.996	6,118.46	5,843.27	5,987.66	5,600.00	650.00	3,404.93	156,112.64
18	4.975	14.003	6,058.33	5,820.79	5,927.68	5,600.00	650.00	3,091.69	159,854.33
19	4.980	14.009	6,002.61	5,800.12	5,872.10	5,600.00	650.00	2,803.47	163,307.80
20	4.985	14.014	5,951.02	5,781.10	5,820.63	5,600.00	650.00	2,538.03	166,495.83
21	4.990	14.020	5,903.27	5,763.58	5,773.01	5,600.00	650.00	2,293.35	169,439.17
22	4.995	14.024	5,859.11	5,747.44	5,728.97	5,600.00	650.00	2,067.68	172,156.86
23	4.999	14.029	5,818.28	5,732.55	5,688.25	5,600.00	650.00	1,859.47	174,666.33
24	5.003	14.033	5,780.53	5,718.81	5,650.60	5,600.00	650.00	1,667.28	176,983.61
25	5.006	14.036	5,745.65	5,706.14	5,615.82	5,600.00	650.00	1,489.85	179,123.47
26	5.010	14.040	5,713.42	5,694.45	5,583.67	5,600.00	650.00	1,326.02	181,099.48
27	5.013	14.043	5,683.65	5,683.65	5,553.98	5,600.00	650.00	1,174.72	182,924.20
28	5.016	14.046	5,656.14	5,673.69	5,526.55	5,600.00	650.00	1,034.98	184,609.19
29	5.018	14.048	5,630.74	5,664.49	5,501.22	5,600.00	650.00	905.92	186,165.11
30	5.021	14.051	5,607.29	5,655.99	5,477.83	5,600.00	650.00	786.73	187,601.84

rion of 0.01 psi was used. **Fig. 8.21** gives the pressure distribution in the reservoir at $t=60$ days.

Close inspection of Gridblocks (9,3) and (4,4) shows the formation of the two pressure sinks. **Table 8.7** gives a summary of the results at the end of each timestep for 60 consecutive timesteps. It is interesting to note that, at a bottomhole-pressure specification of 5,600 psia, Well W-3 produces for approximately 40 days. At the 40th day, the well gets shut in. This is the reason that the sandface and wellblock pressures for Well W-3 are approximately equal. Similarly, the wellblock pressure for Well W-3 is very close to the specified flowing sandface pressure at $t=39$ days (5,603.59 vs. 5,600). This small pressure drawdown (3.59 psi) creates a flow rate of 50.53 STB/D at $t=39$ days. During the next timestep, the gridblock pressure for Gridblock (4,4) is much closer to the specified sandface pressure of 5,600 psia, which indicates that Well W-3 is not capable of producing under the imposed pressure specification of $p_{wf}=5{,}600$ psia. The pressure drop, with respect to time, observed in Wellblock (4,4) after Well W-3 is shut in is caused by production from Well W-2, which continues to produce at a rate of 650 STB/D.

Single-Phase Compressible Flow. In this exercise, the A-1 reservoir is treated as a single-phase gas reservoir. To make the problem more compatible with gas reservoirs at the onset, the x- and y-direction permeabilities are reduced two orders of magnitude by dividing each gridblock permeability by 100. Wells W-2 and W-3 are the two active wells in the A-1 gas reservoir. **Table 8.8** provides the relevant well information.

The initial formation pressure is assumed to be distributed uniformly throughout the reservoir at 7,750 psia. **Table 8.9** gives information on reservoir-fluid properties used in this single-phase compressible-flow exercise.

Total simulation time is considered to be 100 days. Again, both wells are put on production at the same time. During the first 5 days of simulation, a timestep of 1 day is used. For the remainder of the study, the timestep size is kept at 5 days. Within the iterative solver a pressure convergence criterion of 0.001 psi is applied. **Fig. 8.22** gives the calculated pressure distributions at the end of 5 days and 100 days of production.

Again, Wellblocks (9,3) and (4,4) exhibit the lowest pressure levels compared with their respective neighboring gridblocks at $t=5$ days and $t=100$ days. As one moves away from these wellblocks, pressure values increase.

TABLE 8.7—WELL-REPORT OUTPUT FOR SLIGHTLY-COMPRESSIBLE-FLOW EXERCISE (continued)

Time (days)	Productivity Index (STB/D-psi) W-2	W-3	Wellblock Pressure (psia) (9,3)	(4,4)	Sandface Pressure (psia) W-2	W-3	Flow Rate (STB/D) W-2	W-3	Cumulative Production (STB) Field
31	5.023	14.053	5,585.62	5,648.15	5,456.22	5,600.00	650.00	676.63	188,928.48
32	5.025	14.055	5,565.62	5,640.91	5,436.28	5,600.00	650.00	574.95	190,153.44
33	5.027	14.057	5,547.15	5,634.22	5,417.86	5,600.00	650.00	481.04	191,284.47
34	5.029	14.059	5,530.10	5,628.05	5,400.85	5,600.00	650.00	394.29	192,328.77
35	5.031	14.061	5,514.36	5,622.34	5,385.15	5,600.00	650.00	314.18	193,292.95
36	5.032	14.062	5,499.82	5,617.08	5,370.65	5,600.00	650.00	240.21	194,183.16
37	5.034	14.064	5,486.41	5,612.22	5,357.27	5,600.00	650.00	171.88	195,005.03
38	5.034	14.065	5,474.02	5,607.73	5,344.88	5,600.00	650.00	108.79	195,763.83
39	5.034	14.066	5,462.58	5,603.59	5,333.45	5,600.00	650.00	50.53	196,464.36
40	5.034	14.067	5,452.02	5,599.77	5,322.88	5,600.00	650.00	0.00	197,114.36
41	5.034	14.067	5,442.18	5,594.23	5,313.05	5,594.23	650.00	0.00	197,764.36
42	5.034	14.067	5,432.93	5,588.24	5,303.81	5,588.24	650.00	0.00	198,414.36
43	5.034	14.067	5,424.15	5,581.97	5,295.02	5,581.97	650.00	0.00	199,064.36
44	5.034	14.067	5,415.72	5,575.49	5,286.59	5,575.49	650.00	0.00	199,714.36
45	5.034	14.067	5,407.56	5,568.85	5,278.44	5,568.85	650.00	0.00	200,364.36
46	5.034	14.067	5,399.63	5,562.09	5,270.50	5,562.09	650.00	0.00	201,014.36
47	5.034	14.067	5,391.87	5,555.23	5,262.44	5,555.23	650.00	0.00	201,664.36
48	5.034	14.067	5,384.23	5,548.31	5,255.11	5,548.31	650.00	0.00	202,314.36
49	5.034	14.067	5,376.70	5,541.33	5,247.58	5,541.33	650.00	0.00	202,964.36
50	5.034	14.067	5,369.25	5,534.30	5,240.13	5,534.30	650.00	0.00	203,614.36
51	5.034	14.067	5,361.86	5,527.24	5,232.74	5,527.24	650.00	0.00	204,264.36
52	5.034	14.067	5,354.52	5,520.15	5,225.40	5,520.15	650.00	0.00	204,914.36
53	5.034	14.067	5,347.22	5,513.05	5,218.10	5,513.05	650.00	0.00	205,564.36
54	5.034	14.067	5,339.94	5,505.93	5,210.82	5,505.93	650.00	0.00	206,214.36
55	5.034	14.067	5,332.69	5,498.79	5,203.57	5,498.79	650.00	0.00	206,864.36
56	5.034	14.067	5,325.46	5,491.65	5,196.34	5,491.65	650.00	0.00	207,514.36
57	5.034	14.067	5,318.24	5,484.50	5,189.12	5,484.50	650.00	0.00	208,164.36
58	5.034	14.067	5,311.03	5,477.35	5,181.91	5,477.35	650.00	0.00	208,814.36
59	5.034	14.067	5,303.82	5,470.19	5,174.71	5,470.19	650.00	0.00	209,464.36
60	5.034	14.067	5,296.63	5,463.02	5,167.51	5,463.02	650.00	0.00	210,114.36

Table 8.10 is the summary report provided by the output subroutine of the model. In this report, the changes in pressure and production rates encountered as the simulation progresses can be tracked.

The accuracy of the calculations is monitored throughout the simulation by I_{MB} checks. **Fig. 8.23** shows excellent I_{MB} checks throughout the simulation period. The maximum material-balance error is 0.04%, which occurs at $t=3$ days.

TABLE 8.8—WELL INFORMATION FOR COMPRESSIBLE-FLUID-FLOW EXERCISE

Well	Block	Type	Radius (ft)	Specification
W-2	(9,3)	Producer	0.25	$q_{sc}=-3$ MMscf/D
W-3	(4,4)	Producer	0.25	$p_{wf}=6{,}000$ psia

Exercises

8.1. Consider the 1D, single-phase, incompressible flow of oil taking place in the z direction of the system in **Fig. 8.24** with the gridblock properties given in **Table 8.11**. The boundary conditions are as follows.

1. Pressure of the production gridblock (Gridblock 4) is maintained at 1,000 psia.
2. No-flow boundary at the top of the system.
3. Pressure of the gridblock located at the constant-pressure boundary (Gridblock 1) is maintained at 5,000 psia.

The fluid properties are $\mu_o=2$ cp, $\rho_o=50$ lbm/ft^3, and $B_o=1.0$ RB/STB. With the appropriate PDE and its finite-difference approximation, calculate the pressure distribution in the system.

8.2. Consider the 1D, single-phase, steady-state flow of water taking place in the horizontal, homogeneous reservoir shown in **Fig. 8.25.** The gridblock and fluid properties are $\Delta x=400$ ft, $w=200$ ft, $h=80$ ft, $k_x=60$ md, $\mu_w=0.5$ cp, and $B_w=1$ RB/B. The boundary conditions are as follows.

1. No-flow boundaries.
2. Well in Gridblock 1 produces at a rate of 400 B/D.
3. Pressure of injection Gridblock 4 is 3,600 psia.

Calculate the pressure of all gridblocks with the PSOR solution method with $\omega=1.5$ and a pressure convergence criterion of 3 psi. Use $p_1=3{,}000$ psia, $p_2=3{,}200$ psia, and $p_3=3{,}400$ psia for initial guesses.

TABLE 8.9—RESERVOIR AND COMPRESSIBLE-FLUID PROPERTIES

Reservoir temperature, °F	190
Standard temperature, °F	60
Standard pressure, psia	14.7
Gas molecular weight, lbm/lbm-mol	22.836
Pseudocritical temperature, °R	418.38
Pseudocritical pressure, psia	738.44
Gas density at standard conditions, lbm/ft^3	0.058359
FVF	$B_g = (p_{sc}Tz)/(\alpha_c T_{sc} p)$

Gas Viscosity Data

Pressure (psia)	Viscosity (cp)
3,500	0.0222403
4,000	0.0241128
4,500	0.0259745
5,000	0.0278092
5,500	0.0296024
6,000	0.0313411
6,500	0.0330143
7,000	0.0346133
7,500	0.0361318
8,000	0.0375660

8.3. Consider the single-phase, incompressible flow of oil taking-place in the 2D, homogeneous, isotropic system shown in **Fig. 8.26.** Assume $\Delta x = \Delta y = 1{,}000$ ft, $h = 50$ ft, and $k_x = k_y = 100$ md. A production well in the center gridblock is produced at a rate of 12,000 STB/D (μ_o = 2 cp). If pressure in the boundary gridblocks is kept at 2,000 psia, calculate the pressure distribution in the system and the flowing sandface pressure in the wellbore.

8.4. Consider the 1D, single-phase, steady-state flow of oil in the horizontal, heterogeneous system shown in **Fig. 8.27**. **Table 8.12** gives the gridblock properties. The boundary conditions are as follows.

1. Pressure in Gridblock 1 is maintained at 3,000 psia.
2. Production rate from Gridblock 2 is specified as 1,000 STB/D.
3. The pressure gradient at the extreme right of the system is given as 0.2 psi/ft.

The fluid properties are $\mu_o = 2$ cp and $B_o = 1$ RB/STB. With the appropriate PDE and its finite-difference approximation, calculate the pressure distribution in the system.

8.5. Consider the incompressible-fluid-flow problem in the heterogeneous, anisotropic porous medium shown in **Fig. 8.28**. The fluid properties for this problem are $\mu = 1$ cp and $\rho = 62.4$ lbm/ft^3. **Table 8.13** shows the gridblock properties. Ignoring the potential gradient, calculate the pressure distribution in the system and determine the nature of the boundary condition on the lowest z boundary of the system. Quantify the boundary conditions and provide the dimensionality of the problem; boundary conditions are as follows.

1. All boundary planes perpendicular to the z direction except the bottom plane of Gridblock 1, which is the unknown of the problem, are no-flow boundaries.
2. All boundary planes perpendicular to the y direction, except the extreme right face of Gridblock 4, are no-flow boundaries.
3. Gridblock 4 represents a constant-pressure gridblock of 2,800 psia and the well in Gridblock 3 produces at a rate of 300 STB/D.

8.6. Consider the 2D single-phase flow of incompressible oil taking place in the horizontal, homogeneous reservoir shown in **Fig. 8.29**. The gridblock and fluid properties for this problem are $\Delta x = \Delta y = 400$ ft, $k_x = 200$ md, $k_y = 200$ md, $h = 40$ ft, $\mu_o = 2$ cp, and $B_o = 1$ RB/STB. The boundary conditions are as follows.

1. No-flow boundaries.
2. Pressure of each injection gridblock is 5,000 psia.
3. Pressure of production gridblock is 2,000 psia.

Calculate (1) the pressure of all gridblocks using the direct solution method, (2) the injection rate for each injection well, and (3) the production rate for the production well. Hint: Observe the symmetry.

8.7. Simulate the flow of an incompressible oil in the horizontal reservoir represented by the grid shown in **Fig. 8.30**. **Table 8.14** gives gridblock permeabilities and thicknesses. Fluid viscosity is 0.2 mPa · s. There are wells at Nodes (1,1), (2,3), and (3,2). The well at Node (2,3) produces at a rate of 103.68 std m^3/d. The pressures at Nodes (1,1) and (3,2) are maintained at $p_{1,1} = 3500$ kPa and $p_{3,2} = 100$ kPa.

Use the (1) direct solution method, (2) Jacobi solution method, (3) Gauss-Seidel method, and the (4) PSOR method to obtain the pressure distribution in the reservoir. Calculate well flow rates at Nodes (1,1) and (3,2) and check the material balance for each method. Use a tolerance of 1 kPa with iterative methods.

PRESSURE DISTRIBUTION AT 5 DAYS, psia

```
*******  7744.5  7740.0  7728.6  **********************************************************
 7743.4  7739.2  7725.1  7688.8  7709.1  **********************  7486.1  7683.5  **************
 7739.5  7729.7  7691.5  7594.6  7681.2  7727.4  7739.0  7664.4  7230.4  7667.5  7729.0  7745.2
 7734.5  7712.9  7622.9  7333.2  7637.5  7723.1  7743.6  7720.5  7642.1  7717.4  7738.4  7747.4
 7735.4  7719.2  7664.4  7598.4  7696.1  7734.8  7746.7  7739.1  7717.3  7735.0  **************
**********************  7660.1  7717.1  7740.7  7748.1  7745.0  7734.5  7741.1  **************
**************************************  7745.3  7749.1  7748.2  ******************************
**********************************************  7749.7  7749.6  7749.9  *********************
**********************************************  7749.9  7749.9  7750.0  *********************
```

PRESSURE DISTRIBUTION AT 100 DAYS, psia

```
*******  6922.8  6910.5  6886.6  **********************************************************
 6916.4  6907.6  6884.1  6841.1  6860.7  **********************  6411.0  6675.2  **************
 6905.6  6890.3  6847.5  6775.4  6854.1  6941.6  6994.4  6799.2  6245.2  6705.8  6837.9  6916.2
 6894.3  6867.6  6793.7  6636.6  6837.9  6951.6  7018.6  6905.9  6738.4  6804.4  6862.0  6933.1
 6889.7  6865.0  6810.7  6773.9  6885.4  6976.2  7047.9  6979.1  6878.0  6857.4  **************
**********************  6815.2  6912.0  6997.1  7074.4  7037.7  6933.8  6884.0  **************
**************************************  7032.6  7114.0  7113.8  ******************************
**********************************************  7172.0  7191.6  7246.6  *********************
**********************************************  7218.7  7240.7  7294.3  *********************
```

Fig. 8.22—Pressure distributions in the A-1 gas reservoir at $t = 5$ days and $t = 100$ days.

TABLE 8.10—WELL-REPORT OUTPUT FOR COMPRESSIBLE-FLOW EXERCISE

	Productivity Index (Mscf/D-psi)		Wellblock Pressure (psia)		Sandface Pressure (psia)		Flow Rate (Mscf/D)		Cumulative Production (Mscf)
Time (days)	W-2	W-3	(9,3)	(4,4)	W-2	W-3	W-2	W-3	Field
1	2.465	6.898	7,556.46	7,589.05	6,339.59	6,000	3,000	10,960.56	13,960.56
2	2.475	6.917	7,430.02	7,487.94	6,217.73	6,000	3,000	10,292.32	27,252.88
3	2.481	6.932	7,342.54	7,419.73	6,133.56	6,000	3,000	9,841.71	40,094.59
4	2.486	6.943	7,278.86	7370.64	6,072.24	6,000	3,000	9,515.97	52,610.56
5	2.490	6.951	7,230.36	7,333.22	6,025.52	6,000	3,000	9,266.94	64,877.51
10	2.499	6.972	7,104.27	7,231.58	5,903.95	6,000	3,000	8,587.15	122,813.25
15	2.505	6.987	7,020.77	7,162.02	5,823.35	6,000	3,000	8,119.02	178,408.31
20	2.511	6.998	6,955.01	7,107.21	5,760.08	6,000	3,000	7,748.62	232,151.42
25	2.515	7.008	6,897.75	7,060.57	5,705.05	6,000	3,000	7,432.32	284,313.06
30	2.520	7.016	6,845.11	7,019.11	5,654.42	6,000	3,000	7,150.31	335,064.56
35	2.524	7.024	6,795.26	6,981.26	5,606.46	6,000	3,000	6,892.78	384,528.44
40	2.527	7.033	6,747.30	6,946.13	5,560.29	6,000	3,000	6,653.71	432,797.00
45	2.531	7.040	6,700.79	6,913.19	5,515.48	6,000	3,000	6,428.97	479,941.84
50	2.534	7.047	6,655.42	6,882.09	5,471.75	6,000	3,000	6,216.26	526,023.12
55	2.538	7.054	6,611.02	6,852.57	5,428.92	6,000	3,000	6,013.95	571,092.88
60	2.541	7.060	6,567.47	6,824.45	5,386.90	6,000	3,000	5,820.78	615,196.75
65	2.544	7.066	6,524.72	6,797.57	5,345.62	6,000	3,000	5,635.80	658,375.75
70	2.548	7.072	6,482.71	6,771.82	5,305.13	6,000	3,000	5,458.28	700,667.12
75	2.551	7.077	6,441.43	6,747.11	5,265.45	6,000	3,000	5,287.59	742,105.06
80	2.554	7.083	6,400.82	6,723.35	5,226.39	6,000	3,000	5,123.24	782,721.25
85	2.558	7.088	6,360.95	6,700.48	5,188.02	6,000	3,000	4,964.77	822,545.06
90	2.561	7.092	6,321.73	6,678.44	5,150.25	6,000	3,000	4,811.79	861,604.06
95	2.564	7.097	6,283.16	6,657.17	5,113.09	6,000	3,000	4,663.95	899,923.75
100	2.567	7.101	6,245.25	6,636.63	5,076.53	6,000	3,000	4,520.95	937,528.50

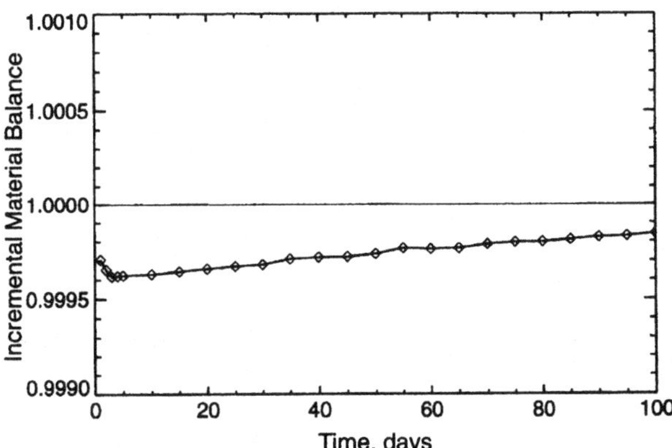

Fig. 8.23—I_{MB} checks during compressible-flow exercise.

8.8. Consider the single-phase, steady-state flow in the horizontal porous medium shown in **Fig. 8.31**, which has heterogeneous permeability distribution. The boundary conditions are as follows.

1. On the extreme right of the system, the pressure gradient is specified as -0.2 psi/ft.

2. On the extreme left of the system, the pressure gradient is specified as -0.8 psi/ft.

3. The well in Gridblock 4 produces with a constant gridblock pressure of 100 psia.

The gridblock and fluid properties for this problem are $\Delta x = 600$ ft, $w = 100$ ft, $h = 80$ ft, $k_{x_1} = 40$ md, $k_{x_2} = 60$ md, $k_{x_3} = 68$ md, $k_{x_4} = 46$ md, $\mu = 1$ cp, and $B = 1$ RB/STB.

Solve for the steady-state-pressure distribution in the system. In the solution of the finite-difference equations, use Thomas' algorithm. Calculate the production rate of the well.

8.9. Consider the 2D slightly-compressible flow of oil in the porous medium shown in **Fig. 8.32**. Assume that the system is horizontal. The gridblock and fluid properties are $\phi = 20\%$, $k_x = k_y = 100$ md, $\Delta x = \Delta y = 600$ ft, $h = 40$ ft, $\mu = 4$ cp, $c = 5 \times 10^{-5}$ psi^{-1}, and $B = 1.2$ RB/STB. Assume that oil FVF, viscosity, and compressibility are not changing with pressure in the range in which you are working. The boundary condition are as follows.

1. The east, north, and south boundaries are no-flow boundaries.

2. In the west boundary, the pressure gradient is specified as $\partial p/\partial x = 0.1$ psi/ft.

3. The production gridblock is kept at 200 psia.

The initial condition of all gridblock pressures = 3,600 psia at $t = 0$.

With the appropriate PDE and its backward finite-difference approximation, calculate the pressure distribution and production rates at the end of 15 and 30 days, respectively. Use a timestep of 15 days.

8.10. Consider the 1D, single-phase unsteady-state flow of oil in the system shown in **Fig. 8.33**. Uniform porosity, ϕ, and permeability, k, distributions exist in the system. Fluid properties are compressibility, c_o, viscosity, μ_o, and FVF, B_o. The initial pressure distribution at $t = 0$ is uniform for all gridblocks and equals p_i.

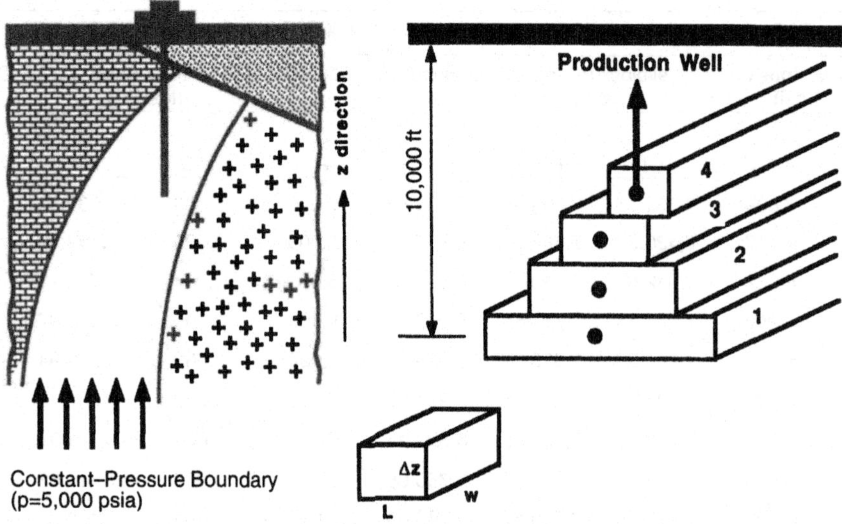

Fig. 8.24—Actual and discretized reservoir in Exercise 8.1.

TABLE 8.11—GRIDBLOCK PROPERTIES FOR EXERCISE 8.1

Gridblock	Δz (ft)	w (ft)	L (ft)	k_z (md)
1	400	1,200	200	100
2	600	1,200	180	100
3	600	1,200	160	100
4	200	1,200	140	100

1. State the PDE that describes the flow of oil in the porous medium described.

2. Using the backward finite-difference approximation, obtain the necessary system of equations to solve the pressure distribution in the system after a time period of Δt.

3. Express the system of equations obtained in Part 2 in a matrix form so that Thomas' algorithm is readily applicable.

8.11. Consider the unsteady-state single-phase flow of oil taking place in the 2D, homogeneous, isotropic, horizontal reservoir shown in **Fig. 8.34**. All boundaries are no-flow boundaries and production from the center gridblock = 400 STB/D. The initial condition of all gridblock pressures = 4,000 psia. The fluid properties are $\mu = 10$ cp, $c = 1\times10^{-5}$ psi^{-1}, and $B = 1$ RB/STB. The gridblock properties are $\Delta x = 400$ ft, $\Delta y = 400$ ft, $k_x = 88.7$ md, $k_y = 88.7$ md, $\phi = 20\%$, and $h = 100$ ft. Assume that FVF and viscosity are unchanged within the pressure range.

TABLE 8.12—GRIDBLOCK PROPERTIES FOR EXERCISE 8.4

Gridblock	Δx (ft)	h (ft)	w (ft)	k_x (md)
1	200	40	100	200
2	400	60	100	160
3	300	20	100	180

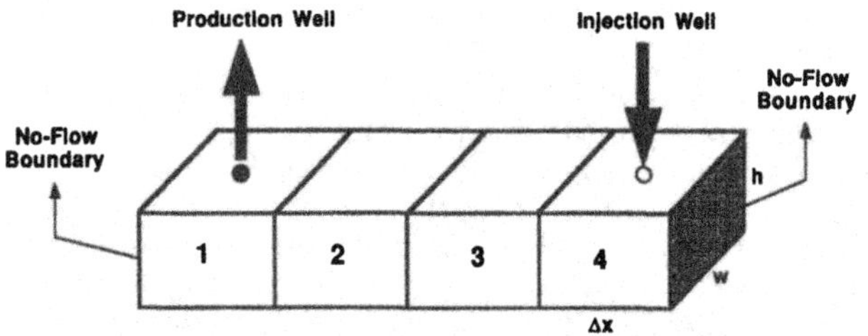

Fig. 8.25—Discretized 1D reservoir in Exercise 8.2.

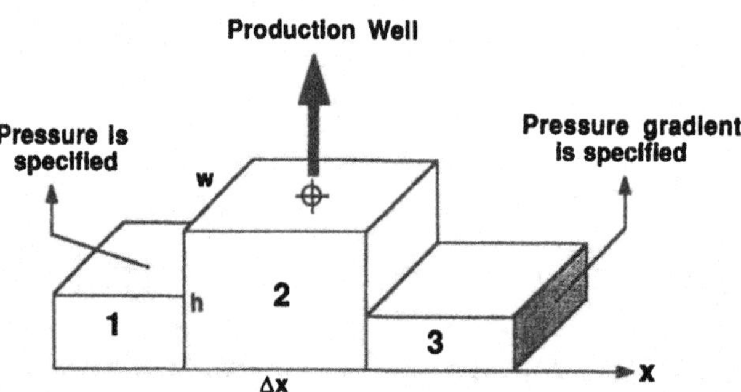

Fig. 8.27—Discretized 1D reservoir in Exercise 8.4.

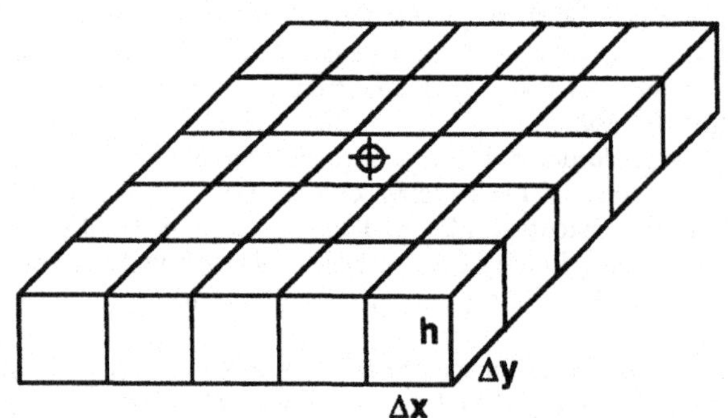

Fig. 8.26—Discretized 2D reservoir in Exercise 8.3.

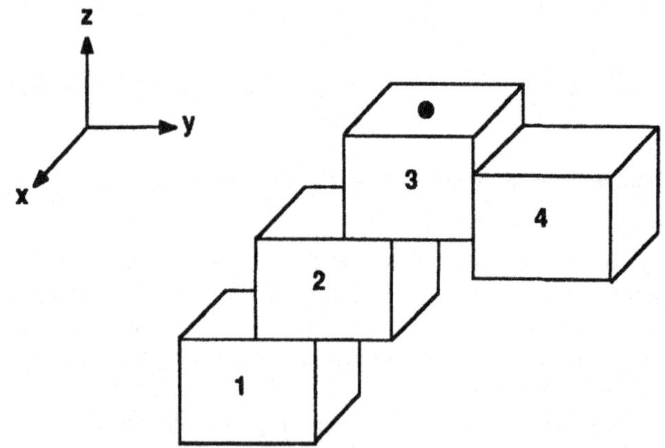

Fig. 8.28—Discretized reservoir in Exercise 8.5.

TABLE 8.13—GRIDBLOCK PROPERTIES FOR EXERCISE 8.5

	Gridblock			
	1	2	3	4
k_z, md	46	37	18	13
k_y, md	32	26	24	28
ϕ, fraction	0.14	0.17	0.13	0.19
Δx, ft	400	600	700	500
Δy, ft	800	600	600	700
Δz, ft	40	24	31	18

Calculate the pressure distribution in the reservoir after 10 and 20 days, respectively. Use the appropriate PDE and its backward finite-difference approximation in the solution. Use a timestep of 10 days.

8.12. Consider the 2D single-phase flow of slightly compressible oil taking place in the horizontal homogeneous reservoir shown in **Fig. 8.35**. A production well, located in the center (Gridblock 5), is produced at a constant rate of 400 STB/D. No-flow boundaries are prescribed along all boundaries. **Table 8.15** gives the pressure distribution in the reservoir at $t = 10$ days. The gridblock properties are $\Delta x = 400$ ft, $\Delta y = 400$ ft, $k_x = 88.7$ md, $k_y = 88.7$ md, $h = 100$ ft, and $\phi = 20\%$. The fluid properties are $\mu_o = 10$ cp (at all pressures), $B_o = 1$ RB/STB (at all pressures), and $c_o = 1 \times 10^{-5}$ psi^{-1}. Calculate the pressure distribution at $t = 20$ days by use of the ADIP solution method.

8.13. Referring to the reservoir described in Exercise 8.7, consider the flow of a slightly compressible oil with a compressibility of 7.3×10^{-5} kPa^{-1}. The porosities of Gridblocks (1,1), (2,1), (1,2), (2,2), and (3,2) are 0.2, 0.25, 0.18, 0.27, and 0.30, respectively. The porosity of Gridblock (2,3) is 0.40 because of fractures. Initially, the pressure at all gridblocks is 3500 kPa.

Calculate the pressure distribution in the reservoir at the end of 20 and 50 days with the (1) explicit-formulation scheme, (2) implicit-formulation scheme using direct-solution method, (3) implicit-formulation scheme using the PSOR solution method with a convergence criterion of 2 kPa, and (4) implicit-formulation scheme using ADIP. Obtain the material-balance error in each case.

8.14. Consider a 2D, single-phase slightly-compressible-flow problem simulated for the reservoir shown in **Fig. 8.36**. The two wellblocks are kept at 1,400 psia. The gridblock properties are $\Delta x = \Delta y = 600$ ft, $k_x = 100$ md, $k_y = 80$ md, $h = 70$ ft, and $\phi = 18\%$. The fluid properties are $c = 4 \times 10^{-7}$ psi^{-1}, $\mu = 1$ cp, and $B = 1$ RB/STB. Implement ADIP for at least one iteration to solve for the pressure distribution at $t = 30$ days. Start with an initial guess of 3,000 psia and do not use iteration parameters.

8.15. Consider the flow of a compressible fluid in the 1D heterogeneous porous medium shown in **Fig. 8.37**. The initial pressure at every point in the system is 3,600 psia before the well is put on production. The boundary conditions are as follows.

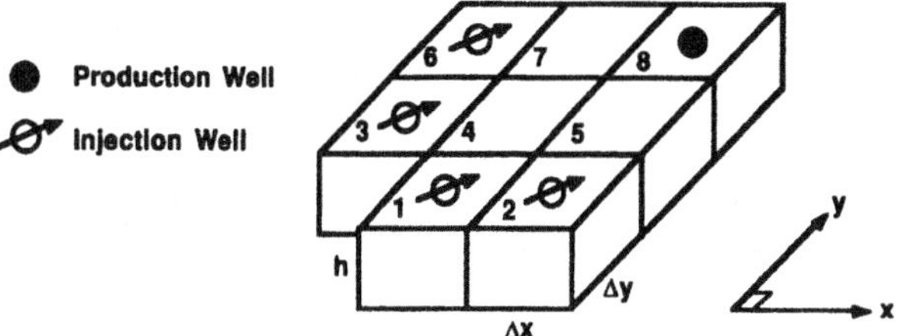

Fig. 8.29—Discretized 2D reservoir in Exercise 8.6.

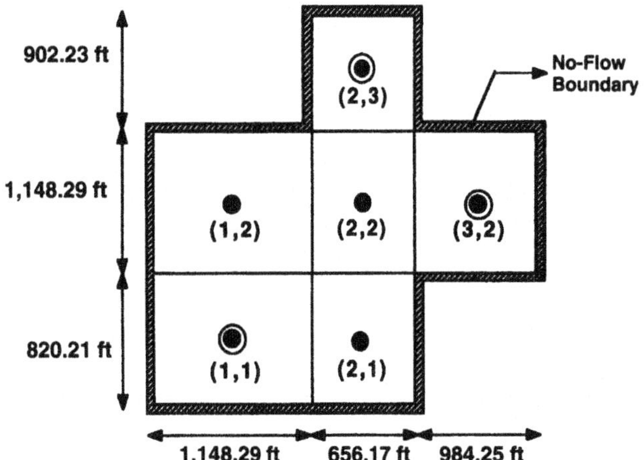

Fig. 8.30—Reservoir description in Exercise 8.7.

1. No-flow boundaries exist at the ends of the system.
2. Production gridblock is kept at 1,200 psia.

Table 8.16 shows the gridblock properties. The fluid properties at $T = 120°$F are $\mu_g = (5.306531 \times 10^{-6})p + 0.00829716$ and $z = (4.949892 \times 10^{-8})p^2 - (2.30415 \times 10^{-4})p + 1.00563$, where p is in psia and μ_g is in cp. The standard conditions are $p_{sc} = 14.7$ psia and $T_{sc} = 520°$R.

Calculate the pressure distribution in the system at the end of 20 days of production. Also calculate the production rate of the well. Use the backward-difference scheme with a pressure convergence tolerance of 10 psia. Use a timestep of 20 days.

8.16. Consider the 2D, horizontal, isotropic, homogeneous porous medium shown in **Fig. 8.38**, in which incompressible single-phase fluid flow is taking place. Assume $\Delta x = \Delta y = 400$ ft, $\mu = 1$ cp, $\phi = 20\%$, $k_x = k_y = 200$ md, $h = 10$ ft, and $B = 1$ RB/STB.

1. State the PDE that describes the fluid flow dynamics in the system.
2. Write the finite-difference approximation of the equation of Part 1.
3. If pressure of the boundary gridblocks is specified as 1,000 psia and the production well is produced at a rate of 1,000 STB/D, generate the system of linear equations necessary to find the pressure distribution in the system. Write the linear equations in matrix form and solve the system of equations using the conjugate gradient method.

TABLE 8.14—GRIDBLOCK PROPERTIES FOR EXERCISE 8.7

Node (i,j)	$h_{i,j}$ (m)	$k_{x_{i,j}}$ (μm^2)	$k_{y_{i,j}}$ (μm^2)
(1,1)	12	0.02	0.02
(1,2)	15	0.15	0.15
(2,1)	10	0.30	0.30
(2,2)	18	0.03	0.03
(2,3)	5	0.06	0.06
(3,2)	6	0.04	0.04

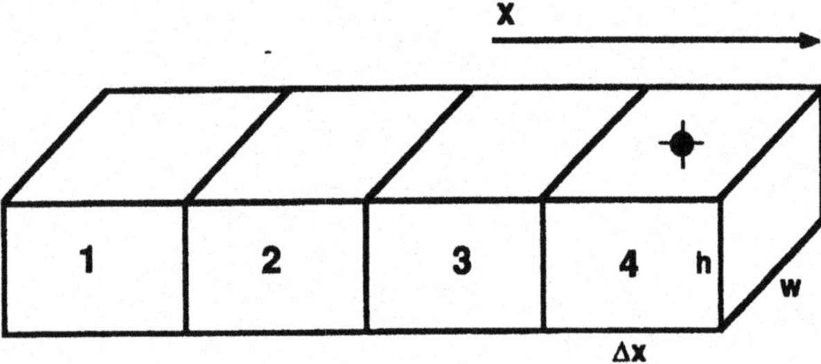

Fig. 8.31—Discretized reservoir in Exercise 8.8.

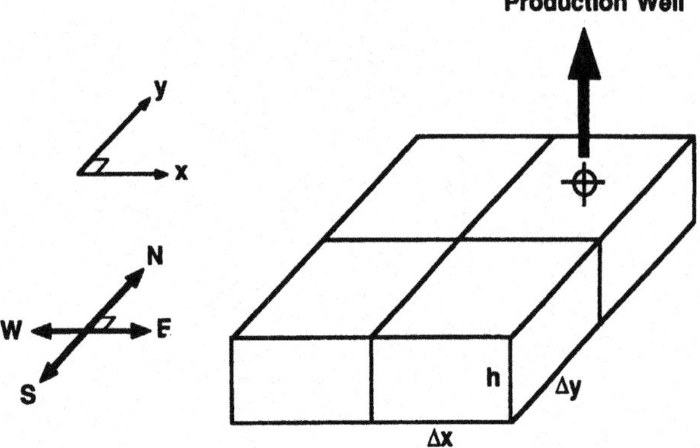

Fig. 8.32—Discretized 2D reservoir in Exercise 8.9.

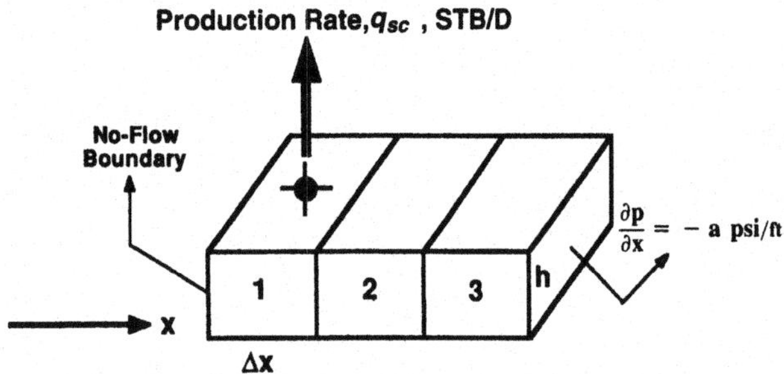

Fig. 8.33—Discretized 1D reservoir in Exercise 8.10.

TABLE 8.15—INITIAL GRIDBLOCK PRESSURES AT t=10 DAYS FOR EXERCISE 8.12	
Gridblock	Pressure (psia)
1	3,867
2	3,830
3	3,867
4	3,830
5	3,763
6	3,830
7	3,867
8	3,830
9	3,867

8.17. Consider the 3D system shown in **Fig. 8.39**. A steady-state flow of water is taking place in this completely closed system, and the system is known to be anisotropic and homogeneous. Note the existence of two wells in Gridblocks (1,3,2) and (4,1,2). These wells penetrate only the top layer. Assume that potential gradients for this

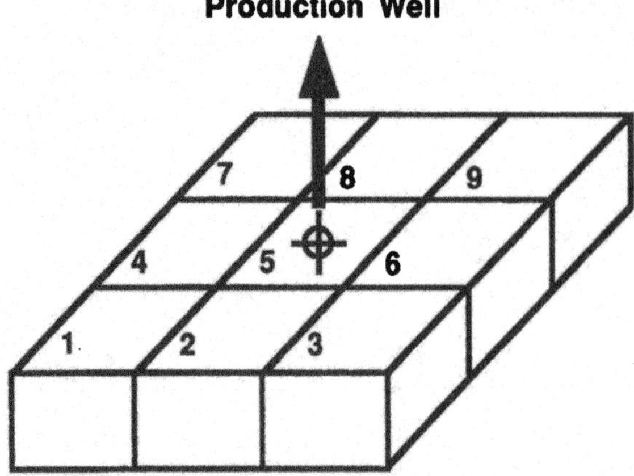

Fig. 8.34—Discretized 2D reservoir in Exercise 8.11.

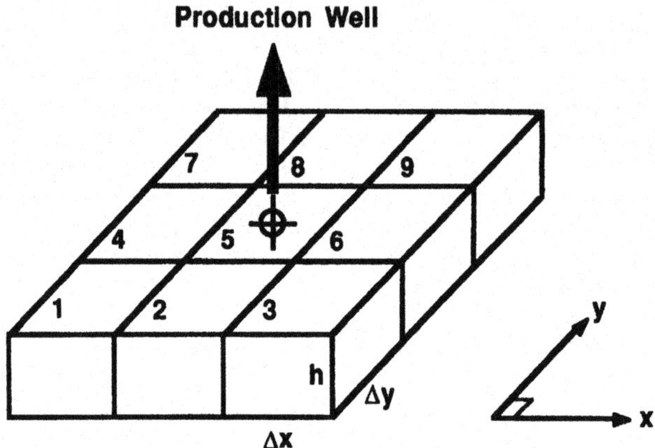

Fig. 8.35—Discretized 2D reservoir in Exercise 8.12.

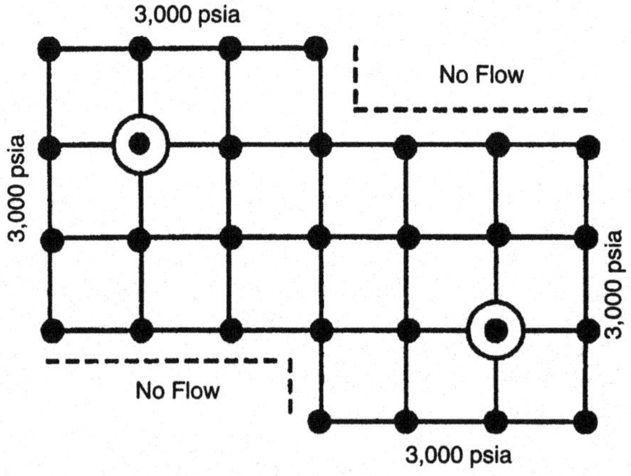

Fig. 8.36—Discretized 2D reservoir in Exercise 8.14.

problem can be approximated by pressure gradients. Other relevant data are $\Delta x=100$ ft, $\Delta y=200$ ft, $\Delta z=40$ ft, $\mu_w=1$ cp, $B_w=1$ RB/B, $k_x=400$ md, $k_y=200$ md, and $k_z=100$ md.

1. Write the PDE that describes the flow problem in the given system.
2. Give the finite-difference approximation for the PDE.
3. The production well in Gridblock (4,1,2) is maintained at atmospheric pressure (you can assume that pressure in this gridblock is kept at 14.7 psia), while 300 B/D of water is injected through the injection well in Gridblock (1,3,2). Write the finite-difference equation for each gridblock and generate the system of linear equations from which the pressure distribution in the system and rate of production from the production well can be solved. Do not attempt to solve the equations.

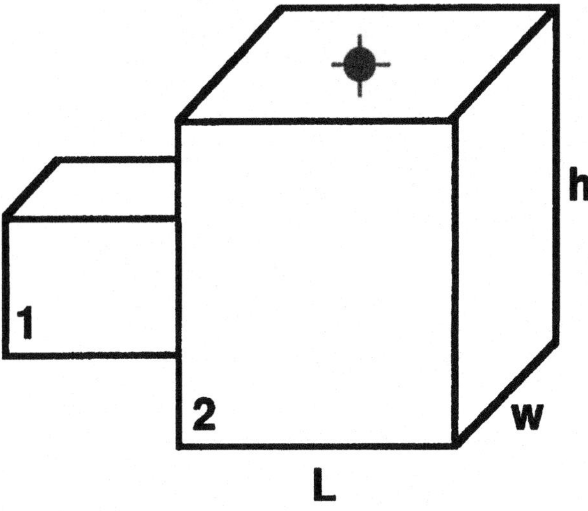

Fig. 8.37—Reservoir described in Exercise 8.15.

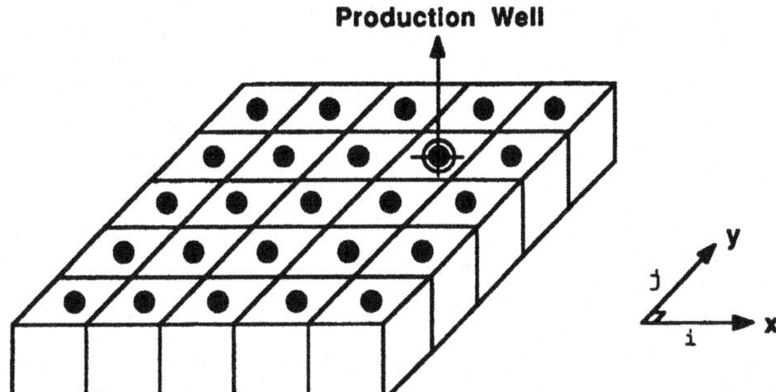

Fig. 8.38—Discretized 2D reservoir in Exercise 8.16.

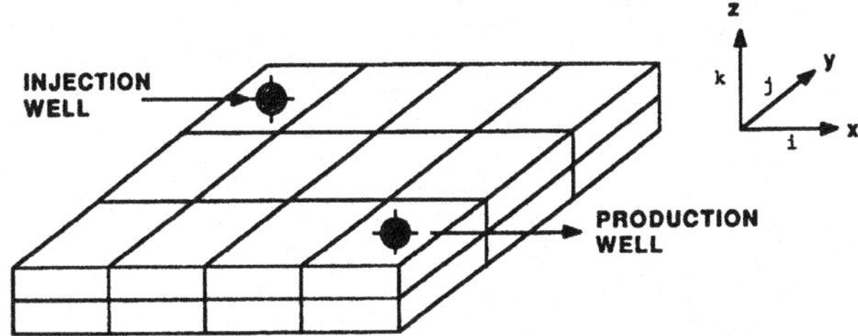

Fig. 8.39—Discretized 3D reservoir in Exercise 8.17.

TABLE 8.16—GRIDBLOCK PROPERTIES FOR EXERCISE 8.15		
	Gridblock 1	Gridblock 2
w, ft	200	220
L, ft	400	400
h, ft	60	80
k, md	1	1.2
ϕ, %	7	8

4. If the pressure in the injection gridblock is specified as 1,500 psia and the production gridblock is kept at atmospheric pressure, how would you modify the equations of Part 3?

8.18. Consider the incompressible flow of water in the 3D structure (Japanese crystal puzzle) shown in **Fig. 8.40**. Four injection wells are located in the outermost gridblocks of the largest x-y plane, and one production well is located in the central gridblock of the same x-y plane. The boundary conditions are as follows.

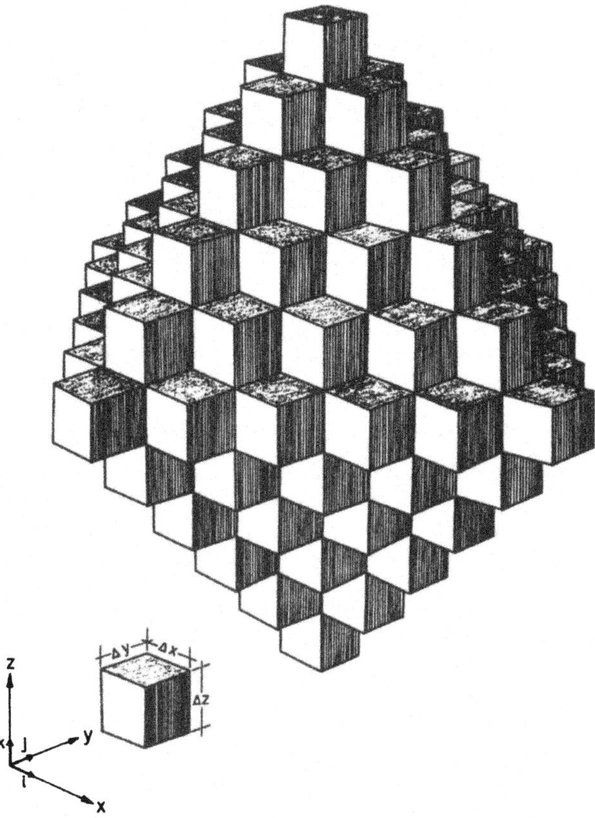

Fig. 8.40—Three-dimensional reservoir described in Exercise 8.18.

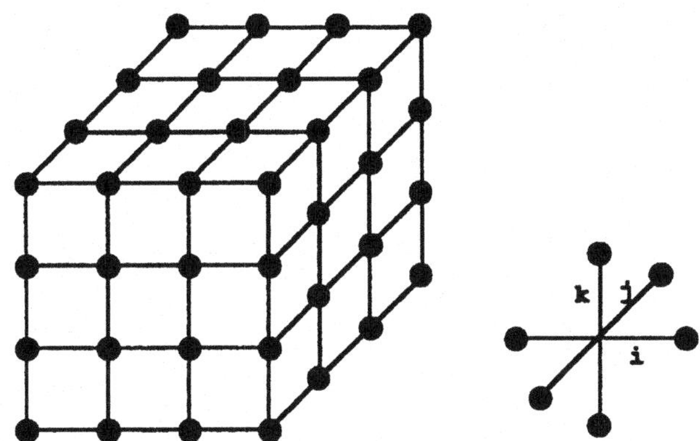

Fig. 8.41—4×4×4 grid system in Exercise 8.19.

1. System is surrounded by no-flow boundaries.
2. Injection rate at injection wells is specified as 3,000 STB/D.
3. The production gridblock is kept at a pressure of 100 psia.

The uniform gridblock properties are $\Delta x = \Delta y = \Delta z = 100$ ft and $k_x = k_y = k_z = 100$ md. The fluid properties are $\mu_w = 1.0$ cp and $B_w = 1.0$ RB/B. Assume that potential gradients for this problem can be approximated by pressure gradients.

With the finite-difference approximation to the governing flow equation, determine the steady-state pressure distribution and flow rate into the production well. Solve the linear equations of the finite-difference approximation by the (1) Jacobi iterative method, (2) Gauss-Seidel iterative method, and (3) PSOR method with ω_{opt}. Use a pressure tolerance of 0.1 psi for each algorithm. Print out the number of iterations with the solutions obtained. Check the material balances.

8.19. Explain how you approximately would solve Laplace's equation in three dimensions: $\partial^2 f/\partial x^2 + \partial^2 f/\partial y^2 + \partial^2 f/\partial z^2 = 0$ inside a cube (**Fig. 8.41**) with an edge of unit length if $f = f(x,y,z)$ is equal to 1 on one face and 0 on the remaining faces. Illustrate your proce-

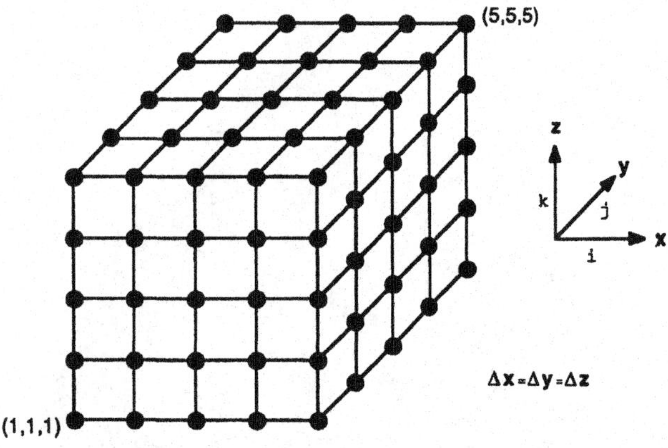

Fig. 8.42—5×5×5 grid system in Exercise 8.20.

dure by finding the approximate value of f at $x = 1/3$, $y = 1/3$, and $z = 1/3$. In the discretization process use a 4×4×4 grid system and base your finite-difference equations on the computational molecule (seven-point finite-difference scheme) in Fig. 8.41.

8.20. Calculate the steady-state pressure distribution in the 3D porous medium shown in **Fig. 8.42**, in which a production well at Node (3,3,3) is completed. Also, calculate the flow rate of the well. Ignore gravitational effects.

The boundary conditions are as follows.

1. Nodes on the outer surfaces of the body are kept at 2,000 psia.
2. Pressure of Gridblock (3,3,3) is kept at 400 psia.

The porous-medium and fluid properties are $k_x = k_y = k_z = 8.88$ md, $\Delta x = \Delta y = \Delta z = 100$ ft (uniform), $\phi = 11\%$, $\mu = 10$ cp, and $B = 1$ RB/STB.

8.21. What are the definitions of $\Gamma_{g_{i,j,k}}$ in terms of p/z for a compressible-flow system when the definition of $B_{g_{i,j,k}}$ as given by Eq. 2.83 is used in $(V_{b_{i,j,k}}/\alpha_c \Delta t)[(\phi^{n+1}/B_g^{n+1}) - (\phi^n/B_g^n)]_{i,j,k}$? Hint: Consider all the permutations of the time levels and pressure-dependent terms ϕ, p, z.

8.22.[4] Consider the steady-state flow of a single-phase incompressible liquid as shown in the reservoir in **Fig. 8.43**. Permeability and thickness maps are provided. Well 1 produces at a flow rate of 600 STB/D, and Well 2 produces at a rate of 400 STB/D. The known boundary conditions are shown along the three external boundaries. Calculate the value of the pressure gradient along the south boundary of the reservoir. Other relevant data are $\Delta x = \Delta y = 1{,}000$ ft (uniform), $\mu = 1.0$ cp, $B = 1.0$ RB/STB, and $\phi = 16\%$.

8.23. Consider the 2D, heterogeneous, anisotropic, volumetric single-phase gas reservoir shown in **Fig. 8.44**. Assume that you are constructing a simulator using the Newton-Raphson procedure.

Use the notation introduced in this chapter to complete the following tasks.

1. Write a characteristic finite-difference equation in an explicit form that generates the system of nonlinear algebraic equations for this reservoir (definition of residual).
2. Write the characteristic linear equation that generates the coefficient matrix (Jacobian), unknown vector, and the right-side vector.
3. Construct the coefficient matrix, unknown vector, and the right-side vector with only generic expressions. Do not write the explicit description of the derivatives and the other entries.

8.24. Consider the flow of a slightly compressible fluid in a 2D, homogeneous, isotropic porous medium as shown in **Fig. 8.45**. The entire reservoir is surrounded by no-flow boundaries. Initial pressure of the reservoir is determined to be 2,800 psia. The well in Gridblock 2 produces at a constant rate of 400 STB/D. Find the flowing sandface pressure of the well after 20 days of production. Use the ADIP solution technique. The uniform gridblock properties are $\Delta x = \Delta y = 600$ ft, $\phi = 24\%$, $k_x = k_y = 200$ md, $h = 60$ ft, and $r_w = 0.24$ ft. The fluid properties are $c = 8 \times 10^{-5}$ psi^{-1}, $B = 0.98$ RB/STB, and $\mu = 1.2$ cp.

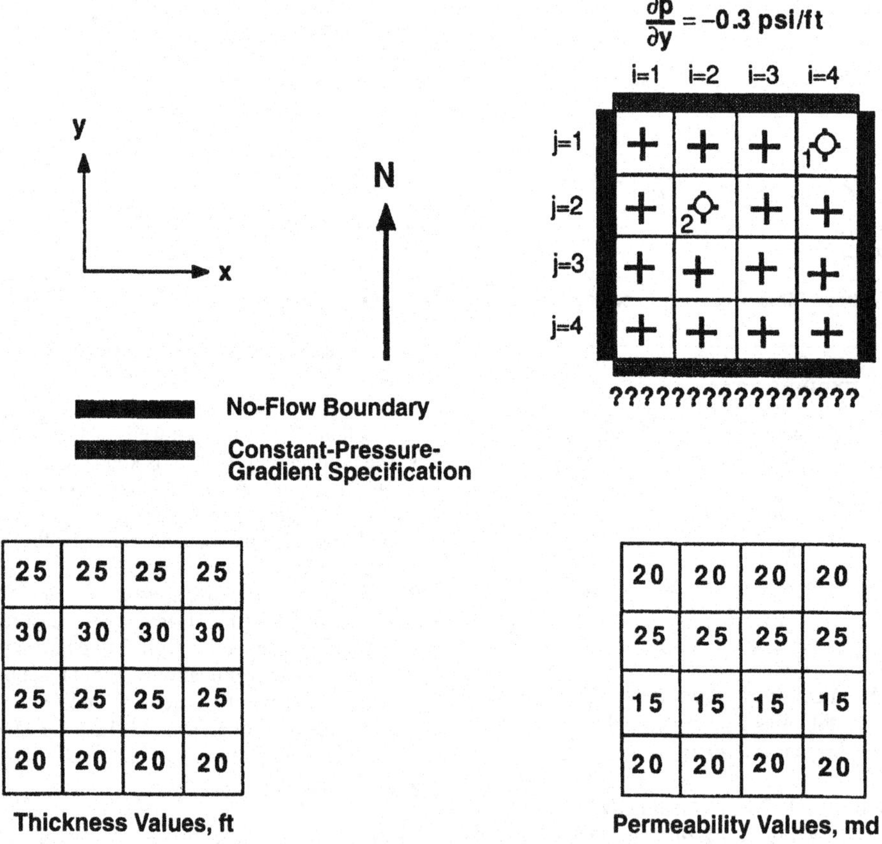

Fig. 8.43—Reservoir presented in Exercise 8.22.

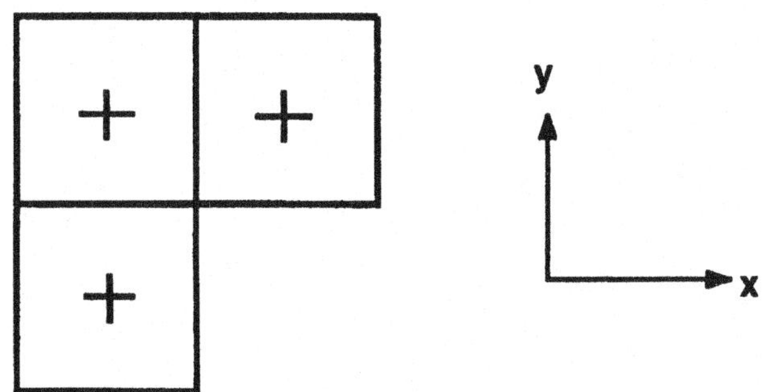

Fig. 8.44—Two-dimensional reservoir of Exercise 8.23.

8.25. The reservoir in **Fig. 8.46** has homogeneous property distribution but exhibits a pronounced permeability anisotropy. Initial reservoir pressure is 3,000 psia and depth gradients are ignored. The gridblock properties are $\Delta x = 1{,}000$ ft, $\Delta y = 800$ ft, $\phi = 18\%$, $k_x = 100$ md, $k_y = 50$ md, $h = 40$ ft, and $r_w = 0.2$ ft. The fluid properties are $c = 1 \times 10^{-6}$ psi^{-1}, $B = 1.0$ RB/STB, and $\mu = 0.87$ cp.

1. Write the finite-difference equations for Gridblocks 1, 18, and 25 at $t = 10$ days if the injection rate of the well in Gridblock 18 is 1,000 STB/D.
2. Write the finite-difference equations for Gridblocks 8 and 18 at $t = 10$ days if the sandface pressure is 4,100 psia.
3. What is the minimum number of unknowns for Parts 1 and 2 of this problem? What are they?

8.26. Use the generalized Newton-Raphson procedure to solve the following two equations in two unknowns. Start with an initial guess of $x_1^0 = 1$ and $x_2^0 = 1$.

1. $x_1^2 + x_2^2 = 1$.
2. $(x_1 - 1)^2 + x_2^2 = 1$.

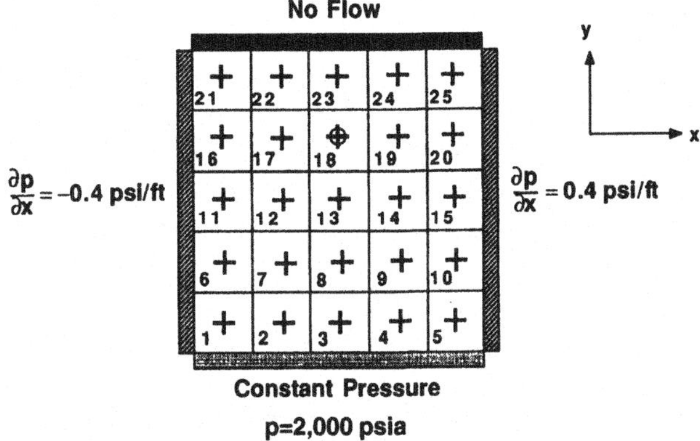

Fig. 8.46—Reservoir described in Exercise 8.25.

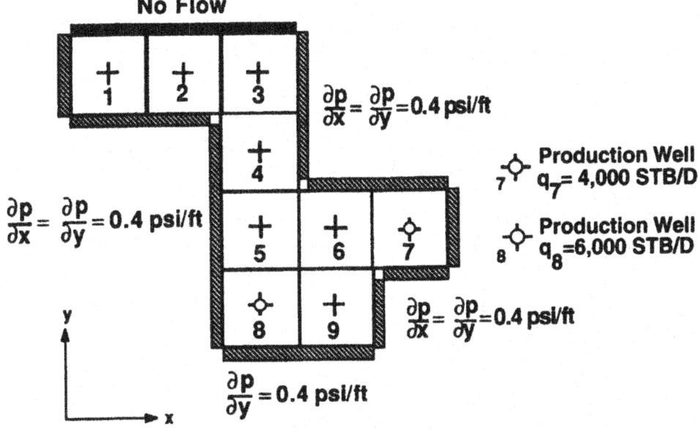

Fig. 8.47—Reservoir described in Exercise 8.27.

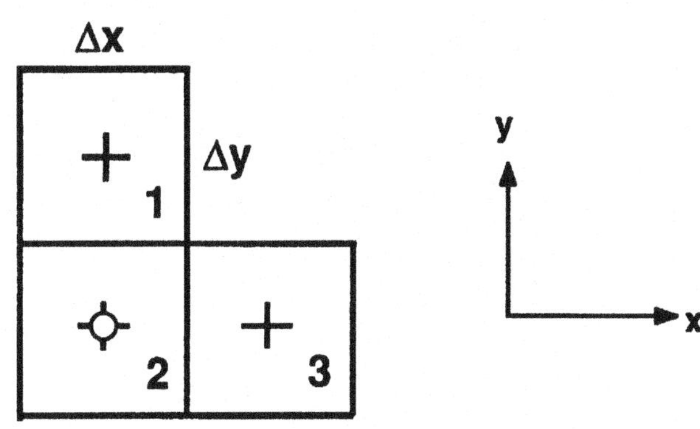

Fig. 8.45—Reservoir presented in Exercise 8.24.

8.27. Consider the 2D incompressible-fluid-flow problem to be studied for the pressure distribution in the reservoir shown in **Fig. 8.47**. **Fig. 8.48** provides additional maps. The gridblock properties are $\Delta x = 800$ ft, $\Delta y = 1{,}000$ ft, and $r_w = 0.2$ ft. The fluid properties are $\rho = 61$ lbm/ft^3 and $\mu = 1.2$ cp.

1. Write the PDE that describes the flow problem in this reservoir. Also, write the characteristic finite-difference approximation to the PDE and express it by use of the SIP notation.
2. Write the finite-difference equation for Gridblock 7 and calculate the numerical values of all coefficients.
3. Set up the finite-difference equations in a matrix form. Fill in the entries of the coefficient matrix, unknown vector, and the right-side vector. Use SIP notation.

8.28. Find the pressure distribution in the reservoir represented by the 2D mesh-centered grid system shown in **Fig. 8.49**. Assume that the reservoir fluid is an incompressible liquid and has a viscosity of 1.0 cp. Gridblocks at the outer boundaries of the reservoir represent a constant-pressure aquifer surrounding the reservoir. The aquifer

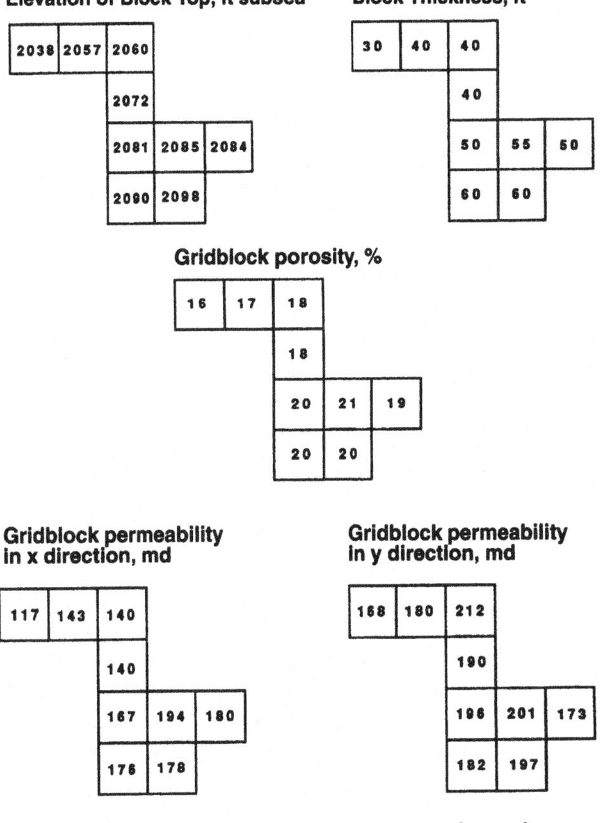

Fig. 8.48—Gridblock elevation, thickness, porosity, and permeability in Exercise 8.27.

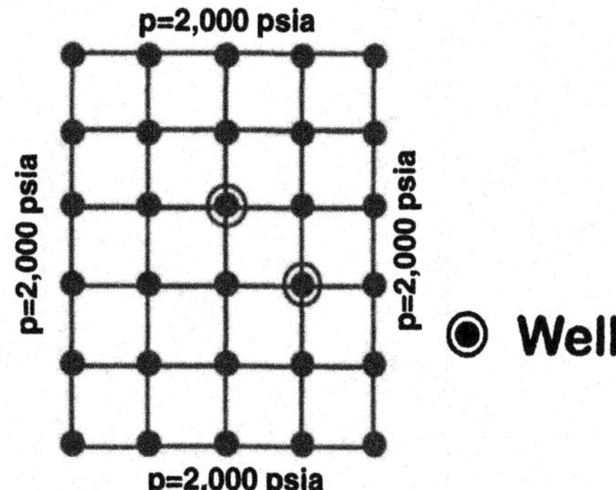

Fig. 8.49—Discretized 2D reservoir in Exercise 8.28.

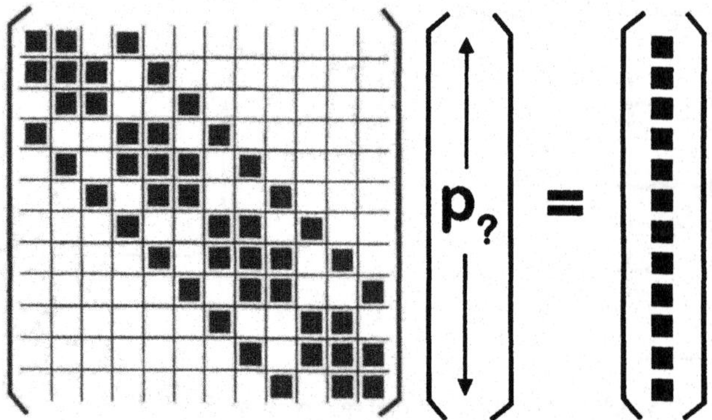

Fig. 8.50—Matrix representation of equations in Exercise 8.28.

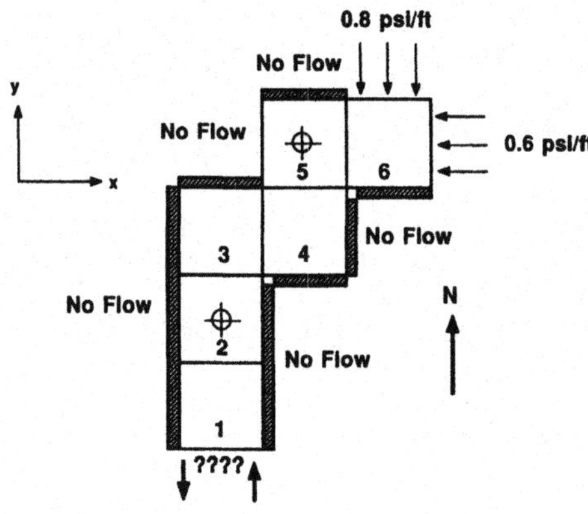

Fig. 8.51—Two-dimensional reservoir described in Exercise 8.29.

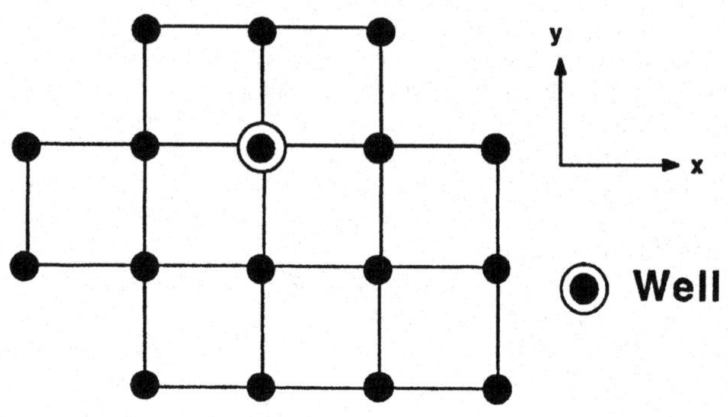

Fig. 8.52—Two-dimensional reservoir described in Exercise 8.32.

pressure is 2,000 psia. Both of the wells drilled in this reservoir are producing at a constant sandface pressure of 1,650 psia.

1. If the coefficient matrix is structured to have the pentadiagonal structure shown in **Fig. 8.50**, how would you number the gridblocks?

2. Calculate the entries for the coefficient matrix and right-side vector.

8.29. Consider the 2D incompressible-fluid-flow problem in the homogeneous anisotropic porous medium shown in **Fig. 8.51**. The gridblock properties are $\Delta x = \Delta y = 175$ ft, $k_x = 100$ md, $k_y = 150$ md, $h = 40$ ft, $r_w = 0.3$ ft, and $s = 0$. The fluid properties are $\mu = 1.2$ cp and $B = 1.05$ RB/STB.

The north and east boundaries of Gridblock 6 have pressure support as shown. The nonproducing observation well in Gridblock 5 gives a pressure reading of 2,054 psia. Moreover, the well in Gridblock 2 is put on production with a sandface-pressure specification of 1,000 psia, leading to production of 2,066 STB/D.

Determine the pressure distribution in the system and whether the south boundary of Gridblock 1 is sealed.

8.30. In constructing the Jacobian matrix for a 1D, single-phase compressible-flow problem, an analytical expression representing the general form of the main diagonal entries for a wellblock with sandface-pressure specification is needed. Derive a generic expression that can be used for such entries.

8.31. A 1D flow equation in the matrix notation for compressible flow is given as

$$W_i^{n+1}{}^{(\nu)} p_{i-1}^{n+1}{}^{(\nu+1)} + C_i^{n+1}{}^{(\nu)} p_i^{n+1}{}^{(\nu+1)} - E_i^{n+1}{}^{(\nu)} p_{i+1}^{n+1}{}^{(\nu+1)} = Q_i^{(\nu)}.$$

Write an algorithmic expression for implementation of the PSOR iterative-solution procedure to solve for pressures at Time Level $n+1$ and Iteration Level $(\nu+1)$.

8.32. Consider the steady-state flow of a single-phase incompressible liquid in the reservoir shown in **Fig. 8.52**. The gridblock properties are $\Delta x = \Delta y = 400$ ft, $k_x = 60$ md, $k_y = 30$ md, and $h = 17$ ft. The fluid properties are $\mu = 1.2$ cp and $B = 1.0$ RB/STB.

The pressure along the external boundaries of the reservoir is 4,000 psia. Flowing sandface pressure at the well ($r_w = 0.25$ ft) is controlled at 1,300 psia. What will be the flow rate into the well? Perform a material-balance check to verify the accuracy of your

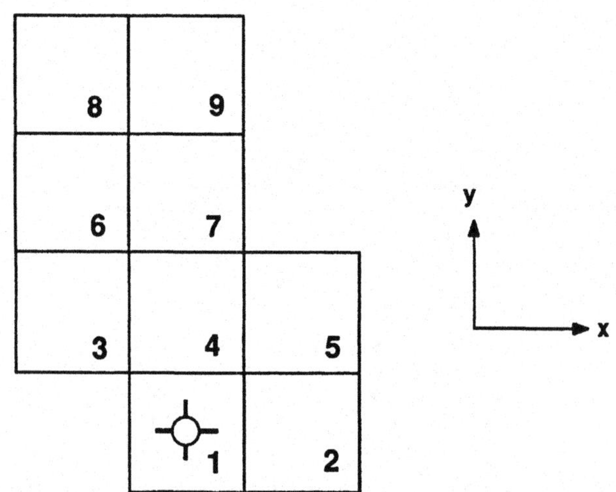

Fig. 8.53—Discretized reservoir described in Exercise 8.33.

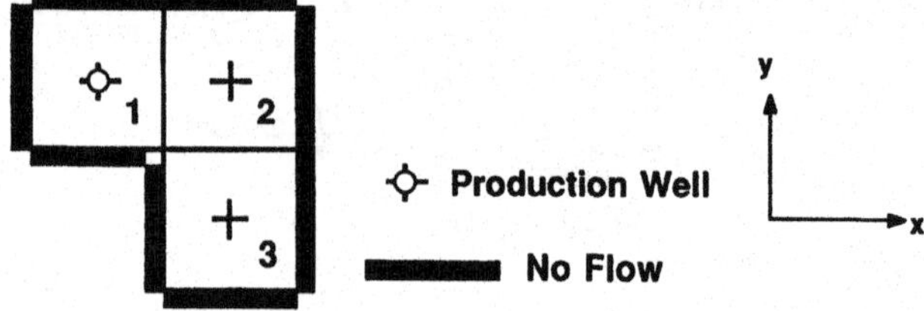

Fig. 8.54—Discretized reservoir described in Exercise 8.34.

solution. In the solution of finite-difference equations, use the Gauss-Seidel procedure with a pressure tolerance of 1 psi.

8.33. Consider the 2D gas reservoir shown in **Fig. 8.53**. The reservoir is surrounded by no-flow boundaries.

Use the generalized Newton-Raphson procedure to solve for the pressure distribution in the reservoir. In the solution of the system of equations generated by the generalized Newton-Raphson procedure, use the line successive overrelaxation (LSOR) procedure with $\omega_{opt} = 1.00$.

1. Write a characteristic equation that will generate the system of nonlinear equations.
2. Write the system of nonlinear equations generated by the equation of Part 1 with a closed form, i.e., $f_{i,j}\ (p_{i\,j}, p_{i-1,j}, \ldots$, etc.).
3. Write a characteristic LSOR equation that will solve the system of equations generated by the generalized Newton-Raphson procedure sweeping the system parallel to the y direction.

8.34. Consider the slightly-compressible-fluid flow through the 2D porous medium shown in **Fig. 8.54**. The porous medium has homogeneous but anisotropic property distribution, and all external boundaries are no-flow boundaries. The pressure at $t=0$ for all gridblocks is 4,000 psia.

Can the well sustain a flow rate of 500 STB/D for 5 days? Justify your answer. Use $h=5$ ft, $k_x=100$ md, $k_y=150$ md, $\Delta x=\Delta y=1{,}320$ ft, $\phi=20\%$, $\mu=1.2$ cp, $c=1\times10^{-6}$ psi^{-1}, $B=1.0$ RB/STB, $r_{eq}=263$ ft, $p_i=4{,}000$ psia, $r_w=0.2$ ft, and skin factor $=+2.0$. In the solution of finite-difference equations written for a timestep size of 5 days, use the PSOR procedure with a pressure tolerance of 1 psi.

8.35. Regardless of the answer to Exercise 8.34, calculate the exact number of days Well 1 can sustain a specified flow rate of 500 STB/D.

8.36.[4] Consider the flow of a single-phase incompressible fluid in a reservoir represented by the body-centered grid in **Fig. 8.55**. The reservoir has homogeneous but anisotropic property distribution with $k_x=100$ md and $k_y=200$ md. The thickness of the formation is uniform and equal to 60 ft. The reservoir is surrounded by no-flow boundaries with the exception of the two locations indicated. Flowing sandface pressure of the well in Gridblock 3 is kept at 600 psia. Assume that the entire top surface of the reservoir is 6,000 ft below the datum level. Wellbore radius is 0.24 ft, and fluid viscosity is 2 cp. Use the LSOR procedure with $\omega_{opt}=1.00$ to solve for the pressure distribution in the reservoir.

8.37. Use the following four equations in four unknowns to obtain an approximate coefficient matrix that is easy to factor.

1. $x_1 + 2x_3 + 4x_4 = -8$
2. $3x_1 + 6x_2 + x_3 = 3$
3. $x_2 + 3x_3 + 2x_4 = 4$
4. $4x_1 + 2x_2 + x_4 = -9$

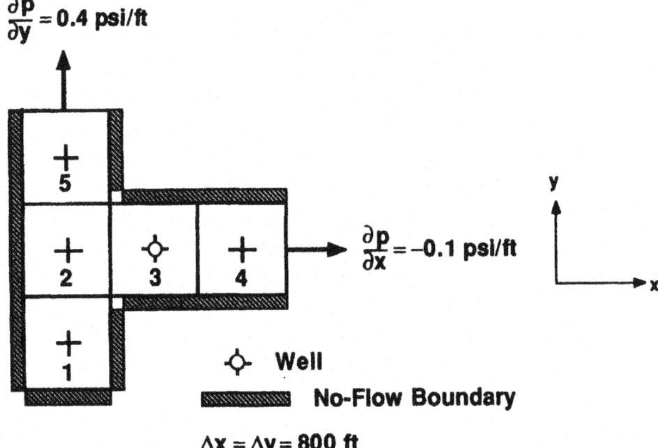

Fig. 8.55—Discretized 2D reservoir described in Exercise 8.36.

Find the entries of the upper and lower tridiagonal matrices that are formed as a consequence of this factorization. Do not use an iteration parameter.

8.38. Rework Example 8.2 for a reservoir dipping at a constant dip angle of 10° from left to right.

Nomenclature

a = constant
a_n = the nth value for a property
$\overline{A}$ = arithmetic average
$A_{G_{i,j,k}}$ = modified transmissibility coefficient of $Z_{i\,j\,k+1}$, L^2/t, STB/(D-ft) [std m^3/(d·m)]
$A_{i,j,k}$ = transmissibility coefficient of $p_{i,j,k+1}$ in matrix notation, L^4t/m, STB/(D-psi) [std m^3/(d·kPa)]
$A_{J_{i,j,k}}$ = Jacobian matrix entry as defined by Eq. 8.169
A_x = cross-sectional area normal to the x direction, L^2, ft^2 [m^2]
$A_{x_{i,j,k}}$ = cross-sectional area normal to the x direction for Gridblock (i,j,k), L^2, ft^2 [m^2]
A_y = cross-sectional area normal to the y direction, L^2, ft^2 [m^2]
$A_{y_{i,j,k}}$ = cross-sectional area normal to the y direction for Gridblock (i,j,k), L^2, ft^2 [m^2]
A_z = cross-sectional area normal to the z direction, L^2, ft^2 [m^2]
B = FVF, L^3/L^3, reservoir volume/volume at standard conditions
B_g = gas FVF, L^3/L^3, RB/scf [m^3/std m^3]
$B_{G_{i,j,k}}$ = modified transmissibility coefficient of $Z_{i\,j\,k-1}$, L^2/t, STB/(D-ft) [std m^3/(d·m)]
$B_{i,j,k}$ = transmissibility coefficient of $p_{i,j,k-1}$ in matrix notation, L^4t/m, STB/(D-psi) [std m^3/(d·kPa)]
$B_{J_{i,j,k}}$ = Jacobian matrix entry as defined by Eq. 8.163
B_l = FVF of Phase l, L^3/L^3, reservoir volume/volume at standard conditions
B_l^n = FVF of phase l at time level n, L^3/L^3, reservoir volume/volume at standard conditions
B_o = oil FVF, L^3/L^3, RB/STB [m^3/std m^3]
B_w = water FVF, L^3/L^3, RB/B [m^3/std m^3]
c = compressibility, Lt^2/m, psi^{-1} [kPa^{-1}]
c_l = compressibility of Phase l, Lt^2/m, psi^{-1} [kPa^{-1}]
c_o = oil compressibility, Lt^2/m, psi^{-1} [kPa^{-1}]
c_ϕ = porosity compressibility, Lt^2/m, psi^{-1} [kPa^{-1}]
$C_{G_{i,j,k}}$ = modified transmissibility coefficient of $Z_{i\,j\,k}$, L^2/t, STB/(D-ft) [std m^3/(d·m)]
$C_{i,j,k}$ = transmissibility coefficient of $p_{i,j,k}$ in matrix notation, L^4t/m, STB/(D-psi) [std m^3/(d·kPa)]
$C_{J_{i,j,k}}$ = Jacobian matrix entry as defined by Eq. 8.166
C_{MB} = cumulative material balance, dimensionless
$d^{(k)}$ = maximum deviation of unknowns between the $k+1$ iteration and kth iteration
$E_{G_{i,j,k}}$ = modified transmissibility coefficient of $Z_{i+1\,j\,k}$, L^2/t, STB/(D-ft) [std m^3/(d·m)]
$E_{i,j,k}$ = transmissibility coefficient of $p_{i+1,j,k}$ in matrix notation, L^4t/m, STB/(D-psi) [std m^3/(d·kPa)]
$E_{J_{i,j,k}}$ = Jacobian matrix entry as defined by Eq. 8.167
F = factor (F=½ for steadystate, F=¾ for pseudosteadystate)
g = acceleration of gravity, L/t^2, ft/sec^2 [m/s^2]
g_{pbx} = specified pressure-gradient boundary in the x direction, m/L^{2}t^2, psi/ft [kPa/m]
g_{pby} = specified pressure-gradient boundary in the y direction, m/L^{2}t^2, psi/ft [kPa/m]
$\overline{G}$ = geometric average
$\overline{H}$ = harmonic average
h = thickness, L, ft [m]

I_{MB} = incremental material balance, dimensionless
j = index in the y direction
$J^n_{w_{i,j,k}}$ = productivity index of a well in Gridblock (i,j,k) as calculated at the old time level, L^4t/m, STB/(D–psi) [std $m^3/(d\cdot kPa)$]
[J] = Jacobian matrix
k = permeability, L^2, darcy [μm^2]
k_H = horizontal permeability, L^2, darcy [μm^2]
k_x = x-direction permeability, L^2, darcy [μm^2]
$k_{x_{i,j,k}}$ = x-direction permeability for Gridblock (i,j,k), L^2, darcy [μm^2]
k_y = y-direction permeability, L^2, darcy [μm^2]
$k_{y_{i,j,k}}$ = y-direction permeability for Gridblock (i,j,k), L^2, darcy [μm^2]
k_z = z-direction permeability, L^2, darcy [μm^2]
L = distance, L, ft [m]
m = dummy index
n = old time level
n_x = number of gridblocks in the x direction
n_y = number of gridblocks in the y direction
n_z = number of gridblocks in the z direction
$N_{G_{i,j,k}}$ = modified transmissibility coefficient of $Z_{i,j+1,k}$, L^2/t, STB/(D-ft) [std $m^3/(d\cdot m)$]
$N_{i,j,k}$ = transmissibility coefficient of $p_{i,j+1,k}$ in matrix notation, L^4t/m, STB/(D-psi) [std $m^3/(d\cdot kPa)$]
$N_{J_{i,j,k}}$ = Jacobian matrix entry defined by Eq. 8.168
p = pressure, m/Lt^2, psia [kPa]
p_i = pressure of Gridblock i, m/Lt^2, psia [kPa]
$p_{i,j,k}$ = pressure of Gridblock (i,j,k), m/Lt^2, psia [kPa]
p^{n+1} = pressure at current (new) time level, m/Lt^2, psia [kPa]
p_{n_x} = pressure of Gridblock n_x, m/Lt^2, psia [kPa]
p° = reference pressure, m/Lt^2, psia [kPa]
$\hat{p}_{i,j,k}$ = datum-corrected pressure of $p_{i,j,k}$ at the depth of topmost perforation, m/Lt^2, psia [kPa]
p_{sc} = pressure at standard conditions, m/Lt^2, psia [kPa]
p_{wf} = flowing-well bottomhole pressure, m/Lt^2, psia [kPa]
$p_{wf_{i,j,k}}$ = flowing-well bottomhole pressure opposite Wellblock (i,j,k), m/Lt^2, psia [kPa]
$\vec{p}$ = pressure vector
Δp = difference in pressure, m/Lt^2, psia [kPa]
q = production or flow rate, L^3/t, RB/D [m^3/d]
q_{gsc} = gas production rate at standard conditions, L^3/t, scf/D [std m^3/d]
q_{gsc_i} = gas production at standard conditions from Wellblock i, L^3/t, scf/D [std m^3/d]
q_l = production or flow rate of Phase l, L^3/t, RB/D [m^3/d]
q_{lsc} = production rate of Phase l at standard conditions, L^3/t, volume at standard conditions/time
$q_{lsc_{i,j,k}}$ = production rate of Phase l at standard conditions from Wellblock (i,j,k), L^3/t, volume at standard conditions/time
$q^m_{lsc_{i,j,k}}$ = production rate of Phase l at standard conditions from Wellblock (i,j,k) at the mth time, L^3/t, volume at standard conditions/time
$q_{lsc_{nx}}$ = production of Phase l at standard conditions from Wellblock n_x, L^3/t, volume at standard conditions/time
q_{spsc} = specified well flow rate at standard conditions, L^3/t, volume at standard conditions/time
Q_G = gravity term on the right side of the finite-difference equation, defined by Eq. 8.70
$Q^{n+1}_{G_{i,j,k}}$ = gravity term on the right side of the finite-difference equation for Gridblock (i,j,k) calculated at the current time level
$Q_{i,j,k}$ = known right side of a flow equation for Gridblock (i,j,k) in matrix notation, L^3/t, volume at standard conditions/time
r_{eq} = equivalent wellblock radius, L, ft [m]
r_w = well radius, L, ft [m]
$\vec{r}^{\,n+1}$ = residual vector at Time Level $n+1$ as defined in Eq. 8.160
s = skin factor
$S_{G_{i,j,k}}$ = modified transmissibility coefficient of $Z_{i,j-1,k}$, L^2/t, STB/(D-ft) [std $m^3/(d\cdot m)$]
$S_{i,j,k}$ = transmissibility coefficient of $p_{i,j-1,k}$ in matrix notation, L^4t/m, STB/(D-psi) [std $m^3/(d\cdot kPa)$]
$S_{J_{i,j,k}}$ = Jacobian matrix entry as defined by Eq. 8.164
t = time, t, days
t^n = old time, t, days
Δt = timestep ($\Delta t = t^{n+1} - t^n$), t, days
Δt^m = the mth timestep, t, days
T = reservoir temperature, T, °R [K]
T_{sc} = temperature at standard conditions, T, °R [K]
v = iteration level
V_b = gridblock bulk volume, L^3, ft^3 [m^3]
$V_{b_{i,j,k}}$ = bulk volume for Gridblock (i,j,k), L^3, ft^3 [m^3]
w = width, L, ft [m]
$\overline{W}$ = weighted average
$W_{G_{i,j,k}}$ = modified transmissibility coefficient of $Z_{i-1,j,k}$, L^2/t, STB/(D-ft) [std $m^3/(d\cdot m)$]
W_i = transmissibility coefficient of p_{i-1} in matrix notation, L^4t/m, STB/(D-psi) [std $m^3/(d\cdot kPa)$]
$W_{i,j,k}$ = transmissibility coefficient of $p_{i-1,j,k}$ in matrix notation, L^4t/m, STB/(D-psi) [std $m^3/(d\cdot kPa)$]
$W_{J_{i,j,k}}$ = Jacobian matrix entry as defined by Eq. 8.165
x = distance in the x direction in the Cartesian coordinate system, L, ft [m]
Δx = difference along the x direction ($\Delta x = x_{i+1} - x_i$), L, ft [m]
y = distance in the y direction in the Cartesian coordinate system, L, ft [m]
Δy = difference along the y direction ($\Delta y = y_{j+1} - y_j$), L, ft [m]
$\Delta y_{i,j,k}$ = size of Gridblock (i,j,k) along the y direction ($\Delta y_{i,j,k} = y_{i,j+1/2,k} - y_{i,j-1/2,k}$), L, ft [m]
z = distance in the z direction in the Cartesian coordinate system, L, ft [m]
z = gas-compressibility factor, dimensionless
Δz = difference along the z direction $= z_{k+1} - z_k$, L, ft [m]
z_k = distance along the z direction at Gridblock k, L, ft [m]
Z = elevation referred to datum (positive downward), L, ft [m]
$Z_{i,j,k}$ = depth to Gridblock (i,j,k) from datum (positive downward), L, ft [m]
α_c = volume conversion factor whose numerical value is given in Table 4.1
β_c = transmissibility conversion factor whose numerical value is given in Table 4.1
Γ_g = accumulation term coefficient for the gas phase
$\Gamma^{n+1}_{g_{i,j,k}}$ = accumulation term coefficient for the gas equation calculated at Time Level $n+1$ for Gridblock (i,j,k), Eq. 8.133
Γ_l = accumulation term coefficient for Phase l
$\Gamma^{n+1}_{l_{i,j,k}}$ = accumulation term coefficient for Phase l as defined by Eq. 8.94 and calculated at the new time level
Γ^n_o = accumulation term coefficient for the oil phase evaluated at the old time level
$\Gamma^{n+1}_{o_{i,j,k}}$ = accumulation term coefficient for the oil phase evaluated at the new time level for Gridblock (i,j,k)
γ_l = gravity of Phase l, m/L^2t^2, psi/ft [kPa/m]

$\gamma_{l_{i,j,k}}$ = gravity of Phase l in Gridblock (i,j,k), m/L^{2}t^2, psi/ft [kPa/m]

$\vec{\delta p}^{\,n+1}$ = $\vec{p}^{\,n+1} - \vec{p}^{\,n}$ = unknown vector in the Newton-Raphson iteration

$\delta p_{i,j,k}$ = change in pressure of Gridblock (i,j,k), m/Lt^2, psia [kPa]

δT_{ox} = change in oil transmissibility

ε = tolerance

μ_g = gas viscosity, m/Lt, cp [Pa·s]

μ_l = viscosity of Phase l, m/Lt, cp [Pa·s]

$\mu_{l_{i,j,k}}$ = viscosity of Phase l in Gridblock (i,j,k), m/Lt, cp [Pa·s]

μ_o = oil viscosity, m/Lt, cp [Pa·s]

μ_w = water viscosity, m/Lt, cp [Pa·s]

ρ_{GS} = spectral radius of the Gauss-Seidel iteration matrix

ρ_l = density of Phase l, m/L^3, lbm/ft^3 [kg/m^3]

ρ_{lsc} = density of Phase l at standard conditions, m/L^3, lbm/ft^3 [kg/m^3]

ρ_l° = density of Phase l at reference pressure, m/L^3, lbm/ft^3 [kg/m^3]

ρ_o = oil-phase density, m/L^3, lbm/ft^3 [kg/m^3]

T_g = gas-phase transmissibility, L^{4}t/m, scf/(D-psi) [std m^3/(d·kPa)]

T_{gx} = gas-phase transmissibility in the x direction, L^{4}t/m, scf/(D-psi) [std m^3/(d·kPa)]

$T^n_{gx_{i\pm 1/2,j,k}}$ = gas-phase transmissibility in the x direction at Boundary $(i \pm 1/2, j, k)$ as calculated at the old time level, L^{4}t/m, scf/(D-psi) [std m^3/(d·kPa)]

$T^n_{gy_{i,j\pm 1/2,k}}$ = gas-phase transmissibility in the y direction at Boundary $(i, j \pm 1/2, k)$ as calculated at the old time level, L^{4}t/m, scf/(D-psi) [std m^3/(d·kPa)]

$T^n_{gz_{i,j,k\pm 1/2}}$ = gas-phase transmissibility in the z direction at Boundary $(i, j, k \pm 1/2)$ as calculated at the old time level, L^{4}t/m, scf/(D-psi) [std m^3/(d·kPa)]

T_l = transmissibility of Phase l

$T_{lx_{i\pm 1/2,j,k}}$ = transmissibility of Phase l in the x direction at Boundary $(i \pm 1/2, j, k)$, L^{4}t/m, STB/(D-psi) [std m^3/(d·kPa)]

$T_{ly_{i,j\pm 1/2,k}}$ = transmissibility of Phase l in the y direction at Boundary $(i, j \pm 1/2, k)$, L^{4}t/m, STB/(D-psi) [std m^3/(d·kPa)]

$T_{lz_{i,j,k\pm 1/2}}$ = transmissibility of Phase l in the z direction at Boundary $(i, j, k \pm 1/2)$, L^{4}t/m, STB/(D-psi) [std m^3/(d·kPa)]

T_{ox} = oil-phase transmissibility in the x direction, L^{4}t/m, STB/(D-psi) [std m^3/(d·kPa)]

ϕ = porosity, fraction

ϕ° = porosity at reference pressure, p°, fraction

Φ_l = potential of Phase l, m/Lt^2, psia [kPa]

Φ_l° = potential of Phase l at absolute datum, m/Lt^2, psia [kPa]

ω = overrelaxation parameter

ω_{opt} = optimum overrelaxation parameter

Ω = weighting factor $(0 \leqq \Omega \leqq 1)$

Subscripts

avg = average value

g = gas phase

i = x-direction index

j = y-direction index

k = z-direction index

l = Phase l

o = oil phase

w = water phase

Superscripts

m = time index

n = old timestep

$n+1$ = current (or new) timestep

(v) = old iteration

$(v+1)$ = current iteration

0 = initial pressure

$\circ$ = reference

$*$ = extrapolated value

References

1. Odeh, A.S.: "An Overview of Mathematical Modeling of the Behavior of Hydrocarbon Reservoirs," *SIAM Review* (July 1982), **24,** No. 3, 263.
2. Aziz, K. and Settari, A.: *Petroleum Reservoir Simulation*, Applied Science Publishers Ltd., London (1979), 104.
3. *The Theory and Practice of the Testing of Gas Wells,* third edition, manual, Energy Resources Conservation Board, Calgary (1975), A1–A23.
4. Ertekin, T. and Adewumi, M.A.: *Reservoir Simulation*, IHRDC Video Library for E&P Specialists, Boston, Massachusetts (1995) 163.

SI Metric Conversion Factors

bbl	× 1.589 873	E − 01	= m^3
cp	× 1.0*	E − 03	= Pa·s
ft	× 3.048*	E − 01	= m
ft^3	× 2.831 685	E − 02	= m^3
°F	(°F + 459.67)/1.8		= K
lbm	× 4.535 924	E − 01	= kg
md	× 9.869 233	E − 04	= μm^2
psi	× 6.894 757	E + 00	= kPa
psi^{-1}	× 1.450 377	E − 01	= kPa^{-1}
°R	5/9		= K

*Conversion factor is exact.

Chapter 9
Multiphase-Flow Simulation in Petroleum Reservoirs

9.1 Introduction

In the first eight chapters of this book, we discussed the procedures used in the development of finite-difference simulators. **Fig. 9.1** shows these procedures for multiphase-flow systems. In this chapter, we discuss these procedures as they apply to multiphase-flow problems.

In the formulation procedure discussed in Chap. 4, the continuity equation (differential mass balance), an equation of state [mathematical description of the pressure/volume/temperature (PVT) behavior of the flowing fluid], and a transport equation (Darcy's law) were combined to develop a partial-differential equation (PDE) that describes single-phase flow through porous media. When these equations are applied to multiphase-flow problems, as described in Secs. 9.2 through 9.4, a system of PDE's is generated with one equation for each hydrocarbon component and one equation for the water phase. These PDE's are coupled to each other by additional constraint equations and capillary pressure relationships.

In Chap. 5, we discussed application of the discretization procedure to the single-phase-flow equation. For multiphase-flow systems, the spatial-discretization procedure is used to convert continuous differential operators of the form $(\partial/\partial x)[\xi^*(\partial\eta/\partial x)]\Delta x$ to an algebraic form. For single-phase flow, the variable ξ^* in the differential operator is defined by $\xi^* = \beta_c k_x A_x/\mu_l B_l$ and the variable η is the pressure, p. For multiphase flow, the variables ξ^* and η can have several definitions. To assist in the discussion of spatial discretization, we introduce a new terminology for multidimensional multiphase-flow systems. Sec. 9.5.1 discusses the discretization process for multiphase systems

The discretization process results in a system of nonlinear algebraic equations. In Chap. 8, we discussed several methods for linearizing the nonlinear, pressure-dependent terms in the single-phase-flow equation. These methods are the explicit treatment, extrapolation treatment, simple-iteration treatment, and the fully-implicit treatment of the transmissibility terms. In this chapter, we discuss how these methods are applied to multiphase-flow situations and we introduce additional methods that can be used to linearize the saturation-dependent terms in multiphase-flow systems. Sec. 9.5.2 discusses the linerization process for multiphase systems.

In multiphase-flow systems, we deal with multiple equations in multiple unknowns for each gridblock. We can formulate the final equation set in several ways, depending on which unknowns are solved directly from the flow equations (the principal unknowns) and which are solved from the constraint equations. Once formulated, several solution methods can be used to generate the coefficient matrix. These are the simultaneous solution (SS) method, the implicit pressure explicit saturation (IMPES) method, and the sequential solution (SEQ) method. Sec. 9.6 discusses these solution methods.

Finally, the representation of wells in reservoir simulation is complicated in the presence of multiphase production. In single-phase flow, the two possible well specifications are bottomhole pressure and production/injection rate. For multiphase-flow systems, there are many more possible specifications. These include bottomhole pressure, oil production/injection rate, water production/injection rate, gas production/injection rate, liquid production rate, and reservoir-voidage rate (reservoir conditions).

In Secs. 9.7.3 and 9.7.4, we discuss these specifications for production and injection wells, respectively. In the remainder of the chapter, we discuss the details of applying the finite-difference technique to multiphase-flow problems.

9.2 Mass-Conservation Equations in a Multiphase-Flow System

Multiphase flow in petroleum reservoirs involves the simultaneous flow of, at most, three phases (oil, water, and gas) transporting multiple fluid components. For black-oil systems, the three fluid components present are oil, water, and gas, all at standard conditions. If there is no mass transfer between phases, each fluid component is contained within its own phase, as **Fig. 9.2** schematically shows. **Fig. 9.3** shows a more realistic representation of a black-oil fluid. In this representation, the oil and water components are assumed to be immiscible; therefore, there is no mass transfer between these phases. The gas component is assumed to be soluble in oil but usually not in water; therefore, mass transfer of the gas component occurs between the oil and gas phases only. The portion of the gas component dissolved in the oil phase is known as solution gas. For the purpose of deriving a general mass-conservation equation, the gas component is split fictitiously into a free-gas component (contained in the gas phase) and a solution-gas component (contained in the oil phase). Furthermore, the mass-transfer rate of gas between the oil and gas phases $(q_{mt_{fg}}, q_{mt_{sg}})$ is treated as a generation term. Other generation terms expressing rates of mass transfer of oil and water, which are zero, are q_{mt_o} and q_{mt_w}.

The material-balance equation for Component c written over a finite control volume of the porous reservoir over Time Interval Δt is

$$(m_i)_c - (m_o)_c + s_c = (m_a)_c. \quad \text{(9.1)}$$

In rectangular coordinates, where the control volume is shown in Fig. 4.7, the physical interpretation of the terms in Eq. 9.1 are $(m_i)_c$ = sum of mass inflows of Component c across the control-volume surfaces at $x-\Delta x/2$, $y-\Delta y/2$, and $z-\Delta z/2$ over Time Interval Δt; $(m_o)_c$ = sum of mass outflows of Component c across the control-volume surfaces at $x+\Delta x/2$, $y+\Delta y/2$, and $z+\Delta z/2$ over Time Interval Δt; s_c = sum of mass generation and mass depletion through wells of Component c over Time Interval Δt; and $(m_a)_c$ = mass ac-

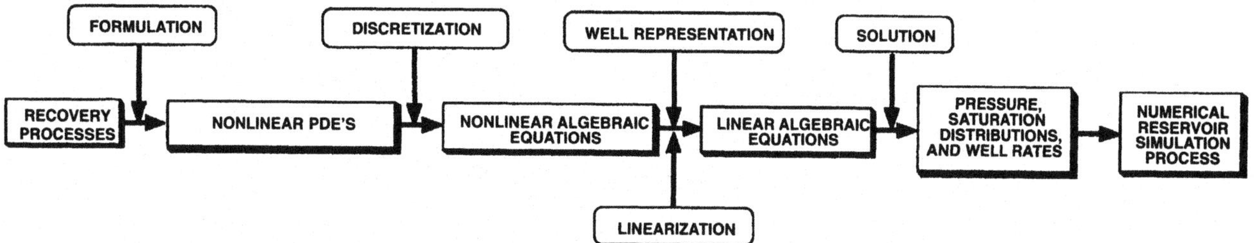

Fig. 9.1—Major steps used in development of multiphase reservoir simulators (redrawn from Ref. 1).

cumulation of Component c caused by compressibility and fluid saturation changes in the control volume over Time Interval Δt.

For Component $c=o, w, fg$, and sg, these terms can be expressed as

$$(m_i)_c = \left[\left(\dot{m}_{cx}A_x\right)_{x-\Delta x/2} + \left(\dot{m}_{cy}A_y\right)_{y-\Delta y/2} + \left(\dot{m}_{cz}A_z\right)_{z-\Delta z/2}\right]\Delta t, \quad \text{(9.2)}$$

$$(m_o)_c = \left[\left(\dot{m}_{cx}A_x\right)_{x+\Delta x/2} + \left(\dot{m}_{cy}A_y\right)_{y+\Delta y/2} + \left(\dot{m}_{cz}A_z\right)_{z+\Delta z/2}\right]\Delta t, \quad \text{(9.3)}$$

$$s_c = \left(q_{mt_c} + q_{m_c}\right)\Delta t, \quad \text{(9.4)}$$

and $(m_a)_c = V_b\left[\left(m_{v_c}\right)_{t+\Delta t} - \left(m_{v_c}\right)_t\right]$, ... (9.5)

where $\dot{m}_c$ = mass flux; A = the area perpendicular to the flux; m_{v_c} = mass per unit volume of porous medium; q_{mt_c} = rate of mass transfer between phases, which is positive for generation and negative otherwise; q_{m_c} = rate of mass depletion through wells, which is positive for injection and negative for production; and V_b = bulk volume of control volume.

Substituting Eqs. 9.2 through 9.5 into Eq. 9.1 and rearranging terms yields

$$-\left[\left(\dot{m}_{cx}A_x\right)_{x+\Delta x/2} - \left(\dot{m}_{cx}A_x\right)_{x-\Delta x/2}\right]\Delta t$$
$$-\left[\left(\dot{m}_{cy}A_y\right)_{y+\Delta y/2} - \left(\dot{m}_{cy}A_y\right)_{y-\Delta y/2}\right]\Delta t$$
$$-\left[\left(\dot{m}_{cz}A_z\right)_{z+\Delta z/2} - \left(\dot{m}_{cz}A_z\right)_{z-\Delta z/2}\right]\Delta t + \left(q_{mt_c} + q_{m_c}\right)\Delta t$$
$$= V_b\left[\left(m_{v_c}\right)_{t+\Delta t} - \left(m_{v_c}\right)_t\right], \quad \text{(9.6)}$$

where $c=o, w, fg$, and sg.

Dividing Eq. 9.6 by Δt and multiplying and dividing the first, second, and third terms on the left side by a nonzero Δx, Δy, and Δz, respectively, gives

$$-\left[\frac{\left(\dot{m}_{cx}A_x\right)_{x+\Delta x/2} - \left(\dot{m}_{cx}A_x\right)_{x-\Delta x/2}}{\Delta x}\right]\Delta x$$
$$-\left[\frac{\left(\dot{m}_{cy}A_y\right)_{y+\Delta y/2} - \left(\dot{m}_{cy}A_y\right)_{y-\Delta y/2}}{\Delta y}\right]\Delta y$$
$$-\left[\frac{\left(\dot{m}_{cz}A_z\right)_{z+\Delta z/2} - \left(\dot{m}_{cz}A_z\right)_{z-\Delta z/2}}{\Delta z}\right]\Delta z + q_{mt_c} + q_{m_c}$$
$$= V_b\left[\frac{\left(m_{v_c}\right)_{t+\Delta t} - \left(m_{v_c}\right)_t}{\Delta t}\right], \quad \text{(9.7)}$$

where $c=o, w, fg$, and sg.

Taking the limit of the terms enclosed in the brackets as Δx, Δy, Δz, and Δt approach zero and substituting the definition of the partial derivative, Eq. 9.7 becomes

$$-\frac{\partial}{\partial x}\left(\dot{m}_{cx}A_x\right)\Delta x - \frac{\partial}{\partial y}\left(\dot{m}_{cy}A_y\right)\Delta y - \frac{\partial}{\partial z}\left(\dot{m}_{cz}A_z\right)\Delta z$$
$$= V_b\frac{\partial}{\partial t}\left(m_{v_c}\right) - q_{m_c} - q_{mt_c}, \quad \text{(9.8)}$$

where $c=o, w, fg$, and sg; $\Delta x \neq 0$, $\Delta y \neq 0$, $\Delta z \neq 0$; and $V_b \neq 0$. It should be emphasized that Eq. 9.8 is an engineering approximation because only the values of Δx, Δy, and Δz in the denominators of Eq. 9.7 were allowed to vanish in the limiting process.

For reservoirs of uniform thickness, we assume A_x, A_y, and A_z are independent of x, y, and z, respectively. In this case, $V_b = \Delta x \Delta y \Delta z = A_x\Delta x = A_y\Delta y = A_z\Delta z$ and $\partial A_x/\partial x = \partial A_y/\partial y = \partial A_z/\partial z = 0$. With these assumptions, Eq. 9.8 can be simplified and expressed in a form similar to Eq. 2.181 for single-phase flow. The present form of Eq. 9.8, however, is more general because it considers changes in the cross-sectional areas in the three coordinate directions.

For the oil, water, and free-gas components, it is possible to express mass flux as the product of density and Darcy's velocity for Phase l; mass per unit volume of reservoir (or concentration) as the product of porosity, phase saturation, and phase density; and mass flow rate as the product of volumetric (phase) -flow rate and phase density. For the solution-gas component, mass flux, mass per unit volume, and mass-flow rate may be expressed in terms of the oil-phase properties R_s and B_o and the gas-phase density at standard conditions, ρ_{gsc}. Mass per unit volume, mass flux, and mass-flow rate are quantities that describe components ($c=o, w, fg$, or sg), whereas flux (volumetric velocity), volumetric-flow rate, density, formation volume factor (FVF), saturation, and solution-gas/oil ratio describe phases ($l=o, w$, or g). The terms in Eq. 9.8 may be expressed as

$$\vec{\dot{m}}_c = \alpha_c \rho_c \vec{u}_c, \quad \text{(9.9a)}$$

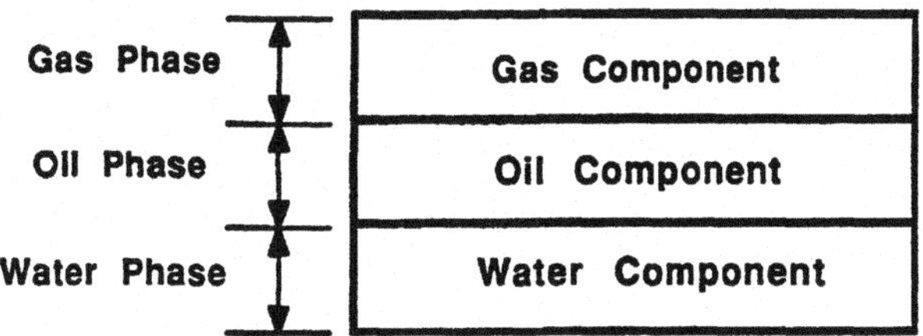

Fig. 9.2—Distribution of components among phases in multiphase flow with no interphase mass transfer.

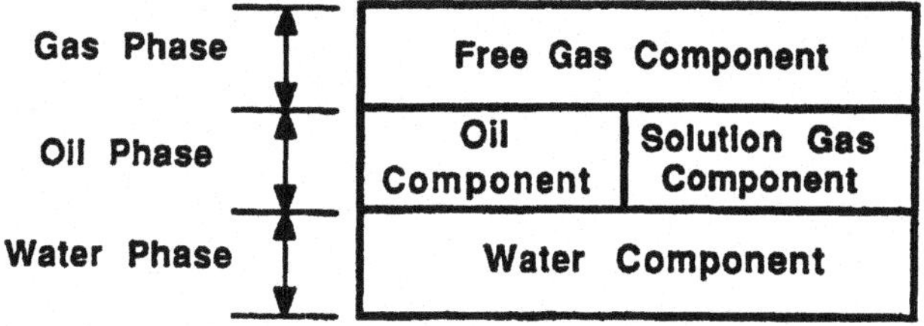

Fig. 9.3—Distribution of components among phases in multiphase flow with gas transfer between the oil and gas phases.

where $c=o$, w, and fg;

$$\vec{\dot{m}}_c = \left(\rho_{gsc}\frac{R_s}{B_o}\right)\vec{u}_o, \quad (9.9b)$$

where $c = sg$;

$$\dot{m}_{cx} = \alpha_c \rho_c u_{cx}, \quad (9.10a)$$

where $c=o$, w, and fg;

$$\dot{m}_{cx} = \left(\rho_{gsc}\frac{R_s}{B_o}\right)u_{ox}, \quad (9.10b)$$

where $c = sg$;

$$\dot{m}_{cy} = \alpha_c \rho_c u_{cy}, \quad (9.11a)$$

where $c=o$, w, and fg;

$$\dot{m}_{cy} = \left(\rho_{gsc}\frac{R_s}{B_o}\right)u_{oy}, \quad (9.11b)$$

where $c = sg$;

$$\dot{m}_{cz} = \alpha_c \rho_c u_{cz}, \quad (9.12a)$$

where $c=o$, w, and fg;

$$\dot{m}_{cz} = \left(\rho_{gsc}\frac{R_s}{B_o}\right)u_{oz}, \quad (9.12b)$$

where $c = sg$;

$$m_{v_c} = \phi \rho_c S_c, \quad (9.13a)$$

where $c=o$, w, and fg;

$$m_{v_c} = \frac{\phi}{\alpha_c}\left(\rho_{gsc}\frac{R_s}{B_o}\right)S_o, \quad (9.13b)$$

where $c = sg$;

$$q_{m_c} = \alpha_c \rho_c q_c, \quad (9.14a)$$

where $c=o$, w, and fg;

$$\text{and } q_{m_c} = \left(\rho_{gsc}\frac{R_s}{B_o}\right)q_o, \quad (9.14b)$$

where $c = sg$. The generation terms may be defined as

$$q_{mt_c} = 0, \quad (9.15a)$$

where $c=o$ or w;

$$q_{mt_c} = q_{mt_{sg}}, \quad (9.15b)$$

where $c=sg$; and

$$q_{mt_c} = -q_{mt_{sg}}, \quad (9.15c)$$

where $c=fg$. In Eqs. 9.15b and 9.15c, $q_{mt_{sg}}$ = rate of mass transfer of gas component between the oil and gas phases (or between the free-gas component and solution-gas component). Note that $g=fg+sg$ for the gas component, whereas $\rho_g = \rho_{fg}$, $S_g = S_{fg}$, and $u_g = u_{fg}$ for the gas phase.

The mass-conservation equation for the oil component may now be obtained by combining Eqs. 9.8 and 9.10 through 9.15 for $c=o$. By dividing the resulting equation by $\alpha_c \rho_{osc}$, using the definition of B_o given by Eq. 2.80, $B_o = \rho_{osc}/\rho_o$, and observing that $q_{osc} = q_o/B_o$, the mass-conservation equation for the oil component becomes

$$-\frac{\partial}{\partial x}\left(\frac{A_x}{B_o}u_{ox}\right)\Delta x - \frac{\partial}{\partial y}\left(\frac{A_y}{B_o}u_{oy}\right)\Delta y - \frac{\partial}{\partial z}\left(\frac{A_z}{B_o}u_{oz}\right)\Delta z$$

$$= \frac{V_b}{\alpha_c}\frac{\partial}{\partial t}\left(\frac{\phi S_o}{B_o}\right) - q_{osc}. \quad (9.16)$$

Similarly, the mass-conservation equation for the water component is

$$-\frac{\partial}{\partial x}\left(\frac{A_x}{B_w}u_{wx}\right)\Delta x - \frac{\partial}{\partial y}\left(\frac{A_y}{B_w}u_{wy}\right)\Delta y - \frac{\partial}{\partial z}\left(\frac{A_z}{B_w}u_{wz}\right)\Delta z$$

$$= \frac{V_b}{\alpha_c}\frac{\partial}{\partial t}\left(\frac{\phi S_w}{B_w}\right) - q_{wsc}. \quad (9.17)$$

The mass-conservation equation for the gas component ($c=g$) is obtained by writing Eq. 9.8 for free gas and solution gas and adding the two equations to eliminate $q_{mt_{sg}}$. The resulting equation is

$$-\frac{\partial}{\partial x}\left(\dot{m}_{fgx}A_x + \dot{m}_{sgx}A_x\right)\Delta x - \frac{\partial}{\partial y}\left(\dot{m}_{fgy}A_y + \dot{m}_{sgy}A_y\right)\Delta y$$

$$-\frac{\partial}{\partial z}\left(\dot{m}_{fgz}A_z + \dot{m}_{sgz}A_z\right)\Delta z$$

$$= V_b\frac{\partial}{\partial t}\left(m_{v_{fg}} + m_{v_{sg}}\right) - \left(q_{m_{fg}} + q_{m_{sg}}\right). \quad (9.18)$$

By substituting Eqs. 9.10 through 9.14 into Eq. 9.18 and dividing the resulting equation by ρ_{gsc} and using the definition of $B_g = \rho_{gsc}/\alpha_c\rho_g$ and observing that $q_{osc} = q_o/B_o$ and $q_{fgsc} = q_{fg}/B_g$, the following mass-conservation equation for the gas component is obtained.

$$-\frac{\partial}{\partial x}\left(\frac{A_x}{B_g}u_{fgx} + A_x\frac{R_s}{B_o}u_{ox}\right)\Delta x - \frac{\partial}{\partial y}\left(\frac{A_y}{B_g}u_{fgy} + A_y\frac{R_s}{B_o}u_{oy}\right)\Delta y$$

$$-\frac{\partial}{\partial z}\left(\frac{A_z}{B_g}u_{fgz} + A_z\frac{R_s}{B_o}u_{oz}\right)\Delta z$$

$$= \frac{V_b}{\alpha_c}\frac{\partial}{\partial t}\left(\frac{\phi S_g}{B_g} + \phi\frac{R_s}{B_o}S_o\right) - q_{gsc}, \quad (9.19)$$

$$\text{where } q_{gsc} = q_{fgsc} + R_s q_{osc}. \quad (9.20)$$

Eqs. 9.16, 9.17, and 9.19 are, respectively, the mass-conservation equations for the oil, water, and gas components for three-dimensional (3D) (rectangular) flow of a multiphase black-oil system. The various terms in these equations have the units of volume at standard conditions per unit time.

9.3 Flow Equations in Multiphase Flow

Darcy's law for multiphase flow, Eq. 2.25, may be substituted into the mass-conservation Eqs. 9.16, 9.17, and 9.19 to obtain the following fluid-flow equations.

$$\frac{\partial}{\partial x}\left[\beta_c k_x A_x \frac{k_{ro}}{\mu_o B_o}\left(\frac{\partial p_o}{\partial x} - \gamma_o\frac{\partial Z}{\partial x}\right)\right]\Delta x$$

$$+\frac{\partial}{\partial y}\left[\beta_c k_y A_y \frac{k_{ro}}{\mu_o B_o}\left(\frac{\partial p_o}{\partial y} - \gamma_o\frac{\partial Z}{\partial y}\right)\right]\Delta y$$

$$+\frac{\partial}{\partial z}\left[\beta_c k_z A_z \frac{k_{ro}}{\mu_o B_o}\left(\frac{\partial p_o}{\partial z} - \gamma_o\frac{\partial Z}{\partial z}\right)\right]\Delta z$$

$$= \frac{V_b}{\alpha_c}\frac{\partial}{\partial t}\left(\frac{\phi S_o}{B_o}\right) - q_{osc}, \quad (9.21)$$

$$\frac{\partial}{\partial x}\left[\beta_c k_x A_x \frac{k_{rw}}{\mu_w B_w}\left(\frac{\partial p_w}{\partial x} - \gamma_w\frac{\partial Z}{\partial x}\right)\right]\Delta x$$

$$+\frac{\partial}{\partial y}\left[\beta_c k_y A_y \frac{k_{rw}}{\mu_w B_w}\left(\frac{\partial p_w}{\partial y} - \gamma_w\frac{\partial Z}{\partial y}\right)\right]\Delta y$$

$$+\frac{\partial}{\partial z}\left[\beta_c k_z A_z \frac{k_{rw}}{\mu_w B_w}\left(\frac{\partial p_w}{\partial z} - \gamma_w\frac{\partial Z}{\partial z}\right)\right]\Delta z$$

$$= \frac{V_b}{\alpha_c}\frac{\partial}{\partial t}\left(\frac{\phi S_w}{B_w}\right) - q_{wsc}, \quad (9.22)$$

and
$$\frac{\partial}{\partial x}\left[\beta_c k_x A_x \frac{k_{rg}}{\mu_g B_g}\left(\frac{\partial p_g}{\partial x} - \gamma_g \frac{\partial Z}{\partial x}\right) + \beta_c k_x A_x \frac{k_{ro} R_s}{\mu_o B_o}\left(\frac{\partial p_o}{\partial x} - \gamma_o \frac{\partial Z}{\partial x}\right)\right]\Delta x$$
$$+ \frac{\partial}{\partial y}\left[\beta_c k_y A_y \frac{k_{rg}}{\mu_g B_g}\left(\frac{\partial p_g}{\partial y} - \gamma_g \frac{\partial Z}{\partial y}\right) + \beta_c k_y A_y \frac{k_{ro} R_s}{\mu_o B_o}\left(\frac{\partial p_o}{\partial y} - \gamma_o \frac{\partial Z}{\partial y}\right)\right]\Delta y$$
$$+ \frac{\partial}{\partial z}\left[\beta_c k_z A_z \frac{k_{rg}}{\mu_g B_g}\left(\frac{\partial p_g}{\partial z} - \gamma_g \frac{\partial Z}{\partial z}\right) + \beta_c k_z A_z \frac{k_{ro} R_s}{\mu_o B_o}\left(\frac{\partial p_o}{\partial z} - \gamma_o \frac{\partial Z}{\partial z}\right)\right]\Delta z$$
$$= \frac{V_b}{\alpha_c}\frac{\partial}{\partial t}\left(\frac{\phi S_g}{B_g} + \frac{\phi R_s S_o}{B_o}\right) - q_{gsc}, \quad (9.23)$$

where q_{gsc} = production (injection) rate of the gas component and is defined by Eq. 9.20 for production.

Eqs. 9.21, 9.22, and 9.23 are the flow equations for the oil, water, and gas components, respectively. When describing these equations, the word component is often dropped, causing some confusion among simulation practitioners. These equations are sometimes mistakenly described as flow equations for phases. The reason for this confusion is that the properties involved in these equations (μ_l, B_l, γ_l, k_{rl}, S_l, p_l, R_s, and q_{lsc}, where $l = o$, w, or g) are all properties of the phases and not properties of the components. In addition, the flow equations for components and phases are identical when there is no mass transfer. Nevertheless, these equations are very general in that they describe 3D, multiphase flow in rectangular coordinates and account for the effects of viscous, capillary, and gravity forces. When these equations are discretized (Sec. 9.5), the resulting finite-difference equations allow for irregular boundaries and changes in cross-sectional area in multiple directions. These finite-difference equations are compatible with the engineer's way of thinking because they are derived from mass-balance considerations and are related to the mathematician's integral-method approach for deriving difference equations from differential equations.[2]

Eqs. 9.21 through 9.23 are the general forms of multiphase-flow equations. These equations can be simplified, depending on the prevailing reservoir conditions, to reduce the complexity of the equation set. Examples 9.1 and 9.2 illustrate this.

Example 9.1. Write the flow equations for an oil reservoir undergoing water injection. Pressure support from water injection is expected to keep reservoir pressure above the bubblepoint pressure. The oil-bearing formation is thin and horizontal but has heterogeneous rock properties.

Solution. The first two statements in this problem imply simultaneous flow of oil and water through the reservoir; therefore, Eqs. 9.21 and 9.22 adequately describe the flow problem.

$$\frac{\partial}{\partial x}\left[\beta_c k_x A_x \frac{k_{rl}}{\mu_l B_l}\left(\frac{\partial p_l}{\partial x} - \gamma_l \frac{\partial Z}{\partial x}\right)\right]\Delta x + \frac{\partial}{\partial y}\left[\beta_c k_y A_y \frac{k_{rl}}{\mu_l B_l}\left(\frac{\partial p_l}{\partial y} - \gamma_l \frac{\partial Z}{\partial y}\right)\right]\Delta y$$
$$+ \frac{\partial}{\partial z}\left[\beta_c k_z A_z \frac{k_{rl}}{\mu_l B_l}\left(\frac{\partial p_l}{\partial z} - \gamma_l \frac{\partial Z}{\partial z}\right)\right]\Delta z$$
$$= \frac{V_b}{\alpha_c}\frac{\partial}{\partial t}\left(\frac{\phi S_l}{B_l}\right) - q_{lsc}, \quad (9.24)$$

where $l = o$ or w.

The third statement in this problem implies that it is sufficient to consider fluid flow in the x and y directions and neglect flow in the z direction. Therefore, Eq. 9.24 reduces to

$$\frac{\partial}{\partial x}\left[\beta_c k_x A_x \frac{k_{rl}}{\mu_l B_l}\left(\frac{\partial p_l}{\partial x} - \gamma_l \frac{\partial Z}{\partial x}\right)\right]\Delta x + \frac{\partial}{\partial y}\left[\beta_c k_y A_y \frac{k_{rl}}{\mu_l B_l}\left(\frac{\partial p_l}{\partial y} - \gamma_l \frac{\partial Z}{\partial y}\right)\right]\Delta y$$
$$= \frac{V_b}{\alpha_c}\frac{\partial}{\partial t}\left(\frac{\phi S_l}{B_l}\right) - q_{lsc}, \quad (9.25)$$

where $l = o$ or w. Furthermore, a horizontal reservoir implies that depth gradients in the x and y directions vanish. That is,

$$\partial Z/\partial x = \partial Z/\partial y = 0, \quad (9.26)$$

which, on substitution in this flow equation, results in

$$\frac{\partial}{\partial x}\left(\beta_c k_x A_x \frac{k_{rl}}{\mu_l B_l}\frac{\partial p_l}{\partial x}\right)\Delta x + \frac{\partial}{\partial y}\left(\beta_c k_y A_y \frac{k_{rl}}{\mu_l B_l}\frac{\partial p_l}{\partial y}\right)\Delta y$$
$$= \frac{V_b}{\alpha_c}\frac{\partial}{\partial t}\left(\frac{\phi S_l}{B_l}\right) - q_{lsc}, \quad (9.27a)$$

where $l = o$ or w.

A heterogeneous reservoir implies that rock properties, such as ϕ, k_x, and k_y, vary from one point to another; therefore, there are no further simplifications. The flow equations for oil and water in this reservoir may be obtained by writing Eq. 9.27a for $l = o$ and w.

$$\frac{\partial}{\partial x}\left(\beta_c k_x A_x \frac{k_{ro}}{\mu_o B_o}\frac{\partial p_o}{\partial x}\right)\Delta x + \frac{\partial}{\partial y}\left(\beta_c k_y A_y \frac{k_{ro}}{\mu_o B_o}\frac{\partial p_o}{\partial y}\right)\Delta y$$
$$= \frac{V_b}{\alpha_c}\frac{\partial}{\partial t}\left(\frac{\phi S_o}{B_o}\right) - q_{osc} \quad (9.27b)$$

and
$$\frac{\partial}{\partial x}\left(\beta_c k_x A_x \frac{k_{rw}}{\mu_w B_w}\frac{\partial p_w}{\partial x}\right)\Delta x + \frac{\partial}{\partial y}\left(\beta_c k_y A_y \frac{k_{rw}}{\mu_w B_w}\frac{\partial p_w}{\partial y}\right)\Delta y$$
$$= \frac{V_b}{\alpha_c}\frac{\partial}{\partial t}\left(\frac{\phi S_w}{B_w}\right) - q_{wsc}. \quad (9.27c)$$

Example 9.2. A sandstone gas reservoir is coproducing gas and water. The gas-bearing formation is thin and dipping with an angle Θ. Knowing that fluid flow takes place along the dip and that capillary forces and solution gas in water are negligible, write the flow equations for this reservoir.

Solution. This problem involves the flow of gas and water only. Considering the multiphase-flow equations previously presented in this section, the oil component and phase do not exist. Therefore, the flow equation for oil can be discarded and the solution-gas term in the gas-flow equation can be dropped. This results in

$$\frac{\partial}{\partial x}\left[\beta_c k_x A_x \frac{k_{rw}}{\mu_w B_w}\left(\frac{\partial p_w}{\partial x} - \gamma_w \frac{\partial Z}{\partial x}\right)\right]\Delta x + \frac{\partial}{\partial y}\left[\beta_c k_y A_y \frac{k_{rw}}{\mu_w B_w}\left(\frac{\partial p_w}{\partial y} - \gamma_w \frac{\partial Z}{\partial y}\right)\right]\Delta y$$
$$+ \frac{\partial}{\partial z}\left[\beta_c k_z A_z \frac{k_{rw}}{\mu_w B_w}\left(\frac{\partial p_w}{\partial z} - \gamma_w \frac{\partial Z}{\partial z}\right)\right]\Delta z$$
$$= \frac{V_b}{\alpha_c}\frac{\partial}{\partial t}\left(\frac{\phi S_w}{B_w}\right) - q_{wsc} \quad (9.22)$$

$$\text{and } \frac{\partial}{\partial x}\left[\beta_c k_x A_x \frac{k_{rg}}{\mu_g B_g}\left(\frac{\partial p_g}{\partial x} - \gamma_g \frac{\partial Z}{\partial x}\right)\right]\Delta x$$

$$+ \frac{\partial}{\partial y}\left[\beta_c k_y A_y \frac{k_{rg}}{\mu_g B_g}\left(\frac{\partial p_g}{\partial y} - \gamma_g \frac{\partial Z}{\partial y}\right)\right]\Delta y$$

$$+ \frac{\partial}{\partial z}\left[\beta_c k_z A_z \frac{k_{rg}}{\mu_g B_g}\left(\frac{\partial p_g}{\partial z} - \gamma_g \frac{\partial Z}{\partial z}\right)\right]\Delta z$$

$$= \frac{V_b}{\alpha_c}\frac{\partial}{\partial t}\left(\frac{\phi S_g}{B_g}\right) - q_{gsc}, \quad \text{.................... (9.28)}$$

where $q_{gsc} = q_{fgsc}$.

Fluid movement in this reservoir may be described by considering only the x and z directions because fluids flow along the dip in this thin formation. A more efficient description of fluid flow is possible by assuming that the x axis coincides with the dip. For a thin formation, flow is one-dimensional (1D) along the new x axis. This reduces Eqs. 9.22 and 9.28 to

$$\frac{\partial}{\partial x}\left[\beta_c k_x A_x \frac{k_{rw}}{\mu_w B_w}\left(\frac{\partial p_w}{\partial x} - \gamma_w \frac{\partial Z}{\partial x}\right)\right]\Delta x = \frac{V_b}{\alpha_c}\frac{\partial}{\partial t}\left(\frac{\phi S_w}{B_w}\right) - q_{wsc}$$

$$\text{.................... (9.29)}$$

$$\text{and } \frac{\partial}{\partial x}\left[\beta_c k_x A_x \frac{k_{rg}}{\mu_g B_g}\left(\frac{\partial p_g}{\partial x} - \gamma_g \frac{\partial Z}{\partial x}\right)\right]\Delta x = \frac{V_b}{\alpha_c}\frac{\partial}{\partial t}\left(\frac{\phi S_g}{B_g}\right) - q_{gsc}.$$

$$\text{.................... (9.30)}$$

For negligible capillary forces, $p_w = p_g$, and for the x axis that dips downward with an angle Θ, $\partial Z/\partial x = \sin\Theta$, Eqs. 9.29 and 9.30 reduce to

$$\frac{\partial}{\partial x}\left[\beta_c k_x A_x \frac{k_{rw}}{\mu_w B_w}\left(\frac{\partial p_g}{\partial x} - \gamma_w \sin\Theta\right)\right]\Delta x$$

$$= \frac{V_b}{\alpha_c}\frac{\partial}{\partial t}\left(\frac{\phi S_w}{B_w}\right) - q_{wsc} \quad \text{.................... (9.31)}$$

$$\text{and } \frac{\partial}{\partial x}\left[\beta_c k_x A_x \frac{k_{rg}}{\mu_g B_g}\left(\frac{\partial p_g}{\partial x} - \gamma_g \sin\Theta\right)\right]\Delta x$$

$$= \frac{V_b}{\alpha_c}\frac{\partial}{\partial t}\left(\frac{\phi S_g}{B_g}\right) - q_{gsc}. \quad \text{.................... (9.32)}$$

9.4 Flow Models for Basic Flow Systems

The mathematical formulation for multiphase flow in petroleum reservoirs consists of the flow equations for all fluid components in the reservoir, additional relationships necessary to complete the flow description, and the initial and boundary conditions. In Sec. 9.3, the flow equations are obtained by combining the appropriate forms of the mass-conservation equation, equation of state, and Darcy's law. The additional relationships include the phase-saturation constraint and capillary pressures as functions of phase saturations. Initial and boundary conditions are needed to obtain a solution for the mathematical model. Sec. 9.7 presents the treatment of these conditions.

The flow systems considered in this chapter are most often encountered in black-oil modeling of hydrocarbon reservoirs. These are two-phase flow of oil and water; two-phase flow of oil and gas; and three-phase flow of oil, water, and gas in oil reservoirs. Modeling of two-phase flow of gas and water in gas reservoirs is similar to modeling that of oil and gas, where water replaces oil in the formulation. Finally, a modified black-oil description can be used to describe liquid dropout in two-phase flow in gas-condensate systems.

9.4.1 Oil/Water Flow Model. In an oil/water flow system, it is assumed that there are two fluid components and two phases. The oil and water components are assumed to be immiscible; therefore, there is no mass transfer between the oil and water phases. In addition, it is assumed that flow is isothermal and the phases are in a state of thermodynamic equilibrium.

Sec. 9.3 presented the flow equations for oil and water as Eqs. 9.21 and 9.22.

$$\frac{\partial}{\partial x}\left[\beta_c k_x A_x \frac{k_{ro}}{\mu_o B_o}\left(\frac{\partial p_o}{\partial x} - \gamma_o \frac{\partial Z}{\partial x}\right)\right]\Delta x$$

$$+ \frac{\partial}{\partial y}\left[\beta_c k_y A_y \frac{k_{ro}}{\mu_o B_o}\left(\frac{\partial p_o}{\partial y} - \gamma_o \frac{\partial Z}{\partial y}\right)\right]\Delta y$$

$$+ \frac{\partial}{\partial z}\left[\beta_c k_z A_z \frac{k_{ro}}{\mu_o B_o}\left(\frac{\partial p_o}{\partial z} - \gamma_o \frac{\partial Z}{\partial z}\right)\right]\Delta z$$

$$= \frac{V_b}{\alpha_c}\frac{\partial}{\partial t}\left(\frac{\phi S_o}{B_o}\right) - q_{osc} \quad \text{..................... (9.21)}$$

$$\text{and } \frac{\partial}{\partial x}\left[\beta_c k_x A_x \frac{k_{rw}}{\mu_w B_w}\left(\frac{\partial p_w}{\partial x} - \gamma_w \frac{\partial Z}{\partial x}\right)\right]\Delta x$$

$$+ \frac{\partial}{\partial y}\left[\beta_c k_y A_y \frac{k_{rw}}{\mu_w B_w}\left(\frac{\partial p_w}{\partial y} - \gamma_w \frac{\partial Z}{\partial y}\right)\right]\Delta y$$

$$+ \frac{\partial}{\partial z}\left[\beta_c k_z A_z \frac{k_{rw}}{\mu_w B_w}\left(\frac{\partial p_w}{\partial z} - \gamma_w \frac{\partial Z}{\partial z}\right)\right]\Delta z$$

$$= \frac{V_b}{\alpha_c}\frac{\partial}{\partial t}\left(\frac{\phi S_w}{B_w}\right) - q_{wsc}. \quad \text{.................... (9.22)}$$

The phase-saturation equation, which is a constraint on the sum of phase saturations, is

$$S_o + S_w = 1, \quad \text{.............................. (9.33)}$$

and the oil/water capillary pressure relationship is

$$P_{cow} = p_o - p_w = f(S_w). \quad \text{.................... (9.34)}$$

Eqs. 9.21, 9.22, 9.33, and 9.34 constitute the oil/water flow model. These equations contain four unknowns, p_o, p_w, S_o, and S_w. The relationships expressed by Eqs. 9.33 and 9.34 can be used to eliminate two of the unknowns in the flow equations, resulting in two equations in two principal unknowns. These two unknowns can be taken as two phase pressures, one phase pressure and oil/water capillary pressure, or one phase pressure and one phase saturation. Expressing the flow equations in terms of the selected unknowns is part of the formulation process. Throughout this chapter, the formulation that uses oil pressure and phase saturations as the principal unknowns is adopted.

The formulation for this model, in terms of p_o and S_w, may be obtained with Eqs. 9.33 and 9.34 to express S_o and p_w as

$$S_o = 1 - S_w \quad \text{.............................. (9.35)}$$

$$\text{and } p_w = p_o - P_{cow}, \quad \text{......................... (9.36)}$$

which when substituted into Eqs. 9.21 and 9.22 results in

$$\frac{\partial}{\partial x}\left[\beta_c k_x A_x \frac{k_{ro}}{\mu_o B_o}\left(\frac{\partial p_o}{\partial x} - \gamma_o \frac{\partial Z}{\partial x}\right)\right]\Delta x$$

$$+\frac{\partial}{\partial y}\left[\beta_c k_y A_y \frac{k_{ro}}{\mu_o B_o}\left(\frac{\partial p_o}{\partial y}-\gamma_o\frac{\partial Z}{\partial y}\right)\right]\Delta y$$

$$+\frac{\partial}{\partial z}\left[\beta_c k_z A_z \frac{k_{ro}}{\mu_o B_o}\left(\frac{\partial p_o}{\partial z}-\gamma_o\frac{\partial Z}{\partial z}\right)\right]\Delta z$$

$$=\frac{V_b}{\alpha_c}\frac{\partial}{\partial t}\left[\frac{\phi(1-S_w)}{B_o}\right]-q_{osc} \quad \text{.................} \quad (9.37)$$

and
$$\frac{\partial}{\partial x}\left[\beta_c k_x A_x \frac{k_{rw}}{\mu_w B_w}\left(\frac{\partial p_o}{\partial x}-\frac{\partial P_{cow}}{\partial x}-\gamma_w\frac{\partial Z}{\partial x}\right)\right]\Delta x$$

$$+\frac{\partial}{\partial y}\left[\beta_c k_y A_y \frac{k_{rw}}{\mu_w B_w}\left(\frac{\partial p_o}{\partial y}-\frac{\partial P_{cow}}{\partial y}-\gamma_w\frac{\partial Z}{\partial y}\right)\right]\Delta y$$

$$+\frac{\partial}{\partial z}\left[\beta_c k_z A_z \frac{k_{rw}}{\mu_w B_w}\left(\frac{\partial p_o}{\partial z}-\frac{\partial P_{cow}}{\partial z}-\gamma_w\frac{\partial Z}{\partial z}\right)\right]\Delta z$$

$$=\frac{V_b}{\alpha_c}\frac{\partial}{\partial t}\left(\frac{\phi S_w}{B_w}\right)-q_{wsc}. \quad \text{.....................} \quad (9.38)$$

Given the initial and boundary conditions, Eqs. 9.37 and 9.38 can be solved for the unknowns p_o and S_w. The other two unknowns, S_o and p_w, can be obtained by substituting the principal unknowns into Eqs. 9.35 and 9.36.

9.4.2 Oil/Gas Flow Model. In an oil/gas flow system, oil and gas at standard conditions are the two fluid components. These two components are distributed in, at most, two distinct phases, oil and gas. Mass transfer of only the gas component occurs between the two phases. Also, it is assumed that fluids are at constant temperature (isothermal conditions) and are in thermodynamic equilibrium throughout the reservoir. Generally, oil is the wetting phase and gas is the nonwetting phase in this system.

The flow equations for oil and gas are expressed by Eqs. 9.21 and 9.23.

$$\frac{\partial}{\partial x}\left[\beta_c k_x A_x \frac{k_{ro}}{\mu_o B_o}\left(\frac{\partial p_o}{\partial x}-\gamma_o\frac{\partial Z}{\partial x}\right)\right]\Delta x$$

$$+\frac{\partial}{\partial y}\left[\beta_c k_y A_y \frac{k_{ro}}{\mu_o B_o}\left(\frac{\partial p_o}{\partial y}-\gamma_o\frac{\partial Z}{\partial y}\right)\right]\Delta y$$

$$+\frac{\partial}{\partial z}\left[\beta_c k_z A_z \frac{k_{ro}}{\mu_o B_o}\left(\frac{\partial p_o}{\partial z}-\gamma_o\frac{\partial Z}{\partial z}\right)\right]\Delta z$$

$$=\frac{V_b}{\alpha_c}\frac{\partial}{\partial t}\left(\frac{\phi S_o}{B_o}\right)-q_{osc} \quad \text{.....................} \quad (9.21)$$

and
$$\frac{\partial}{\partial x}\left[\beta_c k_x A_x \frac{k_{rg}}{\mu_g B_g}\left(\frac{\partial p_g}{\partial x}-\gamma_g\frac{\partial Z}{\partial x}\right)\right.$$

$$\left.+\beta_c k_x A_x \frac{k_{ro}R_s}{\mu_o B_o}\left(\frac{\partial p_o}{\partial x}-\gamma_o\frac{\partial Z}{\partial x}\right)\right]\Delta x$$

$$+\frac{\partial}{\partial y}\left[\beta_c k_y A_y \frac{k_{rg}}{\mu_g B_g}\left(\frac{\partial p_g}{\partial y}-\gamma_g\frac{\partial Z}{\partial y}\right)\right.$$

$$\left.+\beta_c k_y A_y \frac{k_{ro}R_s}{\mu_o B_o}\left(\frac{\partial p_o}{\partial y}-\gamma_o\frac{\partial Z}{\partial y}\right)\right]\Delta y$$

$$+\frac{\partial}{\partial z}\left[\beta_c k_z A_z \frac{k_{rg}}{\mu_g B_g}\left(\frac{\partial p_g}{\partial z}-\gamma_g\frac{\partial Z}{\partial z}\right)\right.$$

$$\left.+\beta_c k_z A_z \frac{k_{ro}R_s}{\mu_o B_o}\left(\frac{\partial p_o}{\partial z}-\gamma_o\frac{\partial Z}{\partial z}\right)\right]\Delta z$$

$$=\frac{V_b}{\alpha_c}\frac{\partial}{\partial t}\left(\frac{\phi S_g}{B_g}+\frac{\phi R_s S_o}{B_o}\right)-q_{gsc}, \quad \text{............} \quad (9.23)$$

where q_{gsc} is given by Eq. 9.20.

The additional relationships completing the flow description are

$$S_g+S_o=1 \quad \text{..............................} \quad (9.39)$$

and $P_{cgo}=p_g-p_o=f(S_g)$. .... (9.40)

This flow model consists of Eqs. 9.21, 9.23, 9.39, and 9.40, in four unknowns, p_o, p_g, S_o, and S_g. Again, Eqs. 9.39 and 9.40 may be used to eliminate two of the unknowns in the flow equations, resulting in two equations in two principal unknowns.

The formulation of the oil/gas flow model in terms of p_o and S_g may be obtained by expressing S_o as a function of S_g by use of Eq. 9.39, expressing p_g as a function of p_o and S_g by use of Eq. 9.40, and substituting for S_o and p_g in Eqs. 9.21 and 9.23. The final form of the flow equations in this formulation is

$$\frac{\partial}{\partial x}\left[\beta_c k_x A_x \frac{k_{ro}}{\mu_o B_o}\left(\frac{\partial p_o}{\partial x}-\gamma_o\frac{\partial Z}{\partial x}\right)\right]\Delta x$$

$$+\frac{\partial}{\partial y}\left[\beta_c k_y A_y \frac{k_{ro}}{\mu_o B_o}\left(\frac{\partial p_o}{\partial y}-\gamma_o\frac{\partial Z}{\partial y}\right)\right]\Delta y$$

$$+\frac{\partial}{\partial z}\left[\beta_c k_z A_z \frac{k_{ro}}{\mu_o B_o}\left(\frac{\partial p_o}{\partial z}-\gamma_o\frac{\partial Z}{\partial z}\right)\right]\Delta z$$

$$=\frac{V_b}{\alpha_c}\frac{\partial}{\partial t}\left[\frac{\phi(1-S_g)}{B_o}\right]-q_{osc} \quad \text{................} \quad (9.41)$$

and
$$\frac{\partial}{\partial x}\left[\beta_c k_x A_x \frac{k_{rg}}{\mu_g B_g}\left(\frac{\partial p_o}{\partial x}+\frac{\partial P_{cgo}}{\partial x}-\gamma_g\frac{\partial Z}{\partial x}\right)\right.$$

$$\left.+\beta_c k_x A_x \frac{k_{ro}R_s}{\mu_o B_o}\left(\frac{\partial p_o}{\partial x}-\gamma_o\frac{\partial Z}{\partial x}\right)\right]\Delta x$$

$$+\frac{\partial}{\partial y}\left[\beta_c k_y A_y \frac{k_{rg}}{\mu_g B_g}\left(\frac{\partial p_o}{\partial y}+\frac{\partial P_{cgo}}{\partial y}-\gamma_g\frac{\partial Z}{\partial y}\right)\right.$$

$$\left.+\beta_c k_y A_y \frac{k_{ro}R_s}{\mu_o B_o}\left(\frac{\partial p_o}{\partial y}-\gamma_o\frac{\partial Z}{\partial y}\right)\right]\Delta y$$

$$+\frac{\partial}{\partial z}\left[\beta_c k_z A_z \frac{k_{rg}}{\mu_g B_g}\left(\frac{\partial p_o}{\partial z}+\frac{\partial P_{cgo}}{\partial z}-\gamma_g\frac{\partial Z}{\partial z}\right)\right.$$

$$\left.+\beta_c k_z A_z \frac{k_{ro}R_s}{\mu_o B_o}\left(\frac{\partial p_o}{\partial z}-\gamma_o\frac{\partial Z}{\partial z}\right)\right]\Delta z$$

$$=\frac{V_b}{\alpha_c}\frac{\partial}{\partial t}\left[\frac{\phi S_g}{B_g}+\frac{\phi R_s(1-S_g)}{B_o}\right]-q_{gsc}, \quad \text{........} \quad (9.42)$$

where q_{gsc} is expressed by Eq. 9.20.

Given initial and boundary conditions, Eqs. 9.41 and 9.42 can be solved for the principal unknowns p_o and S_g. The other two unknowns, S_o and p_g, can be obtained by substituting the principal unknowns into Eqs. 9.39 and 9.40, respectively.

9.4.3 Oil/Water/Gas Flow Model. The three-phase oil/water/gas flow model is known as the black-oil model (or sometimes the β model). This model consists of three fluid components, oil, water, and gas at standard conditions, that are distributed in three distinct phases, oil, water, and gas. While oil and water are immiscible, gas may exist as free or solution gas. The reservoir is assumed to be at constant temperature, and fluids are assumed to be in thermodynamic equilibrium throughout the reservoir. Usually, water is the wetting phase, gas is the nonwetting phase, and oil is an intermediate wetting phase.

The flow equations for this black-oil model are expressed as Eqs. 9.21 through 9.23.

$$\frac{\partial}{\partial x}\left[\beta_c k_x A_x \frac{k_{ro}}{\mu_o B_o}\left(\frac{\partial p_o}{\partial x} - \gamma_o \frac{\partial Z}{\partial x}\right)\right]\Delta x + \frac{\partial}{\partial y}\left[\beta_c k_y A_y \frac{k_{ro}}{\mu_o B_o}\left(\frac{\partial p_o}{\partial y} - \gamma_o \frac{\partial Z}{\partial y}\right)\right]\Delta y + \frac{\partial}{\partial z}\left[\beta_c k_z A_z \frac{k_{ro}}{\mu_o B_o}\left(\frac{\partial p_o}{\partial z} - \gamma_o \frac{\partial Z}{\partial z}\right)\right]\Delta z = \frac{V_b}{\alpha_c}\frac{\partial}{\partial t}\left(\frac{\phi S_o}{B_o}\right) - q_{osc}, \quad (9.21)$$

$$\frac{\partial}{\partial x}\left[\beta_c k_x A_x \frac{k_{rw}}{\mu_w B_w}\left(\frac{\partial p_w}{\partial x} - \gamma_w \frac{\partial Z}{\partial x}\right)\right]\Delta x + \frac{\partial}{\partial y}\left[\beta_c k_y A_y \frac{k_{rw}}{\mu_w B_w}\left(\frac{\partial p_w}{\partial y} - \gamma_w \frac{\partial Z}{\partial y}\right)\right]\Delta y + \frac{\partial}{\partial z}\left[\beta_c k_z A_z \frac{k_{rw}}{\mu_w B_w}\left(\frac{\partial p_w}{\partial z} - \gamma_w \frac{\partial Z}{\partial z}\right)\right]\Delta z = \frac{V_b}{\alpha_c}\frac{\partial}{\partial t}\left(\frac{\phi S_w}{B_w}\right) - q_{wsc}, \quad (9.22)$$

and
$$\frac{\partial}{\partial x}\left[\beta_c k_x A_x \frac{k_{rg}}{\mu_g B_g}\left(\frac{\partial p_g}{\partial x} - \gamma_g \frac{\partial Z}{\partial x}\right) + \beta_c k_x A_x \frac{k_{ro} R_s}{\mu_o B_o}\left(\frac{\partial p_o}{\partial x} - \gamma_o \frac{\partial Z}{\partial x}\right)\right]\Delta x + \frac{\partial}{\partial y}\left[\beta_c k_y A_y \frac{k_{rg}}{\mu_g B_g}\left(\frac{\partial p_g}{\partial y} - \gamma_g \frac{\partial Z}{\partial y}\right) + \beta_c k_y A_y \frac{k_{ro} R_s}{\mu_o B_o}\left(\frac{\partial p_o}{\partial y} - \gamma_o \frac{\partial Z}{\partial y}\right)\right]\Delta y + \frac{\partial}{\partial z}\left[\beta_c k_z A_z \frac{k_{rg}}{\mu_g B_g}\left(\frac{\partial p_g}{\partial z} - \gamma_g \frac{\partial Z}{\partial z}\right) + \beta_c k_z A_z \frac{k_{ro} R_s}{\mu_o B_o}\left(\frac{\partial p_o}{\partial z} - \gamma_o \frac{\partial Z}{\partial z}\right)\right]\Delta z = \frac{V_b}{\alpha_c}\frac{\partial}{\partial t}\left(\frac{\phi S_g}{B_g} + \frac{\phi R_s S_o}{B_o}\right) - q_{gsc}, \quad (9.23)$$

where q_{gsc} is given by Eq. 9.20.

Additional relationships needed to complete the flow description are

$$S_o + S_w + S_g = 1, \quad (9.43)$$

$$P_{cow} = p_o - p_w = f(S_w), \quad (9.34)$$

and $$P_{cgo} = p_g - p_o = f(S_g). \quad (9.44)$$

Eqs. 9.21 through 9.23 and Eqs. 9.43, 9.34, and 9.44 contain six unknowns: p_o, p_w, p_g, S_o, S_w, and S_g. The last three equations may be used to eliminate three unknowns in the first three equations.

The black-oil-model formulation, in terms of p_o, S_w, and S_g, may be obtained by eliminating S_o, p_w, and p_g by the aid of Eqs. 9.43, 9.34, and 9.44. The flow equations of the black-oil model in this formulation become

$$\frac{\partial}{\partial x}\left[\beta_c k_x A_x \frac{k_{ro}}{\mu_o B_o}\left(\frac{\partial p_o}{\partial x} - \gamma_o \frac{\partial Z}{\partial x}\right)\right]\Delta x + \frac{\partial}{\partial y}\left[\beta_c k_y A_y \frac{k_{ro}}{\mu_o B_o}\left(\frac{\partial p_o}{\partial y} - \gamma_o \frac{\partial Z}{\partial y}\right)\right]\Delta y + \frac{\partial}{\partial z}\left[\beta_c k_z A_z \frac{k_{ro}}{\mu_o B_o}\left(\frac{\partial p_o}{\partial z} - \gamma_o \frac{\partial Z}{\partial z}\right)\right]\Delta z = \frac{V_b}{\alpha_c}\frac{\partial}{\partial t}\left[\frac{\phi(1 - S_w - S_g)}{B_o}\right] - q_{osc}, \quad (9.45)$$

$$\frac{\partial}{\partial x}\left[\beta_c k_x A_x \frac{k_{rw}}{\mu_w B_w}\left(\frac{\partial p_o}{\partial x} - \frac{\partial P_{cow}}{\partial x} - \gamma_w \frac{\partial Z}{\partial x}\right)\right]\Delta x + \frac{\partial}{\partial y}\left[\beta_c k_y A_y \frac{k_{rw}}{\mu_w B_w}\left(\frac{\partial p_o}{\partial y} - \frac{\partial P_{cow}}{\partial y} - \gamma_w \frac{\partial Z}{\partial y}\right)\right]\Delta y + \frac{\partial}{\partial z}\left[\beta_c k_z A_z \frac{k_{rw}}{\mu_w B_w}\left(\frac{\partial p_o}{\partial z} - \frac{\partial P_{cow}}{\partial z} - \gamma_w \frac{\partial Z}{\partial z}\right)\right]\Delta z = \frac{V_b}{\alpha_c}\frac{\partial}{\partial t}\left(\frac{\phi S_w}{B_w}\right) - q_{wsc}, \quad (9.38)$$

and
$$\frac{\partial}{\partial x}\left[\beta_c k_x A_x \frac{k_{rg}}{\mu_g B_g}\left(\frac{\partial p_o}{\partial x} + \frac{\partial P_{cgo}}{\partial x} - \gamma_g \frac{\partial Z}{\partial x}\right) + \beta_c k_x A_x \frac{k_{ro} R_s}{\mu_o B_o}\left(\frac{\partial p_o}{\partial x} - \gamma_o \frac{\partial Z}{\partial x}\right)\right]\Delta x + \frac{\partial}{\partial y}\left[\beta_c k_y A_y \frac{k_{rg}}{\mu_g B_g}\left(\frac{\partial p_o}{\partial y} + \frac{\partial P_{cgo}}{\partial y} - \gamma_g \frac{\partial Z}{\partial y}\right) + \beta_c k_y A_y \frac{k_{ro} R_s}{\mu_o B_o}\left(\frac{\partial p_o}{\partial y} - \gamma_o \frac{\partial Z}{\partial y}\right)\right]\Delta y + \frac{\partial}{\partial z}\left[\beta_c k_z A_z \frac{k_{rg}}{\mu_g B_g}\left(\frac{\partial p_o}{\partial z} + \frac{\partial P_{cgo}}{\partial z} - \gamma_g \frac{\partial Z}{\partial z}\right) + \beta_c k_z A_z \frac{k_{ro} R_s}{\mu_o B_o}\left(\frac{\partial p_o}{\partial z} - \gamma_o \frac{\partial Z}{\partial z}\right)\right]\Delta z = \frac{V_b}{\alpha_c}\frac{\partial}{\partial t}\left[\frac{\phi S_g}{B_g} + \frac{\phi R_s(1 - S_w - S_g)}{B_o}\right] - q_{gsc}, \quad (9.46)$$

where q_{gsc} is given by Eq. 9.20.

Given initial and boundary conditions, Eqs. 9.45, 9.38, and 9.46 may be solved for the principal unknowns p_o, S_w, and S_g. Then, it is possible to solve explicitly for the remaining unknowns, S_o, p_w, and p_g, by substitution of the principal unknowns into Eqs. 9.43, 9.34, and 9.44.

The black-oil-model formulation expressed by Eqs. 9.45, 9.38, and 9.46 encompasses the formulations of the other models. The oil/water flow model, the oil/gas flow model, and the water/gas flow model are all subsets of the three-phase-flow model.

Example 9.3. Write the flow model for a solution-gas-drive reservoir. The producing formation is relatively thin and has a large areal extension with several wells drilled and on production.

Solution. Solution-gas drive is an oil-production mechanism that involves simultaneous flow of oil and gas. Evolution of gas from oil is an important drive mechanism in this system; therefore, the applicable flow model for this system is described by Eqs. 9.41 and 9.42.

For a relatively thin formation that extends areally and from which several wells are producing, flow can be assumed to be two-dimensional (2D) in the x-y plane parallel to the producing formation. Therefore, Eqs. 9.41 and 9.42 reduce to

$$\frac{\partial}{\partial x}\left[\beta_c k_x A_x \frac{k_{ro}}{\mu_o B_o}\left(\frac{\partial p_o}{\partial x} - \gamma_o \frac{\partial Z}{\partial x}\right)\right]\Delta x + \frac{\partial}{\partial y}\left[\beta_c k_y A_y \frac{k_{ro}}{\mu_o B_o}\left(\frac{\partial p_o}{\partial y} - \gamma_o \frac{\partial Z}{\partial y}\right)\right]\Delta y = \frac{V_b}{\alpha_c}\frac{\partial}{\partial t}\left[\frac{\phi(1-S_g)}{B_o}\right] - q_{osc} \qquad (9.47)$$

and

$$\frac{\partial}{\partial x}\left[\beta_c k_x A_x \frac{k_{rg}}{\mu_g B_g}\left(\frac{\partial p_o}{\partial x} + \frac{\partial P_{cgo}}{\partial x} - \gamma_g \frac{\partial Z}{\partial x}\right) + \beta_c k_x A_x \frac{k_{ro}R_s}{\mu_o B_o}\left(\frac{\partial p_o}{\partial x} - \gamma_o \frac{\partial Z}{\partial x}\right)\right]\Delta x$$
$$+ \frac{\partial}{\partial y}\left[\beta_c k_y A_y \frac{k_{rg}}{\mu_g B_g}\left(\frac{\partial p_o}{\partial y} + \frac{\partial P_{cgo}}{\partial y} - \gamma_g \frac{\partial Z}{\partial y}\right) + \beta_c k_y A_y \frac{k_{ro}R_s}{\mu_o B_o}\left(\frac{\partial p_o}{\partial y} - \gamma_o \frac{\partial Z}{\partial y}\right)\right]\Delta y$$
$$= \frac{V_b}{\alpha_c}\frac{\partial}{\partial t}\left[\frac{\phi S_g}{B_g} + \frac{\phi R_s(1-S_g)}{B_o}\right] - q_{gsc}, \qquad (9.48)$$

where $q_{gsc} = q_{fgsc} + R_s q_{osc}$. .... (9.20)

Eqs. 9.47 and 9.48 constitute the flow model for this reservoir expressed in the (p_o-S_g) formulation. The same equations may be obtained from the black-oil model by considering Eqs. 9.45 and 9.46, with $S_w = 0$ (or $S_w = S_{iw}$), and discarding Eq. 9.38 for water.

Example 9.4. Express the oil and water flow equations of Example 9.1 in the (p_o-S_o) formulation.

Solution. The oil and water flow equations derived in Example 9.1 are

$$\frac{\partial}{\partial x}\left(\beta_c k_x A_x \frac{k_{ro}}{\mu_o B_o}\frac{\partial p_o}{\partial x}\right)\Delta x + \frac{\partial}{\partial y}\left(\beta_c k_y A_y \frac{k_{ro}}{\mu_o B_o}\frac{\partial p_o}{\partial y}\right)\Delta y = \frac{V_b}{\alpha_c}\frac{\partial}{\partial t}\left(\frac{\phi S_o}{B_o}\right) - q_{osc} \qquad (9.27b)$$

and

$$\frac{\partial}{\partial x}\left(\beta_c k_x A_x \frac{k_{rw}}{\mu_w B_w}\frac{\partial p_w}{\partial x}\right)\Delta x + \frac{\partial}{\partial y}\left(\beta_c k_y A_y \frac{k_{rw}}{\mu_w B_w}\frac{\partial p_w}{\partial y}\right)\Delta y = \frac{V_b}{\alpha_c}\frac{\partial}{\partial t}\left(\frac{\phi S_w}{B_w}\right) - q_{wsc}. \qquad (9.27c)$$

The oil equation, Eq. 9.27b, is expressed in terms of p_o and S_o. The water equation, Eq. 9.27c, may be expressed in terms of p_o and S_o if it is combined with

$$S_w = 1 - S_o \qquad (9.49)$$

and

$$p_w = p_o - P_{cow}(S_o). \qquad (9.50)$$

The resulting water equation is

$$\frac{\partial}{\partial x}\left[\beta_c k_x A_x \frac{k_{rw}}{\mu_w B_w}\left(\frac{\partial p_o}{\partial x} - \frac{\partial P_{cow}}{\partial x}\right)\right]\Delta x + \frac{\partial}{\partial y}\left[\beta_c k_y A_y \frac{k_{rw}}{\mu_w B_w}\left(\frac{\partial p_o}{\partial y} - \frac{\partial P_{cow}}{\partial y}\right)\right]\Delta y = \frac{V_b}{\alpha_c}\frac{\partial}{\partial t}\left[\frac{\phi(1-S_o)}{B_w}\right] - q_{wsc}. \qquad (9.51)$$

Eqs. 9.27b and 9.51 are the oil/water flow equations in the (p_o-S_o) formulation.

9.5 Finite-Difference Approximation of the Flow Equations

The previous section shows that the equations for any of the basic flow models can be expressed in terms of oil pressure and fluid saturations in the (p_o-S_w-S_g) formulation. These flow equations are strongly nonlinear PDE's with analytical solutions too complex, if not impossible, to obtain. Therefore, numerical methods are required to obtain engineering solutions to the flow problem. As with single-phase-flow systems discussed in earlier chapters, the finite-difference approach is used to obtain the numerical solution to multiphase-flow systems. In this approach, the flow equations are discretized by the use of algebraic approximations of the second-order derivatives with respect to space and the first-order derivatives with respect to time. Depending on the approximation of the derivatives with respect to time, one may obtain explicit or implicit finite-difference equations.

9.5.1 Discretization of the Multiphase-Flow Equations. As discussed in Chap. 5, discretization is the process of approximating a differential equation by a set of finite-difference equations. The basic idea behind the discretization process is to replace the derivatives in the differential equation with algebraic approximations. For time-dependent problems, the solution of a differential equation is continuous in both space and time. In contrast, the solution of finite-difference equations is defined only on a finite set of discrete points in space and only at discrete time levels, $t_0 = 0$, $t_1 = t_0 + \Delta t_1$, $t_2 = t_1 + \Delta t_2, \ldots, t^n = t^{n-1} + \Delta t^n$.

Consider the black-oil model in the (p_o-S_w-S_g) formulation (Eqs. 9.38, 9.45, and 9.46). The discretization of these equations involves the following three mathematical operations.

1. The finite-difference approximation of the second-order-derivative terms in the x, y, and z directions, which appear on the left side of the equations. For example, the various second-order-derivative terms in the x direction are

$$\frac{\partial}{\partial x}\left(\beta_c k_x A_x \frac{k_{rl}}{\mu_l B_l}\frac{\partial p_o}{\partial x}\right)\Delta x,$$

$$\frac{\partial}{\partial x}\left(\beta_c k_x A_x \frac{k_{rl}\gamma_l}{\mu_l B_l}\frac{\partial Z}{\partial x}\right)\Delta x,$$

$$\frac{\partial}{\partial x}\left(\beta_c k_x A_x \frac{k_{rw}}{\mu_w B_w}\frac{\partial P_{cow}}{\partial x}\right)\Delta x,$$

$$\frac{\partial}{\partial x}\left(\beta_c k_x A_x \frac{k_{rg}}{\mu_g B_g}\frac{\partial P_{cgo}}{\partial x}\right)\Delta x,$$

$$\frac{\partial}{\partial x}\left(\beta_c k_x A_x \frac{k_{ro}R_s}{\mu_o B_o}\frac{\partial p_o}{\partial x}\right)\Delta x,$$

and

$$\frac{\partial}{\partial x}\left(\beta_c k_x A_x \frac{k_{ro}R_s\gamma_o}{\mu_o B_o}\frac{\partial Z}{\partial x}\right)\Delta x,$$

where $l = o$, w, or g. These terms have the general form of the second-order differential operator $(\partial/\partial x)[\xi_x^*(\partial\eta/\partial x)]\Delta x$, where ξ_x^* may assume the functions $\beta_c k_x A_x(k_{rl}/\mu_l B_l)$, $\beta_c k_x A_x(k_{rl}\gamma_l/\mu_l B_l)$, $\beta_c k_x A_x(k_{ro}R_s/\mu_o B_o)$, or $\beta_c k_x A_x(k_{ro}R_s\gamma_o/\mu_o B_o)$ and η may assume p_o, P_{cow}, P_{cgo}, or Z.

The finite-difference operator form of approximating these differential operators may be expressed in the compact notation $\Delta(\xi\Delta\eta)_{i,j,k}$, which is defined as the sum of its ith, jth, and kth components, $\Delta_x(\xi_x\Delta_x\eta)$, $\Delta_y(\xi_y\Delta_y\eta)$, $\Delta_z(\xi_z\Delta_z\eta)$, in the x, y, and z directions, each evaluated at Point (i,j,k). That is,

$$\Delta(\xi\Delta\eta)_{i,j,k} = \Delta_x(\xi_x\Delta_x\eta)_{i,j,k} + \Delta_y(\xi_y\Delta_y\eta)_{i,j,k} + \Delta_z(\xi_z\Delta_z\eta)_{i,j,k}. \quad (9.52)$$

The finite-difference approximations of the second-order partial derivatives in the x, y, and z directions are

$$\frac{\partial}{\partial x}\left(\xi_x^*\frac{\partial\eta}{\partial x}\right)\Delta x \approx \Delta_x(\xi_x\Delta_x\eta), \quad (9.53)$$

$$\frac{\partial}{\partial y}\left(\xi_y^*\frac{\partial\eta}{\partial y}\right)\Delta y \approx \Delta_y(\xi_y\Delta_y\eta), \quad (9.54)$$

and $$\frac{\partial}{\partial z}\left(\xi_z^*\frac{\partial\eta}{\partial z}\right)\Delta z \approx \Delta_z(\xi_z\Delta_z\eta), \quad (9.55)$$

where $\xi_x = \xi_x^*/\Delta x$, $\xi_y = \xi_y^*/\Delta y$, and $\xi_z = \xi_z^*/\Delta z$. This section presents the expansions defining $\Delta_x(\xi_x\Delta_x\eta)_{i,j,k}$, $\Delta_y(\xi_y\Delta_y\eta)_{i,j,k}$, and $\Delta_z(\xi_z\Delta_z\eta)_{i,j,k}$.

2. The finite-difference approximation of the first-order derivatives, with respect to time, which appear on the right side of the equations. The first-order derivatives include $(\partial/\partial t)(\phi S_l/B_l)$ for $l=w$ or g, $(\partial/\partial t)[\phi(1-S_w-S_g)/B_o]$, and $(\partial/\partial t)[\phi R_s(1-S_w-S_g)/B_o]$. All of these have the general form of the first-order derivative operator $(\partial/\partial t)(f)$, where f may assume the functions $(\phi S_l)/B_l$, $[\phi(1-S_w-S_g)]/B_o$, or $[\phi R_s(1-S_w-S_g)]/B_o$.

The first-order finite-difference operator, which approximates the first-order differential operator as

$$\frac{\partial}{\partial t}(f) \approx \frac{1}{\Delta t}\Delta_t(f) \equiv \frac{1}{\Delta t}(f^{n+1} - f^n), \quad (9.56)$$

is discussed in detail in this section. The difference $\Delta_t(f)$ is called the accumulation term.

3. The conservative expansion of accumulation terms $\Delta_t(f)$ in terms of the unknowns p_o, S_w, and S_g of the formulation, which is discussed in this section.

If a reservoir is represented by a set of discrete gridpoints (or rectangular gridblocks) (i,j,k), $i=1,2,\ldots,n_x$; $j=1,2,\ldots,n_y$; $k=1,2,\ldots,n_z$; then, the finite-difference approximation to the flow equations of the black-oil model, Eqs. 9.45, 9.38, and 9.46, may be written for each Gridblock (i,j,k) as

$$\Delta_x\left[\beta_c\frac{k_xA_x}{\Delta x}\frac{k_{ro}}{\mu_oB_o}(\Delta_xp_o - \gamma_o\Delta_xZ)\right]_{i,j,k} + \Delta_y\left[\beta_c\frac{k_yA_y}{\Delta y}\frac{k_{ro}}{\mu_oB_o}(\Delta_yp_o - \gamma_o\Delta_yZ)\right]_{i,j,k} + \Delta_z\left[\beta_c\frac{k_zA_z}{\Delta z}\frac{k_{ro}}{\mu_oB_o}(\Delta_zp_o - \gamma_o\Delta_zZ)\right]_{i,j,k}$$
$$= \frac{V_{b_{i,j,k}}}{\alpha_c\Delta t}\Delta_t\left[\frac{\phi(1-S_w-S_g)}{B_o}\right]_{i,j,k} - q_{osc_{i,j,k}}, \quad (9.57)$$

$$\Delta_x\left[\beta_c\frac{k_xA_x}{\Delta x}\frac{k_{rw}}{\mu_wB_w}(\Delta_xp_o - \Delta_xP_{cow} - \gamma_w\Delta_xZ)\right]_{i,j,k} + \Delta_y\left[\beta_c\frac{k_yA_y}{\Delta y}\frac{k_{rw}}{\mu_wB_w}(\Delta_yp_o - \Delta_yP_{cow} - \gamma_w\Delta_yZ)\right]_{i,j,k} + \Delta_z\left[\beta_c\frac{k_zA_z}{\Delta z}\frac{k_{rw}}{\mu_wB_w}(\Delta_zp_o - \Delta_zP_{cow} - \gamma_w\Delta_zZ)\right]_{i,j,k}$$
$$= \frac{V_{b_{i,j,k}}}{\alpha_c\Delta t}\Delta_t\left(\frac{\phi S_w}{B_o}\right)_{i,j,k} - q_{wsc_{i,j,k}}, \quad (9.58)$$

and $$\Delta_x\left[\beta_c\frac{k_xA_x}{\Delta x}\frac{k_{rg}}{\mu_gB_g}(\Delta_xp_o + \Delta_xP_{cgo} - \gamma_g\Delta_xZ)\right]_{i,j,k} + \Delta_x\left[\beta_c\frac{k_xA_x}{\Delta x}\frac{k_{ro}R_s}{\mu_oB_o}(\Delta_xp_o - \gamma_o\Delta_xZ)\right]_{i,j,k}$$
$$+ \Delta_y\left[\beta_c\frac{k_yA_y}{\Delta y}\frac{k_{rg}}{\mu_gB_g}(\Delta_yp_o + \Delta_yP_{cgo} - \gamma_g\Delta_yZ)\right]_{i,j,k} + \Delta_y\left[\beta_c\frac{k_yA_y}{\Delta y}\frac{k_{ro}R_s}{\mu_oB_o}(\Delta_yp_o - \gamma_o\Delta_yZ)\right]_{i,j,k}$$
$$+ \Delta_z\left[\beta_c\frac{k_zA_z}{\Delta z}\frac{k_{rg}}{\mu_gB_g}(\Delta_zp_o + \Delta_zP_{cgo} - \gamma_g\Delta_zZ)\right]_{i,j,k} + \Delta_z\left[\beta_c\frac{k_zA_z}{\Delta z}\frac{k_{ro}R_s}{\mu_oB_o}(\Delta_zp_o - \gamma_o\Delta_zZ)\right]_{i,j,k}$$
$$= \frac{V_{b_{i,j,k}}}{\alpha_c\Delta t}\left\{\Delta_t\left(\frac{\phi S_g}{B_g}\right)_{i,j,k} + \Delta_t\left[\frac{\phi R_s(1-S_w-S_g)}{B_o}\right]_{i,j,k}\right\} - q_{gsc_{i,j,k}}, \quad (9.59)$$

With the notation given by Eq. 9.52 for the second-order finite-difference operator, Eqs. 9.57 through 9.59 may be written compactly as

$$\Delta[\mathrm{T}_o(\Delta p_o - \gamma_o\Delta Z)] = \frac{V_b}{\alpha_c\Delta t}\Delta_t\left[\frac{\phi(1-S_w-S_g)}{B_o}\right] - q_{osc}, \quad (9.60)$$

$$\Delta[\mathrm{T}_w(\Delta p_o - \Delta P_{cow} - \gamma_w\Delta Z)] = \frac{V_b}{\alpha_c\Delta t}\Delta_t\left(\frac{\phi S_w}{B_w}\right) - q_{wsc}, \quad (9.61)$$

and $$\Delta[\mathrm{T}_g(\Delta p_o + \Delta P_{cgo} - \gamma_g\Delta Z)] + \Delta[\mathrm{T}_oR_s(\Delta p_o - \gamma_o\Delta Z)]$$
$$= \frac{V_b}{\alpha_c\Delta t}\left\{\Delta_t\left(\frac{\phi S_g}{B_g}\right) + \Delta_t\left[\frac{\phi R_s(1-S_w-S_g)}{B_o}\right]\right\} - q_{gsc}, \quad (9.62)$$

where q_{gsc} is defined by Eq. 9.20 and the directional transmissibilities for Phase $l=o$, w, or g are defined by

$$\mathrm{T}_{lx} = \beta_c\frac{k_xA_x}{\Delta x}\frac{k_{rl}}{\mu_lB_l}, \quad (9.63)$$

$$\mathrm{T}_{ly} = \beta_c\frac{k_yA_y}{\Delta y}\frac{k_{rl}}{\mu_lB_l}, \quad (9.64)$$

and $$\mathrm{T}_{lz} = \beta_c\frac{k_zA_z}{\Delta z}\frac{k_{rl}}{\mu_lB_l}. \quad (9.65)$$

The transmissibilities defined by Eqs. 9.63 through 9.65 are similar to the definitions for single-phase flow with the inclusion of relative permeability, k_{rl}, the only difference (see Eq. 5.48).

Eqs. 9.60 through 9.62 are strongly nonlinear, coupled, algebraic equations. When written for all gridblocks in the reservoir, these three equations represent the finite-difference approximation to Eqs. 9.45, 9.38, and 9.46.

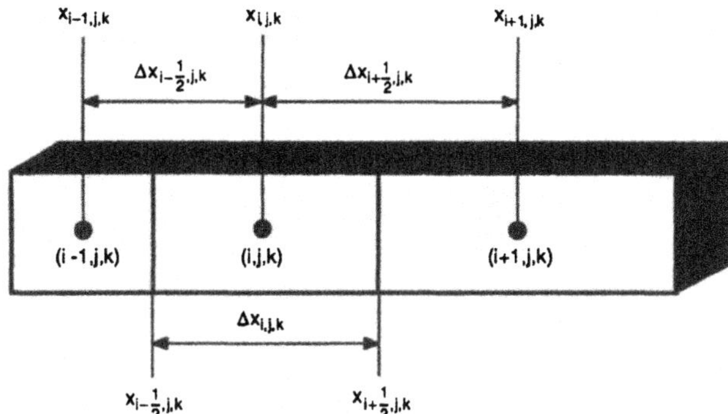

Fig. 9.4—Discretization in the *x* direction.

Discretization in Space. The process of applying the finite-difference approximation to the second-order derivative terms in the x, y, and z directions is called discretization in space. In this section, we derive the finite-difference approximation of the general form of the second-order differential operator in the x direction, $(\partial/\partial x)[\xi_x^*(\partial\eta/\partial x)]\Delta x$ at Gridpoint (i,j,k). In **Fig. 9.4**, the gridblock dimension is $\Delta x_{i,j,k}$, the distance between Gridpoints (i,j,k) and $(i-1,j,k)$ is $\Delta x_{i-½,j,k}$, and the distance between Gridpoints (i,j,k) and $(i+1,j,k)$ is $\Delta x_{i+½,j,k}$. The following relationships hold for both block-centered and point-distributed grids.

$$\Delta x_{i,j,k} = x_{i+½,j,k} - x_{i-½,j,k}, \quad \text{(9.66)}$$

$$\Delta x_{i-½,j,k} = x_{i,j,k} - x_{i-1,j,k}, \quad \text{(9.67)}$$

and $$\Delta x_{i+½,j,k} = x_{i+1,j,k} - x_{i,j,k}. \quad \text{(9.68)}$$

Let f be defined as

$$f = \xi_x^* \frac{\partial\eta}{\partial x}; \quad \text{(9.69)}$$

then, $$\frac{\partial}{\partial x}\left(\xi_x^* \frac{\partial\eta}{\partial x}\right)_{i,j,k} \Delta x_{i,j,k} = \left(\frac{\partial f}{\partial x}\right)_{i,j,k} \Delta x_{i,j,k}, \quad \text{(9.70)}$$

Approximate the first derivative, $(\partial f/\partial x)_{i,j,k}$, by the central-difference approximation with f evaluated at the gridblock boundaries $(i+½,j,k)$ and $(i-½,j,k)$ in the x direction.

$$\left(\frac{\partial f}{\partial x}\right)_{i,j,k} \approx \frac{f_{i+½,j,k} - f_{i-½,j,k}}{\Delta x_{i,j,k}}, \quad \text{(9.71)}$$

where, according to Eq. 9.69,

$$f_{i\pm½,j,k} = \xi_{x_{i\pm½,j,k}}^* \left(\frac{\partial\eta}{\partial x}\right)_{i\pm½,j,k}. \quad \text{(9.72)}$$

Again, approximate the first derivatives, $(\partial\eta/\partial x)_{i\pm½,j,k}$, by the central-difference approximation.

$$\left(\frac{\partial\eta}{\partial x}\right)_{i+½,j,k} \approx \frac{\eta_{i+1,j,k} - \eta_{i,j,k}}{\Delta x_{i+½,j,k}} \quad \text{(9.73)}$$

and $$\left(\frac{\partial\eta}{\partial x}\right)_{i-½,j,k} \approx \frac{\eta_{i,j,k} - \eta_{i-1,j,k}}{\Delta x_{i-½,j,k}}. \quad \text{(9.74)}$$

Substituting Eqs. 9.73 and 9.74 into Eq. 9.72 gives

$$f_{i+½,j,k} \approx \xi_{x_{i+½,j,k}}^* \left(\frac{\eta_{i+1,j,k} - \eta_{i,j,k}}{\Delta x_{i+½,j,k}}\right) \quad \text{(9.75)}$$

and $$f_{i-½,j,k} \approx \xi_{x_{i-½,j,k}}^* \left(\frac{\eta_{i,j,k} - \eta_{i-1,j,k}}{\Delta x_{i-½,j,k}}\right), \quad \text{(9.76)}$$

which, when substituted into Eq. 9.71, results in

$$\left(\frac{\partial f}{\partial x}\right)_{i,j,k} \Delta x_{i,j,k} \approx \left(\frac{\xi_x^*}{\Delta x}\right)_{i+½,j,k} \left(\eta_{i+1,j,k} - \eta_{i,j,k}\right) - \left(\frac{\xi_x^*}{\Delta x}\right)_{i-½,j,k} \left(\eta_{i,j,k} - \eta_{i-1,j,k}\right). \quad \text{(9.77)}$$

Combining Eqs. 9.70 and 9.77 yields

$$\frac{\partial}{\partial x}\left(\xi_x^* \frac{\partial\eta}{\partial x}\right)_{i,j,k} \Delta x_{i,j,k} \approx \left(\frac{\xi_x^*}{\Delta x}\right)_{i+½,j,k} \left(\eta_{i+1,j,k} - \eta_{i,j,k}\right) - \left(\frac{\xi_x^*}{\Delta x}\right)_{i-½,j,k} \left(\eta_{i,j,k} - \eta_{i-1,j,k}\right). \quad \text{(9.78)}$$

Define

$$\xi_x = \frac{\xi_x^*}{\Delta x}; \quad \text{(9.79)}$$

then, $$\frac{\partial}{\partial x}\left(\xi_x^* \frac{\partial\eta}{\partial x}\right)_{i,j,k} \Delta x_{i,j,k} \approx \xi_{x_{i+½,j,k}}\left(\eta_{i+1,j,k} - \eta_{i,j,k}\right) - \xi_{x_{i-½,j,k}}\left(\eta_{i,j,k} - \eta_{i-1,j,k}\right)$$
$$\approx \xi_{x_{i-½,j,k}}\left(\eta_{i-1,j,k} - \eta_{i,j,k}\right) + \xi_{x_{i+½,j,k}}\left(\eta_{i+1,j,k} - \eta_{i,j,k}\right). \quad \text{(9.80)}$$

Defining the right side of Eq. 9.80 as the x component of the second-order finite-difference operator,

$$\Delta_x(\xi_x\Delta_x\eta)_{i,j,k} \equiv \xi_{x_{i-½,j,k}}\left(\eta_{i-1,j,k} - \eta_{i,j,k}\right) + \xi_{x_{i+½,j,k}}\left(\eta_{i+1,j,k} - \eta_{i,j,k}\right); \quad \text{(9.81)}$$

then, $$\frac{\partial}{\partial x}\left(\xi_x^* \frac{\partial\eta}{\partial x}\right)_{i,j,k} \Delta x_{i,j,k} \approx \Delta_x(\xi_x\Delta_x\eta)_{i,j,k}, \quad \text{(9.82)}$$

where ξ_x is related to ξ_x^* through Eq. 9.79.

The finite-difference approximation to the second-order differential term in the y direction, $(\partial/\partial y)[\xi_y^*(\partial\eta/\partial y)]_{i,j,k}\Delta y_{i,j,k}$, may be derived with a procedure similiar to the one just presented for the x direction term, but in this case we consider Gridpoint (i,j,k), with its gridblock boundaries $(i,j-½,k)$ and $(i,j+½,k)$ and its neighboring gridblocks, $(i,j-1,k)$ and $(i,j+1,k)$, in the y direction. The approximation in the y direction may be expressed as

$$\frac{\partial}{\partial y}\left(\xi_y^* \frac{\partial\eta}{\partial y}\right)_{i,j,k} \Delta y_{i,j,k} \approx \Delta_y(\xi_y\Delta_y\eta)_{i,j,k}, \quad \text{(9.83)}$$

where $$\xi_y = \frac{\xi_y^*}{\Delta y} \quad \text{(9.84)}$$

and $$\Delta_y\left(\xi_y\Delta_y\eta\right)_{i,j,k} \equiv \xi_{y_{i,j-½,k}}\left(\eta_{i,j-1,k} - \eta_{i,j,k}\right) + \xi_{y_{i,j+½,k}}\left(\eta_{i,j+1,k} - \eta_{i,j,k}\right), \quad \text{(9.85)}$$

where $\Delta y_{i,j,k}$ and $\Delta y_{i,j\pm½,k}$ are defined by

$$\Delta y_{i,j,k} = y_{i,j+½,k} - y_{i,j-½,k}, \quad \text{(9.86)}$$

$$\Delta y_{i,j-½,k} = y_{i,j,k} - y_{i,j-1,k}, \quad \text{(9.87)}$$

and $$\Delta y_{i,j+½,k} = y_{i,j+1,k} - y_{i,j,k}. \quad \text{(9.88)}$$

The finite-difference approximation to the second-order differential term in the z direction also may be expressed as the z component of the finite-difference operator at Gridpoint (i,j,k).

$$\frac{\partial}{\partial z}\left(\xi_z^* \frac{\partial\eta}{\partial z}\right)_{i,j,k} \Delta z_{i,j,k} \approx \Delta_z(\xi_z\Delta_z\eta)_{i,j,k}, \quad \text{(9.89)}$$

where $\xi_z = \dfrac{\xi_z^*}{\Delta z}$ .... (9.90)

and $\Delta_z\left(\xi_z\Delta_z\eta\right)_{i,j,k} \equiv \xi_{z_{i,j,k-½}}\left(\eta_{i,j,k-1} - \eta_{i,j,k}\right)$

$$+ \xi_{z_{i,j,k+½}}\left(\eta_{i,j,k+1} - \eta_{i,j,k}\right), \quad \text{........ (9.91)}$$

where $\Delta z_{i,j,k}$ and $\Delta z_{i,j,k\pm½}$ are defined by

$$\Delta z_{i,j,k} = z_{i,j,k+½} - z_{i,j,k-½}, \quad \text{.................... (9.92)}$$

$$\Delta z_{i,j,k-½} = z_{i,j,k} - z_{i,j,k-1}, \quad \text{..................... (9.93)}$$

and $\Delta z_{i,j,k+½} = z_{i,j,k+1} - z_{i,j,k}$. .... (9.94)

Adding Eqs. 9.82, 9.83, and 9.89 results in

$$\frac{\partial}{\partial x}\left(\xi_x^*\frac{\partial\eta}{\partial x}\right)_{i,j,k}\Delta x_{i,j,k} + \frac{\partial}{\partial y}\left(\xi_y^*\frac{\partial\eta}{\partial y}\right)_{i,j,k}\Delta y_{i,j,k} + \frac{\partial}{\partial z}\left(\xi_z^*\frac{\partial\eta}{\partial z}\right)_{i,j,k}\Delta z_{i,j,k}$$

$$\approx \Delta_x\left(\xi_x\Delta_x\eta\right)_{i,j,k} + \Delta_y\left(\xi_y\Delta_y\eta\right)_{i,j,k} + \Delta_z\left(\xi_z\Delta_z\eta\right)_{i,j,k},$$

.... (9.95)

which defines the second-order finite-difference operator in 3D Cartesian space. Let $\Delta(\xi\Delta\eta)_{i,j,k}$ denote this operator where the subscripts i, j, and k indicate the x, y, and z directions, respectively. With this notation,

$$\Delta(\xi\Delta\eta)_{i,j,k} \approx \frac{\partial}{\partial x}\left(\xi_x^*\frac{\partial\eta}{\partial x}\right)_{i,j,k}\Delta x_{i,j,k} + \frac{\partial}{\partial y}\left(\xi_y^*\frac{\partial\eta}{\partial y}\right)_{i,j,k}\Delta y_{i,j,k}$$

$$+ \frac{\partial}{\partial z}\left(\xi_z^*\frac{\partial\eta}{\partial z}\right)_{i,j,k}\Delta z_{i,j,k}, \quad \text{............... (9.96)}$$

where $\Delta(\xi\Delta\eta)_{i,j,k} \equiv \Delta_x\left(\xi_x\Delta_x\eta\right)_{i,j,k} + \Delta_y\left(\xi_y\Delta_y\eta\right)_{i,j,k}$

$$+ \Delta_z\left(\xi_z\Delta_z\eta\right)_{i,j,k}, \quad \text{............... (9.97)}$$

$$\xi_x = \frac{\xi_x^*}{\Delta x}, \quad \text{.................................. (9.79)}$$

$$\xi_y = \frac{\xi_y^*}{\Delta y}, \quad \text{.................................. (9.84)}$$

and $\xi_z = \dfrac{\xi_z^*}{\Delta z}$, ... (9.90)

Substituting the expansions given by Eqs. 9.81, 9.85, and 9.91 into Eq. 9.97 results in the expansion of the finite-difference operator in 3D space.

$$\Delta(\xi\Delta\eta)_{i,j,k} \equiv \xi_{x_{i-½,j,k}}\left(\eta_{i-1,j,k} - \eta_{i,j,k}\right) + \xi_{x_{i+½,j,k}}\left(\eta_{i+1,j,k} - \eta_{i,j,k}\right)$$

$$+ \xi_{y_{i,j-½,k}}\left(\eta_{i,j-1,k} - \eta_{i,j,k}\right) + \xi_{y_{i,j+½,k}}\left(\eta_{i,j+1,k} - \eta_{i,j,k}\right)$$

$$+ \xi_{z_{i,j,k-½}}\left(\eta_{i,j,k-1} - \eta_{i,j,k}\right) + \xi_{z_{i,j,k+½}}\left(\eta_{i,j,k+1} - \eta_{i,j,k}\right).$$

.... (9.98)

Eq. 9.98 defines the finite-difference operator in the 3D Cartesian space. The finite-difference operator in 2D space has two directional components only; one in each direction indicated by the subscripts of the operator. Eqs. 9.99 through 9.101 give the definitions of 2D finite-difference operators.

In the x-y plane,

$$\Delta(\xi\Delta\eta)_{i,j} \equiv \Delta_x\left(\xi_x\Delta_x\eta\right)_{i,j} + \Delta_y\left(\xi_y\Delta_y\eta\right)_{i,j}. \quad \text{....... (9.99)}$$

In the x-z plane,

$$\Delta(\xi\Delta\eta)_{i,k} \equiv \Delta_x\left(\xi_x\Delta_x\eta\right)_{i,k} + \Delta_z\left(\xi_z\Delta_z\eta\right)_{i,k}. \quad \text{...... (9.100)}$$

In the y-z plane,

$$\Delta(\xi\Delta\eta)_{j,k} \equiv \Delta_y\left(\xi_y\Delta_y\eta\right)_{j,k} + \Delta_z\left(\xi_z\Delta_z\eta\right)_{j,k}. \quad \text{...... (9.101)}$$

A second-order finite-difference operator in 1D space has only one directional component indicated by the subscript of the operator. Eqs. 9.102 through 9.104 give the definitions of the 1D operators. In the x direction,

$$\Delta(\xi\Delta\eta)_i \equiv \Delta_x\left(\xi_x\Delta_x\eta\right)_i. \quad \text{..................... (9.102)}$$

In the y direction,

$$\Delta(\xi\Delta\eta)_j \equiv \Delta_y\left(\xi_y\Delta_y\eta\right)_j. \quad \text{..................... (9.103)}$$

In the z direction,

$$\Delta(\xi\Delta\eta)_k \equiv \Delta_z\left(\xi_z\Delta_z\eta\right)_k. \quad \text{..................... (9.104)}$$

Examples 9.5 through 9.8 demonstrate the use of these second-order finite-difference operators.

Example 9.5. Write the finite-difference approximations to the following partial-differential terms using the appropriate second-order finite-difference operator.

1. $\dfrac{\partial}{\partial x}\left(\beta_c k_x A_x \dfrac{k_{ro}}{\mu_o B_o}\dfrac{\partial p_o}{\partial x}\right)_{i,j,k}\Delta x_{i,j,k}$.

2. $\dfrac{\partial}{\partial y}\left(\beta_c k_y A_y \dfrac{k_{rw}}{\mu_w B_w}\dfrac{\partial P_{cow}}{\partial y}\right)_{i,j}\Delta y_{i,j}$.

3. $\dfrac{\partial}{\partial z}\left(\beta_c k_z A_z \dfrac{k_{rg}\gamma_g}{\mu_g B_g}\dfrac{\partial Z}{\partial z}\right)_k\Delta z_k$.

Solution. 1. The finite-difference approximation of the partial-differential term $(\partial/\partial x)\{\beta_c k_x A_x[k_{ro}/(\mu_o B_o)](\partial p_o/\partial x)\}_{i,j,k}\Delta x_{i,j,k}$ may be obtained by applying Eq. 9.82,

$$\frac{\partial}{\partial x}\left(\xi_x^*\frac{\partial\eta}{\partial x}\right)_{i,j,k}\Delta x_{i,j,k} \approx \Delta_x\left(\xi_x\Delta_x\eta\right)_{i,j,k}, \quad \text{........... (9.82)}$$

where $\xi_x = \dfrac{\xi_x^*}{\Delta x}$, ... (9.79)

and the finite-difference operator in the x direction at Gridpoint (i,j,k) is defined by Eq. 9.81 as

$$\Delta_x\left(\xi_x\Delta_x\eta\right)_{i,j,k} \equiv \xi_{x_{i-½,j,k}}\left(\eta_{i-1,j,k} - \eta_{i,j,k}\right)$$

$$+ \xi_{x_{i+½,j,k}}\left(\eta_{i+1,j,k} - \eta_{i,j,k}\right). \quad \text{........... (9.81)}$$

Let $\xi_x^* = \beta_c k_x A_x \dfrac{k_{ro}}{\mu_o B_o}$ .... (9.105)

and $\eta = p_o$. .... (9.106)

Application of Eq. 9.79 gives

$$\xi_x = \beta_c\frac{k_x A_x}{\Delta x}\frac{k_{ro}}{\mu_o B_o}. \quad \text{........................ (9.107)}$$

Substitution for ξ_x^*, ξ_x, and η into Eqs. 9.82 and 9.81 yields

$$\frac{\partial}{\partial x}\left(\beta_c k_x A_x\frac{k_{ro}}{\mu_o B_o}\frac{\partial p_o}{\partial x}\right)_{i,j,k}\Delta x_{i,j,k}$$

$$\approx \Delta_x\left(\beta_c\frac{k_x A_x}{\Delta x}\frac{k_{ro}}{\mu_o B_o}\Delta_x p_o\right)_{i,j,k} \quad \text{............... (9.108)}$$

and $\Delta_x\left(\beta_c \frac{k_x A_x}{\Delta x}\frac{k_{ro}}{\mu_o B_o}\Delta_x p_o\right)_{i,j,k}$

$$= \left(\beta_c \frac{k_x A_x}{\Delta x}\frac{k_{ro}}{\mu_o B_o}\right)_{i-½,j,k}\left(p_{o_{i-1,j,k}} - p_{o_{i,j,k}}\right)$$

$$+ \left(\beta_c \frac{k_x A_x}{\Delta x}\frac{k_{ro}}{\mu_o B_o}\right)_{i+½,j,k}\left(p_{o_{i+1,j,k}} - p_{o_{i,j,k}}\right), \quad \ldots\ldots (9.109)$$

which, when combined, result in the finite-difference approximation

$$\frac{\partial}{\partial x}\left(\beta_c k_x A_x \frac{k_{ro}}{\mu_o B_o}\frac{\partial p_o}{\partial x}\right)_{i,j,k}\Delta x_{i,j,k} \approx \left(\beta_c \frac{k_x A_x}{\Delta x}\frac{k_{ro}}{\mu_o B_o}\right)_{i-½,j,k} p_{o_{i-1,j,k}}$$

$$- \left[\left(\beta_c \frac{k_x A_x}{\Delta x}\frac{k_{ro}}{\mu_o B_o}\right)_{i-½,j,k} + \left(\beta_c \frac{k_x A_x}{\Delta x}\frac{k_{ro}}{\mu_o B_o}\right)_{i+½,j,k}\right] p_{o_{i,j,k}}$$

$$+ \left(\beta_c \frac{k_x A_x}{\Delta x}\frac{k_{ro}}{\mu_o B_o}\right)_{i+½,j,k} p_{o_{i+1,j,k}}. \quad \ldots\ldots (9.110)$$

Eq. 9.110 often is expressed as

$$\frac{\partial}{\partial x}\left(\beta_c k_x A_x \frac{k_{ro}}{\mu_o B_o}\frac{\partial p_o}{\partial x}\right)_{i,j,k}\Delta x_{i,j,k} \approx T_{ox_{i-½,j,k}} p_{o_{i-1,j,k}}$$

$$- \left(T_{ox_{i-½,j,k}} + T_{ox_{i+½,j,k}}\right) p_{o_{i,j,k}} + T_{ox_{i+½,j,k}} p_{o_{i+1,j,k}}, \quad \ldots\ldots (9.111)$$

$$\text{where } T_{ox} = \beta_c \frac{k_x A_x}{\Delta x}\frac{k_{ro}}{\mu_o B_o} \quad \ldots\ldots (9.112)$$

and is the oil-phase transmissibility in the x direction.

2. In this part of the problem, we need to write the finite-difference approximation of the partial-differential term in the y direction at Gridpoint (i,j) in the x-y plane. Let

$$\xi_y^* = \beta_c k_y A_y \frac{k_{rw}}{\mu_w B_w} \quad \ldots\ldots (9.113)$$

$$\text{and } \eta = P_{cow}; \quad \ldots\ldots (9.114)$$

$$\text{then, } \xi_y = \beta_c \frac{k_y A_y}{\Delta y}\frac{k_{rw}}{\mu_w B_w} = T_{wy}, \quad \ldots\ldots (9.115)$$

where T_{wy} = water-phase transmissibility in the y direction. Therefore, according to Eq. 9.83, we may write the finite-difference approximation as

$$\frac{\partial}{\partial y}\left(\beta_c k_y A_y \frac{k_{rw}}{\mu_w B_w}\frac{\partial P_{cow}}{\partial y}\right)_{i,j}\Delta y_{i,j} \approx \Delta_y\left(T_{wy}\Delta_y P_{cow}\right)_{i,j}. \quad \ldots\ldots (9.116)$$

Substituting $\xi_y = T_{wy}$ and $\eta = P_{cow}$ in the expansion of $\Delta_y(\xi_y\Delta_y\eta)_{i,j,k}$ given by Eq. 9.85 (where Subscript k is discarded) results in

$$\Delta_y\left(T_{wy}\Delta_y P_{cow}\right)_{i,j} = T_{wy_{i,j-½}}\left(P_{cow_{i,j-1}} - P_{cow_{i,j}}\right)$$

$$+ T_{wy_{i,j+½}}\left(P_{cow_{i,j+1}} - P_{cow_{i,j}}\right). \quad \ldots\ldots (9.117)$$

Combining Eqs. 9.116 and 9.117 and collecting like terms yields the desired approximation

$$\frac{\partial}{\partial y}\left(\beta_c k_y A_y \frac{k_{rw}}{\mu_w B_w}\frac{\partial P_{cow}}{\partial y}\right)_{i,j}\Delta y_{i,j} \approx T_{wy_{i,j-½}} P_{cow_{i,j-1}}$$

$$- \left(T_{wy_{i,j-½}} + T_{wy_{i,j+½}}\right) P_{cow_{i,j}} + T_{wy_{i,j+½}} P_{cow_{i,j+1}}, \quad \ldots\ldots (9.118)$$

$$\text{where } T_{wy} = \beta_c \frac{k_y A_y}{\Delta y}\frac{k_{rw}}{\mu_w B_w}, \quad \ldots\ldots (9.119)$$

3. To write the finite-difference approximation of the partial-differential term in the z direction evaluated at Gridpoint k, let

$$\xi_z^* = \beta_c k_z A_z \frac{k_{rg}}{\mu_g B_g}\gamma_g \quad \ldots\ldots (9.120)$$

$$\text{and } \eta = Z; \quad \ldots\ldots (9.121)$$

$$\text{then, } \xi_z = \frac{\xi_z^*}{\Delta z} = \beta_c \frac{k_z A_z}{\Delta z}\frac{k_{rg}}{\mu_g B_g}\gamma_g = T_{gz}\gamma_g, \quad \ldots\ldots (9.122)$$

where T_{gz} = gas-phase transmissibility in the z direction.

According to Eq. 9.89, the finite-difference approximation may be written as

$$\frac{\partial}{\partial z}\left(\beta_c k_z A_z \frac{k_{rg}}{\mu_g B_g}\gamma_g \frac{\partial Z}{\partial z}\right)_k \Delta z_k \approx \Delta_z\left(T_{gz}\gamma_g\Delta_z Z\right)_k. \quad \ldots\ldots (9.123)$$

Substituting $\xi_z = T_{gz}\gamma_g$ and $\eta = Z$ in the expansion of $\Delta_z(\xi_z\Delta_z\eta)_{i,j,k}$ given by Eq. 9.91 (discarding Subscripts i and j) results in

$$\Delta_z\left(T_{gz}\gamma_g\Delta_z Z\right)_k = \left(T_{gz}\gamma_g\right)_{k-½}\left(Z_{k-1} - Z_k\right)$$

$$+ \left(T_{gz}\gamma_g\right)_{k+½}\left(Z_{k+1} - Z_k\right). \quad \ldots\ldots (9.124)$$

Combining Eqs. 9.123 and 9.124 yields

$$\frac{\partial}{\partial z}\left(\beta_c k_z A_z \frac{k_{rg}}{\mu_g B_g}\gamma_g \frac{\partial Z}{\partial z}\right)_k \Delta z_k \approx \left(T_{gz}\gamma_g\right)_{k-½}\left(Z_{k-1} - Z_k\right)$$

$$+ \left(T_{gz}\gamma_g\right)_{k+½}\left(Z_{k+1} - Z_k\right), \quad \ldots\ldots (9.125)$$

$$\text{where } T_{gz} = \beta_c \frac{k_z A_z}{\Delta z}\frac{k_{rg}}{\mu_g B_g}. \quad \ldots\ldots (9.126)$$

Example 9.6. Write the finite-difference approximation for the oil and water flow equations of Example 9.4.

Solution. Example 9.4 gives the oil and water flow equations in differential form as

$$\frac{\partial}{\partial x}\left(\beta_c k_x A_x \frac{k_{ro}}{\mu_o B_o}\frac{\partial p_o}{\partial x}\right)\Delta x + \frac{\partial}{\partial y}\left(\beta_c k_y A_y \frac{k_{ro}}{\mu_o B_o}\frac{\partial p_o}{\partial y}\right)\Delta y$$

$$= \frac{V_b}{\alpha_c}\frac{\partial}{\partial t}\left(\frac{\phi S_o}{B_o}\right) - q_{osc} \quad \ldots\ldots (9.27b)$$

$$\text{and } \frac{\partial}{\partial x}\left[\beta_c k_x A_x \frac{k_{rw}}{\mu_w B_w}\left(\frac{\partial p_o}{\partial x} - \frac{\partial P_{cow}}{\partial x}\right)\right]\Delta x$$

$$+ \frac{\partial}{\partial y}\left[\beta_c k_y A_y \frac{k_{rw}}{\mu_w B_w}\left(\frac{\partial p_o}{\partial y} - \frac{\partial P_{cow}}{\partial y}\right)\right]\Delta y$$

$$= \frac{V_b}{\alpha_c}\frac{\partial}{\partial t}\left[\frac{\phi(1 - S_o)}{B_w}\right] - q_{wsc}. \quad \ldots\ldots (9.51)$$

These equations represent flow in the 2D x-y plane, which we approximate at a set of discrete points (i,j).

To write the finite-difference approximation for the oil equation, for example, Eq. 9.27b is written at Gridpoint (i,j) and each partial-differential operator is replaced by its corresponding finite-difference operator. Hence, the differential operator represented by the left side of Eq. 9.27b may be replaced by the difference operator given by Eq. 9.99.

$$\frac{\partial}{\partial x}\left(\beta_c k_x A_x \frac{k_{ro}}{\mu_o B_o}\frac{\partial p_o}{\partial x}\right)\Delta x + \frac{\partial}{\partial y}\left(\beta_c k_y A_y \frac{k_{ro}}{\mu_o B_o}\frac{\partial p_o}{\partial y}\right)\Delta y$$

$$\approx \Delta(\mathrm{T}_o \Delta p_o)_{i,j}, \quad \text{.......................... (9.127)}$$

where $\Delta(\mathrm{T}_o\Delta p_o)_{i,j} = \Delta_x\left(\mathrm{T}_{ox}\Delta_x p_o\right)_{i,j} + \Delta_y\left(\mathrm{T}_{oy}\Delta_y p_o\right)_{i,j}$

$$\text{.................... (9.128)}$$

$$\text{and } \mathrm{T}_{ox} = \beta_c \frac{k_x A_x}{\Delta x}\frac{k_{ro}}{\mu_o B_o} \quad \text{........................ (9.112)}$$

$$\text{because } \xi_x^* = \beta_c k_x A_x \frac{k_{ro}}{\mu_o B_o} \quad \text{.................... (9.105)}$$

$$\text{and } \xi_x = \frac{\xi_x^*}{\Delta x} = \mathrm{T}_{ox} \quad \text{.......................... (9.129)}$$

$$\text{and } \mathrm{T}_{oy} = \beta_c \frac{k_y A_y}{\Delta y}\frac{k_{ro}}{\mu_o B_o} \quad \text{...................... (9.130)}$$

$$\text{because } \xi_y^* = \beta_c k_y A_y \frac{k_{ro}}{\mu_o B_o} \quad \text{.................... (9.131)}$$

$$\text{and } \xi_y = \frac{\xi_y^*}{\Delta y} = \mathrm{T}_{oy}. \quad \text{.......................... (9.132)}$$

Also, the differential operator on the right side of Eq. 9.27b may be replaced by the difference operator given by Eq. 9.56.

$$\frac{\partial}{\partial t}\left(\frac{\phi S_o}{B_o}\right) \approx \frac{1}{\Delta t}\Delta_t\left(\frac{\phi S_o}{B_o}\right). \quad \text{.................... (9.133)}$$

Therefore, the finite-difference approximation to the oil equation at Gridpoint (i,j) may now be written in compact form as

$$\Delta(\mathrm{T}_o\Delta p_o)_{i,j} = \frac{V_{b_{i,j}}}{\alpha_c \Delta t}\Delta_t\left(\frac{\phi S_o}{B_o}\right)_{i,j} - q_{osc_{i,j}} \quad \text{.......... (9.134)}$$

$$\text{or } \Delta_x\left(\mathrm{T}_{ox}\Delta_x p_o\right)_{i,j} + \Delta_y\left(\mathrm{T}_{oy}\Delta_y p_o\right)_{i,j} = \frac{V_{b_{i,j}}}{\alpha_c \Delta t}\Delta_t\left(\frac{\phi S_o}{B_o}\right)_{i,j} - q_{osc_{i,j}},$$

$$\text{.................... (9.135)}$$

where T_{ox} and T_{oy} are defined in Eqs. 9.112 and 9.130, respectively.

Similarly, the finite-difference approximation for the water equation, Eq. 9.51, may be written in a compact form as

$$\Delta[\mathrm{T}_w\Delta(p_o - P_{cow})]_{i,j} = \frac{V_{b_{i,j}}}{\alpha_c \Delta t}\Delta_t\left[\frac{\phi(1-S_o)}{B_w}\right]_{i,j} - q_{wsc_{i,j}}$$

$$\text{.................... (9.136)}$$

$$\text{or } \Delta_x\left[\mathrm{T}_{wx}\Delta_x(p_o - P_{cow})\right]_{i,j} + \Delta_y\left[\mathrm{T}_{wy}\Delta_y(p_o - P_{cow})\right]_{i,j}$$

$$= \frac{V_{b_{i,j}}}{\alpha_c \Delta t}\Delta_t\left[\frac{\phi(1-S_o)}{B_w}\right]_{i,j} - q_{wsc_{i,j}}, \quad \text{........... (9.137)}$$

$$\text{where } \mathrm{T}_{wx} = \beta_c \frac{k_x A_x}{\Delta x}\frac{k_{rw}}{\mu_w B_w} \quad \text{.................... (9.138)}$$

$$\text{and } \mathrm{T}_{wy} = \beta_c \frac{k_y A_y}{\Delta y}\frac{k_{rw}}{\mu_w B_w}. \quad \text{...................... (9.119)}$$

In arriving at Eq. 9.137, we let

$$\eta = (p_o - P_{cow}) \quad \text{........................ (9.139)}$$

$$\text{and } \xi^* = \beta_c k A \frac{k_{rw}}{\mu_w B_w}. \quad \text{........................ (9.140)}$$

This results in

$$\xi_x = \beta_c \frac{k_x A_x}{\Delta x}\frac{k_{rw}}{\mu_w B_w} = \mathrm{T}_{wx} \quad \text{.................. (9.141)}$$

$$\text{and } \xi_y = \beta_c \frac{k_y A_y}{\Delta y}\frac{k_{rw}}{\mu_w B_w} = \mathrm{T}_{wy}. \quad \text{.................. (9.115)}$$

Expanding the difference operators on the left side of Eqs. 9.135 and 9.137 using the definitions given by Eqs. 9.81 and 9.85 (with Subscript k discarded), using the definition of the time difference operator given by Eq. 9.56, and collecting terms results in the desired finite-difference approximations.

$$\mathrm{T}_{oy_{i,j-1/2}} p_{o_{i,j-1}} + \mathrm{T}_{ox_{i-1/2,j}} p_{o_{i-1,j}}$$

$$- \left(\mathrm{T}_{oy_{i,j-1/2}} + \mathrm{T}_{ox_{i-1/2,j}} + \mathrm{T}_{ox_{i+1/2,j}} + \mathrm{T}_{oy_{i,j+1/2}}\right) p_{o_{i,j}}$$

$$+ \mathrm{T}_{ox_{i+1/2,j}} p_{o_{i+1,j}} + \mathrm{T}_{oy_{i,j+1/2}} p_{o_{i,j+1}}$$

$$= \frac{V_{b_{i,j}}}{\alpha_c \Delta t}\left[\left(\frac{\phi S_o}{B_o}\right)_{i,j}^{n+1} - \left(\frac{\phi S_o}{B_o}\right)_{i,j}^{n}\right] - q_{osc_{i,j}} \quad \text{..... (9.142)}$$

$$\text{and } \mathrm{T}_{wy_{i,j-1/2}}\left(p_{o_{i,j-1}} - P_{cow_{i,j-1}}\right) + \mathrm{T}_{wx_{i-1/2,j}}\left(p_{o_{i-1,j}} - P_{cow_{i-1,j}}\right)$$

$$- \left(\mathrm{T}_{wy_{i,j-1/2}} + \mathrm{T}_{wx_{i-1/2,j}} + \mathrm{T}_{wx_{i+1/2,j}} + \mathrm{T}_{wy_{i,j+1/2}}\right)\left(p_{o_{i,j}} - P_{cow_{i,j}}\right)$$

$$+ \mathrm{T}_{wx_{i+1/2,j}}\left(p_{o_{i+1,j}} - P_{cow_{i+1,j}}\right) + \mathrm{T}_{wy_{i,j+1/2}}\left(p_{o_{i,j+1}} - P_{cow_{i,j+1}}\right)$$

$$= \frac{V_{b_{i,j}}}{\alpha_c \Delta t}\left\{\left[\frac{\phi(1-S_o)}{B_w}\right]_{i,j}^{n+1} - \left[\frac{\phi(1-S_o)}{B_w}\right]_{i,j}^{n}\right\} - q_{wsc_{i,j}}.$$

$$\text{.................... (9.143)}$$

Example 9.7. Write the finite-difference approximation in the $(p_g\text{-}S_g)$ formulation for the gas reservoir described in Example 9.2.

Solution. The flow equations for this two-phase, 1D gas reservoir with negligible capillary pressure were obtained in Example 9.2 as

$$\frac{\partial}{\partial x}\left[\beta_c k_x A_x \frac{k_{rw}}{\mu_w B_w}\left(\frac{\partial p_g}{\partial x} - \gamma_w \frac{\partial Z}{\partial x}\right)\right]\Delta x = \frac{V_b}{\alpha_c}\frac{\partial}{\partial t}\left(\frac{\phi S_w}{B_w}\right) - q_{wsc}$$

$$\text{.................... (9.144)}$$

for water, and

$$\frac{\partial}{\partial x}\left[\beta_c k_x A_x \frac{k_{rg}}{\mu_g B_g}\left(\frac{\partial p_g}{\partial x} - \gamma_g \frac{\partial Z}{\partial x}\right)\right]\Delta x = \frac{V_b}{\alpha_c}\frac{\partial}{\partial t}\left(\frac{\phi S_g}{B_g}\right) - q_{gsc}$$

$$\text{.................... (9.30)}$$

for gas. These equations may be expressed in a single form as

$$\frac{\partial}{\partial x}\left[\beta_c k_x A_x \frac{k_{rl}}{\mu_l B_l}\left(\frac{\partial p_g}{\partial x} - \gamma_l \frac{\partial Z}{\partial x}\right)\right]\Delta x = \frac{V_b}{\alpha_c}\frac{\partial}{\partial t}\left(\frac{\phi S_l}{B_l}\right) - q_{lsc},$$

$$\text{.................... (9.145)}$$

where $l = w$ or g.

The finite-difference approximation to Eq. 9.145 may be obtained by replacing the continuous-differential operators by their corresponding finite-difference operators. The result is the finite-difference equation at Gridpoint i expressed in compact form as

$$\Delta\left[\mathrm{T}_l(\Delta p_g - \gamma_l \Delta Z)\right]_i = \frac{V_{b_i}}{\alpha_c \Delta t}\Delta_t\left(\frac{\phi S_l}{B_l}\right)_i - q_{lsc_i}, \quad \text{.... (9.146)}$$

$$\Delta(\mathrm{T}_l\Delta p_g)_i - \Delta(\mathrm{T}_l\gamma_l\Delta Z)_i = \frac{V_{b_i}}{\alpha_c \Delta t}\Delta_t\left(\frac{\phi S_l}{B_l}\right)_i - q_{lsc_i},$$

$$\text{.................... (9.147)}$$

or $\Delta_x\left(T_{lx}\Delta_x p_g\right)_i - \Delta_x\left(T_{lx}\gamma_l\Delta_x Z\right)_i = \frac{V_{b_i}}{\alpha_c\Delta t}\Delta_t\left(\frac{\phi S_l}{B_l}\right)_i - q_{lsc_i},$ .... (9.148)

where $l = w$ and g. From Eq. 9.56, we have

$$\frac{V_{b_i}}{\alpha_c\Delta t}\Delta_t\left(\frac{\phi S_l}{B_l}\right)_i = \frac{V_{b_i}}{\alpha_c\Delta t}\left[\left(\frac{\phi S_l}{B_l}\right)_i^{n+1} - \left(\frac{\phi S_l}{B_l}\right)_i^n\right]. \quad (9.149)$$

Also from Eq. 9.81 (with Subscripts j and k discarded), we have the expansions

$$\Delta_x\left(T_{lx}\Delta_x p_g\right)_i = T_{lx_{i-1/2}}\left(p_{g_{i-1}} - p_{g_i}\right) + T_{lx_{i+1/2}}\left(p_{g_{i+1}} - p_{g_i}\right) \quad (9.150)$$

and $\Delta_x(T_{lx}\gamma_l\Delta_x Z)_i = (T_{lx}\gamma_l)_{i-1/2}(Z_{i-1} - Z_i)$

$$+ (T_{lx}\gamma_l)_{i+1/2}(Z_{i+1} - Z_i). \quad (9.151)$$

Substituting Eqs. 9.149 through 9.151 into Eq. 9.148 yields the following finite-difference approximation.

$$T_{lx_{i-1/2}}p_{g_{i-1}} - \left(T_{lx_{i-1/2}} + T_{lx_{i+1/2}}\right)p_{g_i} + T_{lx_{i+1/2}}p_{g_{i+1}} - (T_{lx}\gamma_l)_{i-1/2}(Z_{i-1} - Z_i) - (T_{lx}\gamma_l)_{i+1/2}(Z_{i+1} - Z_i)$$
$$= \frac{V_{b_i}}{\alpha_c\Delta t}\left[\left(\frac{\phi S_l}{B_l}\right)_i^{n+1} - \left(\frac{\phi S_l}{B_l}\right)_i^n\right] - q_{lsc_i}, \quad (9.152)$$

where $l = w$ and g.

Eq. 9.152 written for gas ($l = g$) becomes

$$T_{gx_{i-1/2}}p_{g_{i-1}} - \left(T_{gx_{i-1/2}} + T_{gx_{i+1/2}}\right)p_{g_i} + T_{gx_{i+1/2}}p_{g_{i+1}} - (T_{gx}\gamma_g)_{i-1/2}(Z_{i-1} - Z_i) - (T_{gx}\gamma_g)_{i+1/2}(Z_{i+1} - Z_i)$$
$$= \frac{V_{b_i}}{\alpha_c\Delta t}\left[\left(\frac{\phi S_g}{B_g}\right)_i^{n+1} - \left(\frac{\phi S_g}{B_g}\right)_i^n\right] - q_{gsc_i}, \quad (9.153)$$

which is expressed in terms of p_g and S_g.

Eq. 9.152 written for water ($l = w$) becomes

$$T_{wx_{i-1/2}}p_{g_{i-1}} - \left(T_{wx_{i-1/2}} + T_{wx_{i+1/2}}\right)p_{g_i} + T_{wx_{i+1/2}}p_{g_{i+1}} - (T_{wx}\gamma_w)_{i-1/2}(Z_{i-1} - Z_i) - (T_{wx}\gamma_w)_{i+1/2}(Z_{i+1} - Z_i)$$
$$= \frac{V_{b_i}}{\alpha_c\Delta t}\left[\left(\frac{\phi S_w}{B_w}\right)_i^{n+1} - \left(\frac{\phi S_w}{B_w}\right)_i^n\right] - q_{wsc_i}, \quad (9.154)$$

which may be expressed in terms of p_g and S_g if we set $S_w = 1 - S_g$.

$$T_{wx_{i-1/2}}p_{g_{i-1}} - \left(T_{wx_{i-1/2}} + T_{wx_{i+1/2}}\right)p_{g_i} + T_{wx_{i+1/2}}p_{g_{i+1}} - (T_{wx}\gamma_w)_{i-1/2}(Z_{i-1} - Z_i) - (T_{wx}\gamma_w)_{i+1/2}(Z_{i+1} - Z_i)$$
$$= \frac{V_{b_i}}{\alpha_c\Delta t}\left\{\left[\frac{\phi(1 - S_g)}{B_w}\right]_i^{n+1} - \left[\frac{\phi(1 - S_g)}{B_w}\right]_i^n\right\} - q_{wsc_i}. \quad (9.155)$$

Eqs. 9.153 and 9.155 are the desired finite-difference approximations for the flow equations in this gas reservoir.

Example 9.8. Demonstrate that the 1D finite-difference equation for oil,

$$\Delta_x\left[\beta_c\frac{k_x A_x}{\Delta x}\frac{k_{ro}}{\mu_o B_o}\left(\Delta_x p_o - \gamma_o\Delta_x Z\right)\right]_i = \frac{V_{b_i}}{\alpha_c\Delta t}\Delta_t\left[\frac{\phi(1 - S_w - S_g)}{B_o}\right]_i - q_{osc_i}, \quad (9.156)$$

is Eq. 9.6 in the x direction combined with Eqs. 9.10a, 9.13a, 9.14a, and 9.15a for $c = o$ and Eq. 2.25 for $l = o$.

Solution. Eq. 9.6 for $c = o$ in the x direction is

$$-\left[(\dot{m}_{ox}A_x)_{x+\Delta x/2} - (\dot{m}_{ox}A_x)_{x-\Delta x/2}\right]\Delta t + \left(q_{mt_o} + q_{m_o}\right)\Delta t = V_b\left[(m_{v_o})_{t+\Delta t} - (m_{v_o})_t\right]. \quad (9.157)$$

Eqs. 9.10a, 9.13a, 9.14a, and 9.15a for $c = o$ and Eq. 2.25 for $l = o$ are

$$\dot{m}_{ox} = \alpha_c\rho_o u_{ox}, \quad (9.158)$$

$$m_{v_o} = \phi\rho_o S_o, \quad (9.159)$$

$$q_{m_o} = \alpha_c\rho_o q_o, \quad (9.160)$$

$$q_{mt_o} = 0, \quad (9.161)$$

and $u_{ox} = -\beta_c\frac{k_x k_{ro}}{\mu_o}\left(\frac{\partial p_o}{\partial x} - \gamma_o\frac{\partial Z}{\partial x}\right),$ .... (9.162)

which, on substitution into Eq. 9.157, results in

$$\left\{\left[\beta_c\alpha_c k_x A_x\rho_o\frac{k_{ro}}{\mu_o}\left(\frac{\partial p_o}{\partial x} - \gamma_o\frac{\partial Z}{\partial x}\right)\right]_{x+\Delta x/2} - \left[\beta_c\alpha_c k_x A_x\rho_o\frac{k_{ro}}{\mu_o}\left(\frac{\partial p_o}{\partial x} - \gamma_o\frac{\partial Z}{\partial x}\right)\right]_{x-\Delta x/2}\right\}\Delta t$$
$$+ \left(0 + \alpha_c\rho_o q_o\right)\Delta t = V_b\left[(\phi\rho_o S_o)_{t+\Delta t} - (\phi\rho_o S_o)_t\right]. \quad (9.163)$$

Dividing Eq. 9.163 by $\alpha_c\rho_{osc}\Delta t$; substituting $\rho_o/\rho_{osc} = 1/B_o$, $q_o/B_o = q_{osc}$, and $S_o = 1 - S_w - S_g$; and letting $t = t^n$ and $t + \Delta t = t^{n+1}$ gives

$$\left\{\left[\beta_c A_x k_x\frac{k_{ro}}{\mu_o B_o}\left(\frac{\partial p_o}{\partial x} - \gamma_o\frac{\partial Z}{\partial x}\right)\right]_{x+\Delta x/2} - \left[\beta_c A_x k_x\frac{k_{ro}}{\mu_o B_o}\left(\frac{\partial p_o}{\partial x} - \gamma_o\frac{\partial Z}{\partial x}\right)\right]_{x-\Delta x/2}\right\}$$
$$= \frac{V_b}{\alpha_c\Delta t}\left\{\left[\frac{\phi(1 - S_w - S_g)}{B_o}\right]^{n+1} - \left[\frac{\phi(1 - S_w - S_g)}{B_o}\right]^n\right\} - q_{osc}. \quad (9.164)$$

With the central-difference approximation for the partial derivatives at $x + \Delta x/2$ and $x - \Delta x/2$, the terms on the left side of Eq. 9.164 may be approximated as

$$\left[\beta_c k_x A_x \frac{k_{ro}}{\mu_o B_o}\left(\frac{\partial p_o}{\partial x} - \gamma_o \frac{\partial Z}{\partial x}\right)\right]_{x+\Delta x/2}$$

$$\approx \left(\beta_c k_x A_x \frac{k_{ro}}{\mu_o B_o}\right)_{x+\Delta x/2}$$

$$\times \left[\left(\frac{p_{o_{i+1}} - p_{o_i}}{\Delta x_{i+½}}\right) - (\gamma_o)_{x+\Delta x/2}\left(\frac{Z_{i+1} - Z_i}{\Delta x_{i+½}}\right)\right]$$

$$= \left(\beta_c \frac{k_x A_x}{\Delta x_{i+½}} \frac{k_{ro}}{\mu_o B_o}\right)_{x+\Delta x/2}$$

$$\times \left[\left(p_{o_{i+1}} - p_{o_i}\right) - (\gamma_o)_{x+\Delta x/2}(Z_{i+1} - Z_i)\right] \quad \text{..... (9.165)}$$

and $$- \left[\beta_c k_x A_x \frac{k_{ro}}{\mu_o B_o}\left(\frac{\partial p_o}{\partial x} - \gamma_o \frac{\partial Z}{\partial x}\right)\right]_{x-\Delta x/2}$$

$$\approx -\left(\beta_c k_x A_x \frac{k_{ro}}{\mu_o B_o}\right)_{x-\Delta x/2}$$

$$\times \left[\left(\frac{p_{o_i} - p_{o_{i-1}}}{\Delta x_{i-½}}\right) - (\gamma_o)_{x-\Delta x/2}\left(\frac{Z_i - Z_{i-1}}{\Delta x_{i-½}}\right)\right]$$

$$= \left(\beta_c \frac{k_x A_x}{\Delta x_{i-½}} \frac{k_{ro}}{\mu_o B_o}\right)_{x-\Delta x/2}$$

$$\times \left[\left(p_{o_{i-1}} - p_{o_i}\right) - (\gamma_o)_{x-\Delta x/2}(Z_{i-1} - Z_i)\right], \quad \text{.... (9.166)}$$

where $\Delta x_{i+½}$ and $\Delta x_{i-½}$ are defined in Fig. 9.5.

Substituting Eqs. 9.165 and 9.166 into Eq. 9.164 and replacing $x \pm \Delta x/2$ with $i \pm ½$ gives

$$\left(\beta_c \frac{k_x A_x}{\Delta x} \frac{k_{ro}}{\mu_o B_o}\right)_{i+½} \left[\left(p_{o_{i+1}} - p_{o_i}\right) - \gamma_{o_{i+½}}(Z_{i+1} - Z_i)\right]$$

$$+ \left(\beta_c \frac{k_x A_x}{\Delta x} \frac{k_{ro}}{\mu_o B_o}\right)_{i-½} \left[\left(p_{o_{i-1}} - p_{o_i}\right) - \gamma_{o_{i-½}}(Z_{i-1} - Z_i)\right]$$

$$= \frac{V_b}{\alpha_c \Delta t}\left\{\left[\frac{\phi(1 - S_w - S_g)}{B_o}\right]^{n+1}\right.$$

$$\left. - \left[\frac{\phi(1 - S_w - S_g)}{B_o}\right]^n\right\} - q_{osc}. \quad \text{............ (9.167)}$$

The left side of Eq. 9.167 may be rearranged as

$$S_L = \left(\beta_c \frac{k_x A_x}{\Delta x} \frac{k_{ro}}{\mu_o B_o}\right)_{i+½} \left(p_{o_{i+1}} - p_{o_i}\right)$$

$$+ \left(\beta_c \frac{k_x A_x}{\Delta x} \frac{k_{ro}}{\mu_o B_o}\right)_{i-½} \left(p_{o_{i-1}} - p_{o_i}\right)$$

$$- \left(\beta_c \frac{k_x A_x}{\Delta x} \frac{k_{ro}\gamma_o}{\mu_o B_o}\right)_{i+½} (Z_{i+1} - Z_i)$$

$$- \left(\beta_c \frac{k_x A_x}{\Delta x} \frac{k_{ro}\gamma_o}{\mu_o B_o}\right)_{i-½} (Z_{i-1} - Z_i), \quad \text{.......... (9.168)}$$

which, with the aid of Eq. 9.81, can be expressed as

$$S_L = \Delta_x\left[\left(\beta_c \frac{k_x A_x}{\Delta x} \frac{k_{ro}}{\mu_o B_o}\right)_x \Delta_x p_o\right]_i$$

$$- \Delta_x\left[\left(\beta_c \frac{k_x A_x}{\Delta x} \frac{k_{ro}}{\mu_o B_o}\gamma_o\right)_x \Delta_x Z\right]_i$$

$$= \Delta_x\left[\left(\beta_c \frac{k_x A_x}{\Delta x} \frac{k_{ro}}{\mu_o B_o}\right)_x \left(\Delta_x p_o - \gamma_{ox}\Delta_x Z\right)\right]_i.$$

$$\text{.................. (9.169)}$$

The right side of Eq. 9.167, with the aid of Eq. 9.56, may be expressed as

$$S_R = \frac{V_b}{\alpha_c \Delta t}\Delta_t\left[\frac{\phi(1 - S_w - S_g)}{B_o}\right] - q_{osc}. \quad \text{........ (9.170)}$$

Note that it is implicit in Eq. 9.6 that expression given under Eq. 9.170 is for Point x or Gridpoint i. Therefore, Eq. 9.167 may be written as

$$\Delta_x\left[\left(\beta_c \frac{k_x A_x}{\Delta x} \frac{k_{ro}}{\mu_o B_o}\right)_x \left(\Delta_x p_o - \gamma_{ox}\Delta_x Z\right)\right]_i$$

$$= \frac{V_{b_i}}{\alpha_c \Delta t}\Delta_t\left[\frac{\phi(1 - S_w - S_g)}{B_o}\right]_i - q_{osc_i}, \quad \text{....... (9.156)}$$

which is the desired equation.

Discretization in Time. For time-dependent problems, the finite-difference approximation of the first-order derivative term in time is called discretization in time. Consider the differential operator in time, $(\partial/\partial t)(f)$ at Gridpoint (i,j,k). If we fix the space domain at a given point, the partial derivative with respect to time becomes an ordinary derivative evaluated at the given point.

$$\left[\frac{\partial}{\partial t}(f)\right]_{i,j,k} = \frac{\mathrm{d}}{\mathrm{d}t}\left(f_{i,j,k}\right). \quad \text{...................... (9.171)}$$

Eq. 9.171 may be approximated by a first-order finite-difference operator,

$$\frac{\mathrm{d}}{\mathrm{d}t}\left(f_{i,j,k}\right) \approx \frac{1}{\Delta t}\Delta_t\left(f_{i,j,k}\right), \quad \text{...................... (9.172)}$$

which is defined as

$$\frac{1}{\Delta t}\Delta_t\left(f_{i,j,k}\right) \equiv \frac{1}{\Delta t}\left(f^{n+1}_{i,j,k} - f^n_{i,j,k}\right). \quad \text{................ (9.173)}$$

Consider the finite-difference flow equation (Eq. 9.60) for oil as an example.

$$\Delta[\mathrm{T}_o(\Delta p_o - \gamma_o \Delta Z)] = \frac{V_b}{\alpha_c \Delta t}\Delta_t\left[\frac{\phi(1 - S_w - S_g)}{B_o}\right] - q_{osc}.$$

$$\text{.................... (9.60)}$$

Function f in Eq. 9.60 is $[\phi(1-S_w-S_g)]/B_o$. If every term on both sides of this equation is dated at Time Level n, the definition given by Eq. 9.173 represents a forward-difference (explicit) operator in time.

$$\Delta[\mathrm{T}_o(\Delta p_o - \gamma_o \Delta Z)]^n = \frac{V_b}{\alpha_c \Delta t}\left\{\left[\frac{\phi(1 - S_w - S_g)}{B_o}\right]^{n+1}\right.$$

$$-\left[\frac{\phi(1-S_w-S_g)}{B_o}\right]^n\Bigg\} - q_{osc}^n. \quad \text{............} \quad (9.174)$$

If, on the other hand, every term on both sides of Eq. 9.60 is dated at Time Level $n+1$, the definition given by Eq. 9.173 represents a backward-difference (implicit) operator in time.

$$\Delta\left[\mathrm{T}_o(\Delta p_o - \gamma_o\Delta Z)\right]^{n+1} = \frac{V_b}{\alpha_c\Delta t}\left\{\left[\frac{\phi(1-S_w-S_g)}{B_o}\right]^{n+1}\right.$$

$$-\left.\left[\frac{\phi(1-S_w-S_g)}{B_o}\right]^n\right\} - q_{osc}^{n+1}. \quad \text{...........} \quad (9.175)$$

The explicit finite-difference equations for all components in the black-oil model may now be written in a compact form.

For the oil equation,

$$\Delta[\mathrm{T}_o(\Delta p_o - \gamma_o\Delta Z)]^n = \frac{V_b}{\alpha_c\Delta t}\left\{\left[\frac{\phi(1-S_w-S_g)}{B_o}\right]^{n+1}\right.$$

$$-\left.\left[\frac{\phi(1-S_w-S_g)}{B_o}\right]^n\right\} - q_{osc}^n. \quad \text{............} \quad (9.174)$$

For the water equation,

$$\Delta[\mathrm{T}_w(\Delta p_o - \Delta P_{cow} - \gamma_w\Delta Z)]^n$$

$$= \frac{V_b}{\alpha_c\Delta t}\left[\left(\frac{\phi S_w}{B_w}\right)^{n+1} - \left(\frac{\phi S_w}{B_w}\right)^n\right] - q_{wsc}^n. \quad \text{.....} \quad (9.176)$$

For the gas equation,

$$\Delta\left[\mathrm{T}_g(\Delta p_o + \Delta P_{cgo} - \gamma_g\Delta Z)\right]^n + \Delta\left[\mathrm{T}_o R_s(\Delta p_o - \gamma_o\Delta Z)\right]^n$$

$$= \frac{V_b}{\alpha_c\Delta t}\left\{\left[\frac{\phi S_g}{B_g} + \frac{\phi R_s(1-S_w-S_g)}{B_o}\right]^{n+1}\right.$$

$$-\left.\left[\frac{\phi S_g}{B_g} + \frac{\phi R_s(1-S_w-S_g)}{B_o}\right]^n\right\} - q_{gsc}^n, \quad \text{....} \quad (9.178)$$

where q_{gsc}^n is defined by Eq. 9.20 evaluated at Time Level n.

These three equations, written for a gridblock, can be solved for the gridblock unknowns p_o^{n+1}, S_w^{n+1}, and S_g^{n+1} independently of the equations for other gridblocks. Because the flow equations for multiphase flow are strongly nonlinear, coupled equations, the explicit finite-difference approximation has severe stability limitations that render it inappropriate in most reservoir modeling situations.

The implicit finite-difference equations for all components in the black-oil model may also be written in a compact form.

For the oil equation,

$$\Delta[\mathrm{T}_o(\Delta p_o - \gamma_o\Delta Z)]^{n+1} = \frac{V_b}{\alpha_c\Delta t}\left\{\left[\frac{\phi(1-S_w-S_g)}{B_o}\right]^{n+1}\right.$$

$$-\left.\left[\frac{\phi(1-S_w-S_g)}{B_o}\right]^n\right\} - q_{osc}^{n+1}. \quad \text{...........} \quad (9.175)$$

For the water equation,

$$\Delta[\mathrm{T}_w(\Delta p_o - \Delta P_{cow} - \gamma_w\Delta Z)]^{n+1}$$

$$= \frac{V_b}{\alpha_c\Delta t}\left[\left(\frac{\phi S_w}{B_w}\right)^{n+1} - \left(\frac{\phi S_w}{B_w}\right)^n\right] - q_{wsc}^{n+1}. \quad \text{....} \quad (9.179)$$

For the gas equation,

$$\Delta\left[\mathrm{T}_g(\Delta p_o + \Delta P_{cgo} - \gamma_g\Delta Z)\right]^{n+1} + \Delta\left[\mathrm{T}_o R_s(\Delta p_o - \gamma_o\Delta Z)\right]^{n+1}$$

$$= \frac{V_b}{\alpha_c\Delta t}\left\{\left[\frac{\phi S_g}{B_g} + \frac{\phi R_s(1-S_w-S_g)}{B_o}\right]^{n+1}\right.$$

$$-\left.\left[\frac{\phi S_g}{B_g} + \frac{\phi R_s(1-S_w-S_g)}{B_o}\right]^n\right\} - q_{gsc}^{n+1},$$

$$\text{...................} \quad (9.180)$$

where q_{gsc}^{n+1} is defined by Eq. 9.20 evaluated at Time Level $n+1$.

Eqs. 9.175, 9.179, and 9.180 are unconditionally stable. Hence, the implicit, backward-in-time discretization is used almost exclusively in modeling black-oil reservoirs.

Expansion of Accumulation Terms. The expansion of an accumulation term is the process in which the time-difference operator, acting on a function, is expressed in terms of the difference of the unknowns to preserve mass conservation. An expansion scheme is described as conservative if the following identity is satisfied.

$$\Delta_t f = f^{n+1} - f^n. \quad \text{..........................} \quad (9.181)$$

The use of nonconservative schemes in finite-difference equations does not necessarily produce meaningless results. However, for strongly nonlinear differential equations, such as those encountered in multiphase flow, it may induce instability in addition to producing large material-balance errors.[3] Therefore, this book is concerned with conservative expansion schemes of accumulation terms.

The time difference of functions encountered in multiphase-flow equations are $\Delta_t[(\phi S_l)/B_l]$ for $l=o$, w, or g and $\Delta_t[(\phi R_s S_o)/B_o]$, where $S_o = 1 - S_w - S_g$. For single-phase flow, the time difference of a function can be either $\Delta_t(1/B)$ or $\Delta_t(\phi/B)$. That is, the function f is made of one variable $(1/B)$ or the product of two variables $(\phi, 1/B)$, three variables $(\phi, 1/B_l, S_l)$, or four variables $(\phi, 1/B_o, R_s, S_o)$. The function f may, in general, be expressed as

$$f = UVXY, \quad \text{..............................} \quad (9.182)$$

where $U \equiv \phi$, $V \equiv 1/B_l$, $X \equiv R_s$, and $Y \equiv S_l$. For a three-variable function $f = (\phi S_l)/B_l$, we set $X=1$; for a two-variable function $f = (\phi/B)$, we set $X=Y=1$; and for a one-variable function $f = (1/B)$, we set $U=X=Y=1$.

Substituting Eq. 9.182 into Eq. 9.181 yields the general form for the time difference of a function,

$$\Delta_t(UVXY) = (UVXY)^{n+1} - (UVXY)^n, \quad \text{.........} \quad (9.183)$$

from which we derive the following conservative expansion formula (see Example 9.9).

$$\Delta_t(UVXY) = (VXY)^n\Delta_t U + U^{n+1}(XY)^n\Delta_t V$$

$$+ (UV)^{n+1}Y^n\Delta_t X + (UVX)^{n+1}\Delta_t Y.$$

$$\text{...................} \quad (9.184)$$

The final step in the expansion of the accumulation terms is to express the time difference of U, V, X, and Y ($\Delta_t U$, $\Delta_t V$, $\Delta_t X$, and $\Delta_t Y$) on the right side of Eq. 9.184 in terms of the time difference of the unknowns: $\Delta_t p_o$, $\Delta_t S_w$, and $\Delta_t S_g$. To preserve the conservative property of the expansion given by Eq. 9.184, $\Delta_t U$, $\Delta_t V$, $\Delta_t X$, and $\Delta_t Y$ must be expressed as the product of the chord slope between successive time levels (n and $n+1$) and the time difference of the unknowns. That is,

$$\Delta_t U \equiv \Delta_t \phi = \phi' \Delta_t p_o \quad \text{(9.185)}$$

$$\text{and } \Delta_t V \equiv \Delta_t\left(\frac{1}{B_l}\right) = \left(\frac{1}{B_l}\right)' \Delta_t p_o, \quad \text{(9.186)}$$

where $l = o$, w, or g,

$$\text{and } \Delta_t X \equiv \Delta_t R_s = R_s' \Delta_t p_o \quad \text{(9.187)}$$

$$\text{and } \Delta_t Y \equiv \Delta_t S_l, \quad \text{(9.188a)}$$

where $l = w$ or g,

$$\text{and } \Delta_t Y \equiv \Delta_t S_l = -\Delta_t S_w - \Delta_t S_g, \quad \text{(9.188b)}$$

where $l = o$ and where ϕ', R_s', and $(1/B_l)'$ are defined as chord slopes so that $\Delta_t \phi$, $\Delta_t R_s$, and $\Delta_t (1/B_l)$ are exact. That is,

$$\phi' = \frac{(\phi^{n+1} - \phi^n)}{(p_o^{n+1} - p_o^n)}, \quad \text{(9.189)}$$

$$R_s' = \frac{(R_s^{n+1} - R_s^n)}{(p_o^{n+1} - p_o^n)}, \quad \text{(9.190)}$$

$$\text{and } \left(\frac{1}{B_l}\right)' = \frac{(1/B_l^{n+1}) - (1/B_l^n)}{(p_o^{n+1} - p_o^n)}, \quad \text{(9.191)}$$

where $l = o$, w, or g.

Applying this conservative expansion scheme for $\Delta_t[(\phi S_l)/B_l]$ for $l = o$, w, or g and $\Delta_t[(\phi R_s S_o)/B_o]$ found in Eqs. 9.60 through 9.62, we obtain

$$\Delta_t\left(\frac{\phi S_l}{B_l}\right) = \left[\frac{\phi'}{B_l^n} + \phi^{n+1}\left(\frac{1}{B_l}\right)'\right] S_l^n \Delta_t p_o + \left(\frac{\phi}{B_l}\right)^{n+1} \Delta_t S_l \quad \text{(9.192)}$$

$$\text{and } \Delta_t\left(\frac{\phi R_s S_o}{B_o}\right) = \left\{\left[\frac{\phi'}{B_o^n} + \phi^{n+1}\left(\frac{1}{B_l}\right)'\right] R_s^n + \left(\frac{\phi}{B_o}\right)^{n+1} R_s'\right\} \times S_o^n \Delta_t p_o + \left(\frac{\phi}{B_o}\right)^{n+1} R_s^{n+1} \Delta_t S_o. \quad \text{(9.193)}$$

But in the (p_o-S_w-S_g) formulation, $S_o = 1 - S_w - S_g$ and $\Delta_t S_o = -\Delta_t S_w - \Delta_t S_g$ as given earlier; therefore, $\Delta_t[(\phi S_o)/B_o]$ and $\Delta_t[(\phi R_s S_o)/B_o]$ may be expressed as

$$\Delta_t\left[\frac{\phi(1 - S_w - S_g)}{B_o}\right] = \left[\frac{\phi'}{B_o^n} + \phi^{n+1}\left(\frac{1}{B_o}\right)'\right](1 - S_w^n - S_g^n) \times \Delta_t p_o - \left(\frac{\phi}{B_o}\right)^{n+1} \Delta_t S_w - \left(\frac{\phi}{B_o}\right)^{n+1} \Delta_t S_g \quad \text{(9.194)}$$

$$\text{and } \Delta_t\left[\frac{\phi R_s(1 - S_w - S_g)}{B_o}\right] = \left\{\left[\frac{\phi'}{B_o^n} + \phi^{n+1}\left(\frac{1}{B_o}\right)'\right] R_s^n + \left(\frac{\phi}{B_o}\right)^{n+1} R_s'\right\}(1 - S_w^n - S_g^n)\Delta_t p_o - \left(\frac{\phi}{B_o}\right)^{n+1} R_s^{n+1} \Delta_t S_w - \left(\frac{\phi}{B_o}\right)^{n+1} R_s^{n+1} \Delta_t S_g. \quad \text{(9.195)}$$

All functions dated at Time Level $n+1$ (ϕ^{n+1}, B_l^{n+1}, R_s^{n+1}, p_o^{n+1}) in Eqs. 9.189 through 9.195 are approximated by their values at Time Level $n+1$ but at Iteration Level ν.

The expansions provided by Eq. 9.184 and Eqs. 9.192 through 9.195 are not the only conservative expansions, but experience indicates that they may promote slightly faster convergence during iterations because they keep unknowns associated with strong nonlinearities at Time Level n.

Example 9.9. Derive the conservative-expansion formula for the time difference of function ($UVXY$) as expressed by Eq. 9.184. Determine whether there are other conservative expansions of $\Delta_t(UVXY)$ and, if so, how many.

Solution. Eq. 9.183 gives the time difference of ($UVXY$) as

$$\Delta_t(UVXY) = (UVXY)^{n+1} - (UVXY)^n. \quad \text{(9.183)}$$

Eq. 9.183 satisfies the conservation property expressed by Eq. 9.181. To preserve this property, we may add and subtract the term $(UVX)^{n+1}Y^n$ from the right side of this equation, then collect and factor terms as

$$\begin{aligned}\Delta_t(UVXY) &= (UVXY)^{n+1} + \left[-(UVX)^{n+1}Y^n + (UVX)^{n+1}Y^n\right] - (UVXY)^n \\ &= \left[(UVXY)^{n+1} - (UVX)^{n+1}Y^n\right] + \left[(UVX)^{n+1}Y^n - (UVXY)^n\right] \\ &= \left[(UVX)^{n+1}(Y^{n+1} - Y^n)\right] + Y^n\left[(UVX)^{n+1} - (UVX)^n\right] \\ &= (UVX)^{n+1}\Delta_t Y + Y^n \Delta_t(UVX) \quad \text{(9.196)}\end{aligned}$$

$$\text{where } \Delta_t Y = Y^{n+1} - Y^n \quad \text{(9.197)}$$

$$\text{and } \Delta_t(UVX) = (UVX)^{n+1} - (UVX)^n. \quad \text{(9.198)}$$

The next step is to expand $\Delta_t(UVX)$ so that Eq. 9.198 is preserved. To accomplish this, we add and subtract the term $(UV)^{n+1}X^n$ and proceed as earlier. That is,

$$\begin{aligned}\Delta_t(UVX) &= (UVX)^{n+1} + \left[-(UV)^{n+1}X^n + (UV)^{n+1}X^n\right] - (UVX)^n \\ &= \left[(UVX)^{n+1} - (UV)^{n+1}X^n\right] + \left[(UV)^{n+1}X^n - (UVX)^n\right] \\ &= \left[(UV)^{n+1}(X^{n+1} - X^n)\right] + X^n\left[(UV)^{n+1} - (UV)^n\right] \quad \text{(9.199a)}\end{aligned}$$

$$\text{or } \Delta_t(UVX) = (UV)^{n+1}\Delta_t X + X^n \Delta_t(UV), \quad \text{(9.199b)}$$

$$\text{where } \Delta_t X = X^{n+1} - X^n \quad \text{(9.200)}$$

$$\text{and } \Delta_t(UV) = (UV)^{n+1} - (UV)^n. \quad \text{(9.201)}$$

The identity expressed by Eq. 9.201 may now be expanded as before with the term $U^{n+1}V^n$ added and subtracted. That is,

$$\begin{aligned}\Delta_t(UV) &= (UV)^{n+1} + \left(-U^{n+1}V^n + U^{n+1}V^n\right) - (UV)^n \\ &= \left[(UV)^{n+1} - U^{n+1}V^n\right] + \left[U^{n+1}V^n - (UV)^n\right]\end{aligned}$$

$$= \left[U^{n+1}\left(V^{n+1} - V^n\right)\right] + \left[V^n\left(U^{n+1} - U^n\right)\right] \quad \text{(9.202a)}$$

$$\text{or } \Delta_t(UV) = U^{n+1}\Delta_t V + V^n\Delta_t U, \quad \text{(9.202b)}$$

$$\text{where } \Delta_t V = V^{n+1} - V^n \quad \text{(9.203)}$$

$$\text{and } \Delta_t U = U^{n+1} - U^n. \quad \text{(9.204)}$$

Substituting Eq. 9.202b into Eq. 9.199b and rearranging yields

$$\Delta_t(UVX) = (VX)^n\Delta_t U + U^{n+1}X^n\Delta_t V + (UV)^{n+1}\Delta_t X, \quad \text{(9.205)}$$

which, when substituted into Eq. 9.196, results in the conservative expansion

$$\begin{aligned}\Delta_t(UVXY) &= (UVX)^{n+1}\Delta_t Y \\ &+ Y^n\left[(VX)^n\Delta_t U + U^{n+1}X^n\Delta_t V + (UV)^{n+1}\Delta_t X\right] \\ &= (UVX)^{n+1}\Delta_t Y + Y^n(VX)^n\Delta_t U + Y^nU^{n+1}X^n\Delta_t V \\ &+ Y^n(UV)^{n+1}\Delta_t X \\ &= (UVX)^{n+1}\Delta_t Y + (VXY)^n\Delta_t U + U^{n+1}(XY)^n\Delta_t V \\ &+ (UV)^{n+1}Y^n\Delta_t X \quad \text{(9.206)}\end{aligned}$$

$$\begin{aligned}\text{or } \Delta_t(UVXY) &= (VXY)^n\Delta_t U + U^{n+1}(XY)^n\Delta_t V \\ &+ (UV)^{n+1}Y^n\Delta_t X + (UVX)^{n+1}\Delta_t Y, \quad \text{(9.184)}\end{aligned}$$

which is the equation reported earlier.

To answer the second part of this problem, we may derive two different conservative expansions for $\Delta_t(UV)$, one of which is given as Eq. 9.202b. These are

$$\Delta_t(UV) = U^{n+1}\Delta_t V + V^n\Delta_t U \quad \text{(9.202b)}$$

$$\text{and } \Delta_t(UV) = \Delta_t(VU) = V^{n+1}\Delta_t U + U^n\Delta_t V. \quad \text{(9.207)}$$

For the expansion of $\Delta_t(UVX)$, there are six different conservative expansions, one of which is given as Eq. 9.205. These expansions are

$$\Delta_t(UVX) = V^nX^n\Delta_t U + U^{n+1}X^n\Delta_t V + U^{n+1}V^{n+1}\Delta_t X, \quad \text{(9.205)}$$

$$\Delta_t(UVX) = \Delta_t(VUX) = V^{n+1}X^n\Delta_t U + U^nX^n\Delta_t V + V^{n+1}U^{n+1}\Delta_t X, \quad \text{(9.208)}$$

$$\Delta_t(UVX) = \Delta_t(UXV) = X^nV^n\Delta_t U + U^{n+1}X^{n+1}\Delta_t V + U^{n+1}V^n\Delta_t X, \quad \text{(9.209)}$$

$$\Delta_t(UVX) = \Delta_t(XUV) = X^{n+1}V^n\Delta_t U + X^{n+1}U^{n+1}\Delta_t V + U^nV^n\Delta_t X, \quad \text{(9.210)}$$

$$\Delta_t(UVX) = \Delta_t(XVU) = X^{n+1}V^{n+1}\Delta_t U + X^{n+1}U^n\Delta_t V + V^nU^n\Delta_t X, \quad \text{(9.211)}$$

$$\text{and } \Delta_t(UVX) = \Delta_t(VXU) = X^{n+1}V^{n+1}\Delta_t U + X^nU^n\Delta_t V + V^{n+1}U^n\Delta_t X. \quad \text{(9.212)}$$

In summary, there are two (2!) possible conservative expansions for $\Delta_t(UV)$ and six (3!) possible conservative expansions for $\Delta_t(UVX)$. The number of possible conservative expansions for a time difference of a function is equal to $N!$ where N is the number of variables in the function. Therefore, there are 24 (or 4!) possible conservative expansions for $\Delta_t(UVXY)$.

Example 9.10. Obtain the conservative expansion for $\Delta_t[(\phi S_w)/B_w]$ expressed by Eq. 9.192 for $l = w$ using the general conservative-expansion formula given by Eq. 9.184.

Solution. The general conservative expansion formula is

$$\begin{aligned}\Delta_t(UVXY) &= (VXY)^n\Delta_t U + U^{n+1}(XY)^n\Delta_t V \\ &+ (UV)^{n+1}Y^n\Delta_t X + (UVX)^{n+1}\Delta_t Y, \quad \text{(9.184)}\end{aligned}$$

where $f = UVXY$, $U \equiv \phi$, $V \equiv 1/B_l$, $X \equiv R_s$, and $Y = S_l$.

Following the procedure for a conservative expansion of $\Delta_t[(\phi S_w)/B_w]$, we let $f = (\phi S_w)/B_w = UVY$. Setting $X = 1$ reduces Eq. 9.184 to

$$\begin{aligned}\Delta_t(UVY) &= (VY)^n\Delta_t U + U^{n+1}Y^n\Delta_t V \\ &+ (UV)^{n+1}Y^n\Delta_t(1) + (UV)^{n+1}\Delta_t Y. \quad \text{(9.213)}\end{aligned}$$

Observing that $\Delta_t(1) = 0$,

$$\begin{aligned}\Delta_t(UVY) &= (VY)^n\Delta_t U + U^{n+1}Y^n\Delta_t V \\ &+ (UV)^{n+1}\Delta_t Y. \quad \text{(9.214)}\end{aligned}$$

Substituting the definitions of U, V, and Y into Eq. 9.214 yields

$$\begin{aligned}\Delta_t\left[\phi\left(\frac{1}{B_w}\right)S_w\right] &= \left(\frac{S_w}{B_w}\right)^n\Delta_t\phi + \phi^{n+1}S_w^n\Delta_t\left(\frac{1}{B_w}\right) \\ &+ \left(\frac{\phi}{B_w}\right)^{n+1}\Delta_t S_w. \quad \text{(9.215)}\end{aligned}$$

The time difference of functions ϕ and $(1/B_w)$ must be expressed as

$$\Delta_t\phi = \phi'\Delta_t p_o \quad \text{(9.216)}$$

$$\text{and } \Delta_t\left(\frac{1}{B_w}\right) = \left(\frac{1}{B_w}\right)'\Delta_t p_o. \quad \text{(9.217)}$$

where ϕ' and $(1/B_w)'$ are chord slopes given by Eqs. 9.189 and 9.191, respectively. Substituting $\Delta_t\phi$ and $\Delta_t(1/B_w)$ into Eq. 9.215 gives

$$\begin{aligned}\Delta_t\left(\frac{\phi S_w}{B_w}\right) &= \left(\frac{S_w}{B_w}\right)^n\phi'\Delta_t p_o + \phi^{n+1}S_w^n\left(\frac{1}{B_w}\right)'\Delta_t p_o \\ &+ \left(\frac{\phi}{B_w}\right)^{n+1}\Delta_t S_w \quad \text{(9.218)}\end{aligned}$$

or, after factorization,

$$\Delta_t\left(\frac{\phi S_w}{B_w}\right) = \left[\frac{\phi'}{B_w^n} + \phi^{n+1}\left(\frac{1}{B_w}\right)'\right]S_w^n\Delta_t p_o + \left(\frac{\phi}{B_w}\right)^{n+1}\Delta_t S_w, \quad \text{(9.219)}$$

which is Eq. 9.192 for $l = w$.

Example 9.11. Given the finite-difference flow equations for oil and water of Example 9.6 and using the (p_o-S_o) formulation, write the conservative expansions for $\Delta_t[(\phi S_o)/B_o]$ and $\Delta_t[\phi(1 - S_o)/B_w]$.

Solution. Eq. 9.192 is a conservative expansion of $\Delta_t[(\phi S_l)/B_l]$ in terms p_o and S_l.

$$\begin{aligned}\Delta_t\left(\frac{\phi S_l}{B_l}\right) &= \left[\frac{\phi'}{B_l^n} + \phi^{n+1}\left(\frac{1}{B_l}\right)'\right]S_l^n\Delta_t p_o \\ &+ \left(\frac{\phi}{B_l}\right)^{n+1}\Delta_t S_l. \quad \text{(9.192)}\end{aligned}$$

where $l=o$, w, or g. For $l=o$, Eq. 9.192 becomes

$$\Delta_t\left(\frac{\phi S_o}{B_o}\right) = \left[\frac{\phi'}{B_o^n} + \phi^{n+1}\left(\frac{1}{B_o}\right)'\right]S_o^n\Delta_t p_o + \left(\frac{\phi}{B_o}\right)^{n+1}\Delta_t S_o. \quad (9.220)$$

For $l=w$, Eq. 9.192 becomes

$$\Delta_t\left(\frac{\phi S_w}{B_w}\right) = \left[\frac{\phi'}{B_w^n} + \phi^{n+1}\left(\frac{1}{B_w}\right)'\right]S_w^n\Delta_t p_o + \left(\frac{\phi}{B_w}\right)^{n+1}\Delta_t S_w. \quad (9.219)$$

For the (p_o,-S_o) formulation, we express S_w in Eq. 9.219 in terms of S_o.

$$S_w = 1 - S_o \quad (9.221)$$

and $\Delta_t S_w = -\Delta_t S_o$, ... (9.222)

which on substitution into Eq. 9.219 results in

$$\Delta_t\left[\frac{\phi(1-S_o)}{B_w}\right] = \left[\frac{\phi'}{B_w^n} + \phi^{n+1}\left(\frac{1}{B_w}\right)'\right](1-S_o^n)\Delta_t p_o - \left(\frac{\phi}{B_w}\right)^{n+1}\Delta_t S_o. \quad (9.223)$$

Both $\Delta_t\,[(\phi S_o)/B_o]$ and $\Delta_t\,[\phi(1-S_o)/B_w]$are now expressed in terms of p_o and S_o in Eqs. 9.220 and 9.223.

Finite-Difference Equations. We can now present the implicit (backward) finite-difference equations for the black-oil model, Eqs. 9.175, 9.178, and 9.180, in a compact form.

$$\Delta[\mathrm{T}_o(\Delta p_o - \gamma_o\Delta Z)]^{n+1} = C_{op}\Delta_t p_o + C_{ow}\Delta_t S_w + C_{og}\Delta_t S_g - q_{osc}^{n+1}, \quad (9.224)$$

$$\Delta\left[\mathrm{T}_w(\Delta p_o - \Delta P_{cow} - \gamma_w\Delta Z)\right]^{n+1} = C_{wp}\Delta_t p_o + C_{ww}\Delta_t S_w + C_{wg}\Delta_t S_g - q_{wsc}^{n+1}, \quad (9.225)$$

and
$$\Delta\left[\mathrm{T}_g(\Delta p_o + \Delta P_{cgo} - \gamma_g\Delta Z)\right]^{n+1} + \Delta\left[\mathrm{T}_o R_s(\Delta p_o - \gamma_o\Delta Z)\right]^{n+1} = C_{gp}\Delta_t p_o + C_{gw}\Delta_t S_w + C_{gg}\Delta_t S_g - q_{gsc}^{n+1}, \quad (9.226)$$

where
$$q_{gsc}^{n+1} = \left(q_{fgsc}^{n+1} + R_s^{n+1}q_{osc}^{n+1}\right). \quad (9.227)$$

These equations were developed with the following steps.

1. Discretize the second-order partial-derivative terms with respect to the spatial variables.
2. Discretize the first-order partial-derivative terms with respect to time with the backward-difference approximation.
3. Expand the time-difference terms with a conservative expansion scheme.

The finite-difference space operators, depending on the dimensionality of the problem, are defined by Eq. 9.96 for 3D flow; Eq. 9.99, 9.100, or 9.101 for 2D flow; and Eq. 9.102, 9.103, or 9.104 for 1D flow where the finite-difference space operators in the x, y, and z directions are defined by Eqs. 9.81, 9.85, and 9.91, respectively. The coefficients C_{lu} (where $l=o$, w or g and $u=p_o$, S_w, or S_g) are obtained from Eq. 9.192 for $l=w$, from Eq. 9.194 for $l=o$, and from both Eqs. 9.192 for $l=g$ and 9.195.

$$C_{op} = \frac{V_b}{\alpha_c\Delta t}\left[\frac{\phi'}{B_o^n} + \phi^{n+1}\left(\frac{1}{B_o}\right)'\right]\left(1 - S_w^n - S_g^n\right). \quad (9.228)$$

$$C_{ow} = -\frac{V_b}{\alpha_c\Delta t}\left(\frac{\phi}{B_o}\right)^{n+1}. \quad (9.229)$$

$$C_{og} = -\frac{V_b}{\alpha_c\Delta t}\left(\frac{\phi}{B_o}\right)^{n+1}. \quad (9.230)$$

$$C_{wp} = \frac{V_b}{\alpha_c\Delta t}\left[\frac{\phi'}{B_w^n} + \phi^{n+1}\left(\frac{1}{B_w}\right)'\right]S_w^n. \quad (9.231)$$

$$C_{ww} = \frac{V_b}{\alpha_c\Delta t}\left(\frac{\phi}{B_w}\right)^{n+1}. \quad (9.232)$$

$$C_{wg} = 0. \quad (9.233)$$

$$C_{gp} = \frac{V_b}{\alpha_c\Delta t}\left(\left\{\left[\frac{\phi'}{B_o^n} + \phi^{n+1}\left(\frac{1}{B_o}\right)'\right]R_s^n + \left(\frac{\phi}{B_o}\right)^{n+1}R_s'\right\} \times \left(1 - S_w^n - S_g^n\right) + \left[\frac{\phi'}{B_g^n} + \phi^{n+1}\left(\frac{1}{B_g}\right)'\right]S_g^n\right). \quad (9.234)$$

$$C_{gw} = -\frac{V_b}{\alpha_c\Delta t}\left[\left(\frac{\phi}{B_o}\right)^{n+1}R_s^{n+1}\right]. \quad (9.235)$$

$$C_{gg} = \frac{V_b}{\alpha_c\Delta t}\left[\left(\frac{\phi}{B_g}\right)^{n+1} - \left(\frac{\phi}{B_o}\right)^{n+1}R_s^{n+1}\right]. \quad (9.236)$$

The derivatives ϕ', R_s', and $(1/B_l)'$ are the chord slopes defined by Eqs. 9.189, 9.190, and 9.191, respectively.

$$\phi' = \frac{(\phi^{n+1} - \phi^n)}{(p_o^{n+1} - p_o^n)}, \quad (9.189)$$

$$R_s' = \frac{(R_s^{n+1} - R_s^n)}{(p_o^{n+1} - p_o^n)}, \quad (9.190)$$

and
$$\left(\frac{1}{B_l}\right)' = \frac{\left[(1/B_l^{n+1}) - (1/B_l^n)\right]}{(p_o^{n+1} - p_o^n)}, \quad (9.191)$$

where $l=o$, w, or g.

The implicit-finite-difference equations for two-phase oil/water-, oil/gas-, and water/gas-flow models are subsets of the black-oil model presented in this section. Secs. 9.3 and 9.4 discuss reducing the three-phase-flow model to two-phase-flow models.

Example 9.12. Write the implicit finite-difference equations for two-phase flow of oil and water in 1D horizontal reservoir. Assume negligible capillary forces.

Solution. The implicit finite-difference equations for oil and water flow in this reservoir may be obtained from the difference equations for black-oil model.

To model the flow of oil and water, consider Eqs. 9.224 and 9.225 only. In these two equations, $S_g=0$ and $\Delta_t S_g=0$. For negligible capillary forces, $P_{cow}=0$. For a horizontal reservoir, the gravity terms can be dropped (set $\Delta Z=0$). For 1D flow in the x direction, we use the resulting equations with Subscript i only. Consequently, Eqs. 9.224 and 9.225 reduce to

$$\Delta(\mathrm{T}_o\Delta p_o)_i^{n+1} = \left(C_{op}\Delta_t p_o + C_{ow}\Delta_t S_w - q_{osc}^{n+1}\right)_i \quad (9.237)$$

and
$$\Delta(\mathrm{T}_w\Delta p_o)_i^{n+1} = \left(C_{wp}\Delta_t p_o + C_{ww}\Delta_t S_w - q_{wsc}^{n+1}\right)_i, \quad (9.238)$$

where C_{op}, C_{ow}, C_{wp}, and C_{ww} are obtained from Eqs. 9.228, 9.229, 9.231, and 9.232 with $S_g=0$ as

$$C_{op} = \frac{V_b}{\alpha_c \Delta t}\left[\frac{\phi'}{B_o^n} + \phi^{n+1}\left(\frac{1}{B_o}\right)'\right](1 - S_w^n), \quad \ldots\ldots\ (9.239)$$

$$C_{ow} = -\frac{V_b}{\alpha_c \Delta t}\left(\frac{\phi}{B_o}\right)^{n+1}, \quad \ldots\ldots\ (9.229)$$

$$C_{wp} = \frac{V_b}{\alpha_c \Delta t}\left[\frac{\phi'}{B_w^n} + \phi^{n+1}\left(\frac{1}{B_w}\right)'\right]S_w^n, \quad \ldots\ldots\ (9.231)$$

and $$C_{ww} = \frac{V_b}{\alpha_c \Delta t}\left(\frac{\phi}{B_w}\right)^{n+1}, \quad \ldots\ldots\ (9.232)$$

where ϕ' and $(1/B_l)'$ for $l=o$ or w are expressed by Eqs. 9.189 and 9.191.

With the definitions given by Eq. 9.102 for $\Delta(\mathrm{T}_l\Delta p_o)_i$ and by Eq. 9.81 for $\Delta_x(\mathrm{T}_{lx}\Delta_x p_o)_i$ where Subscripts j and k are dropped, we may write

$$\Delta(\mathrm{T}_l\Delta p_o)_i \equiv \Delta_x(\mathrm{T}_{lx}\Delta_x p_o)_i \quad \ldots\ldots\ (9.240)$$

and $$\Delta_x(\mathrm{T}_{lx}\Delta_x p_o)_i = \mathrm{T}_{lx_{i-1/2}}\left(p_{o_{i-1}} - p_{o_i}\right) + \mathrm{T}_{lx_{i+1/2}}\left(p_{o_{i+1}} - p_{o_i}\right), \quad \ldots\ldots\ (9.241)$$

or $$\Delta(\mathrm{T}_l\Delta p_o)_i = \mathrm{T}_{lx_{i-1/2}}p_{o_{i-1}} - \left(\mathrm{T}_{lx_{i-1/2}} + \mathrm{T}_{lx_{i+1/2}}\right)p_{o_i} + \mathrm{T}_{lx_{i+1/2}}p_{o_{i+1}}, \quad \ldots\ldots\ (9.242)$$

where $l=o$ or w and T_{lx} is defined by Eq. 9.63 as

$$\mathrm{T}_{lx_{i\pm1/2}} = \beta_c\left(\frac{k_x A_x}{\Delta x}\right)_{i\pm1/2}\left(\frac{k_{rl}}{\mu_l B_l}\right)_{i\pm1/2}, \quad \ldots\ldots\ (9.243)$$

where $l=o$ or w.

Substituting Eq. 9.242 into Eqs. 9.237 and 9.238 and using $\Delta_t p_o = p_o^{n+1} - p_o^n$ and $\Delta_t S_w = S_w^{n+1} - S_w^n$ yields

$$\mathrm{T}_{ox_{i-1/2}}^{n+1}p_{o_{i-1}}^{n+1} - \left(\mathrm{T}_{ox_{i-1/2}}^{n+1} + \mathrm{T}_{ox_{i+1/2}}^{n+1}\right)p_{o_i}^{n+1} + \mathrm{T}_{ox_{i+1/2}}^{n+1}p_{o_{i+1}}^{n+1} = C_{op_i}\left(p_{o_i}^{n+1} - p_{o_i}^n\right) + C_{ow_i}\left(S_{w_i}^{n+1} - S_{w_i}^n\right) - q_{osc_i}^{n+1} \quad \ldots\ldots\ (9.244)$$

and $$\mathrm{T}_{wx_{i-1/2}}^{n+1}p_{o_{i-1}}^{n+1} - \left(\mathrm{T}_{wx_{i-1/2}}^{n+1} + \mathrm{T}_{wx_{i+1/2}}^{n+1}\right)p_{o_i}^{n+1} + \mathrm{T}_{wx_{i+1/2}}^{n+1}p_{o_{i+1}}^{n+1} = C_{wp_i}\left(p_{o_i}^{n+1} - p_{o_i}^n\right) + C_{ww_i}\left(S_{w_i}^{n+1} - S_{w_i}^n\right) - q_{wsc_i}^{n+1}. \quad \ldots\ldots\ (9.245)$$

Eqs. 9.244 and 9.245 are written for each Gridblock i in the 1D reservoir.

Example 9.13. If capillary forces are important for the flow problem described in Example 9.12, write the implicit finite-difference equations for both oil and water.

Solution. With the argument presented in Example 9.12 and in light of the importance of capillary forces, the black-oil-model finite-difference equations reduce to

$$\Delta(\mathrm{T}_o\Delta p_o)_i^{n+1} = \left(C_{op}\Delta_t p_o + C_{ow}\Delta_t S_w - q_{osc}^{n+1}\right)_i \quad \ldots\ldots\ (9.237)$$

and $$\Delta[\mathrm{T}_w(\Delta p_o - \Delta P_{cow})]_i^{n+1} = \left(C_{wp}\Delta_t p_o + C_{ww}\Delta_t S_w - q_{wsc}^{n+1}\right)_i. \quad \ldots\ldots\ (9.246)$$

Comparing these two equations with those in Example 9.12, we conclude that the oil equation, Eq. 9.237, is the same, and only the left side of the water equation is different. Specifically, the space operator $\Delta(\mathrm{T}_w\Delta p_o)_i^{n+1}$ is replaced by $\Delta[\mathrm{T}_w(\Delta p_o - \Delta P_{cow})]_i^{n+1}$; therefore, we consider only the expansion of the space operator $\Delta[\mathrm{T}_w(\Delta p_o - \Delta P_{cow})]_i^{n+1}$. Because of the linear nature of the Δ operator, the left side of Eq. 9.246 can be expanded as

$$\Delta[\mathrm{T}_w(\Delta p_o - \Delta P_{cow})]_i = \Delta(\mathrm{T}_w\Delta p_o)_i - \Delta(\mathrm{T}_w\Delta P_{cow})_i. \quad \ldots\ldots\ (9.247)$$

The expansion of $\Delta(\mathrm{T}_w\Delta p_o)_i$ is obtained as Eq. 9.242 for $l=w$ in Example 9.12.

$$\Delta(\mathrm{T}_w\Delta p_o)_i \equiv \Delta_x(\mathrm{T}_{wx}\Delta_x p_o)_i = \mathrm{T}_{wx_{i-1/2}}p_{o_{i-1}} - \left(\mathrm{T}_{wx_{i-1/2}} + \mathrm{T}_{wx_{i+1/2}}\right)p_{o_i} + \mathrm{T}_{wx_{i+1/2}}p_{o_{i+1}}. \quad \ldots\ldots\ (9.248)$$

Similarly, $\Delta(\mathrm{T}_w\Delta P_{cow})_i$ may be expanded as

$$\Delta(\mathrm{T}_w\Delta P_{cow})_i \equiv \Delta_x(\mathrm{T}_{wx}\Delta_x P_{cow})_i = \mathrm{T}_{wx_{i-1/2}}P_{cow_{i-1}} - \left(\mathrm{T}_{wx_{i-1/2}} + \mathrm{T}_{wx_{i+1/2}}\right)P_{cow_i} + \mathrm{T}_{wx_{i+1/2}}P_{cow_{i+1}}. \quad \ldots\ldots\ (9.249)$$

In an implicit formulation, $\Delta(\mathrm{T}_w\Delta P_{cow})$ has to be expanded in terms of S_w.

$$\Delta P_{cow} = P'_{cow}\Delta S_w. \quad \ldots\ldots\ (9.250)$$

For example, in the x direction,

$$\frac{\partial P_{cow}}{\partial x} = \frac{dP_{cow}}{dS_w}\frac{\partial S_w}{\partial x}. \quad \ldots\ldots\ (9.251)$$

Then, $$\Delta(\mathrm{T}_w\Delta P_{cow})_i = \Delta\left[\mathrm{T}_w\left(P'_{cow}\ \Delta S_w\right)\right]_i, \quad \ldots\ldots\ (9.252)$$

where $$P'_{cow} = \frac{dP_{cow}}{dS_w}, \quad \ldots\ldots\ (9.253)$$

Therefore, $$\Delta(\mathrm{T}_w\Delta P_{cow})_i = \Delta\left[\left(\mathrm{T}_w P'_{cow}\right)\Delta S_w\right]_i \equiv \Delta_x\left[(\mathrm{T}_{wx}P'_{cow})\Delta_x S_w\right]_i, \quad \ldots\ldots\ (9.254)$$

which is defined by Eq. 9.81 as

$$\Delta_x\left[(\mathrm{T}_{wx}P'_{cow})\Delta_x S_w\right]_i = \mathrm{T}_{wx_{i-1/2}}P'_{cow_{i-1/2}}\left(S_{w_{i-1}} - S_{w_i}\right) + \mathrm{T}_{wx_{i+1/2}}P'_{cow_{i+1/2}}\left(S_{w_{i+1}} - S_{w_i}\right). \quad \ldots\ldots\ (9.255)$$

Substituting Eqs. 9.248, 9.254, and 9.255 into Eq. 9.247 yields

$$\Delta[\mathrm{T}_w(\Delta p_o - \Delta P_{cow})]_i = \mathrm{T}_{wx_{i-1/2}}p_{o_{i-1}} - \mathrm{T}_{wx_{i-1/2}}P'_{cow_{i-1/2}} \times S_{w_{i-1}} - \left(\mathrm{T}_{wx_{i-1/2}} + \mathrm{T}_{wx_{i+1/2}}\right)p_{o_i} + \left(\mathrm{T}_{wx_{i-1/2}}P'_{cow_{i-1/2}} + \mathrm{T}_{wx_{i+1/2}}P'_{cow_{i+1/2}}\right)S_{w_i} + \mathrm{T}_{wx_{i+1/2}}p_{o_{i+1}} - \mathrm{T}_{wx_{i+1/2}}P'_{cow_{i+1/2}}S_{w_{i+1}}. \quad \ldots\ldots\ (9.256)$$

The water equation may now be obtained by combining Eqs. 9.246 and 9.256.

$$\mathrm{T}_{wx_{i-1/2}}^{n+1}p_{o_{i-1}}^{n+1} - \mathrm{T}_{wx_{i-1/2}}^{n+1}P'^{\,n+1}_{cow_{i-1/2}}S_{w_{i-1}}^{n+1} - \left(\mathrm{T}_{wx_{i-1/2}}^{n+1} + \mathrm{T}_{wx_{i+1/2}}^{n+1}\right)p_{o_i}^{n+1} + \left(\mathrm{T}_{wx_{i-1/2}}^{n+1}P'^{\,n+1}_{cow_{i-1/2}} + \mathrm{T}_{wx_{i+1/2}}^{n+1}P'^{\,n+1}_{cow_{i+1/2}}\right)S_{w_i}^{n+1}$$

$$+ \mathrm{T}_{wx_{i+1/2}}^{n+1} p_{o_{i+1}}^{n+1} - \mathrm{T}_{wx_{i+1/2}}^{n+1} P'^{\,n+1}_{cow_{i+1/2}} S_{w_{i+1}}^{n+1}$$

$$= C_{wp_i}\left(p_{o_i}^{n+1} - p_{o_i}^{n}\right) + C_{ww_i}\left(S_{w_i}^{n+1} - S_{w_i}^{n}\right) - q_{wsc_i}^{n+1}. \quad \text{(9.257)}$$

The oil equation is identical to Eq. 9.244 in Example 9.12. Eqs. 9.244 and 9.257 are the implicit finite-difference flow equations for oil and water, respectively.

Example 9.14. Write the backward-difference equations for the two-phase-flow problem described in Example 9.3, neglecting gravity and capillary forces.

Solution. Considering Example 9.3, the backward-difference equations for this problem may be obtained from the black-oil-model equations. For this problem, we need (1) to consider Eq. 9.224 for oil and Eq. 9.226 for gas and discard Eq. 9.225 for water; (2) to set $S_w = 0$ and $\Delta_t S_w = 0$ in these equations; (3) to neglect terms that include P_{cgo} and oil and gas gravities (i.e., set $P_{cgo} = 0$ and $\Delta Z = 0$); and (4) to use the equations with subscript (i,j) because flow is in the x-y plane. The resulting equations are

$$\Delta(\mathrm{T}_o \Delta p_o)_{i,j}^{n+1} = \left(C_{op}\Delta_t p_o + C_{og}\Delta_t S_g - q_{osc}^{n+1}\right)_{i,j} \quad \text{(9.258)}$$

and $\Delta\left(\mathrm{T}_g \Delta p_o\right)_{i,j}^{n+1} + \Delta(\mathrm{T}_o R_s \Delta p_o)_{i,j}^{n+1}$

$$= \left[C_{gp}\Delta_t p_o + C_{gg}\Delta_t S_g - \left(q_{fgsc}^{n+1} + R_s^{n+1} q_{osc}^{n+1}\right)\right]_{i,j}, \quad \text{(9.259)}$$

where C_{op}, C_{og}, C_{gp}, and C_{gg} are obtained from Eqs. 9.228, 9.230, 9.234, and 9.236 with $S_w = 0$.

$$C_{op} = \frac{V_b}{\alpha_c \Delta t}\left[\frac{\phi'}{B_o^n} + \phi^{n+1}\left(\frac{1}{B_o}\right)'\right](1 - S_g^n), \quad \text{(9.260)}$$

$$C_{og} = -\frac{V_b}{\alpha_c \Delta t}\left(\frac{\phi}{B_o}\right)^{n+1}, \quad \text{(9.230)}$$

$$C_{gp} = \frac{V_b}{\alpha_c \Delta t}\left(\left[\frac{\phi'}{B_g^n} + \phi^{n+1}\left(\frac{1}{B_g}\right)'\right]S_g^n + \left\{\left[\frac{\phi'}{B_o^n} + \phi^{n+1}\left(\frac{1}{B_o}\right)'\right]R_s^n + \left(\frac{\phi}{B_o}\right)^{n+1} R_s'\right\}(1 - S_g^n)\right), \quad \text{(9.261)}$$

$$C_{gg} = \frac{V_b}{\alpha_c \Delta t}\left[\left(\frac{\phi}{B_g}\right)^{n+1} - \left(\frac{\phi}{B_o}\right)^{n+1} R_s^{n+1}\right], \quad \text{(9.236)}$$

and ϕ', R_s', and $(1/B_l)'$ for $l = o$ or g are expressed by Eqs. 9.189, 9.190, and 9.191, respectively.

The next step involves the expansion of the space operator on the left side of Eqs. 9.258 and 9.259. The space operator in the 2D x-y plane is defined by Eq. 9.99.

$$\Delta(\xi\Delta\eta)_{i,j} \equiv \Delta_x(\xi_x \Delta_x \eta)_{i,j} + \Delta_y\left(\xi_y \Delta_y \eta\right)_{i,j}, \quad \text{(9.99)}$$

where $\Delta_x(\xi_x \Delta_x \eta)_{i,j}$ and $\Delta_y(\xi_y \Delta_y \eta)_{i,j}$ are defined by Eqs. 9.81 and 9.85, respectively, and Subscript k is discarded. Therefore,

$$\Delta(\xi\Delta\eta)_{i,j} = \xi_{y_{i,j-1/2}}\eta_{i,j-1} + \xi_{x_{i-1/2,j}}\eta_{i-1,j} - \left(\xi_{y_{i,j-1/2}} + \xi_{x_{i-1/2,j}} + \xi_{x_{i+1/2,j}} + \xi_{y_{i,j+1/2}}\right)\eta_{i,j} + \xi_{x_{i+1/2,j}}\eta_{i+1,j} + \xi_{y_{i,j+1/2}}\eta_{i,j+1}. \quad \text{(9.262)}$$

To expand $\Delta(\mathrm{T}_l \Delta p_o)_{i,j}$ for $l = o$ or g, let $\xi = \mathrm{T}_l$ and $\eta = p_o$ and substitute into Eq. 9.262 to obtain

$$\Delta(\mathrm{T}_l \Delta p_o)_{i,j} = \mathrm{T}_{ly_{i,j-1/2}} p_{o_{i,j-1}} + \mathrm{T}_{lx_{i-1/2,j}} p_{o_{i-1,j}} - \left(\mathrm{T}_{ly_{i,j-1/2}} + \mathrm{T}_{lx_{i-1/2,j}} + \mathrm{T}_{lx_{i+1/2,j}} + \mathrm{T}_{ly_{i,j+1/2}}\right)p_{o_{i,j}} + \mathrm{T}_{lx_{i+1/2,j}} p_{o_{i+1,j}} + \mathrm{T}_{ly_{i,j+1/2}} p_{o_{i,j+1}}, \quad \text{(9.263)}$$

where $\mathrm{T}_{ly} = \beta_c[(k_y A_y)/\Delta y][k_{rl}/(\mu_l B_l)]$ and $\mathrm{T}_{lx} = \beta_c[(k_x A_x)/\Delta x] \times [(k_{rl}/(\mu_l B_l))]$ where $l = o$ or g. To expand $\Delta(\mathrm{T}_o R_s \Delta p_o)_{i,j}$, let $\xi = \mathrm{T}_o R_s$ and $\eta = p_o$ and substitute into Eq. 9.262 to obtain

$$\Delta(\mathrm{T}_o R_s \Delta p_o)_{i,j} = (\mathrm{T}_{oy}R_s)_{i,j-1/2} p_{o_{i,j-1}} + (\mathrm{T}_{ox}R_s)_{i-1/2,j} p_{o_{i-1,j}} - \left[(\mathrm{T}_{oy}R_s)_{i,j-1/2} + (\mathrm{T}_{ox}R_s)_{i-1/2,j} + (\mathrm{T}_{ox}R_s)_{i+1/2,j} + (\mathrm{T}_{oy}R_s)_{i,j+1/2}\right]p_{o_{i,j}} + (\mathrm{T}_{ox}R_s)_{i+1/2,j} p_{o_{i+1,j}} + (\mathrm{T}_{oy}R_s)_{i,j+1/2} p_{o_{i,j+1}}. \quad \text{(9.264)}$$

Substituting the definition of the space operators given by Eqs. 9.263 and 9.264 into Eqs. 9.258 and 9.259 produces the implicit (backward) difference equations for this flow problem.

$$\mathrm{T}_{oy_{i,j-1/2}}^{n+1} p_{o_{i,j-1}}^{n+1} + \mathrm{T}_{ox_{i-1/2,j}}^{n+1} p_{o_{i-1,j}}^{n+1} - \left(\mathrm{T}_{oy_{i,j-1/2}}^{n+1} + \mathrm{T}_{ox_{i-1/2,j}}^{n+1} + \mathrm{T}_{ox_{i+1/2,j}}^{n+1} + \mathrm{T}_{oy_{i,j+1/2}}^{n+1}\right)p_{o_{i,j}}^{n+1} + \mathrm{T}_{ox_{i+1/2,j}}^{n+1} p_{o_{i+1,j}}^{n+1} + \mathrm{T}_{oy_{i,j+1/2}}^{n+1} p_{o_{i,j+1}}^{n+1}$$

$$= C_{op_{i,j}}\left(p_{o_{i,j}}^{n+1} - p_{o_{i,j}}^{n}\right) + C_{og_{i,j}}\left(S_{g_{i,j}}^{n+1} - S_{g_{i,j}}^{n}\right) - q_{osc_{i,j}}^{n+1} \quad \text{(9.265)}$$

and $\left(\mathrm{T}_{gy} + \mathrm{T}_{oy}R_s\right)_{i,j-1/2}^{n+1} p_{o_{i,j-1}}^{n+1} + \left(\mathrm{T}_{gx} + \mathrm{T}_{ox}R_s\right)_{i-1/2,j}^{n+1} p_{o_{i-1,j}}^{n+1}$

$$- \left[\left(\mathrm{T}_{gy} + \mathrm{T}_{oy}R_s\right)_{i,j-1/2}^{n+1} + \left(\mathrm{T}_{gx} + \mathrm{T}_{ox}R_s\right)_{i-1/2,j}^{n+1} + \left(\mathrm{T}_{gx} + \mathrm{T}_{ox}R_s\right)_{i+1/2,j}^{n+1} + \left(\mathrm{T}_{gy} + \mathrm{T}_{oy}R_s\right)_{i,j+1/2}^{n+1}\right]p_{o_{i,j}}^{n+1}$$

$$+ \left(\mathrm{T}_{gx} + \mathrm{T}_{ox}R_s\right)_{i+1/2,j}^{n+1} p_{o_{i+1,j}}^{n+1} + \left(\mathrm{T}_{gy} + \mathrm{T}_{oy}R_s\right)_{i,j+1/2}^{n+1} p_{o_{i,j+1}}^{n+1}$$

$$= C_{gp_{i,j}}\left(p_{o_{i,j}}^{n+1} - p_{o_{i,j}}^{n}\right) + C_{gg_{i,j}}\left(S_{g_{i,j}}^{n+1} - S_{g_{i,j}}^{n}\right) - \left(q_{fgsc}^{n+1} + R_s^{n+1} q_{osc}^{n+1}\right)_{i,j}. \quad \text{(9.266)}$$

9.5.2 Linearization of the Multiphase-Flow Equations. The continuous PDE's describing multiphase-flow problems in porous media are strongly nonlinear. The discretization of these equations, presented in Sec. 9.5.1, produces a set of coupled, nonlinear finite-difference equations. To use the linear-matrix methods discussed in Chap. 7 and Appendix B, these finite-difference equations must be linearized. In Chap. 8, we discussed the linearization of the finite-difference equations for single-phase flow. In that chapter, we discussed the explicit, extrapolation, simple-iteration, and fully-implicit methods of linearizing the finite-difference equations (as they pertain to single-phase flow). In this section, we discuss how these methods are applied to multiphase-flow problems and discuss other methods for linearizing strongly nonlinear terms resulting from saturation-dependent properties.

In numerical reservoir simulation, the nonlinear nature of the finite-difference equations arises because the coefficients of the unknowns are also functions of the unknowns. These nonlinear terms include phase transmissibilities, capillary pressures, phase densities, solution-gas/oil ratio in the interblock flow terms occurring in the finite-difference space operators, coefficients of the time difference of the accumulation terms, and phase production (injection) rates. Precisely, the nonlinearities in Eqs. 9.224 through 9.226 for the black-oil model are T_l^{n+1}, which involves B_l^{n+1}, μ_l^{n+1}, and k_{rl}^{n+1}; P_{cow}^{n+1} and P_{cgo}^{n+1}; γ_l^{n+1}; R_s^{n+1}; the coefficients C_{lp}, C_{lw}, and C_{lg}, which involve ϕ^{n+1}, B_l^{n+1}, R_s^{n+1}, ϕ', $(1/B_l)'$, and R_s'; and q_{lsc}^{n+1} for $l=o$, w, or g. All these are functions of the unknowns p_o^{n+1}, S_w^{n+1}, and/or S_g^{n+1}. These nonlinearities can be divided into two groups: weak and strong.

Weak nonlinearities include all functions that depend on the pressure of one phase, such as B_l^{n+1}, μ_l^{n+1}, γ_l^{n+1}, R_s^{n+1}, ϕ^{n+1}, ϕ', $(1/B_l)'$, and R_s'. The effect of these nonlinearities depends on the magnitude of the pressure change during a timestep. Although phase properties should be evaluated at the corresponding phase pressure, Coats *et al.*[4] have shown that such properties can be evaluated at the oil-phase pressure with little or no loss of accuracy.

Strong nonlinearities include all functions that depend on phase saturation or capillary pressure, such as k_{rl}, P_{cow}', and P_{cgo}', in the (p_o-S_w-S_g) formulation. The nonlinearity caused by capillary pressure disappears if P_{cow} and P_{cgo} are linear functions of S_w and S_g, respectively (see Eq. 9.255 in Example 9.13), or if they are neglected. This is not true for k_{rl}; therefore, the principal nonlinearity in the flow equations is caused by k_{rl}.

Because phase PVT properties are functions of oil pressure and capillary pressure and relative permeability are functions of one saturation, T_l^{n+1} is a function of p_o, S_w, and S_g. Therefore, T_l^{n+1} incorporates both weak and strong nonlinearities. In addition to the transmissibility terms, other nonlinear terms appear on the left side of the flow equations, including $(T_l\gamma_l)^{n+1}$, $(T_w P_{cow}')$, $(T_g P_{cgo}')$, $(T_o R_s)$, and $(T_o R_s \gamma_o)$. There are also nonlinear terms on the right side of the finite-difference equations, including the coefficients of the time difference of unknowns (C_{lp}, C_{lw}, and C_{lg}) and the well flow rates (q_{lsc}^{n+1}). Finally, q_{lsc}^{n+1} is also a function of p_{wf} for a fully-implicit production formulation. In this section we discuss the available methods for the linearization of these nonlinear terms.

Treatment of Interblock Transmissibilities. In multidimensional, multiphase-flow problems, phase transmissibilities between Gridblock (i,j,k) and its neighboring gridblocks in the x, y, and z directions are defined, respectively, for $l=o$, w, or g as

$$T_{lx_{i\pm 1/2,j,k}} = \beta_c\left(\frac{k_x A_x}{\Delta x}\right)_{i\pm 1/2,j,k}\left(\frac{1}{\mu_l B_l}\right)_{i\pm 1/2,j,k} k_{rl_{i\pm 1/2,j,k}}, \qquad (9.267)$$

$$T_{ly_{i,j\pm 1/2,k}} = \beta_c\left(\frac{k_y A_y}{\Delta y}\right)_{i,j\pm 1/2,k}\left(\frac{1}{\mu_l B_l}\right)_{i,j\pm 1/2,k} k_{rl_{i,j\pm 1/2,k}}, \qquad (9.268)$$

and $$T_{lz_{i,j,k\pm 1/2}} = \beta_c\left(\frac{k_z A_z}{\Delta z}\right)_{i,j,k\pm 1/2}\left(\frac{1}{\mu_l B_l}\right)_{i,j,k\pm 1/2} k_{rl_{i,j,k\pm 1/2}}, \qquad (9.269)$$

where the plus and minus signs in the subscripts are used to identify gridblock boundaries in the positive and negative directions of the Cartesian coordinates.

Other terms, such as $(T_{lx}\gamma_l)$, $(T_{ox}R_s)$, and $(T_{ox}R_s\gamma_o)$, may replace T_{lx} given by Eq. 9.267 if the pressure-dependent term $1/(\mu_l B_l)$ on the right side is replaced with $\gamma_l/(\mu_l B_l)$, $R_s/(\mu_o B_o)$, and $(R_s\gamma_o)/(\mu_o B_o)$, respectively. Also, for saturation-dependent terms [such as $(T_{lx}P_{col}')$], k_{rl} may be replaced with $(k_{rl}P_{col}')$. The same can be said of other terms in the y and z directions. As in Sec. 9.5.1., if $\xi=(T_l)$, $(T_l\gamma_l)$, (T_oR_s), $(T_oR_s\gamma_o)$, or (T_lP_{col}'), then ξ_x in the x direction assumes T_{lx}, $(T_{lx}\gamma_l)$, $(T_{ox}R_s)$, $(T_{ox}R_s\gamma_o)$, or $(T_{lx}P_{col}')$, respectively. For further discussion, ξ is denoted as

$$\xi = Gf_p(p_o)f_s(S_w, S_g) = Gf_pf_s, \qquad (9.270)$$

where $G=$ a geometric factor, $f_p=$ a pressure-dependent function, and $f_s=$ a saturation-dependent function. These functions are defined by

$$G \equiv \beta_c\left(\frac{k_x A_x}{\Delta x}\right), \qquad (9.271a)$$

$$G \equiv \beta_c\left(\frac{k_y A_y}{\Delta y}\right), \qquad (9.271b)$$

or $$G \equiv \beta_c\left(\frac{k_z A_z}{\Delta z}\right); \qquad (9.271c)$$

$$f_p \equiv \left(\frac{1}{\mu_l B_l}\right), \qquad (9.272a)$$

$$f_p \equiv \left(\frac{\gamma_l}{\mu_l B_l}\right), \qquad (9.272b)$$

$$f_p \equiv \left(\frac{R_s}{\mu_o B_o}\right), \qquad (9.272c)$$

or $$f_p \equiv \left(\frac{R_s\gamma_o}{\mu_o B_o}\right); \qquad (9.272d)$$

and $$f_s \equiv (k_{rl}) \qquad (9.273a)$$

or $$f_s \equiv \left(k_{rl}P_{col}'\right). \qquad (9.273b)$$

Functions f_p and f_s have different degrees of nonlinearity and, therefore, need to be approximated differently both in space and time.

Weighting of Geometric Factors. The geometric factors, G, in the x, y, and z directions can be derived by use of the procedure discussed in Sec. 8.2.2 (see Example 8.1) for block-centered and point-distributed grids. The following definitions are valid for an irregular grid system.

For a block-centered rectangular grid,

$$G_{i\pm 1/2,j,k} = \beta_c\left(\frac{k_x A_x}{\Delta x}\right)_{i\pm 1/2,j,k} = \beta_c\frac{2A_{x_{i,j,k}}k_{x_{i,j,k}}A_{x_{i\pm 1,j,k}}k_{x_{i\pm 1,j,k}}}{A_{x_{i,j,k}}k_{x_{i,j,k}}\Delta x_{i\pm 1,j,k} + A_{x_{i\pm 1,j,k}}k_{x_{i\pm 1,j,k}}\Delta x_{i,j,k}}, \qquad (9.274)$$

$$G_{i,j\pm 1/2,k} = \beta_c\left(\frac{k_y A_y}{\Delta y}\right)_{i,j\pm 1/2,k} = \beta_c\frac{2A_{y_{i,j,k}}k_{y_{i,j,k}}A_{y_{i,j\pm 1,k}}k_{y_{i,j\pm 1,k}}}{A_{y_{i,j,k}}k_{y_{i,j,k}}\Delta y_{i,j\pm 1,k} + A_{y_{i,j\pm 1,k}}k_{y_{i,j\pm 1,k}}\Delta y_{i,j,k}}, \qquad (9.275)$$

and $$G_{i,j,k\pm 1/2} = \beta_c\left(\frac{k_z A_z}{\Delta z}\right)_{i,j,k\pm 1/2} = \beta_c\frac{2A_{z_{i,j,k}}k_{z_{i,j,k}}A_{z_{i,j,k\pm 1}}k_{z_{i,j,k\pm 1}}}{A_{z_{i,j,k}}k_{z_{i,j,k}}\Delta z_{i,j,k\pm 1} + A_{z_{i,j,k\pm 1}}k_{z_{i,j,k\pm 1}}\Delta z_{i,j,k}}. \qquad (9.276)$$

For a point-distributed rectangular grid,

$$G_{i\pm 1/2,j,k} = \beta_c\left(\frac{k_x A_x}{\Delta x}\right)_{i\pm 1/2,j,k} = \beta_c\frac{2A_{x_{i,j,k}}k_{x_{i,j,k}}A_{x_{i\pm 1,j,k}}k_{x_{i\pm 1,j,k}}}{A_{x_{i,j,k}}k_{x_{i,j,k}}\Delta x_{i\pm 1/2,j,k} + A_{x_{i\pm 1,j,k}}k_{x_{i\pm 1,j,k}}\Delta x_{i\pm 1/2,j,k}}, \qquad (9.277)$$

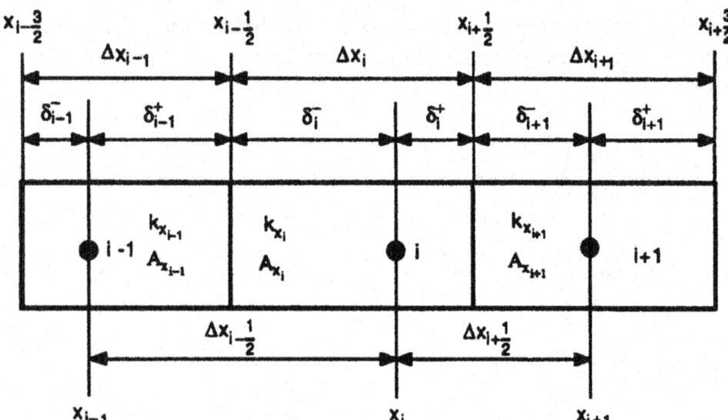

Fig. 9.5—Irregular grid-size distribution.

$$G_{i,j\pm½,k} = \beta_c\left(\frac{k_yA_y}{\Delta y}\right)_{i,j\pm½,k}$$

$$= \beta_c\frac{2A_{y_{i,j,k}}k_{y_{i,j,k}}A_{y_{i,j\pm1,k}}k_{y_{i,j\pm1,k}}}{A_{y_{i,j,k}}k_{y_{i,j,k}}\Delta y_{i,j\pm½,k} + A_{y_{i,j\pm1,k}}k_{y_{i,j\pm1,k}}\Delta y_{i,j\pm½,k}}, \quad (9.278)$$

$$\text{and } G_{i,j,k\pm½} = \beta_c\left(\frac{k_zA_z}{\Delta z}\right)_{i,j,k\pm½}$$

$$= \beta_c\frac{2A_{z_{i,j,k}}k_{z_{i,j,k}}A_{z_{i,j,k\pm1}}k_{z_{i,j,k\pm1}}}{A_{z_{i,j,k}}k_{z_{i,j,k}}\Delta z_{i,j,k\pm½} + A_{z_{i,j,k\pm1}}k_{z_{i,j,k\pm1}}\Delta z_{i,j,k\pm½}}. \quad (9.279)$$

Table 6.6 lists the definitions of the geometric factors for cylindrical coordinate systems.

Example 9.15. Derive expressions for the geometric factor $\beta_c[(k_xA_x)/\Delta x]_{i+½}$ for both block-centered and point-distributed grids with an irregular grid system.

Solution. Consider a 1D reservoir that has been discretized with an irregular numerical grid. **Fig. 9.5** shows Gridpoints $i-1$, i, and $i+1$ and their associated gridblock dimensions. Fig. 9.5 also shows the terminology used to derive expressions applicable to both block-centered and point-distributed grids.

The following relationships hold for both block-centered and point-distributed grid systems.

$$\delta_i^- = x_i - x_{i-½}. \quad (9.280)$$

$$\delta_i^+ = x_{i+½} - x_i. \quad (9.281)$$

$$\Delta x_i = x_{i+½} - x_{i-½}$$

$$= (x_{i+½} - x_i) + (x_i - x_{i-½}) \quad (9.282)$$

$$\text{or } \Delta x_i = \delta_i^+ + \delta_i^-, \quad (9.283)$$

$$\Delta x_{i+½} = x_{i+1} - x_i$$

$$= (x_{i+1} - x_{i+½}) + (x_{i+½} - x_i) \quad (9.284)$$

$$\text{or } \Delta x_{i+½} = \delta_{i+1}^- + \delta_i^+. \quad (9.285)$$

$$\Delta x_{i-½} = x_i - x_{i-1}$$

$$= (x_i - x_{i-½}) + (x_{i-½} - x_{i-1}) \quad (9.286)$$

$$\text{or } \Delta x_{i-½} = \delta_i^- + \delta_{i-1}^+. \quad (9.287)$$

For a block-centered grid system, the following relationship also holds.

$$\delta_i^+ = \delta_i^-, \quad (9.288)$$

where δ_i^+ need not equal δ_{i+1}^- and δ_i^- need not equal δ_{i-1}^+.

For a point-distributed grid system, the following relationships hold.

$$\delta_i^- = \delta_{i-1}^+ \quad (9.289)$$

$$\text{and } \delta_i^+ = \delta_{i+1}^-, \quad (9.290)$$

where δ_i^- need not equal δ_i^+.

The procedure for deriving an expression for $\beta_c[(k_xA_x)/\Delta x]_{i+½}$ is the same as in Example 8.1; however, we use the terminology in Fig. 9.5. Consider the flow of an incompressible fluid from Gridpoint i to Gridpoint $i+1$. Let p_i, $p_{i+½}$, and p_{i+1} be the fluid pressure at x_i, $x_{i+½}$, and x_{i+1}, respectively. The pressure drop between Gridpoints i and $i+1$ may be expressed as

$$\Delta p = p_i - p_{i+1} = (p_i - p_{i+½}) + (p_{i+½} - p_{i+1}). \quad (9.291)$$

We now can write Darcy's law for fluid flow between Gridpoint i and Gridblock Boundary $i+½$ as

$$p_i - p_{i+½} = \frac{q_x\delta_i^+\mu}{\beta_ck_{x_i}A_{x_i}} \quad (9.292)$$

and Darcy's law for fluid flow between Gridblock Boundary $i+½$ and Gridpoint $i+1$ as

$$p_{i+½} - p_{i+1} = \frac{q_x\delta_{i+1}^-\mu}{\beta_ck_{x_{i+1}}A_{x_{i+1}}}. \quad (9.293)$$

For fluid flow between Gridpoints i and $i+1$, we have

$$p_i - p_{i+1} = \frac{q_x\Delta x_{i+½}\mu}{\beta_ck_{x_{i+½}}A_{x_{i+½}}}. \quad (9.294)$$

It follows that

$$\Delta p = \frac{q_x\mu}{\beta_c[(k_xA_x)/\Delta x]_{i+½}} = \frac{q_x\delta_i^+\mu}{\beta_ck_{x_i}A_{x_i}} + \frac{q_x\delta_{i+1}^-\mu}{\beta_ck_{x_{i+1}}A_{x_{i+1}}}, \quad (9.295)$$

$$\text{or } \frac{1}{[(k_xA_x)/\Delta x]_{i+½}} = \frac{\delta_i^+}{k_{x_i}A_{x_i}} + \frac{\delta_{i+1}^-}{k_{x_{i+1}}A_{x_{i+1}}}$$

$$= \frac{A_{x_{i+1}}k_{x_{i+1}}\delta_i^+ + A_{x_i}k_{x_i}\delta_{i+1}^-}{A_{x_i}k_{x_i}A_{x_{i+1}}k_{x_{i+1}}}, \quad (9.296)$$

$$\text{or } \beta_c\left(\frac{k_xA_x}{\Delta x}\right)_{i+½} = \beta_c\frac{A_{x_i}k_{x_i}A_{x_{i+1}}k_{x_{i+1}}}{A_{x_i}k_{x_i}\delta_{i+1}^- + A_{x_{i+1}}k_{x_{i+1}}\delta_i^+}. \quad (9.297)$$

Eq. 9.297 is applicable to both block-centered and point-distributed grids. For a block-centered grid system,

$$\Delta x_i = \delta_i^+ + \delta_i^- = 2\delta_i^+ \quad (9.298)$$

$$\text{or } \delta_i^+ = \Delta x_i/2. \quad (9.299)$$

Similarly,

$$\delta_{i+1}^- = \Delta x_{i+1}/2. \quad (9.300)$$

Substituting these relationships into Eq. 9.297, we obtain

$$\beta_c\left(\frac{k_xA_x}{\Delta x}\right)_{i+½} = \beta_c\frac{2A_{x_i}k_{x_i}A_{x_{i+1}}k_{x_{i+1}}}{A_{x_i}k_{x_i}\Delta x_{i+1} + A_{x_{i+1}}k_{x_{i+1}}\Delta x_i}, \quad (9.301)$$

which is Eq. 9.274 with Subscripts j and k discarded.

For a point-distributed grid system,

$$\Delta x_{i+½} = \delta_{i+1}^- + \delta_i^+ = 2\delta_{i+1}^- = 2\delta_i^+ \quad (9.302)$$

or $\delta_i^+ = \Delta x_{i+1/2}/2$ .... (9.303)

and $\delta_{i+1}^- = \Delta x_{i+1/2}/2,$ .... (9.304)

which, when substituted into Eq. 9.297, results in

$$\beta_c\left(\frac{k_xA_x}{\Delta x}\right)_{i+1/2} = \beta_c\frac{2A_{x_i}k_{x_i}A_{x_{i+1}}k_{x_{i+1}}}{A_{x_i}k_{x_i}\Delta x_{i+1/2} + A_{x_{i+1}}k_{x_{i+1}}\Delta x_{i+1/2}}, \qquad (9.305)$$

which is Eq. 9.277 with Subscripts j and k discarded.

Example 9.16. Write the expression for the geometric factor $\beta_c[(k_xA_x)/\Delta x]_{i+1/2}$ for a block-centered grid system. Simplify this expression and comment on the averaging of Δx, A_x, and k_x for Gridblocks i and $i+1$ for the following cases.

1. Cross-sectional area A_x is independent of x.
2. Permeability in x direction, k_x, is independent of x.
3. Gridblock size Δx is independent of x.
4. Both A_x and Δx are independent of x.
5. Both k_x and Δx are independent of x.
6. Both A_x and k_x (or the product A_xk_x) are independent of x.
7. All A_x, k_x , and Δx are independent of x.

Solution. The geometric factor $\beta_c[(k_xA_x)/\Delta x]_{i+1/2}$ for a block-centered grid may be obtained from Eq. 9.274 by discarding Subscripts j and k as

$$\beta_c\left(\frac{k_xA_x}{\Delta x}\right)_{i+1/2} = \beta_c\frac{2A_{x_i}k_{x_i}A_{x_{i+1}}k_{x_{i+1}}}{A_{x_i}k_{x_i}\Delta x_{i+1} + A_{x_{i+1}}k_{x_{i+1}}\Delta x_i}. \qquad (9.301)$$

This equation may be rewritten as

$$\left(\frac{k_xA_x}{\Delta x}\right)_{i+1/2} = \frac{1}{\left(\frac{1}{2}\right)\left(\frac{\Delta x_{i+1}}{A_{x_{i+1}}k_{x_{i+1}}} + \frac{\Delta x_i}{A_{x_i}k_{x_i}}\right)}. \qquad (9.306)$$

Multiply and divide the right side of Eq. 9.306 by $(\Delta x_{i+1} + \Delta x_i)$.

$$\left(\frac{k_xA_x}{\Delta x}\right)_{i+1/2} = \frac{1}{\left(\frac{\Delta x_{i+1}+\Delta x_i}{2}\right)}\frac{(\Delta x_{i+1} + \Delta x_i)}{\left(\frac{\Delta x_{i+1}}{A_{x_{i+1}}k_{x_{i+1}}} + \frac{\Delta x_i}{A_{x_i}k_{x_i}}\right)}. \qquad (9.307)$$

For a block-centered grid,

$$\Delta x_{i+1/2} = \frac{1}{2}(\Delta x_{i+1} + \Delta x_i)\,. \qquad (9.308)$$

Then,

$$\left(\frac{k_xA_x}{\Delta x}\right)_{i+1/2} = \frac{1}{\Delta x_{i+1/2}}\frac{(\Delta x_{i+1} + \Delta x_i)}{\left[\frac{\Delta x_{i+1}}{(A_xk_x)_{i+1}} + \frac{\Delta x_i}{(A_xk_x)_i}\right]} \qquad (9.309)$$

or $$\frac{\Delta x_{i+1} + \Delta x_i}{(k_xA_x)_{i+1/2}} = \frac{\Delta x_{i+1}}{(A_xk_x)_{i+1}} + \frac{\Delta x_i}{(A_xk_x)_i}. \qquad (9.310)$$

Therefore, $\Delta x_{i+1/2}$ is estimated as the arithmetic average of Δx_i and Δx_{i+1} (Eq. 9.308), and $(k_xA_x)_{i+1/2}$ is the harmonic average of $(k_xA_x)_i$ and $(k_xA_x)_{i+1}$, with the corresponding Δx_i and Δx_{i+1} as weighting factors (Eq. 9.310).

Because the conclusion concerning the averaging of $\Delta x_{i+1/2}$ is obtained from the manipulation of the general expression for $\beta_c[(k_xA_x)/\Delta x]_{i+1/2}$, $\Delta x_{i+1/2}$ is the arithmetic average of gridblock sizes for the two gridblocks surrounding the interface $i+1/2$ (Δx_i and Δx_{i+1}) for all cases considered in Parts 1 through 7 of this problem.

The averaging of k_x and A_x for the various cases must still be found.

1. If A_x is constant with respect to x, $A_{x_i} = A_{x_{i+1}} = A_x =$ constant. Substituting into Eq. 9.310 yields

$$\frac{\Delta x_i + \Delta x_{i+1}}{k_{x_{i+1/2}}} = \frac{\Delta x_{i+1}}{k_{x_{i+1}}} + \frac{\Delta x_i}{k_{x_i}}. \qquad (9.311)$$

Hence, if A_x is constant, k_x is harmonically averaged with the gridblock sizes acting as weighting factors.

2. If k_x is constant with respect to x, $k_{x_i} = k_{x_{i+1}} = k_x =$ constant. Substituting into Eq. 9.310 yields

$$\frac{\Delta x_i + \Delta x_{i+1}}{A_{x_{i+1/2}}} = \frac{\Delta x_{i+1}}{A_{x_{i+1}}} + \frac{\Delta x_i}{A_{x_i}}. \qquad (9.312)$$

Hence, if k_x is constant, A_x is harmonically averaged with the gridblock sizes acting as weighting factors.

3. If Δx is constant with respect to x, $\Delta x_i = \Delta x_{i+1} = \Delta x =$ constant. Substitution into Eq. 9.310 yields

$$\frac{2}{(k_xA_x)_{i+1/2}} = \frac{1}{(k_xA_x)_{i+1}} + \frac{1}{(k_xA_x)_i}. \qquad (9.313)$$

Hence, if Δx is constant, the product A_xk_x is harmonically averaged.

4. If A_x and Δx are constants, Eq. 9.310 becomes

$$\frac{2}{k_{x_{i+1/2}}} = \frac{1}{k_{x_{i+1}}} + \frac{1}{k_{x_i}}. \qquad (9.314)$$

Hence, if A_x and Δx are constants, k_x is harmonically averaged.

5. If k_x and Δx are constants, Eq. 9.310 becomes

$$\frac{2}{A_{x_{i+1/2}}} = \frac{1}{A_{x_{i+1}}} + \frac{1}{A_{x_i}}. \qquad (9.315)$$

Hence, if k_x and Δx are constants, A_x is harmonically averaged (not arithmetically averaged).

6. If A_x and k_x are constants, Eq. 9.310 becomes equal to unity. Hence, whether the product k_xA_x is constant or not, Δx is arithmetically averaged.

7. If A_x , k_x , and Δx are constants, Eq. 9.301 becomes

$$\beta_c\left(\frac{k_xA_x}{\Delta x}\right)_{i+1/2} = \beta_c\frac{k_xA_x}{\Delta x}. \qquad (9.316)$$

Hence, if A_x, k_x, and Δx are constants, there is no need to use any averaging technique and the geometric factor can be calculated directly.

Spatial Weighting of Weak Nonlinearities. The weak nonlinearities in the flow terms, represented by f_p, arise from the pressure-dependent properties in the flow equations and assume the following forms.

$$f_p \equiv \left(\frac{1}{\mu_lB_l}\right), \qquad (9.272a)$$

$$f_p \equiv \left(\frac{\gamma_l}{\mu_lB_l}\right), \qquad (9.272b)$$

$$f_p \equiv \left(\frac{R_s}{\mu_oB_o}\right), \qquad (9.272c)$$

or $$f_p \equiv \left(\frac{R_s\gamma_o}{\mu_oB_o}\right). \qquad (9.272d)$$

Because the pressures are calculated at the interiors of the gridblocks but the nonlinear terms (transmissibility terms, etc.) are evaluated at the gridblock boundaries, we must average, or weight, the pressure-dependent properties between adjacent gridblocks. Weighting the weak nonlinearities is not crucial; that is, they may be evaluated by use of either upstream weighting or midpoint weighting for f_p at gridblock boundaries. For example, if $f_p = [(R_s\gamma_o)/(\mu_oB_o)]_{i+1/2,j,k}$ at the boundary $(i+\frac{1}{2},j,k)$ between Gridblocks (i,j,k) and $(i+1,j,k)$, then f_p may be approximated in two different ways.

Upstream Weighting.

$$\left(\frac{R_s\gamma_o}{\mu_o B_o}\right)_{i+\frac{1}{2},j,k} = \left(\frac{R_s\gamma_o}{\mu_o B_o}\right)_{i,j,k} \quad \text{.................. (9.317a)}$$

if oil flow is from Gridblock (i, j, k) to Gridblock $(i+1, j, k)$, and

$$\left(\frac{R_s\gamma_o}{\mu_o B_o}\right)_{i+\frac{1}{2},j,k} = \left(\frac{R_s\gamma_o}{\mu_o B_o}\right)_{i+1,j,k} \quad \text{.............. (9.317b)}$$

if oil flow is from Gridblock $(i+1, j, k)$ to Gridblock (i, j, k). This approach is a first-order correct approximation.

Midpoint Weighting. The function f_p may be approximated at the gridblock boundary using midpoint weighting with one of three methods.

Method 1.

$$\left(\frac{R_s\gamma_o}{\mu_o B_o}\right)_{i+\frac{1}{2},j,k} = \frac{1}{2}\left[\left(\frac{R_s\gamma_o}{\mu_o B_o}\right)_{i,j,k} + \left(\frac{R_s\gamma_o}{\mu_o B_o}\right)_{i+1,j,k}\right]. \quad \text{.................. (9.318)}$$

Method 2.

$$\left(\frac{R_s\gamma_o}{\mu_o B_o}\right)_{i+\frac{1}{2},j,k} = \frac{R_s(\overline{p})\gamma_o(\overline{p})}{\mu_o(\overline{p})B_o(\overline{p})}. \quad \text{................ (9.319)}$$

Method 3.

$$\left(\frac{R_s\gamma_o}{\mu_o B_o}\right)_{i+\frac{1}{2},j,k} = \frac{\overline{R}_s\overline{\gamma}_o}{\overline{\mu}_o\overline{B}_o}, \quad \text{..................... (9.320)}$$

where $\overline{p} = \frac{1}{2}\left(p_{o_{i+1,j,k}} + p_{o_{i,j,k}}\right)$, ... (9.321)

$$\overline{R}_s = \frac{1}{2}\left(R_{s_{i,j,k}} + R_{s_{i+1,j,k}}\right), \quad \text{.................... (9.322)}$$

$$\overline{\gamma}_o = \frac{1}{2}\left(\gamma_{o_{i,j,k}} + \gamma_{o_{i+1,j,k}}\right), \quad \text{................... (9.323)}$$

$$\overline{\mu}_o = \frac{1}{2}\left(\mu_{o_{i,j,k}} + \mu_{o_{i+1,j,k}}\right), \quad \text{................... (9.324)}$$

and $\overline{B}_o = \frac{1}{2}\left(B_{o_{i,j,k}} + B_{o_{i+1,j,k}}\right)$. .... (9.325)

All three variants of the midpoint-weighting approach are second-order correct. There are similar weighting formulas for $[(R_s\gamma_o) \div (\mu_o B_o)]_{i\pm\frac{1}{2},j,k}$, $[(R_s\gamma_o)/(\mu_o B_o)]_{i,j\pm\frac{1}{2},k}$, and $[(R_s\gamma_o)/(\mu_o B_o)]_{i,j,k\pm\frac{1}{2}}$.

Spatial Weighting of Strong Nonlinearities. The strong nonlinearities in the flow terms, represented by f_s, arise from the saturation-dependent properties in the flow equations and assume the following forms.

$$f_s \equiv (k_{rl}) \quad \text{............................... (9.273a)}$$

or $f_s \equiv (k_{rl}P'_{col})$. .... (9.273b)

In other words, strong nonlinearities include k_{rl} for $l = o$, w, or g, and P'_{cgo} and P'_{cow}. The weighting of the strong nonlinearities is very critical for obtaining physically meaningful results. Slopes of capillary pressures, P'_{cgo} and P'_{cow}, are generally approximated using single-point upstream weighting (sometimes simply referred to as upstream weighting), whereas k_{rl} may be approximated using single-point upstream weighting or two-point upstream weighting. Although it is a second-order approximation, the midpoint weighting of strong nonlinearities is seldom used because it can cause the solution of the finite-difference equations in two-phase flow to converge to a mathematically possible but physically incorrect solution.[2]

As stated earlier, there are two possible weighting schemes for k_{rl} where $l = o$, w, and g.

Single-Point Upstream Weighting. Consider the term $k_{rl_{i+\frac{1}{2},j,k}}$, at the boundary $(i+\frac{1}{2},j,k)$ between Gridblocks (i,j,k) and $(i+1,j,k)$ in the x direction.

$$k_{rl_{i+\frac{1}{2},j,k}} = k_{rl_{i,j,k}} \quad \text{.......................... (9.326a)}$$

if flow of Phase l is from Gridblock (i,j,k) to Gridblock $(i+1,j,k)$, and

$$k_{rl_{i+\frac{1}{2},j,k}} = k_{rl_{i+1,j,k}} \quad \text{......................... (9.326b)}$$

if flow of Phase l is from Gridblock $(i+1,j,k)$ to Gridblock (i,j,k), where the direction of flow for Phase l between Gridblocks (i,j,k) and $(i+1,j,k)$ is determined according to the phase-potential difference

$$\Delta\Phi_{l_{i+\frac{1}{2},j,k}} = \left[\left(p_{l_{i+1,j,k}} - p_{l_{i,j,k}}\right) - \gamma_{l_{i+\frac{1}{2},j,k}}\left(Z_{i+1,j,k} - Z_{i,j,k}\right)\right]. \quad \text{.................. (9.327)}$$

Flow of Phase l is from Gridblock (i,j,k) to Gridblock $(i+1,j,k)$ if $\Delta\Phi_{l_{i+\frac{1}{2},j,k}} < 0$. In this case, Gridblock (i,j,k) is the upstream gridblock for Phase l and Gridblock $(i+1,j,k)$ is the downstream gridblock for Phase l. If $\Delta\Phi_{l_{i+\frac{1}{2},j,k}} > 0$, then Phase l flows from the upstream Gridblock $(i+1,j,k)$ to the downstream Gridblock (i,j,k).

Two-Point Upstream Weighting. Two-point upstream weighting is an extrapolation approach in which $k_{rl_{i+\frac{1}{2},j,k}}$ is expressed in terms of k_{rl} at the two upstream points.[5] The weighting of $k_{rl_{i+\frac{1}{2},j,k}}$ is often reported for uniform grid-size distribution.

$$k_{rl_{i+\frac{1}{2},j,k}} = (1+\Omega)k_{rl_{i,j,k}} - \Omega k_{rl_{i-1,j,k}} \quad \text{........... (9.328a)}$$

if flow of Phase l is from Gridblock (i,j,k) to Gridblock $(i+1,j,k)$, and

$$k_{rl_{i+\frac{1}{2},j,k}} = (1+\Omega)k_{rl_{i+1,j,k}} - \Omega k_{rl_{i+2,j,k}} \quad \text{......... (9.328b)}$$

if flow of Phase l is from Gridblock $(i+1,j,k)$ to Gridblock (i,j,k). In Eqs. 9.328a and 9.328b, $\Omega = \frac{1}{2}$ (for uniform grids) and the resulting value of k_{rl} is constrained between zero and one; i.e., $0 \leqq k_{rl_{i+\frac{1}{2},j,k}} \leqq 1$.

The two-point upstream weighting of $k_{rl_{i+\frac{1}{2},j,k}}$ between Gridblocks (i,j,k) and $(i+1,j,k)$ for a nonuniform grid-size distribution in block-centered and point-distributed grids are derived in Example 9.17.

While the single-point upstream weighting is a first-order approximation and the two-point upstream weighting is a second-order approximation, both approaches converge to a physically correct solution. However, it is reported that the latter approach produces sharper displacement fronts for the same number of gridblocks.[5] If relative permeability is linearized by use of the explicit treatment (that is, relative permeabilities are evaluated at Time Level n), then the two weighting schemes require the same computational effort. However, if the relative permeability is linearized with the fully-implicit treatment, the use of two-point upstream weighting increases the bandwidth of the Jacobian matrix and, hence, the computational effort.

Wheatley[6] presented a version of two-point upstream weighting that does not increase the bandwidth of the Jacobian matrix in implicit simulators, but the scheme is not fully implicit. It reduces spatial truncation errors noticeably, but it may exhibit slight oscillations behind the displacement front. In this approach, $k_{rl_{i+\frac{1}{2},j,k}}$ is approximated in terms of the relative permeability evaluated at Gridblocks (i,j,k) and $(i+1,j,k)$ in the neighborhood of the gridblock boundary $(i+\frac{1}{2},j,k)$.

$$k_{rl_{i+\frac{1}{2},j,k}} = \omega^n_{l_{i,j,k}} k_{rl_{i,j,k}} + \left(1 - \omega^n_{l_{i,j,k}}\right)k_{rl_{i+1,j,k}}, \quad \text{...... (9.329)}$$

$$\text{where } \omega^n_{l_{i,j,k}} = 1 - \Omega_{i,j,k}\left(k^n_{rl_{i,j,k}} - k^n_{rl_{i-1,j,k}}\right)\Big/\left(k^n_{rl_{i+1,j,k}} - k^n_{rl_{i,j,k}}\right) \quad \text{.................. (9.330a)}$$

if flow of Phase l is from Gridblock (i,j,k) to Gridblock $(i+1,j,k)$, and

$$\omega^n_{l_{i,j,k}} = \Omega_{i+1,j,k}\left(k^n_{rl_{i+2,j,k}} - k^n_{rl_{i+1,j,k}}\right)\Big/\left(k^n_{rl_{i+1,j,k}} - k^n_{rl_{i,j,k}}\right) \quad \text{.................. (9.330b)}$$

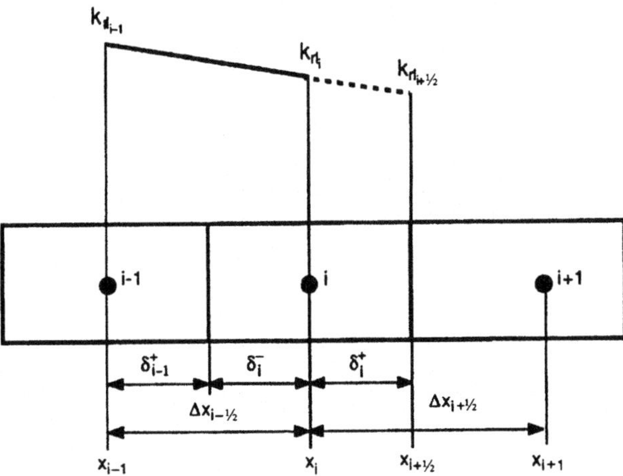

Fig. 9.6—Linear extrapolation of k_{rl} for flow from i to $i+1$.

if flow of Phase l is from Gridblock $(i+1,j,k)$ to Gridblock (i,j,k). Eqs. 9.330a and 9.330b include the constraints $\Omega_{i,j,k} \leqq \omega^n_{li,j,k} \leqq 1$ for flow from Gridblock (i,j,k) to Gridblock $(i+1,j,k)$ and $0 \leqq \omega^n_{li,j,k} \leqq \Omega_{i+1,j,k}$ for flow from Gridblock $(i+1,j,k)$ to Gridblock (i,j,k). The definitions of geometric factors $\Omega_{i,j,k}$ and $\Omega_{i+1,j,k}$ depend on the grid system used (see Example 9.18).

For a block-centered grid system,

$$\Omega_{i,j,k} = \frac{1}{2}\Delta x_{i,j,k}/\Delta x_{i-\frac{1}{2},j,k} \quad \text{(9.331)}$$

$$\text{and } \Omega_{i+1,j,k} = \frac{1}{2}\Delta x_{i+1,j,k}/\Delta x_{i+3/2,j,k}. \quad \text{(9.332)}$$

For a point-distributed grid system,

$$\Omega_{i,j,k} = \frac{1}{2}\Delta x_{i+\frac{1}{2},j,k}/\Delta x_{i-\frac{1}{2},j,k} \quad \text{(9.333)}$$

$$\text{and } \Omega_{i+1,j,k} = \frac{1}{2}\Delta x_{i+\frac{1}{2},j,k}/\Delta x_{i+3/2,j,k}. \quad \text{(9.334)}$$

If in the application of Eqs. 9.328 and 9.329 there are terms that refer to gridblocks that are lying outside the reservoir boundaries, then the geometric factor Ω, $\Omega_{i,j,k}$, or $\Omega_{i+1,j,k}$ is set equal to zero. This reduces the two-point upstream weighting approach to the single-point upstream weighting approach for these gridblocks.

Example 9.17. Derive the two-point upstream weighting of $k_{rl_{i+\frac{1}{2}}}$ for an irregular grid-size distribution for both block-centered and point-distributed grids.

Solution. Use the terminology introduced in Example 9.15 and Fig. 9.5 for irregular grid systems.

For flow from i to $i+1$, the downstream point is $i+1$ and the upstream points are i and $i-1$. **Fig. 9.6** shows the equation of the straight line that passes through the two upstream points $(x_{i-1}, k_{rl_{i-1}})$ and (x_i, k_{rl_i}) and extrapolated to the boundary point $(x_{i+\frac{1}{2}}, k_{rl_{i+\frac{1}{2}}})$.

$$\frac{k_{rl_{i-1}} - k_{rl_{i+\frac{1}{2}}}}{x_{i-1} - x_{i+\frac{1}{2}}} = \frac{k_{rl_i} - k_{rl_{i+\frac{1}{2}}}}{x_i - x_{i+\frac{1}{2}}} \quad \text{(9.335)}$$

or, with the grid dimensions in Fig. 9.6,

$$\frac{k_{rl_{i-1}} - k_{rl_{i+\frac{1}{2}}}}{\delta^+_{i-1} + \delta^-_i + \delta^+_i} = \frac{k_{rl_i} - k_{rl_{i+\frac{1}{2}}}}{\delta^+_i}. \quad \text{(9.336)}$$

Multiplying through by the denominators,

$$\delta^+_i\left(k_{rl_{i-1}} - k_{rl_{i+\frac{1}{2}}}\right) = \left(\delta^+_{i-1} + \delta^-_i + \delta^+_i\right)\left(k_{rl_i} - k_{rl_{i+\frac{1}{2}}}\right). \quad \text{(9.337)}$$

Solving for $k_{rl_{i+\frac{1}{2}}}$,

$$\left(\delta^+_{i-1} + \delta^-_i + \delta^+_i - \delta^+_i\right)k_{rl_{i+\frac{1}{2}}} = \left(\delta^+_{i-1} + \delta^-_i + \delta^+_i\right)k_{rl_i} - \delta^+_i k_{rl_{i-1}} \quad \text{(9.338)}$$

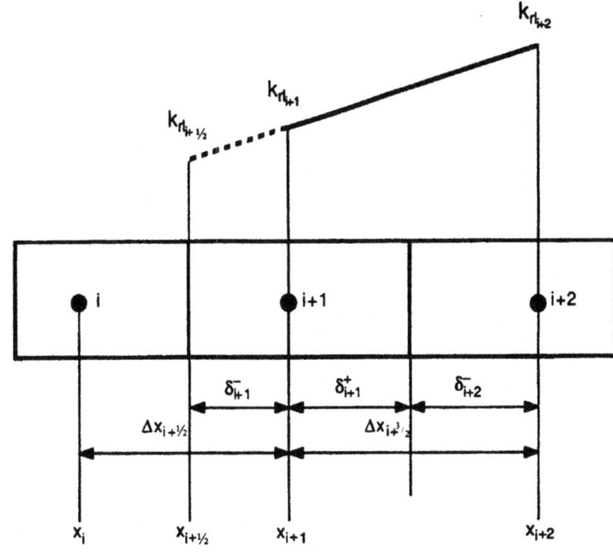

Fig. 9.7—Linear extrapolation of k_{rl} for flow from $i+1$ to i.

$$\text{or } k_{rl_{i+\frac{1}{2}}} = \left(\frac{\delta^+_{i-1} + \delta^-_i + \delta^+_i}{\delta^+_{i-1} + \delta^-_i}\right)k_{rl_i} - \left(\frac{\delta^+_i}{\delta^+_{i-1} + \delta^-_i}\right)k_{rl_{i-1}}, \quad \text{(9.339)}$$

which can be put in the form of Eq. 9.328 for $k_{rl_{i+\frac{1}{2}}}$.

$$k_{rl_{i+\frac{1}{2}}} = (1 + \Omega_i)k_{rl_i} - \Omega_i k_{rl_{i-1}}, \quad \text{(9.340)}$$

$$\text{where } \Omega_i = \frac{\delta^+_i}{\delta^+_{i-1} + \delta^-_i} = \frac{\delta^+_i}{\Delta x_{i-\frac{1}{2}}}. \quad \text{(9.341)}$$

For block-centered grid systems,

$$\Omega_i = \frac{1}{2}\frac{\Delta x_i}{\Delta x_{i-\frac{1}{2}}}, \quad \text{(9.342)}$$

where $0 < \Omega_i < 1$, and for point-distributed grid systems,

$$\Omega_i = \frac{1}{2}\frac{\Delta x_{i+\frac{1}{2}}}{\Delta x_{i-\frac{1}{2}}}, \quad \text{(9.343)}$$

where $\Omega_i > 0$. For regular grid-size distributions, $\Delta x_i = \Delta x_{i+\frac{1}{2}} = \Delta x_{i-\frac{1}{2}}$. Hence,

$$\Omega_i = \tfrac{1}{2}, \quad \text{(9.344)}$$

For flow from $i+1$ to i, the downstream point is i and the upstream points are $i+1$ and $i+2$. Referring to **Fig. 9.7**, the linear-extrapolation equation is

$$\frac{k_{rl_{i+2}} - k_{rl_{i+\frac{1}{2}}}}{x_{i+2} - x_{i+\frac{1}{2}}} = \frac{k_{rl_{i+1}} - k_{rl_{i+\frac{1}{2}}}}{x_{i+1} - x_{i+\frac{1}{2}}} \quad \text{(9.345)}$$

$$\text{or } \frac{k_{rl_{i+2}} - k_{rl_{i+\frac{1}{2}}}}{\delta^-_{i+1} + \delta^+_{i+1} + \delta^-_{i+2}} = \frac{k_{rl_{i+1}} - k_{rl_{i+\frac{1}{2}}}}{\delta^-_{i+1}}, \quad \text{(9.346)}$$

which can be solved for $k_{rl_{i+\frac{1}{2}}}$. Multiplying through by the denominators,

$$\delta^-_{i+1}\left(k_{rl_{i+2}} - k_{rl_{i+\frac{1}{2}}}\right) = \left(\delta^-_{i+1} + \delta^+_{i+1} + \delta^-_{i+2}\right)\left(k_{rl_{i+1}} - k_{rl_{i+\frac{1}{2}}}\right). \quad \text{(9.347)}$$

Factoring out $k_{rl_{i+\frac{1}{2}}}$,

$$\left(-\delta^-_{i+1} + \delta^-_{i+1} + \delta^+_{i+1} + \delta^-_{i+2}\right)k_{rl_{i+\frac{1}{2}}} = \left(\delta^-_{i+1} + \delta^+_{i+1} + \delta^-_{i+2}\right)k_{rl_{i+1}} - \delta^-_{i+1}k_{rl_{i+2}}. \quad \text{(9.348)}$$

Finally, solving for $k_{rl_{i+½}}$,

$$k_{rl_{i+½}} = \left(\frac{\delta_{i+1}^- + \delta_{i+1}^+ + \delta_{i+2}^-}{\delta_{i+1}^+ + \delta_{i+2}^-}\right)k_{rl_{i+1}} - \left(\frac{\delta_{i+1}^-}{\delta_{i+1}^+ + \delta_{i+2}^-}\right)k_{rl_{i+2}} \qquad (9.349)$$

or $k_{rl_{i+½}} = (1 + \Omega_{i+1})k_{rl_{i+1}} - \Omega_{i+1}k_{rl_{i+2}}$, ... (9.350)

where $\Omega_{i+1} = \dfrac{\delta_{i+1}^-}{\delta_{i+1}^+ + \delta_{i+2}^-} = \dfrac{\delta_{i+1}^-}{\Delta x_{i+3/2}}$. .... (9.351)

For block-centered grid systems,

$$\Omega_{i+1} = \frac{1}{2}\frac{\Delta x_{i+1}}{\Delta x_{i+3/2}}, \qquad (9.352)$$

where $0 < \Omega_{i+1} < 1$, and for point-distributed grid systems,

$$\Omega_{i+1} = \frac{1}{2}\frac{\Delta x_{i+½}}{\Delta x_{i+3/2}}, \qquad (9.353)$$

where $\Omega_{i+1} > 0$. For regular grid-size distributions, $\Delta x_{i+1} = \Delta x_{i+½} = \Delta x_{i+3/2}$. Hence,

$$\Omega_{i+1} = ½. \qquad (9.354)$$

Because the two-point upstream weighting of k_{rl} is an extrapolation scheme, it is possible to obtain values for $k_{rl_{i+½}} > 1$ or $k_{rl_{i+½}} < 0$. Therefore, it is necessary to impose constraints on the extrapolated values. These constraints keep $k_{rl_{i+½}}$ within the physically acceptable range of $0 \leqq k_{rl_{i+½}} \leqq 1$.

Eqs. 9.340 and 9.350 are rewritten here for $\Omega_i = \Omega_{i+1} = ½$ for regular block-centered or point-distributed grids as

$$k_{rl_{i+½}} = 1.5k_{rl_i} - 0.5k_{rl_{i-1}} \qquad (9.355a)$$

if flow of Phase l is from i to $i+1$, and

$$k_{rl_{i+½}} = 1.5k_{rl_{i+1}} - 0.5k_{rl_{i+2}} \qquad (9.355b)$$

if flow of Phase l is from $i+1$ to i. This is the Todd *et al.*[5] two-point upstream relative permeability formula.

Example 9.18. Derive the equations for Wheatley's version of two-point upstream weighting of $k_{rl_{i+½}}$.

Solution. The two-point upstream weighting of $k_{rl_{i+½}}$ is an approximation expressed in terms of k_{rl} for the two points that are upstream to $i+½$, whereas Wheatley's version is an approximation of $k_{rl_{i+½}}$ in terms of k_{rl} for the upstream and downstream points. Therefore, k_{rl} for the downstream point has to be incorporated into the approximation of two-point upstream weighting.

For flow from i to $i+1$, the upstream point is i and the downstream point is $i+1$. The two-point upstream weighting formula was obtained in Example 9.17 as

$$k_{rl_{i+½}} = (1 + \Omega_i)k_{rl_i} - \Omega_i k_{rl_{i-1}}, \qquad (9.340)$$

where $\Omega_i = \dfrac{\delta_i^+}{\delta_{i-1}^+ + \delta_i^-} = \dfrac{\delta_i^+}{\Delta x_{i-½}}$. .... (9.341)

Add and subtract $k_{rl_{i+1}}$ for the downstream point to the right side of Eq. 9.340.

$$\begin{aligned} k_{rl_{i+½}} &= (1 + \Omega_i)k_{rl_i} - \Omega_i k_{rl_{i-1}} - k_{rl_{i+1}} + k_{rl_{i+1}} \\ &= k_{rl_{i+1}} - \left[-(1 + \Omega_i)k_{rl_i} + \Omega_i k_{rl_{i-1}} + k_{rl_{i+1}}\right] \\ &= k_{rl_{i+1}} - \left[-k_{rl_i} - \Omega_i k_{rl_i} + \Omega_i k_{rl_{i-1}} + k_{rl_{i+1}}\right] \\ &= k_{rl_{i+1}} - \left[\left(k_{rl_{i+1}} - k_{rl_i}\right) + \Omega_i\left(k_{rl_{i-1}} - k_{rl_i}\right)\right] \\ &= k_{rl_{i+1}} - \left[1 - \Omega_i\left(\frac{k_{rl_i} - k_{rl_{i-1}}}{k_{rl_{i+1}} - k_{rl_i}}\right)\right]\left(k_{rl_{i+1}} - k_{rl_i}\right) \\ &= \left[1 - \Omega_i\left(\frac{k_{rl_i} - k_{rl_{i-1}}}{k_{rl_{i+1}} - k_{rl_i}}\right)\right]k_{rl_i} \\ &\quad + \left[\Omega_i\left(\frac{k_{rl_i} - k_{rl_{i-1}}}{k_{rl_{i+1}} - k_{rl_i}}\right)\right]k_{rl_{i+1}} \qquad (9.356) \end{aligned}$$

If we define ω_i as

$$\omega_i = 1 - \Omega_i\left(\frac{k_{rl_i} - k_{rl_{i-1}}}{k_{rl_{i+1}} - k_{rl_i}}\right), \qquad (9.357)$$

then $k_{rl_{i+½}} = \omega_i k_{rl_i} + (1 - \omega_i)k_{rl_{i+1}}$. .... (9.358)

Eq. 9.358 still expresses $k_{rl_{i+½}}$ in terms of k_{rl_i}, $k_{rl_{i+1}}$, and $k_{rl_{i-1}}$; however, if ω_i is dated at Time Level n, it expresses $k_{rl_{i+½}}$ in terms of k_{rl_i} and $k_{rl_{i+1}}$ only.

$$k_{rl_{i+½}} = \omega_i^n k_{rl_i} + (1 - \omega_i^n)k_{rl_{i+1}}, \qquad (9.359)$$

where $\omega_i^n = 1 - \Omega_i\left(\dfrac{k_{rl_i}^n - k_{rl_{i-1}}^n}{k_{rl_{i+1}}^n - k_{rl_i}^n}\right)$ .... (9.360)

and $\Omega_i = \dfrac{\delta_i^+}{\delta_{i-1}^+ + \delta_i^-} = \dfrac{\delta_i^+}{\Delta x_{i-½}}$. .... (9.341)

For flow from $i+1$ to i, the upstream point is $i+1$ and the downstream point is i. The two-point upstream weighting formula was obtained in Example 9.17 as

$$k_{rl_{i+½}} = (1 + \Omega_{i+1})k_{rl_{i+1}} - \Omega_{i+1}k_{rl_{i+2}}, \qquad (9.350)$$

where $\Omega_{i+1} = \dfrac{\delta_{i+1}^-}{\delta_{i+1}^+ + \delta_{i+2}^-} = \dfrac{\delta_{i+1}^-}{\Delta x_{i+3/2}}$. .... (9.351)

Because $k_{rl_{i+½}}$ has to be expressed in terms of $k_{rl_{i+1}}$ and k_{rl_i}, add and subtract the missing term k_{rl_i} for the downstream point to the right side of Eq. 9.350.

$$\begin{aligned} k_{rl_{i+½}} &= (1 + \Omega_{i+1})k_{rl_{i+1}} - \Omega_{i+1}k_{rl_{i+2}} - k_{rl_i} + k_{rl_i} \\ &= k_{rl_i} + \left[(1 + \Omega_{i+1})k_{rl_{i+1}} - \Omega_{i+1}k_{rl_{i+2}} - k_{rl_i}\right] \\ &= k_{rl_i} + \left[\left(k_{rl_{i+1}} - k_{rl_i}\right) - \Omega_{i+1}\left(k_{rl_{i+2}} - k_{rl_{i+1}}\right)\right] \\ &= k_{rl_i} + \left[1 - \Omega_{i+1}\left(\frac{k_{rl_{i+2}} - k_{rl_{i+1}}}{k_{rl_{i+1}} - k_{rl_i}}\right)\right]\left(k_{rl_{i+1}} - k_{rl_i}\right) \\ &= \left[\Omega_{i+1}\left(\frac{k_{rl_{i+2}} - k_{rl_{i+1}}}{k_{rl_{i+1}} - k_{rl_i}}\right)\right]k_{rl_i} \\ &\quad + \left[1 - \Omega_{i+1}\left(\frac{k_{rl_{i+2}} - k_{rl_{i+1}}}{k_{rl_{i+1}} - k_{rl_i}}\right)\right]k_{rl_{i+1}}. \qquad (9.361) \end{aligned}$$

If we define ω_i as

$$\omega_i = \Omega_{i+1}\left(\frac{k_{rl_{i+2}} - k_{rl_{i+1}}}{k_{rl_{i+1}} - k_{rl_i}}\right), \qquad (9.362)$$

then $k_{rl_{i+½}} + \omega_i k_{rl_i} + (1 - \omega_i)k_{rl_{i+1}}$. .... (9.358)

TABLE 9.1—RESERVOIR AND GRIDBLOCK PROPERTIES FOR EXAMPLE 9.19

Layer	Δx (ft)	Δy (ft)	Δz (ft)	k_x (md)	k_y (md)	k_z (md)	Z (ft)	ϕ	p_i (psia)
3 (top)	1,000	1,000	20	500	500	50	8,335	0.30	4,783.5
2	1,000	1,000	30	50	50	50	8,360	0.30	4,789.8
1 (bottom)	1,000	1,000	50	200	200	19.23	8,400	0.30	4,800.0

TABLE 9.2—FLUID PVT DATA IN PRESSURE RANGE OF INTEREST FOR EXAMPLE 9.19

		Oil			Gas		
p (psia)	R_s (scf/STB)	B_o (RB/STB)	μ_o (cp)	ρ_o (lbm/ft³)	B_g (RB/scf)	μ_g (cp)	ρ_g (lbm/ft³)
3,014.7	930.	1.5650	0.5940	37.781	0.00108	0.0228	9.984
4,014.7	1,270.	1.6950	0.5100	37.046	0.00081	0.0268	13.295
5,014.7	1,618.	1.8270	0.4490	36.424	0.00065	0.0309	16.614

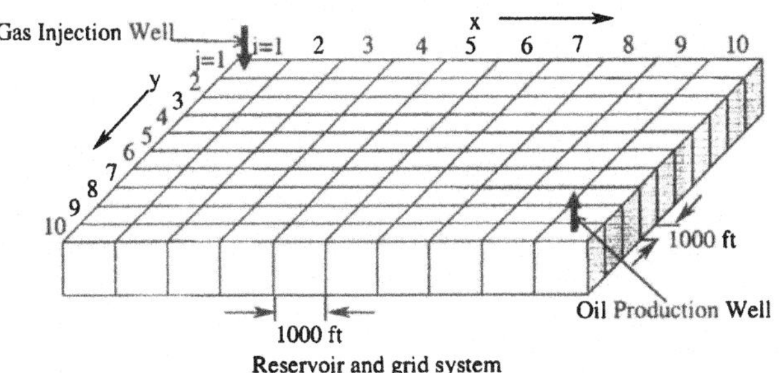

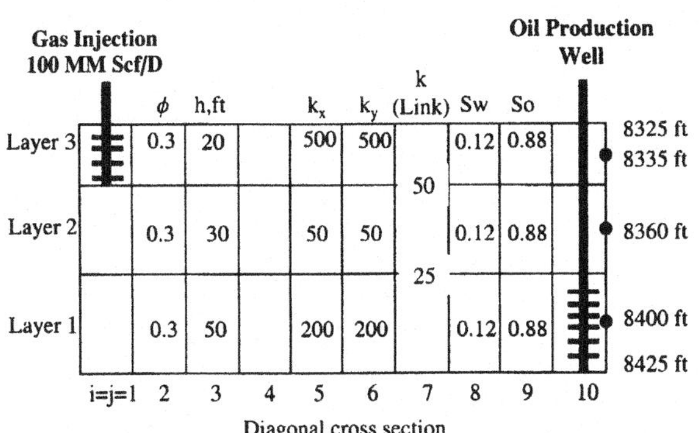

Fig. 9.8—Grid system and diagonal cross section of the reservoir described in Example 9.19 (after Odeh[7]).

TABLE 9.3—TWO-PHASE OIL/GAS RELATIVE PERMEABILITY AND CAPILLARY PRESSURE DATA (FROM ODEH[7])

S_g	k_{rg}	k_{ro}	P_{cgo}
0.000	0.0000	1.0000	0.0
0.001	0.0000	1.0000	0.0
0.020	0.0000	0.9970	0.0
0.050	0.0050	0.9800	0.0
0.120	0.0250	0.7000	0.0
0.200	0.0750	0.3500	0.0
0.250	0.1250	0.2000	0.0
0.300	0.1900	0.0900	0.0
0.400	0.4100	0.0210	0.0
0.450	0.6000	0.0100	0.0
0.500	0.7200	0.0010	0.0
0.600	0.8700	0.0001	0.0
0.700	0.9400	0.0000	0.0
0.850	1.0000	0.0000	0.0

TABLE 9.4—OIL PRESSURE AND FLUID SATURATIONS AT THE WELLBLOCK AND ITS NEIGHBORING GRIDBLOCKS

Gridblock (i,j,k)	p_o (psia)	S_o	S_g	S_w
(10,10,1)	3,315.7	0.6406	0.2391	0.1203
(9,10,1)	3,533.9	0.8520	0.0267	0.1212
(10,9,1)	3,533.9	0.8520	0.0267	0.1212
(10,10,2)	3,325.4	0.5258	0.3541	0.1200
(8,10,1)	3,661.5	0.8528	0.0259	0.1213
(10,10,3)	3,325.3	0.3963	0.4837	0.1200

To express $k_{rl_{i+1/2}}$ in terms of k_{rl_i} and $k_{rl_{i+1}}$ only, ω_i must be dated at Time Level n.

$$k_{rl_{i+1/2}} = \omega_i^n k_{rl_i} + \left(1 - \omega_i^n\right) k_{rl_{i+1}}, \qquad (9.359)$$

$$\text{where } \omega_i^n = \Omega_{i+1}\left(\frac{k^n_{rl_{i+2}} - k^n_{rl_{i+1}}}{k^n_{rl_{i+1}} - k^n_{rl_i}}\right) \qquad (9.363)$$

$$\text{and } \Omega_{i+1} = \frac{\delta^-_{i+1}}{\delta^+_{i+1} + \delta^-_{i+2}} = \frac{\delta^-_{i+1}}{\Delta x_{i+3/2}}. \qquad (9.351)$$

Example 9.19. Consider the oil reservoir described by Odeh[7] and shown in **Fig. 9.8.** It is one-quarter of five-spot pattern (with no flow boundaries). The reservoir consists of three layers showing vertical heterogeneity. It is discretized into $10 \times 10 \times 3$ equal gridblocks with a block-centered grid. **Table 9.1** reports gridblock properties, dimensions, and initial conditions. Initially, the reservoir is undersaturated with R_{si} = 1,270 scf/STB. Initial fluid saturations are $S_{oi} = 0.88$ and $S_{wi} = S_{iw} = 0.12$. **Tables 9.2 and 9.3** give PVT data and relative permeability data, respectively.

Gas is injected in the Upper Corner Gridblock (1,1,3) at a rate of 100 MMscf/D and oil is produced from the Lower Corner Gridblock (10,10,1) at a rate of 20 MSTB/D as long as $p_{w_f} \geqq 1{,}000$ psia, then the production well is operated with constant bottomhole pressure p_{wf} = 1,000 psia until t = 10 years.

Table 9.4 reports the oil pressure and fluid saturations for Production Wellblock (10,10,1) and its neighboring gridblocks, Gridblocks (9,10,1), (10,9,1), (10,10,2), (8,10,1) and (10,10,3) at t = 10 years.

Consider the horizontal flow component of oil in the x direction between Gridblocks (9,10,1) and (10,10,1). Calculate the elements G, f_p, and f_s for $T_{ox_{9½,10,1}}$ and compare the results obtained for different weighting methods discussed in the text.

Solution. In **Table 9.5**, the oil properties B_o, μ_o, and ρ_o at gridblock pressures and k_{ro} at gridblock gas saturation are calculated with linear interpolation (see Appendix A). Also, at $\bar{p}$ = (3,315.7 + 3,533.9)/2 = 3,424.8 psia, B_o = 1.6183 RB/STB and μ_o = 0.5596 cp.

Eq. 9.267 for $l = o$ expresses the oil-phase transmissibility in the x direction between Gridblocks (10,10,1) and (9,10,1), with (i,j,k) representing (10,10,1).

$$T_{ox_{i-1/2,j,k}} = \beta_c \left(\frac{k_x A_x}{\Delta x}\right)_{i-1/2,j,k} \left(\frac{1}{\mu_o B_o}\right)_{i-1/2,j,k} k_{ro_{i-1/2,j,k}} \qquad (9.364)$$

TABLE 9.5—FLUID PROPERTIES CALCULATED BY LINEAR INTERPOLATION

Gridblock (i,j,k)	p_o (psia)	B_o (RB/STB)	μ_o (cp)	ρ_o (lbm/ft^3)	S_g	k_{ro}
(10,10,1)	3,315.7	1.6041	0.5687	37.560	0.2391	0.2327
(9,10,1)	3,533.9	1.6325	0.5504		0.0267	0.9932
(10,9,1)	3,533.9	1.6325	0.5504		0.0267	0.9932
(10,10,2)	3,325.4	1.6054	0.5679	37.553	0.3541	0.0527
(8,10,1)					0.0259	0.9937
(10,10,3)					0.4837	0.0039

or $T_{ox_{i-½,j,k}} = Gf_pf_s$, ... (9.365)

where $G = \beta_c\left(\dfrac{k_xA_x}{\Delta x}\right)_{i-½,j,k}$, ... (9.366)

$$f_p = \left(\frac{1}{\mu_oB_o}\right)_{i-½,j,k}, \quad (9.367)$$

and $f_s = k_{ro_{i-½,j,k}}$. .... (9.368)

In calculating G, the geometric factor $\beta_c[k_xA_x/\Delta x]_{i-½,j,k}$ for a block-centered grid system is expressed by Eq. 9.274.

$$\beta_c\left(\frac{k_xA_x}{\Delta x}\right)_{i-½,j,k} = \beta_c\frac{2A_{x_{i,j,k}}k_{x_{i,j,k}}A_{x_{i-1,j,k}}k_{x_{i-1,j,k}}}{A_{x_{i,j,k}}k_{x_{i,j,k}}\Delta x_{i-1,j,k} + A_{x_{i-1,j,k}}k_{x_{i-1,j,k}}\Delta x_{i,j,k}}, \quad (9.369)$$

where, in this problem,

$$A_{x_{i,j,k}} = A_{x_{i-1,j,k}} = A_x = \Delta y_{i,j,k}\Delta z_{i,j,k} = 1,000 \times 50 \text{ ft}^2,$$

$$k_{x_{i,j,k}} = k_{x_{i-1,j,k}} = k_x = 0.200 \text{ darcy},$$

and $\Delta x_{i,j,k} = \Delta x_{i-1,j,k} = \Delta x = 1,000$ ft.

Because A_x, k_x, and Δx are all uniform, Eq. 9.369 reduces to (see Example 9.16, Part 7),

$$\beta_c\left(\frac{k_xA_x}{\Delta x}\right)_{i-½,j,k} = \beta_c\frac{k_xA_x}{\Delta x} \quad (9.370)$$

$$= \frac{(1.127)0.200(1,000 \times 50)}{1,000}$$

$$= 11.27 \text{ cp-RB/D-psi}.$$

To calculate the weak nonlinearity, f_p may be approximated in four different ways: one that uses upstream weighting and three that use midpoint weighting.

For upstream weighting, determine the upstream gridblock for the oil phase, between Gridblocks (10,10,1) and (9,10,1).

$$\Delta\Phi_{o_{i-½,j,k}} = \left(p_{o_{i-1,j,k}} - p_{o_{i,j,k}}\right) - \gamma_{o_{i-½,j,k}}\left(Z_{i-1,j,k} - Z_{i,j,k}\right) \quad (9.371)$$

$$= 3,533.9 - 3,315.7 - \gamma_{o_{i-½,j,k}}(8,400 - 8,400)$$

$$= 218.2 \text{ psi}.$$

Therefore, Gridblock (9,10,1) defined here as $(i-1,j,k)$, is the upstream gridblock. Hence, for upstream weighting,

$$f_p = \left(\frac{1}{\mu_oB_o}\right)_{i-1,j,k} \quad (9.372)$$

$$= \frac{1}{0.5504 \times 1.6325}$$

$$= 1.113 \text{ STB/RB-cp}.$$

For midpoint weighting by Method 1,

$$f_p = \frac{1}{2}\left[\left(\frac{1}{\mu_oB_o}\right)_{i-1,j,k} + \left(\frac{1}{\mu_oB_o}\right)_{i,j,k}\right] \quad (9.373)$$

$$= \frac{1}{2}\left(\frac{1}{0.5504 \times 1.6325} + \frac{1}{0.5687 \times 1.6041}\right)$$

$$= 1.105 \text{ STB/RB-cp};$$

or, by Method 2,

$$f_p = \left[\frac{1}{\mu_o(\bar{p}_o)B_o(\bar{p}_o)}\right] \quad (9.374)$$

$$= \frac{1}{0.5596 \times 1.6183}$$

$$= 1.104 \text{ STB/RB-cp},$$

where $\bar{p} = (p_{o_{i-1,j,k}} + p_{o_{i,j,k}})/2$ and because $\bar{p}_o = 3,424.8$ psia; or, by Method 3,

$$f_p = \left[\frac{1}{\bar{\mu}_o\bar{B}_o}\right] = \frac{1}{[(\mu_{o_{i-1,j,k}} + \mu_{o_{i,j,k}})/2][(B_{o_{i-1,j,k}} + B_{o_{i,j,k}})/2]} \quad (9.375)$$

$$= \frac{1}{[(0.5504 + 0.5687)/2][(1.6325 + 1.6041)/2]}$$

$$= 1.104 \text{ STB/RB-cp}.$$

For this example, the four different approximation methods for the weak nonlinearity, f_p, produce reasonably close results ($f_p = 1.113$, 1.105, 1.104, or 1.104).

To calculate strong nonlinearity, f_s, for single-point upstream weighting,

$$f_s = k_{ro_{i-1,j,k}} \quad (9.376)$$

$$= k_{ro}(S_g = 0.0267)$$

$$= 0.9932$$

because $(i-1,j,k)$ is upstream to (i,j,k). For two-point upstream weighting where grid size is uniform,

$$f_s = 1.5 \times k_{ro_{i-1,j,k}} - 0.5 \times k_{ro_{i-2,j,k}} \quad (9.377)$$

$$= 1.5 \times (k_{ro})_{S_g=0.0267} - 0.5 \times (k_{ro})_{S_g=0.0259}$$

$$= 1.5 \times 0.9932 - 0.5 \times 0.9937$$

$$= 0.9930.$$

To calculate the value of f_s for midpoint weighting,

$$f_s = k_{ro_{i-½,j,k}} = \frac{1}{2}\left[k_{ro_{i-1,j,k}} + k_{ro_{i,j,k}}\right] \quad (9.378)$$

$$= \frac{1}{2}\left[(k_{ro})_{S_g=0.0267} + (k_{ro})_{S_g=0.2391}\right]$$

$$= \frac{1}{2}(0.9932 + 0.2327)$$

$$= 0.6130.$$

The weighting of the strong nonlinearity f_s provided by the single-point upstream and two-point upstream methods are very close ($f_s = 0.9932$ or 0.9930), while both estimates are noticeably different from the midpoint weighting ($f_s = 0.6130$).

Example 9.20. Given the oil reservoir described in Example 9.19, calculate the interblock oil-flow-rate components in the *x, y,* and *z* directions between Production Gridblock (10,10,1) and its neighboring gridblocks at $t = 10$ years. Use the single-point upstream weighting for the approximation of interblock transmissibilities.

Solution. The implicit finite-difference equation for oil written for Gridblock (10,10,1), defined here as *(i,j,k)*, is expressed as Eq. 9.224.

$$\Delta[\mathrm{T}_o(\Delta p_o - \gamma_o \Delta Z)]^{n+1}_{i,j,k} = \left(C_{op}\Delta_t p_o + C_{ow}\Delta_t S_w + C_{og}\Delta_t S_g - q^{n+1}_{osc}\right)_{i,j,k}, \quad (9.379)$$

where

$$\Delta[\mathrm{T}_o(\Delta p_o - \gamma_o \Delta Z)]_{i,j,k} = \Delta(\mathrm{T}_o \Delta p_o)_{i,j,k} - \Delta(\mathrm{T}_o \gamma_o \Delta Z)_{i,j,k}. \quad (9.380)$$

With the expansion of the space operators on the right side of Eq. 9.380 defined by Eq. 9.97,

$$\Delta(\mathrm{T}_o \Delta p_o)_{i,j,k} \equiv \Delta_x(\mathrm{T}_{ox}\Delta_x p_o)_{i,j,k} + \Delta_y(\mathrm{T}_{oy}\Delta_y p_o)_{i,j,k} + \Delta_z(\mathrm{T}_{oz}\Delta_z p_o)_{i,j,k} \quad (9.381)$$

and

$$\Delta(\mathrm{T}_o \gamma_o \Delta Z)_{i,j,k} \equiv \Delta_x(\mathrm{T}_{ox}\gamma_o \Delta_x Z)_{i,j,k} + \Delta_y(\mathrm{T}_{oy}\gamma_o \Delta_y Z)_{i,j,k} + \Delta_z(\mathrm{T}_{oz}\gamma_o \Delta_z Z)_{i,j,k}. \quad (9.382)$$

In the development of Eq. 9.381, we let ξ in Eq. 9.97 equal T_o and $\eta = p_o$. In the development of Eq. 9.382, we let $\xi = \mathrm{T}_o\gamma_o$ and $\eta = Z$.

Again, the expansion of the space operators on the right side of Eqs. 9.381 and 9.382 are obtained by applying the definitions given by Eqs. 9.81, 9.85, and 9.91. Apply Eq. 9.98 to Eq. 9.381, where ξ_x, ξ_y, and ξ_z assume the values of T_{ox}, T_{oy}, and T_{oz}, respectively, and η assumes the value of p_o. The resulting expansion is

$$\begin{aligned}\Delta(\mathrm{T}_o \Delta p_o)_{i,j,k} &= \mathrm{T}_{ox_{i-1/2,j,k}}\left(p_{o_{i-1,j,k}} - p_{o_{i,j,k}}\right) + \mathrm{T}_{ox_{i+1/2,j,k}}\left(p_{o_{i+1,j,k}} - p_{o_{i,j,k}}\right) \\ &+ \mathrm{T}_{oy_{i,j-1/2,k}}\left(p_{o_{i,j-1,k}} - p_{o_{i,j,k}}\right) + \mathrm{T}_{oy_{i,j+1/2,k}}\left(p_{o_{i,j+1,k}} - p_{o_{i,j,k}}\right) \\ &+ \mathrm{T}_{oz_{i,j,k-1/2}}\left(p_{o_{i,j,k-1}} - p_{o_{i,j,k}}\right) + \mathrm{T}_{oz_{i,j,k+1/2}}\left(p_{o_{i,j,k+1}} - p_{o_{i,j,k}}\right). \quad (9.383)\end{aligned}$$

For Eq. 9.382, we let ξ_x, ξ_y, ξ_z, and η assume $\mathrm{T}_{ox}\gamma_o, \mathrm{T}_{oy}\gamma_o, \mathrm{T}_{oz}\gamma_o$, and Z, respectively. The resulting expansion is

$$\begin{aligned}\Delta(\mathrm{T}_o \gamma_o \Delta Z)_{i,j,k} &= (\mathrm{T}_{ox}\gamma_o)_{i-1/2,j,k}\left(Z_{i-1,j,k} - Z_{i,j,k}\right) + (\mathrm{T}_{ox}\gamma_o)_{i+1/2,j,k}\left(Z_{i+1,j,k} - Z_{i,j,k}\right) \\ &+ (\mathrm{T}_{oy}\gamma_o)_{i,j-1/2,k}\left(Z_{i,j-1,k} - Z_{i,j,k}\right) + (\mathrm{T}_{oy}\gamma_o)_{i,j+1/2,k}\left(Z_{i,j+1,k} - Z_{i,j,k}\right) \\ &+ (\mathrm{T}_{oz}\gamma_o)_{i,j,k-1/2}\left(Z_{i,j,k-1} - Z_{i,j,k}\right) + (\mathrm{T}_{oz}\gamma_o)_{i,j,k+1/2}\left(Z_{i,j,k+1} - Z_{i,j,k}\right). \quad (9.384)\end{aligned}$$

Substituting Eqs. 9.383 and 9.384 into Eq. 9.380 and combining the resulting equation with Eq. 9.379 yields

$$\begin{aligned}&\mathrm{T}^{n+1}_{ox_{i-1/2,j,k}}\left[\left(p^{n+1}_{o_{i-1,j,k}} - p^{n+1}_{o_{i,j,k}}\right) - \gamma^{n+1}_{o_{i-1/2,j,k}}\left(Z_{i-1,j,k} - Z_{i,j,k}\right)\right] \\ &+ \mathrm{T}^{n+1}_{ox_{i+1/2,j,k}}\left[\left(p^{n+1}_{o_{i+1,j,k}} - p^{n+1}_{o_{i,j,k}}\right) - \gamma^{n+1}_{o_{i+1/2,j,k}}\left(Z_{i+1,j,k} - Z_{i,j,k}\right)\right] \\ &+ \mathrm{T}^{n+1}_{oy_{i,j-1/2,k}}\left[\left(p^{n+1}_{o_{i,j-1,k}} - p^{n+1}_{o_{i,j,k}}\right) - \gamma^{n+1}_{o_{i,j-1/2,k}}\left(Z_{i,j-1,k} - Z_{i,j,k}\right)\right] \\ &+ \mathrm{T}^{n+1}_{oy_{i,j+1/2,k}}\left[\left(p^{n+1}_{o_{i,j+1,k}} - p^{n+1}_{o_{i,j,k}}\right) - \gamma^{n+1}_{o_{i,j+1/2,k}}\left(Z_{i,j+1,k} - Z_{i,j,k}\right)\right] \\ &+ \mathrm{T}^{n+1}_{oz_{i,j,k-1/2}}\left[\left(p^{n+1}_{o_{i,j,k-1}} - p^{n+1}_{o_{i,j,k}}\right) - \gamma^{n+1}_{o_{i,j,k-1/2}}\left(Z_{i,j,k-1} - Z_{i,j,k}\right)\right] \\ &+ \mathrm{T}^{n+1}_{oz_{i,j,k+1/2}}\left[\left(p^{n+1}_{o_{i,j,k+1}} - p^{n+1}_{o_{i,j,k}}\right) - \gamma^{n+1}_{o_{i,j,k+1/2}}\left(Z_{i,j,k+1} - Z_{i,j,k}\right)\right] \\ &= \left(C_{op}\Delta_t p_o + C_{ow}\Delta_t S_w + C_{og}\Delta_t S_g - q^{n+1}_{osc}\right)_{i,j,k}. \quad (9.385)\end{aligned}$$

For interior gridblocks, the first, third, and fifth terms on the left side of Eq. 9.385 represent the interblock oil flow rates between Gridblock *(i,j,k)* and its neighboring gridblocks in the negative *x, y,* and *z* directions, respectively. The second, fourth, and sixth terms on the left side of Eq. 9.385 represent interblock oil flow rates between Gridblock *(i,j,k)* and its neighboring gridblocks in the positive *x, y,* and *z* directions, respectively.

For Production Gridblock (10,10,1), there are three no-flow boundaries in the negative direction of *z* and the positive directions of *x* and *y*. Therefore, the second, fourth, and fifth terms on the left side of Eq. 9.385 can be set equal to zero for this gridblock (see Example 5.5). The first, third, and sixth terms on the left side represent, respectively, the interblock flow rates $q^{n+1}_{ox_{i-1/2,j,k}}$, $q^{n+1}_{oy_{i,j-1/2,k}}$ and $q^{n+1}_{oz_{i,j,k+1/2}}$ for the production gridblock. In other words,

$$q^{n+1}_{ox_{i-1/2,j,k}} = \mathrm{T}^{n+1}_{ox_{i-1/2,j,k}}\left[\left(p^{n+1}_{o_{i-1,j,k}} - p^{n+1}_{o_{i,j,k}}\right) - \gamma^{n+1}_{o_{i-1/2,j,k}}\left(Z_{i-1,j,k} - Z_{i,j,k}\right)\right], \quad (9.386)$$

$$q^{n+1}_{oy_{i,j-1/2,k}} = \mathrm{T}^{n+1}_{oy_{i,j-1/2,k}}\left[\left(p^{n+1}_{o_{i,j-1,k}} - p^{n+1}_{o_{i,j,k}}\right) - \gamma^{n+1}_{o_{i,j-1/2,k}}\left(Z_{i,j-1,k} - Z_{i,j,k}\right)\right], \quad (9.387)$$

and

$$q^{n+1}_{oz_{i,j,k+1/2}} = \mathrm{T}^{n+1}_{oz_{i,j,k+1/2}}\left[\left(p^{n+1}_{o_{i,j,k+1}} - p^{n+1}_{o_{i,j,k}}\right) - \gamma^{n+1}_{o_{i,j,k+1/2}}\left(Z_{i,j,k+1} - Z_{i,j,k}\right)\right]. \quad (9.388)$$

Applying Eqs. 9.63 through 9.65 for directional transmissibilities,

$$\mathrm{T}_{ox_{i-1/2,j,k}} = \beta_c\left(\frac{k_x A_x}{\Delta x}\right)_{i-1/2,j,k}\left(\frac{1}{\mu_o B_o}\right)_{i-1/2,j,k} k_{ro_{i-1/2,j,k}}, \quad (9.389)$$

$$T_{oy_{i,j-1/2,k}} = \beta_c \left(\frac{k_y A_y}{\Delta y}\right)_{i,j-1/2,k} \left(\frac{1}{\mu_o B_o}\right)_{i,j-1/2,k} k_{ro_{i,j-1/2,k}}, \quad \text{(9.390)}$$

$$\text{and } T_{oz_{i,j,k+1/2}} = \beta_c \left(\frac{k_z A_z}{\Delta z}\right)_{i,j,k+1/2} \left(\frac{1}{\mu_o B_o}\right)_{i,j,k+1/2} k_{ro_{i,j,k+1/2}}. \quad \text{(9.391)}$$

For the x component of interblock oil flow between Gridblocks (10,10,1) and (9,10,1) and for single-point upstream weighting, we obtained from Example 9.19,

$$\beta_c \left(\frac{k_x A_x}{\Delta x}\right)_{i-1/2,j,k} = 11.27 \text{ cp-RB/D-psi},$$

$$\left(\frac{1}{\mu_o B_o}\right)^{n+1}_{i-1/2,j,k} = 1.113 \text{ STB/RB-cp},$$

$$k^{n+1}_{ro_{i-1/2,j,k}} = 0.9932,$$

and $\Delta\Phi_{o_{i-1/2,j,k}} = 218.2$ psi.

Substituting the first three results into Eq. 9.389 results in

$$T_{ox_{i-1/2,j,k}} = 11.27 \times 1.113 \times 0.9932 = 12.458 \text{ STB/D-psi}.$$

Then, applying Eq. 9.386 and $\Delta\Phi_{o_{i-1/2,j,k}} = 218.2$ psi yields

$$q^{n+1}_{ox_{i-1/2,j,k}} = T_{ox_{i-1/2,j,k}} \Delta\Phi_{o_{i-1/2,j,k}} \quad \text{(9.392)}$$

$$= 12.458 \times 218.2$$

$$= 2{,}718.3 \text{ STB/D}.$$

For the y component of interblock oil flow between Gridblocks (10,10,1) and (10,9,1), there is symmetry about the vertical plane that passes through the centers of Gridblocks (1,1,1) and (10,10,1) because the reservoir is horizontal and $\Delta x = \Delta y$, $k_x = k_y$, and Δz, Z, and ϕ are constants for all the gridblocks (Table 9.1). This is in addition to having the plane of symmetry pass through the production and injection wells. Initial oil pressure and fluid saturations for Gridblocks (9,10,1) and (10,9,1) and those at $t = 10$ years confirm this symmetry. As a result of this symmetry

$$q^{n+1}_{oy_{i,j-1/2,k}} = q^{n+1}_{ox_{i-1/2,j,k}} \quad \text{(9.393)}$$

or $q^{n+1}_{oy_{i,j-1/2,k}} = 2{,}718.3$ STB/D.

Also, $q^{n+1}_{oy_{i,j-1/2,k}}$ and $T_{oy_{i,j-1/2,k}}$ can be estimated with Eq. 9.387 and Eq. 9.390, respectively, after the upstream point between Gridblocks (10,9,1) and (10,10,1) is determined for the oil phase.

For the z component of interblock oil flow between Gridblocks (10,10,1) and (10,10,2), the first step involves determining the upstream gridblock for the oil phase between Gridblocks (10,10,2) and (10,10,1).

$$\Delta\Phi^{n+1}_{o_{i,j,k+1/2}} = \left(p^{n+1}_{o_{i,j,k+1}} - p^{n+1}_{o_{i,j,k}}\right) - \gamma^{n+1}_{o_{i,j,k+1/2}}\left(Z_{i,j,k+1} - Z_{i,j,k}\right), \quad \text{(9.394)}$$

$$\text{where } \gamma^{n+1}_{o_{i,j,k+1/2}} = \bar{\gamma}^{n+1}_o = \frac{1}{2}\left(\gamma^{n+1}_{o_{i,j,k+1}} + \gamma^{n+1}_{o_{i,j,k}}\right) \quad \text{(9.395)}$$

$$= \frac{1}{2}\left[(0.21584 \times 10^{-3})37.553 \times 32.17 + (0.21584 \times 10^{-3})37.560 \times 32.17\right]$$

$$= 0.261 \text{ psi/ft}.$$

Therefore,

$$\Delta\Phi^{n+1}_{o_{i,j,k+1/2}} = (3{,}325.4 - 3{,}315.7) - 0.261(8{,}360 - 8{,}400)$$

$$= 9.7 + 10.44$$

$$= 20.14 \text{ psi}.$$

Because $\Delta\Phi_{o_{i,j,k+1/2}}$ is positive, Gridblock (10,10,2) is upstream to Gridblock (10,10,1) for the oil phase. Therefore, Eq. 9.391 becomes

$$T_{oz_{i,j,k+1/2}} = \beta_c \left(\frac{k_z A_z}{\Delta z}\right)_{i,j,k+1/2} \left(\frac{1}{\mu_o B_o}\right)^{n+1}_{i,j,k+1} k^{n+1}_{ro_{i,j,k+1}}, \quad \text{(9.396)}$$

with Eq. 9.276 for a block-centered grid,

$$\beta_c \left(\frac{k_z A_z}{\Delta z}\right)_{i,j,k+1/2} = \beta_c \frac{2A_{z_{i,j,k}} k_{z_{i,j,k}} A_{z_{i,j,k+1}} k_{z_{i,j,k+1}}}{A_{z_{i,j,k}} k_{z_{i,j,k}} \Delta z_{i,j,k+1} + A_{z_{i,j,k+1}} k_{z_{i,j,k+1}} \Delta z_{i,j,k}} \quad \text{(9.397)}$$

$$= \frac{(1.127)(2)(10^6)(0.01923)(10^6)(0.05)}{(10^6)(0.01923)(30) + (10^6)(0.05)(50)}$$

$$= 704.38 \text{ cp-RB/D-psi}.$$

Alternatively, because $A_{z_{i,j,k}} = A_{z_{i,j,k+1}} = A_z = 1{,}000 \times 1{,}000 = 10^6$ ft^2, we can calculate $\beta_c[(k_z A_z)/\Delta z]_{i,j,k+1/2}$ using the results of Example 9.16, Part 1.

$$\Delta z_{i,j,k+1/2} = \left(\Delta z_{i,j,k} + \Delta z_{i,j,k+1}\right)/2 \quad \text{(9.398)}$$

$$= (50 + 30)/2$$

$$= 40 \text{ ft}$$

$$\text{and } \frac{\Delta z_{i,j,k} + \Delta z_{i,j,k+1}}{k_{z_{i,j,k+1/2}}} = \frac{\Delta z_{i,j,k+1}}{k_{z_{i,j,k+1}}} + \frac{\Delta z_{i,j,k}}{k_{z_{i,j,k}}}, \quad \text{(9.399)}$$

which, on substitution of values gives

$$\frac{(50 + 30)}{k_{z_{i,j,k+1/2}}} = \frac{30}{0.05} + \frac{50}{0.01923},$$

which yields

$$k_{z_{i,j,k+1/2}} = 0.02500 \text{ darcy}.$$

Then, for G,

$$G = \beta_c \left(\frac{k_z A_z}{\Delta z}\right)_{i,j,k+1/2}$$

$$= \beta_c \frac{A_z k_{z_{i,j,k+1/2}}}{\Delta z_{i,j,k+1/2}} \quad \text{(9.400)}$$

$$= 1.127 \frac{10^6 \times 0.02500}{40}$$

$$= 707.38 \text{ cp-RB/D-psi}.$$

For f_p,

$$f_p = \left(\frac{1}{\mu_o B_o}\right)^{n+1}_{i,j,k+1/2}$$

$$= \left(\frac{1}{\mu_o B_o}\right)^{n+1}_{i,j,k+1} \quad \text{(9.401)}$$

$$= \frac{1}{0.5679 \times 1.6054}$$

$$= 1.097 \text{ STB/RB-cp},$$

and for f_s,

$$f_s = k_{ro_{i,j,k+½}}$$

$$= k_{ro_{i,j,k+1}} \quad \text{(9.402)}$$

$$= k_{ro}\left(S_g = 0.3541\right)$$

$$= 0.0527.$$

Therefore,

$$\mathrm{T}^{n+1}_{oz_{i,j,k+½}} = 704.38 \times 1.097 \times 0.0527$$

$$= 40.721 \text{ STB/D-psi}$$

and $q^{n+1}_{oz_{i,j,k+½}} = \mathrm{T}^{n+1}_{oz_{i,j,k+½}} \Delta\Phi^{n+1}_{o_{i,j,k+½}}$

$$= 40.721 \times 20.14$$

$$= 820.12 \text{ STB/D}.$$

Linearization of Weak Nonlinearities. As discussed previously, the pressure-dependent properties of the finite-difference equations represent weak nonlinearities. In this book, we have denoted these properties by the generic term f_p. The effect of these weak nonlinearities on the stability of a model depends on the magnitude of pressure change during a timestep. As Sec. 8.4.1 showed, several methods are available for linearizing pressure-dependent properties in single-phase-flow problems: the explicit method, the simple-iteration method, and the fully-implicit method. Although these methods are equally valid for multiphase-flow situations, we discuss only the explicit and fully-implicit treatments.

Explicit Method. Sec. 8.4.1 discussed the explicit treatment of $f^{n+1}_{p_{i+½}}$. This treatment involves approximating $f_{p_{i+½}}$ by its value at Time Level n,

$$f^{n+1}_{p_{i+½}} \approx f^{n}_{p_{i+½}} = f_{p_{i+½}}\left(p^{n}_{o_i}, p^{n}_{o_{i+1}}\right). \quad \text{(9.403)}$$

Implicit Method. The implicit treatment involves use of the first-order approximation,

$$f^{n+1}_{p_{i+½}} \approx \overset{(v+1)}{f^{n+1}_{p_{i+½}}}$$

$$\approx f^{(v)}_{p_{i+½}} + \left(\frac{\partial f_{p_{i+½}}}{\partial p_{o_i}}\right)^{(v)} \delta p_{o_i} + \left(\frac{\partial f_{p_{i+½}}}{\partial p_{o_{i+1}}}\right)^{(v)} \delta p_{o_{i+1}}. \quad \text{(9.404)}$$

It is recognized, however, that the linearization of weak nonlinearities generally is not crucial for the stability of the solution of the finite-difference equations. Therefore, it is acceptable to use the explicit linearization expressed by Eq. 9.403. The implicit treatment of weak nonlinearities expressed by Eq. 9.404 is used frequently in fully-implicit models linearized by Newton's iteration. Other linearization methods discussed in Sec. 8.4.1 may be used also.

Linearization of Strong Nonlinearities. The saturation-dependent properties in the finite-difference equations represent strong nonlinearities for multiphase-flow problems. In this book, we denote these strong nonlinearities by the generic term f_s. In contrast to the treatment of the weak nonlinearities, the assignment of the time level of the strong nonlinearities is crucial for the solution stability of finite-difference equations. Linearization methods range from the explicit treatment, which is conditionally stable, to the fully-implicit treatment, which is unconditionally stable. The basic methods used in linearizing the strong nonlinearities in the transmissibility, k_{rl} specifically, are discussed next.[2] We consider single-point upstream weighting of transmissibility in the following presentation.

Explicit Method. The explicit method, discussed for pressure-dependent properties in Sec. 8.4.1 for single-phase flow and in this section for multiphase flow, is the simplest and least stable method because the evaluation of f^{n+1}_s is allowed to lag one timestep behind the desired solution.

$$f^{n+1}_s \approx f^n_s = f_s\left(S^n_w, S^n_g\right). \quad \text{(9.405)}$$

This approximation is only conditionally stable, and it can cause severe stability problems especially in single-well simulation where high flow velocities are encountered because of near-wellbore flow convergence.

Extrapolation Method. The extrapolation method, discussed in Sec. 8.4.1 for pressure-dependent properties in single-phase flow, is also applicable for saturation-dependent properties. This method is based on

$$f^{n+1}_s \approx f^{*}_s = f_s\left(S^{*}_w, S^{*}_g\right), \quad \text{(9.406)}$$

where S^*_w and S^*_g = estimates of S^{n+1}_w and S^{n+1}_g extrapolated from Time Levels n and $n-1$.

$$S^{*}_l = S^n_l + \frac{\left(t^{n+1} - t^n\right)}{\left(t^n - t^{n-1}\right)}\left(S^n_l - S^{n-1}_l\right), \quad \text{(9.407)}$$

where $l = w$ or g. Because of the explicit nature of the extrapolation defined by Eq. 9.407, the use of Eq. 9.406 provides only a slight improvement in stability over that of Eq. 9.405.

Simple-Iteration Method. The simple-iteration method, discussed in Sec. 8.4.1, is one of the easiest methods to implement and the most frequently attempted method of linearization. In this method, f^{n+1}_s is evaluated one iteration behind the desired solution,

$$f^{n+1}_s \approx \overset{(v)}{f^{n+1}_s} = f^{(v)}_s = f_s\left[S^{(v)}_w, S^{(v)}_g\right]. \quad \text{(9.408)}$$

This linearization method has the same stability limit as that of the explicit method, and it may not converge when the stability limit on Δt is exceeded.

Linearized Implicit Method. The linearized implicit method is implemented in two steps. In the first step, f^{n+1}_s is approximated by use of the first-order terms of the Taylor's series expansion about the old time level n,

$$f^{n+1}_s \approx f^n_s + \left(\frac{\partial f_s}{\partial S_w}\right)^n \left(S^{n+1}_w - S^n_w\right) + \left(\frac{\partial f_s}{\partial S_g}\right)^n \left(S^{n+1}_g - S^n_g\right), \quad \text{(9.409)}$$

where $\left(\partial f_s / \partial S_l\right)^n$ = the partial derivative of f_s with respect to S_l evaluated at t^n and $\left(S^{n+1}_l - S^n_l\right)$ = the time difference of S_l for the upstream point of the phase under consideration ($l = o$ or w). The second step involves introducing the approximation given by Eq. 9.409 into the interblock flow terms and linearizing the nonlinear terms. For example, introducing Eq. 9.409 into the 1D difference operator $\Delta_x[\mathrm{T}_{ox}\Delta_x p_o]^{n+1}_i$ results in the flow terms,

$$\mathrm{T}^{n+1}_{ox_{i\pm½}}\left(p^{n+1}_{o_{i\pm1}} - p^{n+1}_{o_i}\right) \approx \left[\mathrm{T}^n_{ox_\pm} + \sum_{l=w,g}\left(\frac{\partial \mathrm{T}_{ox}}{\partial S_l}\right)^n_\pm \left(S^{n+1}_l - S^n_l\right)_\pm\right]$$

$$\times \left(p^{n+1}_{o_{i\pm1}} - p^{n+1}_{o_i}\right) \approx \mathrm{T}^n_{ox_\pm}\left(p^{n+1}_{o_{i\pm1}} - p^{n+1}_{o_i}\right)$$

$$+ \sum_{l=w,g}\left(\frac{\partial \mathrm{T}_{ox}}{\partial S_l}\right)^n_\pm \left(p^{n+1}_{o_{i\pm1}} - p^{n+1}_{o_i}\right)\left(S^{n+1}_l - S^n_l\right)_\pm, \quad \text{(9.410)}$$

where $\left(\frac{\partial \mathrm{T}_{ox}}{\partial S_l}\right)^n_\pm = \left[G f_{po}\left(\frac{\partial f_{so}}{\partial S_l}\right)^n\right]_\pm. \quad \text{(9.411)}$

$\mathrm{T}^n_{ox_+}$ and $\left(\partial \mathrm{T}_{ox}/\partial S_l\right)^n_+$ are T_{ox} and its partial derivative with respect to S_l at the upstream point between Gridblocks i and $i+1$, and $\mathrm{T}^n_{ox_-}$ and $\left(\partial \mathrm{T}_{ox}/\partial S_l\right)^n_-$ are T_{ox} and its partial derivative with respect to S_l at the upstream point between Gridblocks i and $i-1$. All are evaluated at Time Level n. The nonlinear terms inside the summation operator

$$\sum_{l=w,g}$$

may be linearized by the following assumption.

$$\left(\frac{\partial T_{ox}}{\partial S_l}\right)^n_{\pm}\left(p^{n+1}_{o_{i\pm1}} - p^{n+1}_{o_i}\right)\left(S^{n+1}_l - S^n_l\right)_{\pm}$$

$$\approx \left(\frac{\partial T_{ox}}{\partial S_l}\right)^n_{\pm}\left(p^n_{o_{i\pm1}} - p^n_{o_i}\right)\left(S^{n+1}_l - S^n_l\right)_{\pm}. \quad \ldots\ldots\ (9.412)$$

Substituting Eq. 9.412 into Eq. 9.410 yields the linearized interblock flow terms,

$$T^{n+1}_{ox_{i\pm1/2}}\left(p^{n+1}_{o_{i\pm1}} - p^{n+1}_{o_i}\right) \approx T^n_{ox_\pm}\left(p^{n+1}_{o_{i\pm1}} - p^{n+1}_{o_i}\right)$$

$$+ \sum_{l=w,g}\left(\frac{\partial T_{ox}}{\partial S_l}\right)^n_{\pm}\left(p^n_{o_{i\pm1}} - p^n_{o_i}\right)\left(S^{n+1}_l - S^n_l\right)_{\pm}. \quad \ldots\ (9.413)$$

Therefore, the linearized implicit approximation for the difference operator $\Delta_x[T_{px}\Delta_x p_o]^{n+1}_i$ for $p=o$, w, or g may be written as

$$\Delta_x\left[T_{px}\Delta_x p_o\right]^{n+1}_i \approx T^n_{px_+}\left(p^{n+1}_{o_{i+1}} - p^{n+1}_{o_i}\right) + T^n_{px_-}\left(p^{n+1}_{o_{i-1}} - p^{n+1}_{o_i}\right)$$

$$+ \sum_{l=w,g}\left(\frac{\partial T_{px}}{\partial S_l}\right)^n_{+}\left(p^n_{o_{i+1}} - p^n_{o_i}\right)\left(S^{n+1}_l - S^n_l\right)_{+}$$

$$+ \sum_{l=w,g}\left(\frac{\partial T_{px}}{\partial S_l}\right)^n_{-}\left(p^n_{o_{i-1}} - p^n_{o_i}\right)\left(S^{n+1}_l - S^n_l\right)_{-}, \quad \ldots\ (9.414)$$

where $p=o$, w, and g and

$$\left(\frac{\partial T_{wx}}{\partial S_g}\right)^n_{\pm} = \left(\frac{\partial T_{gx}}{\partial S_w}\right)^n_{\pm} = 0. \quad \ldots\ldots\ (9.415)$$

In a similar process, we may write the linearized implicit approximation for the spatial-difference operator $\Delta_x[T_{lx}\Delta_x P_{col}]^{n+1}_i$ for $l=w$ or g as

$$\Delta_x\left[T_{lx}\Delta_x P_{col}\right]^{n+1}_i \approx T^n_{lx_+}P'^n_{col_+}\left(S^{n+1}_{l_{i+1}} - S^n_{l_i}\right)$$

$$+ T^n_{lx_-}P'^n_{col_-}\left(S^{n+1}_{l_{i-1}} - S^n_{l_i}\right)$$

$$+ \left(\frac{\partial T_{lx}}{\partial S_l}\right)^n_{+}\left(P^n_{col_{i+1}} - P^n_{col_i}\right)\left(S^{n+1}_l - S^n_l\right)_{+}$$

$$+ \left(\frac{\partial T_{lx}}{\partial S_l}\right)^n_{-}\left(P^n_{col_{i-1}} - P^n_{col_i}\right)\left(S^{n+1}_l - S^n_l\right)_{-},$$

$$\ldots\ldots\ (9.416a)$$

where $l = w$ or g, or

$$\Delta_x\left[T_{lx}\Delta_x P_{col}\right]^{n+1}_i \approx T^n_{lx_+}\left(P^n_{col_{i+1}} - P^n_{col_i}\right)$$

$$+ T^n_{lx_-}\left(P^n_{col_{i-1}} - P^n_{col_i}\right)$$

$$+ \left(\frac{\partial T_{lx}}{\partial S_l}\right)^n_{+}\left(P^n_{col_{i+1}} - P^n_{col_i}\right)\left(S^{n+1}_l - S^n_l\right)_{+}$$

$$+ \left(\frac{\partial T_{lx}}{\partial S_l}\right)^n_{-}\left(P^n_{col_{i-1}} - P^n_{col_i}\right)\left(S^{n+1}_l - S^n_l\right)_{-}$$

$$+ T^n_{lx_+}P'^n_{col_{i+1}}\left(S^{n+1}_{l_{i+1}} - S^n_{l_{i+1}}\right)$$

$$+ T^n_{lx_-}P'^n_{col_{i-1}}\left(S^{n+1}_{l_{i-1}} - S^n_{l_{i-1}}\right)$$

$$- \left(T^n_{lx_+} + T^n_{lx_-}\right)P'^n_{col_i}\left(S^{n+1}_{l_i} - S^n_{l_i}\right),$$

$$\ldots\ldots\ (9.416b)$$

where $l=w$ or g, and where

$$P'^n_{col_\pm} = \left(\frac{dP_{col}}{dS_l}\right)^n_{\pm}, \quad \ldots\ldots\ (9.417)$$

for $l=w$ or g.

Aziz and Settari[2] demonstrated that the linearized implicit method is twice as stable as the explicit method for 1D problems and that the stability is much larger for multidimensional problems. This method does not require iterating on f_s and, in turn, on transmissibility.

Semi-Implicit Method of Nolen and Berry.[8] In the semi-implicit method of Nolen and Berry[8], the nonlinearity on the left side of Eq. 9.412 is retained but solved with Newton's iteration.

$$\left(\frac{\partial T_{ox}}{\partial S_l}\right)^n_{\pm}\left(p^{n+1}_{o_{i\pm1}} - p^{n+1}_{o_i}\right)\left(S^{n+1}_l - S^n_l\right)_{\pm}$$

$$\approx \left(\frac{\partial T_{ox}}{\partial S_l}\right)^n_{\pm}\left[p^{(\nu+1)}_{o_{i\pm1}} - p^{(\nu+1)}_{o_i}\right]\left[S^{(\nu+1)}_l - S^n_l\right]_{\pm}$$

$$\approx \left(\frac{\partial T_{ox}}{\partial S_l}\right)^n_{\pm}\left[p^{(\nu)}_{o_{i\pm1}} - p^{(\nu)}_{o_i}\right]\left[S^{(\nu)}_l - S^n_l\right]_{\pm}$$

$$+ \left(\frac{\partial T_{ox}}{\partial S_l}\right)^n_{\pm}\left[p^{(\nu)}_{o_{i\pm1}} - p^{(\nu)}_{o_i}\right]\left(\delta S_l\right)_{\pm}$$

$$+ \left(\frac{\partial T_{ox}}{\partial S_l}\right)^n_{\pm}\left[S^{(\nu)}_l - S^n_l\right]_{\pm}\left(\delta p_{o_{i\pm1}} - \delta p_{o_i}\right), \quad \ldots\ (9.418)$$

for $\nu = 0,1,2,\ldots$, and where $\delta p_{o_i} = [p^{(\nu+1)}_{o_i} - p^{(\nu)}_{o_i}]$, $\delta S_l = [S^{(\nu+1)}_l - S^{(\nu)}_l]$, and $[(\partial T_{ox})/(\partial S_l)]^n_{\pm}$ are defined by Eq. 9.411, but the partial derivatives are approximated by a chord between $S^n_{l_\pm}$ and a reasonable estimate of $S^{n+1}_{l_\pm}$ (say $S^{n+1}_{l_\pm} - S^n_{l_\pm} = 0.5$).

$$\left(\frac{\partial f_{so}}{\partial S_w}\right)_{\pm} = \frac{f_{so}\left(S^{n+1}_{w_\pm}, S^n_{g_\pm}\right) - f_{so}\left(S^n_{w_\pm}, S^n_{g_\pm}\right)}{S^{n+1}_{w_\pm} - S^n_{w_\pm}} \quad \ldots\ldots\ (9.419)$$

and

$$\left(\frac{\partial f_{so}}{\partial S_g}\right)_{\pm} = \frac{f_{so}\left(S^n_{w_\pm}, S^{n+1}_{g_\pm}\right) - f_{so}\left(S^n_{w_\pm}, S^n_{g_\pm}\right)}{S^{n+1}_{g_\pm} - S^n_{g_\pm}}. \quad \ldots\ (9.420)$$

A reasonable estimate of a fixed chord is calculated from the maximum anticipated saturation change; therefore, the interblock oil flow terms may be approximated as

$$T^{n+1}_{ox_{i\pm1/2}}\left(p^{n+1}_{o_{i\pm1}} - p^{n+1}_{o_i}\right) \approx T^n_{ox_\pm}\left(p^{n+1}_{o_{i\pm1}} - p^{n+1}_{o_i}\right)$$

$$+ \sum_{l=w,g}\left\{\left(\frac{\partial T_{ox}}{\partial S_l}\right)^n_{\pm}\left[p^{(\nu)}_{o_{i\pm1}} - p^{(\nu)}_{o_i}\right]\left[S^{(\nu)}_l - S^n_l\right]_{\pm}\right.$$

$$+ \left(\frac{\partial T_{ox}}{\partial S_l}\right)^n_{\pm}\left[p^{(\nu)}_{o_{i\pm1}} - p^{(\nu)}_{o_i}\right]\left(\delta S_l\right)_{\pm}$$

$$\left.+ \left(\frac{\partial T_{ox}}{\partial S_l}\right)^n_{\pm}\left[S^{(\nu)}_l - S^n_l\right]_{\pm}\left(\delta p_{o_{i\pm1}} - \delta p_{o_i}\right)\right\} \quad \ldots\ (9.421a)$$

or $T^{n+1}_{ox_{i\pm1/2}}\left(p^{n+1}_{o_{i\pm1}} - p^{n+1}_{o_i}\right)$

$$\approx \left\{T^n_{ox_\pm} + \sum_{l=w,g}\left(\frac{\partial T_{ox}}{\partial S_l}\right)^n_{\pm}\left[S^{(\nu)}_l - S^n_l\right]_{\pm}\right\}\left[p^{(\nu)}_{o_{i\pm1}} - p^{(\nu)}_{o_i}\right]$$

$$+ \left\{T^n_{ox_\pm} + \sum_{l=w,g}\left(\frac{\partial T_{ox}}{\partial S_l}\right)^n_{\pm}\left[S^{(\nu)}_l - S^n_l\right]_{\pm}\right\}\left(\delta p_{o_{i\pm1}} - \delta p_{o_i}\right)$$

$$+ \sum_{l=w,g}\left(\frac{\partial T_{ox}}{\partial S_l}\right)^n_{\pm}\left[p^{(\nu)}_{o_{i\pm1}} - p^{(\nu)}_{o_i}\right]\left(\delta S_l\right)_{\pm}. \quad \ldots\ldots\ (9.421b)$$

Nolen and Berry's[8] semi-implicit approximation for the difference operator $\Delta_x[\mathrm{T}_{px}\Delta_x p_o]_i^{n+1}$ for $p=o$, w, or g now may be written as

$$\Delta_x\left[\mathrm{T}_{px}\Delta_x p_o\right]_i^{n+1}$$

$$\approx \left\{\mathrm{T}_{px+}^{n} + \sum_{l=w,g}\left(\frac{\partial \mathrm{T}_{px}}{\partial S_l}\right)_+^n \left[S_l^{(\nu)} - S_l^n\right]_+\right\}\left[p_{o_{i+1}}^{(\nu)} - p_{o_i}^{(\nu)}\right]$$

$$+ \left\{\mathrm{T}_{px-}^{n} + \sum_{l=w,g}\left(\frac{\partial \mathrm{T}_{px}}{\partial S_l}\right)_-^n \left[S_l^{(\nu)} - S_l^n\right]_-\right\}\left[p_{o_{i-1}}^{(\nu)} - p_{o_i}^{(\nu)}\right]$$

$$+ \left\{\mathrm{T}_{px+}^{n} + \sum_{l=w,g}\left(\frac{\partial \mathrm{T}_{px}}{\partial S_l}\right)_+^n \left[S_l^{(\nu)} - S_l^n\right]_+\right\}\left(\delta p_{o_{i+1}} - \delta p_{o_i}\right)$$

$$+ \left\{\mathrm{T}_{px-}^{n} + \sum_{l=w,g}\left(\frac{\partial \mathrm{T}_{px}}{\partial S_l}\right)_-^n \left[S_l^{(\nu)} - S_l^n\right]_-\right\}\left(\delta p_{o_{i-1}} - \delta p_{o_i}\right)$$

$$+ \sum_{l=w,g}\left(\frac{\partial \mathrm{T}_{px}}{\partial S_l}\right)_+^n \left[p_{o_{i+1}}^{(\nu)} - p_{o_i}^{(\nu)}\right](\delta S_l)_+$$

$$+ \sum_{l=w,g}\left(\frac{\partial \mathrm{T}_{px}}{\partial S_l}\right)_-^n \left[p_{o_{i-1}}^{(\nu)} - p_{o_i}^{(\nu)}\right](\delta S_l)_-, \quad \text{......... (9.422)}$$

where $p=o$, w, or g, and where $[(\partial \mathrm{T}_{wx})/(\partial S_g)]_\pm^n = [(\partial \mathrm{T}_{gx})/(\partial S_w)]_\pm^n = 0$ and $[(\partial \mathrm{T}_{px})/(\partial S_l)]_\pm^n$ is a chord slope between $S_{l\pm}^n$ and a reasonable estimate of $S_{l\pm}^{n+1}$.

Eq. 9.422, which represents the semi-implicit method of Nolen and Berry, reduces to Eq. 9.414, which represents the linearized implicit method (1) if the derivative $(\partial \mathrm{T}_{px}/\partial S_l)_\pm^n$ is a tangent, (2) if only one iteration is performed ($\nu+1=1$ or $\nu=0$), and (3) if the zero iteration estimates of the unknowns are those at Time Level n [$p_o^{(0)} = p_o^n$, $S_w^{(0)} = S_w^n$, and $S_g^{(0)} = S_g^n$].

Fully-Implicit Method. The fully-implicit method, also known as Newton's iteration, was discussed for pressure-dependent properties in Sec. 8.4.1 for single-phase flow and is presented in this section for multiphase flow. It is a powerful method that works well for strongly nonlinear problems because it is unconditionally stable. In this method, a flow term at Time Level $n+1$ is approximated by its value at Iteration Level $\nu+1$, which in turn can be approximated by its value at Iteration ν plus a linear combination of the unknowns arising from partial differentiation with respect to all unknown variables. For example, the nonlinearity on the left side of Eq. 9.410 is approximated by

$$\mathrm{T}_{ox_{i\pm 1/2}}^{n+1}\left(p_{o_{i\pm1}}^{n+1} - p_{o_i}^{n+1}\right) \approx \mathrm{T}_{ox_{\pm 1/2}}^{(\nu+1)}\left[p_{o_{i\pm1}}^{(\nu+1)} - p_{o_i}^{(\nu+1)}\right]$$

$$\approx \mathrm{T}_{ox\pm}^{(\nu)}\left[p_{o_{i\pm1}}^{(\nu)} - p_{o_i}^{(\nu)}\right] + \mathrm{T}_{ox_{i\pm}}^{(\nu)}\left(\delta p_{o_{i\pm1}} - \delta p_{o_i}\right)$$

$$+ \left[p_{o_{i\pm1}}^{(\nu)} - p_{o_i}^{(\nu)}\right]\left[\sum_{l=w,g}\left(\frac{\partial \mathrm{T}_{ox}}{\partial S_l}\right)_\pm^{(\nu)}(\delta S_l)_\pm + \left(\frac{\partial \mathrm{T}_{ox}}{\partial p_o}\right)_\pm^{(\nu)}(\delta p_o)_\pm\right], \quad \text{.................... (9.423)}$$

$$\text{where } \left(\frac{\partial \mathrm{T}_{ox}}{\partial S_l}\right)_\pm^{(\nu)} = G f_{po}^{(\nu)}\left(\frac{\partial f_{so}}{\partial S_l}\right)_\pm^{(\nu)} \quad \text{................ (9.424)}$$

$$\text{and } \left(\frac{\partial \mathrm{T}_{ox}}{\partial p_o}\right)_\pm^{(\nu)} = G f_{so}^{(\nu)}\left(\frac{\partial f_{po}}{\partial p_o}\right)_\pm^{(\nu)} \quad \text{................. (9.425)}$$

are partial derivatives evaluated as tangents at Iteration Level ν and the operator δ is defined as

$$\delta X = X^{(\nu+1)} - X^{(\nu)}. \quad \text{........................ (9.426)}$$

Now we may write the fully-implicit approximation for the difference operator $\Delta_x[\mathrm{T}_{px}\Delta_x p_o]_i^{n+1}$ for $p=o$, w, or g as

$$\Delta_x[\mathrm{T}_{px}\Delta_x p_o]_i^{n+1} \approx \mathrm{T}_{px+}^{(\nu)}\left[p_{o_{i+1}}^{(\nu)} - p_{o_i}^{(\nu)}\right] + \mathrm{T}_{px-}^{(\nu)}\left[p_{o_{i-1}}^{(\nu)} - p_{o_i}^{(\nu)}\right]$$

$$+ \mathrm{T}_{px+}^{(\nu)}\left[\delta p_{o_{i+1}}^{(\nu)} - \delta p_{o_i}^{(\nu)}\right]$$

$$+ \mathrm{T}_{px-}^{(\nu)}\left[\delta p_{o_{i-1}}^{(\nu)} - \delta p_{o_i}^{(\nu)}\right]$$

$$+ \sum_{l=w,g}\left[p_{o_{i+1}}^{(\nu)} - p_{o_i}^{(\nu)}\right]\left(\frac{\partial \mathrm{T}_{px}}{\partial S_l}\right)_+^{(\nu)}(\delta S_l)_+$$

$$+ \sum_{l=w,g}\left[p_{o_{i-1}}^{(\nu)} - p_{o_i}^{(\nu)}\right]\left(\frac{\partial \mathrm{T}_{px}}{\partial S_l}\right)_-^{(\nu)}(\delta S_l)_-$$

$$+ \left[p_{o_{i+1}}^{(\nu)} - p_{o_i}^{(\nu)}\right]\left(\frac{\partial \mathrm{T}_{px}}{\partial p_o}\right)_+^{(\nu)}(\delta p_o)_+$$

$$+ \left[p_{o_{i-1}}^{(\nu)} - p_{o_i}^{(\nu)}\right]\left(\frac{\partial \mathrm{T}_{px}}{\partial p_o}\right)_-^{(\nu)}(\delta p_o)_-,$$

$$\text{................... (9.427)}$$

where $p=o$, w, and g, $(\partial \mathrm{T}_{wx}/\partial S_g)_\pm^{(\nu)} = (\partial \mathrm{T}_{gx}/\partial S_w)_\pm^{(\nu)} = 0$ and $(\partial \mathrm{T}_{px}/\partial S_l)_\pm^{(\nu)}$ and $(\partial \mathrm{T}_{px}/\partial p_o)_\pm^{(\nu)}$ are tangents evaluated at the latest iteration for the upstream points between $i \pm 1$ and i.

Eq. 9.427 reduces to Eq. 9.414 for $\nu=0$ and if the nonlinearity of the transmissibility caused by pressure is neglected. Therefore, as far as the linearization of f_s is concerned, the linearized implicit method is the first iteration of Newton's method. Eq. 9.427 reduces to Eq. 9.422 if $f_p^{n+1} \approx f_p^n$ and f_s is a straight line. In other words, for the treatment of f_s, the semi-implicit method of Nolen and Berry[8] and Newton's method are the same for straight-line relative permeabilities.

In conclusion, all linearization methods are special cases of the fully-implicit method. The closer the linearization method is to Newton's method, the more implicit it is and, hence, more stable. This stability is, however, at the expense of greater truncation errors. For black-oil simulation, the best compromise between stability and truncation errors is offered by the linearized implicit method,[2] but recent trends in reservoir modeling tend to favor the use of Newton's method for difficult problems in compositional and thermal simulation. The semi-implicit method has less truncation error than Newton's method but is sensitive to the choice of chord slopes.

Treatment of Coefficients of Time Derivatives. The time derivative coefficients C_{lp}, C_{lw}, and C_{lg} for $l=o$, w, and g, that appear on the right side of Eqs. 9.224 through 9.226 involve the functions ϕ^{n+1}, B_l^{n+1}, R_s^{n+1}, ϕ', $(1/B_l)'$, and R_s' and generally are considered to be weak nonlinearities. These nonlinearities are evaluated in space at the gridblock for which the flow equations are written and can be linearized in time with simple iteration. That is, they are evaluated at p_o^{n+1}, which is evaluated at Iteration Level ν.

It should be emphasized that these nonlinearities cannot be linearized explicitly because the conservative property of the expansion of accumulation terms would be violated, which would introduce material-balance errors. Also, any implicit linearization method other than simple iteration introduces additional nonlinear terms that need further linearization (see Sec. 8.4.1).

Treatment of Production (Injection) Terms. The production and injection terms, q_{osc}^{n+1}, q_{wsc}^{n+1}, and q_{gsc}^{n+1}, where $q_{gsc}^{n+1} = q_{fgsc}^{n+1} + R_s^{n+1} \times q_{osc}^{n+1}$, are evaluated in space at the gridblock for which the flow equations are written. To avoid introducing instabilities, the linearization of the rate terms should be compatible with the linearization of the strong nonlinearities in the transmissibility terms. Therefore, we may approximate the flow rates q_{lsc}^{n+1} for $l=o$, w, and g with the following methods.

With the explicit method,

$$q_{lsc}^{n+1} \approx q_{lsc}^{n}. \quad \text{.............................. (9.428)}$$

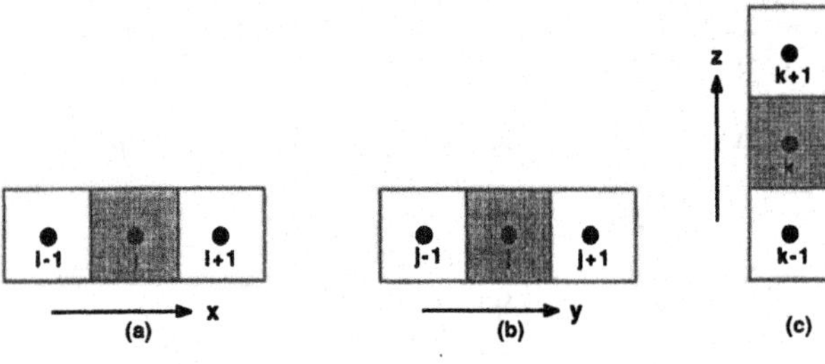

Fig. 9.9—Gridblock sets associated with a general gridblock in one dimension. (a) $\psi_l = \psi_x = \{l-1,\ l+1\}$ (b) $\psi_j = \psi_y = \{j-1,\ j+1\}$ (c) $\psi_k = \psi_z = \{k-1,\ k+1\}$

With the simple-iteration method,

$$\overset{(\nu+1)}{q}{}^{n+1}_{lsc} \approx \overset{(\nu)}{q}{}^{n+1}_{lsc}. \quad \text{(9.429)}$$

With the linearized-implicit method,

$$\begin{aligned} q^{n+1}_{lsc_{i,j,k}} \approx\ & q^{n}_{lsc_{i,j,k}} + \left.\frac{\partial q_{lsc}}{\partial S_w}\right|^{n}_{i,j,k}\left[S^{n+1}_{w_{i,j,k}} - S^{n}_{w_{i,j,k}}\right] \\ & + \left.\frac{\partial q_{lsc}}{\partial S_g}\right|^{n}_{i,j,k}\left[S^{n+1}_{g_{i,j,k}} - S^{n}_{g_{i,j,k}}\right] \\ & + \left.\frac{\partial q_{lsc}}{\partial p_o}\right|^{n}_{i,j,k}\left[p^{n+1}_{o_{i,j,k}} - p^{n}_{o_{i,j,k}}\right] \\ & + \left.\frac{\partial q_{lsc}}{\partial p_{wf_{ref}}}\right|^{n}_{i,j,k}\left[p^{n+1}_{wf_{ref}} - p^{n}_{wf_{ref}}\right]. \end{aligned} \quad \text{(9.430)}$$

With the semi-implicit method of Nolen and Berry,[8]

$$\begin{aligned} \overset{(\nu+1)}{q}{}^{n+1}_{lsc_{i,j,k}} \approx\ & \overset{(\nu)}{q}{}^{n+1}_{lsc_{i,j,k}} + \left.\frac{\Delta q_{lsc}}{\Delta S_w}\right|^{n}_{i,j,k}\left[\overset{(\nu+1)}{S}{}^{n+1}_{w_{i,j,k}} - \overset{(\nu)}{S}{}^{n+1}_{w_{i,j,k}}\right] \\ & + \left.\frac{\Delta q_{lsc}}{\Delta S_g}\right|^{n}_{i,j,k}\left[\overset{(\nu+1)}{S}{}^{n+1}_{g_{i,j,k}} - \overset{(\nu)}{S}{}^{n+1}_{g_{i,j,k}}\right] + \left.\frac{\Delta q_{lsc}}{\Delta p_o}\right|^{n}_{i,j,k} \\ & \times \left[\overset{(\nu+1)}{p}{}^{n+1}_{o_{i,j,k}} - \overset{(\nu)}{p}{}^{n+1}_{o_{i,j,k}}\right] + \left.\frac{\Delta q_{lsc}}{\Delta p_{wf_{ref}}}\right|^{n}_{i,j,k}\left[\overset{(\nu+1)}{p}{}^{n+1}_{wf_{ref}} - \overset{(\nu)}{p}{}^{n+1}_{wf_{ref}}\right]. \end{aligned} \quad \text{(9.431)}$$

With the fully-implicit method,

$$\begin{aligned} \overset{(\nu+1)}{q}{}^{n+1}_{lsc_{i,j,k}} \approx\ & \overset{(\nu)}{q}{}^{n+1}_{lsc_{i,j,k}} + \left.\frac{\partial q_{lsc}}{\partial S_w}\right|^{\overset{(\nu)}{n+1}}_{i,j,k}\left[\overset{(\nu+1)}{S}{}^{n+1}_{w_{i,j,k}} - \overset{(\nu)}{S}{}^{n+1}_{w_{i,j,k}}\right] \\ & + \left.\frac{\partial q_{lsc}}{\partial S_g}\right|^{\overset{(\nu)}{n+1}}_{i,j,k}\left[\overset{(\nu+1)}{S}{}^{n+1}_{g_{i,j,k}} - \overset{(\nu)}{S}{}^{n+1}_{g_{i,j,k}}\right] \\ & + \left.\frac{\partial q_{lsc}}{\partial p_o}\right|^{\overset{(\nu)}{n+1}}_{i,j,k}\left[\overset{(\nu+1)}{p}{}^{n+1}_{o_{i,j,k}} - \overset{(\nu)}{p}{}^{n+1}_{o_{i,j,k}}\right] \\ & + \left.\frac{\partial q_{lsc}}{\partial p_{wf_{ref}}}\right|^{\overset{(\nu)}{n+1}}_{i,j,k}\left[\overset{(\nu+1)}{p}{}^{n+1}_{wf_{ref}} - \overset{(\nu)}{p}{}^{n+1}_{wf_{ref}}\right]. \end{aligned} \quad \text{(9.432)}$$

In Eqs. 9.428 through 9.432, we introduced an additional unknown, $p_{wf_{ref}}$, into the formulation for gridblocks penetrated and perforated by a well. The partial-derivative terms in Eqs. 9.430 and 9.432 are derivatives of the inflow performance relationship, Eq. 6.93, with respect to the principal unknowns. In Eq. 9.431, the terms $\Delta q_{lsc}/\Delta S_w$, $\Delta q_{lsc}/\Delta S_g$, $\Delta q_{lsc}/\Delta p_{wf_{ref}}$, and $\Delta q_{lsc}/\Delta p_o$ are chord slopes between the unknowns at Time Level n and a reasonable estimate of the unknowns at Time Level $n+1$. Secs. 9.7.3 and 9.74, respectively, provide additional discussion on multiphase production and injection.

9.5.3 Finite-Difference Equations. Application of the linearization methods presented in Sec. 9.5.2 to the nonlinearities in space and time in a flow equation produces a linearized finite-difference equation. As we have seen, there are five methods of linearization that range from the explicit treatment to the fully-implicit treatment. In this section, we present the finite-difference equations for the black-oil model written for a general gridblock and linearized by the explicit and fully-implicit treatments. Writing these equations in one, two, and three dimensions is an arduous task; therefore, we introduce a new terminology for writing the expansion of the spatial finite-difference operator where the dimension of the problem is arbitrary. This new method of writing flow equations is known as the control volume finite-difference (CVFD) method.[9]

CVFD Method Terminology. This method was first introduced by Abou-Kassem[10] for 1D and 2D simulations and extended to 3D simulations by Lutchmansingh[11] and Abou-Kassem and Farouq Ali[12] as a means to express equations in a compact form that is consistent with do-loops used in computer programming.

CVFD Method Terminology That Uses Gridblock Coordinates. Consider the expansion of the second-order finite-difference operator at a given point in 1D space. For example, consider $\Delta[\xi\Delta\eta]_i$, which is defined by Eq. 9.102 as $\Delta_x[\xi_x\Delta_x\eta]_i$ with the expansion given by Eq. 9.81. That is,

$$\begin{aligned} \Delta(\xi\Delta\eta)_i &\equiv \Delta_x(\xi_x\Delta_x\eta)_i \\ &= \xi_{x_{i-1/2}}(\eta_{i-1} - \eta_i) + \xi_{x_{i+1/2}}(\eta_{i+1} - \eta_i). \end{aligned} \quad \text{(9.433)}$$

In light of **Fig. 9.9a** and Eq. 9.433, the expansion of the spatial-difference operator $\Delta[\xi\Delta\eta]$ at Gridpoint (or Gridblock) i, $\Delta[\xi\Delta\eta]_i$, is an algebraic combination of the differences $(\eta_{i-1}-\eta_i)$ and $(\eta_{i+1}-\eta_i)$, where $i-1$ and $i+1$ are the immediate neighbors of Gridblock i in the x direction. The coefficient of the difference $(\eta_{i-1}-\eta_i)$ represents the interaction between Gridblock i and its neighboring gridblock, Gridblock $i-1$, and the coefficient of the difference $(\eta_{i+1}-\eta_i)$ represents the interaction between Gridblock i and its neighboring gridblock, Gridblock $i+1$. These coefficients are denoted by $\xi_{x_{i-1/2}}$ and $\xi_{x_{i+1/2}}$, respectively.

If we define ψ_x as the set of gridblocks associated with (but excluding) Gridblock i in the x direction (see Fig. 9.9a), $\psi_x = \{i-1,\ i+1\}$; the coefficient of $(\eta_{i-1}-\eta_i)$ as $\xi_{i,i-1}$ (or $\xi_{i-1,i}$); and the coefficient of $(\eta_{i+1}-\eta_i)$ as $\xi_{i,i+1}$ (or $\xi_{i+1,i}$), we get

$$\xi_{i,m} = \xi_{m,i} = \xi_{x_{i-1/2}} \quad \text{(9.434a)}$$

for $m = i-1$, and

$$\xi_{i,m} = \xi_{m,i} = \xi_{x_{i+1/2}} \quad \text{(9.434b)}$$

for $m = i+1$. Then, Eq. 9.433 may be rewritten as

$$\begin{aligned} \Delta(\xi\Delta\eta)_i &\equiv \Delta_x(\xi_x\Delta_x\eta)_i \\ &= \xi_{i,i-1}(\eta_{i-1} - \eta_i) + \xi_{i,i+1}(\eta_{i+1} - \eta_i) \\ &= \sum_{m\in\psi_x} \xi_{i,m}(\eta_m - \eta_i). \end{aligned} \quad \text{(9.435)}$$

Similarly, we may write the expansion of $\Delta[\xi\Delta\eta]_j$ in the form of Eq. 9.435 as

$$\Delta(\xi\Delta\eta)_j \equiv \Delta_y(\xi_y\Delta_y\eta)_j = \sum_{m\in\psi_y} \xi_{j,m}(\eta_m - \eta_j), \quad \text{(9.436)}$$

where from **Fig. 9.9b**, $\psi_y = \{j-1, j+1\}$. η_m is variable η for Element m contained in the set ψ_y, and $\xi_{j,m}$ is the ξ interaction between Gridblock j and its neighboring gridblock, Gridblock m, of the set ψ_y. This interaction is defined as

$$\xi_{j,m} = \xi_{m,j} = \xi_{y_{j-1/2}} \quad \text{(9.437a)}$$

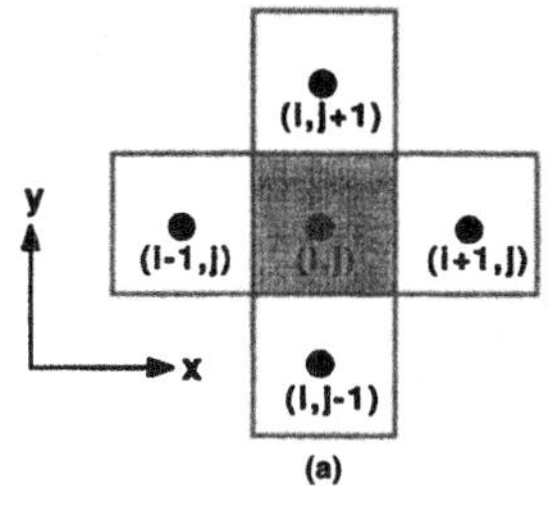

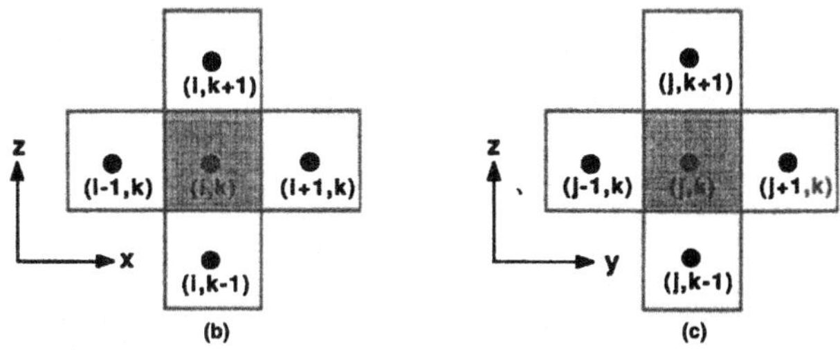

Fig. 9.10—Gridblock sets associated with a general gridblock in two dimensions. (a) $\psi_{i,j}=\psi_x \cup \psi_y=\{(i, j-1), (i-1, j), (i+1, j), (i, j+1)\}$ (b) $\psi_{i,k}=\psi_x \cup \psi_z=\{(i, k-1), (i-1, k), (i+1, k), (i, k+1)\}$ (c) $\psi_{j,k}=\psi_y \cup \psi_z=\{(j, k-1), (j-1, k), (j+1, k), (j, k+1)\}$

for $m=j-1$, and

$$\xi_{j,m} = \xi_{m,j} = \xi_{y_{j+½}} \quad \text{(9.437b)}$$

for $m=j+1$. The expansion of $\Delta[\xi\Delta\eta]_k$ also may be expressed in the form of Eq. 9.435 as

$$\Delta(\xi\Delta\eta)_k \equiv \Delta_z(\xi_z\Delta_z\eta)_k = \sum_{m\in\psi_z} \xi_{k,m}(\eta_m - \eta_k), \quad \text{(9.438)}$$

where from **Fig. 9.9c**, $\psi_z=\{k-1,k+1\}$. η_m is variable η for Element m contained in ψ_z, and $\xi_{k,m}$ is the ξ interaction between Gridblock k and its neighboring gridblock, Gridblock m, of the set ψ_z. Again, this interaction is defined as

$$\xi_{k,m} = \xi_{m,k} = \xi_{z_{k-½}} \quad \text{(9.439a)}$$

for $m=k-1$, and

$$\xi_{k,m} = \xi_{m,k} = \xi_{z_{k+½}} \quad \text{(9.439b)}$$

for $m=k+1$.

The expansion of the spatial difference operator in multidimensions now may be written with the CVFD method by combining the definitions given by Eqs. 9.99 through 9.101 or Eq. 9.97, with Eqs. 9.435, 9.436, and 9.438. For example, the expansion of $\Delta[\xi\Delta\eta]$ at Gridpoint (i,j) in the x-y plane may be obtained as follows.

$$\Delta(\xi\Delta\eta)_{i,j} \equiv \Delta_x(\xi_x\Delta_x\eta)_{i,j} + \Delta_y(\xi_y\Delta_y\eta)_{i,j}, \quad \text{(9.440)}$$

which when combined with Eqs. 9.435 and 9.436 results in

$$\Delta(\xi\Delta\eta)_{i,j} = \sum_{m\in\psi_x} \xi_{(i,j),m}(\eta_m - \eta_{i,j}) + \sum_{m\in\psi_y} \xi_{(i,j),m}(\eta_m - \eta_{i,j})$$

$$= \sum_{m\in\psi_{i,j}} \xi_{(i,j),m}(\eta_m - \eta_{i,j}), \quad \text{(9.441)}$$

where $\psi_{i,j} = \psi_x \cup \psi_y$

$$= \{(i,j-1), (i-1,j), (i+1,j), (i,j+1)\}, \quad \text{(9.442)}$$

is the set of gridblocks associated with but excluding Gridblock (i,j) as shown in **Fig. 9.10a**. η_m is variable η for Element m contained in the set $\psi_{i,j}$, and $\xi_{(i,j),m}$ is the ξ interaction between Gridblock (i,j) and its neighboring gridblock, Gridblock m.

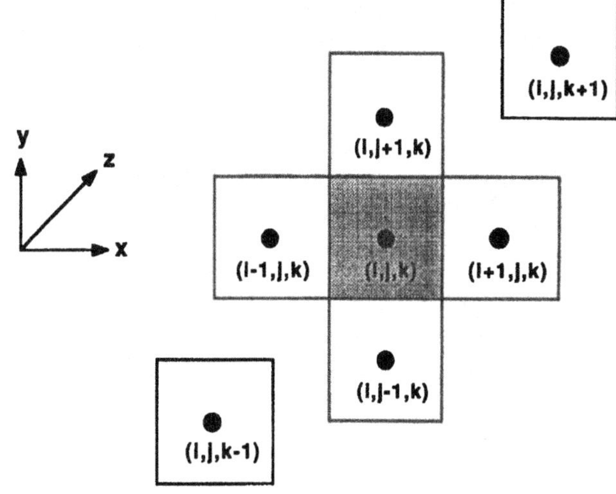

Fig. 9.11—Gridblock set associated with a general gridblock in three dimensions. $\psi_{i,j,k}=\psi_x \cup \psi_y \cup \psi_z=\{(i, j, k-1), (i, j-1, k), (i-1, j, k), (i+1, j, k), (i, j+1, k), (i, j, k+1)\}$

$$\xi_{(i,j),m} = \xi_{m,(i,j)} = \xi_{y_{i,j-½}} \quad \text{(9.443a)}$$

for $m=(i,j-1)$,

$$\xi_{(i,j),m} = \xi_{m,(i,j)} = \xi_{y_{i,j+½}} \quad \text{(9.443b)}$$

for $m=(i,j+1)$,

$$\xi_{(i,j),m} = \xi_{m,(i,j)} = \xi_{x_{i-½,j}} \quad \text{(9.443c)}$$

for $m=(i-1,j)$, and

$$\xi_{(i,j),m} = \xi_{m,(i,j)} = \xi_{x_{i+½,j}} \quad \text{(9.443d)}$$

for $m=(i+1,j)$.

The expansion of the general form of the spatial difference operator at a given point or gridblock in 3D space may be expressed with the CVFD method as

$$\Delta(\xi\Delta\eta)_{i,j,k} = \sum_{m\in\psi_{i,j,k}} \xi_{(i,j,k),m}(\eta_m - \eta_{i,j,k}). \quad \text{(9.444)}$$

In Eq. 9.444, the summation is carried over all the elements contained in the set of gridblocks $\psi_{i,j,k}$. **Figs. 9.9 through 9.11** show that the elements of ψ include the immediate neighboring gridblocks along the x, y, and z directions. Mathematically,

$$\psi_{i,j,k} = \psi_x \cup \psi_y \cup \psi_z. \quad \text{(9.445)}$$

In Eq. 9.445, ψ_x is defined as the set of neighboring gridblocks associated with Gridblock (i,j,k) along the x direction,

$$\psi_x = \{(i-1,j,k), (i+1,j,k)\}; \quad \text{(9.446)}$$

ψ_y is defined as the set of neighboring gridblocks associated with Gridblock (i,j,k) along the y direction,

$$\psi_y = \{(i,j-1,k), (i,j+1,k)\}; \quad \text{(9.447)}$$

and ψ_z is defined as the set of neighboring gridblocks associated with Gridblock (i,j,k) along the z direction,

$$\psi_z = \{(i,j,k-1), (i,j,k+1)\}. \quad \text{(9.448)}$$

The variable η_m is the value of η at Gridblock $m\in\psi_{i,j,k}$. The coefficient $\xi_{(i,j,k),m}$ is the ξ interaction between Gridblock (i,j,k) and its immediate neighboring gridblock, Gridblock $m\in\psi_{i,j,k}$.

$$\xi_{(i,j,k),m} = \xi_{m,(i,j,k)} = \xi_{x_{i\pm½,j,k}} \quad \text{(9.449a)}$$

for $m=(i\pm1,j,k)$,

$$\xi_{(i,j,k),m} = \xi_{m,(i,j,k)} = \xi_{x_{i,j\pm½,k}} \quad \text{(9.449b)}$$

TABLE 9.6—CORRESPONDENCE BETWEEN GRIDBLOCK COORDINATES AND NUMBER IN NATURAL ORDERING

Gridlock Coordinates*	Gridblock Number**
(i,j,k–1)	$n-n_x n_y$
(i,j–1,k)	$n-n_x$
(i–1,j,k)	$n-1$
(i,j,k)	n
(i+1,j,k)	$n+1$
(i,j+1,k)	$n+n_x$
(i,j,k+1)	$n+n_x n_y$

*$i \geqq 1$, $j \geqq 1$, and $k \geqq 1$
** $n_x \geqq 1$, $n_y \geqq 1$, and $n_z \geqq 1$

for $m=(i,j\pm 1,k)$, and

$$\xi_{(i,j,k),m} = \xi_{m,(i,j,k)} = \xi_{x_{i,j,k\pm 1/2}} \quad \text{(9.449c)}$$

for $m=(i,j,k\pm 1)$.

Example 9.21. Use the terminology for the CVFD method presented in Eqs. 9.444 through 9.449 for the expansion of spatial difference operators to derive the expansion of $\Delta[\xi\Delta\eta]_i$ at Gridpoint i in 1D space along the x direction.

$$\Delta(\xi\Delta\eta)_i = \xi_{x_{i-1/2}}\eta_{i-1} - \left(\xi_{x_{i-1/2}} + \xi_{x_{i+1/2}}\right)\eta_i + \xi_{x_{i+1/2}}\eta_{i+1}. \quad \text{(9.450)}$$

Solution. Consider Gridpoint i in the 1D space along the x direction in Fig. 9.9a. From the figure, $\psi_x = \{i-1, i+1\}$, $\psi_y = \{0\}$, and $\psi_z = \{0\}$. Substituting these three sets of gridblocks into Eq. 9.445 gives

$$\begin{aligned}\psi_i &= \psi_x \cup \psi_y \cup \psi_z \\ &= \{i-1, i+1\} \cup \{0\} \cup \{0\} \\ &= \{i-1, i+1\} \\ &= \psi_x. \end{aligned} \quad \text{(9.451)}$$

For $j=k=1$, Subscripts j and k may be suppressed in Eq. 9.449, giving

$$\xi_{i,m} = \begin{cases} \xi_{x_{i-1/2}} \text{ for } m = i-1 \\ \xi_{x_{i+1/2}} \text{ for } m = i+1 \end{cases}, \quad \text{(9.452)}$$

and Eq. 9.444 becomes

$$\Delta(\xi\Delta\eta)_i = \sum_{m\in\psi_i} \xi_{i,m}(\eta_m - \eta_i), \quad \text{(9.453)}$$

where Eq. 9.451 gives ψ_i as $\psi_i = \{i-1, i+1\}$. Therefore,

$$\Delta(\xi\Delta\eta)_i = \xi_{i-1,i}(\eta_{i-1} - \eta_i) + \xi_{i+1,i}(\eta_{i+1} - \eta_i). \quad \text{(9.454)}$$

Substituting Eq. 9.452 into Eq. 9.454 yields

$$\Delta(\xi\Delta\eta)_i = \xi_{x_{i-1/2}}(\eta_{i-1} - \eta_i) + \xi_{x_{i+1/2}}(\eta_{i+1} - \eta_i), \quad \text{(9.455)}$$

which on rearrangement gives the desired expansion

$$\Delta(\xi\Delta\eta)_i = \xi_{x_{i-1/2}}\eta_{i-1} - \left(\xi_{x_{i-1/2}} + \xi_{x_{i+1/2}}\right)\eta_i + \xi_{x_{i+1/2}}\eta_{i+1}. \quad \text{(9.450)}$$

Example 9.22. Derive the expansion of the spatial-difference operator $\Delta[\xi\Delta\eta]_{i,k}$ in the x-z plane using Eqs. 9.444 through 9.449.

Solution. **Fig. 9.10b** shows Gridpoint (i,k) and its immediate neighbors in the x-z plane. From the figure, $\psi_x = \{(i-1,k),(i+1,k)\}$, $\psi_y = \{0\}$, and $\psi_z = \{(i,k-1),(i,k+1)\}$, which when substituted into Eq. 9.445 yields

$$\begin{aligned}\psi_{i,k} &= \psi_x \cup \psi_y \cup \psi_z \\ &= \{(i-1,k),(i+1,k)\} \cup \{0\} \cup \{(i,k-1),(i,k+1)\} \\ &= \{(i-1,k),(i+1,k),(i,k-1)(i,k+1)\} \end{aligned} \quad \text{(9.456a)}$$

or $\psi_{i,k} = \{(i,k-1),(i-1,k),(i+1,k),(i,k+1)\}$. (9.456b)

Suppressing Subscript j (because $j=1$) in Eq. 9.449, we may write

$$\xi_{(i,k),m} = \xi_{x_{i-1/2,k}} \quad \text{(9.457a)}$$

for $m=(i-1,k)$,

$$\xi_{(i,k),m} = \xi_{x_{i+1/2,k}} \quad \text{(9.457b)}$$

for $m=(i+1,k)$,

$$\xi_{(i,k),m} = \xi_{z_{i,k-1/2}} \quad \text{(9.457c)}$$

for $m=(i,k-1)$, and

$$\xi_{(i,k),m} = \xi_{z_{i,k+1/2}} \quad \text{(9.457d)}$$

for $m=(i,k+1)$.

Writing Eq. 9.444 for $\psi_{i,k}$ defined by Eq. 9.456b gives

$$\begin{aligned}\Delta(\xi\Delta\eta)_{i,k} &= \sum_{m\in\psi_{i,k}} \xi_{(i,k),m}(\eta_m - \eta_{i,k}) \\ &= \xi_{(i,k),(i,k-1)}(\eta_{i,k-1} - \eta_{i,k}) \\ &+ \xi_{(i,k),(i-1,k)}(\eta_{i-1,k} - \eta_{i,k}) \\ &+ \xi_{(i,k),(i+1,k)}(\eta_{i+1,k} - \eta_{i,k}) \\ &+ \xi_{(i,k),(i,k+1)}(\eta_{i,k+1} - \eta_{i,k}). \end{aligned} \quad \text{(9.458)}$$

Substituting Eq. 9.457 into Eq. 9.458 and collecting terms yield the desired expansion,

$$\begin{aligned}\Delta(\xi\Delta\eta)_{i,k} &= \xi_{z_{i,k-1/2}}\eta_{i,k-1} + \xi_{z_{i-1/2,k}}\eta_{i-1,k} \\ &- \left(\xi_{z_{i,k-1/2}} + \xi_{z_{i-1/2,k}} + \xi_{z_{i+1/2,k}} + \xi_{z_{i,k+1/2}}\right)\eta_{i,k} \\ &+ \xi_{z_{i+1/2,k}}\eta_{i+1,k} + \xi_{z_{i,k+1/2}}\eta_{i,k+1}. \end{aligned} \quad \text{(9.459)}$$

CVFD Method Terminology That Uses Gridblock Order in Natural Ordering. The terminology for the CVFD method discussed in the previous section, which is used for the expansion of the spatial-difference operator at a given gridblock in multidimensional space, is applicable for any gridblock-ordering scheme. For the natural ordering scheme, which numbers the gridblocks along the x direction first, the y direction second, and the z direction last, **Table 9.6** shows the correspondence between gridblock coordinates and gridblock number.

In this natural ordering scheme, expansion of the general form of the spatial-difference operator at Gridblock n in multidimensional space maybe expressed with the CVFD method as

$$\Delta(\xi\Delta\eta)_n = \sum_{m\in\psi_n} \xi_{n,m}(\eta_m - \eta_n), \quad \text{(9.460)}$$

where $\psi_n = \psi_x \cup \psi_y \cup \psi_z$, (9.461)

$\psi_x = \{n-1, n+1\}$. (9.462)

$\psi_y = \{n-n_x, n+n_x\}$, (9.463)

and $\psi_z = \{n - n_x n_y, n + n_x n_y\}$. (9.464)

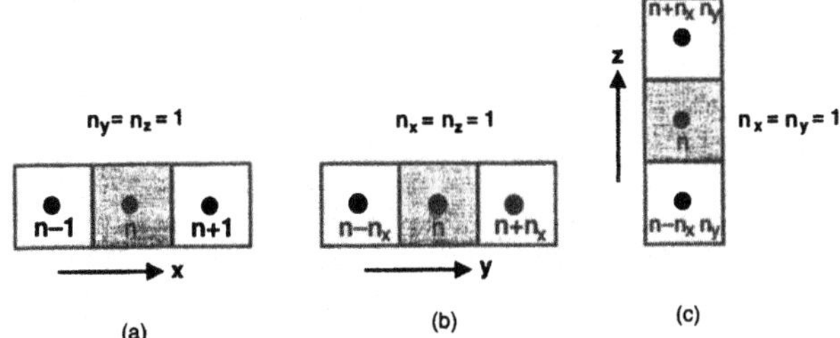

Fig. 9.12—Gridblock sets associated with Gridblock n in one dimension. (a) $\psi_n = \psi_x = \{n-1, n+1\}$ (b) $\psi_n = \psi_y = \{n-n_x, n+n_x\}$ (c) $\psi_n = \psi_z = \{n_x - n_x n_y, n+n_x n_y\}$

The variable η_m is the value of η defined only at Gridblock $m \in \psi_n$. The coefficient $\xi_{n,m}$ is the ξ interaction between Gridblock n and its immediate neighboring gridblock, Gridblock $m \in \psi_n$, and is defined as

$$\xi_{n,m} = \xi_{m,n} = \xi_{x_{i\pm 1/2,j,k}} \qquad (9.465a)$$

for $m = n \pm 1$,

$$\xi_{n,m} = \xi_{m,n} = \xi_{y_{i,j\pm 1/2,k}} \qquad (9.465b)$$

for $m = n \pm n_x$, and

$$\xi_{n,m} = \xi_{m,n} = \xi_{z_{i,j,k\pm 1/2}} \qquad (9.465c)$$

for $m = n \pm n_x n_y$. Eqs. 9.460 through 9.465 hold true for 1D, 2D, and 3D space. **Figs. 9.12 through 9.14** show Gridblock n and the order of its neighboring gridblocks.

Difference Equations Using the CVFD Method. The black-oil-model finite-difference equations, Eqs. 9.224 through 9.226, may be expressed with the CVFD method for Gridblock n as follows.

For the oil equation,

$$\sum_{m\in\psi_n} \mathrm{T}^{n+1}_{o_{n,m}}\left(\Delta_m p_o^{n+1} - \bar{\gamma}^n_{o_{n,m}}\Delta_m Z\right) = C_{op_n}\Delta_t p_{o_n} + C_{ow_n}\Delta_t S_{w_n} + C_{og_n}\Delta_t S_{g_n} - q^{n+1}_{osc_n}. \qquad (9.466)$$

For the water equation,

$$\sum_{m\in\psi_n} \mathrm{T}^{n+1}_{w_{n,m}}\left(\Delta_m p_o^{n+1} - \Delta_m p^{n+1}_{cow} - \bar{\gamma}^n_{w_{n,m}}\Delta_m Z\right) = C_{wp_n}\Delta_t p_{o_n} + C_{ww_n}\Delta_t S_{w_n} + C_{wg_n}\Delta_t S_{g_n} - q^{n+1}_{wsc_n}. \qquad (9.467)$$

For the gas equation,

$$\sum_{m\in\psi_n}\left[\mathrm{T}^{n+1}_{g_{n,m}}\left(\Delta_m p_o^{n+1} + \Delta_m p^{n+1}_{cgo} - \bar{\gamma}^n_{g_{n,m}}\Delta_m Z\right) + \left(\mathrm{T}_o R_s\right)^{n+1}_{n,m} \times \left(\Delta_m p_o^{n+1} - \bar{\gamma}^n_{o_{n,m}}\Delta_m Z\right)\right] = C_{gp_n}\Delta_t p_{o_n} + C_{gw_n}\Delta_t S_{w_n} + C_{gg_n}\Delta_t S_{g_n} - q^{n+1}_{gsc_n}, \qquad (9.468)$$

where $q^{n+1}_{gsc_n} = (q^{n+1}_{fgsc_n} + R^{n+1}_{s_n} q^{n+1}_{osc_n})$, (9.469)

$$\Delta_m p_o = p_{o_m} - p_{o_n}, \qquad (9.470a)$$

$$\Delta_m P_{cow} = P_{cow_m} - P_{cow_n}, \qquad (9.470b)$$

$$\Delta_m P_{cgo} = P_{cgo_m} - P_{cgo_n}, \qquad (9.470c)$$

and $\Delta_m Z = Z_m - Z_n$, (9.470d)

where $m \in \psi_n$; and $\psi_n = \psi_x \cup \psi_y \cup \psi_z$ with ψ_x, ψ_y, and ψ_z defined by Eqs. 9.446 through 9.448 or Eqs. 9.462 through 9.464, depending on the choice of identifying gridblocks by either their coordinates

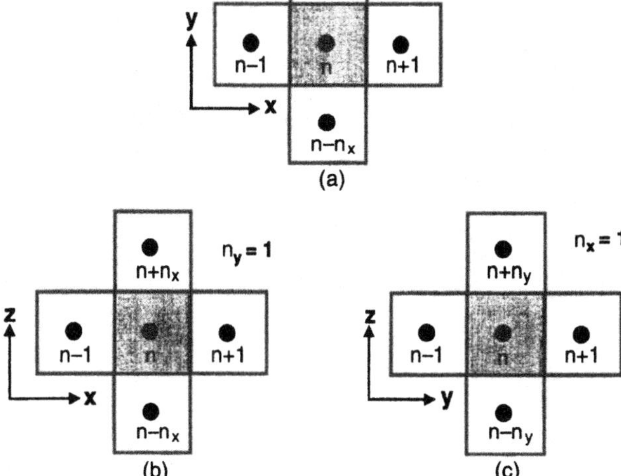

Fig. 9.13—Gridblock sets associated with Gridblock n in two dimensions. (a) $\psi_n = \psi_x \cup \psi_y = \{n-n_x, n-1, n+1, n+n_x\}$ (b) $\psi_n = \psi_x \cup \psi_z = \{n-n_x, n-1, n+1, n+n_x\}$ (c) $\psi_n = \psi_y \cup \psi_z = \{n-n_y, n-1, n+1, n+n_y\}$

(i,j,k) or their order (n) in a natural ordering scheme. For the same reason the interaction $\xi_{n,m}$, which may assume any of the functions $\mathrm{T}^{n+1}_{o_{n,m}}$, $\mathrm{T}^{n+1}_{w_{n,m}}$, $\mathrm{T}^{n+1}_{g_{n,m}}$, $(\mathrm{T}_o R_s)^{n+1}_{n,m}$, $(\mathrm{T}_o\bar{\gamma}_o)^{n+1}_{n,m}$, $(\mathrm{T}_w\bar{\gamma}_w)^{n+1}_{n,m}$, $(\mathrm{T}_g\bar{\gamma}_g)^{n+1}_{n,m}$, $(\mathrm{T}_o R_s\bar{\gamma}_o)^{n+1}_{n,m}$, is defined by Eq. 9.449 or 9.465. Phase transmissibilities defined by Eqs. 9.267 through 9.269 may now be expressed as

$$\mathrm{T}_{l_{n,m}} = G_{n,m}\left(\frac{1}{\mu_l B_l}\right)_{n,m} k_{rl_{n,m}}, \qquad (9.471)$$

where $l = o$, w, or g; $m \in \psi_n$; and $G_{n,m}$ is defined in terms of $G_{i\pm 1/2,j,k}$, $G_{i,j\pm 1/2,k}$, and $G_{i,j,k\pm 1/2}$ given by Eqs. 9.274 through 9.279.

$$G_{n,m} = G_{i\pm 1/2,j,k} \qquad (9.472a)$$

for $m = n \pm 1$,

$$G_{n,m} = G_{i,j\pm 1/2,k} \qquad (9.472b)$$

for $m = n \pm n_x$, and

$$G_{n,m} = G_{i,j,k\pm 1/2} \qquad (9.472c)$$

for $m = n \pm n_x n_y$.

It should be emphasized at this point that the interaction $\xi_{n,m}$ is a function of the unknowns of both the center gridblock, Gridblock n

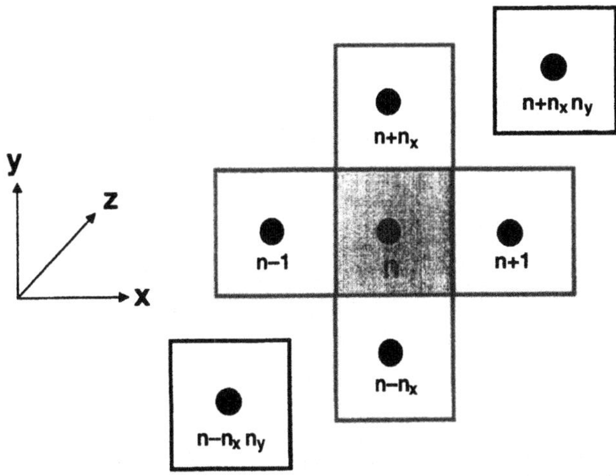

Fig. 9.14—Gridblock set associated with Gridblock n in three dimensions. $\psi_n = \psi_x \cup \psi_y \cup \psi_z = \{n-n_x n_y, n-n_x, n-1, n+1, n+n_x, n+n_x n_y\}$

[or Gridblock(i,j,k)], for which the finite-difference equation is written, and its surrounding or neighboring gridblock, Gridblock m, which is a member of the set ψ_n. For single-point upstream weighting, $\xi_{n,m}$ is evaluated at the upstream gridblock (for the specific phase), which is either the center gridblock or the neighboring gridblock. An exception is that $\bar{\gamma}_{o_{n,m}}$, $\bar{\gamma}_{w_{n,m}}$, and $\bar{\gamma}_{g_{n,m}}$ are the arithmetic average values for the two gridblocks. The variables p_o, P_{cow}, P_{cgo}, and Z in Eq. 9.470 are point values defined at Gridblock n and Gridblock $m \in \psi_n$.

Explicitly Linearized Finite-Difference Equations. Explicit linearization of the finite-difference equations for the black-oil model involves evaluating phase transmissibilities, phase gravities, and phase flow rates at Time Level n. In addition, capillary pressure terms $\Delta(T_w \Delta P_{cow})$ and $\Delta(T_g \Delta P_{cgo})$ are expressed as $\Delta(T_w P'_{cow} \Delta S_w)$ and $\Delta[T_g P'_{cgo} \Delta S_g]$, respectively.

The linearized equations may be rearranged so that the unknown variables appear on the left side and the known quantities appear on the right side of the equations. With natural ordering of gridblocks, Eqs. 9.466 through 9.470 for Gridblock $n = 1,2,\dots,N$ can be expressed with the CVFD method terminology.

For the oil equation,

$$\sum_{m\in\psi_n} T^n_{o_{n,m}} p^{n+1}_{o_m} - \left(C_{op_n} + \sum_{m\in\psi_n} T^n_{o_{n,m}}\right) p^{n+1}_{o_n} - C_{ow_n} S^{n+1}_{w_n} - C_{og_n} S^{n+1}_{g_n}$$
$$= -\left(C_{op_n} p^n_{o_n} + C_{ow_n} S^n_{w_n} + C_{og_n} S^n_{g_n}\right) - q^n_{osc_n} + \sum_{m\in\psi_n} (T_o \bar{\gamma}_o)^n_{n,m} \Delta_m Z. \quad \text{(9.473)}$$

For the water equation,

$$\sum_{m\in\psi_n} T^n_{w_{n,m}} p^{n+1}_{o_m} - \left(C_{wp_n} + \sum_{m\in\psi_n} T^n_{w_{n,m}}\right) p^{n+1}_{o_n} - \sum_{m\in\psi_n} (T_w P'_{cow})^n_{n,m} S^{n+1}_{w_m} - \left[C_{ww_n} - \sum_{m\in\psi_n} (T_w P'_{cow})^n_{n,m}\right]$$
$$\times S^{n+1}_{w_n} - C_{wg_n} S^{n+1}_{g_n} = -\left(C_{wp_n} p^n_{o_n} + C_{ww_n} S^n_{w_n} + C_{wg_n} S^n_{g_n}\right) - q^n_{wsc_n} + \sum_{m\in\psi_n} (T_w \bar{\gamma}_w)^n_{n,m} \Delta_m Z. \quad \text{(9.474)}$$

For the gas equation,

$$\sum_{m\in\psi_n} (T_g + T_o R_s)^n_{n,m} p^{n+1}_{o_m} - \left[C_{gp_n} + \sum_{m\in\psi_n} (T_g + T_o R_s)^n_{n,m}\right] p^{n+1}_{o_n} - C_{wg_n} S^{n+1}_{w_n} + \sum_{m\in\psi_n} (T_g P'_{cgo})^n_{n,m} S^{n+1}_{g_m}$$
$$- \left[C_{gg_n} + \sum_{m\in\psi_n} (T_g P'_{cgo})^n_{n,m}\right] S^{n+1}_{g_n}$$
$$= -\left(C_{gp_n} p^n_{o_n} + C_{gw_n} S^n_w + C_{gg_n} S^n_g\right) - q^n_{gsc_n} + \sum_{m\in\psi_n} \left(T_g \bar{\gamma}_g + T_o R_s \bar{\gamma}_o\right)^n_{n,m} \Delta_m Z, \quad \text{(9.475)}$$

where Eq. 9.469 gives $q^n_{gsc_n} = q^n_{fgsc_n} + R^n_{s_n} q^n_{osc_n}$ and Eqs. 9.461 through 9.464 give ψ_n. Subscript n refers to the gridblock, whereas Superscript n refers to the time level.

The evaluation of the interactions between Gridblock n and Gridblock $m \in \psi_n$ depends on the upstream gridblock between the two gridblocks for the oil phase for $T_{o_{n,m}}$ and $R_{s_{n,m}}$, the water phase for $T_{w_{n,m}}$ and $P'_{cow_{n,m}}$, and the gas phase for $T_{g_{n,m}}$ and $P'_{cgo_{n,m}}$. The terms $\bar{\gamma}_{o_{n,m}}$, $\bar{\gamma}_{w_{n,m}}$, or $\bar{\gamma}_{g_{n,m}}$ are taken as the arithmetic average gravities of the specific phase for the two gridblocks.

Fully-Implicit Finite-Difference Equations. The fully-implicit finite-difference equations for the black-oil model are those expressed by Eqs. 9.466 through 9.468, written for a given gridblock. The nonlinearities in these equations are retained but are linearized by Newton's iteration. Secs. 8.4.1 and 9.5.2 discussed the basic ideas of this linearization procedure.

The derivation of Newton's iterative equations for black-oil model involves four steps.

1. Expressing the equations for Gridblock n in a residual form,

$$R^{n+1}_{l_n} = 0, \quad \text{(9.476)}$$

where $l = o$, w, or g and where

$$R^{n+1}_{o_n} = \left\{\sum_{m\in\psi_n}\left[T^{n+1}_{o_{n,m}}\left(\Delta_m p^{n+1}_o - \bar{\gamma}^n_{o_{n,m}} \Delta_m Z\right)\right] - C_{op_n}\left(p^{n+1}_{o_n} - p^n_{o_n}\right) - C_{ow_n}\left(S^{n+1}_{w_n} - S^n_{w_n}\right) - C_{og_n}\left(S^{n+1}_{g_n} - S^n_{g_n}\right) + q^{n+1}_{osc_n}\right\}, \quad \text{(9.477)}$$

$$R^{n+1}_{w_n} = \left\{\sum_{m\in\psi_n}\left[T^{n+1}_{w_{n,m}}\left(\Delta_m p^{n+1}_o - \Delta_m P^{n+1}_{cow} - \bar{\gamma}^n_{w_{n,m}} \Delta_m Z\right)\right] - C_{wp_n}\left(p^{n+1}_{o_n} - p^n_{o_n}\right) - C_{ww_n}\left(S^{n+1}_{w_n} - S^n_{w_n}\right) - C_{wg_n}\left(S^{n+1}_{g_n} - S^n_{g_n}\right) + q^{n+1}_{wsc_n}\right\}, \quad \text{(9.478)}$$

and

$$R^{n+1}_{g_n} = \left\{\sum_{m\in\psi_n}\left[T^{n+1}_{g_{n,m}}\left(\Delta_m p^{n+1}_o + \Delta_m P^{n+1}_{cgo} - \bar{\gamma}^n_{g_{n,m}} \Delta_m Z\right) + (T_o R_s)^{n+1}_{n,m}\left(\Delta_m p^{n+1}_o - \bar{\gamma}^n_{o_{n,m}} \Delta_m Z\right)\right] - C_{gp_n}\left(p^{n+1}_{o_n} - p^n_{o_n}\right) - C_{gw_n}\left(S^{n+1}_{w_n} - S^n_{w_n}\right) - C_{gg_n}\left(S^{n+1}_{g_n} - S^n_{g_n}\right) + q^{n+1}_{gsc_n}\right\}, \quad \text{(9.479)}$$

where

$$q^{n+1}_{gsc_n} = \left(q^{n+1}_{fgsc_n} + R^{n+1}_{s_n} q^{n+1}_{osc_n}\right). \quad \text{(9.469)}$$

2. Approximating the residuals at Time Level $n+1$ by their estimates at Iteration Level $\nu+1$,

$$R^{n+1}_{l_n} \approx R^{\overset{(\nu+1)}{n+1}}_{l_n}, \quad \text{(9.480)}$$

where $l = o$, w, or g.

3. Approximating the residuals at Iteration Level $\nu+1$ by their estimates at Iteration Level ν plus a linear combination of the unknowns arising from partial differentiation of R_{l_n} with respect to all unknown variables,

$$R^{\overset{(\nu+1)}{n+1}}_{l_n} \approx R^{\overset{(\nu)}{n+1}}_{l_n} + \sum_{m\in\psi_n}\left[\left(\frac{\partial R_{l_n}}{\partial p_{o_m}}\right)^{(\nu)} \delta p_{o_m} + \left(\frac{\partial R_{l_n}}{\partial S_{w_m}}\right)^{(\nu)} \delta S_{w_m}\right.$$

$$+ \left(\frac{\partial R_{l_n}}{\partial S_{g_m}}\right)^{(\nu)} \delta S_{g_m} \Bigg]$$

$$+ \left[\left(\frac{\partial R_{l_n}}{\partial p_{o_n}}\right)^{(\nu)} \delta p_{o_n} + \left(\frac{\partial R_{l_n}}{\partial S_{w_n}}\right)^{(\nu)} \delta S_{w_n} \right.$$

$$\left. + \left(\frac{\partial R_{l_n}}{\partial S_{g_n}}\right)^{(\nu)} \delta S_{g_n} \right], \quad \text{.......... (9.481)}$$

where $l = o, w,$ or g; $m \in \psi_n$;

$$\delta p_{o_m} = \overset{(\nu+1)}{p_{o_m}^{n+1}} - \overset{(\nu)}{p_{o_m}^{n+1}}, \quad \text{.......... (9.482a)}$$

$$\delta S_{w_m} = \overset{(\nu+1)}{S_{w_m}^{n+1}} - \overset{(\nu)}{S_{w_m}^{n+1}}, \quad \text{.......... (9.482b)}$$

and $\delta S_{g_m} = \overset{(\nu+1)}{S_{g_m}^{n+1}} - \overset{(\nu)}{S_{g_m}^{n+1}}$, ... (9.482c)

where $m \in \psi_n \cup \{n\}$ and the set ψ_n is defined by Eqs. 9.461 through 9.464. The partial derivatives obtained from Eqs. 9.477 through 9.479 follow. Eqs. 9.483 through 9.491 occur where $m \in \psi_n$.

$$\left(\frac{\partial R_{o_n}}{\partial p_{o_m}}\right)^{(\nu)} = \left\{ \mathrm{T}_{o_{n,m}}^{(\nu)} + \left[\Delta_m p_o^{(\nu)} - \bar{\gamma}_{o_{n,m}}^{n} \Delta_m Z\right] \left(\frac{\partial \mathrm{T}_{o_{n,m}}}{\partial p_{o_m}}\right)^{(\nu)} \right\}. \quad \text{.......... (9.483)}$$

$$\left(\frac{\partial R_{o_n}}{\partial S_{w_m}}\right)^{(\nu)} = \left\{ \left[\Delta_m p_o^{(\nu)} - \bar{\gamma}_{o_{n,m}}^{n} \Delta_m Z\right] \left(\frac{\partial \mathrm{T}_{o_{n,m}}}{\partial S_{w_m}}\right)^{(\nu)} \right\}. \quad \text{.......... (9.484)}$$

$$\left(\frac{\partial R_{o_n}}{\partial S_{g_m}}\right)^{(\nu)} = \left\{ \left[\Delta_m p_o^{(\nu)} - \bar{\gamma}_{o_{n,m}}^{n} \Delta_m Z\right] \left(\frac{\partial \mathrm{T}_{o_{n,m}}}{\partial S_{g_m}}\right)^{(\nu)} \right\}. \quad \text{.......... (9.485)}$$

$$\left(\frac{\partial R_{w_n}}{\partial p_{o_m}}\right)^{(\nu)} = \left\{ \mathrm{T}_{w_{n,m}}^{(\nu)} + \left[\Delta_m p_o^{(\nu)} - \Delta_m P_{cow}^{(\nu)} - \bar{\gamma}_{w_{n,m}}^{n} \Delta_m Z\right] \times \left(\frac{\partial \mathrm{T}_{w_{n,m}}}{\partial p_{o_m}}\right)^{(\nu)} \right\}. \quad \text{.......... (9.486)}$$

$$\left(\frac{\partial R_{w_n}}{\partial S_{w_m}}\right)^{(\nu)} = \left\{ \left[\Delta_m p_o^{(\nu)} - \Delta_m P_{cow}^{(\nu)} - \bar{\gamma}_{w_{n,m}}^{n} \Delta_m Z\right] \left(\frac{\partial \mathrm{T}_{w_{n,m}}}{\partial S_{w_m}}\right)^{(\nu)} - \mathrm{T}_{w_{n,m}}^{(\nu)} \overset{(\nu)}{P'_{cow_m}} \right\}. \quad \text{.......... (9.487)}$$

$$\left(\frac{\partial R_{w_n}}{\partial S_{g_m}}\right)^{(\nu)} = \{0\}. \quad \text{.......... (9.488)}$$

$$\left(\frac{\partial R_{g_n}}{\partial p_{o_m}}\right)^{(\nu)} = \left\{ \mathrm{T}_{g_{n,m}}^{(\nu)} + \left[\Delta_m p_o^{(\nu)} + \Delta_m P_{cgo}^{(\nu)} - \bar{\gamma}_{g_{n,m}}^{n} \Delta_m Z\right] \times \left(\frac{\partial \mathrm{T}_{g_{n,m}}}{\partial p_{o_m}}\right)^{(\nu)} + (\mathrm{T}_o R_s)_{n,m}^{(\nu)} \right.$$

$$\left. + \left[\Delta_m p_o^{(\nu)} - \bar{\gamma}_{o_{n,m}}^{n} \Delta_m Z\right] \left[\frac{\partial (\mathrm{T}_o R_s)_{n,m}}{\partial p_{o_m}}\right]^{(\nu)} \right\}. \quad \text{.......... (9.489)}$$

$$\left(\frac{\partial R_{g_n}}{\partial S_{w_m}}\right)^{(\nu)} = \left\{ \left[\Delta_m p_o^{(\nu)} - \bar{\gamma}_{o_{n,m}}^{n} \Delta_m Z\right] \left[\frac{\partial (\mathrm{T}_o R_s)_{n,m}}{\partial S_{w_m}}\right]^{(\nu)} \right\}. \quad \text{.......... (9.490)}$$

$$\left(\frac{\partial R_{g_n}}{\partial S_{g_m}}\right)^{(\nu)} = \left\{ \left[\Delta_m p_o^{(\nu)} + \Delta_m P_{cgo}^{(\nu)} - \bar{\gamma}_{g_{n,m}}^{n} \Delta_m Z\right] \left(\frac{\partial \mathrm{T}_{g_{n,m}}}{\partial S_{g_m}}\right)^{(\nu)} + \mathrm{T}_{g_{n,m}}^{(\nu)} \overset{(\nu)}{P'_{cgo_m}} + \left[\Delta_m p_o^{(\nu)} - \bar{\gamma}_{o_{n,m}}^{n} \Delta_m Z\right] \times \left[\frac{\partial (\mathrm{T}_o R_s)_{n,m}}{\partial S_{g_m}}\right]^{(\nu)} \right\}. \quad \text{.......... (9.491)}$$

$$\left(\frac{\partial R_{o_n}}{\partial p_{o_n}}\right)^{(\nu)} = \left[\left\{ \sum_{m \in \psi_n} \left(-\mathrm{T}_{o_{n,m}}^{(\nu)} + \left[\Delta_m p_o^{(\nu)} - \bar{\gamma}_{o_{n,m}}^{n} \Delta_m Z\right] \times \left(\frac{\partial \mathrm{T}_{o_{n,m}}}{\partial p_{o_n}}\right)^{(\nu)} \right) \right\} - C_{op_n}^{(\nu)} + \left(\frac{\partial q_{osc_n}}{\partial p_{o_n}}\right)^{(\nu)} \right]. \quad \text{.......... (9.492)}$$

$$\left(\frac{\partial R_{o_n}}{\partial S_{w_n}}\right)^{(\nu)} = \left[\left\{ \sum_{m \in \psi_n} \left(\left[\Delta_m p_o^{(\nu)} - \bar{\gamma}_{o_{n,m}}^{n} \Delta_m Z\right] \times \left(\frac{\partial \mathrm{T}_{o_{n,m}}}{\partial S_{w_n}}\right)^{(\nu)} \right) \right\} - C_{ow_n}^{(\nu)} + \left(\frac{\partial q_{osc_n}}{\partial S_{w_n}}\right)^{(\nu)} \right]. \quad \text{.......... (9.493)}$$

$$\left(\frac{\partial R_{o_n}}{\partial S_{g_n}}\right)^{(\nu)} = \left[\left\{ \sum_{m \in \psi_n} \left(\left[\Delta_m p_o^{(\nu)} - \bar{\gamma}_{o_{n,m}}^{n} \Delta_m Z\right] \times \left(\frac{\partial \mathrm{T}_{o_{n,m}}}{\partial S_{g_n}}\right)^{(\nu)} \right) \right\} - C_{og_n}^{(\nu)} + \left(\frac{\partial q_{osc_n}}{\partial S_{g_n}}\right)^{(\nu)} \right]. \quad \text{.......... (9.494)}$$

$$\left(\frac{\partial R_{w_n}}{\partial p_{o_n}}\right)^{(\nu)} = \left[\left\{ \sum_{m \in \psi_n} \left(-\mathrm{T}_{w_{n,m}}^{(\nu)} \right.\right.\right.$$

$$+ \left[\Delta_m p_o^{(\nu)} - \Delta_m P_{cow}^{(\nu)} - \bar{\gamma}_{wo_{n,m}}^n \Delta_m Z\right]$$

$$\times \left(\frac{\partial \mathrm{T}_{w_{n,m}}}{\partial p_{o_n}}\right)^{(\nu)} \Bigg) \Bigg\} - C_{wp_n}^{(\nu)} + \left(\frac{\partial q_{wsc_n}}{\partial p_{o_n}}\right)^{(\nu)} \Bigg]. \quad (9.495)$$

$$\left(\frac{\partial R_{w_n}}{\partial S_{w_n}}\right)^{(\nu)} = \Bigg[\Bigg\{ \sum_{m \in \psi_n} \Bigg(\left[\Delta_m p_o^{(\nu)} - \Delta_m P_{cow}^{(\nu)} - \bar{\gamma}_{w_{n,m}}^n \Delta_m Z\right]$$

$$\times \left(\frac{\partial \mathrm{T}_{w_{n,m}}}{\partial S_{w_n}}\right)^{(\nu)} + \mathrm{T}_{w_{n,m}}^{(\nu)} P_{cow_n}'^{(\nu)} \Bigg) \Bigg\}$$

$$- C_{ww_n}^{(\nu)} + \left(\frac{\partial q_{wsc_n}}{\partial S_{w_n}}\right)^{(\nu)} \Bigg]. \quad (9.496)$$

$$\left(\frac{\partial R_{w_n}}{\partial S_{g_n}}\right)^{(\nu)} = \left[\{0\} - C_{wg_n}^{(\nu)} + \left(\frac{\partial q_{wsc_n}}{\partial S_{g_n}}\right)^{(\nu)}\right]. \quad (9.497)$$

$$\left(\frac{\partial R_{g_n}}{\partial p_{o_n}}\right)^{(\nu)} = \Bigg[\Bigg\{ \sum_{m \in \psi_n} \Bigg(- \mathrm{T}_{g_{n,m}}^{(\nu)}$$

$$+ \left[\Delta_m p_o^{(\nu)} + \Delta_m P_{cgo}^{(\nu)} - \bar{\gamma}_{g_{n,m}}^n \Delta_m Z\right] \left(\frac{\partial \mathrm{T}_{g_{n,m}}}{\partial p_{o_n}}\right)^{(\nu)}$$

$$- (\mathrm{T}_o R_s)_{n,m}^{(\nu)} + \left[\Delta_m p_o^{(\nu)} - \bar{\gamma}_{o_{n,m}}^n \Delta_m Z\right]$$

$$\times \left[\frac{\partial (\mathrm{T}_o R_s)_{n,m}}{\partial p_{o_n}}\right]^{(\nu)} \Bigg) \Bigg\} - C_{gp_n}^{(\nu)} + \left(\frac{\partial q_{gsc_n}}{\partial p_{o_n}}\right)^{(\nu)} \Bigg]. \quad (9.498)$$

$$\left(\frac{\partial R_{g_n}}{\partial S_{w_n}}\right)^{(\nu)} = \Bigg[\Bigg\{ \sum_{m \in \psi_n} \Bigg(\left[\Delta_m p_o^{(\nu)} - \bar{\gamma}_{o_{n,m}}^n \Delta_m Z\right]$$

$$\times \left[\frac{\partial (\mathrm{T}_o R_s)_{n,m}}{\partial S_{w_n}}\right]^{(\nu)} \Bigg) \Bigg\} - C_{gw_n}^{(\nu)} + \left(\frac{\partial q_{gsc_n}}{\partial S_{w_n}}\right)^{(\nu)} \Bigg]. \quad (9.499)$$

$$\left(\frac{\partial R_{g_n}}{\partial S_{g_n}}\right)^{(\nu)} = \Bigg[\Bigg\{ \sum_{m \in \psi_n} \Bigg(\left[\Delta_m p_o^{(\nu)} + \Delta_m P_{cgo}^{(\nu)} - \bar{\gamma}_{g_{n,m}}^n \Delta_m Z\right]$$

$$\times \left(\frac{\partial \mathrm{T}_{g_{n,m}}}{\partial S_{g_n}}\right)^{(\nu)} - \mathrm{T}_{g_{n,m}}^{(\nu)} P_{cgo_n}'^{(\nu)}$$

$$+ \left[\Delta_m p_o^{(\nu)} - \bar{\gamma}_{o_{n,m}}^n \Delta_m Z\right] \left[\frac{\partial (\mathrm{T}_o R_s)_{n,m}}{\partial S_{g_n}}\right]^{(\nu)} \Bigg) \Bigg\}$$

$$- C_{gg_n}^{(\nu)} + \left(\frac{\partial q_{gsc_n}}{\partial S_{g_n}}\right)^{(\nu)} \Bigg]. \quad (9.500)$$

The coefficients C_{op_n}, C_{ow_n}, C_{og_n}, C_{wp_n}, C_{ww_n}, C_{wg_n}, C_{gp_n}, C_{gw_n}, and C_{gg_n} are defined by Eqs. 9.228 through 9.236 and the $n+1$ estimates are evaluated at Iteration Level ν in these equations.

4. Equating the residuals $R_{l_n}^{n+1}$, evaluated at Iteration Level $\nu+1$ and expressed by Eq. 9.481, to zero to provide a means for the estimation of the unknowns for which the residuals are at minimum,

$$\sum_{m \in \psi_n} \left[\left(\frac{\partial R_{l_n}}{\partial p_{o_m}}\right)^{(\nu)} \delta p_{o_m} + \left(\frac{\partial R_{l_n}}{\partial S_{w_m}}\right)^{(\nu)} \delta S_{w_m} + \left(\frac{\partial R_{l_n}}{\partial S_{g_m}}\right)^{(\nu)} \delta S_{g_m} \right]$$

$$+ \left[\left(\frac{\partial R_{l_n}}{\partial p_{o_n}}\right)^{(\nu)} \delta p_{o_n} + \left(\frac{\partial R_{l_n}}{\partial S_{w_n}}\right)^{(\nu)} \delta S_{w_n} + \left(\frac{\partial R_{l_n}}{\partial S_{g_n}}\right)^{(\nu)} \delta S_{g_n} \right]$$

$$= - \overset{(\nu)}{R_{l_n}^{n+1}}, \quad (9.501)$$

where $l = o$, w, or g and $n = 1,2, \ldots, N$.

Eq. 9.501 is Newton's iterative equation. This equation represents $3N$ coupled equations. The iteration process is carried out for iterations $\nu = 0,1,2, \ldots,$ until convergence.

9.6 Methods of Solving Multiphase Difference Equations

In contrast to single-phase flow, multiphase-flow simulation results in multiple finite-difference equations for each gridblock (one equation for each component for each gridblock). In this section, the basic solution methods currently in use for solving equations of multiphase-flow problems are introduced. These are the SS, the IMPES, and the SEQ methods. The most powerful solution method, the fully-implicit method (or Newton's method), is introduced as part of the SS method. The methods discussed here are applied to solve the finite-difference equations for three basic flow systems.

Time-stability analyses for these solution methods follow the same basic principles as those of single-phase flow (discussed in Chap. 5) but often require considerable manipulations. Such analyses, therefore, are not considered here but can be found elsewhere.[2]

9.6.1 Simultaneous Solution, SS, Method. As the name implies, the objective of the SS method is to solve all the equations for multiphase flow simultaneously. Consider a reservoir with no-flow boundaries containing N gridblocks that are ordered with natural ordering. For a black-oil model, each gridblock contributes three equations and, consequently, the total number of equations or unknowns is $3N$. To facilitate the matrix representation of the finite-difference equations, the water, gas, and oil equations and the unknowns, S_w, S_g, and p_o, are considered in that order for each gridblock. Although the ordering of equations and unknowns is arbitrary, it is recommended that the coefficient matrix be constructed with alignment between equations and unknowns. Alignment in this context implies that the equation and phase saturation have the same order. Such alignment avoids division by zero during matrix computations and may provide diagonal dominance of the resulting matrix.

The SS method for the explicitly linearized and fully-implicit difference equations for the black-oil model follow.

SS Method for Explicitly Linearized Black-Oil Model. Let us order the unknowns in a vector

$$\vec{X} = \left(\vec{X}_1, \vec{X}_2, \vec{X}_3, \ldots, \vec{X}_N\right)^T. \quad (9.502)$$

$$\vec{X}_n = \left(S_{w_n}, S_{g_n}, p_{o_n}\right)^T, \quad (9.503)$$

where $n = 1,2,3, \ldots, N$. The finite-difference equations, Eqs. 9.473 through 9.475, written for all gridblocks may be expressed in a matrix form as

$$([\mathbf{T}] - [\mathbf{C}])\vec{X}^{n+1} = -[\mathbf{C}]\vec{X}^n - \vec{Q} + \vec{G}, \quad (9.504)$$

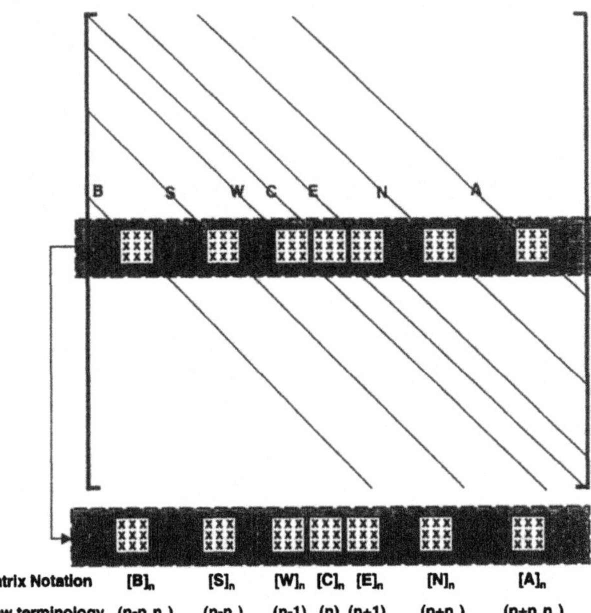

Fig. 9.15—The *n*th block row of Matrix [T] for 3D flow in the CFVD method terminology and in matrix notation. The submatrices of [T] are defined by Eqs. 9.511 through 9.513.

where **[T]** = transmissibility matrix, **[C]** = accumulation matrix, $\vec{Q}$ = source vector, and $\vec{G}$ = vector of gravity terms. The definition of these vectors and matrices follow.

$$\vec{Q} = \left(\vec{Q}_1, \vec{Q}_2, \vec{Q}_3, \ldots, \vec{Q}_N\right)^T. \quad \text{(9.505)}$$

$$\vec{Q}_n = \begin{bmatrix} q^n_{wsc_n} \\ q^n_{gsc_n} \\ q^n_{osc_n} \end{bmatrix}, \quad \text{(9.506)}$$

where $n = 1,2,3, \ldots, N$.

$$\vec{G} = \left(\vec{G}_1, \vec{G}_2, \vec{G}_3, \ldots, \vec{G}_N\right)^T. \quad \text{(9.507)}$$

$$\vec{G}_n = \begin{bmatrix} \sum\limits_{m\in\psi_n} \left(\mathrm{T}_w \bar{\gamma}_w\right)^n_{n,m} \Delta_m Z \\ \sum\limits_{m\in\psi_n} \left(\mathrm{T}_g \bar{\gamma}_g + \mathrm{T}_o R_s \bar{\gamma}_o\right)^n_{n,m} \Delta_m Z \\ \sum\limits_{m\in\psi_n} \left(\mathrm{T}_o \bar{\gamma}_o\right)^n_{n,m} \Delta_m Z \end{bmatrix}, \quad \text{(9.508)}$$

where $n = 1,2,3, \ldots, N$.

$$[\mathbf{C}] = \begin{bmatrix} [\mathbf{C}]_1 & & & \\ & [\mathbf{C}]_2 & & \\ & & [\mathbf{C}]_3 & \\ & & & \ddots \\ & & & & [\mathbf{C}]_N \end{bmatrix}. \quad \text{(9.509)}$$

$$[\mathbf{C}]_n = \begin{bmatrix} C_{ww_n} & C_{wg_n} & C_{wp_n} \\ C_{gw_n} & C_{gg_n} & C_{gp_n} \\ C_{ow_n} & C_{og_n} & C_{op_n} \end{bmatrix}, \quad \text{(9.510)}$$

where $n = 1,2,3, \ldots, N$. In the SS method for multiphase flow, the transmissibility matrix **[T]** has a block structure. That is, the elements of the matrix are submatrices. For the *n*th block row of matrix **[T]** in **Fig. 9.15**, the definition of the submatrices are

$$[\mathbf{T}]_{n,m} = \begin{bmatrix} -\left(\mathrm{T}_w P'_{cow}\right)^n_{n,m} & 0 & \mathrm{T}^n_{w_{n,m}} \\ 0 & \left(\mathrm{T}_g P'_{cgo}\right)^n_{n,m} & \left(\mathrm{T}_g + \mathrm{T}_o R_s\right)^n_{n,m} \\ 0 & 0 & \mathrm{T}^n_{o_{n,m}} \end{bmatrix}, \quad \text{(9.511)}$$

where $m \in \psi_n$ and

$$[\mathbf{T}]_{n,n} = \begin{bmatrix} \sum\limits_{m\in\psi_n} \left(\mathrm{T}_w P'_{cow}\right)^n_{n,m} & 0 & -\sum\limits_{m\in\psi_n} \mathrm{T}^n_{w_{n,m}} \\ 0 & -\sum\limits_{m\in\psi_n} \left(\mathrm{T}_g P'_{cgo}\right)^n_{n,m} & -\sum\limits_{m\in\psi_n} \left(\mathrm{T}_g + \mathrm{T}_o R_s\right)^n_{n,m} \\ 0 & 0 & -\sum\limits_{m\in\psi_n} \mathrm{T}^n_{o_{n,m}} \end{bmatrix} \quad \text{(9.512)}$$

$$\text{or } [\mathbf{T}]_{n,n} = -\sum_{m\in\psi_n} [\mathbf{T}]_{n,m}. \quad \text{(9.513)}$$

For the explicit method of linearization, the elements of the submatrices, $[\mathbf{T}]_{n,m}$ and $[\mathbf{T}]_{n,n}$, are evaluated at Time Level n.

SS Method for Fully-Implicit Black-Oil Model. For multidimensional problems, the SS method is expensive in terms of computation and storage because the number of equations solved is large. Therefore, the value of the SS method lies in its application for fully-implicit models, where, because of the less restrictive stability criteria, large timesteps can be used. Although there are efficient, iterative linear-equation solvers for the fully-implicit black-oil model,[13,14] they are beyond the scope of this book.

Sec. 9.5.3 presents Newton's method for the linearization of the fully-implicit equations for the black-oil model. The linearized equations are expressed as Eq. 9.501. These equations may be expressed in a matrix form as

$$[\mathbf{J}]^{(\nu)} \delta\vec{X} = -\vec{R}^{(\nu)}, \quad \text{(9.514)}$$

where $\nu = 0,1,2, \ldots,$ and where

$$\delta\vec{X} = \vec{X}^{(\nu+1)} - \vec{X}^{(\nu)}; \; \vec{X}^{(0)} = \vec{X}^n. \quad \text{(9.515)}$$

The unknown vector $\vec{X}$ is defined by Eqs. 9.502 and 9.503, and the residual vector $\vec{R}$ is defined as

$$\vec{R} = \left(\vec{R}_1, \vec{R}_2, \vec{R}_3, \ldots, \vec{R}_N\right)^T. \quad \text{(9.516)}$$

$$\vec{R}_n = \left(R_{w_n}, R_{g_n}, R_{o_n}\right)^T, \quad \text{(9.517)}$$

where $n = 1,2,3, \ldots, N$.

In Eq. 9.517, the elements of $\vec{R}_n$ are defined by Eqs. 9.477 through 9.479. The Jacobian Matrix **[J]** is a block-structured matrix similar to [T] (for single-point upstream weighting) and its *n*th block row is shown in Fig. 9.15 where block-row submatrices $[\mathbf{J}]_{n,m}$ for $m \in \psi_n \cup \{n\}$ are defined as

$$[\mathbf{J}]_{n,m} = \begin{bmatrix} \dfrac{\partial R_{w_n}}{\partial S_{w_m}} & \dfrac{\partial R_{w_n}}{\partial S_{g_m}} & \dfrac{\partial R_{w_n}}{\partial p_{o_m}} \\ \dfrac{\partial R_{g_n}}{\partial S_{w_m}} & \dfrac{\partial R_{g_n}}{\partial S_{g_m}} & \dfrac{\partial R_{g_n}}{\partial p_{o_m}} \\ \dfrac{\partial R_{o_n}}{\partial S_{w_m}} & \dfrac{\partial R_{o_n}}{\partial S_{g_m}} & \dfrac{\partial R_{o_n}}{\partial p_{o_m}} \end{bmatrix}, \quad \text{(9.518)}$$

where $m \in \psi_n \cup \{n\}$. Eqs. 9.483 through 9.500 give the elements of the submatrices.

By considering the principal elements forming the residuals defined by Eqs. 9.477 through 9.479, the flow terms, F, the accumulation terms, C, and the production (injection) terms, Q, Newton's iterative equation (Eq. 9.514) may be expressed as

$$\left\{[\mathbf{F}]^{(\nu)} - [\mathbf{C}]^{(\nu)} + [\mathbf{Q}]^{(\nu)}\right\}\delta\vec{X} = -\left\{\vec{F}^{(\nu)} - \left[\vec{C}^{(\nu)} - \vec{C}^{n}\right] + \vec{Q}^{(\nu)}\right\}, \quad \text{(9.519)}$$

where $\nu = 0,1,2, \ldots$, and where the following occurs.

$$\delta\vec{X} = \vec{X}^{(\nu+1)} - \vec{X}^{(\nu)};\ \vec{X}^{(0)} = \vec{X}^{n}. \quad \text{(9.515)}$$

$$\vec{X} = \left(\vec{X}_1, \vec{X}_2, \vec{X}_3, \ldots, \vec{X}_N\right)^T. \quad \text{(9.502)}$$

$$\vec{F} = \left(\vec{F}_1, \vec{F}_2, \vec{F}_3, \ldots, \vec{F}_N\right)^T. \quad \text{(9.520)}$$

$$\vec{C} = \left(\vec{C}_1, \vec{C}_2, \vec{C}_3, \ldots, \vec{C}_N\right)^T. \quad \text{(9.521)}$$

$$\vec{Q} = \left(\vec{Q}_1, \vec{Q}_2, \vec{Q}_3, \ldots, \vec{Q}_N\right)^T. \quad \text{(9.505)}$$

$$\vec{X}_n = \left(S_{w_n}, S_{g_n}, p_{o_n}\right)^T, \quad \text{(9.503)}$$

$$\vec{C}_n = \begin{bmatrix} C_{w_n} \\ C_{g_n} \\ C_{o_n} \end{bmatrix} = \begin{bmatrix} \dfrac{V_b}{\alpha_c \Delta t}\left(\dfrac{\phi S_w}{B_w}\right) \\ \dfrac{V_b}{\alpha_c \Delta t}\left[\dfrac{\phi S_g}{B_g} + \dfrac{\phi R_s(1 - S_w - S_g)}{B_o}\right] \\ \dfrac{V_b}{\alpha_c \Delta t}\left[\dfrac{\phi(1 - S_w - S_g)}{B_o}\right] \end{bmatrix}_n, \quad \text{(9.522)}$$

$$\vec{Q}_n = \begin{bmatrix} Q_{1_n} \\ Q_{2_n} \\ Q_{3_n} \end{bmatrix} = \begin{bmatrix} q_{wsc_n} \\ q_{gsc_n} \\ q_{osc_n} \end{bmatrix}, \quad \text{(9.523)}$$

and

$$\vec{F}_n = \begin{bmatrix} F_{w_n} \\ F_{g_n} \\ F_{o_n} \end{bmatrix} = \begin{bmatrix} \sum\limits_{m\in\psi_n}\left[T_{w_{n,m}}\left(\Delta_m p_o - \Delta_m P_{cow} - \gamma^n_{w_{n,m}}\Delta_m Z\right)\right] \\ \sum\limits_{m\in\psi_n}\left[T_{g_{n,m}}\left(\Delta_m p_o + \Delta_m P_{cgo} - \gamma^n_{g_{n,m}}\Delta_m Z\right) + (T_o R_s)_{n,m}\left(\Delta_m p_o - \gamma^n_{o_{n,m}}\Delta_m Z\right)\right] \\ \sum\limits_{m\in\psi_n}\left[T_{o_{n,m}}\left(\Delta_m p_o - \gamma^n_{o_{n,m}}\Delta_m Z\right)\right] \end{bmatrix}, \quad \text{(9.524)}$$

where $n = 1,2,3, \ldots, N$.

$$[\mathbf{C}] = \begin{bmatrix} [\mathbf{C}]_1 & & & & \\ & [\mathbf{C}]_2 & & & \\ & & [\mathbf{C}]_3 & & \\ & & & \ddots & \\ & & & & [\mathbf{C}]_N \end{bmatrix}. \quad \text{(9.509)}$$

$$[\mathbf{C}]_n = \begin{bmatrix} C_{ww_n} & C_{wg_n} & C_{wp_n} \\ C_{gw_n} & C_{gg_n} & C_{gp_n} \\ C_{ow_n} & C_{og_n} & C_{op_n} \end{bmatrix}, \quad \text{(9.510)}$$

where $n = 1,2,3, \ldots, N$.

$$[\mathbf{Q}] = \begin{bmatrix} [\mathbf{Q}]_1 & & & & \\ & [\mathbf{Q}]_2 & & & \\ & & [\mathbf{Q}]_3 & & \\ & & & \ddots & \\ & & & & [\mathbf{Q}]_N \end{bmatrix}. \quad \text{(9.525)}$$

$$[\mathbf{Q}]_n = \begin{bmatrix} \dfrac{\partial q_{wsc_n}}{\partial S_{w_n}} & \dfrac{\partial q_{wsc_n}}{\partial S_{g_n}} & \dfrac{\partial q_{wsc_n}}{\partial p_{o_n}} \\ \dfrac{\partial q_{gsc_n}}{\partial S_{w_n}} & \dfrac{\partial q_{gsc_n}}{\partial S_{g_n}} & \dfrac{\partial q_{gsc_n}}{\partial p_{o_n}} \\ \dfrac{\partial q_{osc_n}}{\partial S_{w_n}} & \dfrac{\partial q_{osc_n}}{\partial S_{g_n}} & \dfrac{\partial q_{osc_n}}{\partial p_{o_n}} \end{bmatrix}, \quad \text{(9.526)}$$

where $n = 1,2,3, \ldots, N$, and the flow matrix $[\mathbf{F}]$ is a block-structured matrix similar to $[\mathbf{T}]$ (for single-point upstream weighting) and its nth block row is shown in Fig. 9.15 where block row submatrices $[\mathbf{F}]_{n,m}$ for $m \in \psi_n \cup \{n\}$ are defined as

$$[\mathbf{F}]_{n,m} = \begin{bmatrix} \dfrac{\partial F_{w_n}}{\partial S_{w_m}} & \dfrac{\partial F_{w_n}}{\partial S_{g_m}} & \dfrac{\partial F_{w_n}}{\partial p_{o_m}} \\ \dfrac{\partial F_{g_n}}{\partial S_{w_m}} & \dfrac{\partial F_{g_n}}{\partial S_{g_m}} & \dfrac{\partial F_{g_n}}{\partial p_{o_m}} \\ \dfrac{\partial F_{o_n}}{\partial S_{w_m}} & \dfrac{\partial F_{o_n}}{\partial S_{g_m}} & \dfrac{\partial F_{o_n}}{\partial p_{o_m}} \end{bmatrix}, \quad \text{(9.527)}$$

where $m \in \psi_n \cup \{n\}$ and $n = 1,2,3, \ldots, N$. In Eq. 9.527, the partial derivatives of F_{o_n}, F_{w_n}, and F_{g_n} with respect to the unknowns p_o, S_g, and S_w are incorporated into the partial derivatives of R_{l_n} given by Eqs. 9.483 through 9.500.

$$\left(\frac{\partial F_{l_n}}{\partial S_{w_m}}\right)^{(\nu)} = \left(\frac{\partial R_{l_n}}{\partial S_{w_m}}\right)^{(\nu)}, \quad \text{(9.528)}$$

$$\left(\frac{\partial F_{l_n}}{\partial S_{g_m}}\right)^{(\nu)} = \left(\frac{\partial R_{l_n}}{\partial S_{g_m}}\right)^{(\nu)}, \quad \text{(9.529)}$$

and

$$\left(\frac{\partial F_{l_n}}{\partial p_{o_m}}\right)^{(\nu)} = \left(\frac{\partial R_{l_n}}{\partial p_{o_m}}\right)^{(\nu)}, \quad \text{(9.530)}$$

where $l = o$, w, or g, $m \in \psi_n$, and $n = 1,2,3, \ldots, N$. Also, where $(\partial F_{l_n}/\partial S_{w_n})^{(\nu)}$, $(\partial F_{l_n}/\partial S_{g_n})^{(\nu)}$, and $(\partial F_{l_n}/\partial p_{o_n})^{(\nu)}$ are enclosed, respectively, in the braces in the definitions of $(\partial R_{l_n}/\partial S_{w_n})^{(\nu)}$, $(\partial R_{l_n}/\partial S_{g_n})^{(\nu)}$, and $(\partial R_{l_n}/\partial p_{o_n})^{(\nu)}$ given by Eqs. 9.492 through 9.500 for $n = 1,2,3, \ldots, N$.

Newton's iteration starts with the evaluation of the Jacobian matrix,

$$[\mathbf{J}]^{(\nu)} = \left[[\mathbf{F}]^{(\nu)} - [\mathbf{C}]^{(\nu)} - [\mathbf{Q}]^{(\nu)}\right], \quad \text{(9.531)}$$

and the residual,

$$\vec{R}^{(\nu)} = \left\{\vec{F}^{(\nu)} - \left[\vec{C}^{(\nu)} - \vec{C}^{n}\right] + \vec{Q}^{(\nu)}\right\}, \quad \text{(9.532)}$$

at $\vec{X}^{(0)} = \vec{X}^{n}$ for the first iteration ($\nu = 0$). Then $\delta\vec{X}$ is calculated with Eq. 9.514 (or 9.519), from which $\vec{X}^{(1)}$ is estimated with Eq. 9.515. For the second iteration ($\nu = 1$), $[\mathbf{J}]^{(1)}$ and $\vec{R}^{(1)}$ are evaluated at $\vec{X}^{(1)}$ and $\delta\vec{X}$ is determined and an estimate of $\vec{X}^{(2)}$ obtained. The iteration continues as described for $\nu = 2, 3, \ldots$ until convergence is reached.

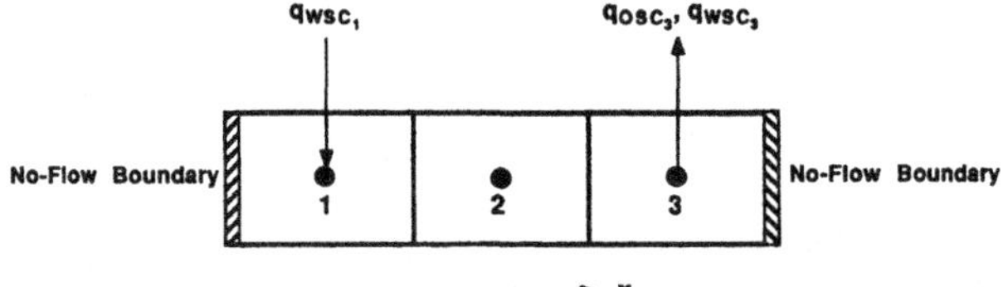

Fig. 9.16—Discretized reservoir for Example 9.23.

SS Method for Two-Phase Models and Flow in Multidimensions. The SS methods for the black-oil model presented previously in this section reduce to the SS methods for two-phase-flow models by changing the definitions of the vectors $\vec{X}_n$, $\vec{Q}_n$, and $\vec{G}_n$, and the matrices $[\mathbf{C}]_n$ and $[\mathbf{T}]_{n,m}$ for $n=1,2,\ldots,N$; and the vectors $\vec{X}_n$, $\vec{R}_n$, $\vec{F}_n$, $\vec{C}_n$, and $\vec{Q}_n$, and the matrices $[\mathbf{C}]_n$, $[\mathbf{Q}]_n$, and $[\mathbf{F}]_{n,m}$ for $n=1,2,\ldots,N$. For two-phase-flow models, the vectors and matrices for Gridblock n are block structured and are obtained by removing the row that corresponds to the extra phase and the column that corresponds to the extra unknown. For example, in the oil/water flow model, the row (second row) that corresponds to gas and the column (second column) that corresponds to S_g are removed (see Example 9.23).

The finite-difference equations written with the CVFD method terminology are applicable for 1D-, 2D-, and 3D-flow problems depending on the definition of Gridblock Set ψ_n. For 1D-flow problems, ψ_n is defined as shown in Fig. 9.12, and matrices **[T]**, **[F]**, and **[J]** have a tridiagonal matrix structure where each element is a $l\times l$ block submatrix (where l is the number of phases). For 2D-flow problems, ψ_n is defined as in Fig. 9.13. Fig. 7.6 shows that matrices **[T]**, **[F]**, and **[J]** have a pentadiagonal matrix structure where each element is a $l\times l$ block submatrix. For 3D-flow problems, ψ_n is defined in Fig. 9.14. Fig. 7.10 shows that matrices **[T]**, **[F]**, and **[J]** have a heptadiagonal matrix structure where each element is a $l\times l$ block submatrix. A $l\times l$ block submatrix is a scalar element for single-phase flow, a 2×2 matrix for two-phase flow, and a 3×3 matrix for three-phase flow.

Example 9.23. Write the fully-implicit finite-difference equations using Newton's iteration for the 1D oil and water flow model of Example 9.12. The reservoir consists of three gridblocks with no-flow boundaries. There is an injection well in Gridblock 1 and a production well in Gridblock 3. Present the equations for this model in matrix form.

Solution. For the 1D reservoir in **Fig. 9.16**, ψ_n is given as

$$\psi_n = \{(n-1),(n+1)\} \quad \text{(9.533)}$$

for $n=1,2,3$ or $\psi_1=\{2\}$, $\psi_2=\{1,3\}$, and $\psi_3=\{2\}$. Gridblocks 0 and 4 are removed from Gridblock Sets ψ_1 and ψ_3, respectively, because Gridblocks 1 and 3 are boundary gridblocks subject to no-flow boundary conditions.

Eq. 9.519 gives the Newton's iterative equation for this problem.

$$\left[[\mathbf{F}]^{(\nu)} - [\mathbf{C}]^{(\nu)} + [\mathbf{Q}]^{(\nu)}\right]\delta\vec{X} = -\left\{\vec{F}^{(\nu)} - \left[\vec{C}^{(\nu)} - \vec{C}^{n}\right] + \vec{Q}^{(\nu)}\right\}, \quad \text{(9.519)}$$

where $\nu=0,1,2,\ldots$, and where

$$\delta\vec{X} = \vec{X}^{(\nu+1)} - \vec{X}^{(\nu)};\ \vec{X}^{(0)} = \vec{X}^{n}, \quad \text{(9.515)}$$

$$\vec{X} = \left(\vec{X}_1,\vec{X}_2,\vec{X}_3\right)^T, \quad \text{(9.534)}$$

$$\vec{F} = \left(\vec{F}_1,\vec{F}_2,\vec{F}_3\right)^T, \quad \text{(9.535)}$$

$$\vec{C} = \left(\vec{C}_1,\vec{C}_2,\vec{C}_3\right)^T, \quad \text{(9.536)}$$

and
$$\vec{Q} = \left(\vec{Q}_1,\vec{Q}_2,\vec{Q}_3\right)^T. \quad \text{(9.537)}$$

The definitions of $\vec{X}_n$, $\vec{F}_n$, $\vec{C}_n$, and $\vec{Q}_n$ are obtained from Eqs. 9.503 and 9.522 through 9.524 by removing the second row entry corresponding to the gas phase in each vector, and setting $S_g=0$.

$$\vec{X}_n = \begin{bmatrix} S_{w_n} \\ p_{o_n} \end{bmatrix}, \quad \text{(9.538)}$$

$$\vec{C}_n = \begin{bmatrix} C_{w_n} \\ C_{o_n} \end{bmatrix} = \begin{bmatrix} \dfrac{V_b}{\alpha_c\Delta t}\left(\dfrac{\phi S_w}{B_w}\right) \\ \dfrac{V_b}{\alpha_c\Delta t}\left[\dfrac{\phi(1-S_w)}{B_o}\right] \end{bmatrix}_n, \quad \text{(9.539)}$$

and
$$\vec{Q}_n = \begin{bmatrix} q_{wsc_n} \\ q_{osc_n} \end{bmatrix}, \quad \text{(9.540)}$$

where $n=1,2,3$, or

$$\vec{Q}_1 = \begin{bmatrix} q_{wsc_1} \\ 0 \end{bmatrix}, \quad \text{(9.541a)}$$

$$\vec{Q}_2 = \begin{bmatrix} 0 \\ 0 \end{bmatrix}, \quad \text{(9.541b)}$$

and
$$\vec{Q}_3 = \begin{bmatrix} q_{wsc_3} \\ q_{osc_3} \end{bmatrix}, \quad \text{(9.541c)}$$

and
$$\vec{F}_n = \begin{bmatrix} F_{w_n} \\ F_{o_n} \end{bmatrix} = \begin{bmatrix} \sum\limits_{m\in\psi_n} T_{w_{n,m}}\Delta_m p_o \\ \sum\limits_{m\in\psi_n} T_{o_{n,m}}\Delta_m p_o \end{bmatrix}, \quad \text{(9.542)}$$

where $n=1,2,3$. Matrices **[C]**, **[Q]**, and **[F]** in Eq. 9.519 are

$$[\mathbf{C}] = \begin{bmatrix} [\mathbf{C}]_1 & & \\ & [\mathbf{C}]_2 & \\ & & [\mathbf{C}]_3 \end{bmatrix}, \quad \text{(9.543)}$$

$$[\mathbf{Q}] = \begin{bmatrix} [\mathbf{Q}]_1 & & \\ & [\mathbf{Q}]_2 & \\ & & [\mathbf{Q}]_3 \end{bmatrix}, \quad \text{(9.544)}$$

and
$$[\mathbf{F}] = \begin{bmatrix} [\mathbf{F}]_{11} & [\mathbf{F}]_{12} & [\mathbf{0}] \\ [\mathbf{F}]_{21} & [\mathbf{F}]_{22} & [\mathbf{F}]_{23} \\ [\mathbf{0}] & [\mathbf{F}]_{32} & [\mathbf{F}]_{33} \end{bmatrix}, \quad \text{(9.545)}$$

The definitions of $[\mathbf{C}]_n$, $[\mathbf{Q}]_n$, and $[\mathbf{F}]_{n,m}$ are obtained from Eqs. 9.510, 9.526, and 9.527, respectively, by removing the second row corresponding to the gas phase and second column corresponding to S_g in each matrix for Gridblock n. Matrix $[\mathbf{C}]_n$ is

$$[\mathbf{C}]_n = \begin{bmatrix} C_{ww_n} & C_{wp_n} \\ C_{ow_n} & C_{op_n} \end{bmatrix}, \quad \text{(9.546)}$$

where $n=1,2,3$ and the coefficients of $[\mathbf{C}]_n$, at the νth iteration, are obtained in Example 9.12.

$$C_{ww_n} = \left[\frac{V_b}{\alpha_c\Delta t}\left(\frac{\phi}{B_w}\right)^{(\nu)}\right]_n, \quad \text{(9.547)}$$

$$C_{wp_n} = \left\{\frac{V_b}{\alpha_c\Delta t}\left[\frac{\phi'}{B_w^n} + \phi\left(\frac{1}{B_w}\right)'\right]^{(\nu)} S_w^n\right\}_n, \quad \text{(9.548)}$$

$$C_{ow_n} = \left[-\frac{V_b}{\alpha_c \Delta t}\left(\frac{\phi}{B_o}\right)^{(\nu)} \right]_n, \quad \text{.................. (9.549)}$$

$$\text{and } C_{op_n} = \left\{ \frac{V_b}{\alpha_c \Delta t}\left[\frac{\phi'}{B_o^n} + \phi\left(\frac{1}{B_o}\right)'\right]^{(\nu)} (1 - S_w^n) \right\}_n. \quad \text{.................. (9.550)}$$

Matrices $[\mathbf{Q}]_n$ are

$$[\mathbf{Q}]_n = \begin{bmatrix} 0 & 0 \\ 0 & 0 \end{bmatrix}, \quad \text{.............................. (9.551)}$$

where $n = 1,2$ and

$$[\mathbf{Q}]_3 = \begin{bmatrix} \dfrac{\partial q_{wsc_3}}{\partial S_{w_3}} & \dfrac{\partial q_{wsc_3}}{\partial p_{o_3}} \\ \dfrac{\partial q_{osc_3}}{\partial S_{w_3}} & \dfrac{\partial q_{osc_3}}{\partial p_{o_3}} \end{bmatrix}. \quad \text{.................... (9.552)}$$

Matrices $[\mathbf{F}]_{n,m}$ are

$$[\mathbf{F}]_{n,m} = \begin{bmatrix} \dfrac{\partial F_{w_n}}{\partial S_{w_m}} & \dfrac{\partial F_{w_n}}{\partial p_{o_m}} \\ \dfrac{\partial F_{o_n}}{\partial S_{w_m}} & \dfrac{\partial F_{o_n}}{\partial p_{o_m}} \end{bmatrix}, \quad \text{...................... (9.553)}$$

where $m \in \psi_n \cup \{n\}$ and $n = 1,2,3$. For $m \in \psi_n$ for $n = 1,2,3$, the application of Eqs. 9.528 and 9.530 for $l = o$ or w gives

$$\left(\frac{\partial F_{w_n}}{\partial S_{w_m}}\right)^{(\nu)} = \left[\Delta_m p_o^{(\nu)}\right]\left(\frac{\partial \mathrm{T}_{w_{n,m}}}{\partial S_{w_m}}\right)^{(\nu)}, \quad \text{.............. (9.554)}$$

$$\left(\frac{\partial F_{w_n}}{\partial p_{o_m}}\right)^{(\nu)} = \mathrm{T}_{w_{n,m}}^{(\nu)} + \left[\Delta_m p_o^{(\nu)}\right]\left(\frac{\partial \mathrm{T}_{w_{n,m}}}{\partial p_{o_m}}\right)^{(\nu)}, \quad \text{....... (9.555)}$$

$$\left(\frac{\partial F_{o_n}}{\partial S_{w_m}}\right)^{(\nu)} = \left[\Delta_m p_o^{(\nu)}\right]\left(\frac{\partial \mathrm{T}_{o_{n,m}}}{\partial S_{w_m}}\right)^{(\nu)}, \quad \text{.............. (9.556)}$$

$$\text{and } \left(\frac{\partial F_{o_n}}{\partial p_{o_m}}\right)^{(\nu)} = \mathrm{T}_{o_{n,m}}^{(\nu)} + \left[\Delta_m p_o^{(\nu)}\right]\left(\frac{\partial \mathrm{T}_{o_{n,m}}}{\partial p_{o_m}}\right)^{(\nu)}. \quad \text{...... (9.557)}$$

For $m = n$ and $n = 1,2,3$, the contents of the brackets in Eqs. 9.492, 9.493, 9.495, and 9.496 reduce to

$$\left(\frac{\partial F_{o_n}}{\partial p_{o_n}}\right)^{(\nu)} = \left\{ \sum_{m \in \psi_n} \left(-\mathrm{T}_{o_{n,m}}^{(\nu)} + \left[\Delta_m p_o^{(\nu)}\right]\left(\frac{\partial \mathrm{T}_{o_{n,m}}}{\partial p_{o_n}}\right)^{(\nu)} \right) \right\}, \quad \text{.................. (9.558)}$$

$$\left(\frac{\partial F_{o_n}}{\partial S_{w_n}}\right)^{(\nu)} = \left\{ \sum_{m \in \psi_n} \left(\left[\Delta_m p_o^{(\nu)}\right]\left(\frac{\partial \mathrm{T}_{o_{n,m}}}{\partial S_{w_n}}\right)^{(\nu)} \right) \right\}, \quad \text{.... (9.559)}$$

$$\left(\frac{\partial F_{w_n}}{\partial p_{o_n}}\right)^{(\nu)} = \left\{ \sum_{m \in \psi_n} \left(-T_{w_{n,m}}^{(\nu)} + \left[\Delta_m p_o^{(\nu)}\right]\left(\frac{\partial T_{w_{n,m}}}{\partial p_{o_n}}\right)^{(\nu)} \right) \right\}, \quad \text{.................. (9.560)}$$

$$\text{and } \left(\frac{\partial F_{w_n}}{\partial S_{w_n}}\right)^{(\nu)} = \left\{ \sum_{m \in \psi_n} \left(\left[\Delta_m p_o^{(\nu)}\right]\left(\frac{\partial \mathrm{T}_{w_{n,m}}}{\partial S_{w_n}}\right)^{(\nu)} \right) \right\}. \quad \text{.................. (9.561)}$$

Example 9.24. Using the single-point upstream weighting for transmissibilities, write the elements of $\vec{F}_n$ and $[\mathbf{F}]_{n,m}$ for $m \in \psi_n \cup \{n\}$, where $n = 1,2,3$ in Example 9.23.

Solution. For the flow problem in Example 9.23, fluids flow from the injection gridblock to the production gridblock. In other words, Gridblock 1 is upstream to Gridblock 2 and Gridblock 2 is upstream to Gridblock 3 for both the oil and water phases.

For single-point upstream transmissibilities,

$$\mathrm{T}_{w_{n,m}} = \left(\mathrm{T}_{w_{n,m}}\right)_n \quad \text{........................... (9.562a)}$$

if Gridblock n is upstream to Gridblock m for water phase,

$$\mathrm{T}_{w_{n,m}} = \left(\mathrm{T}_{w_{n,m}}\right)_m \quad \text{......................... (9.562b)}$$

if Gridblock m is upstream to Gridblock n for water phase,

$$\mathrm{T}_{o_{n,m}} = \left(\mathrm{T}_{o_{n,m}}\right)_n \quad \text{........................... (9.563a)}$$

if Gridblock n is upstream to Gridblock m for oil phase, and

$$\mathrm{T}_{o_{n,m}} = \left(\mathrm{T}_{o_{n,m}}\right)_m \quad \text{......................... (9.563b)}$$

if Gridblock m is upstream to Gridblock n for oil phase.

Substituting Eqs. 9.562 and 9.563 into Eq. 9.542 from Example 9.23 and observing that $\psi_1 = \{2\}$, $\psi_2 = \{1,3\}$, and $\psi_3 = \{2\}$ give

$$\vec{F}_1 = \begin{bmatrix} \left(\mathrm{T}_{w_{1,2}}\right)_1 \left(p_{o_2} - p_{o_1}\right) \\ \left(\mathrm{T}_{o_{1,2}}\right)_1 \left(p_{o_2} - p_{o_1}\right) \end{bmatrix}, \quad \text{................ (9.564)}$$

$$\vec{F}_2 = \begin{bmatrix} \left(\mathrm{T}_{w_{1,2}}\right)_1 \left(p_{o_1} - p_{o_2}\right) + \left(\mathrm{T}_{w_{2,3}}\right)_2 \left(p_{o_3} - p_{o_2}\right) \\ \left(\mathrm{T}_{o_{1,2}}\right)_1 \left(p_{o_1} - p_{o_2}\right) + \left(\mathrm{T}_{o_{2,3}}\right)_2 \left(p_{o_3} - p_{o_2}\right) \end{bmatrix}, \quad \text{.................. (9.565)}$$

$$\text{and } \vec{F}_3 = \begin{bmatrix} \left(\mathrm{T}_{w_{3,2}}\right)_2 \left(p_{o_2} - p_{o_3}\right) \\ \left(\mathrm{T}_{o_{3,2}}\right)_2 \left(p_{o_2} - p_{o_3}\right) \end{bmatrix}. \quad \text{............... (9.566)}$$

Example 9.23 gives the matrix $[\mathbf{F}]$ as

$$[\mathbf{F}] = \begin{bmatrix} [\mathbf{F}]_{11} & [\mathbf{F}]_{12} & [\mathbf{0}] \\ [\mathbf{F}]_{21} & [\mathbf{F}]_{22} & [\mathbf{F}]_{23} \\ [\mathbf{0}] & [\mathbf{F}]_{32} & [\mathbf{F}]_{33} \end{bmatrix} \quad \text{.................... (9.545)}$$

$$\text{and } [\mathbf{F}]_{n,m} = \begin{bmatrix} \dfrac{\partial F_{w_n}}{\partial S_{w_m}} & \dfrac{\partial F_{w_n}}{\partial p_{o_m}} \\ \dfrac{\partial F_{o_n}}{\partial S_{w_m}} & \dfrac{\partial F_{o_n}}{\partial p_{o_m}} \end{bmatrix}, \quad \text{.................... (9.553)}$$

where $m \in \psi_n \cup \{n\}$ and $n = 1,2,3$ and where the elements of $[\mathbf{F}]_{n,m}$ for $m \neq n$ and $n = 1,2,3$ are given by Eqs. 9.554 to 9.557, and those for $[\mathbf{F}]_{n,m}$ for $m = n$ are given by Eqs. 9.558 through 9.561 in Example 9.23. For single-point upstream transmissibilities, the partial derivatives of $\mathrm{T}_{w_{n,m}}$ are obtained with Eq. 9.562.

$$\left(\frac{\partial \mathrm{T}_{w_{n,m}}}{\partial S_{w_m}}\right) = 0 \quad \text{........................... (9.567a)}$$

if Gridblock n is upstream to Gridblock m, and

$$\left(\frac{\partial \mathrm{T}_{w_{n,m}}}{\partial S_{w_m}}\right) = \frac{\partial}{\partial S_{w_m}}\left(\mathrm{T}_{w_{n,m}}\right)_m \quad \text{.................. (9.567b)}$$

if Gridblock m is upstream to Gridblock n.

$$\left(\frac{\partial \mathrm{T}_{w_{n,m}}}{\partial p_{o_m}}\right) = 0 \quad \text{........................... (9.568a)}$$

if Gridblock n is upstream to Gridblock m, and

$$\left(\frac{\partial T_{w_{n,m}}}{\partial p_{o_m}}\right) = \frac{\partial}{\partial p_{o_m}}\left(T_{w_{n,m}}\right)_m \qquad (9.568b)$$

if Gridblock m is upstream to Gridblock n.

$$\left(\frac{\partial T_{w_{n,m}}}{\partial S_{w_n}}\right) = \frac{\partial}{\partial S_{w_n}}\left(T_{w_{n,m}}\right)_n \qquad (9.569a)$$

if Gridblock n is upstream to Gridblock m, and

$$\left(\frac{\partial T_{w_{n,m}}}{\partial S_{w_n}}\right) = 0 \qquad (9.569b)$$

if Gridblock m is upstream to Gridblock n.

$$\left(\frac{\partial T_{w_{n,m}}}{\partial p_{o_n}}\right) = \frac{\partial}{\partial p_{o_n}}\left(T_{w_{n,m}}\right)_n \qquad (9.570a)$$

if Gridblock n is upstream to Gridblock m, and

$$\left(\frac{\partial T_{w_{n,m}}}{\partial p_{o_n}}\right) = 0 \qquad (9.570b)$$

if Gridblock m is upstream to Gridblock n. Similar equations apply for the partial derivatives of the oil-phase transmissibility.

For $n=1$, $\psi_n=\{2\}$; therefore, $m\in\psi_n$ is a member of $\{2\}$, which implies that the first block row of matrix **[F]** has a nonzero diagonal submatrix, $[\mathbf{F}]_{11}$, and only one nonzero off-diagonal submatrix, $[\mathbf{F}]_{12}$. The elements of $[\mathbf{F}]_{12}$ are obtained by substituting Eqs. 9.562, 9.563, 9.567, and 9.568 into Eqs. 9.554 through 9.557 in Example 9.23 for $n=1$ and $m=2$ and observing that Gridblock 1 is upstream to Gridblock 2.

$$\left(\frac{\partial F_{w_1}}{\partial S_{w_2}}\right)^{(\nu)} = \left[p_{o_2}^{(\nu)} - p_{o_1}^{(\nu)}\right](0) = 0, \qquad (9.571)$$

$$\left(\frac{\partial F_{w_1}}{\partial p_{o_2}}\right)^{(\nu)} = \left[T_{w_{1,2}}^{(\nu)}\right]_1 + \left[p_{o_2}^{(\nu)} - p_{o_1}^{(\nu)}\right](0) = \left[T_{w_{1,2}}^{(\nu)}\right]_1, \qquad (9.572)$$

$$\left(\frac{\partial F_{o_1}}{\partial S_{w_2}}\right)^{(\nu)} = \left[p_{o_2}^{(\nu)} - p_{o_1}^{(\nu)}\right](0) = 0, \qquad (9.573)$$

and

$$\left(\frac{\partial F_{o_1}}{\partial p_{o_2}}\right)^{(\nu)} = \left[T_{o_{1,2}}^{(\nu)}\right]_1 + \left[p_{o_2}^{(\nu)} - p_{o_1}^{(\nu)}\right](0) = \left[T_{o_{1,2}}^{(\nu)}\right]_1. \qquad (9.574)$$

The elements of $[\mathbf{F}]_{11}$ are obtained by substituting Eqs. 9.562, 9.563, 9.569, and 9.570 into Eqs. 9.558 through 9.561 for $n=1$ and $m=1$ and observing that Gridblock 1 is upstream to Gridblock 2 and the summation

$\sum_{m\in\psi_n}$ consists of only one term, $\sum_{m\in\{2\}}$.

$$\left(\frac{\partial F_{w_1}}{\partial S_{w_1}}\right)^{(\nu)} = \left\{\left[p_{o_2}^{(\nu)} - p_{o_1}^{(\nu)}\right]\left[\frac{\partial}{\partial S_{w_1}}\left(T_{w_{1,2}}\right)_1\right]^{(\nu)}\right\}, \qquad (9.575)$$

$$\left(\frac{\partial F_{w_1}}{\partial p_{o_1}}\right)^{(\nu)} = \left\{-\left[T_{w_{1,2}}^{(\nu)}\right]_1 + \left[p_{o_2}^{(\nu)} - p_{o_1}^{(\nu)}\right]\left[\frac{\partial}{p_{o_1}}\left(T_{w_{1,2}}\right)_1\right]^{(\nu)}\right\}, \qquad (9.576)$$

$$\left(\frac{\partial F_{o_1}}{\partial S_{w_1}}\right)^{(\nu)} = \left\{\left[p_{o_2}^{(\nu)} - p_{o_1}^{(\nu)}\right]\left[\frac{\partial}{\partial S_{w_1}}\left(T_{o_{1,2}}\right)_1\right]^{(\nu)}\right\}, \qquad (9.577)$$

and

$$\left(\frac{\partial F_{o_1}}{\partial p_{o_1}}\right)^{(\nu)} = \left\{-\left[T_{o_{1,2}}^{(\nu)}\right]_1 + \left[p_{o_2}^{(\nu)} - p_{o_1}^{(\nu)}\right]\left[\frac{\partial}{p_{o_1}}\left(T_{o_{1,2}}\right)_1\right]^{(\nu)}\right\}. \qquad (9.578)$$

For $n=2$, $\psi_2=\{1,3\}$; therefore, $m\in\psi_2$ is a member of $\{1,3\}$, which implies that the second block row of matrix **[F]** has a nonzero diagonal submatrix, $[\mathbf{F}]_{22}$, and two nonzero off-diagonal submatrices, $[\mathbf{F}]_{21}$ and $[\mathbf{F}]_{23}$.

In obtaining the elements of $[\mathbf{F}]_{21}$, note that $n=2$ and $m=1$ and that Gridblock 1 is upstream to Gridblock 2.

$$\left(\frac{\partial F_{w_2}}{\partial S_{w_1}}\right)^{(\nu)} = \left[p_{o_1}^{(\nu)} - p_{o_2}^{(\nu)}\right]\left[\frac{\partial}{\partial S_{w_1}}\left(T_{w_{2,1}}\right)_1\right]^{(\nu)}, \qquad (9.579)$$

$$\left(\frac{\partial F_{w_2}}{\partial p_{o_1}}\right)^{(\nu)} = \left[T_{w_{2,1}}^{(\nu)}\right]_1 + \left[p_{o_1}^{(\nu)} - p_{o_2}^{(\nu)}\right]\left[\frac{\partial}{\partial p_{o_1}}\left(T_{w_{2,1}}\right)_1\right]^{(\nu)}, \qquad (9.580)$$

$$\left(\frac{\partial F_{o_2}}{\partial S_{w_1}}\right)^{(\nu)} = \left[p_{o_1}^{(\nu)} - p_{o_2}^{(\nu)}\right]\left[\frac{\partial}{\partial S_{w_1}}\left(T_{o_{2,1}}\right)_1\right]^{(\nu)}, \qquad (9.581)$$

and

$$\left(\frac{\partial F_{o_2}}{\partial p_{o_1}}\right)^{(\nu)} = \left[T_{o_{1,2}}^{(\nu)}\right]_1 + \left[p_{o_1}^{(\nu)} - p_{o_2}^{(\nu)}\right]\left[\frac{\partial}{p_{o_1}}\left(T_{o_{2,1}}\right)_1\right]^{(\nu)}. \qquad (9.582)$$

In obtaining the elements of $[\mathbf{F}]_{23}$, note that $n=2$ and $m=3$ and that Gridblock 2 is upstream to Gridblock 3.

$$\left(\frac{\partial F_{w_2}}{\partial S_{w_3}}\right)^{(\nu)} = \left[p_{o_3}^{(\nu)} - p_{o_2}^{(\nu)}\right](0) = 0. \qquad (9.583)$$

$$\left(\frac{\partial F_{w_2}}{\partial p_{o_3}}\right)^{(\nu)} = \left[T_{w_{2,3}}^{(\nu)}\right]_2 + \left[p_{o_3}^{(\nu)} - p_{o_2}^{(\nu)}\right](0) = \left[T_{w_{2,3}}^{(\nu)}\right]_2, \qquad (9.584)$$

$$\left(\frac{\partial F_{o_2}}{\partial S_{w_3}}\right)^{(\nu)} = \left[p_{o_3}^{(\nu)} - p_{o_2}^{(\nu)}\right](0) = 0. \qquad (9.585)$$

and

$$\left(\frac{\partial F_{o_2}}{\partial p_{o_3}}\right)^{(\nu)} = \left[T_{o_{2,3}}^{(\nu)}\right]_2 + \left[p_{o_3}^{(\nu)} - p_{o_2}^{(\nu)}\right](0) = \left[T_{o_{2,3}}^{(\nu)}\right]_2. \qquad (9.586)$$

In obtaining the elements of $[\mathbf{F}]_{22}$, note that $n=2$ and $m=2$ and that the summation $\sum_{m\in\psi_n}$ consists of two terms, $\sum_{m\in\{1,3\}}$, and that Gridblock 1 is upstream to Gridblock 2 and Gridblock 2 is upstream to Gridblock 3.

$$\left(\frac{\partial F_{w_2}}{\partial S_{w_2}}\right)^{(\nu)} = \left\{\left[p_{o_1}^{(\nu)} - p_{o_2}^{(\nu)}\right](0) + \left[p_{o_3}^{(\nu)} - p_{o_2}^{(\nu)}\right]\left[\frac{\partial}{\partial S_{w_2}}\left(T_{w_{2,3}}\right)_2\right]^{(\nu)}\right\}$$

$$= \left\{ \left[p_{o_3}^{(\nu)} - p_{o_2}^{(\nu)}\right]\left[\frac{\partial}{\partial S_{w_2}}\left(\mathrm{T}_{w_{2,3}}\right)_2\right]^{(\nu)} \right\}, \qquad (9.587)$$

$$\left(\frac{\partial F_{w_2}}{\partial p_{o_2}}\right)^{(\nu)} = \left\{ -\left[\mathrm{T}^{(\nu)}_{w_{2,1}}\right]_1 + \left[p_{o_1}^{(\nu)} - p_{o_2}^{(\nu)}\right](0) - \left[\mathrm{T}^{(\nu)}_{w_{2,3}}\right]_2 + \left[p_{o_3}^{(\nu)} - p_{o_2}^{(\nu)}\right]\left[\frac{\partial}{\partial p_{o_2}}\left(\mathrm{T}_{w_{2,3}}\right)_2\right]^{(\nu)} \right\}$$

$$= \left(-\left\{\left[\mathrm{T}^{(\nu)}_{w_{2,1}}\right]_1 + \left[\mathrm{T}^{(\nu)}_{w_{2,3}}\right]_2\right\} + \left[p_{o_3}^{(\nu)} - p_{o_2}^{(\nu)}\right]\left[\frac{\partial}{\partial p_{o_2}}\left(\mathrm{T}_{w_{2,3}}\right)_2\right]^{(\nu)} \right), \qquad (9.588)$$

$$\left(\frac{\partial F_{o_2}}{\partial S_{w_2}}\right)^{(\nu)} = \left\{ \left[p_{o_1}^{(\nu)} - p_{o_2}^{(\nu)}\right](0) + \left[p_{o_3}^{(\nu)} - p_{o_2}^{(\nu)}\right]\left[\frac{\partial}{\partial S_{w_2}}\left(\mathrm{T}_{o_{2,3}}\right)_2\right]^{(\nu)} \right\}$$

$$= \left\{ \left[p_{o_3}^{(\nu)} - p_{o_2}^{(\nu)}\right]\left[\frac{\partial}{\partial S_{w_2}}\left(\mathrm{T}_{o_{2,3}}\right)_2\right]^{(\nu)} \right\}, \qquad (9.589)$$

and

$$\left(\frac{\partial F_{o_2}}{\partial p_{o_2}}\right)^{(\nu)} = \left\{ -\left[\mathrm{T}^{(\nu)}_{o_{2,1}}\right]_1 + \left[p_{o_1}^{(\nu)} - p_{o_2}^{(\nu)}\right](0) - \left[\mathrm{T}^{(\nu)}_{o_{2,3}}\right]_2 + \left[p_{o_3}^{(\nu)} - p_{o_2}^{(\nu)}\right]\left[\frac{\partial}{\partial p_{o_2}}\left(\mathrm{T}_{o_{2,3}}\right)_2\right]^{(\nu)} \right\}$$

$$= \left(-\left\{\left[\mathrm{T}^{(\nu)}_{o_{2,1}}\right]_1 + \left[\mathrm{T}^{(\nu)}_{o_{2,3}}\right]_2\right\} + \left[p_{o_3}^{(\nu)} - p_{o_2}^{(\nu)}\right]\left[\frac{\partial}{\partial p_{o_2}}\left(\mathrm{T}_{o_{2,3}}\right)_2\right]^{(\nu)} \right). \qquad (9.590)$$

For $n=3$, $\psi_3=\{2\}$; therefore, $m\in\psi_3$ is a member of $\{2\}$, which implies that the third block row of matrix **[F]** has a nonzero diagonal submatrix, $\mathbf{[F]}_{33}$, and only one nonzero off-diagonal matrix, $\mathbf{[F]}_{32}$.

In obtaining the elements of $\mathbf{[F]}_{32}$, note that $n=3$ and $m=2$ and that Gridblock 2 is upstream to Gridblock 3.

$$\left(\frac{\partial F_{w_3}}{\partial S_{w_2}}\right)^{(\nu)} = \left[p_{o_2}^{(\nu)} - p_{o_3}^{(\nu)}\right]\left[\frac{\partial}{\partial S_{w_2}}\left(\mathrm{T}_{w_{3,2}}\right)_2\right]^{(\nu)}, \qquad (9.591)$$

$$\left(\frac{\partial F_{w_3}}{\partial p_{o_2}}\right)^{(\nu)} = \left[\mathrm{T}^{(\nu)}_{w_{3,2}}\right]_2 + \left[p_{o_2}^{(\nu)} - p_{o_3}^{(\nu)}\right]\left[\frac{\partial}{p_{o_2}}\left(\mathrm{T}_{w_{3,2}}\right)_2\right]^{(\nu)}, \qquad (9.592)$$

$$\left(\frac{\partial F_{o_3}}{\partial S_{w_2}}\right)^{(\nu)} = \left[p_{o_2}^{(\nu)} - p_{o_3}^{(\nu)}\right]\left[\frac{\partial}{\partial S_{w_2}}\left(\mathrm{T}_{o_{3,2}}\right)_2\right]^{(\nu)}, \qquad (9.593)$$

and

$$\left(\frac{\partial F_{o_3}}{\partial p_{o_2}}\right)^{(\nu)} = \left[\mathrm{T}^{(\nu)}_{o_{3,2}}\right]_2 + \left[p_{o_2}^{(\nu)} - p_{o_3}^{(\nu)}\right]\left[\frac{\partial}{p_{o_2}}\left(\mathrm{T}_{o_{3,2}}\right)_2\right]^{(\nu)}. \qquad (9.594)$$

In obtaining the elements of $\mathbf{[F]}_{33}$, note that $n=3$ and $m=3$ and that Gridblock 2 is upstream to Gridblock 3 and the summation $\sum_{m\in\psi_n}$ consists of one term only, $\sum_{m\in\{2\}}$.

$$\left(\frac{\partial F_{w_3}}{\partial S_{w_3}}\right)^{(\nu)} = \left\{\left[p_{o_2}^{(\nu)} - p_{o_3}^{(\nu)}\right](0)\right\} = 0, \qquad (9.595)$$

$$\left(\frac{\partial F_{w_3}}{\partial p_{o_3}}\right)^{(\nu)} = \left\{-\left[\mathrm{T}_{w_{3,2}}\right]_2 + \left[p_{o_2}^{(\nu)} - p_{o_3}^{(\nu)}\right](0)\right\} = -\left[\mathrm{T}^{(\nu)}_{w_{3,2}}\right]_2, \qquad (9.596)$$

$$\left(\frac{\partial F_{o_3}}{\partial S_{w_3}}\right)^{(\nu)} = \left\{\left[p_{o_2}^{(\nu)} - p_{o_3}^{(\nu)}\right](0)\right\} = 0, \qquad (9.597)$$

and

$$\left(\frac{\partial F_{o_3}}{\partial p_{o_3}}\right)^{(\nu)} = \left\{-\left[\mathrm{T}_{o_{3,2}}\right]_2 + \left[p_{o_2}^{(\nu)} - p_{o_3}^{(\nu)}\right](0)\right\} = -\left[\mathrm{T}^{(\nu)}_{o_{3,2}}\right]_2. \qquad (9.598)$$

Note that in Eqs. 9.562 through 9.598, the phase transmissibility between Gridblocks n and m is $\mathrm{T}_{l_{m,n}}$ or $\mathrm{T}_{l_{n,m}}$ for $l=o$ or w, and that phase transmissibility evaluated at the upstream point between Gridblocks n and m is $(\mathrm{T}_{l_{m,n}})_k$ or $(\mathrm{T}_{l_{n,m}})_k$, where k is the upstream gridblock ($k=n$ or m).

9.6.2 IMPES Method. The objective of the IMPES method is to obtain a single pressure equation for each gridblock by combining all flow equations to eliminate the saturation unknowns. To achieve this, capillary pressures and transmissibilities have to be evaluated explicitly (at Time Level n) or at the old iteration level, k. We use the explicit treatment, consequently, the IMPES method is used only when saturations change slowly from one timestep to the next. The pressure equation is written for each gridblock $n=1,2,\ldots,N$, and the resulting set of equations is solved, directly or iteratively, for the oil-phase pressure distribution. The second step in the IMPES method involves the explicit solution for the saturation unknowns by substituting pressures at t^{n+1} into the appropriate flow equations for individual gridblocks. Although the pressure function f_p in the transmissibility can be treated implicitly, it has a weak nonlinearity and, therefore, its explicit evaluation does not cause severe stability problems.

IMPES Method for an Oil/Water Flow Model. The finite-difference equations for the oil/water flow model may be obtained from Eqs. 9.466 and 9.467 by setting $S_{g_n}=0$. For explicit transmissibilities, flow rates, and capillary pressures, the difference equations for Gridblock n become

$$\sum_{m\in\psi_n}\left[\mathrm{T}^n_{o_{n,m}}\left(\Delta_m p_o^{n+1} - \gamma^n_{o_{n,m}}\Delta_m Z\right)\right] = C_{op_n}\Delta_t p_{o_n} + C_{ow_n}\Delta_t S_{w_n} - q^n_{osc_n} \qquad (9.599)$$

and

$$\sum_{m\in\psi_n}\left[\mathrm{T}^n_{w_{n,m}}\left(\Delta_m p_o^{n+1} - \Delta_m P^n_{cow} - \gamma^n_{w_{n,m}}\Delta_m Z\right)\right] = C_{wp_n}\Delta_t p_{o_n} + C_{ww_n}\Delta_t S_{w_n} - q^n_{wsc_n}. \qquad (9.600)$$

The pressure equation for Gridblock n may be obtained by combining these two equations such that the term containing $\Delta_t S_{w_n}$ vanishes. The general procedure for achieving this result is to multiply Eq. 9.600 by a constant, A, add the result to Eq. 9.599, and equate the coefficient of the $\Delta_t S_{w_n}$ term in the resulting equation to zero. This procedure gives the value of A as

$$A = -\frac{C_{ow_n}}{C_{ww_n}}. \qquad (9.601)$$

The combined oil and water equation is

$$\sum_{m\in\psi_n}\left\{\left[\mathrm{T}^n_{o_{n,m}}\left(\Delta_m p_o^{n+1} - \bar{\gamma}^n_{o_{n,m}}\Delta_m Z\right)\right]\right.$$
$$\left.+ A\left[\mathrm{T}^n_{w_{n,m}}\left(\Delta_m p_o^{n+1} - \Delta_m P^n_{cow} - \bar{\gamma}^n_{w_{n,m}}\Delta_m Z\right)\right]\right\}$$
$$= \left(C_{op_n} + AC_{wp_n}\right)\Delta_t p_{o_n} - \left(q^n_{osc_n} + Aq^n_{wsc_n}\right), \quad \text{(9.602)}$$

Substituting Eqs. 9.229 and 9.232 into Eq. 9.601 gives

$$A = -\frac{C_{ow_n}}{C_{ww_n}} = \frac{B^{n+1}_{w_n}}{B^{n+1}_{o_n}}. \quad \text{(9.603)}$$

Substituting Eq. 9.603 into Eq. 9.602 and multiplying the resulting equation by $B^{n+1}_{o_n}$ yields

$$\sum_{m\in\psi_n}\left\{B^{n+1}_{o_n}\left[\mathrm{T}^n_{o_{n,m}}\left(\Delta_m p_o^{n+1} - \bar{\gamma}^n_{o_{n,m}}\Delta_m Z\right)\right]\right.$$
$$\left.+ B^{n+1}_{w_n}\left[\mathrm{T}^n_{w_{n,m}}\left(\Delta_m p_o^{n+1} - \Delta_m P^n_{cow} - \bar{\gamma}^n_{w_{n,m}}\Delta_m Z\right)\right]\right\}$$
$$= \left(B^{n+1}_{o_n}C_{op_n} + B^{n+1}_{w_n}C_{wp_n}\right)\Delta_t p_{o_n}$$
$$- \left(B^{n+1}_{o_n}q^n_{osc_n} + B^{n+1}_{w_n}q^n_{wsc_n}\right). \quad \text{(9.604)}$$

This equation may be rewritten as

$$\sum_{m\in\psi_n}\left(B^{n+1}_{o_n}\mathrm{T}^n_{o_{n,m}} + B^{n+1}_{w_n}\mathrm{T}^n_{w_{n,m}}\right)p^{n+1}_{o_m}$$
$$- \left[\left(B^{n+1}_{o_n}C_{op_n} + B^{n+1}_{w_n}C_{wp_n}\right)\right.$$
$$\left.+ \sum_{m\in\psi_n}\left(B^{n+1}_{o_n}\mathrm{T}^n_{o_{n,m}} + B^{n+1}_{w_n}\mathrm{T}^n_{w_{n,m}}\right)\right]p^{n+1}_{o_n}$$
$$= -\left[\left(B^{n+1}_{o_n}C_{op_n} + B^{n+1}_{w_n}C_{wp_n}\right)p^n_{o_n}\right.$$
$$- \left(B^{n+1}_{o_n}q^n_{osc_n} + B^{n+1}_{w_n}q^n_{wsc_n}\right) + \sum_{m\in\psi_n} B^{n+1}_{w_n}\mathrm{T}^n_{w_{n,m}}\Delta_m P^n_{cow}$$
$$+ \sum_{m\in\psi_n}\left(B^{n+1}_{o_n}\mathrm{T}^n_{o_{n,m}}\bar{\gamma}^n_{o_{n,m}} + B^{n+1}_{w_n}\mathrm{T}^n_{w_{n,m}}\bar{\gamma}^n_{w_{n,m}}\right)\Delta_m Z. \quad \text{(9.605)}$$

Eq. 9.605 is the pressure equation for Gridblock n.

The IMPES method of solution of the oil and water flow model equations consists of two consecutive steps. The first step involves writing Eq. 9.605 for each Gridblock $n = 1,2,\ldots, N$ and solving the system of N-coupled equations for the oil-phase pressure distribution at Time Level $n+1$. In the second step, the water saturation at Time Level $n+1$ is calculated by substituting p_o^{n+1} obtained in the first step into the water equation for individual gridblocks.

$$S^{n+1}_{w_n} = S^n_{w_n} + \frac{1}{C_{ww_n}}$$
$$\times\left\{\sum_{m\in\psi_n}\left[\mathrm{T}^n_{w_{n,m}}\left(\Delta_m p_o^{n+1} - \Delta_m P^n_{cow} - \bar{\gamma}^n_{w_{n,m}}\Delta_m Z\right)\right]\right.$$
$$\left.- C_{wp_n}\left(p^{n+1}_{o_n} - p^n_{o_n}\right) + q^n_{wsc_n}\right\}, \quad \text{(9.606)}$$

where $n = 1,2,\ldots, N$.

While the first step may require iterating on $B^{n+1}_{o_n}$, $B^{n+1}_{w_n}$, C_{op_n}, and C_{wp_n} to preserve material balance, the second step is explicit and C_{ww_n} and C_{wp_n} are evaluated at the converged solution from the first step. The water saturation obtained from Eq. 9.606 is used to calculate $P^{n+1}_{cow_n}$, which is then used as $P^n_{cow_n}$ in the next timestep.

IMPES Method for Oil/Gas Flow Model. The finite-difference equations for the oil/gas flow model may be obtained from Eqs. 9.466 and 9.468 by setting $S_{w_n} = 0$. For explicit transmissibilities, flow rates, and capillary pressures, the difference equations for Gridblock n become

$$\sum_{m\in\psi_n}\left[\mathrm{T}^n_{o_{n,m}}\left(\Delta_m p_o^{n+1} - \bar{\gamma}^n_{o_{n,m}}\Delta_m Z\right)\right]$$
$$= C_{op_n}\Delta_t p_{o_n} + C_{og_n}\Delta_t S_{g_n} - q^n_{osc_n} \quad \text{(9.607)}$$

and
$$\sum_{m\in\psi_n}\left[\mathrm{T}^n_{g_{n,m}}\left(\Delta_m p_o^{n+1} + \Delta_m P^n_{cgo} - \bar{\gamma}^n_{g_{n,m}}\Delta_m Z\right)\right.$$
$$\left.+ \left(\mathrm{T}_o R_s\right)^n_{n,m}\left(\Delta_m p_o^{n+1} - \bar{\gamma}^n_{o_{n,m}}\Delta_m Z\right)\right]$$
$$= C_{gp_n}\Delta_t p_{o_n} + C_{gg_n}\Delta_t S_{g_n} - q^n_{gsc_n}, \quad \text{(9.608)}$$

where
$$q^n_{gsc_n} = \left(q^n_{fgsc_n} + R^n_{s_n}q^n_{osc_n}\right). \quad \text{(9.609)}$$

The pressure equation for Gridblock n may be obtained by combining Eqs. 9.607 and 9.608 such that the term containing $\Delta_t S_{g_n}$ vanishes. Examining the definitions of C_{og_n} and C_{gg_n} given by Eqs. 9.230 and 9.236 suggests that the addition of the oil equation multiplied by $(B_o - R_s B_g)^{n+1}_n$ and the gas equation multiplied by $B^{n+1}_{g_n}$ results in the pressure equation.

$$\sum_{m\in\psi_n}\left\{\left(B_o - R_s B_g\right)^{n+1}_n\left[\mathrm{T}^n_{o_{n,m}}\left(\Delta_m p_o^{n+1} - \bar{\gamma}^n_{o_{n,m}}\Delta_m Z\right)\right]\right.$$
$$+ B^{n+1}_{g_n}\left[\mathrm{T}^n_{g_{n,m}}\left(\Delta_m p_o^{n+1} + \Delta_m P^n_{cgo} - \bar{\gamma}^n_{g_{n,m}}\Delta_m Z\right)\right.$$
$$\left.\left.+ \left(\mathrm{T}_o R_s\right)^n_{n,m}\left(\Delta_m p_o^{n+1} - \bar{\gamma}^n_{o_{n,m}}\Delta_m Z\right)\right]\right\}$$
$$= \left[\left(B_o - R_s B_g\right)^{n+1}_n C_{op_n} + B^{n+1}_{g_n}C_{gp_n}\right]\Delta_t p_{o_n}$$
$$- \left[\left(B_o - R_s B_g\right)^{n+1}_n q^n_{osc_n} + B^{n+1}_{g_n}q^n_{gsc_n}\right], \quad \text{(9.610)}$$

which can be expressed in the form of Eq. 9.605 as

$$\sum_{m\in\psi_n}\left\{\left(B_o - R_s B_g\right)^{n+1}_n \mathrm{T}^n_{o_{n,m}} + B^{n+1}_{g_n}\left[\mathrm{T}^n_{g_{n,m}} + \left(\mathrm{T}_o R_s\right)^n_{n,m}\right]\right\}p^{n+1}_{o_m}$$
$$- \left(\left(B_o - R_s B_g\right)^{n+1}_n C_{op_n} + B^{n+1}_{g_n}C_{gp_n}\right.$$
$$+ \sum_{m\in\psi_n}\left\{\left(B_o - R_s B_g\right)^{n+1}_n \mathrm{T}^n_{o_{n,m}}\right.$$
$$\left.\left.+ B^{n+1}_{g_n}\left[\mathrm{T}^n_{g_{n,m}} + \left(\mathrm{T}_o R_s\right)^n_{n,m}\right]\right\}\right)p^{n+1}_{o_n}$$
$$= -\left[\left(B_o - R_s B_g\right)^{n+1}_n C_{op_n} + B^{n+1}_{g_n}C_{gp_n}\right]p^n_{o_n}$$
$$- \left[\left(B_o - R_s B_g\right)^{n+1}_n q^n_{osc_n} + B^{n+1}_{g_n}q^n_{gsc_n}\right]$$

$$- \sum_{m \in \psi_n} B_{gn}^{n+1} T_{g_{n,m}}^n \Delta_m P_{cgo}^n$$

$$+ \sum_{m \in \psi_n} \left\{ (B_o - R_s B_g)_n^{n+1} T_{o_{n,m}}^n \bar{\gamma}_{o_{n,m}}^n \right.$$

$$\left. + B_{gn}^{n+1} \left[T_{g_{n,m}}^n \bar{\gamma}_{g_{n,m}}^n + (T_o R_s)_{n,m}^n \bar{\gamma}_{o_{n,m}}^n \right] \right\} \Delta_m Z. \quad \ldots\ldots (9.611)$$

Eq. 9.611 is written for each Gridblock $n = 1,2, \ldots, N$, and the system of N-coupled equations is solved for the p_o^{n+1} distribution. We may need to iterate on B_{on}^{n+1}, B_{gn}^{n+1}, R_{sn}^{n+1}, C_{op_n}, and C_{gp_n} until convergence is reached. The gas saturation is obtained by substituting the converged pressure solution in either Eq. 9.607 or 9.608 for Gridblock n. Using Eq. 9.607,

$$S_{g_n}^{n+1} = S_{g_n}^n + \frac{1}{C_{og_n}} \left\{ \sum_{m \in \psi_n} \left[T_{o_{n,m}}^n \left(\Delta_m p_o^{n+1} - \bar{\gamma}_{o_{n,m}}^n \Delta_m Z \right) \right] \right.$$

$$\left. - C_{op_n} \left(p_{o_n}^{n+1} - p_{o_n}^n \right) + q_{osc_n}^n \right\}, \quad \ldots\ldots\ldots\ldots (9.612)$$

where $n = 1,2, \ldots, N$. This gas saturation is used to calculate $P_{cgo_n}^{n+1}$, which, in turn, is used as $P_{cgo_n}^n$ in the calculations involved in the next timestep.

IMPES Method for the Three-Phase Black-Oil Model. Eqs. 9.466 through 9.468 represent the finite-difference equations for the three-phase black-oil model. For explicit transmissibilities, flow rates, and capillary pressures, these equations written for Gridblock n become

$$\sum_{m \in \psi_n} \left[T_{o_{n,m}}^n \left(\Delta_m p_o^{n+1} - \bar{\gamma}_{o_{n,m}}^n \Delta_m Z \right) \right]$$

$$= C_{op_n} \Delta_t p_{o_n} + C_{ow_n} \Delta_t S_{w_n} + C_{og_n} \Delta_t S_{g_n} - q_{osc_n}^n,$$

$$\ldots\ldots\ldots\ldots\ldots\ldots\ldots (9.613)$$

$$\sum_{m \in \psi_n} \left[T_{w_{n,m}}^n \left(\Delta_m p_o^{n+1} - \Delta_m P_{cow}^n - \bar{\gamma}_{w_{n,m}}^n \Delta_m Z \right) \right]$$

$$= C_{wp_n} \Delta_t p_{o_n} + C_{ww_n} \Delta_t S_{w_n} + C_{wg_n} \Delta_t S_{g_n} - q_{wsc_n}^n,$$

$$\ldots\ldots\ldots\ldots\ldots\ldots\ldots (9.614)$$

and $$\sum_{m \in \psi_n} \left[T_{g_{n,m}}^n \left(\Delta_m p_o^{n+1} + \Delta_m P_{cgo}^n - \bar{\gamma}_{g_{n,m}}^n \Delta_m Z \right) \right.$$

$$\left. + (T_o R_s)_{n,m}^n \left(\Delta_m p_o^{n+1} - \bar{\gamma}_{o_{n,m}}^n \Delta_m Z \right) \right]$$

$$= C_{gp_n} \Delta_t p_{o_n} + C_{gw_n} \Delta_t S_{w_n} + C_{gg_n} \Delta_t S_{g_n} - q_{gsc_n}^n,$$

$$\ldots\ldots\ldots\ldots\ldots\ldots\ldots (9.615)$$

where $q_{gsc_n}^n = \left(q_{fgsc_n}^n + R_{sn}^n q_{osc_n}^n \right)$. $\quad \ldots\ldots\ldots\ldots\ldots (9.609)$

The coefficients of $\Delta_t p_o$, $\Delta_t S_w$, and $\Delta_t S_g$ are all defined by Eqs. 9.228 through 9.236 and $C_{wg_n} = 0$, as given by Eq. 9.233.

The pressure equation for Gridblock n may be obtained by combining Eqs. 9.613 through 9.615 such that the terms containing $\Delta_t S_{w_n}$ and $\Delta_t S_{g_n}$ vanish. The general procedure for achieving this result is to multiply the water equation by a constant, A, and the gas equation by a second constant, B, and to add all three equations. This is followed by equating the coefficients of the $\Delta_t S_{w_n}$ and $\Delta_t S_{g_n}$ terms to zero and solving the two resulting equations for the values of A and B. Example 9.25 illustrates this procedure. Alternatively, the pressure equation may be obtained by multiplying the oil equation by $(B_o - R_s B_g)_n^{n+1}$, the water equation by B_{wn}^{n+1}, and the gas equation by B_{gn}^{n+1}, then adding all three equations. The resulting equation is

$$\sum_{m \in \psi_n} \left\{ (B_o - R_s B_g)_n^{n+1} \left[T_{o_{n,m}}^n \left(\Delta_m p_o^{n+1} - \bar{\gamma}_{o_{n,m}}^n \Delta_m Z \right) \right] \right.$$

$$+ B_{wn}^{n+1} \left[T_{w_{n,m}}^n \left(\Delta_m p_o^{n+1} - \Delta_m P_{cow}^n - \bar{\gamma}_{w_{n,m}}^n \Delta_m Z \right) \right]$$

$$+ B_{gn}^{n+1} \left[T_{g_{n,m}}^n \left(\Delta_m p_o^{n+1} + \Delta_m P_{cgo}^n - \bar{\gamma}_{g_{n,m}}^n \Delta_m Z \right) \right.$$

$$\left. \left. + (T_o R_s)_{n,m}^n \left(\Delta_m p_o^{n+1} - \bar{\gamma}_{o_{n,m}}^n \Delta_m Z \right) \right] \right\}$$

$$= \left[(B_o - R_s B_g)_n^{n+1} C_{op_n} + B_{wn}^{n+1} C_{wp_n} + B_{gn}^{n+1} C_{gp_n} \right] \Delta_t p_{o_n}$$

$$- \left[(B_o - R_s B_g)_n^{n+1} q_{osc_n}^n + B_{wn}^{n+1} q_{wsc_n}^n + B_{gn}^{n+1} q_{gsc_n}^n \right],$$

$$\ldots\ldots\ldots\ldots\ldots\ldots\ldots (9.616)$$

which can be rearranged and expressed in the form of Eq. 9.605 as

$$\sum_{m \in \psi_n} \left\{ (B_o - R_s B_g)_n^{n+1} T_{o_{n,m}}^n + B_{wn}^{n+1} T_{w_{n,m}}^n \right.$$

$$\left. + B_{gn}^{n+1} \left[T_{g_{n,m}}^n + (T_o R_s)_{n,m}^n \right] \right\} p_{om}^{n+1}$$

$$- \left((B_o - R_s B_g)_n^{n+1} C_{op_n} + B_{wn}^{n+1} C_{wp_n} + B_{gn}^{n+1} C_{gp_n} \right.$$

$$+ \sum_{m \in \psi_n} \left\{ (B_o - R_s B_g)_n^{n+1} T_{o_{n,m}}^n + B_{wn}^{n+1} T_{w_{n,m}}^n \right.$$

$$\left. \left. + B_{gn}^{n+1} \left[T_{g_{n,m}}^n + (T_o R_s)_{n,m}^n \right] \right\} \right) p_{on}^{n+1}$$

$$= - \left[(B_o - R_s B_g)_n^{n+1} C_{op_n} + B_{wn}^{n+1} C_{wp_n} + B_{gn}^{n+1} C_{gp_n} \right] p_{o_n}^n$$

$$- \left[(B_o - R_s B_g)_n^{n+1} q_{osc_n}^n + B_{wn}^{n+1} q_{wsc_n}^n + B_{gn}^{n+1} q_{gsc_n}^n \right]$$

$$+ \sum_{m \in \psi_n} B_{wn}^{n+1} T_{w_{n,m}}^n \Delta_m P_{cow}^n - \sum_{m \in \psi_n} B_{gn}^{n+1} T_{g_{n,m}}^n \Delta_m P_{cgo}^n$$

$$+ \sum_{m \in \psi_n} \left\{ (B_o - R_s B_g)_n^{n+1} T_{o_{n,m}}^n \bar{\gamma}_{o_{n,m}}^n + B_{wn}^{n+1} T_{w_{n,m}}^n \bar{\gamma}_{w_{n,m}}^n \right.$$

$$\left. + B_{gn}^{n+1} \left[T_{g_{n,m}}^n \bar{\gamma}_{g_{n,m}}^n + (T_o R_s)_{n,m}^n \bar{\gamma}_{o_{n,m}}^n \right] \right\} \Delta_m Z.$$

$$\ldots\ldots\ldots\ldots\ldots\ldots (9.617)$$

Eq. 9.617 is written for each Gridblock $n = 1,2, \ldots, N$, and the system of N-coupled equations is solved for p_o^{n+1} distribution. Note that we may have to iterate on B_{on}^{n+1}, B_{wn}^{n+1}, B_{gn}^{n+1}, R_{sn}^{n+1}, C_{op_n}, C_{wp_n}, and C_{gp_n} during this step. After obtaining the oil-pressure solution, the water and gas saturations at Time Level $n+1$ are solved for explicitly by substituting the pressure solution in the water and oil equations, in that order, for each individual Gridblock n.

$$S_{w_n}^{n+1} = S_{w_n}^n + \frac{1}{C_{ww_n}}$$

$$\times \left\{ \sum_{m \in \psi_n} \left[T_{w_{n,m}}^n \left(\Delta_m p_o^{n+1} - \Delta_m P_{cow}^n - \bar{\gamma}_{w_{n,m}}^n \Delta_m Z \right) \right] \right.$$

$$- C_{wp_n}\left(p_{o_n}^{n+1} - p_{o_n}^n\right) + q_{wsc_n}^n\Bigg\} \quad (9.606)$$

$$\text{and } S_{g_n}^{n+1} = S_{g_n}^n + \frac{1}{C_{og_n}}\left\{\sum_{m\in\psi_n}\left[T_{o_{n,m}}^n\left(\Delta_m p_o^{n+1} - \bar{\gamma}_{o_{n,m}}^n\Delta_m Z\right)\right]\right.$$

$$\left. - C_{op_n}\left(p_{o_n}^{n+1} - p_{o_n}^n\right) - C_{ow_n}\left(S_{w_n}^{n+1} - S_{w_n}^n\right) + q_{osc_n}^n\right\}, \quad (9.618)$$

where $n = 1,2,\ldots,N$. After solving for $S_{w_n}^{n+1}$ and $S_{g_n}^{n+1}$, new capillary pressures $P_{cow_n}^{n+1}$ and $P_{cgo_n}^{n+1}$ are calculated, which are used as $P_{cow_n}^n$ and $P_{cgo_n}^n$ in the calculations involved in the next timestep.

The pressure equation for the three-phase black-oil model, Eq. 9.617, is general because it includes capillary and gravitational forces. Also, it reduces to the pressure equation for the oil/water flow model when terms, including B_g, are dropped and to the pressure equation for the oil/gas flow model when terms, including B_w, are dropped. The pressure and saturation equations in this section are valid for 1D-, 2D-, and 3D-flow problems in Cartesian coordinates.

Example 9.25. Derive the pressure equation for the black-oil model, Eq. 9.617, by combining Eqs. 9.613 through 9.615 using the general procedure discussed in the text.

Solution. As stated, the general procedure for deriving the pressure equation involves multiplying the water equation, Eq. 9.614, by A and the gas equation, Eq. 9.615, by B and then adding the resulting equations to the oil equation, Eq. 9.613. The coefficients of $\Delta_t p_{o_n}$, $\Delta_t S_{w_n}$, and $\Delta_t S_{g_n}$ of the resulting equation are

$$C_{\Delta_t p_{on}} = \left(C_{op_n} + AC_{wp_n} + BC_{gp_n}\right); \quad (9.619)$$

$$C_{\Delta_t S_{gn}} = \left(C_{og_n} + BC_{gg_n}\right) \quad (9.620)$$

because $C_{wg_n} = 0$; and

$$C_{\Delta_t S_{wn}} = \left(C_{ow_n} + AC_{ww_n} + BC_{gw_n}\right). \quad (9.621)$$

Parameters A and B are found by solving

$$C_{og_n} + BC_{gg_n} = 0 \quad (9.622)$$

$$\text{and } C_{ow_n} + AC_{ww_n} + BC_{gw_n} = 0. \quad (9.623)$$

From Eq. 9.622,

$$B = -\frac{C_{og_n}}{C_{gg_n}}, \quad (9.624)$$

and from Eq. 9.623,

$$A = -\frac{\left(BC_{gw_n} + C_{ow_n}\right)}{C_{ww_n}} \quad (9.625a)$$

$$\text{or } A = -B\frac{C_{gw_n}}{C_{ww_n}} - \frac{C_{ow_n}}{C_{ww_n}}. \quad (9.625b)$$

Substituting Eqs. 9.230 and 9.236 into Eq. 9.624 yields

$$B = -\frac{C_{og_n}}{C_{gg_n}} = \frac{-\left[-\dfrac{V_b}{\alpha_c\Delta t}\left(\dfrac{\phi}{B_o}\right)^{n+1}\right]_n}{\left\{\dfrac{V_b}{\alpha_c\Delta t}\left[\left(\dfrac{\phi}{B_g}\right)^{n+1} - \left(\dfrac{\phi}{B_o}\right)^{n+1}R_s^{n+1}\right]\right\}_n}$$

$$= \frac{1}{\left(B_{o_n}^{n+1}/B_{g_n}^{n+1}\right) - R_{s_n}^{n+1}} = \frac{B_{g_n}^{n+1}}{\left(B_o^{n+1} - R_s^{n+1}B_g^{n+1}\right)_n} \quad (9.626a)$$

$$\text{or } B = \frac{B_{g_n}^{n+1}}{\left(B_o - R_sB_g\right)_n^{n+1}}. \quad (9.626b)$$

Substituting Eqs. 9.229, 9.232, and 9.235 into Eq. 9.625b yields

$$A = \frac{-B\left[-\dfrac{V_b}{\alpha_c\Delta t}\left(\dfrac{\phi}{B_o}\right)^{n+1}R_s^{n+1}\right]_n}{\left[\dfrac{V_b}{\alpha_c\Delta t}\left(\dfrac{\phi}{B_w}\right)^{n+1}\right]_n} - \frac{\left[-\dfrac{V_b}{\alpha_c\Delta t}\left(\dfrac{\phi}{B_o}\right)^{n+1}\right]_n}{\left[\dfrac{V_b}{\alpha_c\Delta t}\left(\dfrac{\phi}{B_w}\right)^{n+1}\right]_n}$$

$$= B\left(\frac{R_sB_w}{B_o}\right)_n^{n+1} + \left(\frac{B_w}{B_o}\right)_n^{n+1}. \quad (9.627)$$

Substituting Eq. 9.626b into Eq. 9.627 results in

$$A = \frac{B_{g_n}^{n+1}}{\left(B_o - R_sB_g\right)_n^{n+1}}\left(\frac{R_sB_w}{B_o}\right)_n^{n+1} + \left(\frac{B_w}{B_o}\right)_n^{n+1}$$

$$= \frac{B_{w_n}^{n+1}}{\left(B_o - R_sB_g\right)_n^{n+1}B_{o_n}^{n+1}}\left(B_{g_n}^{n+1}R_{s_n}^{n+1} + B_{o_n}^{n+1} - R_{s_n}^{n+1}B_{g_n}^{n+1}\right) \quad (9.628a)$$

$$\text{or } A = \frac{B_{w_n}^{n+1}}{\left(B_o - R_sB_g\right)_n^{n+1}}. \quad (9.628b)$$

Having determined A and B, given by Eqs. 9.628b and 9.626b, the combined equation becomes

$$\sum_{m\in\psi_n}\left\{\left[T_{o_{n,m}}^n\left(\Delta_m p_o^{n+1} - \bar{\gamma}_{o_{n,m}}^n\Delta_m Z\right)\right]\right.$$

$$+ A\left[T_{w_{n,m}}^n\left(\Delta_m p_o^{n+1} - \Delta_m P_{cow}^n - \bar{\gamma}_{w_{n,m}}^n\Delta_m Z\right)\right]$$

$$+ B\left[T_{g_{n,m}}^n\left(\Delta_m p_o^{n+1} + \Delta_m P_{cgo}^n - \bar{\gamma}_{g_{n,m}}^n\Delta_m Z\right)\right.$$

$$\left.\left. + \left(T_oR_s\right)_{n,m}^n\left(\Delta_m p_o^{n+1} - \bar{\gamma}_{o_{n,m}}^n\Delta_m Z\right)\right]\right\}$$

$$= \left(C_{op_n} + AC_{wp_n} + BC_{gp_n}\right)\Delta_t p_{o_n}$$

$$- \left(q_{osc_n}^n + Aq_{wsc_n}^n + Bq_{gsc_n}^n\right). \quad (9.629)$$

Substituting Eqs. 9.628b and 9.626b (the equations for A and B) into Eq. 9.629 and multiplying through by $\left(B_o - R_sB_g\right)_n^{n+1}$, which is the denominator of both A and B, results in

$$\sum_{m\in\psi_n}\left\{\left(B_o - R_sB_g\right)_n^{n+1}\left[T_{o_{n,m}}^n\left(\Delta_m p_o^{n+1} - \bar{\gamma}_{o_{n,m}}^n\Delta_m Z\right)\right]\right.$$

$$+ B_{w_n}^{n+1}\left[T_{w_{n,m}}^n\left(\Delta_m p_o^{n+1} - \Delta_m P_{cow}^n - \bar{\gamma}_{w_{n,m}}^n\Delta_m Z\right)\right]$$

$$+ B_{g_n}^{n+1}\left[T_{g_{n,m}}^n\left(\Delta_m p_o^{n+1} + \Delta_m P_{cgo}^n - \bar{\gamma}_{g_{n,m}}^n\Delta_m Z\right)\right.$$

$$\left.\left. + \left(T_oR_s\right)_{n,m}^n\left(\Delta_m p_o^{n+1} - \bar{\gamma}_{o_{n,m}}^n\Delta_m Z\right)\right]\right\}$$

$$= \left[\left(B_o - R_sB_g\right)_n^{n+1}C_{op_n} + B_{w_n}^{n+1}C_{wp_n} + B_{g_n}^{n+1}C_{gp_n}\right]\Delta_t p_{o_n}$$

$$- \left[\left(B_o - R_sB_g\right)_n^{n+1}q_{osc_n}^n + B_{w_n}^{n+1}q_{wsc_n}^n + B_{g_n}^{n+1}q_{gsc_n}^n\right], \quad (9.616)$$

TABLE 9.7—RELATIVE PERMEABILITY DATA FOR EXAMPLE 9.26

S_w	k_{rw}	k_{ro}
0.16	0.000	1.000
0.20	0.010	0.700
0.30	0.035	0.325
0.40	0.060	0.140
0.50	0.110	0.045
0.60	0.160	0.031
0.70	0.240	0.015
0.80	0.420	0.000

from which the pressure equation, Eq. 9.617, may be obtained by rearranging terms.

Example 9.26. A homogeneous, 1D horizontal oil reservoir is 1,000 ft long with a cross-sectional area of 10,000 ft^2. It is discretized into four equal gridblocks. Initially, $S_{wi}=S_{iw}=0.160$ and $p_i=1{,}000$ psia everywhere. Water is injected at $x=0$ at a rate of 75.96 B/D at standard conditions, and oil is produced at $x=$ 1,000 ft at the same rate. The gridblock dimensions and properties are $\Delta x=250$ ft, $A_x=10{,}000$ ft^2, $k_x=300$ md, and $\phi=0.20$. The reservoir fluids are incompressible with $B_w=B_o=1$ RB/STB and $\mu_o=\mu_w=1$ cp. The oil/water capillary pressure is zero; **Table 9.7** gives the relative permeability data. (The fluid and rock data are from Ref. 2.)

Using the IMPES solution method, find the pressure and saturation distributions at 100 and 300 days. Use single-point upstream weighting for relative permeabilities. The time-stability limit resulting from explicit transmissibilities for this problem is $\Delta t<\Delta x/0.4453$ or $\Delta t<561$ days.

Solution. **Fig. 9.17** shows the reservoir in this problem. The reservoir is discretized with four gridblocks, ordered as shown, with no-flow boundaries. Injection at $x=0$ and production at $x=1{,}000$ ft are replaced by wells in Gridblocks 1 and 4, respectively. The direction of flow for both oil and water phases is from the injection well to the production well. In other words, fluids flow from Gridblock 1 to Gridblock 2 to Gridblock 3 to Gridblock 4; or Gridblock 1 is upstream to Gridblock 2, Gridblock 2 is upstream to Gridblock 3, and Gridblock 3 is upstream to Gridblock 4.

The pressure and saturation equations for Gridblock n may be obtained from Eqs. 9.605 and 9.606 by substituting for $B_{o_n}=B_{w_n}=1$, $P^n_{cow}=0$, and $\Delta_m Z=0$. The resulting pressure equation is

$$\sum_{m\in\psi_n}\left(T^n_{o_{n,m}}+T^n_{w_{n,m}}\right)p^{n+1}_{o_m} - \left[C_{op_n}+C_{wp_n}+\sum_{m\in\psi_n}\left(T^n_{o_{n,m}}+T^n_{w_{n,m}}\right)\right]p^{n+1}_{o_n} = -\left(C_{op_n}+C_{wp_n}\right)p^n_{o_n}-\left(q^n_{osc_n}+q^n_{wsc_n}\right), \quad (9.630)$$

where $n=1,2,3,4$; and the water-saturation equation is

$$S^{n+1}_{w_n}=S^n_{w_n}+\frac{1}{C_{ww_n}}\times\left[\sum_{m\in\psi_n}T^n_{w_{n,m}}\Delta_m p^{n+1}_o - C_{wp_n}\left(p^{n+1}_{o_n}-p^n_{o_n}\right)+q^n_{wsc_n}\right], \quad (9.631)$$

where $n=1,2,3,4$. For this incompressible fluid-flow problem, application of Eqs. 9.228, 9.231, and 9.232 gives

$$C_{op_n}=0, \quad (9.632)$$

$$C_{wp_n}=0, \quad (9.633)$$

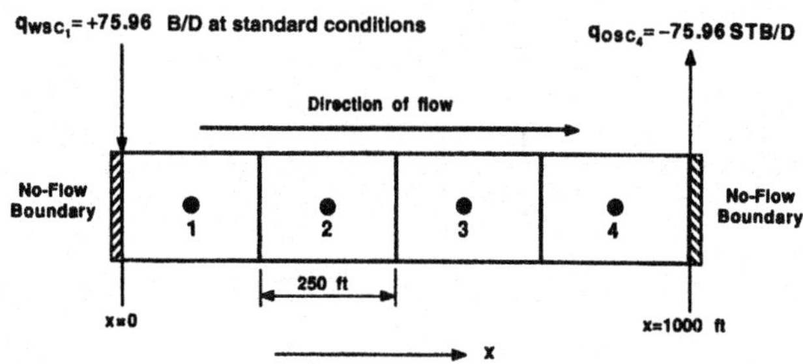

Fig. 9.17—Discretized reservoir for Example 9.26.

$$\text{and } C_{ww_n}=\frac{V_b\phi}{\alpha_c\Delta t} \quad (9.634)$$

because ϕ, B_o, and B_w are independent of pressure and $B_o=B_w=1$ RB/STB. Therefore, Eqs. 9.630 and 9.631 can be simplified to

$$\sum_{m\in\psi_n}\left(T^n_{o_{n,m}}+T^n_{w_{n,m}}\right)p^{n+1}_{o_m}-\sum_{m\in\psi_n}\left(T^n_{o_{n,m}}+T^n_{w_{n,m}}\right)p^{n+1}_{o_n} = -\left(q^n_{osc_n}+q^n_{wsc_n}\right) \quad (9.635)$$

$$\text{and } S^{n+1}_{w_n}=S^n_{w_n}+\frac{1}{(V_b\phi)/(\alpha_c\Delta t)}\left(\sum_{m\in\psi_n}T^n_{w_{n,m}}\Delta_m p^{n+1}_o+q^n_{wsc_n}\right) \quad (9.636)$$

for $n=1,2,3,4$. From Fig. 9.17 for this reservoir,

$$\left.\begin{aligned} n&=1, & \psi_1&=\{2\}\\ n&=2, & \psi_2&=\{1,3\}\\ n&=3, & \psi_3&=\{2,4\}\\ n&=4, & \psi_4&=\{3\}\end{aligned}\right\}. \quad (9.637)$$

For the upstream weighting of transmissibilities between Gridblocks n and $m\in\psi_n$,

$$T^n_{w_{n,m}}=\left(T^n_{w_{n,m}}\right)_n \quad (9.638a)$$

if Gridblock n is upstream to Gridblock m for water phase,

$$T^n_{w_{n,m}}=\left(T^n_{w_{n,m}}\right)_m \quad (9.638b)$$

if Gridblock m is upstream to Gridblock n for water phase,

$$T^n_{o_{n,m}}=\left(T^n_{o_{n,m}}\right)_n \quad (9.639a)$$

if Gridblock n is upstream to Gridblock m for oil phase, and

$$T^n_{o_{n,m}}=\left(T^n_{o_{n,m}}\right)_m \quad (9.639b)$$

if Gridblock m is upstream to Gridblock n for oil phase. Also $q^n_{wsc_2}=q^n_{wsc_3}=q^n_{wsc_4}=0$ and $q^n_{osc_1}=q^n_{osc_2}=q^n_{osc_3}=0$.

Eq. 9.635 may be written for each Gridblock n as follows. For $n=1$,

$$\left[\left(T^n_{w_{1,2}}\right)_1+\left(T^n_{o_{1,2}}\right)_1\right]p^{n+1}_{o_2} - \left[\left(T^n_{w_{1,2}}\right)_1+\left(T^n_{o_{1,2}}\right)_1\right]p^{n+1}_{o_1} = -q^n_{wsc_1}. \quad (9.640)$$

For $n=2$,

$$\left[\left(T^n_{w_{2,1}}\right)_1+\left(T^n_{o_{2,1}}\right)_1\right]p^{n+1}_{o_1}+\left[\left(T^n_{w_{2,3}}\right)_2+\left(T^n_{o_{2,3}}\right)_2\right]p^{n+1}_{o_3}$$

$$-\left\{\left[\left(T^n_{w_{2,1}}\right)_1+\left(T^n_{o_{2,1}}\right)_1\right]+\left[\left(T^n_{w_{2,3}}\right)_2+\left(T^n_{o_{2,3}}\right)_2\right]\right\}p^{n+1}_{o_2}$$

$$=0. \quad \text{(9.641)}$$

For $n=3$,

$$\left[\left(T^n_{w_{3,2}}\right)_2+\left(T^n_{o_{3,2}}\right)_2\right]p^{n+1}_{o_2}+\left[\left(T^n_{w_{3,4}}\right)_3+\left(T^n_{o_{3,4}}\right)_3\right]p^{n+1}_{o_4}$$

$$-\left\{\left[\left(T^n_{w_{3,2}}\right)_2+\left(T^n_{o_{3,2}}\right)_2\right]+\left[\left(T^n_{w_{3,4}}\right)_3+\left(T^n_{o_{3,4}}\right)_3\right]\right\}p^{n+1}_{o_3}$$

$$=0. \quad \text{(9.642)}$$

For $n=4$,

$$\left[\left(T^n_{w_{4,3}}\right)_3+\left(T^n_{o_{4,3}}\right)_3\right]p^{n+1}_{o_3}$$

$$-\left[\left(T^n_{w_{4,3}}\right)_3+\left(T^n_{o_{4,3}}\right)_3\right]p^{n+1}_{o_4}=-q^n_{osc_4}. \quad \text{(9.643)}$$

Eq. 9.636 may be written for each Gridblock n as follows. For $n=1$,

$$S^{n+1}_{w_1}=S^n_{w_1}+\frac{1}{[(V_b\phi)/(\alpha_c\Delta t)]}$$

$$\times\left[\left(T^n_{w_{1,2}}\right)_1\left(p^{n+1}_{o_2}-p^{n+1}_{o_1}\right)+q^n_{wsc_1}\right]. \quad \text{(9.644)}$$

For $n=2$,

$$S^{n+1}_{w_2}=S^n_{w_2}+\frac{1}{[(V_b\phi)/(\alpha_c\Delta t)]}\left[\left(T^n_{w_{2,1}}\right)_1\left(p^{n+1}_{o_1}-p^{n+1}_{o_2}\right)\right.$$

$$\left.+\left(T^n_{w_{2,3}}\right)_2\left(p^{n+1}_{o_3}-p^{n+1}_{o_2}\right)\right]. \quad \text{(9.645)}$$

For $n=3$,

$$S^{n+1}_{w_3}=S^n_{w_3}+\frac{1}{[(V_b\phi)/(\alpha_c\Delta t)]}\left[\left(T^n_{w_{3,2}}\right)_2\left(p^{n+1}_{o_2}-p^{n+1}_{o_3}\right)\right.$$

$$\left.+\left(T^n_{w_{3,4}}\right)_3\left(p^{n+1}_{o_4}-p^{n+1}_{o_3}\right)\right]. \quad \text{(9.646)}$$

For $n=4$,

$$S^{n+1}_{w_4}=S^n_{w_4}+\frac{1}{[(V_b\phi)/(\alpha_c\Delta t)]}\left[\left(T^n_{w_{4,3}}\right)_3\left(p^{n+1}_{o_3}-p^{n+1}_{o_4}\right)\right]. \quad \text{(9.647)}$$

Because all the fluid PVT properties are constant for incompressible-flow problems, the pressure level is immaterial. This implies that the system of equations represented by Eqs. 9.640 through 9.643 does not have a unique solution; therefore, this is an ill-posed problem. If we arbitrarily choose to fix $p^{n+1}_{o_1}$ at 1,000 psia, $p^{n+1}_{o_2}$, $p^{n+1}_{o_3}$, and $p^{n+1}_{o_4}$ can be determined uniquely by solving the modified system of equations simultaneously. Alternatively, the equation for $n=1$ is used to solve for $p^{n+1}_{o_2}$, the equation for $n=2$ is used to solve for $p^{n+1}_{o_3}$, and so on. The last equation for $n=4$ can be used to check the solution. After obtaining the pressure solution at Time Level $n+1$, Eqs. 9.644 through 9.647 are used to solve for $S^{n+1}_{w_1}$, $S^{n+1}_{w_2}$, $S^{n+1}_{w_3}$, and $S^{n+1}_{w_4}$ individually. At the end of each timestep, we perform an incremental material-balance check.

All four gridblocks have the dimensions and rock properties of $\phi=0.20$, $\Delta x=250$ ft, $A_x=10{,}000$ ft^2, and $k_x=0.300$ darcy.

$$V_b=A_x\Delta x \quad \text{(9.648)}$$

$$=10{,}000\times 250=2.5\times 10^6\text{ft}^3.$$

$$T^n_{w_{n,m}}=G_{n,m}\left(\frac{1}{\mu_w B_w}\right)^n_{n,m}(k_{rw})^n_{n,m}. \quad \text{(9.649)}$$

$$G_{n,m}=\beta_c\frac{k_xA_x}{\Delta x} \quad \text{(9.650)}$$

$$=\frac{(1.127)0.300\times 10{,}000}{250}=13.524\text{ RB-cp/(D–psi)}.$$

$$T^n_{w_{n,m}}=13.524\left(\frac{1}{1\times 1}\right)k^n_{rw_{n,m}}=13.524k^n_{rw_{n,m}}. \quad \text{(9.651)}$$

Also,

$$T^n_{o_{n,m}}=G_{n,m}\left(\frac{1}{\mu_oB_o}\right)^n_{n,m}(k_{ro})^n_{n,m} \quad \text{(9.652)}$$

$$=13.524\left(\frac{1}{1\times 1}\right)k^n_{ro_{n,m}}=13.524k^n_{ro_{n,m}}.$$

Therefore, for single-point upstream relative permeabilities,

$$\left(T^n_{w_{2,1}}\right)_1=\left(T^n_{w_{1,2}}\right)_1=13.524k^n_{rw_1}, \quad \text{(9.653)}$$

$$\left(T^n_{w_{3,2}}\right)_2=\left(T^n_{w_{2,3}}\right)_2=13.524k^n_{rw_2}, \quad \text{(9.654)}$$

$$\left(T^n_{w_{4,3}}\right)_3=\left(T^n_{w_{3,4}}\right)_3=13.524k^n_{rw_3}, \quad \text{(9.655)}$$

$$\left(T^n_{o_{2,1}}\right)_1=\left(T^n_{o_{1,2}}\right)_1=13.524k^n_{ro_1}, \quad \text{(9.656)}$$

$$\left(T^n_{o_{3,2}}\right)_2=\left(T^n_{o_{2,3}}\right)_2=13.524k^n_{ro_2}, \quad \text{(9.657)}$$

and $$\left(T^n_{o_{4,3}}\right)_3=\left(T^n_{o_{3,4}}\right)_3=13.524k^n_{ro_3}. \quad \text{(9.658)}$$

The flow rates are $q^n_{wsc_1}=75.96$ B/D and $q^n_{osc_4}=-75.96$ STB/D.

At $t=100$ days. $\Delta t=100-0=100$ days, which may be taken as one timestep because $\Delta t<561$ days.

$$\frac{V_b\phi}{\alpha_c\Delta t}=\frac{(2.5\times 10^6)\times 0.20}{(5.615)(100)}=890.472\text{ RB/D},$$

$$p^{n+1}_{o_1}=1{,}000\text{ psia},$$

$$p^n_{o_1}=p^n_{o_2}=p^n_{o_3}=p^n_{o_4}=1{,}000\text{ psia},$$

and $S^n_{w_1}=S^n_{w_2}=S^n_{w_3}=S^n_{w_4}=0.160$.

Therefore, $k^n_{rw_1}=k^n_{rw_2}=k^n_{rw_3}=(k_{rw})_{S_w=0.16}=0.000$ and $k^n_{ro_1}=k^n_{ro_2}=k^n_{ro_3}=(k_{ro})_{S_w=0.16}=1.000$, which gives the following on substitution into the transmissibilities and into Eqs. 9.640 through 9.643. For $n=1$,

$$13.524(0.000+1.000)p^{n+1}_{o_2}-13.524(0.000+1.000)p^{n+1}_{o_1}$$

$$=-75.96.$$

For $n=2$,

$$13.524(0.000+1.000)p^{n+1}_{o_1}+13.524(0.000+1.000)p^{n+1}_{o_3}$$

$$-[13.524(0.000+1.000)+13.524(0.000+1.000)]p^{n+1}_{o_2}$$

$$=0.$$

For $n=3$,

$$13.524(0.000+1.000)p^{n+1}_{o_2}+13.524(0.000+1.000)p^{n+1}_{o_4}$$

$$-[13.524(0.000+1.000)+13.524(0.000+1.000)]p^{n+1}_{o_3}$$

$$=0.$$

TABLE 9.8—COMPILATION OF SOLUTIONS FOR PRINCIPAL UNKNOWNS FOR ALL GRIDBLOCKS AT 100 DAYS

Gridblock	p_o (psia)	p_w (psia)	S_w	S_o
1	1,000	1,000	0.2453	0.7547
2	994.4	994.4	0.1600	0.8400
3	988.8	988.8	0.1600	0.8400
4	983.2	983.2	0.1600	0.8400

For $n=4$,

$$13.524(0.000+1.000)p_{o_3}^{n+1}-13.524(0.000+1.000)p_{o_4}^{n+1}$$

$$=-(-75.96).$$

The system of equations that describes the pressure distribution becomes

$$-13.524\times 1,000+13.524p_{o_2}^{n+1}=-75.96,$$

$$13.524\times 1,000-27.048p_{o_2}^{n+1}+13.524p_{o_3}^{n+1}=0,$$

$$13.524p_{o_2}^{n+1}-27.048p_{o_3}^{n+1}+13.524p_{o_4}^{n+1}=0,$$

and $13.524p_{o_3}^{n+1}-13.524p_{o_4}^{n+1}=+75.96.$

The solution for this system of equations can be obtained by either a direct solution procedure or an iterative procedure. The solution is $p_{o_1}^{n+1}=1{,}000$ psia (fixed), $p_{o_2}^{n+1}=994.4$ psia, $p_{o_3}^{n+1}=988.8$ psia, and $p_{o_4}^{n+1}=983.2$ psia.

Substituting this pressure solution at $t=100$ days into Eqs. 9.644 through 9.647 gives the following. For $n=1$,

$$S_{w_1}^{n+1}=0.160+\frac{1}{890.472}[0(994.4-1,000)+75.96]$$

$$=0.2453.$$

For $n=2$,

$$S_{w_2}^{n+1}=0.160+\frac{1}{890.472}[0(1,000-994.4)$$

$$+0(988.8-994.4)]=0.160.$$

For $n=3$,

$$S_{w_3}^{n+1}=0.160+\frac{1}{890.472}[0(994.4-988.8)$$

$$+0(983.2-988.8)]=0.160.$$

For $n=4$,

$$S_{w_4}^{n+1}=0.160+\frac{1}{890.472}[0(988.8-983.2)]=0.160.$$

Then, $S_{o_n}^{n+1}=1-S_{w_n}^{n+1}$ and $p_{w_n}^{n+1}=p_{o_n}^{n+1}-p_{cow}^{n+1}=p_{o_n}^{n+1}$, because $P_{cow}=0$, where $n=1,2,3,4$. **Table 9.8** contains a compilation of solutions for the principal unknowns for all gridblocks at 100 days.

For this incompressible-fluid system, it is sufficient to perform the material-balance check for one phase only (water phase, for example).

$$I_{MB}=\frac{\sum_{n=1}^{N}[(V_{b_n}\phi_n)/\alpha_c]\left(S_{w_n}^{n+1}-S_{w_n}^{n}\right)}{\Delta t\sum_{n=1}^{N}q_{wsc_n}^{n}}. \quad\text{.......... (9.659)}$$

For this problem,

$$I_{MB}=\frac{\dfrac{V_b\phi}{\alpha_c\Delta t}\sum_{n=1}^{4}\left(S_{w_n}^{n+1}-S_{w_n}^{n}\right)}{\left(q_{wsc_1}+0+0+0\right)}$$

$$=\frac{890.472}{75.96}[(0.2453-0.160)+(0.160-0.160)$$

$$+(0.160-0.160)+(0.160-0.160)]$$

$$=0.99996.$$

At $t=300$ days. $\Delta t=300-100=200$ days, which may be taken as one timestep because, for stability, $\Delta t<561$ days.

$$\frac{V_b\phi}{\alpha_c\Delta t}=\frac{(2.5\times 10^6)\times 0.20}{(5.615)(200)}=445.236\text{ RB/D}.$$

$p_{o_1}^{n+1}=1{,}000$ psia (fixed), $p_{o_1}^{n}=1{,}000$ psia, $p_{o_2}^{n}=994.4$ psia, $p_{o_3}^{n}=988.8$ psia, and $p_{o_4}^{n}=983.2$ psia. $S_{w_1}^{n}=0.2453$ and $S_{w_2}^{n}=S_{w_3}^{n}=S_{w_4}^{n}=0.160$. Therefore, $k_{rw_1}^{n}=0.0213$ and $k_{rw_2}^{n}=k_{rw_3}^{n}=k_{rw_4}^{n}=0.000$, $k_{ro_1}^{n}=0.5301$, and $k_{ro_2}^{n}=k_{ro_3}^{n}=k_{ro_4}^{n}=1.000$, which results in the following when substituted into the transmissibilities and into Eqs. 9.640 through 9.643. For $n=1$,

$$13.524(0.5301+0.0213)p_{o_2}^{n+1}$$

$$-13.524(0.5301+0.0213)p_{o_1}^{n+1}=-75.96.$$

For $n=2$,

$$13.524(0.5301+0.0213)p_{o_1}^{n+1}+13.524(0.000+1.000)p_{o_3}^{n+1}$$

$$-[13.524(0.5301+0.0213)+13.524$$

$$\times(0.000+1.000)]p_{o_2}^{n+1}=0.$$

For $n=3$,

$$13.524(0.000+1.000)p_{o_2}^{n+1}+13.524(0.000+1.000)p_{o_4}^{n+1}$$

$$-[13.524(0.000+1.000)+13.524(0.000+1.000)]p_{o_3}^{n+1}$$

$$=0.$$

For $n=4$,

$$13.524(0.000+1.000)p_{o_3}^{n+1}-13.524(0.000+1.000)p_{o_4}^{n+1}$$

$$=-(-75.96).$$

The system of equations that describes the pressure distribution is

$$-13.524\times 0.5514\times 1,000+13.524\times 0.5514p_{o_2}^{n+1}$$

$$=-75.96,$$

$$13.524\times 0.5514\times 1,000-13.524\times 1.5514p_{o_2}^{n+1}$$

$$+13.524p_{o_3}^{n+1}=0,$$

$$13.524p_{o_2}^{n+1}-27.048p_{o_3}^{n+1}+13.524p_{o_4}^{n+1}=0,$$

and $13.524p_{o_3}^{n+1}-13.524p_{o_4}^{n+1}=+75.96.$

The solution for this system of equations is $p_{o_1}^{n+1}=1{,}000$ psia (fixed), $p_{o_2}^{n+1}=989.8$ psia, $p_{o_3}^{n+1}=984.2$ psia, and $p_{o_4}^{n+1}=978.6$ psia. Next, we solve for the saturation distribution $S_{w_n}^{n+1}$ using Eqs. 9.644 through 9.647. For $n=1$,

$$S_{w_1}^{n+1}=0.2453+\frac{1}{445.236}$$

$$\times[13.524\times 0.0213(989.8-1,000)+75.96]$$

$$=0.4093.$$

For $n=2$,

$$S_{w_2}^{n+1}=0.160+\frac{1}{445.236}$$

$$\times[13.524\times 0.0213(1,000-989.8)$$

$$+13.524\times 0(984.2-989.8)]=0.1666.$$

TABLE 9.9—COMPILATION OF SOLUTIONS FOR PRINCIPAL UNKNOWNS FOR ALL GRIDBLOCKS AT 300 DAYS

Gridblock	p_o (psia)	p_w (psia)	S_w	S_o
1	1,000	1,000	0.4093	0.5907
2	989.8	989.8	0.1666	0.8334
3	984.2	984.2	0.16	0.84
4	978.6	978.6	0.16	0.84

For $n=3$,

$$S_{w_3}^{n+1} = 0.160 + \frac{1}{445.236}$$
$$\times [13.524 \times 0(989.8 - 984.2)$$
$$+ 13.524 \times 0(978.6 - 984.2)] = 0.160.$$

For $n=4$,

$$S_{w_4}^{n+1} = 0.160 + \frac{1}{445.236}$$
$$\times [13.524 \times 0(984.2 - 978.6)] = 0.160.$$

Then, $S_{o_n}^{n+1} = 1 - S_{w_n}^{n+1}$, where $n=1,2,3,4$ and, because $P_{cow}=0$, $p_{w_n}^{n+1} = p_{o_n}^{n+1}$, where $n=1,2,3,4$. **Table 9.9** contains a compilation of solutions for the principal unknowns for all gridblocks at 300 days. The material-balance check for water at 300 days gives

$$I_{MB} = \frac{V_b\phi}{\alpha_c \Delta t}\frac{1}{q_{wsc_1}}\sum_{n=1}^{4}\left(S_{w_n}^{n+1} - S_{w_n}^{n}\right)$$
$$= \frac{445.236}{75.96}[(0.4093 - 0.2453) + (0.1666 - 0.160)$$
$$+ (0.160 - 0.160) + (0.160 - 0.160)]$$
$$= 0.99996.$$

9.6.3 SEQ Method. The objective of the SEQ method is to improve stability of the IMPES method without solving for the oil pressure and saturations simultaneously. This is accomplished by solving for the pressure implicitly, as in the IMPES method, followed by solving for the saturation implicitly in a subsequent step.[15] The SEQ method, therefore, consists of two consecutive steps. The first step is identical to the IMPES method in which an implicit pressure solution and explicit saturation solution are obtained (Sec. 9.6.2). The second step is an implicit solution of the saturation equations. This method of solution may be derived by the use of either the linearized implicit-flow equations or the mass-conservation equations combined with the fractional-flow equations. Because the oil pressure and saturations are solved for independently, material balance will not be satisfied for all phases.

Derivation of the SEQ Method for the Black-Oil Model. Both steps of the SEQ method can be derived either from the linearized implicit-flow equations or from mass-conservation equations combined with the fractional-flow equations. The flow equations are presented, followed by derivation of the IMPES step and derivation of the implicit-saturation step. The general case represented by the black-oil model is presented here.

Derivation of the SEQ Method From Linearized Implicit Equations. Linearized Implicit Equations. Eqs. 9.466 through 9.468 for the black-oil model may be written in a linearized implicit form with the approximations given by Eqs. 9.414, 9.416b, and 9.430.

For the oil equation,

$$\sum_{m\in\psi_n} T^n_{o_{n,m}}\left(\Delta_m p_o^{n+1} - \bar{\gamma}^n_{o_{n,m}}\Delta_m Z\right)$$
$$+ \sum_{m\in\psi_n}\left(\Delta_m p_o^n - \bar{\gamma}^n_{o_{n,m}}\Delta_m Z\right)\left(\frac{\partial T_{o_{n,m}}}{\partial S_{w_m}}\right)^n \Delta_t S_{w_m}$$
$$+ \left[\sum_{m\in\psi_n}\left(\Delta_m p_o^n - \bar{\gamma}^n_{o_{n,m}}\Delta_m Z\right)\left(\frac{\partial T_{o_{n,m}}}{\partial S_{w_n}}\right)^n\right]\Delta_t S_{w_n}$$
$$+ \sum_{m\in\psi_n}\left(\Delta_m p_o^n - \bar{\gamma}^n_{o_{n,m}}\Delta_m Z\right)\left(\frac{\partial T_{o_{n,m}}}{\partial S_{g_m}}\right)^n \Delta_t S_{g_m}$$
$$+ \left[\sum_{m\in\psi_n}\left(\Delta_m p_o^n - \bar{\gamma}^n_{o_{n,m}}\Delta_m Z\right)\left(\frac{\partial T_{o_{n,m}}}{\partial S_{g_n}}\right)^n\right]\Delta_t S_{g_n}$$
$$= \left(C_{op_n} - q'^{n}_{opsc_n}\right)\Delta_t p_{o_n} + C_{ow_n}\Delta_t S_{w_n}$$
$$+ C_{og_n}\Delta_t S_{g_n} - q'^{n}_{owsc_n}\Delta_t S_{w_n} - q'^{n}_{ogsc_n}\Delta_t S_{g_n} - q^n_{osc_n}. \quad (9.660)$$

For the water equation,

$$\sum_{m\in\psi_n} T^n_{w_{n,m}}\left(\Delta_m p_o^{n+1} - \Delta_m P^n_{cow} - \bar{\gamma}^n_{w_{n,m}}\Delta_m Z\right)$$
$$+ \sum_{m\in\psi_n}\left[\left(\Delta_m p_o^n - \Delta_m P^n_{cow} - \bar{\gamma}^n_{w_{n,m}}\Delta_m Z\right)\right.$$
$$\left.\times\left(\frac{\partial T_{w_{n,m}}}{\partial S_{w_m}}\right)^n - T^n_{w_{n,m}} P'^{n}_{cow_m}\right]\Delta_t S_{w_m}$$
$$+ \left\{\sum_{m\in\psi_n}\left[\left(\Delta_m p_o^n - \Delta_m P^n_{cow} - \bar{\gamma}^n_{w_{n,m}}\Delta_m Z\right)\right.\right.$$
$$\left.\left.\times\left(\frac{\partial T_{w_{n,m}}}{\partial S_{w_n}}\right)^n + T^n_{w_{n,m}} P'^{n}_{cow_n}\right]\right\}\Delta_t S_{w_n}$$
$$= \left(C_{wp_n} - q'^{n}_{wpsc_n}\right)\Delta_t p_{o_n} + C_{ww_n}\Delta_t S_{w_n}$$
$$- q'^{n}_{wwsc_n}\Delta_t S_{w_n} - q'^{n}_{wgsc_n}\Delta_t S_{g_n} - q^n_{wsc_n}. \quad (9.661)$$

For the gas equation,

$$\sum_{m\in\psi_n}\left[T^n_{g_{n,m}}\left(\Delta_m p_o^{n+1} + \Delta_m P^n_{cgo} - \bar{\gamma}^n_{g_{n,m}}\Delta_m Z\right)\right.$$
$$\left.+ (T_o R_s)^n_{n,m}\left(\Delta_m p_o^{n+1} - \bar{\gamma}^n_{o_{n,m}}\Delta_m Z\right)\right]$$
$$+ \sum_{m\in\psi_n}\left(\Delta_m p_o^n - \bar{\gamma}^n_{o_{n,m}}\Delta_m Z\right)\left[\frac{\partial (T_o R_s)_{n,m}}{\partial S_{w_m}}\right]^n \Delta_t S_{w_m}$$
$$+ \left\{\sum_{m\in\psi_n}\left(\Delta_m p_o^n - \bar{\gamma}^n_{o_{n,m}}\Delta_m Z\right)\left[\frac{\partial (T_o R_s)_{n,m}}{\partial S_{w_n}}\right]^n\right\}\Delta_t S_{w_n}$$
$$+ \sum_{m\in\psi_n}\left\{\left(\Delta_m p_o^n + \Delta_m P^n_{cgo} - \bar{\gamma}^n_{g_{n,m}}\Delta_m Z\right)\left(\frac{\partial T_{g_{n,m}}}{\partial S_{g_m}}\right)^n\right.$$
$$+ T^n_{g_{n,m}} P'^{n}_{cgo_m} + \left(\Delta_m p_o^n - \bar{\gamma}^n_{o_{n,m}}\Delta_m Z\right)$$
$$\left.\times\left[\frac{\partial (T_o R_s)_{n,m}}{\partial S_{g_m}}\right]^n\right\}\Delta_t S_{g_m}$$

$$+\left[\sum_{m\in\psi_n}\left\{\left(\Delta_m p_o^n + \Delta_m P_{cgo}^n - \bar{\gamma}_{g_{n,m}}^n \Delta_m Z\right)\left(\frac{\partial \mathrm{T}_{g_{n,m}}}{\partial S_{g_n}}\right)^n\right.\right.$$

$$-\mathrm{T}_{g_{n,m}}^n \overset{n}{P'_{cgo_n}} + \left(\Delta_m p_o^n - \bar{\gamma}_{o_{n,m}}^n \Delta_m Z\right)$$

$$\left.\left.\times\left[\frac{\partial(\mathrm{T}_o R_s)_{n,m}}{\partial S_{g_n}}\right]^n\right\}\right]\Delta_t S_{g_n}$$

$$= \left(C_{gp_n} - \overset{n}{q'_{gpsc_n}}\right)\Delta_t p_{o_n} + C_{gw_n}\Delta_t S_{w_n}$$

$$+ C_{gg_n}\Delta_t S_{g_n} - \overset{n}{q'_{gwsc_n}}\Delta_t S_{w_n} - \overset{n}{q'_{ggsc_n}}\Delta_t S_{g_n} - \overset{n}{q_{gsc_n}}, \quad \text{(9.662)}$$

where $$q_{gsc_n}^n = \left(q_{fgsc_n}^n + R_{s_n}^n q_{osc_n}^n\right), \quad \text{(9.609)}$$

$$\overset{n}{q'_{gpsc_n}} = \left(\frac{\partial q_{gsc_n}}{\partial p_{o_n}}\right)^n$$

$$= \left(\frac{\partial q_{fgsc_n}}{\partial p_{o_n}}\right)^n + R_s^n\left(\frac{\partial q_{osc_n}}{\partial p_{o_n}}\right)^n + q_{osc_n}^n \overset{n}{R'_{s_n}}, \quad \text{(9.663)}$$

$$\overset{n}{q'_{gwsc_n}} = \left(\frac{\partial q_{gsc_n}}{\partial S_{w_n}}\right)^n = \left(\frac{\partial q_{fgsc_n}}{\partial S_{w_n}}\right)^n + R_{s_n}^n\left(\frac{\partial q_{osc_n}}{\partial S_{w_n}}\right)^n, \quad \text{(9.664)}$$

$$\overset{n}{q'_{ggsc_n}} = \left(\frac{\partial q_{gsc_n}}{\partial S_{g_n}}\right)^n = \left(\frac{\partial q_{fgsc_n}}{\partial S_{g_n}}\right)^n + R_{s_n}^n\left(\frac{\partial q_{osc_n}}{\partial S_{g_n}}\right)^n, \quad \text{(9.665)}$$

and where, for single-point upstream weighting of transmissibility of l=o, w, or g,

$$\mathrm{T}_{l_{n,m}}^n = \left(\mathrm{T}_{l_{n,m}}^n\right)_m \quad \text{(9.666a)}$$

for flow from Gridblock m to Gridblock n,

$$\mathrm{T}_{l_{n,m}}^n = \left(\mathrm{T}_{l_{n,m}}^n\right)_n \quad \text{(9.666b)}$$

for flow from Gridblock n to Gridblock m,

$$\left(\frac{\partial \mathrm{T}_{l_{n,m}}}{\partial S_{w_m}}\right)^n = \left[\frac{\partial}{\partial S_{w_m}}\left(\mathrm{T}_{l_{n,m}}\right)_m\right]^n \quad \text{(9.667a)}$$

for flow from Gridblock m to Gridblock n,

$$\left(\frac{\partial \mathrm{T}_{l_{n,m}}}{\partial S_{w_m}}\right)^n = 0 \quad \text{(9.667b)}$$

for flow from Gridblock n to Gridblock m,

$$\left(\frac{\partial \mathrm{T}_{l_{n,m}}}{\partial S_{w_n}}\right)^n = 0 \quad \text{(9.668a)}$$

for flow from Gridblock m to Gridblock n,

$$\left(\frac{\partial \mathrm{T}_{l_{n,m}}}{\partial S_{w_n}}\right)^n = \left[\frac{\partial}{\partial S_{w_n}}\left(\mathrm{T}_{l_{n,m}}\right)_n\right]^n \quad \text{(9.668b)}$$

for flow from Gridblock n to Gridblock m,

$$\left(\frac{\partial \mathrm{T}_{l_{n,m}}}{\partial S_{g_m}}\right)^n = \left[\frac{\partial}{\partial S_{g_m}}\left(\mathrm{T}_{l_{n,m}}\right)_m\right]^n \quad \text{(9.669a)}$$

for flow from Gridblock m to Gridblock n,

$$\left(\frac{\partial \mathrm{T}_{l_{n,m}}}{\partial S_{g_m}}\right)^n = 0 \quad \text{(9.669b)}$$

for flow from Gridblock n to Gridblock m, and

$$\left(\frac{\partial \mathrm{T}_{l_{n,m}}}{\partial S_{g_n}}\right)^n = 0 \quad \text{(9.670a)}$$

for flow from Gridblock m to Gridblock n, and

$$\left(\frac{\partial \mathrm{T}_{l_{n,m}}}{\partial S_{g_n}}\right)^n = \left[\frac{\partial}{\partial S_{g_n}}\left(\mathrm{T}_{l_{n,m}}\right)_n\right]^n \quad \text{(9.670b)}$$

for flow from Gridblock n to Gridblock m.

IMPES Step. In the first step of the SEQ method, the transmissibilities, production, and capillary pressures in the linearized implicit equations, Eqs. 9.660 through 9.662 ,are evaluated explicitly (at Time Level n). The resulting equations are

$$\sum_{m\in\psi_n}\left[\mathrm{T}_{o_{n,m}}^n\left(\Delta_m p_o^{n+1} - \bar{\gamma}_{o_{n,m}}^n \Delta_m Z\right)\right]$$

$$= \left(C_{op_n} - \overset{n}{q'_{opsc_n}}\right)\Delta_t p_{o_n} + C_{ow_n}\Delta_t S_{w_n}$$

$$+ C_{og_n}\Delta_t S_{g_n} - \overset{n}{q_{osc_n}}, \quad \text{(9.671)}$$

$$\sum_{m\in\psi_n}\left[\mathrm{T}_{w_{n,m}}^n\left(\Delta_m p_o^{n+1} - \Delta_m P_{cow}^n - \bar{\gamma}_{w_{n,m}}^n \Delta_m Z\right)\right]$$

$$= \left(C_{wp_n} - \overset{n}{q'_{wpsc_n}}\right)\Delta_t p_{o_n} + C_{ww_n}\Delta_t S_{w_n} - \overset{n}{q_{wsc_n}}, \quad \text{(9.672)}$$

and $$\sum_{m\in\psi_n}\left[\mathrm{T}_{g_{n,m}}^n\left(\Delta_m p_o^{n+1} + \Delta_m P_{cgo}^n - \bar{\gamma}_{g_{n,m}}^n \Delta_m Z\right)\right.$$

$$\left.+ (\mathrm{T}_o R_s)_{n,m}^n\left(\Delta_m p_o^{n+1} - \bar{\gamma}_{o_{n,m}}^n \Delta_m Z\right)\right]$$

$$= \left(C_{gp_n} - \overset{n}{q'_{gpsc_n}}\right)\Delta_t p_{o_n} + C_{gw_n}\Delta_t S_{w_n} + C_{gg_n}\Delta_t S_{g_n}$$

$$- \overset{n}{q_{gsc_n}}. \quad \text{(9.673)}$$

The pressure equation for Gridblock n, obtained by combining Eqs. 9.671 through 9.673 in exactly the same way as for the IMPES method discussed in Sec. 9.6.2, becomes

$$\sum_{m\in\psi_n}\left\{\left(B_o - R_s B_g\right)_n^{n+1}\mathrm{T}_{o_{n,m}}^n + B_{w_n}^{n+1}\mathrm{T}_{w_{n,m}}^n\right.$$

$$\left.+ B_{g_n}^{n+1}\left[\mathrm{T}_{g_{n,m}}^n + (\mathrm{T}_o R_s)_{n,m}^n\right]\right\}p_{o_m}^{n+1}$$

$$-\left(\left[\left(B_o - R_sB_g\right)_n^{n+1}C_{op_n} + B_{wn}^{n+1}C_{wp_n} + B_{gn}^{n+1}C_{gp_n}\right]\right.$$

$$-\left[\left(B_o - R_sB_g\right)_n^{n+1}q'^{\,n}_{opsc_n} + B_{wn}^{n+1}q'^{\,n}_{wpsc_n} + B_{gn}^{n+1}q'^{\,n}_{gpsc_n}\right]$$

$$+\sum_{m\in\psi_n}\left\{\left(B_o - R_sB_g\right)_n^{n+1}T^n_{o_{n,m}} + B_{wn}^{n+1}T^n_{w_{n,m}}\right.$$

$$\left.\left.+ B_{gn}^{n+1}\left[T^n_{g_{n,m}} + \left(T_oR_s\right)^n_{n,m}\right]\right\}\right)p_{o_n}^{n+1}$$

$$= -\left\{\left[\left(B_o - R_sB_g\right)_n^{n+1}C_{op_n} + B_{wn}^{n+1}C_{wp_n} + B_{gn}^{n+1}C_{gp_n}\right]\right.$$

$$\left.-\left[\left(B_o - R_sB_g\right)_n^{n+1}q'^{\,n}_{opsc_n} + B_{wn}^{n+1}q'^{\,n}_{wpsc_n} + B_{gn}^{n+1}q'^{\,n}_{gpsc_n}\right]\right\}p^n_{o_n}$$

$$-\left[\left(B_o - R_sB_g\right)_n^{n+1}q^n_{osc_n} + B_{wn}^{n+1}q^n_{wsc_n} + B_{gn}^{n+1}q^n_{gsc_n}\right]$$

$$+\sum_{m\in\psi_n}B_{wn}^{n+1}T^n_{w_{n,m}}\Delta_mP^n_{cow} - \sum_{m\in\psi_n}B_{gn}^{n+1}T^n_{g_{n,m}}\Delta_mP^n_{cgo}$$

$$+\sum_{m\in\psi_n}\left\{\left(B_o - R_sB_g\right)_n^{n+1}T^n_{o_{n,m}}\bar{\gamma}^n_{o_{n,m}} + B_{wn}^{n+1}T^n_{w_{n,m}}\bar{\gamma}^n_{w_{n,m}}\right.$$

$$\left.+ B_{gn}^{n+1}\left[T^n_{g_{n,m}}\bar{\gamma}^n_{g_{n,m}} + \left(T_oR_s\right)^n_{n,m}\bar{\gamma}^n_{o_{n,m}}\right]\right\}\Delta_mZ. \quad \ldots. \ (9.674)$$

Eq. 9.674 is written for each Gridblock $n = 1,2, \ldots, N$ and the system of N-coupled equations is solved for the p_o^{n+1} distribution. To honor the mass conservation property, B_{on}^{n+1}, B_{wn}^{n+1}, B_{gn}^{n+1}, R_{sn}^{n+1}, C_{op_n}, C_{wp_n}, and C_{gp_n} may have to be iterated on until convergence is reached. After obtaining the oil-pressure solution at Time Level $n+1$, the water and gas saturations, which are called S^*_{wn} and S^*_{gn}, are calculated explicitly by substituting the pressure solution into the water and oil equations, Eqs. 9.672 and 9.671, in that order, for each individual Gridblock n.

$$C_{ww_n}\left(S^*_{wn} - S^n_{wn}\right)$$

$$= \sum_{m\in\psi_n}\left[T^n_{w_{n,m}}\left(\Delta_mp_o^{n+1} - \Delta_mP^n_{cow} - \bar{\gamma}^n_{w_{n,m}}\Delta_mZ\right)\right]$$

$$-\left(C_{wp_n} - q'^{\,n}_{wpsc_n}\right)\left(p^{n+1}_{o_n} - p^n_{o_n}\right) + q^n_{wsc_n} \quad \ldots\ldots \ (9.675)$$

and

$$C_{og_n}\left(S^*_{gn} - S^n_{gn}\right) = \sum_{m\in\psi_n}\left[T^n_{o_{n,m}}\left(\Delta_mp_o^{n+1} - \bar{\gamma}^n_{o_{n,m}}\Delta_mZ\right)\right]$$

$$-\left(C_{op_n} - q'^{\,n}_{opsc_n}\right)\left(p^{n+1}_{o_n} - p^n_{o_n}\right)$$

$$-C_{ow_n}\left(S^*_{wn} - S^n_{wn}\right) + q^n_{osc_n}, \quad \ldots\ldots\ldots\ldots\ldots\ldots \ (9.676)$$

where C_{ww_n}, C_{wp_n}, C_{og_n}, C_{ow_n}, and C_{op_n} are all evaluated at $p^{n+1}_{o_n}$.

Implicit-Saturation Step. In the second step of the SEQ method, the implicit-saturation equations are obtained by adding Eqs. 9.675 and 9.661 for water and Eqs. 9.676 and 9.660 for oil for every Gridblock n and rearranging the resulting equations.

$$\sum_{m\in\psi_n}\left[\left(\Delta_mp^n_o - \Delta_mP^n_{cow} - \bar{\gamma}^n_{w_{n,m}}\Delta_mZ\right)\right.$$

$$\left.\times\left(\frac{\partial T_{w_{n,m}}}{\partial S_{w_m}}\right)^n - T^n_{w_{n,m}}P'^{\,n}_{cow_m}\right]\Delta_tS_{w_m}$$

$$+\left\{\sum_{m\in\psi_n}\left[\left(\Delta_mp^n_o - \Delta_mP^n_{cow} - \bar{\gamma}^n_{w_{n,m}}\Delta_mZ\right)\right.\right.$$

$$\left.\left.\times\left(\frac{\partial T_{w_{n,m}}}{\partial S_{w_n}}\right)^n + T^n_{w_{n,m}}P'^{\,n}_{cow_n}\right] - \left(C_{ww_n} - q'^{\,n}_{wwsc_n}\right)\right\}\Delta_tS_{w_n}$$

$$+ q'^{\,n}_{wgsc_n}\Delta_tS_{g_n} = -C_{ww_n}\left(S^*_{wn} - S^n_{wn}\right) \quad \ldots\ldots\ldots\ldots \ (9.677)$$

and

$$\sum_{m\in\psi_n}\left(\Delta_mp^n_o - \bar{\gamma}^n_{o_{n,m}}\Delta_mZ\right)\left(\frac{\partial T_{o_{n,m}}}{\partial S_{w_m}}\right)^n\Delta_tS_{w_m}$$

$$+\left\{\left[\sum_{m\in\psi_n}\left(\Delta_mp^n_o - \bar{\gamma}^n_{o_{n,m}}\Delta_mZ\right)\left(\frac{\partial T_{o_{n,m}}}{\partial S_{w_n}}\right)^n\right]\right.$$

$$\left.-\left(C_{ow_n} - q'^{\,n}_{owsc_n}\right)\right\}\Delta_tS_{w_n}$$

$$+\sum_{m\in\psi_n}\left(\Delta_mp^n_o - \bar{\gamma}^n_{o_{n,m}}\Delta_mZ\right)\left(\frac{\partial T_{o_{n,m}}}{\partial S_{g_m}}\right)^n\Delta_tS_{g_m} +$$

$$+\left\{\left[\sum_{m\in\psi_n}\left(\Delta_mp^n_o - \bar{\gamma}^n_{o_{n,m}}\Delta_mZ\right)\left(\frac{\partial T_{o_{n,m}}}{\partial S_{g_n}}\right)^n\right]\right.$$

$$\left.-\left(C_{og_n} - q'^{\,n}_{ogsc_n}\right)\right\}\Delta_tS_{g_n}$$

$$= -C_{ow_n}\left(S^*_{wn} - S^n_{wn}\right) - C_{og_n}\left(S^*_{gn} - S^n_{gn}\right), \quad \ldots.. \ (9.678)$$

where $n = 1,2, \ldots, N$.

Eqs. 9.677 and 9.678 form a system of $2N$-coupled equations and can be solved simultaneously for the Δ_tS_w and Δ_tS_g distributions. However, as these equations show, the saturation equations derived from the linearized implicit equations are decoupled if $q'^{\,n}_{wgsc_n}$ is zero. Therefore, the set of N equations represented by Eq. 9.677 can be solved implicitly for the Δ_tS_w distribution first, followed by the Δ_tS_g distribution with the following N equations, which are obtained by rearranging Eq. 9.678.

$$\sum_{m\in\psi_n}\left(\Delta_mp^n_o - \bar{\gamma}^n_{o_{n,m}}\Delta_mZ\right)\left(\frac{\partial T_{o_{n,m}}}{\partial S_{g_m}}\right)^n\Delta_tS_{g_m}$$

$$+\left\{\left[\sum_{m\in\psi_n}\left(\Delta_mp^n_o - \bar{\gamma}^n_{o_{n,m}}\Delta_mZ\right)\left(\frac{\partial T_{o_{n,m}}}{\partial S_{g_n}}\right)^n\right]\right.$$

$$\left.-\left(C_{og_n} - q'^{\,n}_{ogsc_n}\right)\right\}\Delta_tS_{g_n}$$

$$= -C_{ow_n}\left(S^*_{wn} - S^n_{wn}\right) - C_{og_n}\left(S^*_{gn} - S^n_{gn}\right)$$

$$-\sum_{m\in\psi_n}\left(\Delta_mp^n_o - \bar{\gamma}^n_{o_{n,m}}\Delta_mZ\right)\left(\frac{\partial T_{o_{n,m}}}{\partial S_{w_m}}\right)^n\Delta_tS_{w_m}$$

$$-\left\{\left[\sum_{m\in\psi_n}\left(\Delta_mp^n_o - \bar{\gamma}^n_{o_{n,m}}\Delta_mZ\right)\left(\frac{\partial T_{o_{n,m}}}{\partial S_{w_n}}\right)^n\right]\right.$$

$$\left.-\left(C_{ow_n} - q'^{\,n}_{owsc_n}\right)\right\}\Delta_tS_{w_n}, \quad \ldots\ldots\ldots\ldots\ldots\ldots \ (9.679)$$

where $n=1,2,\ldots,N$. In matrix form, Eqs. 9.674, 9.677, and 9.679 have a tri-, penta-, or heptadiagonal structure for 1D-, 2D-, or 3D-flow problems, respectively.

Derivation of SEQ Method With Fractional Flow Equations. Fractional-Flow Equations. The equations in which superficial phase velocities ($\vec{u}_o$, $\vec{u}_w$, $\vec{u}_g$) are expressed in terms of total superficial velocity ($\vec{u}_t$) and fractional-flow functions (f_w, f_o, f_g) are called fractional-flow equations. Darcy's law written for all phases, Eq. 2.25, can be combined as in Example 9.27 to obtain the fractional-flow equations for water, oil, and gas phases in a three-phase flow system.

$$\vec{u}_w = f_w\vec{u}_t + \beta_c k(Y_g + \zeta_w)\left(\vec{\nabla}P_{cow} + \Delta\gamma_{ow}\vec{\nabla}Z\right)$$
$$+ \beta_c kY_g\left(\vec{\nabla}P_{cgo} + \Delta\gamma_{og}\vec{\nabla}Z\right), \quad \ldots\ldots\ldots\ldots (9.680)$$

$$\vec{u}_o = f_o\vec{u}_t - \beta_c k\zeta_w\left(\vec{\nabla}P_{cow} + \Delta\gamma_{ow}\vec{\nabla}Z\right)$$
$$+ \beta_c k\zeta_g\left(\vec{\nabla}P_{cgo} + \Delta\gamma_{og}\vec{\nabla}Z\right), \quad \ldots\ldots\ldots\ldots (9.681)$$

and $$\vec{u}_g = f_g\vec{u}_t - \beta_c kY_g\left(\vec{\nabla}P_{cow} + \Delta\gamma_{ow}\vec{\nabla}Z\right)$$
$$- \beta_c k(Y_g + \zeta_g)\left(\vec{\nabla}P_{cgo} + \Delta\gamma_{og}\vec{\nabla}Z\right), \quad \ldots\ldots\ldots (9.682)$$

where $$\vec{u}_t = -\lambda_t\left[\vec{\nabla}p_o - f_w\left(\vec{\nabla}P_{cow} + \Delta\gamma_{ow}\vec{\nabla}Z\right)\right.$$
$$\left.+ f_g\left(\vec{\nabla}P_{cgo} + \Delta\gamma_{og}\vec{\nabla}Z\right) - \gamma_o\vec{\nabla}Z\right]; \quad \ldots\ldots\ldots (9.683)$$

$$f_l = \frac{\lambda_l}{\lambda_t}, \quad \ldots\ldots\ldots\ldots (9.684)$$

where $l=o$, w, or g;

$$\lambda_l = \beta_c\frac{kk_{rl}}{\mu_l}, \quad \ldots\ldots\ldots\ldots (9.685)$$

where $l=o$, w, or g;

$$\lambda_t = \lambda_o + \lambda_w + \lambda_g; \quad \ldots\ldots\ldots\ldots (9.686)$$

$$Y_g = \frac{k_{rg}}{\mu_g}f_w = \frac{k_{rw}}{\mu_w}f_g; \quad \ldots\ldots\ldots\ldots (9.687)$$

$$\zeta_w = \frac{k_{ro}}{\mu_o}f_w = \frac{k_{rw}}{\mu_w}f_o; \quad \ldots\ldots\ldots\ldots (9.688)$$

$$\zeta_g = \frac{k_{ro}}{\mu_o}f_g = \frac{k_{rg}}{\mu_g}f_o; \quad \ldots\ldots\ldots\ldots (9.689)$$

$$\Delta\gamma_{ow} = \gamma_w - \gamma_o; \quad \ldots\ldots\ldots\ldots (9.690)$$

$$\Delta\gamma_{og} = \gamma_o - \gamma_g; \quad \ldots\ldots\ldots\ldots (9.691)$$

and the gradient vectors are defined as

$$\vec{\nabla}p_o = \frac{\partial p_o}{\partial x}\vec{i} + \frac{\partial p_o}{\partial y}\vec{j} + \frac{\partial p_o}{\partial z}\vec{k}; \quad \ldots\ldots\ldots\ldots (9.692)$$

$$\vec{\nabla}P_{col} = \frac{\partial P_{col}}{\partial x}\vec{i} + \frac{\partial P_{col}}{\partial y}\vec{j} + \frac{\partial P_{col}}{\partial z}\vec{k}, \quad \ldots\ldots\ldots\ldots (9.693)$$

where $l=w$ or g; and

$$\vec{\nabla}Z = \frac{\partial Z}{\partial x}\vec{i} + \frac{\partial Z}{\partial y}\vec{j} + \frac{\partial Z}{\partial z}\vec{k}, \quad \ldots\ldots\ldots\ldots (9.694)$$

where $\vec{i}$, $\vec{j}$, and $\vec{k}$ = unit vectors in the x, y, and z directions, respectively.

The phase velocities can be expressed in terms of their components along the x, y, and z directions. For the water velocity,

$$\vec{u}_w = u_{wx}\vec{i} + u_{wy}\vec{j} + u_{wz}\vec{k}, \quad \ldots\ldots\ldots\ldots (9.695)$$

where $$u_{wx} = f_w u_{tx} + \beta_c k_x(Y_g + \zeta_w)\left(\frac{\partial P_{cow}}{\partial x} + \Delta\gamma_{ow}\frac{\partial Z}{\partial x}\right)$$
$$+ \beta_c k_x Y_g\left(\frac{\partial P_{cgo}}{\partial x} + \Delta\gamma_{og}\frac{\partial Z}{\partial x}\right), \quad \ldots\ldots\ldots\ldots (9.696)$$

$$u_{wy} = f_w u_{ty} + \beta_c k_y(Y_g + \zeta_w)\left(\frac{\partial P_{cow}}{\partial y} + \Delta\gamma_{ow}\frac{\partial Z}{\partial y}\right)$$
$$+ \beta_c k_y Y_g\left(\frac{\partial P_{cgo}}{\partial y} + \Delta\gamma_{og}\frac{\partial Z}{\partial y}\right), \quad \ldots\ldots\ldots\ldots (9.697)$$

and $$u_{wz} = f_w u_{tz} + \beta_c k_z(Y_g + \zeta_w)\left(\frac{\partial P_{cow}}{\partial z} + \Delta\gamma_{ow}\frac{\partial Z}{\partial z}\right)$$
$$+ \beta_c k_z Y_g\left(\frac{\partial P_{cgo}}{\partial z} + \Delta\gamma_{og}\frac{\partial Z}{\partial z}\right). \quad \ldots\ldots\ldots\ldots (9.698)$$

Likewise, the total velocity may be expressed as

$$\vec{u}_t = u_{tx}\vec{i} + u_{ty}\vec{j} + u_{tz}\vec{k}, \quad \ldots\ldots\ldots\ldots (9.699)$$

where $$u_{tx} = \lambda_{tx}\left[\frac{\partial p_o}{\partial x} - f_w\left(\frac{\partial P_{cow}}{\partial x} + \Delta\gamma_{ow}\frac{\partial Z}{\partial x}\right)\right.$$
$$\left.+ f_g\left(\frac{\partial P_{cgo}}{\partial x} + \Delta\gamma_{og}\frac{\partial Z}{\partial x}\right) - \gamma_o\frac{\partial Z}{\partial x}\right], \quad \ldots\ldots\ldots (9.700)$$

$$u_{ty} = -\lambda_{ty}\left[\frac{\partial p_o}{\partial y} - f_w\left(\frac{\partial P_{cow}}{\partial y} + \Delta\gamma_{ow}\frac{\partial Z}{\partial y}\right)\right.$$
$$\left.+ f_g\left(\frac{\partial P_{cgo}}{\partial y} + \Delta\gamma_{og}\frac{\partial Z}{\partial y}\right) - \gamma_o\frac{\partial Z}{\partial y}\right], \quad \ldots\ldots\ldots (9.701)$$

and $$u_{tz} = -\lambda_{tz}\left[\frac{\partial p_o}{\partial z} - f_w\left(\frac{\partial P_{cow}}{\partial z} + \Delta\gamma_{ow}\frac{\partial Z}{\partial z}\right)\right.$$
$$\left.+ f_g\left(\frac{\partial P_{cgo}}{\partial z} + \Delta\gamma_{og}\frac{\partial Z}{\partial z}\right) - \gamma_o\frac{\partial Z}{\partial z}\right]. \quad \ldots\ldots\ldots (9.702)$$

Combined Mass-Conservation and Fractional-Flow Equations. The mass-conservation equations, Eqs. 9.16, 9.17, and 9.19, may be expressed as

$$-\vec{\nabla}\cdot\left(\frac{V_b}{B_o}\vec{u}_o\right) = \frac{V_b}{\alpha_c}\frac{\partial}{\partial t}\left[\phi\frac{(1 - S_w - S_g)}{B_o}\right] - q_{osc},$$
$$\ldots\ldots\ldots\ldots (9.703)$$

$$-\vec{\nabla}\cdot\left(\frac{V_b}{B_w}\vec{u}_w\right) = \frac{V_b}{\alpha_c}\frac{\partial}{\partial t}\left(\frac{\phi S_w}{B_w}\right) - q_{wsc}, \quad \ldots\ldots\ldots (9.704)$$

and $$-\vec{\nabla}\cdot\left(\frac{V_b}{B_g}\vec{u}_g + \frac{V_b R_s}{B_o}\vec{u}_o\right)$$
$$= \frac{V_b}{\alpha_c}\frac{\partial}{\partial t}\left[\frac{\phi S_g}{B_g} + \frac{\phi R_s}{B_o}(1 - S_w - S_g)\right] - q_{gsc},$$
$$\ldots\ldots\ldots\ldots (9.705)$$

where $q_{gsc} = q_{fgsc} + R_s q_{osc}$, $\vec{u}_g$ = velocity of the gas phase (free-gas velocity, $\vec{u}_{fg}$), and $V_b = A_x\Delta x = A_y\Delta y = A_z\Delta z$. The inner (or scalar) products of $\vec{\nabla}$ and the vectors enclosed in the parenthesis on the left side of Eqs. 9.703 through 9.705 produce the left side scalars of Eqs. 9.16, 9.17, and 9.19.

Substituting the fractional-flow equations expressed by Eqs. 9.680 through 9.682 into the mass-conservation equations, Eqs. 9.703 through 9.705, results in following flow equations in differential form.

$$-\vec{\nabla}\cdot\left(\frac{V_b}{B_o}f_o\vec{u}_t\right) + \vec{\nabla}\cdot\left[\frac{\beta_c V_b k}{B_o}\zeta_w\left(\vec{\nabla}P_{cow} + \Delta\gamma_{ow}\vec{\nabla}Z\right)\right]$$

$$-\vec{\nabla}\cdot\left[\frac{\beta_c V_b k}{B_o}\zeta_g\left(\vec{\nabla}P_{cgo}+\Delta\gamma_{og}\vec{\nabla}Z\right)\right]$$

$$=\frac{V_b}{\alpha_c}\frac{\partial}{\partial t}\left[\phi\frac{(1-S_w-S_g)}{B_o}\right]-q_{osc}, \quad (9.706)$$

$$-\vec{\nabla}\cdot\left(\frac{V_b}{B_w}f_w\vec{u}_t\right)-\vec{\nabla}\cdot\left[\frac{\beta_c V_b k}{B_w}(Y_g+\zeta_w)\left(\vec{\nabla}P_{cow}+\Delta\gamma_{ow}\vec{\nabla}Z\right)\right]$$

$$-\vec{\nabla}\cdot\left[\frac{\beta_c V_b k}{B_w}Y_g\left(\vec{\nabla}P_{cgo}+\Delta\gamma_{og}\vec{\nabla}Z\right)\right]$$

$$=\frac{V_b}{\alpha_c}\frac{\partial}{\partial t}\left[\frac{\phi S_w}{B_w}\right]-q_{wsc}, \quad (9.707)$$

and
$$-\vec{\nabla}\cdot\left(\frac{V_b}{B_g}f_g\vec{u}_t\right)+\vec{\nabla}\cdot\left[\frac{\beta_c V_b k}{B_g}Y_g\left(\vec{\nabla}P_{cow}+\Delta\gamma_{ow}\vec{\nabla}Z\right)\right]$$

$$+\vec{\nabla}\cdot\left[\frac{\beta_c V_b k}{B_g}(Y_g+\zeta_g)\left(\vec{\nabla}P_{cgo}+\Delta\gamma_{og}\vec{\nabla}Z\right)\right]$$

$$-\vec{\nabla}\cdot\left(\frac{V_b}{B_o}R_s f_o\vec{u}_t\right)+\vec{\nabla}\cdot\left[\frac{\beta_c V_b k}{B_o}R_s\zeta_w\left(\vec{\nabla}P_{cow}+\Delta\gamma_{ow}\vec{\nabla}Z\right)\right]$$

$$-\vec{\nabla}\cdot\left[\frac{\beta_c V_b k}{B_o}R_s\zeta_g\left(\vec{\nabla}P_{cgo}+\Delta\gamma_{og}\vec{\nabla}Z\right)\right]$$

$$=\frac{V_b}{\alpha_c}\frac{\partial}{\partial t}\left[\frac{\phi S_g}{B_g}+\frac{\phi R_s(1-S_w-S_g)}{B_o}\right]-q_{gsc}. \quad (9.708)$$

The finite-difference approximation of Eqs. 9.706 through 9.708, considering the central-difference approximation for first-order derivatives and after expanding the accumulation terms in terms of p_o, S_w, and S_g, may be expressed in compact form as

$$-\Delta\left(\frac{f_o}{B_o}Au_t\right)^{n+1}+\Delta\left[G\frac{\zeta_w}{B_o}(\Delta P_{cow}+\Delta\gamma_{ow}\Delta Z)\right]^{n+1}$$

$$-\Delta\left[G\frac{\zeta_g}{B_o}(\Delta P_{cgo}+\Delta\gamma_{og}\Delta Z)\right]^{n+1}$$

$$=C_{op}\Delta_t p_o+C_{ow}\Delta_t S_w+C_{og}\Delta_t S_g-q_{osc}^{n+1}, \quad (9.709)$$

$$-\Delta\left(\frac{f_w}{B_w}Au_t\right)^{n+1}$$

$$-\Delta\left[G\frac{(Y_g+\zeta_w)}{B_w}(\Delta P_{cow}+\Delta\gamma_{ow}\Delta Z)\right]^{n+1}$$

$$-\Delta\left[G\frac{Y_g}{B_w}(\Delta P_{cgo}+\Delta\gamma_{og}\Delta Z)\right]^{n+1}$$

$$=C_{wp}\Delta_t p_o+C_{ww}\Delta_t S_w-q_{wsc}^{n+1}, \quad (9.710)$$

and
$$-\Delta\left[\left(\frac{f_g}{B_g}+\frac{R_s}{B_o}f_o\right)Au_t\right]^{n+1}$$

$$+\Delta\left[G\left(\frac{Y_g}{B_g}+\frac{R_s}{B_o}\zeta_w\right)(\Delta P_{cow}+\Delta\gamma_{ow}\Delta Z)\right]^{n+1}$$

$$+\Delta\left\{G\left[\frac{(Y_g+\zeta_g)}{B_g}-\frac{R_s}{B_o}\zeta_g\right](\Delta P_{cgo}+\Delta\gamma_{og}\Delta Z)\right\}^{n+1}$$

$$=C_{gp}\Delta_t p_o+C_{gw}\Delta_t S_w+C_{gg}\Delta_t S_g-q_{gsc}^{n+1}, \quad (9.711)$$

where G = the geometric factor discussed in Sec. 9.5.2; A = cross-sectional area; Eqs. 9.228 through 9.236 give C_{op}, C_{ow}, C_{og}, C_{wp}, C_{ww}, C_{wg}, C_{gp}, C_{gw}, and C_{gg}; Eq. 9.97 defines all second-order finite-difference operators in 3D space; and all first-order finite-difference operators are central-difference operators. A first-order finite-difference operator $\Delta[(f/B)Au_t]_{i,j,k}$ or $\Delta[(f/B)Au_t]_n$, (where f may assume f_o, f_w, f_g, or $R_s f_o$) may be written with the CFVD method terminology as Examples 9.28 and 9.29 show.

$$\Delta\left(\frac{f}{B}Au_t\right)_{i,j,k}\equiv\Delta_x\left(\frac{f}{B}A_x u_{tx}\right)_{i,j,k}+\Delta_y\left(\frac{f}{B}A_y u_{ty}\right)_{i,j,k}+\Delta_z\left(\frac{f}{B}A_z u_{tz}\right)_{i,j,k}$$

$$=-\sum_{m\in\psi_n}\left(\frac{f}{B}\right)_{n,m}q_{t_{n,m}}, \quad (9.712)$$

where
$$\Delta_x\left(\frac{f}{B}A_x u_{tx}\right)_{i,j,k}\equiv\left(\frac{f}{B}A_x\right)_{i+1/2,j,k}u_{tx_{i+1/2,j,k}}-\left(\frac{f}{B}A_x\right)_{i-1/2,j,k}u_{tx_{i-1/2,j,k}}$$

$$=-\sum_{m\in\psi_x}\left(\frac{f}{B}\right)_{n,m}q_{t_{n,m}}, \quad (9.713)$$

$$\Delta_y\left(\frac{f}{B}A_y u_{ty}\right)_{i,j,k}\equiv\left(\frac{f}{B}A_y\right)_{i,j+1/2,k}u_{ty_{i,j+1/2,k}}-\left(\frac{f}{B}A_y\right)_{i,j-1/2,k}u_{ty_{i,j-1/2,k}}$$

$$=-\sum_{m\in\psi_y}\left(\frac{f}{B}\right)_{n,m}q_{t_{n,m}}, \quad (9.714)$$

and
$$\Delta_z\left(\frac{f}{B}A_z u_{tz}\right)_{i,j,k}\equiv\left(\frac{f}{B}A_z\right)_{i,j,k+1/2}u_{tz_{i,j,k+1/2}}-\left(\frac{f}{B}A_z\right)_{i,j,k-1/2}u_{tz_{i,j,k-1/2}}$$

$$=-\sum_{m\in\psi_z}\left(\frac{f}{B}\right)_{n,m}q_{t_{n,m}}, \quad (9.715)$$

where ψ_n is given by Eqs. 9.461 through 9.464.

The interblock total flow rate $q_{t_{n,m}}$ across the boundary (n,m) between Gridblocks n and $m\in\psi_n$ is related to the interblock total velocity across the same boundary.

$$q_{t_{n,m}}=(A_x u_{tx})_{i-1/2,j,k} \quad (9.716a)$$

for $m=n-1$,

$$q_{t_{n,m}}=(A_y u_{ty})_{i,j-1/2,k} \quad (9.716b)$$

for $m=n-n_x$,

$$q_{t_{n,m}}=(A_z u_{tz})_{i,j,k-1/2} \quad (9.716c)$$

for $m=n-n_x n_y$,

$$q_{t_{n,m}}=-(A_x u_{tx})_{i+1/2,j,k} \quad (9.716d)$$

for $m=n+1$,

$$q_{t_{n,m}} = -\left(A_y u_{ty}\right)_{i,j+½,k} \quad \text{(9.716e)}$$

for $m=n+n_x$, and

$$q_{t_{n,m}} = -\left(A_z u_{tz}\right)_{i,j,k+½} \quad \text{(9.716f)}$$

for $m=n+n_x n_y$. $q_{t_{n,m}}$ can be calculated with

$$q_{t_{n,m}} = q_{o_{n,m}} + q_{w_{n,m}} + q_{g_{n,m}}, \quad \text{(9.717)}$$

where $q_{o_{n,m}} = G_{n,m}\left(\frac{k_{ro}}{\mu_o}\right)_{n,m}\left(\Delta_m p_o^{n+1} - \bar{\gamma}^n_{o_{n,m}}\Delta_m Z\right),$

$$\quad \text{(9.718)}$$

$$q_{w_{n,m}} = G_{n,m}\left(\frac{k_{rw}}{\mu_w}\right)_{n,m}\left(\Delta_m p_o^{n+1} - \Delta_m P^n_{cow} - \bar{\gamma}^n_{w_{n,m}}\Delta_m Z\right), \quad \text{(9.719)}$$

and $q_{g_{n,m}} = G_{n,m}\left(\frac{k_{rg}}{\mu_g}\right)_{n,m}\left(\Delta_m p_o^{n+1} + \Delta_m P^n_{cgo} - \bar{\gamma}^n_{g_{n,m}}\Delta_m Z\right),$

$$\quad \text{(9.720)}$$

where $G_{n,m}$ is defined by Eq. 9.472. Alternatively, total velocities across the gridblock boundary along the x, y, and z directions may be obtained by use of a central-difference approximation of Eqs. 9.700, 9.701, and 9.702, respectively.

IMPES Step. The IMPES step can be derived by combining Eqs. 9.709 through 9.711 for Gridblock n. In this step, the transmissibilities and capillary pressures are evaluated explicitly and production rates are approximated by the linearized implicit method (Eq. 9.430) with neglected implicit contributions resulting from saturation changes.

$$-\Delta\left[\left(\frac{f_o}{B_o}\right)^n Au_t\right]_n + \Delta\left[G\frac{\zeta_w}{B_o}\left(\Delta P_{cow} + \overline{\Delta\gamma}^n_{ow}\Delta Z\right)\right]^n_n$$

$$-\Delta\left[G\frac{\zeta_g}{B_o}\left(\Delta P_{cgo} + \overline{\Delta\gamma}^n_{og}\Delta Z\right)\right]^n_n$$

$$= \left(C_{op_n} - \overset{n}{q'_{opsc_n}}\right)\Delta_t p_{o_n} + C_{ow_n}\left(S^*_{w_n} - S^n_{w_n}\right)$$

$$+ C_{og_n}\left(S^*_{g_n} - S^n_{g_n}\right) - \overset{n}{q_{osc_n}}, \quad \text{(9.721)}$$

$$-\Delta\left[\left(\frac{f_w}{B_w}\right)^n Au_t\right]_n - \Delta\left[G\frac{(Y_g+\zeta_w)}{B_w}\left(\Delta P_{cow} + \overline{\Delta\gamma}^n_{ow}\Delta Z\right)\right]^n_n$$

$$-\Delta\left[G\frac{Y_g}{B_w}\left(\Delta P_{cgo} + \overline{\Delta\gamma}^n_{og}\Delta Z\right)\right]^n_n$$

$$= \left(C_{wp_n} - \overset{n}{q'_{wpsc_n}}\right)\Delta_t p_{o_n} + C_{ww_n}\left(S^*_{w_n} - S^n_{w_n}\right) - \overset{n}{q_{wsc_n}}, \quad \text{(9.722)}$$

and $-\Delta\left[\left(\frac{f_g}{B_g} + \frac{R_s}{B_o}f_o\right)^n Au_t\right]_n$

$$+\Delta\left[G\left(\frac{Y_g}{B_g} + \frac{R_s}{B_o}\zeta_w\right)\left(\Delta P_{cow} + \overline{\Delta\gamma}^n_{ow}\Delta Z\right)\right]^n_n$$

$$+\Delta\left\{G\left[\frac{(Y_g+\zeta_g)}{B_g} - \frac{R_s}{B_o}\zeta_g\right]\left(\Delta P_{cgo} + \overline{\Delta\gamma}^n_{og}\Delta Z\right)\right\}^n_n$$

$$= \left(C_{gp_n} - \overset{n}{q'_{gpsc_n}}\right)\Delta_t p_{o_n} + C_{gw_n}\left(S^*_{w_n} - S^n_{w_n}\right)$$

$$+ C_{gg_n}\left(S^*_{g_n} - S^n_{g_n}\right) - \overset{n}{q_{gsc_n}}. \quad \text{(9.723)}$$

Eqs. 9.721 through 9.723 are combined by eliminating $(S^*_{w_n} - S^n_{w_n})$ and $(S^*_{g_n} - S^n_{g_n})$ in the same manner as in the IMPES method (Sec. 9.6.2). Because the left side of Eqs. 9.721 through 9.723 and those of Eqs. 9.671 through 9.673 are the finite-difference approximations to the left side of Eqs. 9.703 through 9.705, Eqs. 9.721, 9.722, and 9.723 are equivalent to Eqs. 9.671, 9.672, and 9.673, respectively. Therefore, the resulting pressure equation is given by Eq. 9.674, which can be solved for the p_o^{n+1} distribution as discussed previously in this section. After obtaining the pressure solution, p_o^{n+1}, interblock total flow rates, u_t, across all boundaries for each Gridblock $n=1,2,\ldots,N$, which are needed to solve the saturation equations in the second step of the SEQ method, can be calculated with Eqs. 9.717 through 9.720. The explicit updating of the water and gas saturations $(S^*_{w_n}, S^*_{g_n})$ is obtained by use of either Eqs. 9.675 and 9.676 or Eqs. 9.722 and 9.721, in that order, for the individual gridblocks.

Implicit-Saturation Step. Implicit-saturation equations may be obtained by first subtracting Eq. 9.721 from Eq. 9.709 for oil and Eq. 9.722 from Eq. 9.710 for water. The linerized-implicit method is used to approximate q^{n+1}_{osc} and q^{n+1}_{wsc} in Eqs. 9.709 and 9.710. The resulting equations written with the CFVD method terminology are

$$\sum_{m\in\psi_n}\frac{1}{B^n_{o_{n,m}}}\Delta_t(f_o q_t)_{n,m}$$

$$+\sum_{m\in\psi_n}G_{n,m}\frac{1}{B^n_{o_{n,m}}}\Delta_t\left[\zeta_{w_{n,m}}\left(\Delta_m P_{cow} + \overline{\Delta\gamma}^n_{ow_{n,m}}\Delta_m Z\right)\right]$$

$$-\sum_{m\in\psi_n}G_{n,m}\frac{1}{B^n_{o_{n,m}}}\Delta_t\left[\zeta_{g_{n,m}}\left(\Delta_m P_{cgo} + \overline{\Delta\gamma}^n_{og_{n,m}}\Delta_m Z\right)\right]$$

$$= \left(C_{ow_n} - \overset{n}{q'_{owsc_n}}\right)\Delta_t S_{w_n} + \left(C_{og_n} - \overset{n}{q'_{ogsc_n}}\right)\Delta_t S_{g_n}$$

$$- C_{ow_n}\left(S^*_{w_n} - S^n_{w_n}\right) - C_{og_n}\left(S^*_{g_n} - S^n_{g_n}\right) \quad \text{(9.724)}$$

and $\sum_{m\in\psi_n}\frac{1}{B^n_{w_{n,m}}}\Delta_t(f_w q_t)_{n,m}$

$$-\sum_{m\in\psi_n}G_{n,m}\frac{1}{B^n_{w_{n,m}}}\Delta_t\left[(Y_g+\zeta_w)_{n,m}\left(\Delta_m P_{cow} + \overline{\Delta\gamma}^n_{ow_{n,m}}\Delta_m Z\right)\right]$$

$$-\sum_{m\in\psi_n}G_{n,m}\frac{1}{B^n_{w_{n,m}}}\Delta_t\left[Y_{g_{n,m}}\left(\Delta_m P_{cgo} + \overline{\Delta\gamma}^n_{og_{n,m}}\Delta_m Z\right)\right]$$

$$= \left(C_{ww_n} - \overset{n}{q'_{wwsc_n}}\right)\Delta_t S_{w_n} - \overset{n}{q'_{wgsc_n}}\Delta_t S_{g_n}$$

$$- C_{ww_n}\left(S^*_{w_n} - S^n_{w_n}\right). \quad \text{(9.725)}$$

Second, Eqs. 9.724 and 9.725 are approximated implicitly. The resulting saturation equations may be rearranged in terms of $\Delta_t S_w$ and $\Delta_t S_g$ only.

$$\sum_{m\in\psi_n}\left[\left(\frac{f_o}{B_o}\right)^n_{n,m}\Delta_t q_{t_{n,m}}\right] + \sum_{m\in\psi_n}\left\{\left(\frac{q_t}{B^n_o}\right)_{n,m}\left(\frac{\partial f_{o_{n,m}}}{\partial S_{w_m}}\right)^n + \frac{G_{n,m}}{B^n_{o_{n,m}}}\right.$$

$$\times\left[\left(\Delta_m P^n_{cow} + \overline{\Delta\gamma}^n_{ow_{n,m}}\Delta_m Z\right)\left(\frac{\partial\zeta_{w_{n,m}}}{\partial S_{w_m}}\right)^n + \zeta^n_{w_{n,m}}\overset{n}{P'_{cow_m}}\right.$$

$$- \left(\Delta_m P^n_{cgo} + \overline{\Delta\gamma}^n_{og_{n,m}} \Delta_m Z\right)\left(\frac{\partial \zeta_{g_{n,m}}}{\partial S_{w_m}}\right)^n \Bigg]\Bigg\} \Delta_t S_{w_m}$$

$$+ \sum_{m\in\psi_n} \Bigg\{ \left(\frac{q_t}{B^n_o}\right)_{n,m} \left(\frac{\partial f_{o_{n,m}}}{\partial S_{g_m}}\right)^n + \frac{G_{n,m}}{B^n_{o_{n,m}}}$$

$$\times \Bigg[\left(\Delta_m P^n_{cow} + \overline{\Delta\gamma}^n_{ow_{n,m}}\Delta_m Z\right)\left(\frac{\partial \zeta_{w_{n,m}}}{\partial S_{g_m}}\right)^n$$

$$- \left(\Delta_m P^n_{cgo} + \overline{\Delta\gamma}^n_{og_{n,m}}\Delta_m Z\right)\left(\frac{\partial \zeta_{g_{n,m}}}{\partial S_{g_m}}\right)^n - \zeta^n_{g_{n,m}} \overset{n}{P'_{cgo_m}} \Bigg]\Bigg\}$$

$$\times \Delta_t S_{g_m} + \Bigg(- \left(C_{ow_n} - \overset{n}{q'_{owsc_n}}\right) + \sum_{m\in\psi_n}\Bigg\{ \left(\frac{q_t}{B^n_o}\right)_{n,m}$$

$$\times \left(\frac{\partial f_{o_{n,m}}}{\partial S_{w_n}}\right)^n + \frac{G_{n,m}}{B^n_{o_{n,m}}}\Bigg[\left(\Delta_m P^n_{cow} + \overline{\Delta\gamma}^n_{ow_{n,m}}\Delta_m Z\right)\left(\frac{\partial\zeta_{w_{n,m}}}{\partial S_{w_n}}\right)^n$$

$$- \zeta^n_{w_{n,m}} \overset{n}{P'_{cow_n}} - \left(\Delta_m P^n_{cgo} + \overline{\Delta\gamma}^n_{og_{n,m}}\Delta_m Z\right)\left(\frac{\partial\zeta_{g_{n,m}}}{\partial S_{w_n}}\right)^n\Bigg]\Bigg\}\Bigg)$$

$$\times \Delta_t S_{w_n} + \Bigg(- \left(C_{og_n} - \overset{n}{q'_{ogsc_n}}\right) + \sum_{m\in\psi_n} \Bigg\{ \left(\frac{q_t}{B^n_o}\right)_{n,m}$$

$$\times \left(\frac{\partial f_{o_{n,m}}}{\partial S_{g_n}}\right)^n + \frac{G_{n,m}}{B^n_{o_{n,m}}}\Bigg[\left(\Delta_m P^n_{cow} + \overline{\Delta\gamma}^n_{ow_{n,m}}\Delta_m Z\right)\left(\frac{\partial\zeta_{w_{n,m}}}{\partial S_{g_n}}\right)^n$$

$$- \left(\Delta_m P^n_{cgo} + \overline{\Delta\gamma}^n_{og_{n,m}}\Delta_m Z\right)\left(\frac{\partial\zeta_{g_{n,m}}}{\partial S_{g_n}}\right)^n + \zeta^n_{g_{n,m}} \overset{n}{P'_{cgo_n}}\Bigg]\Bigg\}\Bigg)$$

$$\times \Delta_t S_{g_n} = - C_{ow_n}\left(S^*_{w_n} - S^n_{w_n}\right) - C_{og_n}\left(S^*_{g_n} - S^n_{g_n}\right) \qquad (9.726)$$

and

$$\sum_{m\in\psi_n}\left[\left(\frac{f_w}{B_w}\right)^n_{n,m}\Delta_t q_{t_{n,m}}\right] + \sum_{m\in\psi_n}\Bigg(\left(\frac{q_t}{B^n_w}\right)_{n,m}\left(\frac{\partial f_{w_{n,m}}}{\partial S_{w_m}}\right)^n$$

$$+ \frac{G_{n,m}}{B^n_{w_{n,m}}}\Bigg\{ - \left(\Delta_m P^n_{cow} + \overline{\Delta\gamma}^n_{ow_{n,m}}\Delta_m Z\right)$$

$$\times \left[\left(\frac{\partial Y_{g_{n,m}}}{\partial S_{w_m}}\right)^n + \left(\frac{\zeta_{w_{n,m}}}{\partial S_{w_m}}\right)^n\right]$$

$$- \left(Y^n_g + \zeta^n_w\right)_{n,m} \overset{n}{P'_{cow_m}} - \left(\Delta_m P^n_{cgo} + \overline{\Delta\gamma}^n_{og_{n,m}}\Delta_m Z\right)$$

$$\times \left(\frac{\partial Y_{g_{n,m}}}{\partial S_{w_m}}\right)^n\Bigg\}\Bigg)\Delta_t S_{w_m} + \sum_{m\in\psi_n}\Bigg(\left(\frac{q_t}{B^n_w}\right)_{n,m}\left(\frac{\partial f_{w_{n,m}}}{\partial S_{g_m}}\right)^n$$

$$+ \frac{G_{n,m}}{B^n_{w_{n,m}}}\Bigg\{ - \left(\Delta_m P^n_{cow} + \overline{\Delta\gamma}^n_{ow_{n,m}}\Delta_m Z\right)$$

$$\times \left[\left(\frac{\partial Y_{g_{n,m}}}{\partial S_{g_m}}\right)^n + \left(\frac{\partial\zeta_{w_{n,m}}}{\partial S_{g_m}}\right)^n\right]$$

$$- \left(\Delta_m P^n_{cgo} + \overline{\Delta\gamma}^n_{og_{n,m}}\Delta_m Z\right)\left(\frac{\partial Y_{g_{n,m}}}{\partial S_{g_m}}\right)^n$$

$$- Y^n_{g_{n,m}} \overset{n}{P'_{cgo_m}} \Bigg\}\Bigg)\Delta_t S_{g_m}$$

$$+ \Bigg(- \left(C_{ww_n} - \overset{n}{q'_{wwsc_n}}\right) + \sum_{m\in\psi_n}\Bigg\{\left(\frac{q_t}{B^n_w}\right)_{n,m}\left(\frac{\partial f_{w_{n,m}}}{\partial S_{w_n}}\right)^n$$

$$+ \frac{G_{n,m}}{B^n_{w_{n,m}}}\Bigg[- \left(\Delta_m P^n_{cow} + \overline{\Delta\gamma}^n_{ow_{n,m}}\Delta_m Z\right)$$

$$\times \left[\left(\frac{\partial Y_{g_{n,m}}}{\partial S_{w_n}}\right)^n + \left(\frac{\partial\zeta_{w_{n,m}}}{\partial S_{w_n}}\right)^n\right] + \left(Y^n_g + \zeta^n_w\right)_{n,m}\overset{n}{P'_{cow_n}}$$

$$- \left(\Delta_m P^n_{cgo} + \overline{\Delta\gamma}^n_{og_{n,m}}\Delta_m Z\right)\left(\frac{\partial Y_{g_{n,m}}}{\partial S_{w_n}}\right)^n\Bigg]\Bigg\}\Bigg)\Delta_t S_{w_n}$$

$$+ \Bigg(\overset{n}{q'_{wgsc_n}} + \sum_{m\in\psi_n}\Bigg\{\left(\frac{q_t}{B^n_w}\right)_{n,m}\left(\frac{\partial f_{w_{n,m}}}{\partial S_{g_n}}\right)^n + \frac{G_{n,m}}{B^n_{w_{n,m}}}$$

$$\times \Bigg[- \left(\Delta_m P^n_{cow} + \overline{\Delta\gamma}^n_{ow_{n,m}}\Delta_m Z\right)\Bigg[\left(\frac{\partial Y_{g_{n,m}}}{\partial S_{g_n}}\right)^n$$

$$+ \left(\frac{\partial\zeta_{w_{n,m}}}{\partial S_{g_n}}\right)^n\Bigg] - \left(\Delta_m P^n_{cgo} + \overline{\Delta\gamma}^n_{og_{n,m}}\Delta_m Z\right)\left(\frac{\partial Y_{g_{n,m}}}{\partial S_{g_n}}\right)^n$$

$$+ Y^n_{g_{n,m}}\overset{n}{P'_{cgo_n}}\Bigg]\Bigg\}\Bigg)\Delta_t S_{g_n} = - C_{ww_n}\left(S^*_{w_n} - S^n_{w_n}\right). \qquad (9.727)$$

The following statements are specific to Eqs. 9.726 and 9.727.

For single-point upstream weighting, function F, which may assume f_w, f_o, ζ_w, Y_g, or ζ_g, and its partial derivatives with respect to saturation S, which may be S_w or S_g, are defined as

$$F^n_{n,m} = \left(F^n_{n,m}\right)_m \qquad (9.728a)$$

for flow from Gridblock m to Gridblock n,

$$F^n_{n,m} = \left(F^n_{n,m}\right)_n \qquad (9.728b)$$

for flow from Gridblock n to Gridblock m,

$$\left(\frac{\partial F_{n,m}}{\partial S_m}\right)^n = \left[\frac{\partial}{\partial S_m}\left(F_{n,m}\right)_m\right]^n \qquad (9.729a)$$

for flow from Gridblock m to Gridblock n,

$$\left(\frac{\partial F_{n,m}}{\partial S_m}\right)^n = 0 \quad \text{(9.729b)}$$

for flow from Gridblock n to Gridblock m,

$$\left(\frac{\partial F_{n,m}}{\partial S_n}\right)^n = 0 \quad \text{(9.730a)}$$

for flow from Gridblock m to Gridblock n, and

$$\left(\frac{\partial F_{n,m}}{\partial S_n}\right)^n = \left[\frac{\partial}{\partial S_n}\left(F_{n,m}\right)_n\right]^n \quad \text{(9.730b)}$$

for flow from Gridblock n to Gridblock m.

Terms of the form $\Delta_m P_c^n(\partial F_{n,m}/\partial S) \pm F^n_{n,m}P_c^{'n}$, where P_c is either P_{cow} or P_{cgo} and $P_c^{'n}$ is defined at Gridblock n or m, may be replaced by terms of the form $F^n_{n,m}P^{'n}_{c_{n,m}}$, where $P^{'n}_{c_{n,m}}$ is defined at the boundary between Gridblocks n and m, as reported by Aziz and Settari.[2]

Phase mobilities λ_w, λ_o, and λ_g and their derivatives ($d\lambda_w/dS_w$, $d\lambda_g/dS_g$, $\partial\lambda_o/\partial S_w$, and $\partial\lambda_o/\partial S_g$), which appear in the definitions of ζ_w, ζ_g, and Y_g and their partial derivatives at gridblock boundaries between Gridblocks n and m, must be evaluated at the saturation of upstream gridblock, either Gridblock n or m, for each phase.

The first term on the left side of Eqs. 9.726 and 9.727 must vanish; that is, $\Delta_t q_{t_{n,m}}$ must vanish independently on each gridblock boundary. This implies that the implicit-saturation step of the SEQ method treats flow as if it were incompressible. Any change in interblock phase flow rates of any two phases in three-phase flow (or any phase in two-phase flow) must be balanced by an opposite change in the interblock flow rate of the remaining phase on a reservoir-volume basis.

The last statement can be used to derive implicit approximations to the saturation equations, Eqs. 9.726 and 9.727. Because $\Delta_t q_{t_{n,m}}$ must vanish independently on each gridblock boundary, we drop the boundary identification [Subscripts (n,m)] and deal with interblock total and phase flow rates as q_t, q_o, q_w, and q_g. Because $\Delta_t q_t = 0$ and

$$q_t = q_o + q_w + q_g \quad \text{(9.731)}$$

the implicit adjustment of the interblock phase flow rates must satisfy

$$\Delta_t q_o + \Delta_t q_w + \Delta_t q_g = 0. \quad \text{(9.732)}$$

The differentiation of Eq. 9.732 with respect to the principal unknowns gives

$$\left(\frac{\partial q_o}{\partial S_w} + \frac{\partial q_w}{\partial S_w} + \frac{\partial q_g}{\partial S_w}\right)\Delta_t S_w + \left(\frac{\partial q_o}{\partial S_g} + \frac{\partial q_w}{\partial S_g} + \frac{\partial q_g}{\partial S_g}\right)\Delta_t S_g = 0 \quad \text{(9.733)}$$

because q_t is evaluated at p_o^{n+1}. Because $\Delta_t S_w$ and $\Delta_t S_g$ are independent in the (p_o-S_w-S_g) formulation, the following conditions must be satisfied.

$$\frac{\partial q_o}{\partial S_w} + \frac{\partial q_w}{\partial S_w} + \frac{\partial q_g}{\partial S_w} = 0 \quad \text{(9.734)}$$

$$\text{and } \frac{\partial q_o}{\partial S_g} + \frac{\partial q_w}{\partial S_g} + \frac{\partial q_g}{\partial S_g} = 0. \quad \text{(9.735)}$$

Now the definitions of q_o, q_w, and q_g must satisfy Eqs. 9.731, 9.734, and 9.735 simultaneously for any gridblock boundary. The definitions of q_o, q_w, and q_g are obtained from the approximation of the fractional-flow equations, Eqs. 9.680 through 9.682, where capillary and gravity forces are neglected.

$$q_o = f_o q_t, \quad \text{(9.736a)}$$

$$q_w = f_w q_t, \quad \text{(9.736b)}$$

$$\text{and } q_g = f_g q_t, \quad \text{(9.736c)}$$

where f_w, f_o, and f_g = fractional-flow functions defined by Eq. 9.684. It is simple to verify that the definitions given by Eq. 9.736 satisfy Eqs. 9.731, 9.734, and 9.735 because q_t is constant and $f_o + f_w + f_g = 1$, from which $(\partial f_o/\partial S_w) + (\partial f_w/\partial S_w) + (\partial f_g/\partial S_w) = 0$ and $(\partial f_o/\partial S_g) + (\partial f_w/\partial S_g) + (\partial f_g/\partial S_g) = 0$.

The implicit approximation to the saturation equations may be obtained by neglecting the capillary and gravity terms in the saturation equations expressed by Eqs. 9.726 and 9.727 (but not in the definition of $q_{t_{n,m}}$).

$$\sum_{m\in\psi_n}\left(\frac{q_t}{B_o^n}\right)_{n,m}\left(\frac{\partial f_{o_{n,m}}}{\partial S_{w_m}}\right)^n \Delta_t S_{w_m} + \sum_{m\in\psi_n}\left(\frac{q_t}{B_o^n}\right)_{n,m}\left(\frac{\partial f_{o_{n,m}}}{\partial S_{g_m}}\right)^n \Delta_t S_{g_m}$$

$$+ \left[-\left(C_{ow_n} - q'^{\,n}_{owsc_n}\right) + \sum_{m\in\psi_n}\left(\frac{q_t}{B_o^n}\right)_{n,m}\left(\frac{\partial f_{o_{n,m}}}{\partial S_{w_n}}\right)^n\right]\Delta_t S_{w_n}$$

$$+ \left[-\left(C_{og_n} - q'^{\,n}_{ogsc_n}\right) + \sum_{m\in\psi_n}\left(\frac{q_t}{B_o^n}\right)_{n,m}\left(\frac{\partial f_{o_{n,m}}}{\partial S_{g_n}}\right)^n\right]\Delta_t S_{g_n}$$

$$= -C_{ow_n}\left(S^*_{w_n} - S^n_{w_n}\right) - C_{og_n}\left(S^*_{g_n} - S^n_{g_n}\right) \quad \text{(9.737)}$$

$$\text{and } \sum_{m\in\psi_n}\left(\frac{q_t}{B_w^n}\right)_{n,m}\left(\frac{\partial f_{w_{n,m}}}{\partial S_{w_m}}\right)^n \Delta_t S_{w_m}$$

$$+ \sum_{m\in\psi_n}\left(\frac{q_t}{B_w^n}\right)_{n,m}\left(\frac{\partial f_{w_{n,m}}}{\partial S_{g_m}}\right)^n \Delta_t S_{g_m}$$

$$+ \left[-\left(C_{ww_n} - q'^{\,n}_{wwsc_n}\right) + \sum_{m\in\psi_n}\left(\frac{q_t}{B_w^n}\right)_{n,m}\left(\frac{\partial f_{w_{n,m}}}{\partial S_{w_n}}\right)^n\right]$$

$$\times \Delta_t S_{w_n} + \left[q'^{\,n}_{wgsc_n} + \sum_{m\in\psi_n}\left(\frac{q_t}{B_w^n}\right)_{n,m}\left(\frac{\partial f_{w_{n,m}}}{\partial S_{g_n}}\right)^n\right]\Delta_t S_{g_n}$$

$$= -C_{ww_n}\left(S^*_{w_n} - S^n_{w_n}\right), \quad \text{(9.738)}$$

where $q_{t_{n,m}}$ is defined by Eqs. 9.717 through 9.720.

Eqs. 9.726 and 9.727 or Eqs. 9.737 and 9.738 are written for Gridblock $n = 1,2,\ldots,N$. The resulting $2N$ equations can be solved simultaneously for $\Delta_t S_w$ and $\Delta_t S_g$ distributions. In matrix form, the system of $2N$ equations has a tri-, penta-, or heptadiagonal structure for 1D-, 2D-, or 3D-flow problems, respectively, with elements that are 2×2 matrices.

Example 9.27. Derive the equation for total velocity and the fractional-flow equation for each phase in a three-phase-, 3D-flow system.

$$\vec{u}_t = -\lambda_t\left[\vec{\nabla}p_o - f_w\left(\vec{\nabla}P_{cow} + \Delta\gamma_{ow}\vec{\nabla}Z\right)\right.$$

$$\left. + f_g\left(\vec{\nabla}P_{cgo} + \Delta\gamma_{og}\vec{\nabla}Z\right) - \gamma_o\vec{\nabla}Z\right], \quad \text{(9.683)}$$

$$\vec{u}_w = f_w\vec{u}_t + \beta_c k\left(Y_g + \zeta_w\right)\left(\vec{\nabla}P_{cow} + \Delta\gamma_{ow}\vec{\nabla}Z\right)$$

$$+ \beta_c k Y_g\left(\vec{\nabla}P_{cgo} + \Delta\gamma_{og}\vec{\nabla}Z\right), \quad \text{(9.680)}$$

$$\vec{u}_o = f_o\vec{u}_t - \beta_c k\zeta_w\left(\vec{\nabla}P_{cow} + \Delta\gamma_{ow}\vec{\nabla}Z\right)$$

$$+ \beta_c k\zeta_g\left(\vec{\nabla}P_{cgo} + \Delta\gamma_{og}\vec{\nabla}Z\right), \quad \text{(9.681)}$$

$$\text{and } \vec{u}_g = f_g\vec{u}_t - \beta_c kY_g\left(\vec{\nabla}P_{cow} + \Delta\gamma_{ow}\vec{\nabla}Z\right)$$

$$- \beta_c k\left(Y_g + \zeta_g\right)\left(\vec{\nabla}P_{cgo} + \Delta\gamma_{og}\vec{\nabla}Z\right), \quad \text{(9.682)}$$

where $\lambda_t = \lambda_o + \lambda_w + \lambda_g$; .... (9.686)

$$\lambda_l = \beta_c \frac{kk_{rl}}{\mu_l}, \quad (9.685)$$

where $l = o$, w, or g;

$$f_l = \frac{\lambda_l}{\lambda_t}, \quad (9.684)$$

where $l = o$, w, or g;

$$f_w + f_o + f_g = 1; \quad (9.739)$$

$$Y_g = \frac{k_{rg}}{\mu_g} f_w = \frac{k_{rw}}{\mu_w} f_g; \quad (9.687)$$

$$\zeta_g = \frac{k_{ro}}{\mu_o} f_g = \frac{k_{rg}}{\mu_g} f_o; \quad (9.689)$$

$$\zeta_w = \frac{k_{ro}}{\mu_o} f_w = \frac{k_{rw}}{\mu_w} f_o; \quad (9.688)$$

$$\Delta\gamma_{ow} = \gamma_w - \gamma_o; \quad (9.690)$$

and $\Delta\gamma_{og} = \gamma_o - \gamma_g$. .... (9.691)

Solution. 1. Define $\vec{u}_w$, $\vec{u}_o$, and $\vec{u}_g$ as the velocity vectors for the water, oil, and gas phases, respectively. The total velocity vector, $\vec{u}_t$, can be defined as the vector sum of all the phase velocity vectors,

$$\vec{u}_t = \vec{u}_w + \vec{u}_o + \vec{u}_g. \quad (9.740)$$

Eq. 2.25 gives the phase velocity vectors as

$$\vec{u}_l = -\beta_c \frac{kk_{rl}}{\mu_l}\left(\vec{\nabla} p_l - \gamma_l \vec{\nabla} Z\right), \quad (9.741)$$

where $l = o$, w, or g, or

$$\vec{u}_o = -\lambda_o\left(\vec{\nabla} p_o - \gamma_o \vec{\nabla} Z\right), \quad (9.742)$$

$$\vec{u}_w = -\lambda_w\left(\vec{\nabla} p_o - \vec{\nabla} P_{cow} - \gamma_o \vec{\nabla} Z\right), \quad (9.743)$$

and $\vec{u}_g = -\lambda_g\left(\vec{\nabla} p_o + \vec{\nabla} P_{cgo} - \gamma_g \vec{\nabla} Z\right)$. .... (9.744)

k is a diagonal tensor with components k_x, k_y, and k_z, provided the grid directions x, y, and z lie on the principal permeability axes of the porous medium. That is,

$$k = \begin{bmatrix} k_x & 0 & 0 \\ 0 & k_y & 0 \\ 0 & 0 & k_z \end{bmatrix}. \quad (9.745)$$

In this book, however, we drop the tensor notation for k with the understanding that k=k_x, k_y, and k_z for fluid flow along the x, y, and z directions, respectively. A velocity vector $\vec{u}$ implies a quantity that has both magnitude and direction with components u_x, u_y, and u_z in the x, y, and z directions, respectively.

Substituting Eqs. 9.742 through 9.744 into Eq. 9.740 yields

$$\vec{u}_t = -\lambda_w\left(\vec{\nabla} p_o - \vec{\nabla} P_{cow} - \gamma_w \vec{\nabla} Z\right) - \lambda_o\left(\vec{\nabla} p_o - \gamma_o \vec{\nabla} Z\right)$$

$$- \lambda_g\left(\vec{\nabla} p_o + \vec{\nabla} P_{cgo} - \gamma_g \vec{\nabla} Z\right)$$

$$= -\left(\lambda_w + \lambda_o + \lambda_g\right)\vec{\nabla} p_o + \lambda_w \vec{\nabla} P_{cow} - \lambda_g \vec{\nabla} P_{cgo}$$

$$+ \left(\lambda_w \gamma_w + \lambda_o \gamma_o + \lambda_g \gamma_g\right)\vec{\nabla} Z$$

$$= -\lambda_t\left[\vec{\nabla} p_o - \frac{\lambda_w}{\lambda_t}\vec{\nabla} P_{cow} + \frac{\lambda_g}{\lambda_t}\vec{\nabla} P_{cgo}\right.$$

$$\left. - \left(\frac{\lambda_w}{\lambda_t}\gamma_w + \frac{\lambda_o}{\lambda_t}\gamma_o + \frac{\lambda_g}{\lambda_t}\gamma_g\right)\vec{\nabla} Z\right] \quad (9.746a)$$

or $\vec{u}_t = -\lambda_t\left[\left(\vec{\nabla} p_o - f_w \vec{\nabla} P_{cow} + f_g \vec{\nabla} P_{cgo}\right)\right.$

$$\left. - \left(f_w \gamma_w + f_o \gamma_o + f_g \gamma_g\right)\vec{\nabla} Z\right], \quad (9.746b)$$

where $\lambda_t = \lambda_w + \lambda_o + \lambda_g$ .... (9.686)

and $f_l = \dfrac{\lambda_l}{\lambda_t}$, ... (9.684)

where $l = o$, w, or g. The last term in the brackets on the right side of Eq. 9.746b can be rearranged as

$$\left(f_w \gamma_w + f_o \gamma_o + f_g \gamma_g\right)\vec{\nabla} Z = \left[f_w \gamma_w + \left(1 - f_w - f_g\right)\gamma_o + f_g \gamma_g\right]\vec{\nabla} Z$$

$$= \left[f_w\left(\gamma_w - \gamma_o\right) - f_g\left(\gamma_o - \gamma_g\right) + \gamma_o\right]\vec{\nabla} Z$$

$$= f_w \Delta\gamma_{ow} \vec{\nabla} Z - f_g \Delta\gamma_{og} \vec{\nabla} Z + \gamma_o \vec{\nabla} Z, \quad (9.747)$$

where $\Delta\gamma_{ow} = \gamma_w - \gamma_o$ and $\Delta\gamma_{og} = \gamma_o - \gamma_g$.

Substituting Eq. 9.747 into Eq. 9.746b and factoring terms results in the desired expression for $\vec{u}_t$.

$$\vec{u}_t = -\lambda_t\left[\vec{\nabla} p_o - f_w\left(\vec{\nabla} P_{cow} + \Delta\gamma_{ow} \vec{\nabla} Z\right)\right.$$

$$\left. + f_g\left(\vec{\nabla} P_{cgo} + \Delta\gamma_{og} \vec{\nabla} Z\right) - \gamma_o \vec{\nabla} Z\right]. \quad (9.683)$$

2. Eq. 9.740 may be rearranged to express $\vec{u}_w$ and then combined with Eqs. 9.742, 9.744, and 9.683 to produce the fractional-flow equation for water.

$$\vec{u}_w = \vec{u}_t - \vec{u}_o - \vec{u}_g$$

$$= \left(f_w + f_o + f_g\right)\vec{u}_t - \left(\vec{u}_o + \vec{u}_g\right)$$

$$= f_w \vec{u}_t + \left(f_o + f_g\right)\vec{u}_t - \left(\vec{u}_o + \vec{u}_g\right)$$

$$= f_w \vec{u}_t - \left(f_o + f_g\right)\lambda_t\left[\vec{\nabla} p_o - f_w\left(\vec{\nabla} P_{cow} + \Delta\gamma_{ow} \vec{\nabla} Z\right)\right.$$

$$\left. + f_g\left(\vec{\nabla} P_{cgo} + \Delta\gamma_{og} \vec{\nabla} Z\right) - \gamma_o \vec{\nabla} Z\right]$$

$$- \left[-\lambda_o\left(\vec{\nabla} p_o - \gamma_o \vec{\nabla} Z\right) - \lambda_g\left(\vec{\nabla} p_o + \vec{\nabla} P_{cgo} - \gamma_g \vec{\nabla} Z\right)\right]$$

$$= f_w \vec{u}_t + \left[-\left(f_o + f_g\right)\lambda_t + \lambda_o + \lambda_g\right]\vec{\nabla} p_o$$

$$+ \left(f_o + f_g\right)\lambda_t f_w\left(\vec{\nabla} P_{cow} + \Delta\gamma_{ow} \vec{\nabla} Z\right)$$

$$- \left(f_o + f_g\right)\lambda_t f_g\left(\vec{\nabla} P_{cgo} + \Delta\gamma_{og} \vec{\nabla} Z\right) + \lambda_g \vec{\nabla} P_{cgo}$$

$$+ \left[\left(f_o + f_g\right)\lambda_t \gamma_o - \lambda_o \gamma_o - \lambda_g \gamma_g\right]\vec{\nabla} Z. \quad (9.748)$$

Using the relationships $\lambda_o = f_o \lambda_t$, $\lambda_g = f_g \lambda_t$, $(f_o + f_g)\lambda_t f_w = (\lambda_o + \lambda_g) f_w$, and $(f_o + f_g)\lambda_t f_g = (\lambda_o + \lambda_g) f_g = (f_o + f_g)\lambda_g$, Eq. 9.748 may be rewritten as

$$\vec{u}_w = f_w \vec{u}_t + \left(\lambda_o + \lambda_g\right) f_w\left(\vec{\nabla} P_{cow} + \Delta\gamma_{ow} \vec{\nabla} Z\right)$$

$$- \left(f_o + f_g\right)\lambda_g\left(\vec{\nabla} P_{cgo} + \Delta\gamma_{og} \vec{\nabla} Z\right) + \lambda_g \vec{\nabla} P_{cgo}$$

$$+ \left(\lambda_o \gamma_o + \lambda_g \gamma_o - \lambda_o \gamma_o - \lambda_g \gamma_g\right)\vec{\nabla} Z$$

$$= f_w \vec{u}_t + \left(\lambda_o + \lambda_g\right) f_w\left(\vec{\nabla} P_{cow} + \Delta\gamma_{ow} \vec{\nabla} Z\right)$$

$$- \left(f_o + f_g\right)\lambda_g\left(\vec{\nabla} P_{cgo} + \Delta\gamma_{og} \vec{\nabla} Z\right) + \lambda_g\left(\vec{\nabla} P_{cgo} + \Delta\gamma_{og} \vec{\nabla} Z\right)$$

$$= f_w\vec{u}_t + (\lambda_o + \lambda_g)f_w\left(\vec{\nabla}P_{cow} + \Delta\gamma_{ow}\vec{\nabla}Z\right)$$

$$+ (1 - f_o - f_g)\lambda_g\left(\vec{\nabla}P_{cgo} + \Delta\gamma_{og}\vec{\nabla}Z\right). \quad \text{(9.749)}$$

With $f_w = (1 - f_o - f_g)$, $\lambda_o = \beta_c[(kk_{ro})/\mu_o]$, and $\lambda_g = \beta_c \times [(kk_{rg})/\mu_g]$ and the definition $Y_g = (k_{rg}/\mu_g)f_w$ and $\zeta_w = (k_{ro} \div \mu_o)f_w$, Eq. 9.749 may be rewritten as

$$\vec{u}_w = f_w\vec{u}_t + \beta_c k(Y_g + \zeta_w)\left(\vec{\nabla}P_{cow} + \Delta\gamma_{ow}\vec{\nabla}Z\right)$$

$$+ \beta_c kY_g\left(\vec{\nabla}P_{cgo} + \Delta\gamma_{og}\vec{\nabla}Z\right). \quad \text{(9.680)}$$

3. The fractional-flow equation for oil may be obtained, as in Part 2, by combining Eqs. 9.740, 9.743, 9.744, and 9.683. In the following derivation, Eq. 9.680 is used instead of Eq. 9.743.

$$\vec{u}_o = \vec{u}_t - \vec{u}_w - \vec{u}_g$$

$$= (f_w + f_o + f_g)\vec{u}_t - \vec{u}_w - \vec{u}_g$$

$$= f_o\vec{u}_t + f_w\vec{u}_t + f_g\vec{u}_t$$

$$- \left[f_w\vec{u}_t + \beta_c k(Y_g + \zeta_w)\left(\vec{\nabla}P_{cow} + \Delta\gamma_{ow}\vec{\nabla}Z\right)\right.$$

$$\left. + \beta_c kY_g\left(\vec{\nabla}P_{cgo} + \Delta\gamma_{og}\vec{\nabla}Z\right)\right]$$

$$- \left[- \lambda_g\left(\vec{\nabla}p_o + \vec{\nabla}P_{cgo} - \gamma_g\vec{\nabla}Z\right)\right]$$

$$= f_o\vec{u}_t + f_w\vec{u}_t - f_g\lambda_t\left[\vec{\nabla}p_o - f_w\left(\vec{\nabla}P_{cow} + \Delta\gamma_{ow}\vec{\nabla}Z\right)\right.$$

$$\left. + f_g\left(\vec{\nabla}P_{cgo} + \Delta\gamma_{og}\vec{\nabla}Z\right) - \gamma_o\vec{\nabla}Z\right]$$

$$- \left[f_w\vec{u}_t + (\lambda_o + \lambda_g)f_w\left(\vec{\nabla}P_{cow} + \Delta\gamma_{ow}\vec{\nabla}Z\right)\right.$$

$$\left. + \lambda_g f_w\left(\vec{\nabla}P_{cgo} + \Delta\gamma_{og}\vec{\nabla}Z\right)\right]$$

$$+ \left[\lambda_g\left(\vec{\nabla}p_o + \vec{\nabla}P_{cgo} - \gamma_g\vec{\nabla}Z\right)\right]. \quad \text{(9.750)}$$

Observing that $f_g\lambda_t = \lambda_g$, Eq. 9.750 may be rewritten as

$$\vec{u}_o = f_o\vec{u}_t + f_w\vec{u}_t - \lambda_g\vec{\nabla}p_o + \lambda_g f_w\left(\vec{\nabla}P_{cow} + \Delta\gamma_{ow}\vec{\nabla}Z\right)$$

$$- \lambda_g f_g\left(\vec{\nabla}P_{cgo} + \Delta\gamma_{og}\vec{\nabla}Z\right) + \lambda_g\gamma_o\vec{\nabla}Z$$

$$- f_w\vec{u}_t - (\lambda_o + \lambda_g)f_w\left(\vec{\nabla}P_{cow} + \Delta\gamma_{ow}\vec{\nabla}Z\right)$$

$$- \lambda_g f_w\left(\vec{\nabla}P_{cgo} + \Delta\gamma_{og}\vec{\nabla}Z\right)$$

$$+ \lambda_g\vec{\nabla}p_o + \lambda_g\vec{\nabla}P_{cgo} - \lambda_g\gamma_g\vec{\nabla}Z, \quad \text{(9.751)}$$

which simplifies to

$$\vec{u}_o = f_o\vec{u}_t - \lambda_g f_g\left(\vec{\nabla}P_{cgo} + \Delta\gamma_{og}\vec{\nabla}Z\right) + \lambda_g\gamma_o\vec{\nabla}Z$$

$$- \lambda_o f_w\left(\vec{\nabla}P_{cow} + \Delta\gamma_{ow}\vec{\nabla}Z\right)$$

$$- \lambda_g f_w\left(\vec{\nabla}P_{cgo} + \Delta\gamma_{og}\vec{\nabla}Z\right) + \lambda_g\vec{\nabla}P_{cgo} - \lambda_g\gamma_g\vec{\nabla}Z$$

$$= f_o\vec{u}_t - \lambda_o f_w\left(\vec{\nabla}P_{cow} + \Delta\gamma_{ow}\vec{\nabla}Z\right)$$

$$- \lambda_g\left[(f_g + f_w)\left(\vec{\nabla}P_{cgo} + \Delta\gamma_{og}\vec{\nabla}Z\right)\right]$$

$$+ \lambda_g\left[\vec{\nabla}P_{cgo} + (\gamma_o - \gamma_g)\vec{\nabla}Z\right]$$

$$= f_o\vec{u}_t - \lambda_o f_w\left(\vec{\nabla}P_{cow} + \Delta\gamma_{ow}\vec{\nabla}Z\right)$$

$$+ \lambda_g\left[(1 - f_w - f_g)\left(\vec{\nabla}P_{cgo} + \Delta\gamma_{og}\vec{\nabla}Z\right)\right]$$

$$= f_o\vec{u}_t - \lambda_o f_w\left(\vec{\nabla}P_{cow} + \Delta\gamma_{ow}\vec{\nabla}Z\right)$$

$$+ \lambda_g f_o\left(\vec{\nabla}P_{cgo} + \Delta\gamma_{og}\vec{\nabla}Z\right), \quad \text{(9.752)}$$

which further simplifies to

$$\vec{u}_o = f_o\vec{u}_t - \beta_c k\zeta_w\left(\vec{\nabla}P_{cow} + \Delta\gamma_{ow}\vec{\nabla}Z\right)$$

$$+ \beta_c k\zeta_g\left(\vec{\nabla}P_{cgo} + \Delta\gamma_{og}\vec{\nabla}Z\right), \quad \text{(9.681)}$$

where $\zeta_w = (k_{ro}/\mu_o)f_w = (k_{rw}/\mu_w)f_o$ and $\zeta_g = (k_{rg}/\mu_g)f_o = (k_{ro}/\mu_o)f_g$.

4. With Eqs. 9.742, 9.743, and 9.683 and the derivation of Eqs. 9.680 and 9.681, there are four different approaches for deriving the fractional-flow equation for gas. The most direct approach uses Eqs. 9.740, 9.680, and 9.681.

$$\vec{u}_g = \vec{u}_t - \vec{u}_w - \vec{u}_o$$

$$= \vec{u}_t - \left[f_w\vec{u}_t + \beta_c k(Y_g + \zeta_w)\left(\vec{\nabla}P_{cow} + \Delta\gamma_{ow}\vec{\nabla}Z\right)\right.$$

$$\left. + \beta_c kY_g\left(\vec{\nabla}P_{cgo} + \Delta\gamma_{og}\vec{\nabla}Z\right)\right]$$

$$- \left[f_o\vec{u}_t - \beta_c k\zeta_w\left(\vec{\nabla}P_{cow} + \Delta\gamma_{ow}\vec{\nabla}Z\right)\right.$$

$$\left. + \beta_c k\zeta_g\left(\vec{\nabla}P_{cgo} + \Delta\gamma_{og}\vec{\nabla}Z\right)\right]$$

$$= (1 - f_w - f_o)\vec{u}_t - \beta_c k(Y_g + \zeta_w - \zeta_w)$$

$$\times \left(\vec{\nabla}P_{cow} + \Delta\gamma_{ow}\vec{\nabla}Z\right) - \beta_c k(Y_g + \zeta_g)\left(\vec{\nabla}P_{cgo} + \Delta\gamma_{og}\vec{\nabla}Z\right), \quad \text{(9.753)}$$

which simplifies to

$$\vec{u}_g = f_g\vec{u}_t - \beta_c kY_g\left(\vec{\nabla}P_{cow} + \Delta\gamma_{ow}\vec{\nabla}Z\right)$$

$$- \beta_c k(Y_g + \zeta_g)\left(\vec{\nabla}P_{cgo} + \Delta\gamma_{og}\vec{\nabla}Z\right), \quad \text{(9.682)}$$

where $f_g = 1 - f_w - f_o$. (9.754)

Example 9.28. Find the finite-difference approximation to the first-order derivative $\vec{\nabla}\cdot[V_b(f/B)\vec{u}_t]$ in rectangular coordinates.

Solution. The vectors $\vec{\nabla}$ and $\vec{u}_t$ in 3D Cartesian space are

$$\vec{\nabla} = \frac{\partial}{\partial x}\vec{i} + \frac{\partial}{\partial y}\vec{j} + \frac{\partial}{\partial y}\vec{k} \quad \text{(9.755)}$$

and $\vec{u}_t = u_{tx}\vec{i} + u_{ty}\vec{j} + u_{tz}\vec{k}$. (9.699)

Then, $\vec{\nabla}\cdot\left(V_b\frac{f}{B}\vec{u}_t\right)$

$$= \frac{\partial}{\partial x}\left(V_b\frac{f}{B}u_{tx}\right) + \frac{\partial}{\partial y}\left(V_b\frac{f}{B}u_{ty}\right) + \frac{\partial}{\partial z}\left(V_b\frac{f}{B}u_{tz}\right). \quad \text{(9.756)}$$

For a Gridblock (i,j,k) with Δx, Δy, and Δz constant and $V_b = A_x \Delta x = A_y \Delta_y = A_z \Delta z$, Eq. 9.756 may be rewritten as

$$\vec{\nabla}\cdot\left(V_b\frac{f}{B}\vec{u}_t\right)_{i,j,k} = \frac{\partial}{\partial x}\left(\frac{f}{B}A_x u_{tx}\right)_{i,j,k}\Delta x_{i,j,k} + \frac{\partial}{\partial y}\left(\frac{f}{B}A_y u_{ty}\right)_{i,j,k}\Delta y_{i,j,k} + \frac{\partial}{\partial z}\left(\frac{f}{B}A_z u_{tz}\right)_{i,j,k}\Delta z_{i,j,k}. \quad \text{(9.757)}$$

In Fig. 9.4, the first derivative in the x direction at Point (i,j,k), $(\partial/\partial x)[(f/B)A_x u_{tx}]$, may be approximated by use of the central-difference approximation with the argument evaluated at the Gridblock Boundaries $(i+½,j,k)$ and $(i-½,j,k)$ in the x direction.

$$\frac{\partial}{\partial x}\left(\frac{f}{B}A_x u_{tx}\right)_{i,j,k} \approx \frac{[(f/B)A_x u_{tx}]_{i+½,j,k} - [(f/B)A_x u_{tx}]_{i-½,j,k}}{\Delta x_{i,j,k}} \quad \text{(9.758)}$$

or $$\frac{\partial}{\partial x}\left(\frac{f}{B}A_x u_{tx}\right)_{i,j,k}\Delta x_{i,j,k} \approx \left(\frac{f}{B}A_x\right)_{i+½,j,k} u_{tx_{i+½,j,k}} - \left(\frac{f}{B}A_x\right)_{i-½,j,k} u_{tx_{i-½,j,k}}. \quad \text{(9.759)}$$

The finite-difference approximation to the first derivative term in the y or z direction may be derived with a procedure similar to the one presented, but in this case we consider Gridpoint (i,j,k) with its gridblock boundaries $(i,j-½,k)$ and $(i,j+½,k)$ in the y direction or $(i,j,k-½)$ and $(i,j,k+½)$ in the z direction. The resulting approximations are

$$\frac{\partial}{\partial y}\left(\frac{f}{B}A_y u_{ty}\right)_{i,j,k}\Delta y_{i,j,k} \approx \left(\frac{f}{B}A_y\right)_{i,j+½,k} u_{ty_{i,j+½,k}} - \left(\frac{f}{B}A_y\right)_{i,j-½,k} u_{ty_{i,j-½,k}} \quad \text{(9.760)}$$

and $$\frac{\partial}{\partial z}\left(\frac{f}{B}A_z u_{tz}\right)_{i,j,k}\Delta z_{i,j,k} \approx \left(\frac{f}{B}A_z\right)_{i,j,k+½} u_{tz_{i,j,k+½}} - \left(\frac{f}{B}A_z\right)_{i,j,k-½} u_{tz_{i,j,k-½}}. \quad \text{(9.761)}$$

Defining the right sides of Eqs. 9.759, 9.760, and 9.761 as the x, y, and z components, respectively, of the first-order finite-difference operator,

$$\Delta_x\left(\frac{f}{B}A_x u_{tx}\right)_{i,j,k} \equiv \left(\frac{f}{B}A_x\right)_{i+½,j,k} u_{tx_{i+½,j,k}} - \left(\frac{f}{B}A_x\right)_{i-½,j,k} u_{tx_{i-½,j,k}}, \quad \text{(9.762)}$$

$$\Delta_y\left(\frac{f}{B}A_y u_{ty}\right)_{i,j,k} \equiv \left(\frac{f}{B}A_y\right)_{i,j+½,k} u_{ty_{i,j+½,k}} - \left(\frac{f}{B}A_y\right)_{i,j-½,k} u_{ty_{i,j-½,k}}, \quad \text{(9.763)}$$

and $$\Delta_z\left(\frac{f}{B}A_z u_{tz}\right)_{i,j,k} \equiv \left(\frac{f}{B}A_z\right)_{i,j,k+½} u_{tz_{i,j,k+½}} - \left(\frac{f}{B}A_z\right)_{i,j,k-½} u_{tz_{i,j,k-½}}; \quad \text{(9.764)}$$

then, $$\frac{\partial}{\partial x}\left(\frac{f}{B}A_x u_{tx}\right)_{i,j,k}\Delta x_{i,j,k} \approx \Delta_x\left(\frac{f}{B}A_x u_{tx}\right)_{i,j,k}, \quad \text{(9.765)}$$

$$\frac{\partial}{\partial y}\left(\frac{f}{B}A_y u_{ty}\right)_{i,j,k}\Delta y_{i,j,k} \approx \Delta_y\left(\frac{f}{B}A_y u_{ty}\right)_{i,j,k}, \quad \text{(9.766)}$$

and $$\frac{\partial}{\partial z}\left(\frac{f}{B}A_z u_{tz}\right)_{i,j,k}\Delta z_{i,j,k} \approx \Delta_z\left(\frac{f}{B}A_z u_{tz}\right)_{i,j,k}. \quad \text{(9.767)}$$

The finite-difference approximation to the first derivative operator in three dimensions may be obtained by combining Eq. 9.757 and Eqs. 9.765 through 9.767.

$$\vec{\nabla}\cdot\left(V_b\frac{f}{B}\vec{u}_t\right)_{i,j,k} \approx \Delta_x\left(\frac{f}{B}A_x u_{tx}\right)_{i,j,k} + \Delta_y\left(\frac{f}{B}A_y u_{ty}\right)_{i,j,k} + \Delta_z\left(\frac{f}{B}A_z u_{tz}\right)_{i,j,k}. \quad \text{(9.768)}$$

Defining the right side of Eq. 9.768 as the first-order difference operator,

$$\Delta\left(\frac{f}{B}A u_t\right)_{i,j,k} \equiv \Delta_x\left(\frac{f}{B}A_x u_{tx}\right)_{i,j,k} + \Delta_y\left(\frac{f}{B}A_y u_{ty}\right)_{i,j,k} + \Delta_z\left(\frac{f}{B}A_z u_{tz}\right)_{i,j,k}; \quad \text{(9.769)}$$

then, Eq. 9.768 may be rewritten as

$$\vec{\nabla}\cdot\left(V_b\frac{f}{B}\vec{u}_t\right)_{i,j,k} \approx \Delta\left(\frac{f}{B}A u_t\right)_{i,j,k}. \quad \text{(9.770)}$$

Example 9.29. Express the definition of the first-order difference operator derived in Example 9.28, $\Delta[(f/B)A u_t]_{i,j,k}$, with the CVFD method terminology for gridblock coordinates and natural ordering presented in Sec. 9.5.3.

Solution. The approximations derived in Example 9.28 are summarized as

$$\vec{\nabla}\cdot\left(V_b\frac{f}{B}\vec{u}_t\right)_{i,j,k} \approx \Delta\left(\frac{f}{B}A u_t\right)_{i,j,k}, \quad \text{(9.770)}$$

where $$\Delta\left(\frac{f}{B}A u_t\right)_{i,j,k} \equiv \Delta_x\left(\frac{f}{B}A_x u_{tx}\right)_{i,j,k} + \Delta_y\left(\frac{f}{B}A_y u_{ty}\right)_{i,j,k} + \Delta_z\left(\frac{f}{B}A_z u_{tz}\right)_{i,j,k}, \quad \text{(9.769)}$$

$$\Delta_x\left(\frac{f}{B}A_x u_{tx}\right)_{i,j,k} \equiv \left(\frac{f}{B}A_x\right)_{i+½,j,k} u_{tx_{i+½,j,k}} - \left(\frac{f}{B}A_x\right)_{i-½,j,k} u_{tx_{i-½,j,k}}, \quad \text{(9.762)}$$

$$\Delta_y\left(\frac{f}{B}A_y u_{ty}\right)_{i,j,k} \equiv \left(\frac{f}{B}A_y\right)_{i,j+½,k} u_{ty_{i,j+½,k}} - \left(\frac{f}{B}A_y\right)_{i,j-½,k} u_{ty_{i,j-½,k}}, \quad \text{(9.763)}$$

and $$\Delta_z\left(\frac{f}{B}A_z u_{tz}\right)_{i,j,k} \equiv \left(\frac{f}{B}A_z\right)_{i,j,k+½} u_{tz_{i,j,k+½}} - \left(\frac{f}{B}A_z\right)_{i,j,k-½} u_{tz_{i,j,k-½}}. \quad \text{(9.764)}$$

For Gridblock (i,j,k) and its surrounding gridblocks, shown in Fig. 9.10, Eq. 9.762 may be expressed with the CVFD method terminology as

$$\Delta_x\left(\frac{f}{B}A_x u_{tx}\right)_{i,j,k} \equiv \left(\frac{f}{B}A\right)_{(i,j,k),(i+1,j,k)} u_{t_{(i,j,k),(i+1,j,k)}} - \left(\frac{f}{B}A\right)_{(i,j,k),(i-1,j,k)} u_{t_{(i,j,k),(i-1,j,k)}}, \quad (9.771)$$

where $$\left(\frac{f}{B}A\right)_{(i,j,k),(i\pm 1,j,k)} = \left(\frac{f}{B}A_x\right)_{i\pm 1/2,j,k} \quad (9.772)$$

and $$u_{t_{(i,j,k),(i\pm 1,j,k)}} = u_{tx_{i\pm 1/2,j,k}}. \quad (9.773)$$

Define $$q_{t_{(i,j,k),(i+1,j,k)}} = -(Au_t)_{(i,j,k),(i+1,j,k)} \quad (9.774)$$

and $$q_{t_{(i,j,k),(i-1,j,k)}} = (Au_t)_{(i,j,k),(i-1,j,k)}. \quad (9.775)$$

Then, Eq. 9.771 may be written as

$$\Delta_x\left(\frac{f}{B}A_x u_{tx}\right)_{i,j,k} \equiv -\left(\frac{f}{B}\right)_{(i,j,k),(i+1,j,k)} q_{t_{(i,j,k),(i+1,j,k)}} - \left(\frac{f}{B}\right)_{(i,j,k),(i-1,j,k)} q_{t_{(i,j,k),(i-1,j,k)}} \quad (9.776a)$$

or $$\Delta_x\left(\frac{f}{B}A_x u_{tx}\right)_{i,j,k} \equiv -\sum_{m\in\psi_x}\left(\frac{f}{B}\right)_{n,m} q_{t_{n,m}}, \quad (9.776b)$$

where $$\psi_x = \{(i-1,j,k),(i+1,j,k)\}. \quad (9.446)$$

According to Eq. 9.775, the difference between $q_{t_{n,m}}$, which appears in Eq. 9.776b, and $(Au_t)_{(i,j,k),(i+1,j,k)}$, which appears in Eq. 9.771, is that, while $q_{t_{n,m}}$ always represents total flow from a surrounding Gridblock m to the center Gridblock n, $(Au_t)_{(i,j,k),(i\pm 1,j,k)}$ represents total flow in the positive direction of x.

Similarly, Eqs. 9.763 and 9.764 may be expressed with the CVFD method terminology as

$$\Delta_y\left(\frac{f}{B}A_y u_{ty}\right)_{i,j,k} \equiv -\sum_{m\in\psi_y}\left(\frac{f}{B}\right)_{n,m} q_{t_{n,m}} \quad (9.777)$$

and $$\Delta_z\left(\frac{f}{B}A_z u_{tz}\right)_{i,j,k} \equiv -\sum_{m\in\psi_z}\left(\frac{f}{B}\right)_{n,m} q_{t_{n,m}}, \quad (9.778)$$

where $$\psi_y = \{(i,j-1,k),(i,j+1,k)\} \quad (9.447)$$

and $$\psi_z = \{(i,j,k-1),(i,j,k+1)\}. \quad (9.448)$$

Combining Eqs. 9.769, 9.776b, 9.777, and 9.778 results in

$$\Delta\left(\frac{f}{B}Au_t\right)_{i,j,k} \equiv -\sum_{m\in\psi_{i,j,k}}\left(\frac{f}{B}\right)_{n,m} q_{t_{n,m}}, \quad (9.779)$$

where $(f/B)_{n,m}$ = interaction between Gridblocks n and m, $q_{t_{n,m}}$ = total flow rate from surrounding Gridblock m to center Gridblock n, where

$$\psi_{i,j,k} = \psi_x \cup \psi_y \cup \psi_z = \{(i,j,k-1),(i,j-1,k),(i-1,j,k),(i+1,j,k),(i,j+1,k),(i,j,k+1)\}. \quad (9.780)$$

For natural ordering, as shown in Fig. 9.13, Eq. 9.779 for Gridblock n may be expressed as

$$\Delta\left(\frac{f}{B}Au_t\right)_n \equiv -\sum_{m\in\psi_n}\left(\frac{f}{B}\right)_{n,m} q_{t_{n,m}}, \quad (9.781)$$

where $$\psi_n = \psi_x \cup \psi_y \cup \psi_z = \{n-n_xn_y, n-n_x, n-1, n+1, n+n_x, n+n_xn_y\} \quad (9.782)$$

Eqs. 9.779 and 9.781 are applicable for 1D, 2D, and 3D flow. In all cases, the gridblock set ψ is defined as shown in Figs. 9.8 through 9.10 for the (i,j,k) notation and Figs. 9.11 through 9.13 for natural ordering of gridblocks.

SEQ Method for Basic Flow Models in Multiple Dimensions. This section has presented the derivation of the SEQ method for the flow equations of the oil, water, and gas model in 3D space by two different approaches. The pressure equation given by Eq. 9.674 and the explicit-saturation-prediction equations for $S^*_{w_n}$ and $S^*_{g_n}$, Eqs. 9.675 and 9.676, for the first step of the SEQ method are the same as for the IMPES method. The implicit-saturation equations in the second step of the SEQ method have three possible forms (represented by Eqs. 9.677 and 9.678, Eqs. 9.726 and 9.727, or Eqs. 9.737 and 9.738), depending on the approach used in their derivation. In this section, we comment on application of these equations for 1D, 2D, and 3D flow, their reduction and use for three basic flow models, the material-balance errors associated with the method, the stability of the method, and the treatment of implicit production rates during the saturation step.

SEQ Method for Multidimensional Flow. Eqs. 9.674 through 9.676 in the IMPES step and Eqs. 9.677 and 9.678, Eqs. 9.726 and 9.727, or Eqs. 9.737 and 9.738 in the implicit-saturation step of the SEQ method are applicable for 1D-, 2D-, and 3D-flow problems, depending on the definition of the gridblock set ψ_n. For 1D-, 2D-, and 3D-flow problems, the sets of the gridblocks surrounding Gridblock n, ψ_n, are defined and shown in Figs. 9.11 through 9.13, respectively. The pressure equation (Eq. 9.674) written for all gridblocks $n = 1,2,\ldots,N$ in the IMPES step has a tri-, penta-, or heptadiagonal structure matrix for 1D, 2D, or 3D flow for natural ordering of the gridblocks. The implicit-saturation equations (Eqs. 9.677 and 9.678, Eqs. 9.726 and 9.727, or Eqs. 9.737 and 9.738) written for all gridblocks $n = 1,2,\ldots,N$ in the implicit-saturation step have a block tri-, block penta-, or block heptadiagonal structure, respectively, for 1D-, 2D-, or 3D-flow problems. The block submatrixes are 2×2 matrices for three-phase flow.

SEQ Method for Basic Flow Models. The equations derived for the SEQ method in this section for the general case are represented by the black-oil model. Specifically, the pressure equation is given as Eq. 9.674; the explicit saturations $S^*_{w_n}$ and $S^*_{g_n}$ are predicted by Eqs. 9.675 and 9.676 in that order; and the implicit-saturation equations are expressed as Eqs. 9.677 and 9.678, Eqs. 9.726 and 9.727, or Eqs. 9.737 and 9.738. The use of the implicit-saturation equations derived from the linearized implicit- flow equations, Eqs. 9.677 and 9.678, are not recommended because they can cause stability problems in a three-phase-flow system.

SEQ Method for the Oil/Water Flow Model. The equations of the SEQ method for the two-phase oil/water flow model can be derived from the appropriate equations previously presented in this section. In the IMPES step, the pressure equation is obtained from Eq. 9.674 by discarding all terms multiplied by $B^{n+1}_{g_n}$ and by setting $S_g = 0$ when necessary. The explicit saturation $S^*_{w_n}$ is obtained with Eq. 9.675. In the saturation step, the water-saturation equation is expressed as Eq. 9.677 or can be obtained from either Eq. 9.727 or 9.738 by setting $S_g = 0$ and $\lambda_g = 0$ (along with functions of either S_g or λ_g, such as Y_g and its partial derivatives). In this case $q_{t_{n,m}} = q_{o_{n,m}} + q_{w_{n,m}}$ and $\lambda_t = \lambda_o + \lambda_w$. Both steps of the SEQ method require solution of matrix equations of the same size. The choice of the implicit-saturation equation (oil or water) to be solved in the saturation step of the SEQ method is not critical for stability. It does affect material balance for the other phase; however, material-balance errors for an oil/water system normally are small.

SEQ Method for the Oil/Gas Flow Model. The equations of the SEQ method for the two-phase oil/gas flow model can be derived from the appropriate equations previously presented in this section. In the IMPES step, the pressure equation is obtained from Eq. 9.674 by discarding all terms multiplied by $B^{n+1}_{w_n}$ and by setting $S_w = 0$ when necessary. The explicit saturation $S^*_{g_n}$ is obtained with Eq. 9.676 with $S^*_{w_n} = S^n_{w_n} = 0$. In the saturation step, the oil-saturation equation can be obtained from Eq. 9.678, 9.726, or 9.737 by setting $S_w=0$ and $\lambda_w=0$ (and functions of either S_w or λ_w, such as Y_w and ζ_w and their partial derivatives). In this case, $q_{t_{n,m}}=q_{o_{n,m}}+q_{g_{n,m}}$ and $\lambda_t=\lambda_o+\lambda_g$. Both steps of the SEQ method require solution of matrix equations of the same size. The choice of the implicit-saturation equation (oil or gas) to be solved in the saturation step of the SEQ method is not critical for stability but does affect material balance for the other phase. Material-balance errors in the gas phase may become unacceptable for this system.

Material-Balance Errors Induced by the SEQ Method. The sequential nature of the SEQ method generally produces equations that are not mass conservative for all phases. It can be proved, by summing Eq. 9.674 for all gridblocks $n=1,2,\ldots,N$, that the IMPES step itself satisfies material balance for two- and three-phase-flow models (see Sec. 8.5). Because implicit-saturation step treats flow as if it were incompressible, it is conservative only for the phases for which we write and solve the saturation equations. Consequently, any change in saturations from the explicit level, S^*, to the new level, S^{n+1}, brings about changes in interblock flow rates and accumulation of the remaining phase. The implicit-saturation step of the SEQ method as presented generally does not satisfy material balance for the nonwetting phase (oil phase in oil/water system and gas phase in oil/gas and black-oil systems). For an oil/water system, the material-balance error is proportional to the areal variation of B_w/B_o but it normally is negligible.[2] For oil/gas and oil/water/gas systems, the material-balance error in the gas phase, which is proportional to the areal variation of B_o/B_g and on variations of the solution GOR, may become unacceptable.[2] The choice of the saturation equations to be solved in the saturation step affects material balance, which will not be satisfied for the remaining phase.

In a black-oil model, the material-balance errors associated with variations of solution GOR can be eliminated by obtaining a simultaneous oil pressure and gas saturation solution in the first step, followed by obtaining an implicit-water-saturation solution in the second step.[16]

Stability of the SEQ Method. The implicit-saturation equations in the saturation step of the SEQ method can be derived in three different ways. For two-phase flow, the derivation method for the saturation equation is not critical for the stability of the SEQ method. For three-phase flow, however, the saturation equations derived as Eqs. 9.677 and 9.678 may cause stability problems; therefore, use of Eqs. 9.726 and 9.727 or Eqs. 9.737 and 9.738 is critical for the stability of the SEQ method. Coats[16] reported that the simultaneous solution for p_o and S_g, followed by an implicit solution for S_w, is more stable than solving for pressure followed by the implicit solution for S_w and S_g for the majority of three-phase-flow simulation problems. In addition, it is necessary for SEQ method stability to include implicit production terms in the saturation step.

Treatment of Production Terms in the Saturation Step. The implicit treatment of production terms in the saturation step is critical for the stability of the SEQ method. Because the saturation step treats fluid flow as if it were incompressible, phase production rates are adjusted so that the change in total production rate on a reservoir volume basis over the timestep must be zero. For Production Gridblock n, $\Delta_t q_{t_n}=0$, where $q_{t_n}=q_{o_n}+q_{w_n}+q_{g_n}$ can be satisfied if $q_{o_n}=f_{o_n}q_{t_n}$, $q_{w_n}=f_{w_n}q_{t_n}$, and $q_{g_n}=f_{g_n}q_{t_n}$, where q_{t_n} is estimated from the well production specified at p_o^{n+1}, S_w^n, and S_g^n. Therefore, the partial derivatives with respect to S_{w_n} and S_{g_n} of production rates at standard conditions in the implicit-saturation equations must be obtained from

$$q_{osc_n}=\frac{f_{o_n}}{B_{o_n}^{n+1}}q_{t_n}, \qquad (9.783)$$

$$q_{wsc_n}=\frac{f_{w_n}}{B_{w_n}^{n+1}}q_{t_n}, \qquad (9.784)$$

and $$q_{gsc_n}=\left(\frac{f_{g_n}}{B_{g_n}^{n+1}}+R_{s_n}^{n+1}\frac{f_{o_n}}{B_{o_n}^{n+1}}\right)q_{t_n}. \qquad (9.785)$$

It should be mentioned, however, that if the production rate of liquid (in three-phase flow) or the production rate of one phase (in two-phase flow) is specified, it will not be maintained after the implicit-saturation step. A solution is possible through iteration, where the rate used in the IMPES step is entered as the specified rate minus the implicit rate change obtained from the implicit-saturation step of the previous iteration.[2] As the number of iterations increases, however, the SEQ method becomes less attractive.

Example 9.30. Consider two-phase flow of oil and water with negligible capillary pressure, in a 1D horizontal reservoir. Write the two forms of the implicit-water-saturation equation that can be derived from Eqs. 9.677 and 9.738. Compare the two forms, pointing out differences, and show how they may collapse to one equation.

Solution. With Eqs. 9.677 and 9.738, $S_g=0$ for two-phase flow of oil and water, $P_{cow}=0$ for negligible capillary pressure, $\psi_n=\{n-1,\ n+1\}$ for a 1D reservoir, and $\Delta_m Z=Z_m-Z_n=0$, where $m\in\psi_n$, for a horizontal reservoir.

For Gridblock n, Eq. 9.677 for this problem reduces to

$$\sum_{m\in\psi_n}\Delta_m p_o^n\left(\frac{\partial T_{w_{n,m}}}{\partial S_{w_m}}\right)^n\Delta_t S_{w_m}+\left[-\left(C_{ww_n}-q'^{\,n}_{wwsc_n}\right)+\sum_{m\in\psi_n}\Delta_m p_o^n\left(\frac{\partial T_{w_{n,m}}}{\partial S_{w_n}}\right)^n\right]\Delta_t S_{w_n}=-C_{ww_n}\left(S_{w_n}^*-S_{w_n}^n\right), \qquad (9.786)$$

where $\psi_n=\{n-1,n+1\}$, $\qquad (9.787)$

where $n=1,2,\ldots,N$;

$$\Delta_m p_o^n=p_{o_m}^n-p_{o_n}^n; \qquad (9.788)$$

where $m\in\psi_n$; and, for gridblock boundary (n,m) where $m\in\psi_n$,

$$T_{w_{n,m}}^n=\left(G\frac{k_{rw}}{\mu_w B_w}\right)_{n,m}^n=G_{n,m}\left(\frac{1}{\mu_w B_w}\right)_{n,m}^n k_{rw_{n,m}}^n, \qquad (9.789)$$

$$\left(\frac{\partial T_{w_{n,m}}}{\partial S_{w_m}}\right)^n=G_{n,m}\left(\frac{1}{\mu_w B_w}\right)_{n,m}^n\left(\frac{dk_{rw_{n,m}}}{dS_{w_m}}\right)^n, \qquad (9.790a)$$

and $$\left(\frac{\partial T_{w_{n,m}}}{\partial S_{w_n}}\right)^n=G_{n,m}\left(\frac{1}{\mu_w B_w}\right)_{n,m}^n\left(\frac{dk_{rw_{n,m}}}{dS_{w_n}}\right)^n. \qquad (9.790b)$$

Applying Eq. 9.786, the implicit-water-saturation equation for Gridblock n is

$$\left(p_{o_{n-1}}^n-p_{o_n}^n\right)\left(\frac{\partial T_{w_{n,n-1}}}{\partial S_{w_{n-1}}}\right)^n\Delta_t S_{w_{n-1}}+\left(p_{o_{n+1}}^n-p_{o_n}^n\right)\left(\frac{\partial T_{w_{n,n+1}}}{\partial S_{w_{n+1}}}\right)^n\Delta_t S_{w_{n+1}}$$
$$+\left[-\left(C_{ww_n}-q'^{\,n}_{wwsc_n}\right)+\left(p_{o_{n-1}}^n-p_{o_n}^n\right)\left(\frac{\partial T_{w_{n,n-1}}}{\partial S_{w_n}}\right)^n+\left(p_{o_{n+1}}^n-p_{o_n}^n\right)\left(\frac{\partial T_{w_{n,n+1}}}{\partial S_{w_n}}\right)^n\right]\Delta_t S_{w_n}$$
$$=-C_{ww_n}\left(S_{w_n}^*-S_{w_n}^n\right). \qquad (9.791)$$

Also for Gridblock n, Eq. 9.738 for this problem reduces to

$$\sum_{m\in\psi_n}\left(\frac{q_t}{B_w^n}\right)_{n,m}\left(\frac{\partial f_{w_{n,m}}}{\partial S_{w_m}}\right)^n \Delta_t S_{w_m}$$

$$+\left[-\left(C_{ww}-q'^{\,n}_{wwsc_n}\right)+\sum_{m\in\psi_n}\left(\frac{q_t}{B_w^n}\right)_{n,m}\left(\frac{\partial f_{w_{n,m}}}{\partial S_{w_n}}\right)^n\right]\Delta_t S_{w_n}$$

$$=-C_{ww_n}\left(S^*_{w_n}-S^n_{w_n}\right), \quad \text{.......} \quad (9.792)$$

where, from Eqs. 9.684 through 9.686,

$$f_w=\frac{\lambda_w}{\lambda_t}, \quad \text{.......} \quad (9.793)$$

$$\lambda_t=\lambda_w+\lambda_o, \quad \text{.......} \quad (9.794)$$

$$\lambda_l=\beta_c\frac{kk_{rl}}{\mu_l}, \quad \text{.......} \quad (9.685)$$

where $l=o$ or w, and from Eqs. 9.717 through 9.719,

$$q_{t_{n,m}}=G_{n,m}\left(\frac{k_{rw}}{\mu_w}+\frac{k_{ro}}{\mu_o}\right)_{n,m}\left(p^{n+1}_{o_m}-p^{n+1}_{o_n}\right), \quad \text{.......} \quad (9.795)$$

where $m\in\psi_n$. Therefore, the implicit-water-saturation equation for Gridblock n is

$$\left(\frac{q_t}{B_w^n}\right)_{n,n-1}\left(\frac{\partial f_{w_{n,n-1}}}{\partial S_{w_{n-1}}}\right)^n\Delta_t S_{w_{n-1}}+\left(\frac{q_t}{B_w^n}\right)_{n,n+1}\left(\frac{\partial f_{w_{n,n+1}}}{\partial S_{w_{n+1}}}\right)^n\Delta_t S_{w_{n+1}}$$

$$+\left[-\left(C_{ww_n}-q'^{\,n}_{wwsc_n}\right)+\left(\frac{q_t}{B_w^n}\right)_{n,n-1}\left(\frac{\partial f_{w_{n,n-1}}}{\partial S_{w_n}}\right)^n\right.$$

$$\left.+\left(\frac{q_t}{B_w^n}\right)_{n,n+1}\left(\frac{\partial f_{w_{n,n+1}}}{\partial S_{w_n}}\right)^n\right]\Delta_t S_{w_n}=-C_{ww_n}\left(S^*_{w_n}-S^n_{w_n}\right).$$

$$\text{.......} \quad (9.796)$$

The two forms of the implicit-water-saturation equation, Eqs. 9.791 and 9.796, differ only in the coefficients of $\Delta_t S_w$. That is,

$$\left(p^n_{o_m}-p^n_{o_n}\right)\left(\frac{\partial T_{w_{n,m}}}{\partial S_w}\right)^n \quad \text{.......} \quad (9.797)$$

in Eq. 9.791 and

$$\left(\frac{q_t}{B_w^n}\right)_{n,m}\left(\frac{\partial f_{w_{n,m}}}{\partial S_w}\right)^n \quad \text{.......} \quad (9.798)$$

in Eq. 9.796. To point out the differences in the coefficients of $\Delta_t S_w$, these coefficients are expressed as

$$\left(p^n_{o_m}-p^n_{o_n}\right)\left(\frac{\partial T_{w_{n,m}}}{\partial S_w}\right)^n$$

$$=G_{n,m}\left(\frac{1}{B_w\mu_w}\right)^n_{n,m}\left(\frac{dk_{rw_{n,m}}}{dS_w}\right)^n\left(p^n_{o_m}-p^n_{o_n}\right) \quad \text{.....} \quad (9.799)$$

and $\left(\frac{q_t}{B_w^n}\right)_{n,m}\left(\frac{\partial f_{w_{n,m}}}{\partial S_w}\right)^n$

$$=\left[G_{n,m}\frac{1}{B^n_{n,m}}\left(\frac{k_{rw}}{\mu_w}+\frac{k_{ro}}{\mu_o}\right)^n_{n,m}\left(p^{n+1}_{o_m}-p^{n+1}_{o_n}\right)\right]$$

$$\times\left[\frac{d}{dS_w}\left(\frac{\beta_c\frac{kk_{rw}}{\mu_w^n}}{\lambda_t}\right)\right]^n_{n,m}$$

$$=G_{n,m}\left(\frac{1}{B_w\mu_w}\right)^n_{n,m}\left[\beta_c k\left(\frac{k_{rw}}{\mu_w}+\frac{k_{ro}}{\mu_o}\right)\right]^n_{n,m}\left(p^{n+1}_{o_m}-p^{n+1}_{o_n}\right)$$

$$\times\left[\frac{d}{dS_w}\left(\frac{k_{rw}}{\lambda_t}\right)_{n,m}\right]^n$$

$$=G_{n,m}\left(\frac{1}{B_w\mu_w}\right)^n_{n,m}\lambda^n_{t_{n,m}}\left[\frac{d}{dS_w}\left(\frac{k_{rw_{n,m}}}{\lambda_{t_{n,m}}}\right)\right]^n\left(p^{n+1}_{o_m}-p^{n+1}_{o_n}\right)$$

$$=G_{n,m}\left(\frac{1}{B_w\mu_w}\right)^n_{n,m}\left[\left(\frac{dk_{rw_{n,m}}}{dS_w}\right)^n-\left(\frac{k_{rw}}{\lambda_t}\right)^n_{n,m}\left(\frac{d\lambda_{t_{n,m}}}{dS_w}\right)^n\right]$$

$$\times\left(p^{n+1}_{o_m}-p^{n+1}_{o_n}\right) \quad \text{.......} \quad (9.800)$$

because $\lambda^n_{t_{n,m}}\left[\frac{d}{dS_w}\left(\frac{k_{rw_{n,m}}}{\lambda_{t_{n,m}}}\right)\right]^n$

$$=\lambda^n_{t_{n,m}}\left(\frac{1}{\lambda_{t_{n,m}}}\frac{dk_{rw_{n,m}}}{dS_w}-\frac{k_{rw_{n,m}}}{\lambda^2_{t_{n,m}}}\frac{d\lambda_{t_{n,m}}}{dS_w}\right)^n$$

$$=\left(\frac{dk_{rw_{n,m}}}{dS_w}\right)^n-\left(\frac{k_{rw}}{\lambda_t}\right)^n_{n,m}\left(\frac{d\lambda_{t_{n,m}}}{dS_w}\right)^n. \quad \text{.......} \quad (9.801)$$

Comparing Eqs. 9.799 and 9.800, we can conclude that $(p^n_{o_m}-p^n_{o_n})(\partial T_{w_{n,m}}/\partial S_w)^n$ is simply an approximation of $(q_t/B^n_w)_{n,m}(\partial f_{w_{n,m}}/\partial S_w)^n$ where $(p^{n+1}_{o_m}-p^{n+1}_{o_n})$ is replaced by $(p^n_{o_m}-p^n_{o_n})$ and the derivative of the total mobility with respect to S_w is neglected. Therefore, Eq. 9.800 collapses to Eq. 9.799 and, in turn, Eq. 9.796 collapses to Eq. 9.791 if $(p^{n+1}_{o_m}-p^{n+1}_{o_n})$ is replaced by $(p^n_{o_m}-p^n_{o_n})$ in the definition of $q_{t_{n,m}}$ and the change in total mobility is ignored. In other words, the two expressions are identical if the total mobility in the definition of the fractional-flow coefficient of water, f_w, is assumed to be constant.

Example 9.31. Write the implicit-water-saturation equation that can be derived from Eq. 9.738 for the incompressible two-phase flow of oil and water with negligible capillary pressure in a 1D horizontal reservoir consisting of N gridblocks. Water is injected at $x=0$ and fluids are produced at $x=L$ at a constant rate q. Use single-point upstream weighting.

Solution. The reservoir is discretized along the x direction into Gridblocks $1,2,\ldots,n-1,n,n+1,\ldots,N$. For Gridblock n, $\psi_n=\{n-1,n+1\}$. For this problem, $P_{cow}=0$, Z is constant, and fluids are incompressible; that is, $B_w=B_o=1$, and μ_w and μ_o are independent of pressure.

For two-phase flow of oil and water, the implicit-water-saturation equation can be obtained from Eq. 9.738 by setting $S_g=0$.

$$\sum_{m\in\psi_n}\left(\frac{q_t}{B_w^n}\right)_{n,m}\left(\frac{\partial f_{w_{n,m}}}{\partial S_{w_m}}\right)^n\Delta_t S_{w_m}$$

$$+\left[-\left(C_{ww_n}-\overset{n}{q'_{wwsc_n}}\right)+\sum_{m\in\psi_n}\left(\frac{q_t}{B_w^n}\right)_{n,m}\left(\frac{\partial f_{w_{n,m}}}{\partial S_{w_n}}\right)^n\right]$$

$$\times\,\Delta_t S_{w_n}=-C_{ww_n}\left(S^*_{w_n}-S^n_{w_n}\right), \quad\quad (9.792)$$

where $\psi_n=\{n-1,n+1\}$, where $n=1,2,\ldots,N$, or

$$\left(\frac{q_t}{B_w^n}\right)_{n,n-1}\left(\frac{\partial f_{w_{n,n-1}}}{\partial S_{w_{n-1}}}\right)^n\Delta_t S_{w_{n-1}}+\left(\frac{q_t}{B_w^n}\right)_{n,n+1}\left(\frac{\partial f_{w_{n,n+1}}}{\partial S_{w_{n+1}}}\right)^n\Delta_t S_{w_{n+1}}$$

$$+\left[-\left(C_{ww_n}-\overset{n}{q'_{wwsc_n}}\right)+\left(\frac{q_t}{B_w^n}\right)_{n,n-1}\left(\frac{\partial f_{w_{n,n-1}}}{\partial S_{w_n}}\right)^n\right.$$

$$\left.+\left(\frac{q_t}{B_w^n}\right)_{n,n+1}\left(\frac{\partial f_{w_{n,n+1}}}{\partial S_{w_n}}\right)^n\right]\Delta_t S_{w_n}=-C_{ww_n}\left(S^*_{w_n}-S^n_{w_n}\right). \quad\quad (9.796)$$

Because the direction of flow is from Gridblock 1 to Gridblock N, Gridblock $n-1$ is upstream to Gridblock n which is upstream to Gridblock $n+1$ for both oil and water phases. For zero capillary pressure and horizontal reservoir,

$$q_{t_{n,n-1}}=0 \quad\quad (9.802)$$

for $n=1$ (no-flow boundary gridblock),

$$q_{t_{n,n-1}}=G_{n,n-1}\left(\frac{k_{rw}}{\mu_w}+\frac{k_{ro}}{\mu_o}\right)^n_{n,n-1}\left(p^{n+1}_{o_{n-1}}-p^{n+1}_{o_n}\right)=q \quad\quad (9.803)$$

for $n=2,3,\ldots,N$,

$$q_{t_{n,n+1}}=G_{n,n+1}\left(\frac{k_{rw}}{\mu_w}+\frac{k_{ro}}{\mu_o}\right)^n_{n,n+1}\left(p^{n+1}_{o_{n+1}}-p^{n+1}_{o_n}\right)=-q \quad\quad (9.804)$$

for $n=1,2,3,\ldots,N-1$, and

$$q_{t_{n,n+1}}=0 \quad\quad (9.805)$$

for $n=N$ (no-flow boundary gridblock). For upstream weighting,

$$\left(\frac{\partial f_{w_{n,n-1}}}{\partial S_{w_{n-1}}}\right)^n=\left[\frac{\partial}{\partial S_{w_{n-1}}}\left(f_{w_{n,n-1}}\right)_{n-1}\right]^n$$

$$=\left(\frac{df_w}{dS_w}\right)^n_{n-1}=\overset{n}{f'_{w_{n-1}}}. \quad\quad (9.806)$$

where $n=2,3,\ldots,N$,

$$\left(\frac{\partial f_{w_{n,n-1}}}{\partial S_{w_n}}\right)^n=\left[\frac{\partial}{\partial S_{w_n}}\left(f_{w_{n,n-1}}\right)_{n-1}\right]^n=0, \quad\quad (9.807)$$

where $n=2,3,\ldots,N$,

$$\left(\frac{\partial f_{w_{n,n+1}}}{\partial S_{w_{n+1}}}\right)^n=\left[\frac{\partial}{\partial S_{w_{n+1}}}\left(f_{w_{n,n+1}}\right)_n\right]^n=0. \quad\quad (9.808)$$

where $n=1,2,3,\ldots,N-1$, and

$$\left(\frac{\partial f_{w_{n,n+1}}}{\partial S_{w_n}}\right)^n=\left[\frac{\partial}{\partial S_{w_n}}\left(f_{w_{n,n+1}}\right)_n\right]^n$$

$$=\left(\frac{df_w}{dS_w}\right)^n_n=\overset{n}{f'_{w_n}}, \quad\quad (9.809)$$

where $n=1,2,3,\ldots,N-1$. For treatment of $\overset{n}{q'_{wwsc_n}}$, $\overset{n}{q'_{wwsc_1}}=0$ because $q_{wsc_1}=q=$constant (injection well) and $\overset{n}{q'_{wwsc_n}}=0$ for $n=2,3,\ldots,N-1$ because $q_{wsc_n}=0$ (no wells).

For the production gridblock, $n=N$, using Eq. 9.784 gives

$$q_{wsc_N}=(-q)\frac{f_{w_N}}{B^n_{w_N}}=-qf_{w_N}, \quad\quad (9.810)$$

from which

$$\overset{n}{q'_{wwsc_N}}=-q\left(\frac{df_{w_N}}{dS_{w_N}}\right)^n=-q\overset{n}{f'_{w_N}}. \quad\quad (9.811)$$

Substituting Eqs. 9.810 and 9.811 into Eq. 9.796 and implementing no-flow boundaries yields the following. For Gridblock $n=1$,

$$0-q(0)\Delta_t S_{w_2}+\left[-\left(C_{ww_1}-0\right)+0-q\overset{n}{f'_{w_1}}\right]\Delta_t S_{w_1}$$

$$=-C_{ww_1}\left(S^*_{w_1}-S^n_{w_1}\right) \quad\quad (9.812a)$$

$$\text{or}\ -\left(C_{ww_1}+q\overset{n}{f'_{w_1}}\right)\Delta_t S_{w_1}=-C_{ww_1}\left(S^*_{w_1}-S^n_{w_1}\right). \quad\quad (9.812b)$$

For Gridblocks $n=2,3,\ldots,N-1$,

$$q\overset{n}{f'_{w_{n-1}}}\Delta_t S_{w_{n-1}}-q(0)\Delta_t S_{w_{n+1}}$$

$$+\left[-\left(C_{ww_n}-0\right)+q(0)-q\overset{n}{f'_{w_n}}\right]\Delta_t S_{w_n}$$

$$=-C_{ww_n}\left(S^*_{w_n}-S^n_{w_n}\right) \quad\quad (9.813a)$$

$$\text{or}\ q\overset{n}{f'_{w_{n-1}}}\Delta_t S_{w_{n-1}}-\left[C_{ww_n}+q\overset{n}{f'_{w_n}}\right]\Delta_t S_{w_n}$$

$$=-C_{ww_n}\left(S^*_{w_n}-S^n_{w_n}\right), \quad\quad (9.813b)$$

where $n=2,3,\ldots,N-1$. For Gridblock $n=N$,

$$q\overset{n}{f'_{w_{N-1}}}\Delta_t S_{w_{N-1}}-0+\left\{-\left[C_{ww_N}-\left(-q\overset{n}{f'_{w_N}}\right)\right]\right.$$

$$\left.+q(0)+0\right\}\Delta_t S_{w_N}$$

$$=-C_{ww_N}\left(S^*_{w_N}-S^n_{w_N}\right) \quad\quad (9.814a)$$

$$\text{or}\ q\overset{n}{f'_{w_{N-1}}}\Delta_t S_{w_{N-1}}-\left(C_{ww_N}+q\overset{n}{f'_{w_N}}\right)\Delta_t S_{w_N}$$

$$=-C_{ww_N}\left(S^*_{w_N}-S^n_{w_N}\right), \quad\quad (9.814b)$$

which is the same as Eq. 9.813b for $n=N$.

Therefore, the implicit-water-saturation equation for this reservoir is given by Eq. 9.812b for Gridblock $n=1$ and by Eq. 9.813b for Gridblocks $n=2,3,\ldots,N$.

TABLE 9.10—COMPARISON OF COMPUTER WORK AND STORAGE REQUIREMENTS FOR MULTIDIMENSIONAL MULTIPHASE FLOW*

Solution Method	Number of Unknowns	Work Per Timestep $W_{\Delta t}$**	Storage S
IMPES	N	$C\,N a_W\,[1]$	$2\,N a_S\,[1]$
SEQ	$N,(l-1)N$	$C\,N a_W\,[1+(l-1)^3]$	$2\,N a_S\,[(l-1)^2]$
SS	lN	$C\,N a_W\,[l^3]$	$2\,N a_S\,[l^2]$

*Entries in table are based on comparisons reported by Aziz and Settari.[2]
**The constant C depends on the machine and programming efficiency.

TABLE 9.11—NUMBER OF GRIDBLOCKS AND DEFINITIONS OF a_W AND a_S FOR BAND-DIRECT ELIMINATION WITH NATURAL ORDERING OF GRIDBLOCKS*,**

Flow Dimension	N	a_W	a_S
2D	$n_{px}n_{py}$	n_{py}^2	n_{py}
3D	$n_{px}n_{py}n_{pz}$	$n_{py}^2 n_{pz}^2$	$n_{py}n_{pz}$

*Entries in this table are based on comparisons reported by Aziz and Settari.[2]
**For $n_{px} \geqq n_{py} \geqq n_{pz}$ with gridblocks ordered in the k direction followed by j and i.

9.6.4 Comparison and Selection of Solution Methods. The multiphase-solution methods discussed in this chapter include IMPES, SEQ, and SS methods. These methods can be used to solve the finite-difference equations describing 1D, 2D, and 3D, two-phase ($l=2$) and three-phase ($l=3$) -flow problems. For a reservoir consisting of N gridblocks, the IMPES method solves one set of N equations; the SS method solves one set of lN equations; and the SEQ method solves two sets of equations, one with N equations and the other with $(l-1)N$ equations.

While the IMPES and SS methods preserve material balance, the SEQ method does not preserve material balance for at least one phase in the saturation step. Implicitness of the methods increases from IMPES to SEQ to SS. While higher degrees of implicitness increase stability, this is achieved at the expense of increased truncation errors. In practical terms, a higher degree of implicitness results in a more robust reservoir model but high truncation errors tend to smear flood fronts.

Comparison of Computer Work and Storage Requirements. The computer cost of solving the finite-difference equations for a given problem depends on the work associated with the solution technique, W; the storage requirements; and the machine type (scalar, vector, or multiprocessor). The computer work required for a given method of solution may be expressed as

$$W = W_{\Delta t} \times n_{\Delta t}, \quad \text{.......................... (9.815)}$$

where $W_{\Delta t}$ = computer work for one timestep and $n_{\Delta t}$ = number of timesteps required to reach the desired simulation time.

Work Per Timestep, $W_{\Delta t}$, and Storage, S. Work per timestep depends on the method of solution used (IMPES, SEQ, or SS), the algorithm used to solve the algebraic equations (either a direct method or an iterative method), the number of gridblocks used to describe the reservoir, the gridblock ordering (natural, D2, cyclic-2, or D4 ordering), the computer, and programming efficiency. The storage requirement depends on the solution algorithm and programming efficiency. In the present context, S and $W_{\Delta t}$ refer to the size of the matrix and work required for a direct solver.

To compare $W_{\Delta t}$ and S requirements for the IMPES, SEQ, and SS methods, consider multiphase flow in a parallelpiped reservoir discretized into $n_{px} \times n_{py}$ or $n_{px} \times n_{py} \times n_{pz}$ active gridblocks for 2D or 3D problems, respectively. Assume that $n_{px} \geqq n_{py} \geqq n_{pz}$ and n_{px}, n_{py}, and n_{pz} are sufficiently large so that most of the work is spent on solving the matrix equation. Also assume that the gridblocks are ordered with natural ordering, with gridblocks ordered in the k direction followed by the j and i directions. Finally, assume that the solution of the matrix equation is obtained by band-direct elimination. **Table 9.10** presents the computer requirements $W_{\Delta t}$ and S for the three methods of solution under these conditions in terms of the parameters N, a_W, and a_S. These parameters depend on the dimensionality of the problem as given in **Table 9.11** as functions of n_{px}, n_{py}, and n_{pz}. Entries in these two tables are based on comparisons reported by Aziz and Settari.[2] Examination and analysis of the entries in Table 9.10 reveal the following observations (assuming that the majority of computational work is incurred during the solution of the linear algebraic equations).

$W_{\Delta t}$ and S for the IMPES method are independent of the number of phases, whereas those for the SEQ and SS methods increase dramatically with increasing number of phases, regardless of the dimensionality of the problem. Normalizing all the results to the IMPES solution,

$$W_{\Delta t_{\text{IMPES}}} : W_{\Delta t_{\text{SEQ}}} : W_{\Delta t_{\text{SS}}} = (1) : \left[1 + (l-1)^3\right] : \left(l^3\right) \quad \text{.................... (9.816)}$$

$$= 1 : 2 : 8 \text{ for } l=2$$

$$= 1 : 9 : 27 \text{ for } l=3$$

and $$S_{\text{IMPES}} : S_{\text{SEQ}} : S_{\text{SS}} = (1) : \left[(l-1)^2\right] : \left(l^2\right) \quad \text{....... (9.817)}$$

$$= 1 : 1 : 4 \text{ for } l=2$$

$$= 1 : 4 : 9 \text{ for } l=3.$$

These simple ratios convey a lot of useful information. Examples include, for three-phase-flow problems, $W_{\Delta t_{SS}}/W_{\Delta t_{SEQ}} = 27/9 = 3$ and $S_{SS}/S_{SEQ} = 9/4 = 2.25$. Also, for the SS method, we can estimate that the $W_{\Delta t}$ and S requirements increase by 27/8 (or 3.4-fold) and 9/4 (or 2.25-fold), respectively, when going from a two-phase problem to a three-phase problem. The numerical value of these ratios is based on the band-direct elimination technique used for solution of the linear algebraic equations. Although the numerical values differ for different linear-equation solvers or ordering schemes, the trends presented in Tables 9.10 and 9.11 are correct.

The computer work per gridblock per timestep, $W_{\Delta t}/N$, for a given method of solution is proportional to the value of a_W defined in Table 9.11.

$$\frac{W_{\Delta t}}{N} \propto n_{py}^2 \quad \text{.............................. (9.818a)}$$

for 2D problems, and

$$\frac{W_{\Delta t}}{N} \propto n_{py}^2 n_{pz}^2 \quad \text{............................ (9.818b)}$$

for 3D problems. That is, the computer work strongly depends on the smaller dimension (n_{py}) for 2D and on the smaller plane ($n_{py}n_{pz}$) for 3D problems. Similarly, the matrix storage requirements per gridblock, S/N, is proportional to the value of a_S defined in Table 9.11

$$\frac{S}{N} \propto n_{py} \quad \text{................................ (9.819a)}$$

for 2D problems, and

$$\frac{S}{N} \propto n_{py}n_{pz} \quad \text{.............................. (9.819b)}$$

for 3D problems. Eqs. 9.818 and 9.819 imply that a band-direct-elimination method can be made efficient with natural ordering if gridblocks along the shortest direction are ordered first and those along the longest direction are ordered last. For $n_{px} \geqq n_{py} \geqq n_{pz}$, the shortest direction is the k direction and the longest direction is the i direction. Also implied is that increasing the number of gridblocks along the shortest direction increases storage requirements per gridblock linearly and increases computer work per gridblock per timestep quadratically. For example, in a 2D reservoir with an $n_{px} \times n_{py}$ grid, doubling n_{py} doubles S/N but quadruples $W_{\Delta t}/N$. For the same example, the number of gridblocks, N, doubles, the storage requirement, S, increases four-fold and the computer work per timestep, $W_{\Delta t}$, increases eight-fold. For the same 2D reservoir, if n_{py} is halved and n_{px} is doubled (that is, N remains unchanged), a band-direct-elimination procedure solves the problem on the $2n_{px} \times (n_{py}/2)$ grid four times faster and requires half the storage requirement than does the $n_{px} \times n_{py}$ grid.

Going from a 2D areal simulation to a 3D simulation with the same n_{px} and n_{py} would increase sharply $W_{\Delta t}$ and S requirements for the same direct-solution method .

$$\frac{W_{\Delta t_{3D}}}{W_{\Delta t_{2D}}} = \frac{(Na_w)_{3D}}{(Na_w)_{2D}} = \frac{(n_{px}n_{py}n_{pz})(n_{py}^2 n^2_{pz})}{(n_{px}n_{py})(n_{py}^2)} = n_{pz}^3 \quad \text{(9.820)}$$

$$\text{and } \frac{S_{3D}}{S_{2D}} = \frac{(Na_S)_{3D}}{(Na_S)_{2D}} = \frac{(n_{px}n_{py}n_{pz})(n_{py}n_{pz})}{(n_{px}n_{py})(n_{py})} = n_{pz}^2. \quad \text{(9.821)}$$

That is, $W_{\Delta t}$ and S increase, respectively, with the third and second powers of the number of layers. For example, if a 2D simulation on 30×20 grid were extended to a 3D simulation on $30 \times 20 \times 3$ grid, the computer work per timestep and storage requirements would increase by a factor of 27 and 9, respectively. Because 3D problems are very expensive to run, we must attempt to simplify the problem to conduct the study with as few layers as possible.

The relative estimates of $W_{\Delta t}$ and S are also appropriate for gridblock-ordering schemes other than natural ordering and for efficient matrix solvers other than standard Gaussian elimination, although the absolute estimates of $W_{\Delta t}$ and S will be different from those reported in Table 9.10.

Number of Required Timesteps, $n_{\Delta t}$. The number of timesteps required to advance the solution to the desired simulation time depends on the duration of the simulation and the maximum allowable timestep size, which in turn depend on the solution method's stability, practical considerations, and accuracy requirements. The solution method's stability increases with the implicitness of the method, thus permitting larger timesteps. Implicitness increases progressively from the IMPES to the SEQ to the implicit SS method. For a given solution method, stability decreases from one to two to three dimensions for the same set of data, but it increases with grid size. In multiple dimensions, stability is controlled by the smaller grid size; that is, a cross-sectional simulation is less stable than a horizontal 2D simulation because Δz is usually small compared with Δx or Δy.[2] In general, for practical problems, it is impossible to predict the number of required timesteps *a priori* without experience with similar problems. Such predictions may require numerical experimentation on a representative set of data.

Selection of Method of Solution. The most inexpensive solution method, in terms of work and storage, should be selected if a choice of IMPES, SEQ, or SS method is available. However, difficult problems may limit this choice. In general, the IMPES method can be used for easy problems and the SS method for difficult problems. Most areal problems can be solved efficiently with the IMPES method, which also can be used to solve coarsely layered, 2D cross-sectional problems with small capillary pressures and little coning tendencies. Most cross-sectional problems and simple coning problems can be solved efficiently by use of the SEQ method. The implicit SS method is reserved for difficult cross-sectional problems, coning problems, and three-phase-flow problems. In this context, a difficult problem can be defined as a problem undergoing large saturation changes during a timestep.

9.7 Treatment of Problems Specific to Multiphase Flow

In this section, we deal with the treatment of problems that are encountered in the simulation of multiphase flow in black-oil reservoirs. The problems in this section include the initialization of reservoir models, treatment of boundary conditions, the distribution of the well flow rate among phases and layers in production wells and injections wells, handling of gas-phase discontinuity, and treatment of slopes of relative permeabilities.

9.7.1 Treatment of Initial Conditions. The solution of multiphase-flow equations requires specification of initial and boundary conditions. Initial conditions in black-oil reservoirs involve the definition of phase pressures and phase saturations for every gridblock in the reservoir model at the beginning of the simulation.

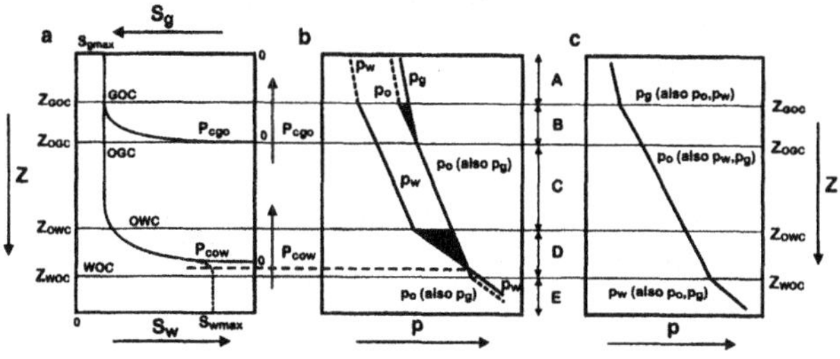

Fig. 9.18—Phase pressure and saturation distributions in the vertical direction: (a) vertical-saturation distribution; (b) vertical-phase-pressure distributions considering capillary pressures; and (c) vertical-phase-pressure distribution neglecting capillary pressures. (A = gas-cap zone, B = oil/gas transition zone, C = oil zone, D = oil/water transition zone, and E = water zone.)[2]

Differences in phase gravities and capillary forces cause fluids to segregate until the reservoir reaches gravity/capillary equilibrium. **Fig. 9.18** schematically shows phase pressure and saturation distributions in a vertical column at $t = 0$.

Up to five different zones may exist vertically; starting from the top of the reservoir and moving downward, these are the gas-cap zone, oil/gas transition zone, oil zone, oil/water transition zone, and water zone. A brief description of these zones is followed by comments on the order of performing calculations for initialization.[17]

Gas-Cap Zone. In the original gas cap, the gas phase is the only continuous phase; therefore, the vertical pressure distribution of the gas phase can be determined from hydrostatic-pressure considerations.

$$\frac{dp_g}{dZ} = \gamma_g \quad \text{(9.822)}$$

$$\text{with } S_o = 0, \quad \text{(9.823)}$$

from which we calculate the oil-phase pressure,

$$p_o = p_g - P_{cgo}(S_{g_{\max}}). \quad \text{(9.824)}$$

Additionally,

$$S_w = S_{iw}, \quad \text{(9.825)}$$

from which we calculate the water-phase pressure,

$$p_w = p_o - P_{cow}(S_{iw}). \quad \text{(9.826)}$$

Finally,

$$S_g = 1 - S_o - S_{iw}. \quad \text{(9.827)}$$

Alternatively, in cases where a historical oil saturation is observed in well logs or core samples, Eq. 9.823 can be replaced with $S_o = S_{org}$.

Oil/Gas Transition Zone. In the oil/gas transition zone, both the oil and gas phases are continuous; therefore, the vertical pressure distribution of these phases can be determined from hydrostatic-pressure considerations.

$$\frac{dp_o}{dZ} = \gamma_o \quad \text{(9.828)}$$

$$\text{and } \frac{dp_g}{dZ} = \gamma_g. \quad \text{(9.829)}$$

From the oil and gas pressures, we calculate the gas/oil capillary pressure,

$$P_{cgo}(S_g) = p_g - p_o, \quad \text{(9.830)}$$

which allows us to calculate the gas-saturation distribution, S_g. In addition,

$$S_w = S_{iw}, \quad \text{(9.825)}$$

from which the water-phase pressure can be calculated,

$$p_w = p_o - P_{cow}(S_{iw}). \quad (9.826)$$

Finally,

$$S_o = 1 - S_g - S_{iw}. \quad (9.831)$$

Oil Zone. In the oil zone, the oil phase is the only continuous phase. Therefore, the vertical oil-phase pressure distribution can be determined from hydrostatic-pressure considerations.

$$\frac{dp_o}{dZ} = \gamma_o. \quad (9.828)$$

Also,

$$S_g = 0, \quad (9.832)$$

from which we calculate the gas-phase pressure,

$$p_g = p_o + P_{cgo}(0). \quad (9.833)$$

In addition,

$$S_w = S_{iw}, \quad (9.825)$$

from which we calculate the water-phase pressure,

$$p_w = p_o - P_{cow}(S_{iw}). \quad (9.826)$$

Finally,

$$S_o = 1 - S_g - S_{iw}. \quad (9.831)$$

Oil/Water Transition Zone. In the oil/water transition zone, both the oil and water phases are continuous; therefore, the vertical pressure distribution of these phases can be determined from hydrostatic-pressure considerations.

$$\frac{dp_o}{dZ} = \gamma_o \quad (9.828)$$

$$\text{and } \frac{dp_w}{dZ} = \gamma_w. \quad (9.834)$$

From the oil and water pressures, we calculate the oil/water capillary pressure,

$$P_{cow}(S_w) = p_o - p_w, \quad (9.835)$$

which allows us to calculate the water-saturation distribution, S_w. In addition,

$$S_g = 0, \quad (9.832)$$

from which the gas-phase pressure can be calculated,

$$p_g = p_o + P_{cgo}(0). \quad (9.833)$$

Finally,

$$S_o = 1 - S_g - S_w. \quad (9.836)$$

Water Zone. In the water zone, the water phase is the only phase present and, consequently, is continuous. Therefore, the vertical water-phase pressure distribution can be determined from hydrostatic-pressure considerations.

$$\frac{dp_w}{dZ} = \gamma_w. \quad (9.834)$$

Also,

$$S_o = 0, \quad (9.823)$$

from which we calculate the oil-phase pressure,

$$p_o = p_w + P_{cow}(S_{w\max}). \quad (9.837)$$

In addition,

$$S_g = 0, \quad (9.832)$$

from which we calculate the gas-phase pressure,

$$p_g = p_o + P_{cgo}(0). \quad (9.833)$$

Finally,

$$S_w = 1. \quad (9.838)$$

Again, if well logs or core data indicate a historical oil saturation in the aquifer, Eq. 9.823 can be replaced with $S_o = S_{orw}$ and Eq. 9.838 can be replaced with $S_w = 1 - S_{orw}$.

In summary, the calculations performed during the model initialization are based on capillary-gravity equilibrium and are dependent on the nature of the fluids occupying the different reservoir zones. For a continuous phase, the initial pressure distribution is determined from hydrostatic considerations, while for a discontinuous phase, the initial pressure distribution is determined from the capillary pressure relationship evaluated at the endpoint saturation. The initial saturation distribution of a continuous phase is obtained from either the capillary pressure relationship or the saturation constraint

$$\sum_l S_l = 1, \quad (9.839)$$

where $l \in \{o, w, g\}$, while the saturation of a discontinuous phase is fixed at the endpoint saturation.

Given the depth of the water/oil contact (WOC), Z_{woc}, the depth of the oil/gas contact (OGC), Z_{ogc}, and the capillary pressure curves, the initial pressure and saturation distributions can be defined uniquely if one specifies a reference pressure (datum pressure) and reference depth (datum depth).[17]

For an unsaturated oil reservoir, the reference pressure and depth are arbitrary and can be specified in any of the five reservoir zones. For a saturated oil reservoir, the datum depth must be Z_{ogc} and the datum pressure must be the initial saturation pressure. If any other values are selected, the simulation model will not initialize to equilibrium conditions. This can be visualized by assuming a reference depth and pressure that yields a reservoir pressure different from the saturation pressure at Z_{ogc}. Even if zero production/injection data were specified in the model, saturations would change as gas goes in or out of solution.

When applying the hydrostatic gradients to obtain the pressure distribution, the simulation model will initialize to equilibrium conditions if the depths used in the initialization algorithm are the same as those in the simulation layers. If, however, a finer grid system is used in the initialization, more accurate volumetrics are achieved but the resulting model is not in hydrostatic equilibrium. Some commercial simulation programs allow for both initialization methods. If the second method is selected, we advise use of several timesteps with no production or injection to allow the model to equilibrate.

If capillary pressure relationships are neglected (or $P_{cow} = P_{cgo} = 0$), the distribution of phase saturations has to be specified (usually the endpoint saturations) but the pressure distribution can be determined from the knowledge of one reference pressure. In this case, it is generally assumed that no transition zones occur in the reservoir. Fig. 9.18c shows the pressure distribution in this case schematically.

Finally, if a transition zone falls within one gridblock, the error in the initial volume of oil can be up to $\frac{1}{2}V_b\phi(S_{w\max} - S_{iw})$ and $\frac{1}{2}V_b\phi(S_{g\max} - S_{gc})$. In many practical field cases, these errors are not serious because of the uncertainties associated with the definition of reservoir limits.[2]

All the equations discussed so far assume hydrostatic (gravity/capillary) equilibrium. There are, however, cases where actual petroleum reservoirs are initially in hydrodynamic equilibrium. These reservoirs, characterized by tilted WOC's, are caused by water flow through the aquifer. Unfortunately, there is no universal method to initialize reservoirs of this type. Generally, a trial-and-error procedure is used to initialize these reservoirs. In this procedure, pseudowells (or flux wells) are placed in the aquifer with pseudoinjection wells in the upstream direction of water movement and pseudoproduction wells in the downstream direction. Identical injection and production rates (in reservoir volumes) are specified from the pseudowells (with all physical wells shut in) and the simulation model is run until the WOC

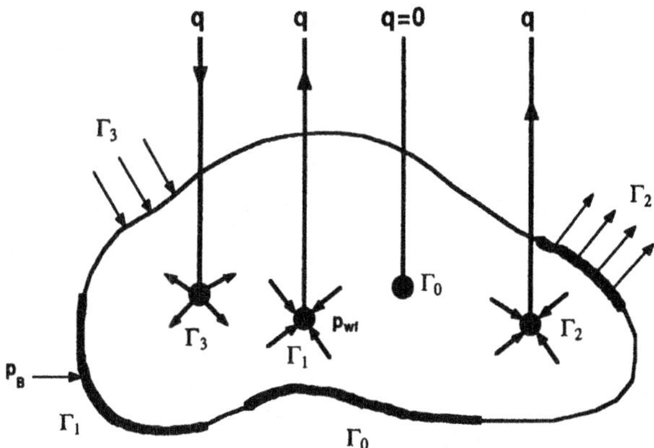

Fig. 9.19—Types of reservoir boundaries. Γ_0=no-flow boundary; Γ_1=constant pressure; Γ_2=specified efflux; and Γ_3=specified influx.

stabilizes. The injection and production rates are then adjusted until the correct dip in the WOC is achieved.

9.7.2 Treatment of Boundary Conditions. Flow in and out of an open system takes place only at the boundaries. A petroleum reservoir is an open system with external boundaries, such as those defining reservoir limits, and internal boundaries, such as wells. **Fig. 9.19** shows that these boundaries may be exposed to constant-pressure conditions, no-flow conditions, and/or finite-flow conditions. A constant-pressure boundary is, in reality, a flow boundary that allows fluid flux in such a manner that the pressure at the boundary is maintained at a constant value. Therefore, for this discussion, we consider no-flow (closed or sealed) boundaries and flow boundaries. At the finite-difference level, any flow boundary condition is equivalent to a no-flow boundary condition coupled with a source (sink) term representing the flow in or out of the reservoir through a fictitious well. Following this approach, it is possible to treat both external and internal boundaries in the same fashion.

We now consider the treatment of reservoir external boundaries at the finite-difference level and demonstrate their application for the oil equation in a 1D horizontal reservoir containing two phases, oil and water.

$$T^{n+1}_{ox_{i-1/2}}\left(p^{n+1}_{o_{i-1}} - p^{n+1}_{o_i}\right) + T^{n+1}_{ox_{i+1/2}}\left(p^{n+1}_{o_{i+1}} - p^{n+1}_{o_i}\right)$$
$$= C_{op_i}\left(p^{n+1}_{o_i} - p^n_{o_i}\right) + C_{ow_i}\left(S^{n+1}_{w_i} - S^n_{w_i}\right) - q^{n+1}_{osc_i}, \quad \text{(9.840)}$$

where $i = 1, \ldots, n_x$.

No-Flow Boundaries. No-flow boundary conditions arise when the external reservoir boundary is sealed to flow because of vanishing reservoir quality (e.g., permeability, thickness) or because of flow symmetry about the boundary, as in the case of elements of symmetry in confined flood patterns. To model no-flow boundaries, phase transmissibilities across such boundaries are set to zero (see Examples 5.5 and 5.6).

For a no-flow boundary condition at Gridblock Boundaries $x_{1/2}$ and $x_{n_x+1/2}$ in a block-centered grid system, interblock flow rates across reservoir boundaries are set to zero.

$$T^{n+1}_{ox_{1/2}}\left(p^{n+1}_{o_0} - p^{n+1}_{o_1}\right) = T^{n+1}_{ox_{n_x+1/2}}\left(p^{n+1}_{o_{n_x+1}} - p^{n+1}_{o_{n_x}}\right) = 0 \quad \text{(9.841)}$$

or, in effect, $T^{n+1}_{ox_{1/2}}$ and $T^{n+1}_{ox_{n_x+1/2}}$ are set equal to zero. Eq. 9.840 for Boundary Gridblock $i = 1$ becomes

$$0 + T^{n+1}_{ox_{1 1/2}}\left(p^{n+1}_{o_2} - p^{n+1}_{o_1}\right) = C_{op_1}\left(p^{n+1}_{o_1} - p^{n+1}_{o_1}\right)$$
$$+ C_{ow_1}\left(S^{n+1}_{w_1} - S^n_{w_1}\right) - q^{n+1}_{osc_1}; \quad \text{(9.842)}$$

and for Boundary Gridblock $i = n_x$, it becomes

$$T^{n+1}_{ox_{n_x-1/2}}\left(p^{n+1}_{o_{n_x-1}} - p^{n+1}_{o_{n_x}}\right) + 0 = C_{op_{n_x}}\left(p^{n+1}_{o_{n_x}} - p^n_{o_{n_x}}\right)$$
$$+ C_{ow_{n_x}}\left(S^{n+1}_{w_{n_x}} - S^n_{w_{n_x}}\right) - q^{n+1}_{osc_{n_x}}. \quad \text{(9.843)}$$

Constant-Pressure Boundaries. Constant-pressure boundary conditions arise when pressure is maintained at a reservoir boundary. A constant-pressure boundary develops when the rate of fluids withdrawn (at reservoir conditions) on one side of the boundary is equal to the rate of fluids being supplied or injected on the other side of the same boundary.

For a constant-pressure boundary, the interblock oil flow rate across the boundary at $x_{1/2}$ in a block-centered grid (Fig. 5.2) may be expressed as

$$T^{n+1}_{ox_{1/2}}\left(p^{n+1}_{o_0} - p^{n+1}_{o_1}\right) = T^{n+1}_{ox_{1/2}}\left(p^{n+1}_{o_0} - p_{x_{1/2}}\right) + T^{n+1}_{ox_{1/2}}\left(p_{x_{1/2}} - p^{n+1}_{o_1}\right)$$
$$= 2T^{n+1}_{ox_{1/2}}\left(p_e - p^{n+1}_{o_1}\right)$$
$$= \left[2\beta_c\left(\frac{k_x A_x}{\Delta x}\right)_1\left(\frac{k_{ro}}{\mu_o B_o}\right)_1\right]\left(p_e - p^{n+1}_{o_1}\right), \quad \text{(9.844)}$$

where $(p_{x_{1/2}} - p_{o_1}) = (p_{o_0} - p_{x_{1/2}}) = (p_e - p_{o_1})$ and $p_{x_{1/2}} = p_e$. Therefore, Eq. 9.840 written for Boundary Gridblock $i = 1$ may be expressed as

$$q^*_{osc_1} + T^{n+1}_{ox_{1 1/2}}\left(p^{n+1}_{o_2} - p^{n+1}_{o_1}\right) = C_{op_1}\left(p^{n+1}_{o_1} - p^n_{o_1}\right)$$
$$+ C_{ow_1}\left(S^{n+1}_{w_1} - S^n_{w_1}\right) - q^{n+1}_{osc_1}, \quad \text{(9.845)}$$

where $$q^*_{osc_1} = \left[\beta_c\left(\frac{k_x A_x}{\Delta x/2}\right)_1\left(\frac{k_{ro}}{\mu_o B_o}\right)_1\right]\left(p_e - p^{n+1}_{o_1}\right). \quad \text{(9.846)}$$

In other words, Eq. 9.840 for Boundary Gridblock $i = 1$ is written for a no-flow boundary (see Eq. 9.842) and the boundary condition is replaced with a fictitious well in the gridblock injecting (or producing) oil at a rate $q^*_{osc_1}$ given by Eq. 9.846.

Similarly, Eq. 9.840 for Boundary Gridblock $i = n_x$ where $x_{n_x+1/2}$ is a constant-pressure boundary in a block-centered grid (Fig. 5.2) becomes

$$T^{n+1}_{ox_{n_x-1/2}}\left(p^{n+1}_{o_{n_x-1}} - p^{n+1}_{o_{n_x}}\right) + q^*_{osc_{n_x}} = C_{op_{n_x}}\left(p^{n+1}_{o_{n_x}} - p^n_{o_{n_x}}\right)$$
$$+ C_{ow_{n_x}}\left(S^{n+1}_{w_{n_x}} - S^n_{w_{n_x}}\right) - q^{n+1}_{osc_{n_x}}, \quad \text{(9.847)}$$

where $$q^*_{osc_{n_x}} = \left[\beta_c\left(\frac{k_x A_x}{\Delta x/2}\right)_{n_x}\left(\frac{k_{ro}}{\mu_o B_o}\right)_{n_x}\right]\left(p_e - p^{n+1}_{o_{n_x}}\right). \quad \text{(9.848)}$$

and where $p_e = p_{n_x+1/2}$.

For a point-distributed grid (Fig. 5.4), $p^{n+1}_{o_1} = p_e$ and $p^{n+1}_{o_{n_x}} = p_e$ because boundary gridpoints fall on reservoir boundaries.

Specified-Efflux Boundaries. Specified-efflux boundary conditions arise when communication exists between the reservoir in question and another reservoir through boundary Γ_2. The boundary condition in this case is replaced with a no-flow boundary and a fictitious production well. The efflux rate can be specified or can result from a specified pressure or potential gradient. Sec. 9.7.3 presents the distribution of the efflux rate among phases and gridblocks sharing the boundary Γ_2.

If gridblock boundary at $x_{1/2}$ represents a boundary with another reservoir through which fluids enter or leave Gridblock 1 at a rate of q_{sp}, Eq. 9.840 for Boundary Gridblock 1 becomes

$$q^*_{osc_1} + T^{n+1}_{ox_{1 1/2}}\left(p^{n+1}_{o_2} - p^{n+1}_{o_1}\right) = C_{op_1}\left(p^{n+1}_{o_1} - p^n_{o_1}\right)$$
$$+ C_{ow_1}\left(S^{n+1}_{w_1} - S^n_{w_1}\right) + q^{n+1}_{osc_1}, \quad \text{(9.849)}$$

TABLE 9.12—PRODUCTION-WELL-SPECIFICATION OPTION AND DEFINITIONS OF q_{sp}, F_o, F_w, AND F_g

Well-Specification Option	Well-Specification Rate q_{sp}	F_o	F_w	F_g
O_{p1}	q_o	k_{ro}/μ_o	0	0
O_{p2}	q_{osc}	$\frac{k_{ro}}{\mu_o B_o}$	0	0
O_{p3}	q_w	0	$\frac{k_{rw}}{\mu_w}$	0
O_{p4}	q_{wsc}	0	$\frac{k_{rw}}{\mu_w B_w}$	0
O_{p5}	q_g	0	0	$\frac{k_{rg}}{\mu_g}$
O_{p6}	q_{gsc}	$\frac{R_s k_{ro}}{\mu_o B_o}$	0	$\frac{k_{rg}}{\mu_g B_g}$
O_{p7}	q_L	$\frac{k_{ro}}{\mu_o}$	$\frac{k_{rw}}{\mu_w}$	0
O_{p8}	q_{Lsc}	$\frac{k_{ro}}{\mu_o B_o}$	$\frac{k_{rw}}{\mu_w B_w}$	0
O_{p9}	q_t	$\frac{k_{ro}}{\mu_o}$	$\frac{k_{rw}}{\mu_w}$	$\frac{k_{rg}}{\mu_g}$
O_{p10}	q_{tsc}	$\frac{\left(1+\frac{R_s}{\alpha_c}\right)k_{rc}}{\mu_o B_o}$	$\frac{k_{rw}}{\mu_w B_w}$	$\frac{k_{rg}}{\alpha_c \mu_g B_g}$

where $$q^*_{osc_1} = \left[\frac{T^{n+1}_{ox_{1/2}}}{\left(T^{n+1}_{ox_{1/2}} + T^{n+1}_{wx_{1/2}}\right)}\right] q_{sp}. \quad \text{(9.850)}$$

If, on the other hand, a pressure gradient is specified as $dp/dx = \alpha$, then

$$q^*_{osc_1} = T^{n+1}_{ox_{1/2}}\left(p^{n+1}_{o_0} - p^{n+1}_{o_1}\right)$$

$$= -T^{n+1}_{ox_{1/2}}\Delta x_{1/2}\left(\frac{p^{n+1}_{o_1} - p^{n+1}_{o_0}}{\Delta x_{1/2}}\right) \quad \text{(9.851a)}$$

or $$q^*_{osc_1} = \left(-T_{ox_{1/2}}\Delta x_{1/2}\right)\alpha. \quad \text{(9.851b)}$$

Specified-Influx Boundaries. Specified-influx boundary conditions arise when the reservoir is in communication with an aquifer supplying water influx through Boundary Γ_3. Again, this boundary condition is replaced with a no-flow boundary and a fictitious injection well with the specified water influx distributed among the boundary gridblocks. In this case, Sec. 9.7.4 presents $q^*_{lsc_n} = 0$ for $l = o$ or g and q^*_{wsc} distributed among the boundary gridblocks.

9.7.3 Treatment of Fluid Production. Unlike production wells in single-phase systems, there are several rate specifications that may be imposed on a production well in multiphase systems. These options include specified oil production rate at reservoir conditions, O_{p1}; specified oil production rate at standard conditions, O_{p2}; specified water production rate at reservoir conditions, O_{p3}; specified water production rate at standard conditions, O_{p4}; specified gas production rate at reservoir conditions, O_{p5}; specified gas production rate at standard conditions, O_{p6}; specified liquid production rate at reservoir conditions, O_{p7}; specified liquid production rate at standard conditions, O_{p8}; specified total production rate at reservoir conditions, O_{p9}; specified total production rate at standard conditions, O_{p10}; and specified sandface pressure, O_{p11}.

The well-production rates q_{osc}, q_{wsc}, and q_{gsc} that appear in the finite-difference equations are related through the flowing bottom-hole pressure of the well. The questions that must be addressed, which were not addressed in Chap. 6, are how to calculate the production rates of the phases that are not specified and how to partition production rates back to individual phases, when a liquid production rate or a total production rate is specified. To answer these questions, we consider a well perforated in a single gridblock and a well that penetrates multiple gridblocks.

Production From Single-Block Wells. The production rate of Phase l at standard conditions from a well perforated in a single gridblock q_{lsc_n} may be expressed as

$$q_{lsc_n} = -G_{w_n}\left(\frac{k_{rl}}{\mu_l B_l}\right)_n \left(p_{l_n} - p_{wf}\right) \quad \text{(9.852a)}$$

for oil and water and as

$$q_{gsc_n} = -G_{w_n}\left[\left(\frac{k_{rg}}{\mu_g B_g}\right)\left(p_{g_n} - p_{wf}\right) + \left(R_{so}\frac{k_{ro}}{\mu_o B_o}\right)\left(p_{o_n} - p_{wf}\right)\right] \quad \text{(9.852b)}$$

for gas. In Eq. 9.852, G_{w_n} = wellblock geometric factor for Gridblock n discussed in Sec. 6.2. The negative sign in Eq. 9.852 arises because of the sign convention of negative for production (mass sink) used in this book.

The flow rates of the various phases are not independent but are related to each other through the flowing bottomhole pressure, p_{wf}.

$$p_{wf} = \frac{G_{w_n}\sum_l F_{l_n} p_{l_n} + q_{sp}}{G_{w_n}\sum_l F_{l_n}}, \quad \text{(9.853a)}$$

where $l \in \{o, w, g\}$ and well-specification options are O_{p1} through O_{p10}.

$$p_{wf} = p_{wf_{sp}}, \quad \text{(9.853b)}$$

where the well-specification option is O_{p11}. For Eq. 9.853a, **Table 9.12** gives the values of q_{sp}, F_o, F_w, and F_g for each well specification option. Eqs. 9.852 and 9.853a are derived with the potential method. This formulation is correct only if p_{wf} is estimated implicitly (at Time Level $n+1$). Stability problems may arise if a simple iteration is used to update p_{wf}. These stability problems may be removed if it is assumed that capillary pressures at the wellblock are negligible. With this assumption, the potential method of allocation reduces to the mobility method of allocation. The mobility method of allocation is defined by

$$q_{lsc_n} = -G_{w_n}\left(\frac{k_{rl}}{\mu_l B_l}\right)_n \left(p_{o_n} - p_{wf}\right) \quad \text{(9.854a)}$$

for oil and water and as

$$q_{gsc_n} = -G_{w_n}\left[\left(\frac{k_{rg}}{\mu_g B_g}\right) + \left(R_{so}\frac{k_{ro}}{\mu_o B_o}\right)\right]\left(p_{o_n} - p_{wf}\right) \quad \text{(9.854b)}$$

for gas. In addition,

$$p_{wf} = p_{o_n} + \frac{q_{sp}}{G_{w_n}\sum_l F_{l_n}}, \quad \text{(9.855)}$$

where $l \in \{o, w, g\}$ and well-specification options are O_{p1} through O_{p10}.

The mobility method of allocating production can be used to help reduce stability problems. Another approach to reduce numerical instability is to estimate p_{wf} by use of pressures and saturations at

Time Level n in Eq. 9.852. To maintain the specified well production rate, q_{sp}, in this approach, Eq. 9.852 should be replaced with

$$q_{lsc_n} = \frac{\left(\frac{k_{rl}}{\mu_l B_l}\right)_n \left(p^n_{l_n} - p^n_{wf}\right)}{\sum_p \left[F_{p_n}\left(p^n_{p_n} - p^n_{wf}\right)\right]} q_{sp}, \quad \text{(9.856)}$$

where $l \in \{o, w, g\}$ and $p \in \{o, w, g\}$.

Production From Multiblock Wells. *Explicit and Simple Iteration Methods for Multiblock Production Wells.* The production rate of Phase l at standard conditions from Gridblock $n \in \psi_w$, where ψ_w is the set of gridblocks penetrated by the well, is expressed by Eq. 9.852. The flowing sandface pressure, assuming negligible pressure drop in the wellbore, can be expressed with the following allocation methods.

Potential Method of Allocation.

$$p_{wf} = \frac{\sum_n \left[G_{w_n} \sum_l (F_l p_l)_n\right] + q_{sp}}{\sum_n \left(G_{w_n} \sum_l F_{l_n}\right)}, \quad \text{(9.857)}$$

where $l \in \{o, w, g\}$; well-specification options are O_{p1} through O_{p10}; and $n \in \psi_w$.

Mobility Method of Allocation.

$$p_{wf} = \frac{\sum_n \left[(G_w p_o)_n \sum_l F_{l_n}\right] + q_{sp}}{\sum_n \left(G_{w_n} \sum_l F_{l_n}\right)}, \quad \text{(9.858)}$$

where $l \in \{o, w, g\}$; well-specification options are O_{p1} through O_{p10}; and $n \in \psi_w$, or

$$p_{wf} = p_{wf_{sp}}, \quad \text{(9.853b)}$$

where the well-specification option is O_{p11}.

Eqs. 9.857 and 9.858 assume negligible pressure drop in the well. Methods that consider pressure drop in the well are discussed later in this section. In addition, in developing Eq. 9.858, we assumed that capillary pressure effects are negligible at the wellbore. Once a flowing sandface pressure is calculated with Eq. 9.857, 9.858, or 9.853b, Eq. 9.852 is used to calculate the gridblock contribution to the production rate from the well. As with single-block wells, to preserve the specified production rate (well-specification options are O_{p1} through O_{p10}), p_{wf} derived by either Eq. 9.857 or 9.858 must be evaluated implicitly at Time Level $n+1$. If p_{wf} is estimated explicitly at Time Level n, the specified well-production rate will not be maintained with Eq. 9.852. To maintain the specified rate when p_{wf} is evaluated explicitly, the following equation is required instead of Eq. 9.852.

$$q_{lsc_n} = G_{w_n}\left(\frac{k_{rl}}{\mu_l B_l}\right)_n \times \frac{\left(p_{l_n} - p^n_{wf}\right)}{\sum_m \left[G_{w_m} \sum_p F_{pm}\left(p_{pm} - p^n_{wf}\right)\right]} q_{sp}, \quad \text{(9.859)}$$

where $l = o, w,$ or g; $p \in \{o, w, g\}$; well-specification options are O_{p1} through O_{p10}; $n \in \psi_w$; and $m \in \psi_w$.

In addition to the potential and mobility allocation methods discussed, Aziz and Settari[2] developed a mobility-allocation method that does not require the intermediate step of calculating p_{wf} for rate-specified wells. If we assume that equal potential gradients exist for all gridblocks, $n \in \psi_w$, then

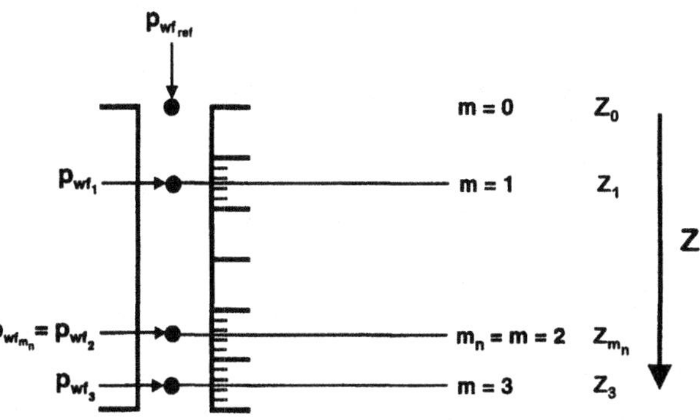

Fig. 9.20—Vertical well penetrating three producing gridblocks.

$$q_{lsc_n} = G_{w_n} \frac{[k_{rl}/(\mu_l B_l)]_n}{\sum_m \left(G_{w_m} \sum_p F_{pm}\right)} q_{sp}, \quad \text{(9.860)}$$

where $l = o, w,$ or g; $p \in \{o, w, g\}$; well-specification options are O_{p1} through O_{p10}; $n \in \psi_w$; and $m \in \psi_w$. Eq. 9.860 is obtained by setting $p_{o_n} = p_o$ in Eq. 9.858, combining the resulting equation with Eq. 9.854, and eliminating the $(p_o - p_{wf})$ term. Aziz and Settari[2] report that the use of Eq. 9.860 may produce erroneous results when the well penetrates noncommunicating layers or when there are large contrasts in layer properties.

In the methods discussed, we have assumed that the pressure drop in the well is negligible. When pressure drop in the well is to be considered, the well-production rate must be made compatible with the pressure distribution in the wellbore. While a rigorous solution to this problem involving multiphase flow through tubing is beyond the scope of this book, we present an approximate solution[18] that has been used successfully in coning, cross-sectional, and 3D simulations.

In this approximate solution, the pressure drop caused by frictional flow in the wellbore is ignored, as are capillary pressures in the producing gridblocks. In this approach,

$$p_{l_n} - p_{wf_n} = p_{o_n} - p_{wf_n}, \quad \text{(9.861)}$$

where $l = o, w,$ or g and $n \in \psi_w$. p_{wf_n} is determined by a reference value, $p_{wf_{ref}}$, and the hydrostatic gradient. If the gridblocks penetrated by a well are numbered sequentially with the top-most gridblock numbered as Wellblock 1 and the bottom-most gridblock numbered as Wellblock n_k (as in **Fig. 9.20**), then, for Wellblock $m \in \psi_w$,

$$p_{wf_m} = p_{wf_{m-1}} + \bar{\gamma}_{w_m}\left(Z_m - Z_{m-1}\right), \quad \text{(9.862)}$$

where $\bar{\gamma}_{w_m}$ = mean gravity of all fluids in the wellbore in the interval $(Z_m - Z_{m-1})$. If the top of the producing zone is taken as the reference depth where $p_{wf} = p_{wf_{ref}}$ at elevation $Z_0 = Z_{ref}$, Eq. 9.862 may be rewritten to express p_{wf_n} (opposite Wellblock m_n) as

$$p_{wf_n} = p_{wf_{ref}} + \sum_{m=1}^{m_n} \bar{\gamma}_{w_m}\left(Z_m - Z_{m-1}\right), \quad \text{(9.863a)}$$

where $n \in \psi_w$ or, if an average wellbore gradient, $\bar{\gamma}_w$, is considered, as

$$p_{wf_n} = p_{wf_{ref}} + \bar{\gamma}_w\left(Z_{m_n} - Z_0\right), \quad \text{(9.863b)}$$

where $n \in \psi_w$ and $Z_{m_n} = Z_n$. In Eqs. 9.863a and 9.863b, the average pressure gradient is defined as

$$\bar{\gamma}_w = \frac{B_o \gamma_o q_{osc} + B_w \gamma_w q_{wsc} + B_g \gamma_g q_{fgsc}}{B_o q_{osc} + B_w q_{wsc} + B_g q_{fgsc}}, \quad \text{(9.864)}$$

where $\gamma_l = \gamma_c \rho_l g$ $\quad$ (9.865)

and where $l = o$, w, or g. If an average well gradient is used, as in Eq. 9.863b, the production rate terms in Eq. 9.864 are the well-production rates. If individual gradients between perforated wellblocks are used, as in Eq. 9.863a, the production rate terms in Eq. 9.864 represent the summation of rates over all upstream wellblocks.

Eqs. 9.863a and 9.863b can be rewritten as

$$p_{wf_n} = p_{wf_{ref}} + H_n, \quad \text{(9.866)}$$

where $n \in \psi_w$. If individual completion gradients are used, then

$$H_n = \sum_{m=1}^{m_n} \bar{\gamma}_{w_m}(Z_m - Z_{m-1}), \quad \text{(9.867a)}$$

where $n \in \psi_w$ or, if an average well gradient is used, then

$$H_n = \bar{\gamma}_w(Z_{m_n} - Z_0), \quad \text{(9.867b)}$$

where $n \in \psi_w$. Substituting Eq. 9.866 into Eq. 9.854 and summing over all perforated wellblocks results in

$$q_{sp} = \sum_n \sum_l q_{l_n}, \quad \text{(9.868a)}$$

where $l \in \{o, w, g\}$; $n \in \psi_w$; and well-specification options are O_{p1} through O_{p10}, or

$$q_{sp} = -\sum_n \left\{ G_{w_n} \sum_l \left[F_{l_n}\left(p_{o_n} - p_{wf_{ref}} - H_n\right)\right]\right\}, \quad \text{(9.868b)}$$

where $l \in \{o, w, g\}$; $n \in \psi_w$; and well-specification options are O_{p1} through O_{p10}. Solving Eq. 9.868b for $p_{wf_{ref}}$,

$$p_{wf_{ref}} = \frac{\sum_n \left[G_{w_n}\left(p_{o_n} - H_n\right) \sum_l F_{l_n}\right] + q_{sp}}{\sum_n \left(G_{w_n} \sum_l F_{l_n}\right)}, \quad \text{(9.869)}$$

where $l \in \{o, w, g\}$; $n \in \psi_w$; and well-specification options are O_{p1} through O_{p10}. Eq. 9.869 is the multiphase version of Eq. 6.105, which was developed for single-phase flow in Example 6.10.

Once $p_{wf_{ref}}$ is calculated with Eq. 9.869, the production rates from the individual wellblocks are calculated by

$$q_{lsc_n} = -G_{w_n}\left(\frac{k_{rl}}{\mu_l B_l}\right)_n \left(p_{o_n} - p_{wf_{ref}} - H_n\right), \quad \text{(9.870)}$$

where $l = o$, w, or g; well-specification options are O_{p1} through O_{p10}; and $n \in \psi_w$.

Implicit Method for Multiblock Production Wells. The implicit treatment method for multiphase flow is identical to the method for single-phase flow described in Sec. 6.2.2. In this method, the contribution of Wellblock n to the specified production rate (q_{sp_n}) is expanded by use of the Taylor series expansion about Iteration Level ν.

$$\begin{aligned} \overset{(\nu+1)}{q}{}^{n+1}_{sp_n} = \overset{(\nu)}{q}{}^{n+1}_{sp_n} &+ \left(\frac{\partial q_{sp_n}}{\partial S_{w_n}}\right)^{\overset{(\nu)}{n+1}} \left[\overset{(\nu+1)}{S}{}^{n+1}_{w_n} - \overset{(\nu)}{S}{}^{n+1}_{w_n}\right] \\ &+ \left(\frac{\partial q_{sp_n}}{\partial S_{g_n}}\right)^{\overset{(\nu)}{n+1}} \left[\overset{(\nu+1)}{S}{}^{n+1}_{g_n} - \overset{(\nu)}{S}{}^{n+1}_{g_n}\right] \\ &+ \left(\frac{\partial q_{sp_n}}{\partial p_{o_n}}\right)^{\overset{(\nu)}{n+1}} \left[\overset{(\nu+1)}{p}{}^{n+1}_{o_n} - \overset{(\nu)}{p}{}^{n+1}_{o_n}\right] \\ &+ \left(\frac{\partial q_{sp_n}}{\partial p_{wf_{ref}}}\right)^{\overset{(\nu)}{n+1}} \left[\overset{(\nu+1)}{p}{}^{n+1}_{wf_{ref}} - \overset{(\nu)}{p}{}^{n+1}_{wf_{ref}}\right], \end{aligned} \quad \text{(9.871)}$$

where well-specification options are O_{p1} through O_{p10} and $n \in \psi_w$. The specified production rate for the well, q_{sp}, is the sum of the production rates from the individual wellblocks. That is,

$$\begin{aligned} \sum_n \overset{(\nu+1)}{q}{}^{n+1}_{sp_n} = \sum_n \overset{(\nu)}{q}{}^{n+1}_{sp_n} + \sum_n &\left\{ \left(\frac{\partial q_{sp_n}}{\partial S_{w_n}}\right)^{\overset{(\nu)}{n+1}} \left[\overset{(\nu+1)}{S}{}^{n+1}_{w_n} - \overset{(\nu)}{S}{}^{n+1}_{w_n}\right] \right. \\ &+ \left(\frac{\partial q_{sp_n}}{\partial S_{g_n}}\right)^{\overset{(\nu)}{n+1}} \left[\overset{(\nu+1)}{S}{}^{n+1}_{g_n} - \overset{(\nu)}{S}{}^{n+1}_{g_n}\right] \\ &+ \left(\frac{\partial q_{sp_n}}{\partial p_{o_n}}\right)^{\overset{(\nu)}{n+1}} \left[\overset{(\nu+1)}{p}{}^{n+1}_{o_n} - \overset{(\nu)}{p}{}^{n+1}_{o_n}\right] \\ &\left. + \left(\frac{\partial q_{sp_n}}{\partial p_{wf_{ref}}}\right)^{\overset{(\nu)}{n+1}} \left[\overset{(\nu+1)}{p}{}^{n+1}_{wf_{ref}} - \overset{(\nu)}{p}{}^{n+1}_{wf_{ref}}\right]\right\}, \end{aligned} \quad \text{(9.872)}$$

where well-specification options are O_{p1} through O_{p10} and $n \in \psi_w$. For well-specification options O_{p1} through O_{p10}, the production rate at Iteration Level $\nu + 1$ must equal the rate at Iteration Level ν. That is,

$$\sum_n \overset{(\nu+1)}{q}{}^{n+1}_{sp_n} = \sum_n \overset{(\nu)}{q}{}^{n+1}_{sp_n} = q_{sp}, \quad \text{(9.873)}$$

where well-specification options are O_{p1} through O_{p10} and $n \in \psi_w$. Substituting Eq. 9.873 into Eq. 9.872 and solving for $p^{n+1}_{wf_{ref}}$ at Iteration Level $\nu + 1$ results in

$$\begin{aligned} \overset{(\nu+1)}{p}{}^{n+1}_{wf_{ref}} = \overset{(\nu)}{p}{}^{n+1}_{wf_{ref}} - &\left(\sum_n \left\{ \left(\frac{\partial q_{sp_n}}{\partial S_{w_n}}\right)^{\overset{(\nu)}{n+1}} \left[\overset{(\nu+1)}{S}{}^{n+1}_{w_n} - \overset{(\nu)}{S}{}^{n+1}_{w_n}\right] \right.\right. \\ &+ \left(\frac{\partial q_{sp_n}}{\partial S_{g_n}}\right)^{\overset{(\nu)}{n+1}} \left[\overset{(\nu+1)}{S}{}^{n+1}_{g_n} - \overset{(\nu)}{S}{}^{n+1}_{g_n}\right] + \left(\frac{\partial q_{sp_n}}{\partial p_{o_n}}\right)^{\overset{(\nu)}{n+1}} \\ &\left.\left. \times \left[\overset{(\nu+1)}{p}{}^{n+1}_{o_n} - \overset{(\nu)}{p}{}^{n+1}_{o_n}\right]\right\}\right) \Big/ \sum_n \left(\frac{\partial q_{sp_n}}{\partial p_{wf_{ref}}}\right)^{\overset{(\nu)}{n+1}}, \end{aligned} \quad \text{(9.874)}$$

where well-specification options are O_{p1} through O_{p10} and $n \in \psi_w$. The derivative terms in Eqs. 9.871, 9.872, and 9.874 can be obtained from the inflow-performance relationship for Wellblock n contribution to the well-specified rate,

$$q_{sp_n} = -G_{w_n} \sum_l F_{l_n}\left(p_{o_n} - p_{wf_{ref}} - H_n\right), \quad \text{(9.875)}$$

where well-specification options are O_{p1} through O_{p10}; $l \in \{o, w, g\}$; and $n \in \psi_w$. In the remainder of this discussion, we use the definition of H_n as stated in Eq. 9.867b.

Taking the partial derivatives of Eq. 9.875, with respect to the unknowns p_o, S_g, S_w, and $p_{wf_{ref}}$ for the $(p_o - S_g - S_w)$ formulation, results in

$$\frac{\partial q_{sp_n}}{\partial S_{w_n}} = -G_{w_n} \sum_l \left[\left(\frac{\partial F_{l_n}}{\partial S_{w_n}}\right)\left(p_{o_n} - p_{wf_{ref}} - H_n\right)\right], \quad \text{(9.876)}$$

where well-specification options are O_{p1} through O_{p10}, $l \in \{o, w, g\}$, and $n \in \psi_w$;

$$\frac{\partial q_{spn}}{\partial S_{gn}} = -G_{w_n}\sum_l\left[\left(\frac{\partial F_{l_n}}{\partial S_{gn}}\right)\left(p_{o_n} - p_{wf_{ref}} - H_n\right)\right], \quad (9.877)$$

where well-specification options are O_{p1} through O_{p10}, $l \in \{o, w, g\}$, $Z_{m_n} = Z_n$, and $n \in \psi_w$;

$$\frac{\partial q_{spn}}{\partial p_{o_n}} = -G_{w_n}\left\{\sum_l\left[\left(\frac{\partial F_{l_n}}{\partial p_{o_n}}\right)\left(p_{o_n} - p_{wf_{ref}} - H_n\right)\right] + \sum_l F_{l_n}\right\}, \quad (9.878)$$

where well-specification options are O_{p1} through O_{p10}, $l \in \{o, w, g\}$, and $n \in \psi_w$; and

$$\frac{\partial q_{spn}}{\partial p_{wf_{ref}}} = G_{w_n}\sum_l\left[F_{l_n}\left(1 + \frac{\partial H_n}{\partial p_{wf_{ref}}}\right)\right], \quad (9.879)$$

where well-specification options are O_{p1} through O_{p10}, $l \in \{o, w, g\}$, and $n \in \psi_w$, and where, from Eq. 9.867b,

$$\frac{\partial H_n}{\partial p_{wf_{ref}}} = \frac{\partial \overline{\gamma}_w}{\partial p_{wf_{ref}}}\left(Z_{m_n} - Z_0\right), \quad (9.880)$$

where $n \in \psi_w$ and $Z_{m_n} = Z_n$.

In Eq. 9.880, $\overline{\gamma}_w$ is the well gradient defined by Eq. 9.864. Because of the difficulty of evaluating $\partial\overline{\gamma}_w/\partial p_{wf_{ref}}$, in practice the wellbore gradient often is evaluated explicitly.[19] That is, $\overline{\gamma}_w = \overline{\gamma}_w^n$ and $\partial\overline{\gamma}_w/\partial p_{wf_{ref}} = 0$. The production rates of various phases from Wellblock n are expressed by Eq. 9.870.

We have not discussed the evaluation of the derivative terms. The method is fully implicit if the derivative terms are updated with each nonlinear iteration. If the derivative terms are evaluated at the beginning of the timestep and held constant with each nonlinear iteration, the resulting formulation is the linearized-implicit method. Finally, if the derivative terms are replaced with chord-slope approximations, the resulting formulation is the semi-implicit method.[8]

9.7.4 Treatment of Fluid Injection. The condition imposed on an injection well in multiphase flow may be specified injection rate at standard conditions of a given phase (usually gas or water), O_{i1}; specified injection rate of water at reservoir conditions (as is the case of balancing reservoir voidage or water influx at the external boundary of the reservoir), O_{i2}; or specified sandface pressure of a well (or pressure at reservoir external boundary), O_{i3}.

The injection rates q_{wsc}, q_{gsc}, and $q_{osc} = 0$ in the finite-difference equations are expressed at standard conditions. Like production rates, injection rates have to be estimated independently from the finite-difference equations. This section shows how to distribute a specified well-injection rate among the wellblocks penetrated by the well $n \in \psi_w$ (or sharing their boundaries with the reservoir boundary). Here again, we consider a well penetrating a single gridblock and a well penetrating multiple gridblocks.

Injection in Single-Block Wells. For injection wells, we make the fundamental assumption that the mobility of the injected fluid is equal to the total mobility of the reservoir fluids at in-situ conditions, in Injection Gridblock n.

$$\left(\frac{k_{r_{inj}}}{\mu_{inj}}\right)_n = \sum_l\left(\frac{k_{rl}}{\mu_l}\right)_n, \quad (9.881)$$

where $l \in \{o, w, g\}$ and $inj = w$ or g. Therefore, the injection rate into Gridblock n, expressed at standard conditions, for a sandface-pressure specification is

$$q_{injsc_n} = -\frac{G_{w_n}}{B_{inj_n}}\sum_l\left(\frac{k_{rl}}{\mu_l}\right)_n\left(p_{o_n} - p_{wf_{sp}}\right), \quad (9.882)$$

where $l \in \{o, w, g\}$ and $inj = w$ or g. For a well-rate specification,

$$q_{injsc_n} = q_{sp}. \quad (9.883a)$$

where well-specification option $= O_{i1}$, and

$$q_{injsc_n} = \frac{q_{sp}}{B_{inj_n}}. \quad (9.883b)$$

where well-specification option $= O_{i2}$, $inj = w$ or g, and B_{inj_n} = FVF of the injected phase at in-situ conditions in the Injection Gridblock n. The bottomhole pressure for a well rate specification can be estimated with Eq. 9.882 as

$$p_{wf} = p_{o_n} + \frac{q_{injsc_n}B_{inj_n}}{\left[G_{w_n}\sum_l\left(k_{rl}/\mu_l\right)_n\right]}, \quad (9.884)$$

where $l \in \{o, w, g\}$ and $inj = w$ or g. In this treatment, we assumed negligible capillary forces.

Injection in Multiblock Wells. *Explicit and Simple Iteration Methods for Multiblock Injection Wells.* The well-specified injection rate may be distributed among Injection Gridblocks $n \in \psi_w$ according to potential allocation or mobility allocation. For potential allocation,

$$q_{injsc_n} = -\frac{G_{w_n}}{B_{inj_n}}\sum_l\left[\left(\frac{k_{rl}}{\mu_l}\right)_n\left(p_{l_n} - p_{wf}\right)\right]. \quad (9.885)$$

where $l \in \{o, w, g\}$; $inj = w$ or g; $n \in \psi_w$; and

$$p_{wf} = \frac{\sum_n\left(G_{w_n}/B_{inj_n}\right)\sum_l\left(k_{rl}/\mu_l\right)_n p_{l_n} + q_{spsc}}{\sum_n\left(G_{w_n}/B_{inj_n}\right)\sum_l\left(k_{rl}/\mu_l\right)_n}. \quad (9.886)$$

where $l \in \{o, w, g\}$; $inj = w$ or g; and $n \in \psi_w$. For mobility allocation,

$$q_{injsc_n} = -\frac{G_{w_n}}{B_{inj_n}}\left[\sum_l\left(\frac{k_{rl}}{\mu_l}\right)_n\right]\left(p_{o_n} - p_{wf}\right), \quad (9.887)$$

where $l \in \{o, w, g\}$; $inj = w$ or g; $n \in \psi_w$; and

$$p_{wf} = \frac{\sum_n\left(G_{w_n}/B_{inj_n}\right)p_{o_n}\sum_l\left(k_{rl}/\mu_l\right)_n + q_{spsc}}{\sum_n\left(G_{w_n}/B_{inj_n}\right)\sum_l\left(k_{rl}/\mu_l\right)_n}, \quad (9.888)$$

where $l \in \{o, w, g\}$, $inj = w$ or g, and $n \in \psi_w$. If the pressure drops $(p_{o_n} - p_{wf})$ for $n \in \psi_w$ are assumed equal, Eq. 9.888 becomes

$$p_{wf} = p_{o_n} + \frac{q_{spsc}}{\left[\sum_m\left(G_{w_m}/B_{inj_m}\right)\sum_l\left(k_{rl}/\mu_l\right)_m\right]}, \quad (9.889)$$

where $l \in \{o, w, g\}$, $inj = w$ or g, $m \in \psi_w$, and $n \in \psi_w$, which when combined with Eq. 9.887 yields

$$q_{injsc_n} = \frac{G_{w_n}}{B_{inj_n}}\left[\sum_l\left(\frac{k_{rl}}{\mu_l}\right)_n\right]\frac{q_{spsc}}{\left[\sum_m\left(G_{w_m}/B_{inj_m}\right)\sum_l\left(k_{rl}/\mu_l\right)_m\right]}, \quad (9.890)$$

where $l \in \{o, w, g\}$, $inj = w$ or g, $m \in \psi_w$, and $n \in \psi_w$. For a bottomhole-pressure specification $p_{wf} = p_{wf_{sp}}$,

$$q_{injsc_n} = -\frac{G_{w_n}}{B_{inj_n}}\sum_l\left(\frac{k_{rl}}{\mu_l}\right)_n\left(p_{l_n} - p_{wf_{sp}}\right). \quad \text{.......... (9.891)}$$

where $l \in \{o,w,g\}$, $inj = w$ or g, and $n \in \psi_w$. The assumptions and remarks related to the allocation methods for injection wells, particularly the assumption of negligible pressure drop in the wellbore, are the same as those discussed in Sec. 9.7.3 for production wells. If p_{wf} is estimated explicitly at Time Level n, then, to preserve the specified injection rate,

$$q_{injsc_n} = \frac{G_{w_n}}{B_{inj_n}}\sum_l\left(\frac{k_{rl}}{\mu_l}\right)_n\left(p_{l_n} - p^n_{wf}\right) \times \frac{q_{spsc}}{\left[\sum_m(G_{w_m}/B_{inj_m})\sum_l(k_{rl}/\mu_l)_m\left(p_{l_m} - p^n_{wf}\right)\right]}, \quad \text{.................... (9.892)}$$

where $l \in \{o, w, g\}$, $inj = w$ or g, $m \in \psi_w$, and $n \in \psi_w$.

An injection profile for the specified injection rate that is compatible with the pressure distribution in the wellbore is also possible. In this case,

$$p_{wf_n} = p_{wf_{ref}} + H_n \quad \text{.......................... (9.866)}$$

$$\text{and } H_n = \sum_{m=1}^{m_n}\bar{\gamma}_{w_m}(Z_m - Z_{m-1}), \quad \text{.................. (9.867a)}$$

$n \in \psi_w$ and $\bar{\gamma}_{w_m}$ = gradient of the injected fluid in the interval $(Z_m - Z_{m-1})$, or, if a uniform well gradient is assumed,

$$H_n = \bar{\gamma}_w\left(Z_{m_n} - Z_0\right), \quad \text{........................ (9.867b)}$$

$$\text{where } \bar{\gamma}_w = \gamma_{inj} \quad \text{.............................. (9.893)}$$

$Z_{m_n} = Z_n$ and $inj = w$ or g. The rate of fluid injection into Injection Gridblock n is expressed as

$$q_{injsc_n} = -\frac{G_{w_n}}{B_{inj_n}}\sum_l\left(\frac{k_{rl}}{\mu_l}\right)_n\left(p_{o_n} - p_{wf_{ref}} - H_n\right), \quad \text{.... (9.894)}$$

$$\text{where } p_{wf_{ref}} = p_{wf_{sp}}, \quad \text{.......................... (9.895)}$$

for specified bottomhole pressure, and as

$$p_{wf_{ref}} = \frac{\sum_n\left[(G_{w_n}/B_{inj_n})(p_{o_n} - H_n)\sum_l(k_{rl}/\mu_l)_n\right] + q_{spsc}}{\sum_n(G_{w_n}/B_{inj_n})\sum_l(k_{rl}/\mu_l)_n}. \quad \text{.................... (9.896)}$$

for flow-rate specification, where $l \in \{o,w,g\}$, $inj = w$ or g, and $n \in \psi_w$.

Implicit Method for Multiblock Injection Wells. The implicit treatment method is similar to that for production wells discussed earlier. Expanding the contribution of Gridblock n to the well injection rate (q_{injsc_n}) with a Taylor series expansion results in

$$\overset{(v+1)}{q^{n+1}_{injsc_n}} = \overset{(v)}{q^{n+1}_{injsc_n}} + \left(\frac{\partial q_{injsc_n}}{\partial S_{w_n}}\right)^{\overset{(v)}{n+1}}\left[\overset{(v+1)}{S^{n+1}_{w_n}} - \overset{(v)}{S^{n+1}_{w_n}}\right] + \left(\frac{\partial q_{injsc_n}}{\partial S_{g_n}}\right)^{\overset{(v)}{n+1}}\left[\overset{(v+1)}{S^{n+1}_{g_n}} - \overset{(v)}{S^{n+1}_{g_n}}\right] + \left(\frac{\partial q_{injsc_n}}{\partial p_{o_n}}\right)^{\overset{(v)}{n+1}}\left[\overset{(v+1)}{p^{n+1}_{o_n}} - \overset{(v)}{p^{n+1}_{o_n}}\right] + \left(\frac{\partial q_{injsc_n}}{\partial p_{wf_{ref}}}\right)^{\overset{(v)}{n+1}}\left[\overset{(v+1)}{p^{n+1}_{wf_{ref}}} - \overset{(v)}{p^{n+1}_{wf_{ref}}}\right], \quad \text{....... (9.897)}$$

where $inj = w$ or g and $n \in \psi_w$. The specified injection rate for the well is the sum of the rates into the individual wellblocks. That is,

$$\sum_n \overset{(v+1)}{q^{n+1}_{injsc_n}} = \sum_n \overset{(v)}{q^{n+1}_{injsc_n}} + \sum_n\left\{\left(\frac{\partial q_{injsc_n}}{\partial S_{w_n}}\right)^{\overset{(v)}{n+1}}\left[\overset{(v+1)}{S^{n+1}_{w_n}} - \overset{(v)}{S^{n+1}_{w_n}}\right] + \left(\frac{\partial q_{injsc_n}}{\partial S_{g_n}}\right)^{\overset{(v)}{n+1}}\left[\overset{(v+1)}{S^{n+1}_{g_n}} - \overset{(v)}{S^{n+1}_{g_n}}\right] + \left(\frac{\partial q_{injsc_n}}{\partial p_{o_n}}\right)^{\overset{(v)}{n+1}}\left[\overset{(v+1)}{p^{n+1}_{o_n}} - \overset{(v)}{p^{n+1}_{o_n}}\right] + \left(\frac{\partial q_{injsc_n}}{\partial p_{wf_{ref}}}\right)^{\overset{(v)}{n+1}}\left[\overset{(v+1)}{p^{n+1}_{wf_{ref}}} - \overset{(v)}{p^{n+1}_{wf_{ref}}}\right]\right\}, \quad \text{... (9.898)}$$

where $inj = w$ or g and $n \in \psi_w$. For a rate specification, the well-injection rate at Iteration Level v must equal the well rate at Iteration Level $v+1$. That is,

$$\sum_n \overset{(v+1)}{q^{n+1}_{injsc_n}} = \sum_n \overset{(v)}{q^{n+1}_{injsc_n}}, \quad \text{...................... (9.899)}$$

where $inj = w$ or g and $n \in \psi_w$. Substituting Eq. 9.899 into Eq. 9.898 and solving for $p^{n+1}_{wf_{ref}}$, at Iteration Level $v+1$, results in

$$\overset{(v+1)}{p^{n+1}_{wf_{ref}}} = \overset{(v)}{p^{n+1}_{wf_{ref}}} - \left(\sum_n\left\{\left(\frac{\partial q_{injsc_n}}{\partial S_{w_n}}\right)^{\overset{(v)}{n+1}}\left[\overset{(v+1)}{S^{n+1}_{w_n}} - \overset{(v)}{S^{n+1}_{w_n}}\right] + \left(\frac{\partial q_{injsc_n}}{\partial S_{g_n}}\right)^{\overset{(v)}{n+1}}\left[\overset{(v+1)}{S^{n+1}_{g_n}} - \overset{(v)}{S^{n+1}_{g_n}}\right] + \left(\frac{\partial q_{injsc_n}}{\partial p_{o_n}}\right)^{\overset{(v)}{n+1}} \times \left[\overset{(v+1)}{p^{n+1}_{o_n}} - \overset{(v)}{p^{n+1}_{o_n}}\right]\right\}\right) \Big/ \sum_n\left(\frac{\partial q_{injsc_n}}{\partial p_{wf_{ref}}}\right)^{\overset{(v)}{n+1}}, \quad \text{.................... (9.900)}$$

where $inj = w$ or g and $n \in \psi_w$. The derivative terms in Eqs. 9.897, 9.898, and 9.900 can be obtained from the injectivity equation, Eq. 9.894.

$$\frac{\partial q_{injsc_n}}{\partial S_{w_n}} = -\frac{G_{w_n}}{B_{inj_n}}\left(\frac{1}{\mu_o}\frac{\partial k_{ro}}{\partial S_w} + \frac{1}{\mu_w}\frac{dk_{rw}}{dS_w}\right)_n \times \left(p_{o_n} - p_{wf_{ref}} - H_n\right). \quad \text{................ (9.901)}$$

where $inj = w$ or g and $n \in \psi_w$.

$$\frac{\partial q_{injsc_n}}{\partial S_{g_n}} = -\frac{G_{w_n}}{B_{inj_n}}\left(\frac{1}{\mu_o}\frac{\partial k_{ro}}{\partial S_g} + \frac{1}{\mu_g}\frac{dk_{rg}}{dS_g}\right)_n$$

$$\times \left(p_{o_n} - p_{wf_{ref}} - H_n\right), \quad \text{.................} (9.902)$$

where $inj = w$ or g and $n \in \psi_w$.

$$\frac{\partial q_{injsc_n}}{\partial p_{o_n}} = -\frac{G_{w_n}}{B_{inj_n}}\left\{\left(\frac{k_{ro}}{\mu_o}\right)_n\left(p_{o_n} - p_{wf_{ref}} - H_n\right)\right.$$

$$\times\left[\frac{1}{\left(p_{o_n} - p_{wf_{ref}} - H_n\right)} - \frac{1}{\mu_{o_n}}\frac{\mathrm{d}\mu_{o_n}}{\mathrm{d}p_{o_n}} - \frac{1}{B_{inj_n}}\frac{\mathrm{d}B_{inj_n}}{\mathrm{d}p_{o_n}}\right]$$

$$+\left(\frac{k_{rw}}{\mu_w}\right)_n\left(p_{o_n} - p_{wf_{ref}} - H_n\right)$$

$$\times\left[\frac{1}{\left(p_{o_n} - p_{wf_{ref}} - H_n\right)} - \frac{1}{\mu_{w_n}}\frac{\mathrm{d}\mu_{w_n}}{\mathrm{d}p_{o_n}} - \frac{1}{B_{inj_n}}\frac{\mathrm{d}B_{inj_n}}{\mathrm{d}p_{o_n}}\right]$$

$$+\left(\frac{k_{rg}}{\mu_g}\right)_n\left(p_{o_n} - p_{wf_{ref}} - H_n\right)$$

$$\left.\times\left[\frac{1}{\left(p_{o_n} - p_{wf_{ref}} - H_n\right)} - \frac{1}{\mu_{g_n}}\frac{\mathrm{d}\mu_{g_n}}{\mathrm{d}p_{o_n}} - \frac{1}{B_{inj_n}}\frac{\mathrm{d}B_{inj_n}}{\mathrm{d}p_{o_n}}\right]\right\},$$

$$\text{...................} (9.903)$$

where $inj = w$ or g and $n \in \psi_w$.

$$\frac{\partial q_{injsc_n}}{\partial p_{wf_{ref}}} = \frac{G_{w_n}}{B_{inj_n}}\sum_l\left[\left(\frac{k_{rl}}{\mu_l}\right)_n\left(1 + \frac{\partial H_n}{\partial p_{wf_{ref}}}\right)\right], \quad \text{.......} (9.904)$$

where $l \in \{o, w, g\}$; $inj = w$ or g; and $n \in \psi_w$.

In our discussion on the derivative terms, we made the following assumptions.

1. Capillary pressure effects are negligible. This assumption implies that all fluid properties B_l and μ_l for $l = o$, w, or g are evaluated with p_o.
2. The relative permeability to oil, k_{ro}, obeys a three-phase relative permeability model of the form $k_{ro} = k_{ro}$ (S_w, S_g).
3. The relative permeability to water, k_{rw}, is a function of water-phase saturation only.
4. The relative permeability to gas, k_{rg}, is a function of gas-phase saturation only.

These assumptions may be relaxed at the expense of more complicated derivative terms. Similar assumptions may be required for the evaluation of the partial derivatives of F_l for $l = o$, w, or g in Eqs. 9.876 through 9.879 for production wells. Also in this discussion, we have assumed that the injection-rate specification was made at standard conditions (O_{i1}). If the injection-rate specification is made at reservoir conditions, (O_{i2}), then set $B_{inj} = 1$ and $\mathrm{d}B_{inj}/\mathrm{d}p_o = 0$ and replace well specification q_{spsc} with q_{sp} in the formulation.

9.7.5 Treatment of Gas-Phase Discontinuity and Variable-Bubblepoint Approach. In multiphase flow, the gas phase may disappear or reappear in regions of an oil reservoir under certain conditions. For example, the gas phase does not exist initially in undersaturated oil reservoirs but appears under primary depletion as the reservoir pressure drops below the bubblepoint pressure. Also, the gas phase may disappear in a saturated oil reservoir undergoing repressurization by water injection. Likewise, it may reappear if gas is injected into an undersaturated reservoir. Also, gas may appear locally because of pressure drawdowns in the near-wellbore vicinity. Therefore, proper handling of gas-phase changes in a black-oil simulation is important. The two most common methods for handling gas-phase change are the variable-substitution method and the pseudosolution GOR method.

Variable-Substitution Method. In the variable-substitution method, the disappearance and reappearance of the gas phase is handled rigorously. The main idea is to identify the prevailing conditions in a given gridblock and then determine the appropriate unknowns and the constraint equation to be used. The variable-substitution method uses the $(p_o\text{-}S_g\text{-}S_w)$ formulation and the $(p_o\text{-}R_s\text{-}S_w)$ formulation. Switching to the appropriate formulation for each gridblock takes place every Newtonian iteration. A gridblock in a reservoir exhibits one of two cases.

Case 1. $S_g^{(\nu)} > 0$ or $R_s^{(\nu)} = f(p_o^{(\nu)})$, which implies that the oil phase in the gridblock is saturated with gas (Point A in **Fig. 9.21**) and, therefore, R_s is not an unknown. The constraint equation in this case is $S_o = 1 - S_w - S_g$, and the unknowns are taken as p_o, S_g, and S_w.

Case 2. $S_g^{(\nu)} = 0$ or $R_s^{(\nu)} < f(p_o^{(\nu)})$, which implies that the oil phase in the gridblock is undersaturated with gas (Point B in Fig. 9.21) and, therefore, R_s is independent of oil pressure. The constraint equation in this case is $S_o = 1 - S_w$, and the unknowns are taken as p_o, R_s, and S_w.

Pseudosolution GOR Method. In this method, the disappearance and reappearance of the gas phase is handled without resorting to the variable-substitution logic in the numerical-solution procedure of a black-oil simulator. This is accomplished through the use of pseudosolution GOR, $\tilde{R}_s$,[18] which is expressed as

$$\tilde{R}_s = R_s(p_o)\Psi(S_g), \quad \text{.........................} (9.905)$$

where $\Psi(S_g) = 1$ .... (9.906a)

if $S_g \gg \varepsilon_g$, and

$$\Psi(S_g) = \frac{S_g}{S_g + \varepsilon_g} \quad \text{..........................} (9.906b)$$

otherwise. In Eq. 9.906, ε_g = tolerance used for the disappearance and reappearance of the gas phase. This method uses the $(p_o\text{-}S_g\text{-}S_w)$ formulation only. The use of Eqs. 9.905, 9.906a, and 9.906b forces the system in each gridblock to act as if there were a small amount of noncondensible gas. In effect, the gas phase is allowed to approach disappearance without achieving it. The success of this method depends on an appropriate initialization of saturations consistent with the pseudosolution GOR equation, a fully-implicit treatment of the pseudosolution GOR function, and an appropriate reassignment of saturations if negative gas saturation is encountered during iteration for a timestep. Eq. 9.907 may be used[20] to reassign gas saturation. If $S_g^{(\nu)}$ is negative,

$$S_g^{(\nu)} = \sqrt{S_g^n \varepsilon_g}. \quad \text{.............................} (9.907)$$

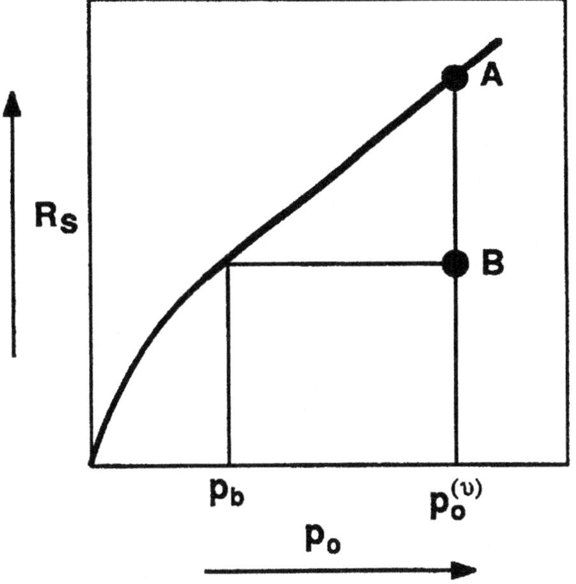

Fig. 9.21—Solution GOR at saturated and undersaturated conditions.

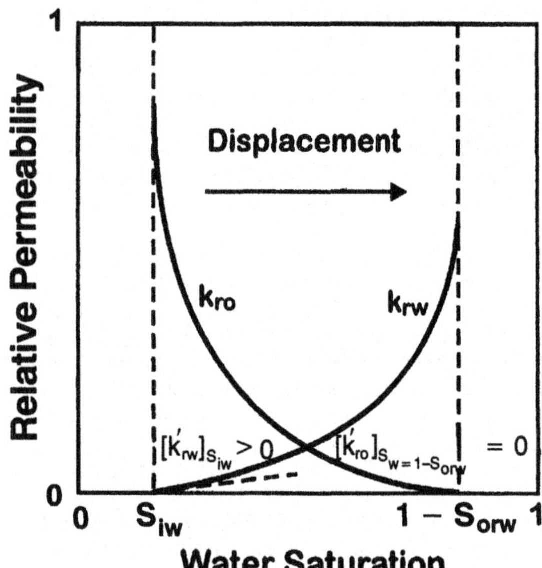

Fig. 9.22—Handling of k_r curves at endpoints for oil/water system.[2]

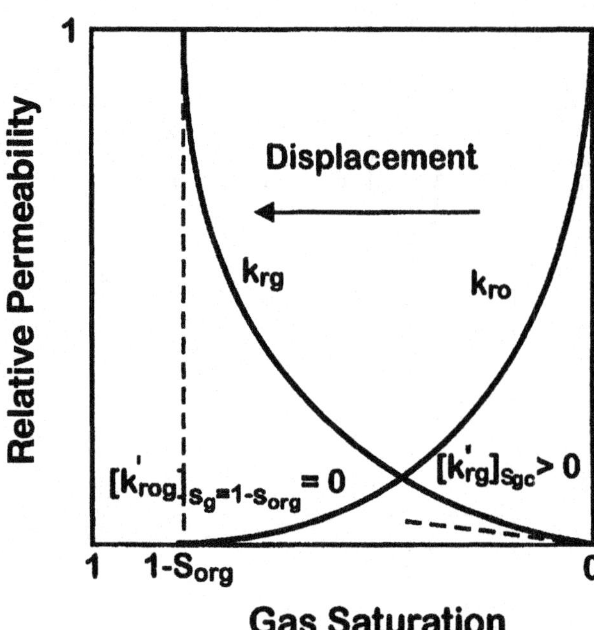

Fig. 9.23—Handling of k_r curves at endpoints for oil/gas system.

9.7.6 Treatment of Slopes of Relative Permeabilities. The implicit treatment of relative permeabilities requires estimates of their slopes. Implicit simulators use tangent slopes, while semi-implicit simulators use chord slopes. Tangent slopes in relative permeability tables are piecewise constant if linear interpolation is used. Chord slopes must be taken in the direction of expected saturation changes. This is important particularly when one of the phases is immobile, for example, $(k'_{rw})_{S_{iw}} > 0$ in **Fig. 9.22** and $(k'_{rg})_{S_{gc}} > 0$ in **Fig. 9.23**.

Neglecting the direction of saturation change may result in an explicit treatment of the relative permeability of the displacing phase near the critical displacing phase saturation (S_{iw} in Fig. 9.22 and $S_g = S_{gc}$ in Fig. 9.23). At the other relative permeability endpoints ($S_w = 1 - S_{orw}$ in Fig. 9.22 and $S_g = 1 - S_{org}$ in Fig. 9.23), the slopes of k_{ro} must be set to zero to prevent overshoot.[2] Overshoot is a term used to describe the situation that exists when predicted saturations fall beyond their physical limits ($S_{iw} \leqq S_w \leqq 1 - S_{orw}$ for oil/water system in Fig. 9.22, and $0 \leqq S_g \leqq 1 - S_{org}$ for oil/gas system in Fig. 9.23).

9.7.7 Automatic Timestep Selection. Most commercial reservoir simulators allow for automatic timestep selection, or automatic timestep control. The most common automatic-timestep-selection procedure is Todd *et al.*'s.[5] The objective of the Todd *et al.* approach is to limit the growth or reduction of successive timesteps on the basis of changes of the principal unknowns. In the (p_o-S_g-S_w) formulation and in conjunction with the (p_o-R_s-S_w) formulation for the variable-substitution method for phase disappearance (Sec. 9.7.5), this approach takes the form

$$\Delta t^{n+1} = \Delta t_{\min} \quad \text{(9.908)}$$

for $n = 0$ and the form

$$\Delta t^{n+1} = \min\left(F_{\Delta t}\Delta t, \Delta t_p^{n+1}, \Delta t_S^{n+1}, \Delta t_{R_s}^{n+1}\right) \quad \text{(9.909)}$$

for $n = 1,2,3\ldots$,

$$\text{where } \Delta t_p^{n+1} = \frac{\Delta p_{\max}}{\max\limits_{i,j,k}\left(\left|p_{i,j,k}^{n+1} - p_{i,j,k}^{n}\right|\right)}\Delta t^n, \quad \text{(9.910)}$$

$$\Delta t_S^{n+1} = \Delta S_{\max} \Big/ \left[\max_{i,j,k}\left(\left|S_{o_{i,j,k}}^{n+1} - S_{o_{i,j,k}}^{n}\right|, \left|S_{g_{i,j,k}}^{n+1} - S_{g_{i,j,k}}^{n}\right|, \left|S_{w_{i,j,k}}^{n+1} - S_{w_{i,j,k}}^{n}\right|\right)\right]$$

$$\times \Delta t^n, \quad \text{(9.911)}$$

$$\text{and } \Delta t_{R_s}^{n+1} = \frac{\Delta R_{s_{\max}}}{\max\limits_{i,j,k}\left(\left|R_{s_{i,j,k}}^{n+1} - R_{s_{i,j,k}}^{n}\right|\right)}\Delta t^n. \quad \text{(9.912)}$$

In Eqs. 9.908 through 9.912, the following are the user-defined input parameters: $\Delta t_{\min}$ = minimum allowable timestep size, $F_{\Delta t}$ = maximum allowable ratio of $\Delta t^{n+1}/\Delta t^n$ ($F_{\Delta t} > 1$ and generally is between 2 and 3), $\Delta p_{\max}$ = maximum allowable pressure change from one timestep to the next, $\Delta S_{\max}$ = maximum allowable saturation change from one timestep to the next, and $\Delta R_{s_{\max}}$ = maximum allowable change in solution-gas/oil ratio from one timestep to the next.

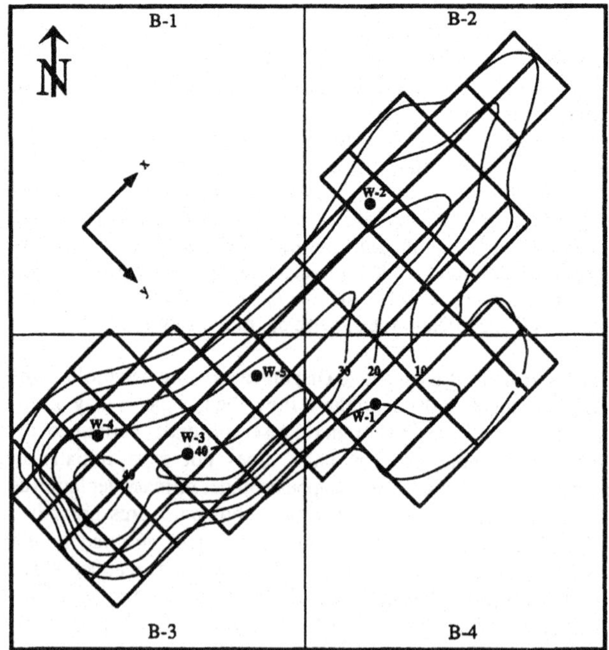

Fig. 9.24—The A-1 reservoir as studied under multiphase-flow conditions.

TABLE 9.13—WELL DATA FOR THREE-PHASE FLOW EXERCISE

Name	Gridblock	Type	Radius, r_w (ft)	Specification
W-1	(7,7)	Producer	0.25	$q_{tsc} = -100{,}000$ STB/D
W-2	(9,3)	Producer	0.25	$p_{sf} = 3{,}400$ psia
W-3	(4,4)	Producer	0.25	$q_{osc} = -100$ STB/D
W-4	(3,2)	Producer	0.25	$q_{gsc} = -1$ MMscf/D
W-5	(6,4)	Producer	0.25	$q_{Lsc} = -150$ STB/D

TABLE 9.14—INITIAL CONDITIONS AND OTHER RESERVOIR PARAMETERS FOR THREE-PHASE EXERCISE

S_{oi}	0.50
S_{gi}	0.08
S_{wi}	0.42
p_{oi}, psia	4,800
c_R, psi^{-1}	3.0×10^{-6}
T_R, °F	190
T_{sc}, °F	60
p_{sc}, psia	14.7

It is important to note that, because of the nonlinear nature of the finite-difference equations, the use of Eqs. 9.908 through 9.912 does not guarantee that the simulated changes in the principal unknowns (e.g., $\max_{i,j,k}|p^{n+1}_{i,j,k} - p^n_{i,j,k}|$) will be less than the desired maximum change (e.g., Δp_{max}). If the simulated change exceeds the desired change, the timestep is reduced by

$$\Delta t^{n+1} = \Delta t^n / F_{\Delta t}. \quad \text{(9.913)}$$

(Note: $F_{\Delta t}$ can have different values when Δt^{n+1} is increased or decreased.) The simulation is terminated if the process of reducing Δt^{n+1} is performed more than a predetermined number of times or if the value of Δt^{n+1} becomes less than Δt_{min} during the process.

9.8 Chapter Project

In Chap. 8, the A-1 reservoir was studied as a single-phase reservoir by considering, individually, flow of an incompressible, a slightly compressible, and a compressible fluid. In this chapter, the A-1 reservoir is a multiphase reservoir. Along these lines, two separate problems are examined: a three-phase, oil/water/gas flow problem and a two-phase problem with water injection into an oil reservoir with no gas. In these two studies, the reservoir rock and fluid properties, as summarized in Chap. 2, are assigned to the extent that they are applicable. **Fig. 9.24** shows the A-1 reservoir's five wells and rectangular grid system.

9.8.1 Three-Phase Flow Problem. In this exercise, the A-1 reservoir is considered to contain oil, water, and gas phases. All five wells (Wells W-1 through W-5) are treated as active wells. **Table 9.13** gives the relevant information, including the various boundary conditions specified at each well location. All the wells are assumed to have no skin. **Table 9.14** provides information on the initial conditions specified and other necessary parameters. The total simulation time was considered to be 60 days. The simulator used the IMPES formulation with nonlinear terms calculated at Time Level $n+½$. In the calculation of the relative permeability to oil, Stone's second model was used (see Sec. 2.3.5). The table-lookup routines that use linear-interpolation technique were used to calculate the nonlinear fluid properties. Numerical-differentiation procedures were implemented when the calculation of the derivatives of the nonlinear terms was required.

Fig. 9.25 gives the calculated pressure distributions for each phase at the end of 60 days of simulation. **Fig. 9.26** presents the saturation distribution at the end of 60 days of simulation. In the wellblocks hosting the five wells of the A-1 reservoir, we can easily recognize the lowest pressure values encountered compared with those in the surrounding four neighboring gridblocks. The phase saturations as presented in Fig. 9.26 do not show noticeable changes specifically for the oil and gas phases. On average, oil saturation decreased by 3 to 4%, and this decrease in oil saturation was replaced by an increase in the gas-phase saturation. This is expected because, as the reservoir pressure decreased, more gas came out of solution and occupied a larger fraction of the available pore space.

Tables 9.15 through 9.19 give the well reports as documented by the output routine of the simulator. In these well reports, flow rates for each phase are listed with the flowing sandface pressure, wellblock pressure (for water phase), and oil and gas saturations. Table 9.15 shows that Well W-1 reacts to 100,000 STB/D total fluid production specification by producing only a few barrels of water, 20

WATER-PHASE PRESSURE DISTRIBUTION AT 60 DAYS (psia)

```
*******  3615.5  3609.2  3608.0  *******  *******  *******  *******  *******  *******  *******  *******
 3619.0  3611.9  3596.0  3598.0  3592.8  *******  *******  *******  3542.8  3571.9  *******  *******
 3619.5  3612.5  3601.1  3589.0  3583.2  3568.1  3585.2  3577.3  3522.7  3573.8  3588.7  3599.5
 3620.7  3613.2  3598.0  3571.5  3574.6  3548.0  3585.7  3587.5  3574.1  3583.5  3590.5  3598.7
 3621.0  3614.3  3600.1  3584.9  3583.1  3578.1  3591.5  3594.4  3587.9  3588.2  *******  *******
*******  *******  *******  3589.1  3586.5  3585.2  3592.3  3599.6  3593.0  3590.8  *******  *******
*******  *******  *******  *******  *******  3588.0  3587.3  3606.7  *******  *******  *******  *******
*******  *******  *******  *******  *******  *******  3602.8  3616.4  3624.5  *******  *******  *******
*******  *******  *******  *******  *******  *******  3615.8  3624.2  3627.8  *******  *******  *******
```

OIL-PHASE PRESSURE DISTRIBUTION AT 60 DAYS (psia)

```
*******  3617.1  3610.8  3609.7  *******  *******  *******  *******  *******  *******  *******  *******
 3620.7  3613.6  3597.7  3599.6  3594.4  *******  *******  *******  3544.4  3573.5  *******  *******
 3621.1  3614.2  3602.8  3590.6  3584.8  3569.7  3586.9  3578.9  3524.3  3575.5  3590.4  3601.2
 3622.3  3614.8  3599.7  3573.2  3576.2  3549.6  3587.3  3589.1  3575.7  3585.1  3592.1  3600.4
 3622.6  3615.9  3601.7  3586.5  3584.8  3579.7  3593.1  3596.1  3589.5  3589.9  *******  *******
*******  *******  *******  3590.8  3588.2  3586.9  3593.9  3601.2  3594.6  3592.4  *******  *******
*******  *******  *******  *******  *******  3589.6  3589.0  3608.3  *******  *******  *******  *******
*******  *******  *******  *******  *******  *******  3604.4  3618.0  3626.1  *******  *******  *******
*******  *******  *******  *******  *******  *******  3617.5  3625.9  3629.5  *******  *******  *******
```

GAS-PHASE PRESSURE DISTRIBUTION AT 60 DAYS (psia)

```
*******  3617.2  3610.9  3609.8  *******  *******  *******  *******  *******  *******  *******  *******
 3620.8  3613.7  3597.8  3599.7  3594.5  *******  *******  *******  3544.5  3573.6  *******  *******
 3621.2  3614.3  3602.9  3590.8  3584.9  3569.9  3587.0  3579.0  3524.4  3575.6  3590.5  3601.3
 3622.4  3614.9  3599.8  3573.3  3576.3  3549.7  3587.4  3589.2  3575.8  3585.2  3592.2  3600.5
 3622.8  3616.0  3601.8  3586.6  3584.9  3579.8  3593.2  3596.2  3589.6  3590.0  *******  *******
*******  *******  *******  3590.9  3588.3  3587.0  3594.0  3601.3  3594.7  3592.5  *******  *******
*******  *******  *******  *******  *******  3589.8  3589.1  3608.4  *******  *******  *******  *******
*******  *******  *******  *******  *******  *******  3604.5  3618.1  3626.2  *******  *******  *******
*******  *******  *******  *******  *******  *******  3617.6  3626.0  3629.6  *******  *******  *******
```

Fig. 9.25—Phase pressure distributions in the A-1 reservoir at $t = 60$ days.

WATER-PHASE SATURATION DISTRIBUTION AT 60 DAYS

```
*******  0.4241  0.4241  0.4240  *******  *******  *******  *******  *******  *******  *******  *******
 0.4242  0.4239  0.4240  0.4242  0.4240  *******  *******  *******  0.4243  0.4243  *******  *******
 0.4241  0.4237  0.4237  0.4241  0.4243  0.4241  0.4240  0.4242  0.4241  0.4240  0.4240  0.4241
 0.4241  0.4239  0.4239  0.4239  0.4240  0.4243  0.4240  0.4240  0.4242  0.4240  0.4239  0.4239
 0.4241  0.4240  0.4242  0.4239  0.4239  0.4239  0.4240  0.4240  0.4240  0.4239  *******  *******
*******  *******  *******  0.4244  0.4239  0.4240  0.4239  0.4239  0.4240  0.4239  *******  *******
*******  *******  *******  *******  *******  0.4240  0.4240  0.4239  *******  *******  *******  *******
*******  *******  *******  *******  *******  *******  0.4239  0.4238  0.4239  *******  *******  *******
*******  *******  *******  *******  *******  *******  0.4239  0.4238  0.4238  *******  *******  *******
```

OIL-PHASE SATURATION DISTRIBUTION AT 60 DAYS

```
*******  0.4605  0.4606  0.4598  *******  *******  *******  *******  *******  *******  *******  *******
 0.4621  0.4586  0.4590  0.4609  0.4589  *******  *******  *******  0.4583  0.4597  *******  *******
 0.4610  0.4573  0.4567  0.4591  0.4604  0.4579  0.4583  0.4613  0.4630  0.4584  0.4587  0.4598
 0.4611  0.4594  0.4584  0.4566  0.4579  0.4587  0.4580  0.4585  0.4610  0.4581  0.4579  0.4580
 0.4609  0.4599  0.4613  0.4574  0.4569  0.4572  0.4587  0.4587  0.4584  0.4577  *******  *******
*******  *******  *******  0.4618  0.4574  0.4578  0.4580  0.4588  0.4587  0.4581  *******  *******
*******  *******  *******  *******  *******  0.4583  0.4579  0.4591  *******  *******  *******  *******
*******  *******  *******  *******  *******  *******  0.4587  0.4586  0.4597  *******  *******  *******
*******  *******  *******  *******  *******  *******  0.4594  0.4591  0.4590  *******  *******  *******
```

GAS-PHASE SATURATION DISTRIBUTION AT 60 DAYS

```
*******  0.1155  0.1153  0.1162  *******  *******  *******  *******  *******  *******  *******  *******
 0.1136  0.1175  0.1170  0.1149  0.1171  *******  *******  *******  0.1174  0.1160  *******  *******
 0.1149  0.1190  0.1196  0.1168  0.1153  0.1181  0.1177  0.1145  0.1129  0.1176  0.1173  0.1160
 0.1148  0.1167  0.1177  0.1195  0.1181  0.1169  0.1180  0.1175  0.1149  0.1179  0.1182  0.1181
 0.1151  0.1161  0.1145  0.1187  0.1192  0.1188  0.1172  0.1173  0.1177  0.1183  *******  *******
*******  *******  *******  0.1138  0.1187  0.1182  0.1181  0.1173  0.1173  0.1179  *******  *******
*******  *******  *******  *******  *******  0.1177  0.1181  0.1170  *******  *******  *******  *******
*******  *******  *******  *******  *******  *******  0.1173  0.1176  0.1164  *******  *******  *******
*******  *******  *******  *******  *******  *******  0.1167  0.1170  0.1172  *******  *******  *******
```

Fig. 9.26—Phase saturation distributions in the A-1 reservoir at $t = 60$ days.

TABLE 9.15—WELL REPORT FOR WELL W-1

Time (days)	Flow Rates q_o (STB/D)	q_w (B/D)	q_g (Mscf/D)	BHP p_{wf} (psia)	Pressure $p_{7,7}$ (psia)	Saturation at Gridblock (7,7) S_o	S_g
1	−51.60	−4.09	−561.19	4,668.88	4,771.59	0.499	0.080
2	−51.08	−4.06	−561.19	4,652.80	4,754.72	0.499	0.081
3	−50.43	−4.03	−561.19	4,632.35	4,733.30	0.498	0.081
4	−49.69	−3.99	−561.20	4,608.85	4,708.70	0.497	0.082
5	−48.92	−3.95	−561.20	4,583.60	4,682.28	0.496	0.083
10	−44.99	−3.74	−561.23	4,446.13	4,538.91	0.492	0.087
15	−40.00	−3.50	−561.26	4,293.41	4,379.45	0.486	0.092
20	−35.83	−3.30	−561.28	4,158.47	4,239.01	0.481	0.097
25	−32.44	−3.14	−561.30	4,033.63	4,109.65	0.476	0.102
30	−29.74	−3.02	−561.32	3,922.50	3,994.88	0.471	0.106
35	−28.14	−2.97	−561.33	3,850.46	3,921.45	0.469	0.108
40	−26.68	−2.93	−561.33	3,780.10	3,849.79	0.466	0.110
45	−25.36	−2.89	−561.34	3,712.70	3,781.20	0.464	0.112
50	−24.17	−2.85	−561.35	3,647.63	3,715.00	0.462	0.114
55	−23.06	−2.82	−561.35	3,584.21	3,650.52	0.460	0.116
60	−22.03	−2.78	−561.36	3,522.04	3,587.33	0.458	0.118

TABLE 9.16—WELL REPORT FOR WELL W-2

Time (days)	Flow Rates q_o (STB/D)	q_w (B/D)	q_g (Mscf/D)	BHP p_{wf} (psia)	Pressure $p_{9,3}$ (psia)	Saturation at Gridblock (9,3) S_o	S_g
1	−636.62	−57.31	−9,465.34	3,400.00	4,297.01	0.483	0.095
2	−578.54	−53.26	−8,978.96	3,400.00	4,229.87	0.481	0.097
3	−543.52	−50.62	−8,613.72	3,400.00	4,186.70	0.480	0.098
4	−513.27	−48.28	−8,277.04	3,400.00	4,148.56	0.479	0.098
5	−487.06	−46.21	−7,973.40	3,400.00	4,115.02	0.478	0.099
10	−390.37	−38.32	−6,771.39	3,400.00	3,988.57	0.475	0.102
15	−328.38	−33.29	−5,896.82	3,400.00	3,909.10	0.474	0.103
20	−278.42	−29.04	−5,169.66	3,400.00	3,842.49	0.473	0.104
25	−238.30	−25.49	−4,569.58	3,400.00	3,787.24	0.471	0.105
30	−203.76	−22.31	−4,032.00	3,400.00	3,738.08	0.470	0.106
35	−173.98	−19.47	−3,547.57	3,400.00	3,694.30	0.469	0.107
40	−148.57	−16.96	−3,114.38	3,400.00	3,655.76	0.467	0.108
45	−125.80	−14.63	−2,707.83	3,400.00	3,620.19	0.466	0.109
50	−104.88	−12.42	−2,316.37	3,400.00	3,586.54	0.465	0.110
55	−85.34	−10.28	−1,932.65	3,400.00	3,554.17	0.464	0.111
60	−66.88	−8.19	−1,552.20	3,400.00	3,522.67	0.463	0.112

TABLE 9.17—WELL REPORT FOR WELL W-3

Time (days)	Flow Rates q_o (STB/D)	q_w (B/D)	q_g (Mscf/D)	BHP p_{wf} (psia)	Pressure $p_{4,4}$ (psia)	Saturation at Gridblock (4,4) S_o	S_g
1	−100	−7.92	−1,084.08	4,732.10	4,777.57	0.499	0.080
2	−100	−7.94	−1,093.57	4,718.73	4,764.29	0.499	0.081
3	−100	−7.96	−1,103.17	4,705.06	4,750.72	0.498	0.081
4	−100	−7.99	−1,113.45	4,690.40	4,736.16	0.498	0.081
5	−100	−8.01	−1,124.50	4,674.64	4,720.53	0.497	0.082
10	−100	−8.17	−1,190.50	4,581.50	4,628.06	0.495	0.085
15	−100	−8.36	−1,273.54	4,466.78	4,514.20	0.491	0.088
20	−100	−8.85	−1,442.42	4,304.75	4,354.44	0.485	0.093
25	−100	−9.41	−1,639.68	4,139.32	4,191.65	0.478	0.099
30	−100	−9.98	−1,838.93	3,987.98	4,042.94	0.473	0.105
35	−100	−10.47	−1,986.45	3,886.18	3,943.52	0.469	0.108
40	−100	−10.91	−2,103.89	3,808.91	3,868.43	0.466	0.110
45	−100	−11.37	−2,226.43	3,731.86	3,793.62	0.464	0.113
50	−100	−11.84	−2,354.56	3,654.93	3,719.00	0.461	0.115
55	−100	−12.33	−2,488.01	3,578.49	3,644.92	0.459	0.117
60	−100	−12.83	−2,626.74	3,502.70	3,571.55	0.457	0.119

to 50 STB/D of oil, and more than 0.5 MMscf/D of gas. Obviously, this production scheme for Well W-1 is undesirable because the producing GOR is very high.

Table 9.16 presents the well report for Well W-2. As Table 9.16 indicates, Well W-2 was produced under a constant flowing sandface pressure specification of 3,400 psia. Under these conditions, oil, water, and gas production rates were relatively larger compared with the production rates from Well W-1.

In Well W-3, an oil production rate of 100 STB/D was specified. Table 9.17 provides information about the performance of Well W-3 under the imposed conditions. It is clear from Table 9.17 that pro-

TABLE 9.18—WELL REPORT FOR WELL W-4

Time (days)	Flow Rates q_o (STB/D)	q_w (B/D)	q_g (Mscf/D)	BHP p_{wf} (psia)	Pressure $p_{3,2}$ (psia)	Saturation at Gridblock (3,2) S_o	S_g
1	−91.92	−7.29	−1,000.00	4,713.24	4,770.50	0.499	0.080
2	−91.25	−7.25	−1,000.00	4,701.27	4,758.21	0.499	0.081
3	−90.64	−7.22	−1,000.00	4,689.93	4,746.58	0.498	0.081
4	−90.01	−7.19	−1,000.00	4,678.19	4,734.55	0.498	0.081
5	−89.36	−7.15	−1,000.00	4,665.77	4,721.82	0.498	0.082
10	−85.53	−6.95	−1,000.00	4,590.67	4,644.91	0.495	0.084
15	−80.91	−6.71	−1,000.00	4,494.19	4,546.26	0.492	0.086
20	−72.49	−6.30	−1,000.00	4,343.32	4,391.81	0.487	0.091
25	−63.60	−5.89	−1,000.00	4,178.49	4,223.31	0.480	0.097
30	−56.65	−5.56	−1,000.00	4,028.43	4,070.35	0.474	0.103
35	−52.24	−5.38	−1,000.00	3,922.25	3,962.51	0.471	0.108
40	−49.62	−5.30	−1,000.00	3,852.09	3,891.64	0.468	0.109
45	−47.05	−5.23	−1,000.00	3,779.20	3,818.04	0.466	0.110
50	−44.61	−5.16	−1,000.00	3,705.60	3,743.75	0.464	0.112
55	−42.31	−5.09	−1,000.00	3,632.14	3,669.61	0.461	0.114
60	−40.17	−5.02	−1,000.00	3,559.20	3,596.01	0.459	0.117

TABLE 9.19—WELL REPORT FOR WELL W-5

Time (days)	Flow Rates q_o (STB/D)	q_w (B/D)	q_g (Mscf/D)	BHP p_{wf} (psia)	Pressure $p_{6,4}$ (psia)	Saturation at Gridblock (6,4) S_o	S_g
1	−138.98	−11.02	−1,513.84	4,686.66	4,767.09	0.499	0.080
2	−138.94	−11.06	−1,529.75	4,664.46	4,748.09	0.499	0.081
3	−138.90	−11.10	−1,546.70	4,644.00	4,727.83	0.498	0.081
4	−138.86	−11.14	−1,564.97	4,622.18	4,706.25	0.497	0.082
5	−138.81	−11.19	−1,584.24	4,599.38	4,683.68	0.497	0.083
10	−138.56	−11.44	−1,690.23	4,476.35	4,561.96	0.493	0.086
15	−138.14	−11.86	−1,848.12	4,333.58	4,421.61	0.488	0.090
20	−137.54	−12.46	−2,060.61	4,180.77	4,272.41	0.483	0.095
25	−136.90	−13.10	−2,286.57	4,030.81	4,126.20	0.477	0.100
30	−136.29	−13.71	−2,506.63	3,895.67	3,994.66	0.472	0.105
35	−135.70	−14.30	−2,656.63	3,804.87	3,907.58	0.470	0.107
40	−135.17	−14.83	−2,790.48	3,725.76	3,831.73	0.467	0.109
45	−134.66	−15.34	−2,923.71	3,649.68	3,758.86	0.465	0.111
50	−134.14	−15.86	−3,059.10	3,575.10	3,687.47	0.463	0.113
55	−133.61	−16.39	−3,197.33	3,501.66	3,617.22	0.461	0.115
60	−133.08	−16.92	−3,338.74	3,429.19	3,547.97	0.459	0.116

TABLE 9.20—WELL DATA FOR TWO-PHASE WATER-INJECTION PROBLEM

Name	Gridblock	Type	Radius, r_w (ft)	Specification
W-2	(9,3)	Producer	0.25	p_{sf} = 5,300 psia
W-3	(4,4)	Injector	0.25	q_{wsc} = 250 B/D
W-4	(3,2)	Producer	0.25	p_{sf} = 5,300 psia

ducing 100 STB/D of oil from Well W-3 is possible only at the expense of increasing water and gas production.

In Well W-4, a gas flow rate of 1 MMscf/D was specified. Oil flow rate was 91.92 STB/D at the end of the first day of production, and this production rate decreased to 40.17 STB/D at the end of 60 days. Similarly, water production rate started at 7.29 B/D and decreased to 5.02 B/D in 60 days. Table 9.18 summarizes these results. Finally, Table 9.19 presents a production report for Well W-5. In this well, another boundary condition specification option, the total liquid production rate of 150 STB/D, was imposed. Performance of this well shows increases in water and gas production rates, accompanied by a slightly steady decrease in oil production rate.

9.8.2 Two-Phase, Water Injection Problem. In this second multiphase-flow exercise, the A-1 reservoir is treated as a two-phase (oil/water) system. Only Wells W-2 through W-4 are designated as active wells. As **Table 9.20** summarizes, Well W-3 is an injector and Wells W-2 and W-4 are producers. All three wells are assumed to have zero skin.

TABLE 9.21—INITIAL CONDITIONS AND OTHER RESERVOIR PARAMETERS USED IN TWO-PHASE WATER INJECTION EXERCISE

S_o	0.50
S_{wi}	0.50
p_{oi}, psia	7,000
c_R, psi^{-1}	5.9×10^{-6}
B_o, RB/STB	$1.0/[1.0+5.0\times10^{-6}(p-14.7)]$
B_w, RB/B	$1.0/[1.0+1.0\times10^{-6}(p-14.7)]$
μ_w, cp	0.52

Pressure (psia)	Oil Viscosity (cp)
5,000.0	0.9200
5,500.0	0.9243
6,000.0	0.9372
6,500.0	0.9494
7,000.0	0.9650
7,500.0	0.9812
8,000.0	1.0019

Table 9.21 provides information on initial conditions and other parameters adapted specially for the two-phase exercise. For the relative permeability data, the two-phase oil/water relative permeability data presented in Fig. 2.27 and Table 2.6 were used.

WATER-PHASE PRESSURE DISTRIBUTION AT 100 DAYS (psia)

```
******* 5406.1 5400.6 5416.9 ***************************************************************
5416.7  5405.3 5384.8 5424.9 5441.6 *********************** 5385.0 5398.4 ***************
5423.3  5415.7 5416.0 5440.0 5450.0 5449.0 5437.1 5414.5 5373.3 5396.6 5402.2 5407.6
5432.2  5429.8 5436.8 5460.0 5452.7 5450.7 5438.5 5420.6 5403.9 5402.0 5402.2 5404.6
5437.1  5437.6 5445.8 5454.0 5449.6 5446.8 5440.2 5424.7 5412.4 5404.5 ***************
*********************** 5457.1 5449.2 5446.0 5440.1 5428.2 5416.1 5406.3 ***************
*************************************** 5445.2 5440.5 5432.6 *******************************
*********************************************** 5441.4 5435.6 5437.9 ***********************
*********************************************** 5443.0 5438.0 5437.8 ***********************
```

OIL-PHASE PRESSURE DISTRIBUTION AT 100 DAYS (psia)

```
******* 5407.3 5401.8 5418.1 ***************************************************************
5417.9  5406.5 5385.9 5426.1 5442.8 *********************** 5386.2 5399.6 ***************
5424.5  5416.8 5417.2 5441.2 5451.2 5450.2 5438.3 5415.7 5374.5 5397.8 5403.3 5408.7
5433.4  5431.0 5438.0 5461.0 5453.9 5451.8 5439.6 5421.8 5405.1 5403.2 5403.4 5405.8
5438.3  5438.8 5447.0 5455.1 5450.8 5448.0 5441.4 5425.9 5413.6 5405.7 ***************
*********************** 5458.3 5450.4 5447.2 5441.3 5429.4 5417.3 5407.5 ***************
*************************************** 5446.4 5441.6 5433.8 *******************************
*********************************************** 5442.6 5436.8 5439.1 ***********************
*********************************************** 5444.2 5439.2 5439.0 ***********************
```

Fig. 9.27—Phase pressure distributions for the water-injection problem at $t = 100$ days.

WATER-PHASE PRESSURE DISTRIBUTION AT 300 DAYS (psia)

```
******* 5368.9 5365.9 5376.6 ***************************************************************
5375.7  5366.9 5354.4 5380.8 5389.6 *********************** 5342.5 5347.8 ***************
5379.5  5372.8 5373.5 5390.8 5393.6 5387.4 5373.2 5357.8 5335.6 5344.8 5346.5 5349.5
5385.9  5383.2 5388.1 5406.7 5393.6 5387.8 5373.5 5360.3 5350.0 5346.9 5345.7 5346.4
5389.3  5388.9 5394.0 5397.2 5388.7 5382.9 5374.1 5361.8 5353.7 5347.4 ***************
*********************** 5398.8 5387.4 5381.3 5372.9 5362.9 5355.3 5348.3 ***************
*************************************** 5379.2 5371.7 5364.2 *******************************
*********************************************** 5370.3 5364.1 5364.6 ***********************
*********************************************** 5369.9 5364.4 5363.6 ***********************
```

OIL-PHASE PRESSURE DISTRIBUTION AT 300 DAYS (psia)

```
******* 5370.1 5367.1 5377.8 ***************************************************************
5376.9  5368.1 5355.6 5382.0 5390.8 *********************** 5343.7 5349.0 ***************
5380.6  5374.0 5374.7 5391.8 5394.8 5388.6 5374.4 5359.0 5336.8 5346.0 5347.7 5350.7
5387.1  5384.3 5389.2 5407.4 5394.8 5389.0 5374.7 5361.5 5351.2 5348.0 5346.9 5347.6
5390.4  5390.1 5395.2 5398.4 5389.9 5384.1 5375.3 5363.0 5354.9 5348.6 ***************
*********************** 5399.9 5388.6 5382.5 5374.1 5364.1 5356.5 5349.4 ***************
*************************************** 5380.4 5372.9 5365.4 *******************************
*********************************************** 5371.5 5365.3 5365.8 ***********************
*********************************************** 5371.1 5365.6 5364.8 ***********************
```

Fig. 9.28—Phase pressure distributions for the water-injection problem at $t = 300$ days.

Figs. 9.27 and 9.28 show the pressure distribution for the water and oil phases at the end of 100 and 300 days of simulation, respectively. **Figs. 9.29 and 9.30** give phase saturation distributions at $t = 100$ and $t = 300$ days. A close look at these figures reveals the formation of a cone of impression around Gridblock (4,4), which is hosting the injection well. Also, two cones of depression are located around the producers [Gridblocks (9,3) and (3,2)]. The decrease in the pressure of Gridblock (4,4) as the water injection continues (from $t = 100$ days to $t = 300$ days) is caused by the higher total reservoir-voidage rate caused by the producers, compared with the 250-B/D injection rate specified at the injector. Also, the increased water saturation value in the injection gridblock improves the injectivity ratios encountered in Well W-3.

Finally, **Tables 9.22 through 9.24** present well reports for Wells W-2 through W-4. Again, a comparison of the reported values in these tables clearly shows that the system starts to behave as if it were in a steady-state regime at approximately $t = 200$ days when the reported values remain almost constant.

Exercises

9.1 Apply the general conservative-expansion formula given by Eq. 9.184 to obtain Eq. 9.193 for the expansion of $\Delta_t[(\phi R_s/B_o)S_o]$.

9.2 Demonstrate that the 1D finite-difference equation for gas,

$$\Delta_x\left[\beta_c\frac{k_xA_x}{\Delta x}\frac{k_{rg}}{\mu_gB_g}(\Delta_xp_g - \gamma_g\Delta_xZ)\right]_i$$

$$+ \Delta_x\left[\beta_c\frac{k_xA_xk_{ro}R_s}{\Delta x\ \mu_oB_o}(\Delta_xp_o - \gamma_o\Delta_xZ)\right]_i$$

$$= \frac{V_{b_i}}{\alpha_c\Delta t}\left\{\left[\frac{\phi S_g}{B_g} + \frac{\phi R_s(1 - S_g)}{B_o}\right]_i^{n+1}\right.$$

$$\left. - \left[\frac{\phi S_g}{B_g} + \frac{\phi R_s(1 - S_g)}{B_o}\right]_i^n\right\} - \left(q_{fgsc_i} + R_{s_i}q_{osc_i}\right),$$

can be derived by combining Eqs. 9.6, 9.10, 9.13 through 9.15, and 2.25.

9.3 Given the 3D oil reservoir described in Example 9.19, calculate the elements G, f_s, and f_p for $T_{gx_{9½,10,1}}$ and $T_{gx_{10,10,1½}}$ using the different weighting methods mentioned in the text.

9.4 Given the 3D oil reservoir described in Example 9.19, calculate the interblock gas flow rate components in the x, y, and z directions between Production Gridblock (10,10,1) and its immediate neighboring gridblocks at 10 years. Use one-point upstream weighting for the approximation of interblock transmissibilities.

9.5 Given the flow model for the reservoir in Example 9.3, write the finite-difference equations for Gridblock n or (i,j) in the 2D x-y space.

9.6 Write the implicit finite-difference equations for two-phase flow of water and gas in 1D horizontal reservoir. Assume negligible gas solution in water. Start with Eqs. 9.224 through 9.226, 9.189 through 9.191, and 9.267 through 9.269 and state all necessary assumptions.

9.7 Derive the linearized-implicit approximations for the difference operator $\Delta_x(T_{wx}\Delta_xP_{cow})$ as expressed by Eqs. 9.416a and 9.416b for $l = w$. State the differences between the two approximations.

WATER-PHASE SATURATION DISTRIBUTION AT 100 DAYS

```
******* 0.5042 0.5042 0.5039 ***************************************************************
0.5045  0.5037 0.5039 0.5029 0.5039 *********************** 0.5042 0.5042 ***************
0.5042  0.5034 0.5034 0.5101 0.5039 0.5038 0.5037 0.5039 0.5038 0.5037 0.5039 0.5041
0.5042  0.5044 0.5045 0.5495 0.5029 0.5043 0.5036 0.5038 0.5038 0.5038 0.5037 0.5037
0.5041  0.5039 0.5042 0.5035 0.5034 0.5036 0.5038 0.5037 0.5037 0.5037 ***************
*********************** 0.5048 0.5035 0.5036 0.5036 0.5037 0.5037 0.5037 ***************
*************************************** 0.5037 0.5037 0.5037 *******************************
*********************************************** 0.5037 0.5036 0.5038 ***********************
*********************************************** 0.5038 0.5037 0.5036 ***********************
```

OIL-PHASE SATURATION DISTRIBUTION AT 100 DAYS

```
******* 0.4958 0.4958 0.4961 ***************************************************************
0.4955  0.4963 0.4961 0.4971 0.4961 *********************** 0.4958 0.4958 ***************
0.4958  0.4966 0.4966 0.4899 0.4961 0.4962 0.4963 0.4961 0.4962 0.4963 0.4961 0.4959
0.4958  0.4956 0.4955 0.4505 0.4971 0.4957 0.4964 0.4962 0.4962 0.4962 0.4963 0.4963
0.4959  0.4961 0.4958 0.4965 0.4966 0.4964 0.4962 0.4963 0.4963 0.4963 ***************
*********************** 0.4952 0.4965 0.4964 0.4964 0.4963 0.4963 0.4963 ***************
*************************************** 0.4963 0.4963 0.4963 *******************************
*********************************************** 0.4963 0.4964 0.4962 ***********************
*********************************************** 0.4962 0.4963 0.4964 ***********************
```

Fig. 9.29—Saturation distributions for the water-injection problem at $t = 100$ days.

WATER-PHASE SATURATION DISTRIBUTION AT 300 DAYS

```
******* 0.5049 0.5051 0.5038 ***************************************************************
0.5060  0.5036 0.5038 0.5017 0.5043 *********************** 0.5051 0.5051 ***************
0.5051  0.5028 0.5026 0.5390 0.5050 0.5040 0.5037 0.5043 0.5039 0.5037 0.5042 0.5049
0.5053  0.5072 0.5086 0.6203 0.5145 0.5042 0.5036 0.5039 0.5040 0.5039 0.5037 0.5036
0.5050  0.5045 0.5053 0.5037 0.5030 0.5034 0.5041 0.5038 0.5038 0.5035 ***************
*********************** 0.5048 0.5033 0.5036 0.5036 0.5037 0.5037 0.5038 ***************
*************************************** 0.5039 0.5037 0.5039 *******************************
*********************************************** 0.5039 0.5035 0.5041 ***********************
*********************************************** 0.5041 0.5037 0.5036 ***********************
```

OIL-PHASE SATURATION DISTRIBUTION AT 300 DAYS

```
******* 0.4951 0.4949 0.4962 ***************************************************************
0.4940  0.4964 0.4962 0.4983 0.4957 *********************** 0.4949 0.4949 ***************
0.4949  0.4972 0.4974 0.4610 0.4950 0.4960 0.4963 0.4957 0.4961 0.4963 0.4958 0.4951
0.4947  0.4928 0.4914 0.3797 0.4855 0.4958 0.4964 0.4961 0.4960 0.4961 0.4963 0.4964
0.4950  0.4955 0.4947 0.4963 0.4970 0.4966 0.4959 0.4962 0.4962 0.4965 ***************
*********************** 0.4952 0.4967 0.4964 0.4964 0.4963 0.4963 0.4962 ***************
*************************************** 0.4961 0.4963 0.4961 *******************************
*********************************************** 0.4961 0.4965 0.4959 ***********************
*********************************************** 0.4959 0.4963 0.4964 ***********************
```

Fig. 9.30—Saturation distributions for the water-injection problem at $t = 300$ days.

TABLE 9.22—WELL REPORT FOR WELL W-2 (PRODUCER)

Time (days)	Flow Rates q_o (STB/D)	q_w (B/D)	Pressure $p_{9,3}$ (psia)	Saturation at Gridblock (9,3) S_o
10	−1,187.27	−161.15	6,081.96	0.498
20	−877.95	−119.51	5,876.98	0.497
30	−649.41	−88.65	5,726.17	0.497
40	−482.21	−65.96	5,616.10	0.497
50	−361.26	−49.48	5,536.62	0.497
60	−274.17	−37.60	5,479.53	0.496
70	−211.62	−29.06	5,438.62	0.496
80	−166.82	−22.93	5,409.30	0.496
90	−134.78	−18.54	5,388.32	0.496
100	−111.85	−15.40	5,373.31	0.496
110	−95.44	−13.14	5,362.56	0.496
120	−83.70	−11.53	5,354.87	0.496
130	−75.30	−10.38	5,349.37	0.496
140	−69.29	−9.55	5,345.43	0.496
150	−64.99	−8.96	5,342.61	0.496
160	−61.92	−8.53	5,340.59	0.496
170	−59.72	−8.23	5,339.15	0.496
180	−58.14	−8.02	5,338.12	0.496
190	−57.02	−7.86	5,337.38	0.496
200	−56.21	−7.75	5,336.85	0.496
210	−55.64	−7.67	5,336.48	0.496
220	−55.23	−7.61	5,336.21	0.496
230	−54.93	−7.57	5,336.02	0.496
240	−54.73	−7.55	5,335.88	0.496
250	−54.58	−7.53	5,335.79	0.496
260	−54.47	−7.51	5,335.72	0.496
270	−54.40	−7.50	5,335.67	0.496
280	−54.35	−7.49	5,335.63	0.496
290	−54.31	−7.49	5,335.61	0.496
300	−54.28	−7.49	5,335.59	0.496

TABLE 9.23—WELL REPORT FOR WELL W-3 (INJECTOR)

Time (days)	Flow Rates q_o (STB/D)	q_w (B/D)	Pressure $p_{4,4}$ (psia)	Saturation at Gridblock (4,4) S_o
10	0.00	250	6,526.75	0.494
20	0.00	250	6,195.31	0.488
30	0.00	250	5,968.98	0.483
40	0.00	250	5,808.64	0.478
50	0.00	250	5,694.05	0.473
60	0.00	250	5,612.02	0.469
70	0.00	250	5,553.36	0.464
80	0.00	250	5,511.43	0.459
90	0.00	250	5,481.44	0.455
100	0.00	250	5,460.01	0.451
110	0.00	250	5,444.72	0.446
120	0.00	250	5,433.80	0.442
130	0.00	250	5,426.02	0.438
140	0.00	250	5,420.49	0.434
150	0.00	250	5,416.57	0.430
160	0.00	250	5,413.73	0.426
170	0.00	250	5,411.71	0.422
180	0.00	250	5,410.27	0.419
190	0.00	250	5,409.25	0.415
200	0.00	250	5,408.54	0.411
210	0.00	250	5,408.04	0.408
220	0.00	250	5,407.70	0.404
230	0.00	250	5,407.46	0.401
240	0.00	250	5,407.27	0.398
250	0.00	250	5,407.10	0.395
260	0.00	250	5,406.97	0.391
270	0.00	250	5,406.87	0.388
280	0.00	250	5,406.79	0.385
290	0.00	250	5,406.73	0.383
300	0.00	250	5,406.68	0.380

9.8 Prove that the fully-implicit approximation for the difference operator $\Delta_x(T_{px}\Delta_x p_o]_i^{n+1}$ given by Eq. 9.427 can be reduced to the semi-implicit approximation of Nolen and Berry[8] of same given by Eq. 9.422. State and implement all necessary assumptions and perform all manipulations.

9.9 Using upstream weighting and knowing that flow is in the direction of increasing i in 1D reservoir, write the finite-difference equations for Gridblock i in an oil and water flow system using the following methods.

1. Simple iteration method.
2. Linearized implicit method.
3. Semi-implicit method of Nolen and Berry.[8]

9.10 Write the equations of the SS method for explicitly linearized oil and gas flow model in 1D reservoir.

9.11 Write the equations of the SS method for explicitly linearized oil and water flow model in a 2D horizontal reservoir. Use natural ordering of gridblocks.

9.12 The reservoir described in Example 9.26 was simulated for $t = 300$ days. Find the pressure and saturation distributions at t = 600 and 800 days. Use single timesteps to progress simulation from 300 to 600 and from 600 to 800 days. Check incremental material balance for both oil and water at the end of each timestep.

9.13 Given the oil reservoir and data described in Example 9.26, the capillary pressure data in **Table 9.25** and fixing the oil pressure for Gridblock 1 at 1,000 psia, find the pressure and saturation distributions at 100 and 300 days using the IMPES method. Compare your simulation results with those obtained in Example 9.26.

9.14 Write the pressure equation and implicit-water-saturation equation of the SEQ method for oil and water flow in 1D reservoir by reducing the general equations for black-oil model. Neglect gravity forces.

TABLE 9.24—WELL REPORT FOR WELL W-4 (PRODUCER)

Time (days)	Flow Rates q_o (STB/D)	q_w (B/D)	Pressure $p_{3,2}$ (psia)	Saturation at Gridblock (3,2) S_o
10	−2,168.64	−295.29	5,998.11	0.498
20	−1,556.44	−212.64	5,800.01	0.497
30	−1,157.42	−158.48	5,671.34	0.497
40	−876.73	−120.22	5,581.02	0.497
50	−675.95	−92.79	5,516.51	0.496
60	−531.90	−73.10	5,470.37	0.496
70	−428.71	−58.99	5,437.36	0.496
80	−354.88	−48.87	5,413.73	0.496
90	−302.13	−41.63	5,396.84	0.496
100	−264.41	−36.45	5,384.75	0.496
110	−237.43	−32.74	5,376.11	0.496
120	−218.13	−30.09	5,369.93	0.496
130	−204.31	−28.19	5,365.50	0.496
140	−194.43	−26.83	5,362.34	0.496
150	−187.35	−25.85	5,360.07	0.496
160	−182.31	−25.16	5,358.45	0.496
170	−178.70	−24.66	5,357.30	0.496
180	−176.12	−24.30	5,356.47	0.496
190	−174.26	−24.05	5,355.87	0.496
200	−172.94	−23.86	5,355.45	0.496
210	−171.99	−23.73	5,355.14	0.496
220	−171.31	−23.63	5,354.92	0.496
230	−170.82	−23.56	5,354.76	0.496
240	−170.48	−23.51	5,354.65	0.496
250	−170.25	−23.48	5,354.57	0.496
260	−170.08	−23.45	5,354.51	0.496
270	−169.96	−23.43	5,354.47	0.496
280	−169.88	−23.41	5,354.44	0.496
290	−169.82	−23.39	5,354.42	0.496
300	−169.78	−23.38	5,354.40	0.496

9.15 Prove that material balance is satisfied for the IMPES method. Use a 1D reservoir with no-flow boundaries.

9.16 For two-phase flow of oil and water, derive the equation for total velocity and fractional-flow equations in the x direction. Check

TABLE 9.25—CAPILLARY PRESSURE DATA FOR EXERCISE 9.13

S_w	P_{cow} (psi)
0.16	0.90
0.20	0.70
0.30	0.50
0.40	0.40
0.50	0.30
0.60	0.22
0.70	0.17
0.80	−0.20

your equations with those obtained from the corresponding equations in three-phase flow.

9.17 The fractional flow coefficients f_w, f_o, and f_g are defined by Eqs. 9.684 and 9.685. Derive the expressions for $\partial f_o/\partial S_w$, $\partial f_o/\partial S_g$, $\partial f_w/\partial S_w$, $\partial f_w/\partial S_g$, $\partial f_g/\partial S_w$, and $\partial f_g/\partial S_g$ in terms of $\partial k_{ro}/\partial S_w$, $\partial k_{ro}/\partial S_g$, dk_{rw}/dS_w, and dk_{rg}/dS_g, which should be used in Eqs. 9.737 and 9.738.

9.18 Using the expressions obtained in Exercise 9.17 and Eq. 9.736, prove that Eqs. 9.731, 9.734, and 9.735 are satisfied.

9.19 Using Eqs. 9.783 through 9.785 and the expressions obtained in Exercise 9.17, derive equations for the partial derivatives of q_{osc_n} and q_{wsc_n} with respect to S_{w_n} and S_{g_n} that should be used in the implicit-saturation equations, Eqs. 9.677 and 9.678, Eqs. 9.726 and 9.727, or Eqs. 9.737 and 9.738, of the second step of the SEQ method.

9.20 Write the implicit-water-saturation equation for Gridblock n for incompressible two-phase flow of oil and water, with negligible capillary pressure, in 2D horizontal reservoir. In your derivation, assume that each Gridblock n may have a production well in it and use the following as your starting points.

1. Eq. 9.677.
2. Eq. 9.727.
3. Eq. 9.738.

9.21 Give a complete formulation of two-phase gas/water flow applicable to a 2D domain with no depth gradients. Assume the solubility of gas in water and the capillary pressure between the two phases to be negligible. Treat the porous medium as homogeneous and isotropic. Reduce the equations to their simplest forms and identify the principal unknowns and the equations that are necessary to solve the problem.

9.22 1. After examining the following formulation, describe the fluid-flow problem and the porous media to the fullest extent.

$$\frac{\partial}{\partial x}\left(\beta_c\frac{k_x k_{ro}}{\mu_o B_o}\frac{\partial p}{\partial x}\right)+\frac{q_o}{V_b}$$

$$=\frac{1}{\alpha_c}\frac{\partial}{\partial t}\left(\frac{\phi S_o}{B_o}\right)+\frac{\partial}{\partial x}\left(\gamma_c\rho_o g\beta_c\frac{k_x k_{ro}}{\mu_o B_o}\frac{\partial Z}{\partial x}\right),$$

$$\frac{\partial}{\partial x}\left(\beta_c\frac{k_x k_{rw}}{\mu_w B_w}\frac{\partial p}{\partial x}\right)+\frac{q_w}{V_b}$$

$$=\frac{1}{\alpha_c}\frac{\partial}{\partial t}\left(\frac{\phi S_w}{B_w}\right)+\frac{\partial}{\partial x}\left(\gamma_c\rho_w g\beta_c\frac{k_x k_{rw}}{\mu_w B_w}\frac{\partial Z}{\partial x}\right).$$

2. What are the principal unknowns of the problem? Provide the necessary auxiliary equations to solve the problem.

Nomenclature

A = cross section, L^2, ft^2 [m^2] (or constant)
A_x = cross section normal to the x direction, L^2, ft^2 [m^2]
A_y = cross section normal to the y direction, L^2, ft^2 [m^2]
A_z = cross section normal to the z direction, L^2, ft^2 [m^2]
[A] = submatrix for Gridblock $(i,j,k+1)$ in matrix notation in Fig. 9.11
B = FVF (or constant)
B_g = gas FVF, L^3/L^3, RB/scf [m^3/std m^3]
B_{inj_n} = injected fluid FVF in Wellblock n, L^3/L^3
B_l = Phase l FVF
B_o = oil FVF, L^3/L^3, RB/STB [m^3/std m^3]
B_w = water FVF, L^3/L^3, RB/B [m^3/std m^3]
[B] = submatrix for Gridblock $(i,j,k-1)$ in matrix notation in Fig. 9.11
c_R = reservoir-rock compressibility, Lt^2/m, psi^{-1} [kPa^{-1}]
$\vec{C}$ = accumulation vector defined by Eq. 9.521
C_{gg} = coefficient of $\Delta_t S_g$ in the expansion of gas accumulation, L^3/t, scf/D [std m^3/d]
C_{gp} = coefficient of $\Delta_t p_o$ in the expansion of gas accumulation, L^4t/m, scf/(D-psi) [std m^3/(d·kPa)]
C_{gw} = coefficient of $\Delta_t S_w$ in the expansion of gas accumulation, L^3/t, scf/D [std m^3/d]
C_{lg} = coefficient of $\Delta_t S_g$ in the expansion of the accumulation of the lth component
C_{lp} = coefficient of $\Delta_t p_o$ in the expansion of the accumulation of the lth component
C_{lu} = coefficient used in describing the expansion of the accumulation term
C_{lw} = coefficient of $\Delta_t S_w$ in the expansion of the accumulation of the lth component
$\vec{C}_n$ = vector defined by Eq. 9.522
C_{og} = coefficient of $\Delta_t S_g$ in the expansion of oil accumulation, L^3/t, STB/D [std m^3/d]
C_{op} = coefficient of $\Delta_t p_o$ in the expansion of oil accumulation, L^4t/m, STB/(D-psi) [std m^3/(d·kPa)]
C_{ow} = coefficient of $\Delta_t S_w$ in the expansion of oil accumulation, L^3/t, STB/D [std m^3/d]
C_{wg} = coefficient of $\Delta_t S_g$ in the expansion of water accumulation, L^3/t, B/D [std m^3/d]
C_{wp} = coefficient of $\Delta_t p_o$ in the expansion of water accumulation, L^4t/m, B/(D-psi) [std m^3/(d·kPa)]
C_{ww} = coefficient of $\Delta_t S_w$ in the expansion of water accumulation, L^3/t, B/D [std m^3/d]
[C] = accumulation matrix or submatrix for Gridblock (i, j, k) in matrix notation in Fig. 9.11
[E] = submatrix for Gridblock $(i+1,j,k)$ in matrix notation in Fig. 9.11
f = function
f_g = gas-fractional-flow coefficient, dimensionless
f_l = Phase l ftractional flow coefficient, dimensionless
f_o = oil-fractional-flow coefficient, dimensionless
f_p = weak nonlinearity function
f_{po} = weak nonlinearity function defined by Eq. 9.272a or 9.272b for l=o
f_s = strong nonlinearity function
f_{so} = strong nonlinearity function defined by Eq. 9.273a or 9.273b for l=o

f_w = water-fractional-flow coefficient, dimensionless
$\vec{F}$ = flow term vector defined by Eq. 9.520
F_g = gas flow term (or gas function defined in Table 9.12)
F_{l_n} = Phase l flow term for Gridblock n (or Phase l function for Gridblock n in Sec. 9.7.3)
$\vec{F}_n$ = flow term vector for Gridblock n
$F_{n,m}$ = flow term between Gridblocks n and m
F_o = oil flow term (or oil function defined in Table 9.12)
F_w = water flow term (or water function defined in Table 9.12)
[F] = flow term matrix
g = acceleration caused by gravity, L/t^2, ft/sec^2 [m/s^2]
G = geometric factor
$G_{i,j,k}$ = geometric factor for Gridblock (i,j,k)
$G_{n,m}$ = geometric factor between Gridblocks n and m defined by Eq. 9.472
G_w = well geometric factor (constant of productivity or injectivity index), L^3, RB-cp/(D–psi) [m^3 · Pa · s/(d · kPa)]
H_n = well gradient function as defined by Eqs. 9.867a and 9.867b, m/Lt^2, psia [kPa]
$\vec{i}$ = unit vector in the x direction
I_{MB} = incremental material balance
$\vec{j}$ = unit vector in the y direction
[J] = Jacobian matrix
$\vec{k}$ = unit vector in the z direction
k_{rg} = relative permeability to gas, dimensionless
$k_{r_{inj}}$ = relative permeability to injected phase, dimensionless
k_{rl} = relative permeability to Phase l, dimensionless
k_{ro} = relative permeability to oil, dimensionless
k'_{rog} = dk_{rog}/dS_g
k_{rw} = relative permeability to water, dimensionless
k_x = permeability in the x direction, L^2, darcy [μm^2]
k_y = permeability in the y direction, L^2, darcy [μm^2]
k_z = permeability in the z direction, L^2, darcy [μm^2]
m = a member of Gridblock Set ψ_n
$(m_a)_c$ = mass accumulation of Component c caused by compressibility and fluid saturation changes in the control volume over Time Interval Δt, m, lbm [kg]
$\vec{\dot m}_c$ = mass flux for Component c, m/L^{2}t, lbm/(D-ft^2) [kg/(d · m^2)]
$\dot m_{c_x}$ = mass flux for Component c along the x direction, m/L^{2}t, lbm/(D-ft^2) [kg/(d · m^2)]
$\dot m_{c_y}$ = mass flux for Component c along the y direction, m/L^{2}t, lbm/(D-ft^2) [kg/(d · m^2)]
$\dot m_{c_z}$ = mass flux for Component c along the z direction, m/L^{2}t, lbm/(D-ft^2) [kg/(d · m^2)]
$\dot m_{fg_x}$ = mass flux for free gas along the x direction, m/L^{2}t, lbm/(D-ft^2) [kg/(d · m^2)]
$\dot m_{fg_y}$ = mass flux for free gas along the y direction, m/L^{2}t, lbm/(D-ft^2) [kg/(d · m^2)]
$\dot m_{fg_z}$ = mass flux for free gas along the z direction, m/L^{2}t, lbm/(D-ft^2) [kg/(d · m^2)]
$(m_i)_c$ = sum of mass inflows of Component c across the control-volume surfaces at $x-\Delta x/2$, $y-\Delta y/2$, and $z-\Delta z/2$ over Time Interval Δt, m, lbm [kg]
$(m_o)_c$ = the sum of mass outflows of Component c across the control-volume surfaces at $x+\Delta x/2$, $y+\Delta y/2$, and $z+\Delta z/2$ over Time Interval Δt, m, lbm, [kg]
$\dot m_{o_x}$ = mass flux of oil along the x direction, m/L^{2}t, lbm/(D–ft^2) [kg/(d · m^2)]
m_{sg} = mass of solution gas, m, lbm [kg]
$\dot m_{sg_x}$ = mass flux for solution gas along the x direction, m/L^{2}t, lbm/(D–ft^2) [kg/(d · m^2)]
$\dot m_{sg_y}$ = mass flux for solution gas along the y direction, m/L^{2}t, lbm/(D–ft^2) [kg/(d · m^2)]
$\dot m_{sg_z}$ = mass flux for solution gas along the z direction, m/L^{2}t, lbm/(D–ft^2) [kg/(d · m^2)]
m_{v_c} = mass of Component c per unit volume of rock, m/L^3, lbm/ft^3 [kg/m^3]
$m_{v_{fg}}$ = mass of free gas per unit volume of rock, m/L^3, lbm/ft^3 [kg/m^3]
m_{v_o} = mass of oil per unit volume of rock, m/L^3, lbm/ft^3 [kg/m^3]
$m_{v_{sg}}$ = mass of solution gas per unit volume of rock, m/L^3, lbm/ft^3 [kg/m^3]
n_{px} = number of gridblocks in the x direction for a parallelpiped reservoir, n
n_{py} = number of gridblocks in the y direction for a parallelpiped reservoir, n
n_{pz} = number of gridblocks in the z direction for a parallelpiped reservoir, n
n_x = number of gridblocks in the x direction, n
n_y = number of gridblocks in the y direction, n
$n_{\Delta t}$ = number of timesteps, n
n_k = number of the bottom-most wellblock, n
N = total number of gridblocks that represent a reservoir, n
[N] = submatrix for Gridblock $(i,j+1,k)$ in matrix notation in Fig. 9.11
O_{i1} = specified injection rate at standard conditions of a given phase (usually gas or water) imposed on an injection well in multiphase flow
O_{i2} = specified injection rate of water or gas at reservoir conditions imposed on an injection well in multiphase flow
O_{i3} = specified sandface pressure imposed on an injection well in multiphase flow
O_{p1} = specified oil production rate at reservoir conditions well-specification option
O_{p2} = specified oil production rate at standard conditions well-specification option
O_{p3} = specified water production rate at reservoir conditions well-specification option
O_{p4} = specified water production rate at standard conditions well-specification option
O_{p5} = specified gas production rate at reservoir conditions well-specification option
O_{p6} = specified gas production rate at standard conditions well-specification option
O_{p7} = specified liquid production rate at reservoir conditions well-specification option
O_{p8} = specified liquid production rate at standard conditions well-specification option
O_{p9} = specified total production rate at reservoir conditions well-specification option
O_{p10} = specified total production rate at standard conditions well-specification option
O_{p11} = specified sandface pressure well-specification option imposed on production well
p = pressure, m/Lt^2, psia [kPa]
p_e = external (boundary) pressure, m/Lt^2, psia [kPa]
p_g = gas pressure, m/Lt^2, psia [kPa]
p_i = initial pressure, m/Lt^2, psia [kPa]
p_l = pressure of Phase l, m/Lt^2, psia [kPa]

p_o = oil pressure, m/Lt^2, psia [kPa]
p_{o_n} = oil pressure for Gridblock n, m/Lt^2, psia [kPa]
p_w = water pressure, m/Lt^2, psia [kPa]
p_{wf_n} = flowing well pressure opposite Gridblock n, m/Lt^2, psia [kPa]
$p_{wf_{ref}}$ = flowing well pressure at reference elevation, m/Lt^2, psia [kPa]
$p_{wf_{sp}}$ = specified flowing well pressure, m/Lt^2, psia [kPa]
Δp_o = pressure difference, m/Lt^2, psi [kPa]
P_{cgo} = gas/oil capillary pressure, m/Lt^2, psi [kPa]
P_{col} = capillary pressure between the oil phase and Phase l, m/Lt^2, psi [kPa]
P_{cow} = oil/water capillary pressure, m/Lt^2, psi [kPa]
q_{fg} = production rate of free-gas component, L^3/t, RB/D [m^3/d]
q_{fgsc} = free gas production rate at standard conditions, L^3/t, scf/D [std m^3/d]
q_{gsc} = gas production rate at standard conditions, L^3/t, scf/D [std m^3/d]
q'_{ggsc_n} = $\partial q_{gsc}/\partial S_g$ for Gridblock n, L^3/t, scf/D [std m^3/d]
q'_{gpsc_n} = $\partial q_{gsc}/\partial p_o$ for Gridblock n, L^{4}t/m, scf/(D-psi) [std m^3/(d·kPa)]
q'_{gwsc_n} = $\partial q_{gsc}/\partial S_w$ for Gridblock n, L^3/t, scf/D [std m^3/d]
$q_{inj_{sc}}$ = injection rate at standard conditions, L^3/t, B/D [std m^3/d] or scf/D [std m^3/d]
q_l = production rate of Phase l at reservoir conditions L^3/t, RB/D [m^3/d]
$q_{l_{sc}}$ = production rate of Phase l at standard conditions, L^3/t, STB/D [std m^3/d] or scf/D [std m^3/d]
q_{m_c} = rate of mass depletion for Component c through wells, m/t, lbm/D [kg/d]
$q_{m_{fg}}$ = rate of mass production (injection) of free-gas component, m/t, lbm/D [kg/d]
q_{mt_c} = rate of mass transfer of Component c between phases, m/t, lbm/D [kg/d]
q_{mt_o} = rate of mass transfer of oil component between phases, m/t, lbm/D [kg/d]
$q_{mt_{sg}}$ = rate of mass transfer of solution gas between phases, m/t, lbm/D [kg/d]
q_{mt_w} = rate of mass transfer of water component between phases, m/t, lbm/D [kg/d]
q_o = oil production rate at reservoir conditions, L^3/t, RB/D [m^3/d]
q'_{ogsc_n} = $\partial q_{osc}/\partial S_g$ for Gridblock n, L^3/t, STB/D [std m^3/d]
q'_{opsc} = $\partial q_{osc}/\partial p_o$, L^{4}t/m, STB/(D-psi) [std m^3/(d·kPa)]
q_{osc} = oil production rate at standard conditions, L^3/t, STB/D [std m^3/d]
$q_{osc_{i,j,k}}$ = oil production rate at standard conditions from Wellblock (i,j,k), L^3/t, STB/D [std m^3/d]
q'_{owsc} = $\partial q_{osc}/\partial S_w$, L^3/t, STB/D [std m^3/d]
$q_{ox_{i-1/2,j,k}}$ = interblock oil flow rate in the x direction between Gridblocks (i,j,k) and (i–1,j,k), L^3/t, STB/D [std m^3/d]
$q_{oy_{i,j-1/2,k}}$ = interblock oil flow rate in the y direction between Gridblocks (i,j,k) and (i,j–1,k), L^3/t, STB/D [std m^3/d]
$q_{oz_{i,j,k+1/2}}$ = interblock oil flow rate in the z direction between Gridblocks (i,j,k) and (i,j,k+1), L^3/t, STB/D [std m^3/d]
q_{sp} = specified well production (injection) rate
q_{spsc} = specified well production (injection) rate at standard conditions
$q_{t_{n,m}}$ = interblock total flow rate between Gridblocks n and m, L^3/t, RB/D [m^3/d]
q_{tsc} = total well flow rate at standard conditions, L^3/t, STB/D [std m^3/d]
q'_{wgsc_n} = $\partial q_{wsc}/\partial S_g$ for Gridblock n, L^3/t, B/D [std m^3/d]
q'_{wpsc_n} = $\partial q_{wsc}/\partial p_o$ for Gridblock n, L^{4}t/m, B/(D-psi) [std m^3/(d·kPa)]
q_{wsc} = water flow rate at standard conditions, L^3/t, B/D [std m^3/d]
q'_{wwsc_n} = $\partial q_{wsc}/\partial S_w$ for Gridblock n, L^3/t, B/D [std m^3/d]
$\vec{Q}$ = production vector defined by Eq. 9.505
[Q] = production (injection) matrix
r_w = well radius, L, ft [m]
$\vec{R}$ = residual vector defined by Eq. 9.516
R_l = residual of Component l
R_{l_n} = residual of Compnent l in Gridblock n
$\vec{R}_n$ = residual vector for Gridblock n
R_{o_n} = oil residual in Gridblock n, L^3/t, STB/D [std m^3/d]
R_s = solution GOR, L^3/L^3, scf/STB [std m^3/std m^3]
$\tilde{R}_s$ = pseudosolution GOR defined by Eq. 9.905, L^3/L^3, scf/STB [std m^3/std m^3]
R_{si} = initial solution GOR, L^3/L^3, scf/STB [std m^3/std m^3]
R_{s_n} = solution GOR in Gridblock n, L^3/L^3, scf/STB [std m^3/std m^3]
$R_{s_{n,m}}$ = solution GOR between neighboring Gridblocks n and m, L^3/L^3, scf/STB [std m^3/std m^3]
R_{w_n} = water residual in Gridblock n, L^3/t, B/D [std m^3/d]
s_c = sum of mass generation and mass depletion through wells of Component c over Time Interval Δt
S = saturation (or memory storage requirements)
S_c = saturation of Phase c (Component $c = o,w,f_g$), fraction
S_{fg} = saturation of free gas ($S_{fg} = S_g$), fraction
S_g = gas saturation, fraction
S_{g_n} = gas saturation for Gridblock n, fraction
S_{gc} = critical gas saturation, fraction
S_{gi} = initial gas saturation, fraction
$S_{g_{max}}$ = maximum gas saturation, fraction
S_{iw} = irreducible water saturation, fraction
S_{IMPES} = memory storage requirements for IMPES method
S_l = Phase l saturation, fraction
S_L = left side
S_o = oil saturation, fraction
S_{oi} = initial oil saturation, fraction
S_{org} = residual oil saturation in oil/gas system, fraction
S_{orw} = residual oil saturation in oil/water system, fraction
S_R = right side
S_{SEQ} = memory storage requirements for SEQ method
S_{SS} = memory storage requirements for SS method
S_w = water saturation, fraction
S_{wi} = initial water saturation, fraction
S_{w_n} = water saturation in Gridblock n, fraction
S_{w_m} = water saturation in Gridblock m, fraction
$S_{w_{max}}$ = maximum water saturation, fraction
[S] = submatrix for Gridblock ($i, j-1, k$) in matrix notation in Fig. 9.11
t = time, t, days
T_R = reservoir temperature, T, °R [K]
Δt = timestep ($\Delta t = t^{n+1} - t^n$), t, days
u = superficial velocity, L/t, RB/(D-ft^2) [m^3/(d·m^2)]

$\vec{u}_c$ = Component c superficial velocity vector, L/t, RB/(D-ft^2) [m^3/(d·m^2)]
u_{cx} = x component of Component c superficial velocity, L/t, RB/(D-ft^2) [m^3/(d·m^2)]
u_{cy} = y component of Component c superficial velocity, L/t, RB/(D-ft^2) [m^3/(d·m^2)]
u_{cz} = z component of Component c superficial velocity, L/t, RB/(D-ft^2) [m^3/(d·m^2)]
u_{fg} = free-gas superficial velocity, L/t, RB/(D-ft^2) [m^3/(d·m^2)]
u_{fgx} = x component of free-gas superficial velocity, L/t, RB/(D-ft^2) [m^3/(d·m^2)]
u_{fgy} = y component of free-gas superficial velocity, L/t, RB/(D-ft^2) [m^3/(d·m^2)]
u_{fgz} = z component of free-gas superficial velocity, L/t, RB/(D-ft^2) [m^3/(d·m^2)]
u_g = gas superficial velocity, L/t, RB/(D-ft^2) [m^3/(d·m^2)]
$\vec{u}_g$ = gas-phase superficial velocity vector, L/t, RB/(D-ft^2) [m^3/(d·m^2)]
$\vec{u}_o$ = oil-phase superficial velocity vector, L/t, RB/(D-ft^2) [m^3/(d·m^2)]
u_{ox} = x component of oil superficial velocity, L/t, RB/(D-ft^2) [m^3/(d·m^2)]
u_{oy} = y component of oil superficial velocity, L/t, RB/(D-ft^2) [m^3/(d·m^2)]
u_{oz} = z component of oil superficial velocity, L/t, RB/(D-ft^2) [m^3/(d·m^2)]
$\vec{u}_t$ = total superficial velocity vector, L/t, RB/(D-ft^2) [m^3/(d·m^2)]
u_{tz} = z component of total superficial velocity, L/t, RB/(D-ft^2) [m^3/(d·m^2)]
$\vec{u}_w$ = water-phase superficial velocity vector, L/t, RB/(D-ft^2) [m^3/(d·m^2)]
u_{wx} = x component of water superficial velocity, L/t, RB/(D-ft^2)[m^3/(d·m^2)]
u_{wy} = y component of water superficial velocity, L/t, RB/(D-ft^2)[m^3/(d·m^2)]
u_{wz} = z component of water superficial velocity, L/t, RB/(D-ft^2)[m^3/(d·m^2)]
U = specified function ($U \equiv \phi$)
v = iteration level
V = specified function ($V \equiv 1/B$)
V_b = gridblock bulk volume, L^3, ft^3 [m^3]
W = computer work requirement
$W_{\Delta t}$ = computer work requirement per timestep
$W_{\Delta t_{\text{IMPES}}}$ = computer work per timestep for the IMPES method
$W_{\Delta t_{\text{SEQ}}}$ = computer work per timestep for the SEQ method
$W_{\Delta t_{\text{SS}}}$ = computer work per timestep for the SS method
[W] = submatrix for Gridblock $(i-1,j,k)$ in matrix notation in Fig. 9.11
x = distance in the x direction in the cartesian coordinate system, L, ft [m]
Δx = difference along the x direction ($\Delta x = x_{i+1} - x_i$), L, ft [m]
$\Delta x_{i,j,k}$ = size of Gridblock (i,j,k) along the x direction ($\Delta x_{i,j,k} = x_{i+1/2,j,k} - x_{i-1/2,j,k}$), L, ft [m]
X = unknown variable, or specified function ($X \equiv R_s$)
$\vec{X}$ = unknown vector defined by Eq. 9.502
y = distance in the y direction in the Cartesian coordinate system, L, ft [m]
Δy = difference along the y direction ($\Delta y = y_{j+1} - y_j$), L, ft [m]
Y = specified function ($Y \equiv S_l$)
Y^n = specified function at Time Level n

Δz = difference along the z direction ($\Delta z = z_{k+1} - z_k$), L, ft [m]
Δz_k = size of gridblock along the z direction, L, ft [m]
Z = elevation referred to datum (positive downward), L, ft [m]
Z_{goc} = elevation of GOC referred to datum, L, ft [m]
Z_{ogc} = elevation of OGC referred to datum, L, ft [m]
Z_{owc} = elevation of OWC referred to datum, L, ft [m]
Z_m = elevation of center of Gridblock m referred to datum, L, ft [m]
Z_{m_n} = elevation of Wellblock n with the terminology in Fig. 9.20, L, ft [m]
Z_n = elevation of Gridblock n, L, ft [m]
Z_{woc} = elevation of WOC referred to datum, L, ft [m]
ΔZ = change in elevation, L, ft [m]
α_c = volumetric conversion factor whose numerical value is given in Table 4.1
α_S = storage function defined in Table 9.11
α_W = work function defined in Table 9.11
β_c = transmissibility conversion factor whose numerical value is given in Table 4.1
γ_g = gas gravity, m/L^{2}t^2, psi/ft [kPa/m]
$\gamma_{g_{n,m}}$ = gas gravity between neighboring Gridblocks n and m, m/L^{2}t^2, psi/ft [kPa/m]
γ_l = gravity of Phase l, m/L^{2}t^2, psi/ft [kPa/m]
γ_o = oil gravity, m/L^{2}t^2, psi/ft [kPa/m]
$\gamma_{o_{n,m}}$ = oil gravity between neighboring Gridblocks n and m, m/L^{2}t^2, psi/ft [kPa/m]
γ_{ox} = oil gravity in the x direction, m/L^{2}t^2, psi/ft [kPa/m]
γ_w = water gravity, m/L^{2}t^2, psi/ft [kPa/m]
$\bar{\gamma}_w$ = average hydrostatic gradient in the wellbore, m/L^{2}t^2, psi/ft [kPa/m]
$\gamma_{w_{n,m}}$ = water gravity between neighboring Gridblocks n and m, m/L^{2}t^2, psi/ft [kPa/m]
$\Delta\gamma_{og}$ = difference between oil and gas gravities ($\Delta\gamma_{og} = \gamma_o - \gamma_g$), m/L^{2}t^2, psi/ft [kPa/m]
$\Delta\gamma_{ow}$ = difference between water and oil gravities ($\Delta\gamma_{ow} = \gamma_w - \gamma_o$), m/L^{2}t^2, psi/ft [kPa/m]
$\Gamma_0 - \Gamma_3$ = types of internal and external reservoir boundaries defined in Fig. 9.19
δ_i = distance between gridblock and gridblock boundary (see Fig. 9.5), L, ft [m]
Δ = difference, difference operator
Δ_m = difference operator defined by Eq. 9.470
Δ_t = difference operator in the time domain
ε_g = gas saturation tolerance used for gas-phase disappearance and reappearance
ζ_g = function defined by Eq. 9.689
ζ_w = function defined by Eq. 9.688
η = dummy variable that assumes p_o, P_{cow}, P_{cgo}, or Z
$\eta_{i,j,k}$ = variable η for Gridblock (i,j,k)
η_m = variable η for Gridblock m
$\Delta\eta$ = difference of variable η
Θ = dip angle
λ_g = gas mobility, L^{3}t/m, RB/(D–psi–ft) [m^3/(d·kPa·m)]
λ_o = oil mobility, L^{3}t/m, RB/(D–psi–ft) [m^3/(d·kPa·m)]
λ_t = total mobility, L^{3}t/m, RB/(D–psi–ft) [m^3/(d·kPa·m)]
λ_w = water mobility, L^{3}t/m, RB/(D–psi–ft) [m^3/(d·kPa·m)]
μ_g = gas viscosity, m/Lt, cp [Pa·s]
μ_{inj} = viscosity of injected fluid, m/Lt, cp [Pa·s]
μ_l = viscosity of Phase l, m/Lt, cp [Pa·s]

μ_o = oil viscosity, m/Lt, cp [Pa·s]
μ_w = water viscosity, m/Lt, cp [Pa·s]
ξ^* = dummy variable that assumes the functions $\beta_c kA[k_{r_l}/(\mu_l B_l)]$, $\beta_c kA[(k_{r_l}\gamma_l)/(\mu_l B_l)]$, $\beta_c kA[(k_{r_o}R_s)/(\mu_o B_o)]$, or $\beta_c kA[(k_{r_o}R_s\gamma_o)/(\mu_o B_o)]$
$\xi_{i,m}$ = interblock coefficient between Gridblocks i and m along the x direction
$\xi_{j,m}$ = interblock coefficient between Gridblocks j and m along the y direction
$\xi_{k,m}$ = interblock coefficient between Gridblocks k and m along the z direction
$\xi_{n,m}$ = interblock coefficient between Gridblock n and its neighboring Gridblock m
ξ_x = $\xi_x^*/\Delta x$
ξ_x^* = dummy variable in the x direction that assumes the function $\beta_c k_x A_x[k_{r_l}/(\mu_l B_l)]$, $\beta_c k_x A_x([k_{r_l}\gamma_l)/(\mu_l B_l)]$, $\beta_c k_x A_x[(k_{r_o}R_s)/(\mu_o B_o)]$, or $\beta_c k_x A_x[(k_{r_o}R_s\gamma_o)/(\mu_o B_o)]$
$\xi_{x_{i\pm 1/2,j,k}}$ = transmissibility in the x direction between Gridblocks (i,j,k) and $(i\pm 1,j,k)$
ξ_y = $\xi_y^*/\Delta y$
ξ_y^* = dummy variable in the y direction that assumes the function $\beta_c k_y A_y[k_{r_l}/(\mu_l B_l)]$, $\beta_c k_y A_y[(k_{r_l}\gamma_l)/(\mu_l B_l)]$, $\beta_c k_y A_y[(k_{r_o}R_s)/(\mu_o B_o)]$, or $\beta_c k_y A_y[(k_{r_o}R_s\gamma_o)/(\mu_o B_o)]$
$\xi_{y_{i,j\pm 1/2,k}}$ = transmissibility in the y direction between Gridblocks (i,j,k) and $(i,j\pm 1,k)$
ξ_z^* = dummy variable in the z direction that assumes the function $\beta_c k_z A_z[k_{r_l}/(\mu_l B_l)]$, $\beta_c k_z A_z[(k_{r_l}\gamma_l)/(\mu_l B_l)]$, $\beta_c k_z A_z[(k_{r_o}R_s)/(\mu_o B_o)]$, or $\beta_c k_z A_z[(k_{r_o}R_s\gamma_o)/(\mu_o B_o)]$
$\xi_{z_{i,j,k\pm 1/2}}$ = transmissibility in the z direction between Gridblocks (i,j,k) and $(i,j,k\pm 1)$
ρ_c = density of Component c, m/L^3, lbm/ft^3 [kg/m^3]
ρ_{fg} = density of free gas, m/L^3, lbm/ft^3 [kg/m^3]
ρ_g = gas-phase density, m/L^3, lbm/ft^3 [kg/m^3]
ρ_{gsc} = gas-phase density at standard conditions, m/L^3, lbm/ft^3 [kg/m^3]
ρ_o = oil-phase density, m/L^3, lbm/ft^3 [kg/m^3]
ρ_{osc} = oil-phase density at standard conditions, m/L^3, lbm/ft^3 [kg/m^3]
T_g = transmissibility of gas phase, L^{4}t/m, scf/(D-psi) [std m^3/(d·kPa)]
$T_{g_{n,m}}$ = gas-phase transmissibility between Gridblocks n and m, L^{4}t/m, scf/(D-psi) [std m^3/(d·kPa)]
T_{gx} = gas-phase transmissibility in the x direction, L^{4}t/m, scf/(D-psi) [std m^3/(d·kPa)]
T_{gz} = gas-phase transmissibility in the z direction
T_{lx} = transmissibility of Phase l in the x direction
T_{ly} = transmissibility of Phase l in the y direction
T_{lz} = transmissibility of Phase l in the z direction
$T_{n,m}$ = transmissibility between Gridblock n and its neighboring Gridblock m
T_o = oil-phase transmissibility, L^{4}t/m, STB/(D-psi) [std m^3/(d·kPa)]
$T_{o_{n,m}}$ = oil-phase transmissibility between neighboring Gridblocks n and m, L^{4}t/m, STB/(D-psi) [std m^3/(d·kPa)]
T_{ox} = oil-phase transmissibility in the x direction, L^{4}t/m, STB/(D-psi) [std m^3/(d·kPa)]
T_{oy} = oil-phase transmissibility in the y direction, L^{4}t/m, STB/(D-psi) [std m^3/(d·kPa)]
T_{oz} = oil-phase transmissibility in the z direction, L^{4}t/m, STB/(D-psi) [std m^3/(d·kPa)]
T_w = water–phase transmissibility, L^{4}t/m, B/(D-psi) [std m^3/(d·kPa)]
$T_{w_{n,m}}$ = water-phase transmissibility between Gridblocks n and m, L^{4}t/m, B/(D-psi) [std m^3/(d·kPa)]
T_{wx} = water-phase transmissibility in the x direction, L^{4}t/m, B/(D-psi) [std m^3/(d·kPa)]
T_{wy} = water-phase transmissibility in the y direction, L^{4}t/m, B/(D-psi) [std m^3/(d·kPa)]
[T] = transmissibility matrix
Y_g = function defined by Eq. 9.687
ϕ = porosity, fraction
Φ_o = potential of oil phase, m/Lt^2, psia [kPa]
$\Delta\Phi$ = phase potential difference, m/Lt^2, psi [kPa]
ψ_i = set of gridblocks associated with (but excluding) Gridblock i in the x direction
ψ_j = set of gridblocks associated with (but excluding) Gridblock j in the y direction
ψ_k = set of gridblocks associated with (but excluding) Gridblock k in the z direction
ψ_n = set of neighboring blocks associated with (but excluding) Gridblock n in natural ordering
ψ_x = set of neighboring gridblocks along the x direction
ψ_y = set of neighboring gridblocks along the y direction
ψ_z = set of neighboring gridblocks along the z direction
Ψ = function defined by Eq. 9.906
ω_l = weighting factor of Phase l
Ω = geometric factor in Eq. 9.328
[0] = matrix whose elements are zeroes (null matrix)

Subscripts

c = component
fg = free gas
g = gas
i = index for blocks in the x direction
inj = injected
j = index for blocks in the y direction
k = index for blocks in the z direction
l = Phase l or Component l
m = neighboring gridblock to Gridblock n
mt = mass transfer
n = gridblock
o = oil
p = phase
sc = standard conditions
sg = solution gas
sp = specified
t = total
w = water

Superscripts

n = old timestep
$n+1$ = current (or new) timestep
(v) = old iteration
$(v+1)$ = current iteration
T = transpose of
° = reference
* = updated explicitly in IMPES step of the SEQ
′ = first derivative
′n = first derivative evaluated at the old timestep level n
→ = vector

References

1. Odeh, A.S.: "An Overview of Mathematical Formulation of the Behavior of Hydrocarbon Reservoirs," *SIAM Review* (July 1982) **24,** No. 3, 263.
2. Aziz, K. and Settari, A.: *Petroleum Reservoir Simulation*, Applied Science Publishers Ltd., London (1979).
3. Arakawa, A.: "Computational Design for Long-Term Numerical Integration of the Equations of Fluid Motion: Two-dimensional Incompressible Flow. Part 1," *J. Computational Physics* (1966) 119.
4. Coats, K.H., *et. al.*: "Three-Dimensional Simulation of Steamflooding," *SPEJ* (December 1974) 573; *Trans.,* AIME, **257**.
5. Todd, M.R., O'Dell, P.M., and Hirasaki, G.J.: "Methods for Increased Accuracy in Numerical Reservoir Simulators," *SPEJ* (December 1972) 515; *Trans.,* AIME, **253.**
6. Wheatley, M.J.: "A Version of Two-Point Upstream Weighting for Use in Implicit Numerical Reservoir Simulation," paper SPE 7677 presented at the 1979 SPE Symposium on Reservoir Simulation, Denver, Colorado, 1–2 February.
7. Odeh, A.S.: "Comparison of Solutions to a Three-Dimensional Black-Oil Reservoir Simulation Problem," *JPT* (January 1981) 13.
8. Nolen, J.S. and Berry, D.W.: "Tests of the Stability and Time-Step Sensitivity of Semi-Implicit Reservoir Simulation Techniques," *SPEJ* (June 1972) 253; *Trans.,* AIME, **253.**
9. Aziz, K.:"Reservoir Simulation Grids: Opportunitites and Problems," paper SPE 25233 presented at the 1993 SPE Symposium on Reservoir Simulation, New Orleans, 28 February–3 March.
10. Abou-Kassem, J.H.: "Investigation of Grid Orientation in a Two-Dimensional, Compositional, Three-Phase Steam Model," PhD dissertation, U. of Calgary, Alberta (1981).
11. Lutchmansingh, P.M.: "Development and Application of a Highly Implicit, Multidimensional Polymer Injection Simulator," PhD dissertation, Pennsylvania State U., University Park, Pennsylvania (1987).
12. Abou-Kassem, J.H. and Farouq Ali, S.M.: "A Unified Approach to the Solution of Reservoir Simulation Equations," paper SPE 17072 presented at the 1987 SPE Eastern Regional Meeting, Pittsburgh, Pennsylvania, 21–23 October.
13. Behie, A. and Vinsome, P.K.W.: "Block Iterative Methods for Fully Implicit Reservoir Simulation," *SPEJ* (October 1982) 658.
14. Appleyard, J.R. and Cheshire, I.M.: "Nested Factorization," paper SPE 12264 presented at the 1983 SPE Reservoir Simulation Symposium, San Francisco, 15–18 November.
15. Spillette, A.G., Hillestad, J.G., and Stone, H.L.: "A High-Stability Sequential Solution Approach to Reservoir Simulation," paper SPE 4542 presented at the 1973 SPE Annual Meeting, Las Vegas, Nevada, 30 September–3 October.
16. Coats, K.H.: "A Highly Implicit Steamflood Model," *SPEJ* (October 1978) 369.
17. Kazemi, H., Vestal, C.R., and Shank, G.D.: "An Efficient Multicomponent Numerical Simulator," *SPEJ* (October 1978) 355.
18. Au, A.D.K. *et al.*: "Techniques for Fully Implicit Reservoir Simulation," paper SPE 9302 presented at the 1980 Annual Technical Conference and Exhibition, Dallas, 21–24 September.
19. Thomas, G.W.: *Principles of Hydrocarbon Reservoir Simulation*, Intl. Human Resources Development Corp., Boston, Massachusetts (1982) 153–158.
20. Abou-Kassem, J.H.: "Practical Considerations in Developing Numerical Simulators for Thermal Recovery," *J. Pet. Sci. Eng.* (1996) **15,** 281.

SI Metric Conversion Factors

bbl	× 1.589 873	E − 01	= m^3
cp	× 1.0*	E − 03	= Pa·s
ft	× 3.048*	E − 01	= m
ft^2	× 9.290 304*	E − 02	= m^2
ft^3	× 2.831 685	E − 02	= m^3
°F	(°F + 459.67) 1.8		= K
lbm	× 4.535 924	E − 01	= kg
md	× 9.869 233	E − 04	= μm^2
psi	× 6.894 757	E + 00	= kPa
°R	× .555 555		= K

*Conversion factor is exact.

Chapter 10
Practical Aspects of Reservoir Simulation

10.1 Introduction

The focus of this book has been on the development of finite-difference simulators; however, the vast majority of engineers working in reservoir simulation probably will never develop a simulator. In most cases, the reservoir engineer performs simulation studies with a commercial or in-house simulator. An SPE monograph[1] is devoted specifically to advanced topics on the subject of conducting simulation studies. This monograph, however, requires previous knowledge of reservoir studies and reservoir simulation. This chapter provides the prospective simulation engineer with the basics of performing a numerical reservoir study. **Fig. 10.1** shows the application of reservoir simulation.

The basic elements of a reservoir simulation study are defining the study objectives, gathering and analyzing data, constructing the reservoir simulation model, history matching the simulation model, running prediction cases, and reporting.

The most important step in a simulation study is the development of a clear set of study objectives. These objectives dictate the amount of company resources that should be allocated to the study, the modeling approach used in the study, the quality of the history match required by the study, and the definition and number of prediction cases considered by the study. All these points are addressed in detail throughout this chapter.

Generally, reservoir simulation is considered the most powerful predictive tool available to the reservoir engineer because reservoir simulation considers much more geologic and reservoir data than any other reservoir-prediction technique. Consequently, reservoir simulation has a much greater data requirement than other techniques.

Reservoir simulation's large data requirement has two important consequences; one is positive for the study and the other is detrimental. The positive aspect of the large data requirement is that data must be gathered from many sources and integrated into a single reservoir model. A properly conducted simulation study uses data from all available sources. The amalgamation of these data into a coherent model requires that all data be gathered, reviewed, and validated. The data review generally requires a multidisciplinary approach to a reservoir study. That is, the engineers performing the study must work with the geophysicists, geologists, formation evaluation specialists, reservoir engineers, production engineers, and operations staff who are familiar with the subject field. The detrimental aspect is that the process is extremely resource intensive.

Once validated, data must be manipulated to ensure that they are technically appropriate for reservoir simulation. This generally requires modifying the data so that they are at the proper scale for the simulation study. This scaleup can best be exemplified by the relative permeability data. The scale at which relative permeability data are measured (core scale) is not appropriate for reservoir simulation. **Fig. 10.2** illustrates this.

In this figure, the relative permeability data measured from the core cannot be expected to be representative of the relative permeability behavior at the reservoir scale because gravity forces act over a much greater distance in the reservoir than in the core sample. Consequently, the degree of fluid segregation occurring in the reservoir is much greater than the degree of segregation in the core sample.

The manipulation of data from several different sources inevitably leads to conflicts in the reservoir data. Even if the data have been validated, there is still a possibility of data conflicts. Again, this is caused by the difference in the scale at which different data are measured. For example, the height of the transition zone measured from a properly conducted and interpreted well log probably will differ from that of a properly conducted capillary pressure test on core samples taken from the same well. The general rule for the resolution of these discrepancies is that the proper measurement to use in a simulation study should be the most reliable measurement that is representative of the property or process occurring at the reservoir scale.

To summarize, the positive consequence of the large data requirement for reservoir simulation is that large volumes of data must be gathered, analyzed, and processed. The validation of these data and the resolution of any data conflicts increase the engineer's knowledge of the reservoir and generally lead to a much greater understanding of the reservoir. This may be true even before any simulation predictions are made.

The detrimental consequence of the large data requirement in reservoir simulation is that conducting a simulation study may be extremely resource intensive. The acquisition, validation, and processing of all data needed for a simulation study require the dedication of large amounts of company resources. These resources include not only the data acquisition costs, but also engineering time; computing costs; and investments in software, development, support, and maintenance.

The large volume of data required for a simulation study often leads to overkill,[3-7] which is one of the most common misuses of reservoir simulation. Overkill is the use of company resources that is not warranted by the quality of input data, quantity of input data, or information to be obtained from the study. To avoid overkill, a limit must be placed on the amount of resources used during a simulation study. This limit can be achieved only by having a clear set of study objectives at the inception of the study. Once study objectives are defined, only the resources required to meet these objec-

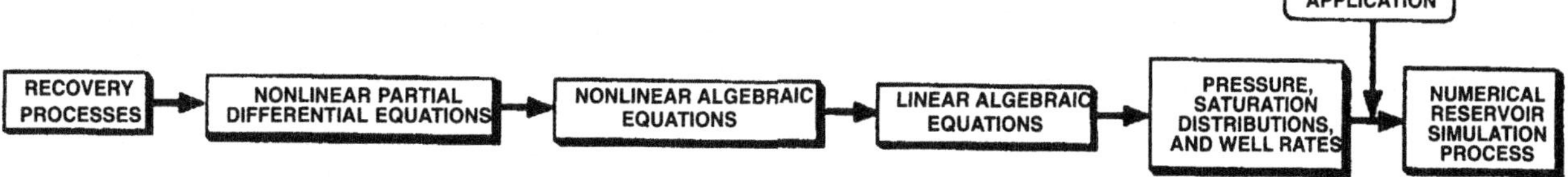

Fig. 10.1—Application of the model as the final phase of a numerical reservoir study (from Odeh [2]).

tives should be used. This leads to a fundamental rule of reservoir simulation: always use the simplest model required to meet study objectives.[8]

After the data have been collected and analyzed, they must be put into a format that can be interpreted by the simulator. This is the model construction phase of the study. During this phase, decisions are made concerning the scope of the simulation model (e.g., model type, model dimensionality, number of active and inactive grid cells, and fluid description). Again, the objectives of the study must dictate the decisions made on these issues.

Once the model is constructed, it must be tuned with known reservoir behavior. This is the history-matching phase of the study. History matching is the process of changing input data to forecast (or, more appropriately, hindcast) past reservoir performance. This is necessary because hydrocarbon-reservoir information is sparse. Even with proactive reservoir-management and data-acquisition programs, the data acquired from the relatively few wellbores that penetrate a reservoir cannot describe the reservoir in its entirety. The history-matching phase of a simulation study, therefore, is used to calibrate "soft" data to known reservoir performance.

After the history-matching phase of the study, the simulation model can be used to forecast future reservoir performance. This is the prediction phase of the study, and most of the study objectives are met during this phase. Appropriate objectives that can be addressed during the prediction phase of the study include selecting and optimizing a field-development plan, performing sensitivity analyses on key reservoir uncertainties, and analyzing various reservoir-management strategies.

Another important activity performed during the prediction phase of the study is to analyze the forecasts generated by the simulator to ensure that they make physical sense. This includes comparing the results with industry standards, with results from other prediction methods (e.g., material balance, Buckley-Leverett analysis, or decline-curve analysis) and analogous fields, and with expected production trends.

This chapter discusses all required simulation study phases. It is impossible to write a comprehensive method or "cookbook" approach for performing a simulation study because each reservoir and reservoir study is different. The objective of this chapter, therefore, is to provide the basics of conducting a reservoir simulation study. It should be emphasized that the material presented in this chapter is only a guideline. Because there are many "correct" ways to perform a simulation study, the method presented here should not be regarded as the only way to conduct such a study. This leads to a second fundamental rule of reservoir simulation: let the nature of the problem dictate the method of solution.[4]

10.2 Study Objectives

The most important step in the application of reservoir simulation to a successful reservoir study is the design of the study objectives. These objectives address the fundamental issue of what is to be learned by performing the study. Once the study objectives are determined, they dictate the type and scope of the reservoir model to be used, the amount of company resources to be used, the quality of the history match required, and the type of prediction cases required.

When developing a set of study objectives, concerns regarding the stage of recovery of the subject field or reservoir, the quantity and quality of the available reservoir data, whether the study warrants further data acquisition, and the time frame in which the study is to be conducted need to be addressed.

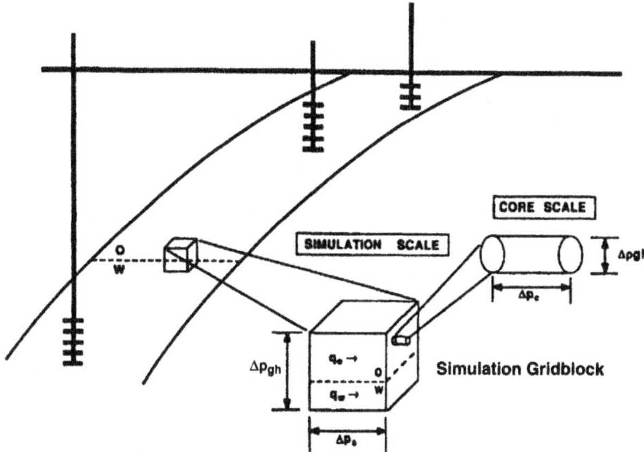

Fig. 10.2—Visualization of scaleup concept.

The stage of recovery of the subject field or reservoir is important in the design of the study objectives because reservoir simulation only yields reliable answers to certain questions provided relevant production history is available. For example, during the appraisal (preproduction) stage of a field, the only available history is from drillstem tests from exploration and appraisal wells. The data from this historical period are very limited and can be used only to history match the reservoir model in a very gross sense. Consequently, the information that can be obtained from the model is very general. The objectives for such a model may include determining the range of reserves for the field and the range in timing of production for the field.

In addition, if it is assumed that the uncertainties in the model will affect the quantitative results of the model but not the relative ranking of alternative production strategies, then the model can be used to screen the different strategies. If this assumption is made, it can be determined whether the subject field or reservoir is a candidate for waterflooding and whether a peripheral waterflood will respond better than a pattern waterflood.

A second example concerning the development stage of the subject field or reservoir is primary production. Even with several years of primary production, a successfully history-matched simulation model may be unable to give reliable results for questions concerning secondary or tertiary recovery because different processes control reservoir behavior during primary recovery and secondary recovery. For example, during primary production, fluid expansion may govern reservoir performance and the presence or absence of vertical shale barriers may not affect production significantly. The presence or absence of these barriers may affect the performance of a displacement process critically if gravity override or underride is anticipated in the reservoir. To make reliable forecasts with a reservoir simulator, significant relevant history is required to history match the model.

To define a proper set of study objectives, the quantity and quality of the available reservoir data must be considered. For example, if gas/oil relative permeability data are unavailable, a study of a potential gasflood will not yield reliable forecasts. If a gasflood is being considered, all relevant data should be acquired or obtained through sound engineering judgment with industry-accepted practices.

Finally, the timing of the study should be considered when developing the study objectives. For example, if the results of a simula-

TABLE 10.1—SOURCES OF RESERVOIR DATA [9,10]

Time/Operation	Predrilling						
		Seismic				Geology Engineering Study	
	Gravity	Time	Velocity	Amplitude	Character	Analogy, Regional Knowledge, and Maps	Depositional Environment
Depth markers		2	2			2	2
Structure and area	2	2	1	3	3	2	
Hydrodynamics						1	
Gross thickness			2		3	2	2
Net thickness				2	2	2	2
Lithology			2	2	3	2	2
Mechanical properties			2	2	3	2	2
Contacts			2	2	2	4	
Pressure			2	3		1	
Porosity			2	2	3	2	2
Permeability					4	2	2
Fluid saturation			3	3	3	4	
Pore sizes						2	
Producing mechanism		4	3	3	3	2	3
Hydrocarbon properties			4	4		2	
Water properties						1	
Production rate						2	2

Code: 1. Best source. 2. Good data source. 3. Average data source. 4. Poor data source.

TABLE 10.1—SOURCES OF RESERVOIR DATA [9,10] (continued)

Time/Operation	Wellbore Operations During Drilling												
						Logs						Wireline	
	Drill Rate	Mud Log	Cuttings	Cores	Drillstem	Electric	SP	Acoustic	Density	Gamma Ray	Neutron	Test	Cores
Depth markers	3	3	2	1	1	1	1	1	1	1	1	2	1
Structure and area					4								
Gross thickness	2	2	3	2	4	1	1	1	1	1	1		
Net thickness	3	3	4	1	4	1	1	1	1	1			
Lithology	3		2	1		3	3	2	2	2	3		1
Mechanical properties	3		2	1				2	2	2	3		2
Contacts		3	2	2	2	1	2	1	1		1	1	2
Pressure		3			1							2	
Porosity	4		3	1		3		1	1		1		2
Permeability			4	1	1	4		3	3		3	2	3
Relative permeability				1									
Fluid saturation		3	3	2	1	1	3	2	2		2	2	3
Pore sizes			2	1	4	4	4	4	4	4	4		3
Water properties				4	1							2	
Production rate				2	2			4	4		4	2	3
Fluids produced					1								

Code: 1. Best source. 2. Good data source. 3. Average data source. 4. Poor data source.
SP = spontaneous potential.

tion study are required in a short time frame (say, a few months), detailed forecasts generally cannot be made. In cases like these, less detailed objectives can be developed for the short term, while more detailed results can be generated once the rush period has passed.

10.3 Data Analysis

As stated in the introduction of this chapter, a properly conducted simulation study uses data from many varied sources. **Table 10.1** presents a list of data sources available to the reservoir engineer.[9,10]

TABLE 10.1—SOURCES OF RESERVOIR DATA [9,10] (continued)

Time/Operation	Post-Development						
	Production						Special Studies
	Flow Test	Pressure	Water Cut	Gas/Oil Ratio	History	Analogy	Engineering and Geology
Depth markers	2						1
Structure and area	2	2	3	3	1		1
Hydrodynamics	2	1			3	1	1
Gross thickness	2						1
Net thickness	2						1
Lithology						2	1
Mechanical properties						2	1
Contacts	1		2	2	2		1
Pressure	1	1				1	1
Porosity	4					2	1
Permeability	2	1				2	1
Relative permeability	1	2	2	2	2	2	1
Fluid saturation	1		1	1	2		1
Pore sizes						2	
Producing mechanism			1	1	1	1	1
Hydrocarbon properties	1	2		1		2	1
Water properties	1		1			2	1
Production rate	1	1			1	2	1
Fluids produced	1		1	1	1	2	1
Well damage	1	1			1		1
Recovery efficiency			2	2	1	2	1

Code: 1. Best source. 2. Good data source. 3. Average data source. 4. Poor data source.

The purpose of this section is to describe briefly some of the more common data sources available along with the role these data play in a numerical reservoir study. This discussion is not meant to be all inclusive because many other data sources are currently available to the reservoir engineer and petroleum research organizations are developing new analysis tools constantly.

In finite-difference simulation, many of the properties entered into the simulator must be consistent with the grid size and layering used in the reservoir model. In this section, we discuss only the aspects of the input data that are independent of the grid-cell size. In the section on model construction, we discuss the methods used to take grid-independent data and convert them to the appropriate grid-specific data.

10.3.1 Geophysical and Geological Data. Geophysical and geological data form the framework of any simulation model. In a broad sense, geophysical data provide the limits (or envelope) of the reservoir, whereas the geological data provide the internal anatomy. Because the practicing reservoir engineer generally is not expected to be able to perform detailed geophysical or geological studies, this section helps illustrate the need for a multidisciplinary approach to reservoir simulation.

Geophysical Data. By far, the geophysical data most commonly used in reservoir simulation are seismic data. Seismic data are obtained by generating acoustic energy at the earth's surface, transmitting this energy toward the target formations, and measuring (and recording) the time required for this energy to be reflected back to the surface through subsurface strata. **Fig. 10.3** shows the seismic-acquisition technique for a two-dimensional (2D) -seismic process and a typical seismic response in the form of a seismic line.

The seismic line shown in Fig. 10.3 represents a cross section through the reservoir and adjacent overburden and underburden formations. Seismic cross sections can be used by geophysicists to generate structure maps (both structure top and base) as well as identify faults, formation pinchouts, unconformities, variations in reservoir thickness, and reservoir continuity. Seismic data are also used to condition geostatistical models (incorporate data trends) in reservoirs where petrophysical properties (e.g., porosity and permeability) correlate to seismic attributes (see Sec. 10.4.3). In addition to the 2D-seismic process, three-dimensional (3D) -seismic, four-dimensional-seismic (time-lapse 3D-seismic), and cross-borehole tomology processes are used routinely for large hydrocarbon accumulations.

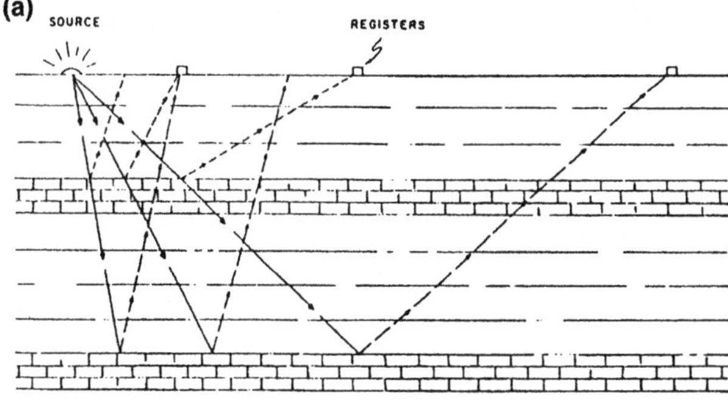

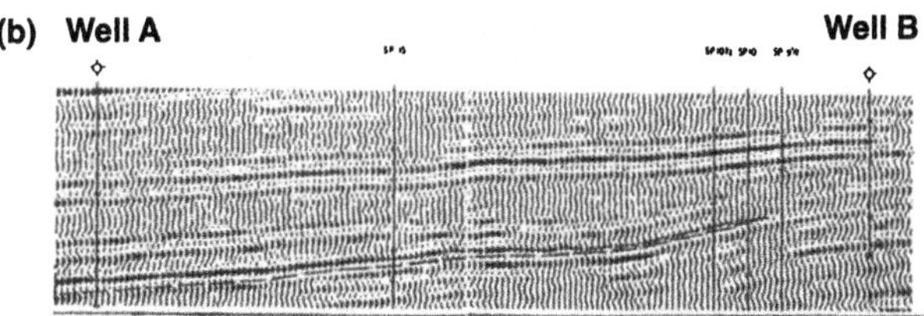

Fig. 10.3—Seismic line across the Brent field (after Campbell *et al.*[11]).

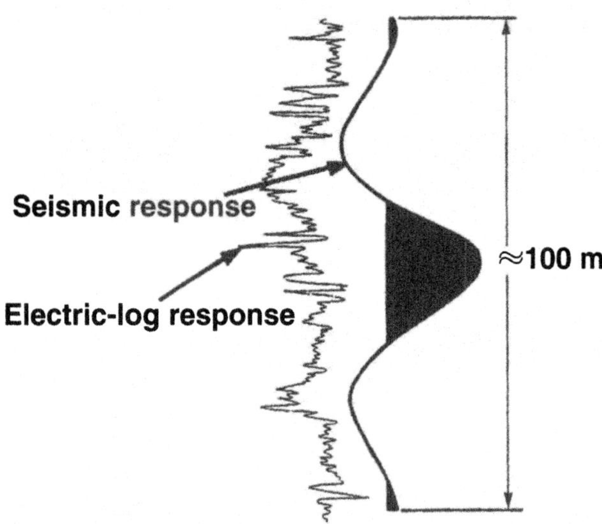

Fig. 10.4—Comparison of the resolution of seismic data and well log data (after Anstey[12]).

One limitation of seismic data is the relatively poor resolution of the technique. **Fig. 10.4** compares the resolution of a typical seismic response and a typical electric-log response. This figure illustrates that seismic techniques are appropriate for defining the reservoir envelope and identifying large-scale reservoir characteristics, such as faults and unconformities. Any reservoir property on a scale smaller than the resolution of the seismic survey cannot be determined by seismic techniques. Fig. 10.4 also illustrates that, for the internal structure of the reservoir, additional geological data must be considered.

Geologic Data. Reservoir simulation is such a powerful reservoir prediction tool because it is the only predictive tool that can account rigorously for reservoir geology. A successful simulation study always incorporates all available geologic data required to meet the study objectives.

The geologic model describes the distribution of reservoir properties, such as permeability, porosity, net pay, and flow barriers, along with the distribution of all reservoir and nonreservoir facies (rock types). Consequently, the geologic model provides the framework on which the reservoir simulation model is built. **Fig. 10.5** illustrates this.

Table 10.2 lists the requirements of the geologic model for reservoir simulation purposes. The map requirement in this table may be as simple as a single value for each simulation layer or as complex as a hand-drawn or computer-generated contour map.

The raw data used in the development of the geologic model consist of much of the same data used in engineering studies: core samples, openhole logs, and pressure-transient data. In addition, the geologic model may be enhanced with data sources normally not considered by reservoir engineers. These include mud logging, stratigraphy, paleontology, geochemistry, scanning electron microscopy, thin-section, and outcrop studies. Harris[13] provides a detailed discussion of the role of geology in reservoir simulation and the synergy between engineering and geologic data.

A good geologic model not only maps various reservoir properties throughout a hydrocarbon accumulation and associated aquifer but also attempts to interpret the processes that governed the distribution of these properties. This allows reservoir properties to be extrapolated to areas of little geologic control. Also, geostatistical analysis can aid in interpolating reservoir data between points of geological control.[14,15] The two main processes that govern the distribution of reservoir properties in hydrocarbon reservoirs are deposition and diagenesis and are discussed in the following sections.

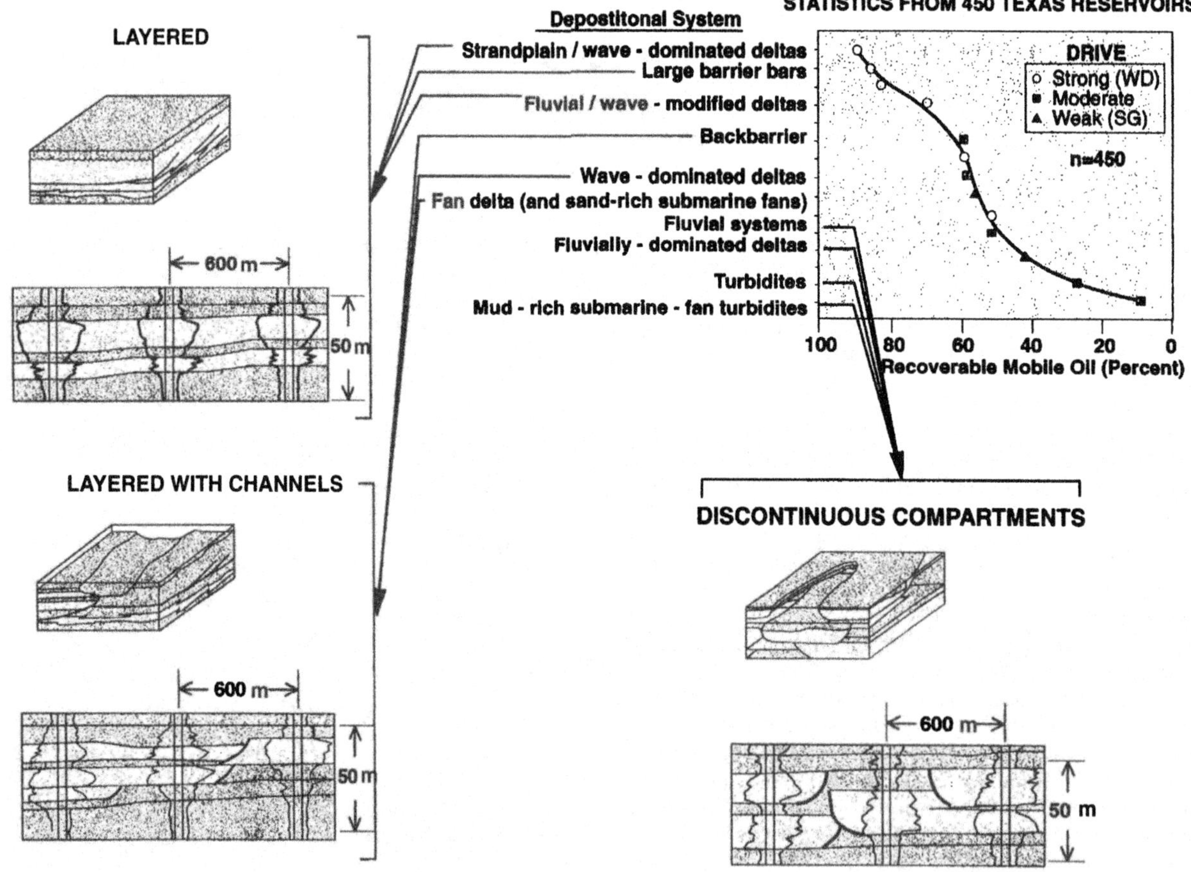

Fig. 10.5—Construction of a geologic model; WD = waterdrive, SG = Solution Gas. [Personal communication with G.M. Flaherty, Chevron Overseas Petroleum Inc., San Ramon, California (6 May 1996).]

TABLE 10.2—MAP REQUIREMENTS OF THE GEOLOGIC MODEL IN RESERVOIR SIMULATION

Property	Use in Simulation	Status
Structure top	Reservoir depth Initial reservoir pressure Original oil in place (OOIP) and original gas in place (OGIP) calculations	Required for the top layer Optional for lower layers (defaults may be obtained from the structure top of the top layer and gross thicknesses)
Net reservoir thickness, h_n	Assignment of cell net thickness values Horizontal-transmissibility calculations PV calculations Calculation of well geometric factors, G_w OOIP and OGIP calculations	Required
Gross reservoir thickness, h_g	Assignment of cell gross thickness values Gravity head calculations Initial reservoir pressures Transition-zone calculations Initial saturation distributions Vertical-transmissibility calculations	Optional (default may be obtained from net thickness, $h_n/h_g=1$)
Net to gross thickness ratio, h_n/h_g	Assignment to cell h_n/h_g values	Optional (default may equal one, $h_n/h_g=1$)
Porosity, ϕ	Assignment of cell ϕ values Development of porosity/permeability transforms Pore volume (PV) calculations OOIP and OGIP calculations	Required for all layers
Horizontal permeability, k_H	Assignment of cell permeability values Horizontal-transmissibility calculations Development of porosity/permeability transforms Calculation of well geometric factors, G_w	Required for all layers
Vertical permeability, k_V	Assignment of cell permeability values Vertical-transmissibility calculations	Optional (default may be obtained from horizontal permeabilities, $k_V/k_H=1$)
Initial saturations S_{wi}, S_{oi}, and S_{gi}	Initial saturation distributions Transition-zone heights OOIP and OGIP calculations	Optional (default may be obtained from initial capillary/gravity equilibrium)
Endpoint saturations S_{iw}, S_{orw}, S_{org} and S_{gc}	Saturation normalization Assignment of cell critical saturation values for saturation unnormalization	Optional (default may be obtained from endpoints of input relative permeability data)
Fluid contacts, OWC and gas/oil contact (GOC)	OOIP and OGIP calculations Initial saturation distributions Initial reservoir pressures	Required

Note: One map per simulation layer is required; however, defaults may be used for optional properties.

Depositional Environment. The depositional environment relates reservoir properties (and their distributions) in today's petroleum reservoirs to the environment present during the original deposition of reservoir rock materials. The fundamental law for the determination of the distribution of properties is that the processes acting today are the same processes that occurred when the reservoir rock originally was deposited.

The depositional model provides insight into the original distribution of reservoir properties, in both the areal and vertical dimensions. These areal and vertical trends can be determined from the depositional environment and incorporated into the model. For example, in the areal sense, a braided-stream depositional environment may exhibit relatively homogeneous reservoir properties throughout the reservoir with directional trends oriented parallel to the long axis of the river bed. These directional trends could affect reservoir behavior and reservoir-management decisions significantly. Consequently, these trends should be considered in the simulation study. Another example of the role of the geologic model, this time in the vertical sense, is a channel-mouth bar sand. Reservoirs deposited in this environment may exhibit the best reservoir quality (high porosity and permeability) at the top of the reservoir where wave action has removed any clay or silt material. Poorer quality sands may exist deeper in the reservoir. In cross-sectional and 3D models, this distribution of reservoir properties can be incorporated into the simulation study.

These examples are meant to illustrate why reservoir simulation is such a powerful tool. Reservoir simulation is the only prediction technique that considers these areal and vertical distributions. Poston and Gross[16] provide a detailed description, based on numerical simulation results, of how formation deposition affects production performance from various sandstone reservoirs. Fig. 10.5 illustrates the effects of depositional environment.

The depositional environment provides the original distribution of reservoir properties. The original distribution, however, is not sufficient for reservoir simulation because over geologic time this distribution may be acted upon by other processes. These processes are the diagenetic processes.

Diagenesis. Diagenetic processes are those processes that alter sediments and sedimentary rocks after their original deposition. They include mechanical processes (such as consolidation and compaction), chemical processes [such as authigenesis (crystal growth) and cementation], and biological processes (such as bioturbation). These processes can affect reservoir performance significantly on a global, regional, or localized scale and should be considered in the geologic and reservoir models. For example, on a global scale, mechanical tectonic forces may induce natural fracturing that would have a major impact on reservoir performance. In this case, the impact of diagenesis on the simulation study would be as fundamental as the selection of the simulator type (dual-porosity vs. single-porosity approach, Sec. 10.4.1) used in the study. On a regional scale, precipitation and cementation from reservoir brine may reduce po-

TABLE 10.3—USE OF CORE DATA IN RESERVOIR SIMULATION		
Property	Use in Simulation	Analysis
Lithology identification	Grid layering Assignment of rock types/facies Assignment of cell h_n/h_g values	Visual inspection
Net reservoir thickness, h_n	Assignment of cell net thickness values Horizontal-transmissibility calculations OOIP and OGIP calculations PV calculations Calculation of well geometric factors, G_w Net pay cutoffs	Routine core analysis Visual inspection Minipermeameter
Gross reservoir thickness, h_g	Assignment of cell gross thickness values Gravity head calculations Initial reservoir pressures Vertical-transmissibility calculations Transition-zone calculations Initial saturation distributions	Visual inspection Minipermeameter
Net to gross thickness ratio, h_n/h_g	Assignment of cell h_n/h_g values	Visual inspection Minipermeameter
Porosity, ϕ	Assignment of cell ϕ values Development of porosity/permeability transforms PV calculations OOIP and OGIP calculations	Routine core analysis
Horizontal permeability, k_H	Assignment of cell permeability values Horizontal-transmissibility calculations Development of permeability transforms Calculation of well geometric factors, G_w	Routine core analysis
Initial saturations, S_{wi}, S_{oi}, and S_{gi}	Initial saturation distributions Transition-zone heights OOIP and OGIP calculations	Routine core analysis
Endpoint saturations, S_{iw}, S_{orw}, S_{org}, and S_{gc}	Assignment of cell critical fluid saturation values Normalization of relative permeability and capillary pressure data Assignment of cell endpoint saturations	Special core analysis
Formation compressibility, c_R	Assignment of cell c_R values	Special core analysis
Relative permeability, k_r	Reservoir "rock curves" Basis for "interblock pseudofunctions" Basis for "well pseudofunctions"	Special core analysis
Capillary pressure, P_c	Reservoir "rock curves" Basis for "interblock pseudofunctions" Basis for "well pseudofunctions" Initial saturation distributions OOIP and OGIP calculations Height of capillary transition zones	Special core analysis

rosity and permeability in the aquifer but not significantly influence these properties in the pay zone. In this case, the impact of diagenesis would influence the selection of reservoir properties above and below the oil/water contact (OWC).

10.3.2 Engineering Data. Engineering data are concerned with the statics and dynamics of reservoir fluids. These data differ from geologic data in that geologic data are concerned with rock properties and the processes that govern the distribution of these properties. Although much of the raw data for engineering and geologic data are identical, the methods in which the data are processed and the objectives of the analyses are significantly different.

Reservoir Description. *Core Data.* Core measurements provide engineers and geologists with the only opportunity for directly observing how actual reservoir rock and fluids behave under controlled conditions. **Table 10.3** shows, for reservoir simulation purposes, the data obtained from core measurements. This table shows that simulation data can be obtained from visual inspection, routine core analysis, and special core analysis. Visual inspection is the process of handling and observing the core material and can be used to obtain fundamental rock properties, including lithology, presence of shale laminations and crossbedding, gross reservoir thickness, and net- to gross-thickness ratio. Routine core analysis is concerned with the measurement of basic formation properties, such as the porosity, absolute permeability, and initial saturations of the core samples. Special core analysis is concerned with the measurement of more complex reservoir properties, such as compressibility, endpoint saturations, relative permeability, and capillary pressure (along with many other reservoir properties, such as electrical properties of the formation).

The measurements made at the core scale can be used directly in reservoir simulation only for very finely layered models. For coarsely layered models, these data must be scaled up to the reservoir scale.

In the following discussions, it is assumed that the core program used in data acquisition is adequate to ensure that all core measurements are representative of the reservoir. This requires that all phases of the core program—core cutting, handling, transport, preservation, sampling, and testing—do not alter core properties. Although the design of a successful core program is beyond the scope of this book, all core data should be validated thoroughly before they are incorporated into the simulation model.

Routine Core Analysis. Routine core analysis, sometimes referred to as PKS (porosity, permeability, and saturation) analysis, is concerned with the measurement of basic formation properties. Generally, these properties must be averaged and scaled up from the

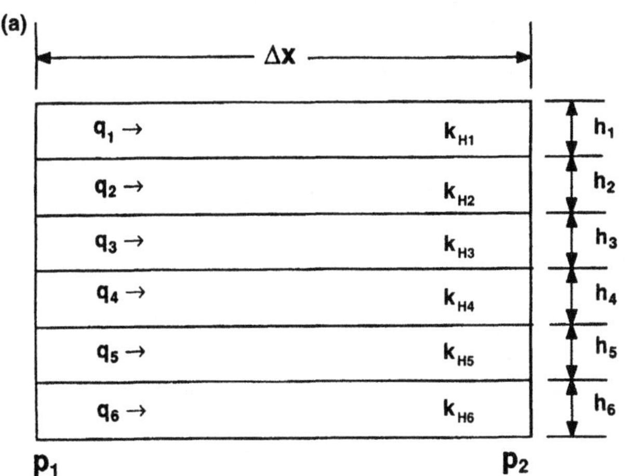

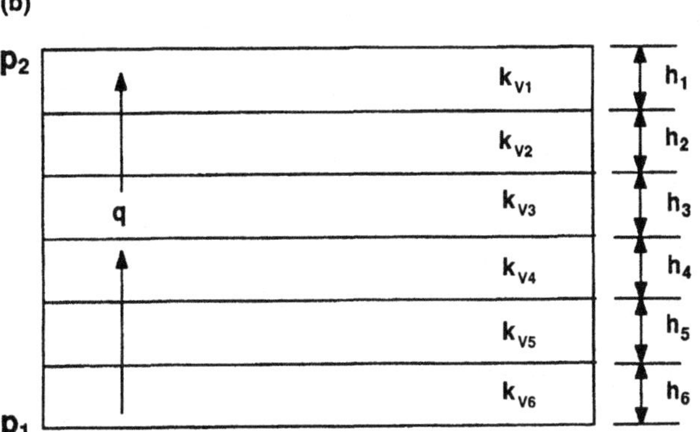

Fig. 10.6—Representation of (a) horizontal flow and (b) vertical flow in a stratified reservoir.

core scale to a scale appropriate for reservoir simulation. The averaging of the results of routine core analysis follows.

The average porosity from a stratified core section can be obtained by a thickness-weighted average.

$$\bar{\phi} = \frac{\sum_{k=1}^{n_k} \phi_k h_k}{\sum_{k=1}^{n_k} h_k}. \quad \text{(10.1)}$$

The determination of the average absolute permeability from a stratified core section is dependent on the direction of flow. To obtain these averages, we must consider the processes occurring in the reservoir. The following discussions consider horizontal and vertical flow. It should be remembered that, if the core is drilled vertically in a dipping reservoir (or, equivalently, obtained from a deviated well through a horizontal reservoir), corrections need to be made before averages can be calculated properly.

Fig. 10.6a is a typical representation of horizontal flow in a hydrocarbon accumulation. This figure shows that, in most cases, flow in the horizontal direction is parallel flow because, in horizontal-flow situations, fluids travel through reservoir strata to production wells and remain in the zone where they originated. For parallel flow, Eq. 10.2 is used to determine average permeability.

$$\bar{k}_H = \frac{\sum_{k=1}^{n_k} k_{H_k} h_k}{\sum_{k=1}^{n_k} h_k}. \quad \text{(10.2)}$$

Horizontal permeability from core data is generally in conflict with data from well-test analysis. Again, this is because core and well-test data are measured at different scales. This requires that core data be scaled up to reservoir scale, which can be done with a permeability transform (discussed later in this section).

Fig. 10.6b is a typical representation of vertical flow. The figure shows that, in most cases, flow in the vertical direction is serial flow. This is because in vertical-flow situations, fluids must pass in series from one zone to the next. For serial flow, Eq. 10.3 is used to determine average permeability.

$$\bar{k}_V = \frac{\sum_{k=1}^{n_k} h_k}{\sum_{k=1}^{n_k} \frac{h_k}{k_{Vk}}}. \quad \text{(10.3)}$$

Again, vertical permeabilities may need to be scaled up for use in reservoir simulation. A k_V/k_H ratio for clean pay can be obtained by dividing the average core vertical permeability by the average core horizontal permeability. For clean pay, once horizontal permeability is chosen for the simulation study, the vertical permeability can be obtained by multiplying it by the core k_V/k_H ratio. In the presence of discontinuous shales, further scaleup of the vertical permeability may be required. In the presence of continuous shales, the vertical transmissibility of a layer bounded by shale will be either reduced or set equal to zero.

The average saturation from a stratified core section can be obtained by PV weighting.

$$\bar{S}_{li} = \frac{\sum_{k=1}^{n_k} S_{li_k} \phi_k h_k}{\sum_{k=1}^{n_k} \phi_k h_k}, \quad \text{(10.4)}$$

where $l = o$, w, or g.

The averaging of data should be done judiciously because the extreme values of data often control the behavior of a process. For example, breakthrough during a secondary recovery project will be controlled by the permeability of the most permeable layer. If this value is lost during the averaging process, the breakthrough time is altered. It is always a good idea to carry all data throughout the study at the scale that they were measured and to perform any averaging or scale-up as the last step before data input into the simulator.

The methods of averaging described by Eqs. 10.1 through 10.4 represent a static approach to upscaling data from the core scale to the reservoir scale. Durlofsky[17] presented a dynamic approach to scaleup based on the incompressible-flow equation and periodic boundary conditions, which has been found to be more representative of reservoir processes than the static approach. In particular, it has been found very effective for upscaling permeability data in the presence of crossbedding.

Example 10.1. Use the core data supplied in **Fig. 10.7** to determine the average porosity, horizontal permeability, and vertical permeability. For this example, assume that within 1 ft intervals the vertical permeability is equal to the horizontal permeability.

Solution. Data for ϕ, k, and h for each 1-ft interval are taken from Fig. 10.7 and tabulated along with ϕh, kh, and h/k in **Table 10.4**. From this table we have

$$\sum h = 14 \text{ ft},$$

$$\sum \phi h = 4.58 \text{ ft},$$

$$\sum kh = 32{,}440 \text{ md-ft},$$

and $\sum h/k = 0.0188$ ft/md.

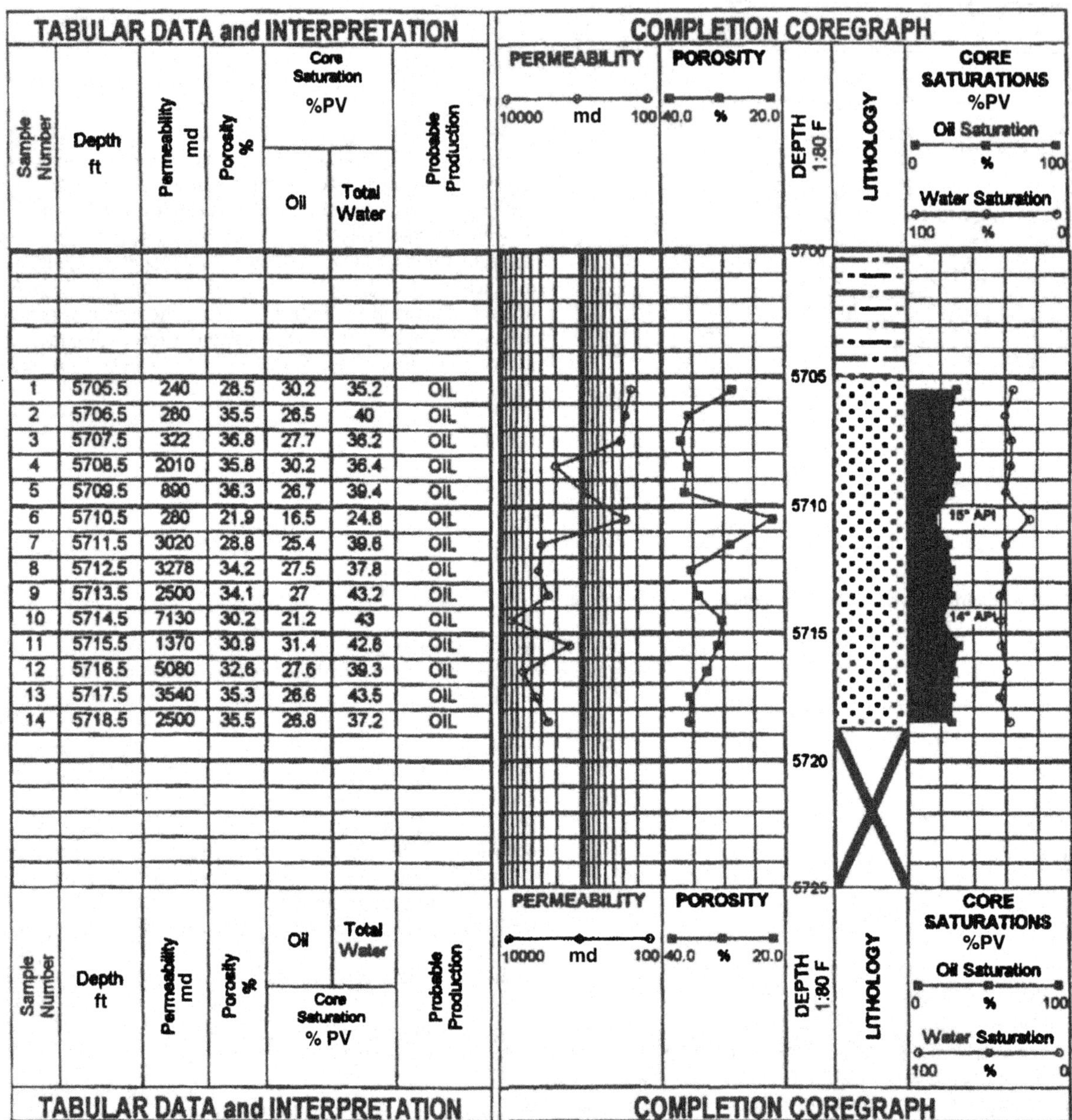

COMPANY: Good Oil Co.
WELL: West No. 2
FIELD: Wildcat
LOCATION: Wood County, Texas

FILE NUMBER: 57161-12345
DEPTH RANGE: 5693 to 5727 ft
DATE: Wednesday, May 29,

FORMATION: Woodbine
CORE TYPE: Diamond
DRILLING FLUID: Water Base Mud

Sand
Silt
No Samples

TABULAR DATA and INTERPRETATION

Sample Number	Depth ft	Permeability md	Porosity %	Core Saturation %PV Oil	Core Saturation %PV Total Water	Probable Production
1	5705.5	240	28.5	30.2	35.2	OIL
2	5706.5	280	35.5	26.5	40	OIL
3	5707.5	322	36.8	27.7	36.2	OIL
4	5708.5	2010	35.8	30.2	36.4	OIL
5	5709.5	890	36.3	26.7	39.4	OIL
6	5710.5	280	21.9	16.5	24.8	OIL
7	5711.5	3020	28.8	25.4	39.6	OIL
8	5712.5	3278	34.2	27.5	37.8	OIL
9	5713.5	2500	34.1	27	43.2	OIL
10	5714.5	7130	30.2	21.2	43	OIL
11	5715.5	1370	30.9	31.4	42.8	OIL
12	5716.5	5080	32.6	27.6	39.3	OIL
13	5717.5	3540	35.3	26.6	43.5	OIL
14	5718.5	2500	35.5	26.8	37.2	OIL

Fig. 10.7—Data and interpretation for Example 10.1 (from Core Laboratories[18]).

From Eq. 10.1,

$$\bar{\phi} = \frac{\sum \phi h}{\sum h} \quad (10.5)$$

$$= \frac{4.58}{14}$$

$$= 0.33.$$

From Eq. 10.2,

$$\bar{k}_H = \frac{\sum kh}{\sum h} \quad (10.6)$$

$$= \frac{32,440 \text{ md-ft}}{14 \text{ ft}}$$

$$= 2,317 \text{ md}.$$

TABLE 10.4—SOLUTION TO EXAMPLE 10.1

Average porosity, fraction	0.33
Horizontal permeability, md	2,317.0
Vertical permeability, md	745.0
k_V/k_H	0.32

Interval Top (ft TVDSS)	Bottom (ft TVDSS)	k (md)	ϕ (fraction)	h (ft)	ϕh (ft)	kh (md-ft)	h/k (ft/md)
5,705.5	5,706.5	240.0	0.29	1.0	0.29	240.0	0.0042
5,706.5	5,707.5	280.0	0.36	1.0	0.36	280.0	0.0036
5,707.5	5,708.5	322.0	0.37	1.0	0.37	322.0	0.0031
5,708.5	5,709.5	2,010.0	0.36	1.0	0.36	2,010.0	0.0005
5,709.5	5,710.5	890.0	0.36	1.0	0.36	890.0	0.0011
5,710.5	5,711.5	280.0	0.22	1.0	0.22	280.0	0.0036
5,711.5	5,712.5	3,020.0	0.29	1.0	0.29	3,020.0	0.0003
5,712.5	5,713.5	3,278.0	0.34	1.0	0.34	3,278.0	0.0003
5,713.5	5,714.5	2,500.0	0.34	1.0	0.34	2,500.0	0.0004
5,714.5	5,715.5	7,130.0	0.30	1.0	0.30	7,130.0	0.0001
5,715.5	5,716.5	1,370.0	0.31	1.0	0.31	1,370.0	0.0007
5,716.5	5,717.5	5,080.0	0.33	1.0	0.33	5,080.0	0.0002
5,717.5	5,718.5	3,540.0	0.35	1.0	0.35	3,540.0	0.0003
5,718.5	5,719.5	2,500.0	0.36	1.0	0.36	2,500.0	0.0004
			Summation:	14.0	4.58	32,440.0	0.0188

SS=subsea.

From Eq. 10.3,

$$\bar{k}_V = \frac{\sum h}{\sum h/k} \quad (10.7)$$

$$= \frac{14 \text{ ft}}{0.0188 \text{ ft/md}}$$

$$= 745 \text{ md}$$

and $$\frac{k_V}{k_H} = \frac{745}{2,317}$$

$$= 0.32.$$

Table 10.4 tabulates these results.

Special Core Analysis. Special core analysis is concerned with the measurement of reservoir properties required for specialized studies. These properties are not measured routinely because of the time frame and costs required for their measurement. While routine-core-analysis results can be obtained within weeks, special core analyses may require several months before reliable results can be obtained. The remainder of this section discusses the averaging of special-core-analysis results.

The use of the appropriate formation (or rock) compressibility in reservoir simulation requires specific knowledge of the reservoir simulator used in the study, along with a general knowledge of the processes occurring in the reservoir because there are several definitions of formation compressibility that, under different circumstances, could be appropriate for reservoir simulation. The formulation of the simulation program and relevant reservoir processes dictate the definition of compressibility appropriate for a particular study.

Compressibility, which relates the relative change in volume to change in reservoir pressure, is discussed in Chap. 2. This property is defined by Eq. 2.39 as

$$c = -\frac{1}{V}\frac{dV}{dp}. \quad (10.8)$$

In porous rock, we must consider the bulk volume, V_b; the PV, V_p; and the solid (or grain) volume, V_s. These volumes are related by

$$V_b = V_p + V_s \quad (10.9)$$

$$\text{and } \phi = \frac{V_p}{V_b} = \frac{V_b - V_s}{V_b}. \quad (10.10)$$

The volume changes for all reservoir volumes are governed by

$$c_b = -\frac{1}{V_b}\frac{dV_b}{dp}, \quad (10.11)$$

$$c_p = -\frac{1}{V_p}\frac{dV_p}{dp}, \quad (10.12)$$

$$c_s = -\frac{1}{V_s}\frac{dV_s}{dp}, \quad (10.13)$$

$$\text{and } c_\phi = \frac{1}{\phi}\frac{d\phi}{dp}. \quad (10.14)$$

Because the rock volumes are related by Eqs. 10.9 and 10.10, the compressibilities associated with these volumes are related. The most relevant relationships for reservoir simulation are

$$c_p = \frac{c_b - c_s}{\phi} + c_s \quad (10.15)$$

$$\text{and } c_\phi = c_p(1 - \phi) - \phi c_s. \quad (10.16)$$

In this book, we assume that the bulk volume is constant, which allows for removal of the bulk volume from the time derivative in the finite-difference equations. That is,

$$\frac{\partial}{\partial t}\left(\frac{V_b \phi S_l}{\alpha_c B_l}\right) = \frac{V_b}{\alpha_c}\frac{\partial}{\partial t}\left(\frac{\phi S_l}{B_l}\right). \quad (10.17)$$

With Eq. 10.17, all expansions of the time derivative require the use of the porosity compressibility. Other equally valid formulations of the finite-difference equations may require the use of the PV compressibility. For the proper simulation of the pressure response to fluid-withdrawal behavior, the engineer performing the simulation

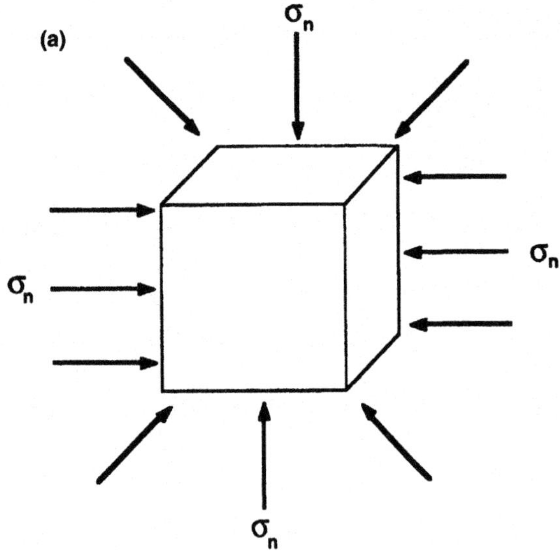

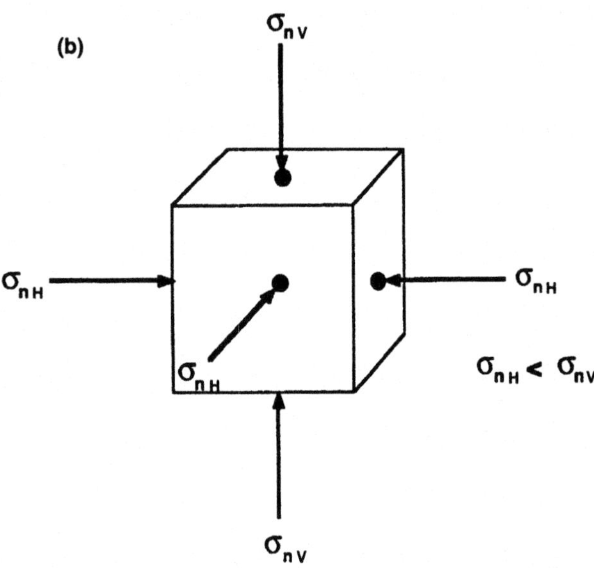

Fig. 10.8—Schematic representations of (a) hydrostatic loading and (b) uniaxial loading.

study must be familiar with the formulation of the finite-difference equations used in the simulator program, as well as the appropriate definition of compressibility used in these equations.

Knowledge of the reservoir processes prevalent in the subject reservoir is also required to determine the appropriate definition of compressibility to use in a simulation study. There are different methods used for measuring formation compressibility that, under certain circumstances, are appropriate for reservoir simulation. The measurement of formation compressibility involves applying stress (load) to the core samples and measuring the volume changes at different stress levels. The core sample can be loaded in several different ways. Two of the more common methods of applying stress are hydrostatic loading and uniaxial loading. Hydrostatic loading involves applying stresses that are equal on all surfaces of the core sample, whereas uniaxial loading involves applying the main stress on one axis of the core while keeping the stresses equal on the other axes (but at a lower stress level). **Fig. 10.8** shows the difference between these two processes schematically.

In deep hydrocarbon reservoirs, the stresses acting on the reservoir rock often can be assumed equal; consequently, compressibility measured under hydrostatic conditions is appropriate for reservoir simulation. On the other hand, in shallow reservoirs the overburden acts as the principal load, while the horizontal stresses are generally less than this principal load. Also, in tectonically active regions, the local stress field may load the reservoir in a manner where there is one principal direction of stress. In such cases, compressibility measured under uniaxial conditions may be more representative of reservoir behavior. Therefore, the knowledge of the state of stress within the reservoir aids in determining the appropriate compressibility measurement for the simulation study.

When the compressibility must be converted from a hydrostatic measurement to an equivalent uniaxial measurement, Eq. 10.18 can be used.

$$c_u = \frac{1}{3}\frac{(1+\nu)}{(1-\nu)}c_h . \qquad (10.18)$$

In Eq. 10.18, ν = Poisson's ratio of the reservoir formation. For typical sandstone reservoirs, Poisson's ratio lies between 0.15 and 0.35. In addition, most hydrocarbon reservoirs contain layers of nonreservoir rock. The expansion of this nonpay zone during reservoir depletion may need to be considered during a reservoir study.

Endpoint fluid saturations, S_{iw}, S_{orw}, S_{org}, and S_{gc}, all can be obtained from special core analysis. While special core analysis is the most common method available to the reservoir engineer for obtaining S_{orw}, S_{org}, and S_{gc}, the value of S_{iw} also can be measured from openhole, cased-hole, and computer-processed-interpretation logs. In general, core-derived S_{iw} does not equal log-derived S_{iw}. Because the value of log-derived S_{iw} is measured at the reservoir scale, this value can be used directly for reservoir simulation. If no estimates at the reservoir scale of S_{orw}, S_{org}, and S_{gc} are available, core-derived values can be scaled up with microscopic displacement efficiencies.

$$E_{Dw} = \frac{1 - S_{iw} - S_{orw}}{1 - S_{iw}} \qquad (10.19)$$

and $$E_{Dg} = \frac{1 - S_{iw} - S_{org}}{1 - S_{iw}}. \qquad (10.20)$$

Solving for S_{orw} and S_{org} results in

$$S_{orw} = (1 - S_{iw})(1 - E_{Dw}) \qquad (10.21)$$

and $$S_{org} = (1 - S_{iw})(1 - E_{Dg}). \qquad (10.22)$$

If it is assumed that the microscopic displacement efficiencies at the reservoir scale and the core scale are equal (or, more realistically, a factor lower than the microscopic displacement efficiency at the core scale), then Eqs. 10.19 through 10.22 can be used to determine the critical saturations to flow at the reservoir scale. The microscopic displacement efficiencies can be obtained with Eqs. 10.19 and 10.20 along with the core-derived values of S_{iw}, S_{orw}, and S_{org}. Then, the values of S_{orw} and S_{org} at the reservoir scale can be obtained by use of Eqs. 10.21 and 10.22 with the calculated values of E_{Dw}, E_{Dg}, and S_{iw} at reservoir scale. It should be emphasized that the values of S_{orw} and S_{org} at the reservoir scale estimated by Eqs. 10.19 through 10.22 are only approximations. Values measured at the reservoir scale are preferable. Methods of obtaining values of S_{org} and S_{orw} at reservoir scale from cased-hole logs are discussed later in this section.

Relative permeability, discussed in Chap. 2, is defined as the effective permeability to a particular fluid divided by a base permeability. Two base permeabilities are in general use in the petroleum industry: absolute (air) permeability, k_a, and effective permeability to oil at irreducible water saturation, $k_{ro}(S_{iw})$. The remainder of this discussion uses absolute permeability as the base permeability. It should be remembered that the base permeability to use in a particular study must be consistent with the permeability values assigned to the cells in the simulation model. Later in this section, the pressure-transient data is discussed further.

The relative permeability curves obtained from core samples from different core plugs in a well are never identical. Before relative permeability data can be incorporated into a reservoir simulator, the individual relative permeability curves must be grouped (if required), validated, and averaged. Grouping relative permeability curves involves collecting all curves with common reservoir characteristics. These characteristics may be related to geologic data, such as reservoir facies, or location, such as proximity to the OWC. The characteristic to use for the grouping of these curves changes from study to study. In many cases, grouping the relative permeability data is not necessary and only one curve is required for the simulation study.

Validation of the relative permeability curves involves inspecting the data to ensure that they are representative of the characteristics of the group to which they are assigned. This requires normalizing the curves to remove the effects of different endpoint saturations (critical saturations to flow) and resolving any conflicts with the resulting curves. This may involve discarding any curve that does not appear representative of the group.

Then, the relative permeability curves for each group can be averaged to obtain a single curve for the group. Again, normalized curves must be used in the averaging process to remove the effects of different endpoint saturations. If unnormalized curves are used in the averaging process, unnatural kinks are obtained in the averaged curves at the individual endpoint saturations.

Normalizing the curves involves scaling the saturation values of the original curves (each curve may have different endpoint saturations) so that all curves have common endpoint saturations. These common normalized endpoint saturations are

$$S_{iwn} = S_{orwn} = 0 \quad \text{.......................... (10.23)}$$

for oil/water curves and

$$S_{gcn} = S_{orgn} = 0 \quad \text{.......................... (10.24)}$$

for oil/gas curves. In other words, the fluid saturations of the original relative permeability curves should be stretched mathematically from the measured endpoint saturations to endpoint saturations of zero and one. The equation used to normalize the water saturations for the two-phase oil/water relative permeability curves is

$$S_{wn} = \frac{S_w - S_{iw}}{1 - S_{iw} - S_{orw}}, \quad \text{...................... (10.25)}$$

while the equations used to normalize the gas saturation for two-phase oil/gas relative permeability are

$$S_{gn}^o = \frac{S_g}{1 - S_{iw} - S_{org}} \quad \text{...................... (10.26)}$$

$$\text{and } S_{gn}^g = \frac{S_g - S_{gc}}{1 - S_{iw} - S_{org} - S_{gc}}. \quad \text{................ (10.27)}$$

Two different definitions of normalized gas saturation are required for oil/gas systems because, in the presence of irreducible water, oil is mobile through the range $0 < S_g < 1 - S_{iw} - S_{org}$, while gas is mobile through the range $S_{gc} < S_g < 1 - S_{iw} - S_{org}$.

These definitions of normalized saturations ensure that all relative permeability curves go from normalized saturation values of zero to one. In Eqs. 10.25 through 10.27, the endpoint saturations of the individual core samples should be used. Once the saturations have been normalized, the relative permeability curves should be inspected visually to ensure that they are representative of the reservoir group to which they are assigned. If a curve differs significantly from other curves in the group, the discrepancy should be resolved. For example, the following questions should be asked. At what conditions were the relative permeability measurements made (reservoir or ambient conditions)? Were the tests made with the same procedures (steady state or unsteady state)? Were different coring fluids used during the coring process and will these fluids alter wettability? Is the core sample actually a member of this group? If the discrepancies cannot be resolved, the curve should be considered carefully before it is included in the average.

Once the representative, normalized curves are assembled, they can be averaged. Because there is no need to weight one curve differently from other curves, a straight arithmetic average is appropriate for relative permeability values and provides a single curve that should be representative of each relative permeability group.

The final step in the averaging process is to denormalize the curves. This involves the use of Eqs. 10.25 through 10.27 to convert the normalized saturations to physical saturations. For this process, the endpoint saturations at the reservoir scale should be used [that is, the log-derived values of S_{iw}, S_{orw} (from Eq. 10.21) and S_{org} (from Eq. 10.22)]. The denormalized curves represent the rock curves to be used in the simulation model. Unless thin simulation layers are used in the study, the rock curves need further scaleup with pseudofunctions. Sec. 10.4.3 discusses this process.

At this point, it is necessary to emphasize the importance of the core program. The most accurate measurement of core relative permeability is with a steady-state method, such as the Penn State method. (The Penn State method, first designed by Morse *et al.*,[19] is a steady-state method for measuring relative permeability.) These methods generally require more time than unsteady-state methods; consequently, they are more expensive to run. Again, the objectives of the study must warrant the additional accuracy.

Finally, we must consider the processes occurring in the reservoir to determine which relative permeability curves should be included in the averaging procedure. Two main saturation paths can be used during measurement of relative permeability curves: drainage (a nonwetting phase displaces a wetting phase) and imbibition (a wetting phase displaces a nonwetting phase). In water-wet reservoirs, water displacing oil is an imbibition process; therefore, imbibition curves should be used in the averaging process for most simulation studies. If significant imbibition and drainage processes are expected during the exploitation of the subject reservoir, both drainage and imbibition curves may be required for the simulation study. Most commercial reservoir simulators allow for hysteresis, and this option should be used if required to meet the study objectives.

Example 10.2. Using the relative permeability data in **Table 10.5**, determine the appropriate relative permeability curves for the reservoir. The irreducible water saturation from the core data is 27%, while it is 22% from well logs.

Solution. To adjust the relative permeability data to reservoir conditions, the core saturations must be converted to normalized saturations with core properties. To do this, we use Eqs. 10.25 through 10.27.

$$S_{wn} = \frac{S_w - S_{iw}}{1 - S_{iw} - S_{orw}} \quad \text{...................... (10.25)}$$

$$= \frac{S_w - 0.27}{1 - 0.27 - 0.25}$$

$$= \frac{S_w - 0.27}{0.48},$$

$$S_{gn}^o = \frac{S_g}{1 - S_{iw} - S_{org}} \quad \text{...................... (10.26)}$$

$$= \frac{S_g}{1 - 0.27 - 0.25}$$

$$= \frac{S_g}{0.48},$$

$$\text{and } S_{gn}^g = \frac{S_g - S_{gc}}{1 - S_{iw} - S_{org} - S_{gc}} \quad \text{................ (10.27)}$$

$$= \frac{S_g - 0.05}{1 - 0.27 - 0.25 - 0.05}$$

$$= \frac{S_g - 0.05}{0.43}.$$

Relative permeability can be tabulated vs. the normalized saturations. The next step is to denormalize the saturation data. No S_{orw} or S_{org} data at reservoir conditions were supplied, so these data must be generated. To generate these data, we use Eqs. 10.19 and 10.20 and assume that the microscopic displacement efficiency at reservoir conditions is equal to that at the core conditions. Eqs. 10.19 and

TABLE 10.5—DATA FOR EXAMPLE 10.2

Oil/Water Curves	Core	Reservoir	Gas/Oil Curves	Core	Reservoir
S_{iw}	0.270	0.220	S_{iw}	0.270	0.220
S_{orw}	0.250	0.267	S_{org}	0.250	0.267
			S_{gc}	0.050	0.053
$k_{row}(S_{iw})$	0.450		$k_{rog}(0)$	0.450	same as $k_{row}(S_{iw})$
$k_{rw}(1-S_{orw})$	0.250		$k_{rog}(S_{gc})$	0.400	
			$k_{rog}(S_g^*)$	0.350	$S_g^*=1-S_{org}-S_{iw}$
			$k_{rg}(1-S_{org})$	0.600	<1.0
E_{Dw}	0.658	0.658	E_{Dg}	0.658	0.658

Oil/Water Curves: Core Water Saturation	k_{row}	k_{rw}	Gas/Oil Curves: Core Gas Saturation	k_{rog}	k_{rg}
0.000	1.000	0.000	0.000	0.450	0.000
0.270	0.450	0.000	0.050	0.400	0.000
0.300	0.340	0.002	0.150	0.250	0.002
0.400	0.100	0.010	0.200	0.150	0.010
0.450	0.030	0.030	0.250	0.075	0.030
0.600	0.009	0.090	0.300	0.050	0.050
0.650	0.003	0.125	0.400	0.010	0.200
0.750	0.000	0.250	0.480	0.000	0.600
1.000	0.000	1.000	1.000	0.000	—

10.20 calculate core conditions, and Eqs. 10.21 and 10.22 calculate reservoir conditions.

$$E_{Dw}=\frac{1-S_{iw}-S_{orw}}{1-S_{iw}} \quad \text{(10.19)}$$

$$=\frac{1-0.27-0.25}{1-0.27}$$

$$=0.658,$$

$$E_{Dg}=\frac{1-S_{iw}-S_{org}}{1-S_{iw}} \quad \text{(10.20)}$$

$$=\frac{1-0.27-0.25}{1-0.27}$$

$$=0.658,$$

$$S_{orw}=(1-S_{iw})(1-E_{Dw}) \quad \text{(10.21)}$$

$$=(1-0.22)(1-0.658)$$

$$=0.267,$$

$$\text{and } S_{org}=(1-S_{iw})(1-E_{Dg}) \quad \text{(10.22)}$$

$$=(1-0.22)(1-0.658)$$

$$=0.267.$$

To denormalize the saturation data, we solve Eqs. 10.25 through 10.27 for S_w and S_g, respectively.

$$S_w=S_{iw}+S_{wn}(1-S_{iw}-S_{orw}) \quad \text{(10.28)}$$

$$=0.22+S_{wn}(1-0.22-0.267)$$

$$=0.22+0.513S_{wn},$$

$$S_g=S_{gn}^o(1-S_{iw}-S_{org}) \quad \text{(10.29)}$$

$$=S_{gn}^o(1-0.22-0.267)$$

$$=0.513S_{gn}^o,$$

$$\text{and } S_g=S_{gn}^g(1-S_{iw}-S_{org}-S_{gc})+S_{gc} \quad \text{(10.30)}$$

$$=S_{gn}^g(1-0.22-0.267-0.05)+0.05$$

$$=0.463S_{gn}^g+0.05.$$

Because we have two definitions of normalized gas saturation, we obtain two different sets of physical gas saturations at the reservoir scale after denormalization. The final step is to interpolate the k_{rog} and k_{rg} data to a common set of gas saturations. **Table 10.6** tabulates these results, and **Figs. 10.9 through 10.12** show the results in relative permeability curves.

Capillary pressure is the property that relates the differences in pressure of reservoir fluids to the fluid saturation. This property has many important consequences in reservoir behavior, including the height of any transition zone, the initial distribution of reservoir fluids, and the retention of the wetting phase in the reservoir.

As with relative permeability data, capillary pressure data should be grouped, validated, and averaged before their use in a simulation study. The methods used to average and incorporate capillary pressure into a simulation model are similar to those used for relative permeability. There are, however, several differences in the averaging process that must be addressed.

In the averaging of relative permeability data, only the saturations (x axis of a relative permeability curve) were normalized because the relative permeability values (y axis), by their very definition, are normalized already. That is, the effective permeability is normalized with the base permeability.

Capillary pressure data (y axis of a capillary pressure curve) are not normalized during their measurement; consequently, both axes must be scaled to obtain representative curves. For the fluid saturations, the normalized saturations defined by Eqs. 10.25 and 10.26 are appropriate for capillary pressure data and no further scaling is required. For the capillary pressure itself, additional scaling may be required.

Capillary pressure is dependent on the pore-size distribution of the reservoir rock. Leverett[20] defined a dimensionless capillary

TABLE 10.6—SOLUTION TO EXAMPLE 10.2

Oil/Water Relative Permeability Curves

Core Water Saturation	k_{row}	k_{rw}	S_{wn} Eq. 10.25	Reservoir Water Saturation
0.000	1.000	0.000	—	0.000
0.270	0.450	0.000	0.000	0.220
0.300	0.340	0.002	0.063	0.252
0.400	0.100	0.010	0.271	0.359
0.450	0.030	0.030	0.375	0.412
0.600	0.009	0.090	0.688	0.573
0.650	0.003	0.125	0.792	0.626
0.750	0.000	0.250	1.000	0.733
1.000	0.000	1.000	—	1.000

Oil/Gas Relative Permeability Curves (Intermediate)

Core Gas Saturation	k_{rog}	S^o_{gn} Eq. 10.26	Reservoir Gas Saturation for Oil Curve	k_{rg}	S^g_{gn} Eq. 10.27	Reservoir Gas Saturation for Gas Curve
0.000	0.450	0.000	0.000	0.000	—	0.000
0.050	0.400	0.104	0.053	0.000	0.000	0.050
0.150	0.250	0.313	0.160	0.002	0.233	0.158
0.200	0.150	0.417	0.214	0.010	0.349	0.212
0.250	0.075	0.521	0.267	0.030	0.465	0.265
0.300	0.050	0.625	0.321	0.050	0.581	0.319
0.400	0.010	0.833	0.427	0.200	0.814	0.423
0.480	0.000	1.000	0.513	0.350	1.000	0.513
0.75	0.000	—	0.733	0.600	—	—

Oil/Gas Relative Permeability Curves (Final)

Core Gas Saturation	k_{rog}	k_{rg}	Common Reservoir Saturation
0.000	0.450	0.000	0.000
0.050	0.403	0.000	0.050
0.150	0.253	0.002	0.158
0.200	0.154	0.010	0.212
0.250	0.078	0.030	0.265
0.300	0.051	0.050	0.319
0.400	0.012	0.200	0.423
0.480	0.000	0.350	0.513
0.75	0.000	0.600	0.733

pressure group, the J function, which includes the effects of pore-size distribution. The J function is defined as

$$J(S_w) = \frac{P_c(S_w)}{\sigma \cos(\Theta_c)}\left(\frac{k}{\phi}\right)^{1/2}. \quad \quad (10.31)$$

Leverett[20] presented experimental evidence that indicated that, within a given reservoir facies, the J function remains relatively uniform. **Fig. 10.13** shows an example of the J function for several sandstones. Eq. 10.31 can be rearranged to obtain

$$P_c(S_w) = \sigma \cos(\Theta_c) J(S_w)\left(\frac{\phi}{k}\right)^{1/2}. \quad \quad (10.32)$$

The use of the J function allows the capillary pressure to be measured from core samples at a given location in the reservoir, be normalized with the local properties of the core (with both the normalized saturations and J function), and be denormalized with properties at a different location in the reservoir. With this approach, the capillary pressure curve measured at one location can be made representative of the capillary pressure curve at other locations in the reservoir.

Once the J-function curves are obtained from available core samples, they can be averaged in the same manner as the relative permeability curves to obtain a representative J-function curve for a given reservoir facies. Again, the curves used during the averaging process should use normalized saturations. Finally, straight arithmetic averaging is appropriate for averaging the J function.

If the calculated height of the capillary transition zone from the core data differs from the measured transition zone determined from well logs, the core-derived capillary pressure data need further scaling for use in reservoir simulation. This scaleup can be accomplished with the simple ratio,

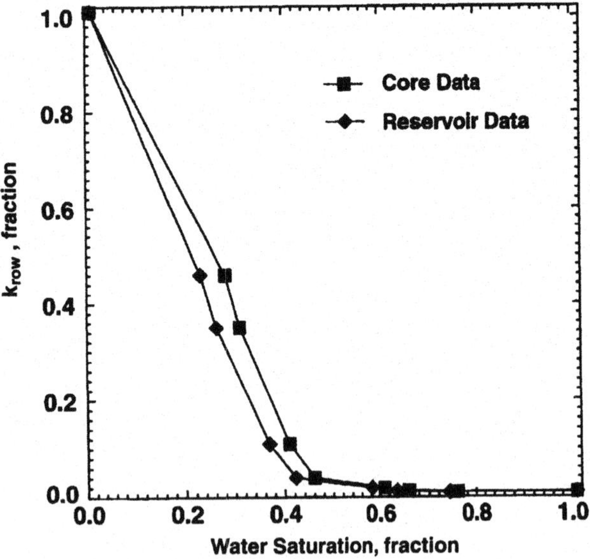

Fig. 10.9—k_{row} data.

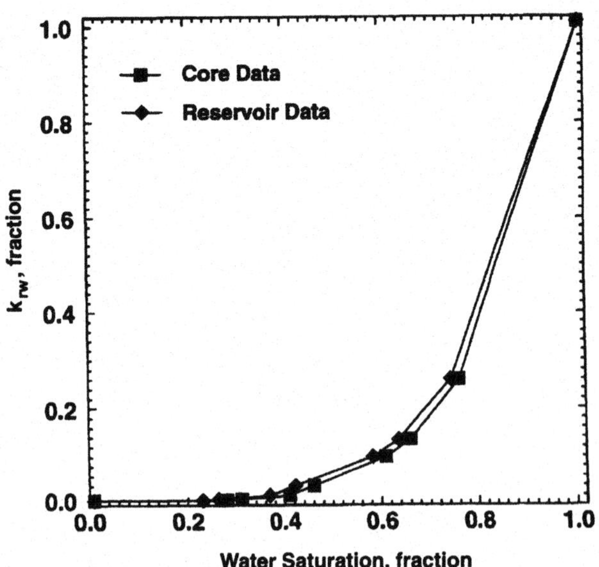

Fig. 10.10—k_{rw} data.

$$P_{cl} = \frac{h_{tzl}}{h_{tzc}} P_{c_c}. \quad \text{(10.33)}$$

The use of this ratio ensures that the height of the transition zone from the core data equals the height of the transition zone measured from well logs while also ensuring that the shape of the core-derived capillary pressure curve is retained.

As with the relative permeability data, a choice must be made between drainage and imbibition data. Unfortunately, a conflict with displacement processes arises when considering which capillary pressure curve to use in a reservoir simulation study. During oil migration into a water-wet reservoir, the influx of oil is a drainage process; consequently, the in-place fluid distribution is governed by the drainage (decreasing the wetting-phase saturation) capillary pressure curve. On the other hand, oil production is an imbibition process; therefore, production performance is governed by the imbibition (increasing the wetting-phase saturation) process.

To resolve this conflict, imbibition capillary pressure curves generally are used in reservoir simulation. The use of these curves ensures that the mechanisms occurring during production are modeled properly in the simulation study. This treatment, however, may result in a discrepancy between the simulator-determined fluid in place and the actual fluid in place. To overcome this discrepancy, porosity multipliers may be required to bring the simulated fluids in place in line with the actual values.

Although some scaleup has been performed already (the use of reservoir-scale endpoint saturations in the denormalization process and the ratio of the log- and core-derived transition-zone heights in Eq. 10.33), the relative permeability and capillary pressure curves derived from the method presented in this book are considered appropriate to describe flow at the core scale. These curves are called rock curves and may require further scaleup for reservoir simulation. This additional scaleup process is accomplished with pseudofunctions, as discussed in Sec. 10.4.3.

Example 10.3. Using the capillary pressure data in **Table 10.7**, determine the appropriate capillary pressure curves for the reservoir. Note the differences between the core data and reservoir data.

Solution. The saturation data used in this example are identical to those used in Example 10.2. These data need to be converted to reservoir conditions in the same way. Because this was already done in Example 10.2, we proceed to normalizing the capillary pressure data.

The first step for converting the capillary pressure to reservoir conditions is to convert the core capillary pressure data to the *J* func-

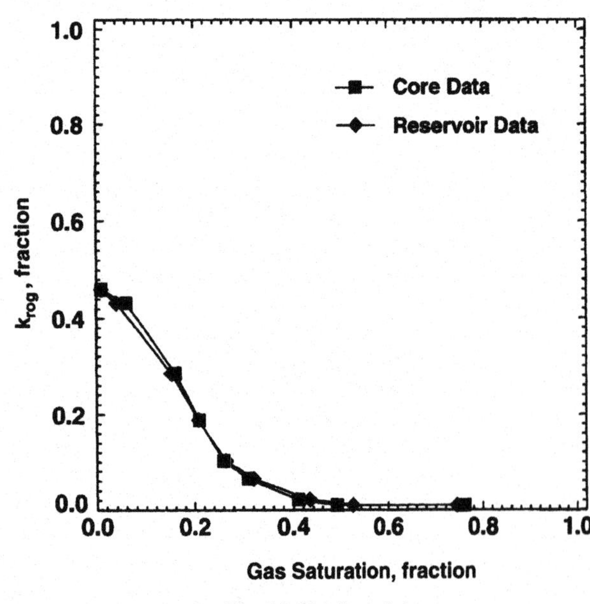

Fig. 10.11—k_{rog} data.

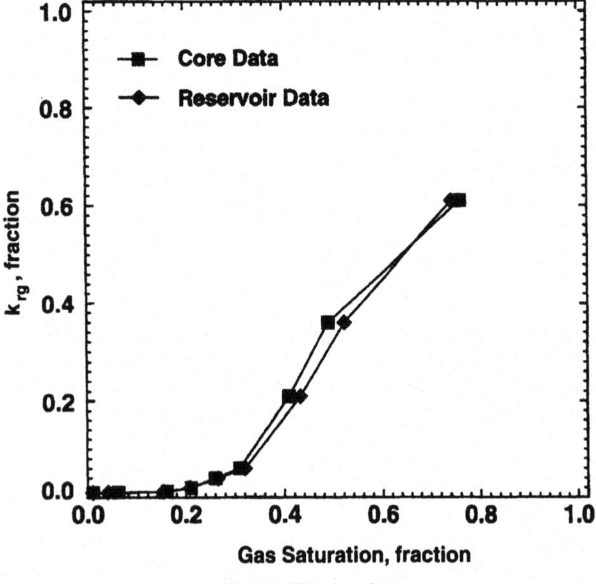

Fig. 10.12—k_{rg} data.

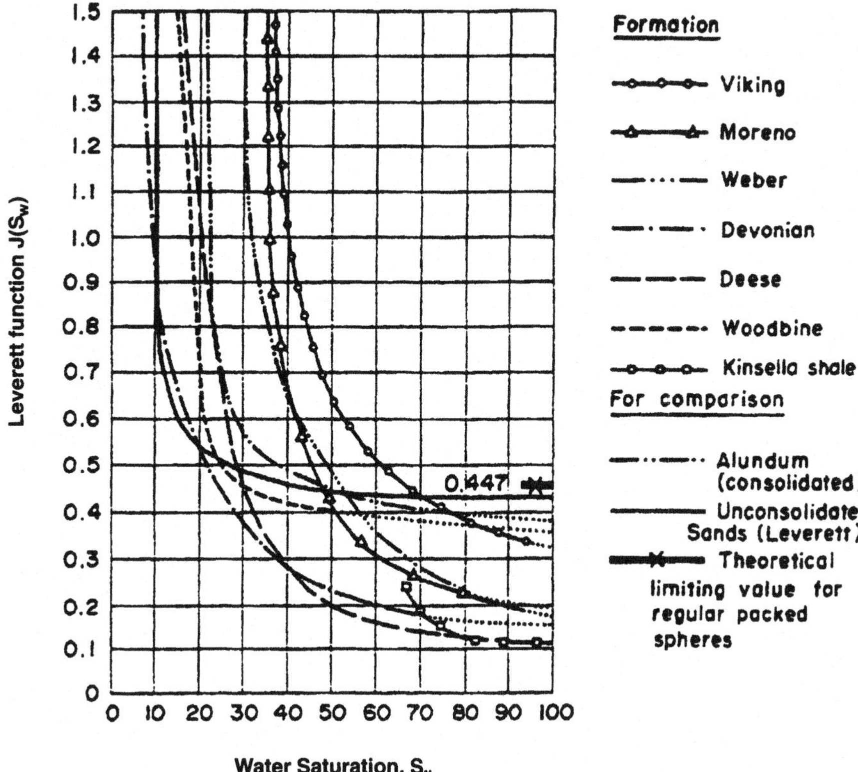

Fig. 10.13—Leverett *J* function for several reservoir rocks (after Bear[21]).

tion. This is done with Eq. 10.31 along with the representative core data.

$$J(S_w) = \frac{P_c(S_w)}{\sigma \cos(\Theta_c)}\left(\frac{k}{\phi}\right)^{1/2} \quad \text{(10.31)}$$

$$= \frac{P_c(S_w)}{45\cos(40)}\left(\frac{22}{0.25}\right)^{1/2}$$

$$= 0.27213 P_c(S_w).$$

TABLE 10.7—CAPILLARY PRESSURE DATA FOR EXAMPLE 10.3

Oil/Water Curves			Gas/Oil Curves		
	Core	Reservoir		Core	Reservoir
S_{iw}	0.270	0.220	S_{iw}	0.270	0.220
S_{orw}	0.250	0.267	S_{org}	0.250	0.267
			S_{gc}	0.050	0.053
k, md	22.0	25.0	k, md	25.0	27.0
ϕ, fraction	0.250	0.20	ϕ, fraction	0.20	0.21
σ, dyne/cm	45.0	38.0	σ, dyne/cm	15.0	18.0
Θ_c, degree	40.0	45.0	Θ_c, degree	1.5	1.5
E_{Dw}	0.658	0.658	E_{Dg}	0.658	0.658
	Core Water Saturation	Core P_{cow} (psi)		Core Gas Saturation	Core P_{cgo} (psi)
	0.000	—		0.000	0.000
	0.270	13.750		0.050	0.240
	0.300	8.640		0.150	0.400
	0.400	4.320		0.200	0.475
	0.450	3.240		0.250	0.715
	0.600	2.160		0.300	0.950
	0.650	1.800		0.400	1.900
	0.750	1.080		0.480	4.000
	1.000	0.000		0.730	—

TABLE 10.8—SOLUTION TO EXAMPLE 10.3

Oil/Water Curves					
Core Water Saturation	Core P_{cow} (psi)	$J(S_w)$	Reservoir P_{cow} (psi)	S_{wn}	Reservoir Water Saturation
0.000	—	—	—	—	0.000
0.270	13.750	3.742	8.993	0.000	0.220
0.300	8.640	2.351	5.651	0.063	0.252
0.400	4.320	1.176	2.825	0.271	0.359
0.450	3.240	0.882	2.119	0.375	0.412
0.600	2.160	0.588	1.413	0.688	0.573
0.650	1.800	0.490	1.177	0.792	0.626
0.750	1.080	0.294	0.706	1.000	0.733
1.000	0.000	0.000	0.000	—	1.000
Gas/Oil Curves					
Core Gas Saturation	Core P_{cgo} (psi)	$J(S_g)$	Reservoir P_{cgo} (psi)	S_{gn}	Reservoir Gas Saturation
0.000	0.000	0.000	0.000	0.000	0.000
0.050	0.240	0.179	0.284	0.104	0.053
0.150	0.400	0.298	0.473	0.313	0.160
0.200	0.475	0.354	0.562	0.417	0.214
0.250	0.715	0.533	0.846	0.521	0.267
0.300	0.950	0.708	1.124	0.625	0.321
0.400	1.900	1.417	2.248	0.833	0.427
0.480	4.000	2.982	4.733	1.000	0.513
0.730	—	—	—	—	0.780

A similar equation can be developed for the gas/oil curves. Then, the J function can be converted to $P_c(S_w)$ at reservoir conditions by use of Eq. 10.32 along with the representative reservoir data.

$$P_c(S_w) = \sigma \cos(\Theta_c) J(S_w) \left(\frac{\phi}{k}\right)^{1/2} \quad \text{(10.32)}$$

$$= 38 \cos(45) J(S_w) \left(\frac{0.20}{25}\right)^{1/2}$$

$$= 2.403 J(S_w).$$

Again, a similar equation can be obtained for the gas/oil curves. **Table 10.8** tabulates these results, and **Figs. 10.14 and 10.15** show the results in capillary pressure curves.

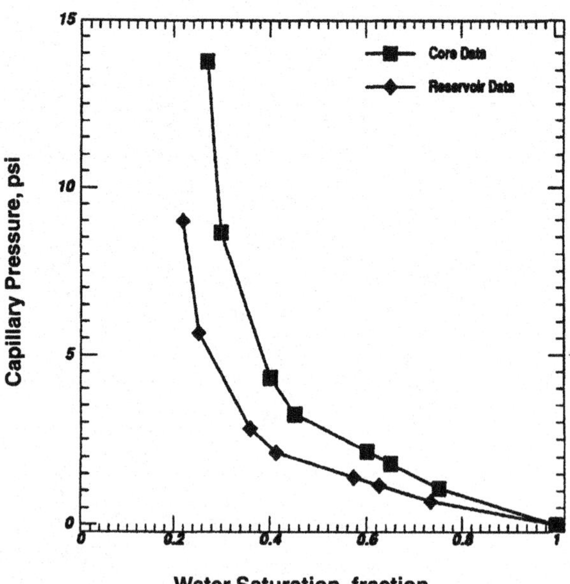

Fig. 10.14—Oil/water capillary pressure data.

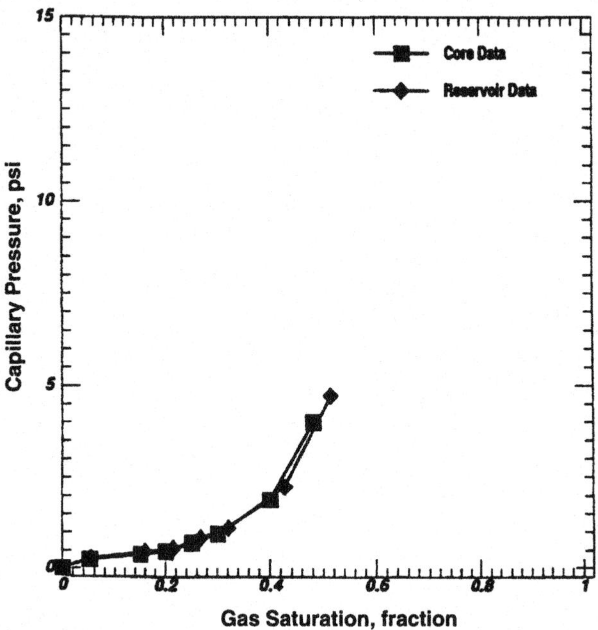

Fig. 10.15—Gas/oil capillary pressure data.

Openhole Well-Log Data. Well log data are important in reservoir simulation because they provide engineers, geologists, and petrophysicists with the opportunity to measure formation properties at the reservoir scale and at in-situ conditions. Consequently, the degree of scaleup required for log-derived data is less than that for core-derived data. In addition, openhole logs are run on almost every well drilled (at the least, a minimal openhole log suite is run to identify perforation intervals). Therefore, openhole log data are the most abundant data available to earth scientists and engineers. **Table 10.9** lists the reservoir simulation input obtained from openhole log data.

Porosity at Reservoir Scale. The average porosity of a stratified log section can be obtained by thickness-weighted averaging. That is, Eq. 10.1 is also applicable for averaging log-derived porosities.

Permeability at Reservoir Scale. Permeability cannot be measured directly from openhole logs but must be estimated with a permeability transform. A permeability transform is a crossplot of core-derived permeability and core-derived porosity. **Fig. 10.16** shows a typical permeability transform. Once the permeability transform is developed, log-derived porosity values can be used to estimate permeability at the reservoir scale.

The basic permeability transform can be enhanced in several ways. They can be improved greatly by developing transforms for individual facies or flow units. Also, multiple transforms can be used. For example, a core-porosity/log-porosity transform (crossplot of core-derived and log-derived porosities) can be used to convert the log porosities to equivalent core porosities. This transform can be followed by a core-permeability/core-porosity transform to estimate the equivalent core permeability. Finally, a core-permeability/buildup-permeability transform (crossplot of core-derived and buildup-derived permeabilities) can be used to convert the core permeability to an equivalent reservoir-scale permeability. A final enhancement to the basic permeability transform is a multivariable transform that includes data other than porosity, such as water saturation, bulk density, or sonic time.

Once the permeability transform (or suite of transforms) has been developed, it can be used to convert log porosities to reservoir-scale permeabilities. Newly drilled wells are not always cored or tested, but they are logged routinely to determine which intervals to perforate. Consequently, the method described in this section is one of the most common methods used to develop permeability distributions and maps for reservoir simulation.

TABLE 10.9—USE OF OPENHOLE LOG DATA IN RESERVOIR SIMULATION

Property	Use in Simulation	Well Logs
Lithology identification	Grid layering Assignment of rock type/facies Formation thickness Net to gross thickness ratio, h_n/h_g	Spontaneous potential (SP) Gamma ray Porosity logs (lithodensity, neutron, sonic)
Water saturation, S_w	Initial water saturation distribution, S_{wi} Fluid contact, OWC Reservoir scale irreducible water saturation, S_{iw} Presence/height of the oil/water transition zone Saturation maps for history matching	Resistivity logs
Gas saturation, S_g	Initial gas saturation distribution, S_{gi} Fluid contact, GOC Presence/height of the gas/oil transition zone Saturation maps for history matching	Compensated neutron logs Bulk density logs
Porosity, ϕ	Assignment of cell porosity values Development of log porosity/permeability transform	Acoustic logs Bulk density logs Neutron logs
Net reservoir thickness, h_n	Assignment of cell net thickness values Horizontal-transmissibility calculations PV calculations Calculation of well geometric factors, G_w Net pay cutoffs	SP Gamma ray Resistivity logs Porosity logs (with appropriate cutoffs)
Gross reservoir thickness, h_g	Assignment of cell gross thickness values Gravity head calculations Initial reservoir pressures Vertical-transmissibility calculations Transition-zone calculations Initial saturation distributions	SP Gamma ray Resistivity logs
Net to gross thickness ratio, h_n/h_g	Assignment of cell h_n/h_g values	SP Gamma ray Resistivity logs
Vertical pressure gradient	Fluid contacts, GOC and OWC Initial reservoir pressure Identification of hydraulic communication Retrieval of fluid samples Oil gravity estimate Nonreservoir rock Initial saturation pressure	Initial wireline formation tester
	Grid layering Zonal reservoir pressures for history matching	Wireline formation tester surveys after depletion

After the log-derived permeabilities have been estimated, Eqs. 10.2 and 10.3 can be used to generate averaged permeabilities from a stratified log section. At this point, we would like to reiterate our warning about the averaging of extreme data.

Initial Saturations at Reservoir Scale and Irreducible Water Saturation at Reservoir Scale. The average initial saturation of a stratified section can be obtained by PV weighting. That is, Eq. 10.4 also is appropriate for log-derived data.

It should be remembered that the initial water saturation, S_{wi}, above the oil/water capillary transition zone is equal to the irreducible water saturation, S_{iw}. Therefore, openhole resistivity logs can be used to make direct measurements of S_{iw} at the reservoir scale.

Vertical Pressure Gradients. Vertical pressure gradients are extremely useful in reservoir simulation studies because they provide varied information that can be incorporated into the study. This information can be used in both the model-construction phase and the history-matching phase of the study. Vertical pressure gradients are measured with a wireline formation tester.

Fig. 10.17 shows a typical pressure-gradient plot of reservoir presssure vs. depth for a reservoir at discovery. In the general case, three vertical pressure gradients may be identified within a single reservoir unit on an initial pressure-gradient plot. These pressure gradients correspond to the gravities of the water, oil, and gas phases within the reservoir unit. Typically, a water pressure gradient is greater than 0.45 psi/ft. The oil pressure gradient is dependent on oil gravity and may range from 0.433 psi/ft for a 10°API oil to 0.347 psi/ft for a 45°API oil. The oil pressure gradient must be corrected for thermal conditions in the reservoir. Finally, the gas pressure gradient is dependent on the reservoir pressure and temperature and is on the order of 0.04 to 0.07 psi/ft. On an initial pressure-gradient plot, such as in Fig. 10.17, the intersection of the gas- and oil-pressure-gradient curves represents the original GOC, whereas the intersection of the oil- and water-pressure-gradient curves represents the original OWC. Finally, the pressure at the GOC can give an indication of the initial saturation pressure. For reservoirs in which the contacts are unknown (for example, only lowest known oil or highest known water are known), pressure-gradient data can be used to estimate the GOC or OWC. Supercharged points on a pressure-gradient plot may represent layers of nonreservoir rock or may indicate tool failure.

For multiple reservoir zones, the initial pressure-gradient plot appears as in **Fig. 10.18**. If the multiple reservoir zones are in a normal pressure regime (Fig. 10.18a), the initial vertical-pressure-gradient plot cannot be used to determine whether the reservoir zones are in hydraulic communication. If, however, the individual reservoir units lie in different pressure regimes (Fig. 10.18b), this indicates that the reservoir units are not in hydraulic communication.

It is a good reservoir-management practice to run wireline tester surveys on infill or development wells drilled after significant pressure depletion. This gives much more reservoir data than the initial pressure-gradient survey alone. **Fig. 10.19** shows a pressure-gradient plot for an undersaturated reservoir after a given production period in

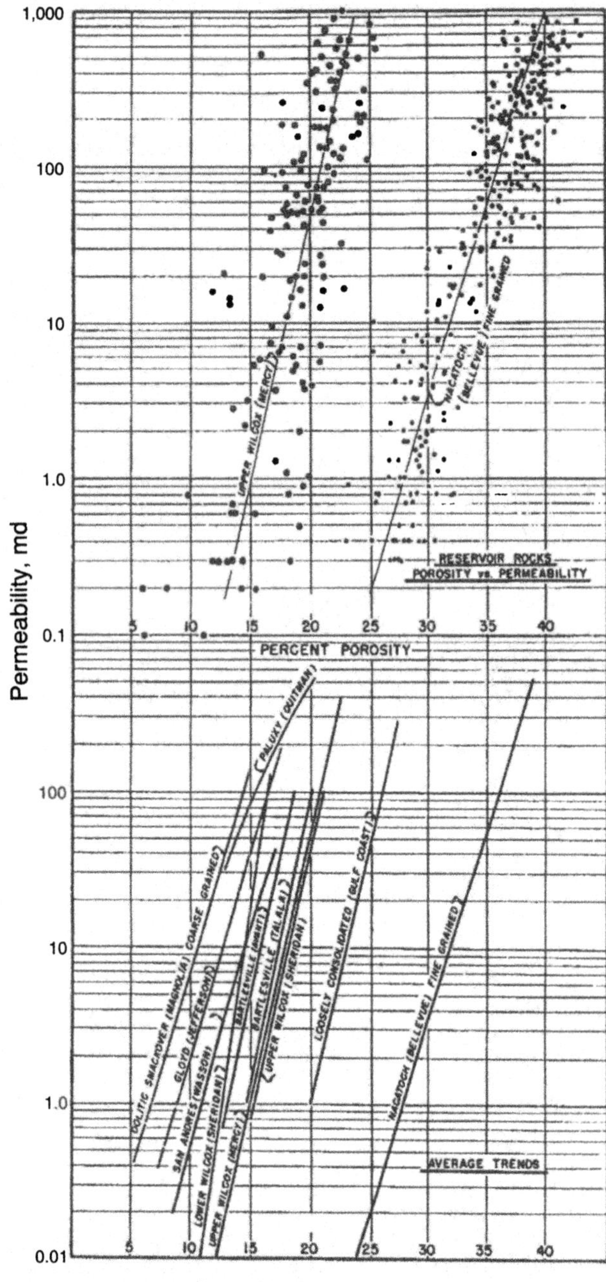

Fig. 10.16—Permeability/porosity relationships for several reservoir formations (after Beaumont and Foster[22]).

the BRENT sequence of the Dunlin field.[23] (BRENT is an acronym for the producing intervals of a prolific North Sea sequence: Broom, Rannoch, Etive, Ness, and Tarbert.) This figure contains several important features that should be incorporated into a reservoir model. The nonuniform gradient (broken gradient line) on a pressure-gradient plot indicates that the reservoir is undergoing preferential depletion (or pressurization through preferential injection) in the separate reservoir units. This preferential production/injection may be caused by the reservoir-management strategy used in the depletion of the field or because the various reservoir units have different properties. Regardless of the reason for the preferential production/injection, discontinuities in the vertical pressure gradient indicate the presence of vertical flow barriers and separate reservoir units.

Example 10.4. Use the pressure-gradient data in Fig. 10.19 to determine the flow units and potential simulation layering strategy for the Dunlin field.

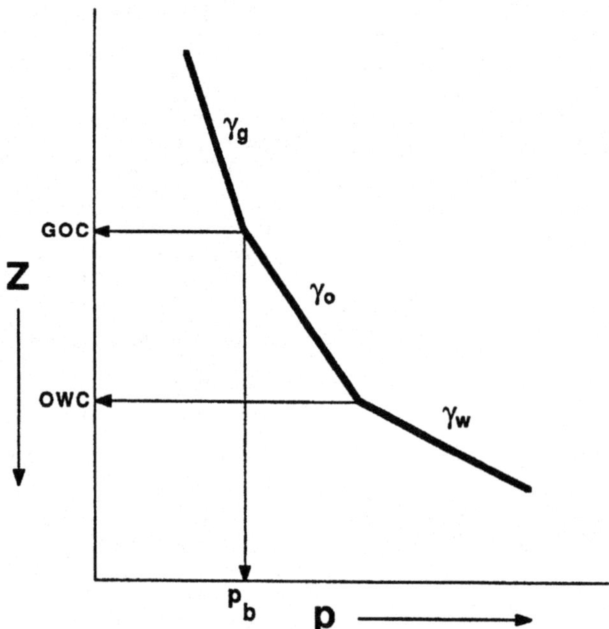

Fig. 10.17—Characteristic repeat formation test (RFT) plot.

Solution. Starting from the top of the well, the break in the pressure gradient between the Tarbert and Ness sands indicates that there is preferential depletion/injection occurring between these stratigraphic units because stratigraphic units with contrasting reservoir properties exhibit differences in the rates of pressure depletion. For example, in stratigraphic units with different permeabilities, the zone with the higher permeability yields higher production rates; consequently, the pressure depletes more rapidly. Unless additional engineering or geologic data suggest otherwise, one simulation layer may be adequate to describe the Tarbert member. In addition, the break in the pressure gradient at the boundary between the Tarbert and Ness units indicates that a vertical flow barrier exists between these units. If no vertical barrier were present, fluids in the high-pressure unit (upper Ness) would flow into the lower-pressure unit (Tarbert) and the pressure in the two units would equilibrate hydrostatically at some intermediate pressure.

The break in the pressure gradient in the middle of the Ness sand at 9,150-ft true vertical depth subsea (TVDSS) suggests that at least two simulation layers may be required for this sand.

The break in the pressure gradient at the midreservoir shale suggests that a simulation layer boundary should be placed on this shale. In addition, the shale separation between the Ness and Etive sands may indicate the need for a reduced transmissibility barrier between the simulation layers. Because the shale is relatively thin, a simulation layer is not required to describe it.

The continuous pressure gradient through the Etive and Rannoch sands suggests that these two geologic units may be combined into a single simulation layer. Additional engineering or geologic data may, however, be used to justify treating the Etive and Rannoch sands as separate layers.

Finally, the discontinuity in the pressure gradient at the boundary of the Rannoch and Broom sands suggests that one simulation layer should be used for the Broom formation. The contrast in the pressure gradient between these stratigraphic units also suggests that a contrast in reservoir properties should be used for the Rannoch and Broom sands and that a vertical flow barrier be placed between these layers.

Pressure-Transient Data. As with log data, pressure-transient data are measured at a scale appropriate for numerical simulation and require little scaleup before use in reservoir modeling. These data are a source of cell permeabilities and well data in the simula-

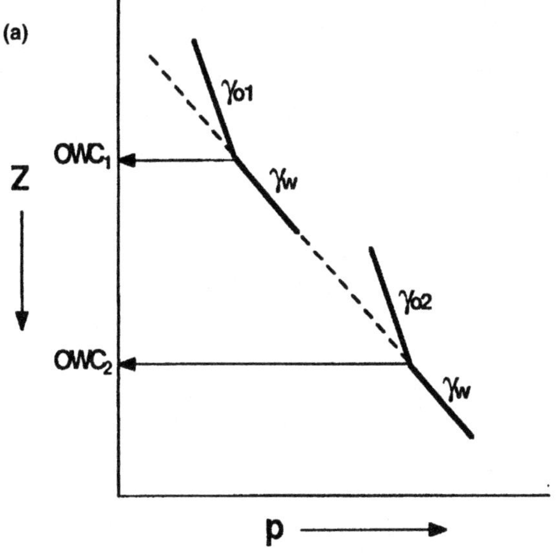

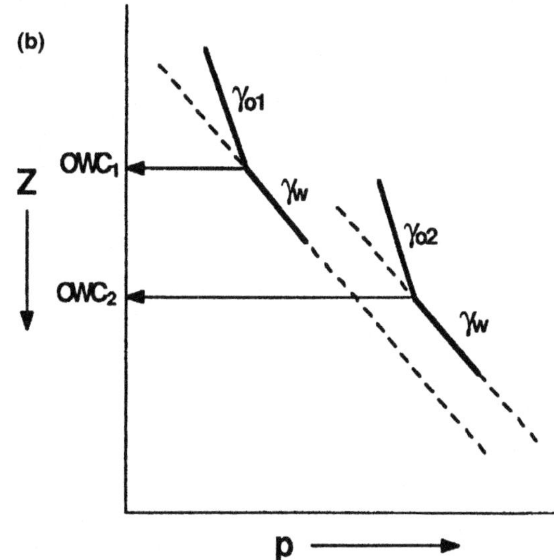

Fig. 10.18—Pressure-gradient plot of a reservoir with multiple zones. (a) Flow units in a normal pressure regime; no inference can be made regarding whether the zones are in hydraulic communication. (b) Flow units in two pressure regimes; these reservoir zones cannot be in hydraulic communication.

tion model. **Table 10.10** lists the data obtained from pressure-transient analysis and describes their role in reservoir simulation.

Horizontal Permeability at Reservoir Scale. The most important consideration for permeability data derived from pressure-transient analysis is that, even if a single phase is produced, these data are measured in the presence of an irreducible water saturation. That is, the permeability obtained from pressure-transient analysis is the effective permeability to oil or gas and not the absolute permeability.

Fig. 10.19—Wireline pressure plot of the Dunlin field (after Barbe[23]).

Consequently, if the base permeability of the relative permeability data is the absolute permeability, then the absolute permeability value must be calculated back from the pressure-transient-derived permeability as

$$k_a = \frac{k_o(S_{iw})}{k_{ro}(S_{iw})}, \qquad (10.34)$$

where $k_o(S_{iw})$ = effective permeability to oil obtained from pressure-transient analysis and $k_{ro}(S_{iw})$ = endpoint relative permeability.

If, on the other hand, the base permeability of the relative permeability data is the oil permeability in the presence of irreducible water, the permeability obtained from pressure-transient analysis requires no correction. The most important point in this discussion is that, when using permeability values from pressure-transient analysis, they must be consistent with the base permeability of the relative permeability data used in the simulation study.

Because well tests are not always run on new wells, it may be necessary to generate permeability data at the reservoir scale. This can be accomplished with a permeability transform.

The constant part of the well inflow performance equation (well geometric factor) used in reservoir simulation has been found to depend on the size of the areal grid used in the simulation model.[24-26] Field-measured data, therefore, must be scaled to reflect the size of the imposed numerical grid. Sec. 10.4.3 discusses this topic further.

In reservoir engineering, formation damage is quantified by the well's skin factor. Skin factors used in reservoir simulation have been found to depend on the layering of the simulation model.[26] Field-measured data, therefore, must be altered to reflect the layering of the imposed numerical grid. Sec. 10.4.3 also discusses this topic further.

The appropriate shut-in well pressures, p_{ws}, from buildup data for use in a history match have been found to be dependent on both the areal size and the layering of the imposed numerical grid used in the model.[24-27] Field-measured pressure data, therefore, must be selected carefully to reflect the grid spacing and layering. Sec. 10.5.3 discusses this topic further.

Production Data. Two forms of production data may be used in reservoir simulation: (1) metered production rates and (2) cased-hole-production-log data. Production-rate histories generally are used during the history-matching phase of a simulation study, whereas cased-hole-production-log data can be used in both the model-construction and history-matching phase of the study.

TABLE 10.10—USE OF PRESSURE-TRANSIENT DATA IN RESERVOIR SIMULATION

Property	Use in Simulation	Test
Horizontal permeability, k_H	Generation of permeability maps and assignment of cell permeability values Calculation of well geometric factors, G_w Horizontal-transmissibility calculations Reservoir-scale porosity/permeability transforms	Buildup Drawdown Interference Drillstem test (DST)
Formation damage	Skin factors Calculation of well geometric factors, G_w	Buildup Drawdown DST
Fluid samples	Fluid PVT properties	Downhole samples Wellhead samples Separator samples
Shut-in well pressures, p_{ws}	Well pressures for history matching (after correction)	Buildup
Static reservoir pressure, $\bar{p}$	Isobaric maps for history matching	Buildup Drawdown DST

TABLE 10.11—USE OF HISTORICAL PRODUCTION DATA IN RESERVOIR SIMULATION

Property	Use in Simulation
Oil rates	Specification of oil rates Matching oil production rates Matching cumulative oil production
Water rates	Matching water-cut behavior Matching water-breakthrough times Matching cumulative water production
Gas rates	Matching GOR behavior Matching gas-breakthrough times Matching cumulative gas production
Flowing bottomhole pressures, p_{wf}	Calibration of well productivities from history mode to prediction mode Matching well pressures (e.g., in the analysis of complex well-test data)
Static reservoir pressure	Development of isobaric maps for cell-by-cell pressure match Matching well pressures (dependent on grid size)
Historical well work	Assignment of open reservoir intervals Assignment of completion productivity indices

Historical Production Data. Metered production rates provide the basis of any history match. **Table 10.11** lists the information from production histories that can be used in the history-matching phase of a simulation study.

For a successful history match, production data should be as detailed as possible. Ideally, these data should be measured for each perforated interval in each well. In reality, these data cannot be metered continuously for each flow unit in each well. In many cases, only the gross well rates or, possibly, gross field rates are known.

If only field data are available, well rates need to be allocated back to the individual wells. This can be done rigorously by constructing a facilities model on a surface network simulator (a simulator for surface pipelines and equipment). Such a model can be used to predict individual well rates from a single or a field rate; however, this may be a time-consuming process that may not be required to fulfill the study objectives. For a more simplified allocation, field production may be prorated by either the most recently tested rates (if wells are periodically flow tested) or by well productivity indices. That is, the production rate from Well n can be obtained from field rates by use of one of the following methods. For proration by flow tests,

$$q_n = \frac{q_{n_{\text{test}}}}{\sum_{i=1}^{n_w} q_{i_{\text{test}}}} q_{\text{field}}, \quad \text{(10.35)}$$

and for proration by productivity indices,

$$q_n = \frac{J_{wn}}{\sum_{i=1}^{n_w} J_{wi}} q_{\text{field}}. \quad \text{(10.36)}$$

Note that the test rates used in Eq. 10.35 are not necessarily measured at the same time but may be measured over a given time interval. In addition, the test separator may not be operating under the same conditions as the production separators. Consequently,

$$\sum_{n=1}^{n_w} q_{n_{\text{test}}} \neq q_{\text{field}}.$$

If well rates are known (or allocated from field data) but rates from perforated intervals are required for a history match, these rates may be prorated by the productivity indices of the individual reservoir layers, J_{w_k}. That is, the production from Zone k in Well n can be determined by

$$q_{n,k} = \frac{J_{w_{n,k}}}{\sum_{i}^{n_k} J_{w_{n,i}}} q_n. \quad \text{(10.37)}$$

Ideally, these zonal production rates should be measured with a production logging tool (PLT).

It should be emphasized that metered data are always preferable to generated data. The proration schemes discussed in this section, therefore, should be used only as a last resort when metered data are not available. If prorated production data are used in a history

TABLE 10.12—USE OF PRODUCTION-LOGGING DATA IN RESERVOIR SIMULATION

Property	Use in Simulation	Production Log
Temperature	Initial reservoir temperature Zonal fluid entry for history matching	Temperature survey
Zonal flow rates/fluid entry points	Grid layering Zonal flow rates for history matching Identification of cross flow for history matching	PLT Temperature survey Acoustic logging Gradiomanometer
Casing/cement/tubing integrity	Quality of water-cut data for history matching Quality of producing GOR data for history matching	Cement-bond log Cement evaluation tool Temperature survey Acoustic logging
Water saturation, S_w	Saturation maps for history matching Front tracking Reservoir-scale residual oil saturation to water, S_{orw}	Pulsed neutron capture (PNC) log Carbon/oxygen (C/O) log
Gas saturation, S_g	Saturation maps for history matching Monitor gas-cap expansion Reservoir-scale residual oil saturation to gas, S_{org}	Neutron log PNC log

match, the quality of the proration scheme needs to be considered. That is, excessive matching may not always be warranted if prorated data are used in the study.

To make the interpretation of historical data easy, many major oil companies have databases that contain the most relevant production data. Modern petroleum databases generally have graphical interfaces that provide the engineer with the ability to look at both historical trends (with *x-y* plots) and areal trends (with bubble plots). These databases can be a substantial aid in the interpretation of historical data, and their use in a history match is recommended strongly if they are available.

Cased-Hole-Production-Logging Data. Cased-hole-production-logging techniques are used to monitor a well after it is cased, completed, and put on production. **Table 10.12** contains information from cased-hole-production logs that can be used in a simulation study.

Reservoir temperature is a required input parameter in many commercial reservoir simulators because all reservoir-fluid pressure/volume/temperature (PVT) properties are temperature dependent. Most commercial simulators have facilities to generate PVT properties internally with empirical correlations, and these correlations require reservoir temperature.

If measured PVT data are to be entered directly into the simulator, accurate temperature surveys allow fluid-property measurements to be made at the correct reservoir temperature. For gas reservoirs or saturated oil reservoirs, reservoir temperature is required to convert measured gas compressibility factors, z, to values of B_g (either internally or externally to the reservoir simulator). In addition, relative permeability data should be measured at reservoir pressures and temperatures.

Zonal fluid production rates and fluid entry points are important for both the model-construction and history-matching phases of a simulation study. During model construction, high contrasts in historical zonal fluid production rates may indicate contrasts in reservoir rock properties and give insight into the reservoir zonation and, consequently, model layering.

During the history-matching phase of a study, the more detail that can be incorporated into the history match, the more the predictions made with the simulation model are improved. Thus, if rates from individual reservoir units can be matched, rather than simply matching well rates, then more confidence can be placed in the predicted reservoir performance. To match these zonal rates, accurate measurements of these rates must be made.

The use of PLT data is very critical for successfully history-matched injection wells because PLT data provide the required data to make adjustments to reservoir data in the immediate vicinity of injection wells to ensure that the injection fluids are entering the various geologic intervals in the proper proportions. Attempting to perform a history match by matching production performance only gives erroneous results if the injection fluids are entering the reservoir in the wrong geologic intervals.

The measurement of zonal production rates is made with a PLT, sometimes referred to as a flowmeter or "spinner" tool. Essentially, a PLT is a propeller attached to a metering device. The rotational speed of the propeller is proportional to the total fluid rate flowing through the tool. **Fig. 10.20** shows a well-profile survey obtained from a PLT (right-most track).[28]

This figure shows the percentage of the well's production rate for each perforated interval. In this example, the contrast in the fluid production rates may indicate a contrast in reservoir properties and, consequently, may indicate separate flow units. On the other hand, these contrasts may indicate different levels of formation damage in an otherwise homogeneous reservoir. Therefore, PLT data may be used in support of other geologic data to determine a simulation layering strategy but cannot, by themselves, be used to define a simulation-layering strategy.

Other production-logging techniques that can be used to determine, but not necessarily quantify, fluid entry into a wellbore include acoustic and temperature logging.

During history matching, water-cut and producing gas/oil ratio (GOR) data are two of the principal trends used as match criteria. The reliability of the match, therefore, is only as good as the quality of the metered water and gas rates. The reservoir simulator only considers flow in the reservoir itself; consequently, the data to be matched should be reservoir data. Water and gas production caused by channelling through cement or tubing/annulus communication should not be used in the history-matching process. In fact, if reservoir properties are altered to match water and gas production from these two mechanisms (if they can be matched), the quality of the predictions is suspect.

During the history match, reservoir trends should be examined to determine whether they make physical sense. If a well appears to water out before downdip offset wells (or, equivalently, a well exhibits gas breakthrough before adjacent updip wells), then the mechanical integrity of the casing, cement, and tubing should be examined. The methods used to determine this integrity include the cement-bond log, the cement evaluation tool, temperature surveys, and acoustic logging.

Cased-hole logs (PNC and C/O) can be used to measure water and gas saturations at the reservoir scale after a well has been on production. This gives geologists and engineers the ability to develop time-lapse saturation maps. During the history-matching phase of the simulation study, these maps can be used to match flood-front advancement and regions/zones of bypassed oil.

During the model-construction phase of the simulation study, cased-hole logs can be used to measure the saturations in watered- or gassed-out regions/zones to estimate reservoir-scale values of S_{orw} and S_{org}. When estimating the endpoint saturations at the reservoir scale, cased-hole logs of injection wells may not give representative results because many more PV's of injected fluids pass through the radius of investigation of the logging tool than are en-

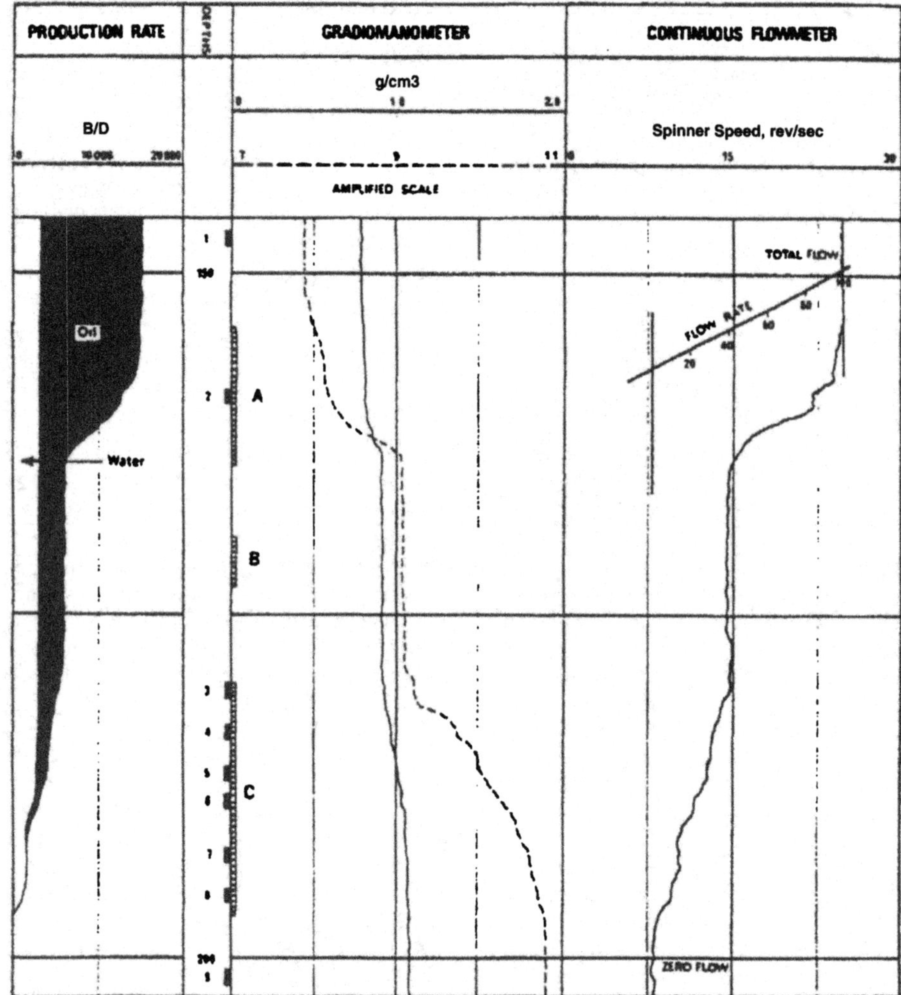

Fig. 10.20—PLT response (right track) showing percentage of total liquid flow rate (after Allan and Roberts[28]).

countered by the majority of the reservoir. Therefore, this method of estimating endpoint saturations is recommended for production wells in swept areas.

Nonreservoir-Rock Description. In the previous sections of this chapter, we discussed the properties of the hydrocarbon-bearing rock associated with subsurface hydrocarbon reservoirs. In most petroleum reservoirs, however, there are sections of the producing formation that are nonhydrocarbon bearing. The performance of the reservoir may be influenced significantly by this nonreservoir rock. The effects of the nonreservoir rock may need to be incorporated into the simulation model.

Shale Description. Most petroleum reservoirs contain some nonpay strata, principally shales and siltstones. The presence of shales and siltstones can have a dramatic impact on reservoir performance, including gas underrunning and water overriding shales; inhibition of coning; primary-production, reservoir-crossflow, wellbore-crossflow, and gravity-drainage effects; nonuniform advancement of GOC and OWC; barriers to upward segregation (percolation) of liberated solution gas and to the preferred direction of oil flow; and waterflooding effects and enhanced-oil-recovery (EOR) -process effects.[29]

To make proper reservoir-management decisions, all these effects must be incorporated into the simulation model. If the shale barrier is continuous (or, for simulation purposes, if the shale is on the same order as the areal grid size), the shale barriers can be represented as zero- or reduced- transmissibility barriers between simulation grid layers. For cases where the shales are not continuous and are smaller than the grid size, Begg and King[30] discussed four techniques that can be used to account for shale effects. These techniques, which define an equivalent vertical permeability in the presence of discontinuous shales, are categorized by the method used to determine the equivalent permeability. These techniques are numerical, analytical, streamline, and statistical methods.

Each of the techniques has advantages and limitations but they give consistent results. The effective vertical permeability defined by the statistical approach can be obtained by

$$k_{V_e} = \frac{k_V(1 - f_{sh})}{[1 + n_{sh}(\bar{l}_{sh}/2)]^2} \quad \text{.......................} \quad (10.38)$$

for 2D problems and

$$k_{Ve} = \frac{k_V(1 - f_{sh})}{[1 + n_{sh}(\bar{l}_{sh}/3)]^2} \quad \text{......................} \quad (10.39)$$

for 3D problems. In Eqs. 10.38 and 10.39, k_V = vertical permeability of the clean sand and k_{Ve} = effective vertical permeability in the presence of discontinuous shale.

Aquifer Description. All hydrocarbon accumulations contain interstitial water, and many are associated with either a bottomwater or peripheral aquifer. These aquifers affect reservoir performance by supplying reservoir energy and, in the case of bottomwater reservoirs, may lead to water coning. The two principal parameters required to characterize an aquifer for reservoir simulation are the aquifer size (and, consequently, strength) and transmissibility. These parameters can be obtained from the same sources as the hydrocarbon-bearing formation: regional maps, and core and log data. Aquifer parameters, however, are considered soft data (mainly, because there is not as much geologic control in the aquifer as in the reservoir) and are, in general, the first parameters to be altered in a history match to obtain a match of the average reservoir pressure.

Fluid Description. Fluids produced from petroleum reservoirs include oil, gas, and water. In reservoir simulation, the two approaches available for characterizing the hydrocarbon fluids (assigning representative fluid properties) are black-oil and compositional characterization.

Black-oil characterization refers to fluid PVT properties that are strictly pressure dependent, while compositional characterization refers to fluid properties that are pressure, temperature, and composition dependent. Both of these characterization methods, in the context of reservoir simulation, are discussed in the following sections.

Black-Oil Description. A survey of major oil companies' simulation efforts in the mid-1980's[31] revealed that the majority of simulation activity was black-oil simulation, with more than 50% of the simulation models classified as black-oil models. Although the trends from this study indicated that the use of black-oil models was on the decline, they still showed that the majority of future simulation models will be black-oil models. Because black-oil models historically have been the workhorse of reservoir simulation and because this is anticipated to continue in the future, we concentrate on the black-oil fluid description.

Properties Required for a Black-Oil Description. The oil properties required for a black-oil fluid description are the saturated-fluid properties (properties below the saturation pressure) B_o, R_s, and μ_o.

These properties are functions of reservoir pressure and generally are obtained from laboratory measurements. In addition to these properties, the oil density at standard conditions, ρ_{osc} [or, equivalently, the oil gravity (in °API) or specific gravity], is also required. The oil density at standard conditions is a single value, not a function of pressure.

To complete the fluid description, properties above the bubblepoint pressure must be supplied. These undersaturated-fluid properties can be determined internally in the reservoir simulator with

$$B_o = B_{ob}/\left[1 + c_o(p - p_b)\right], \quad \text{.................} \quad (10.40)$$

where $p > p_b$,

$$\text{and } \mu_o = \mu_{ob}/\left[1 - c_\mu(p - p_b)\right], \quad \text{.................} \quad (10.41)$$

where $p > p_b$.

Eq. 10.40 is a discretized form of the definition of isothermal oil compressibility, while Eq. 10.41 is strictly an empirical relationship. The parameters c_o and c_μ are required to complete the fluid description. The values of c_o and c_μ can be either constants or functions of solution-gas/oil ratio, depending on the objectives of the simulation study and the requirements of the reservoir simulation program used in the study.

The gas properties required for a black-oil fluid description are B_g (or, equivalently, gas compressibility factor, z) and μ_g. Again, these properties are required as functions of reservoir pressure. In addition, gas density at standard conditions, ρ_{gsc} (or, equivalently, the gas gravity or molecular weight), is required. For oil reservoirs, it is common to use gas properties based on either laboratory-measured properties or published correlations, while laboratory-measured properties generally are used for gas reservoirs.

The required water properties for a black-oil description are B_w, μ_w, R_{sw} (optional in some reservoir simulators), and ρ_{wsc}. These properties can be either functions of reservoir pressure or constant values. In general, these properties can be obtained from published correlations.

Measurement of Black-Oil Properties. As stated earlier, a black-oil description requires the values of saturated-oil properties as a function of pressure. These properties can be obtained from correlations but more commonly are obtained from laboratory measurements of the actual reservoir fluids. Two laboratory procedures can be used to measure PVT properties: flash expansion (constant composition) and differential liberation (constant volume).

In the flash-expansion procedure, reservoir fluids are introduced into the PVT cell at reservoir temperature and the pressure is reduced to various pressure levels. At each pressure level, the gas and oil volumes are measured, with the final measurement made at standard conditions. The formation volume factor (FVF) for the flash-expansion process, B_{of}, can be determined by dividing the oil volume at the cell pressure and reservoir temperature by the oil volume at standard conditions. The solution-gas/oil ratio for the flash process, R_{sf}, also can be obtained from the appropriate gas and oil volumes.

In the differential-liberation process, reservoir fluids are introduced into the PVT cell at reservoir temperature. The pressure in the cell is reduced, and the gas and oil volumes are measured. At this point, all liberated gas is expelled from the PVT cell by displacing the gas at constant pressure. This procedure is repeated for each pressure step. The final measurement is made at standard conditions. The FVF, B_{od}, and solution-gas/oil ratio, R_{sd}, are obtained in the same way as in the flash process.

The values of the FVF and solution-gas/oil ratio obtained from the flash-expansion process generally differ from the values obtained from the differential-liberation process. The decision regarding which set of data to use in a simulation study must be made. To address this issue, the processes occurring in the reservoir must be considered.

In the reservoir, undersaturated oils flow to production wells by fluid expansion (and, possibly, other drive mechanisms). As the oil passes through the bubblepoint pressure, a free-gas saturation begins to develop. Initially, this gas remains where it originally evolved until the critical saturation to gas flow, S_{gc}, is reached. During this stage of depletion, the process occurring in the reservoir is more like the flash-expansion process.

Once the critical gas saturation to flow has been reached, the gas, because of its high mobility and low density, flows readily to production wells or migrates upward to form a secondary gas cap. During this phase of depletion, the process occurring in the reservoir is more like the differential-liberation process. Because different processes are dominant during different phases of depletion, a conflict in reservoir properties occurs during primary depletion of undersaturated reservoirs.

If most of the reservoir depletion occurs before the critical gas saturation is reached, the flash-expansion properties are more appropriate for reservoir simulation. However, if most of the depletion occurs after the critical gas saturation has been reached, the reservoir properties measured under differential liberation are more appropriate. Differential-liberation data are the more commonly used data in reservoir studies.

The use of the differential-liberation data is not as straightforward as it may first appear because processes other than reservoir processes act on the produced fluids before they reach the stock tank, and these processes must be considered in the simulation study. At any given time, both the gas and oil phases travel at approximately the same velocities through the production separators. That is, there is little slippage between the gas and liquid phases in the separator. Under these conditions, the flash-expansion process is most appropriate.

The production-separator properties are required to determine the produced volumes but do not affect reservoir behavior. To properly account for the effect of the separators, flash-expansion data must be used in conjunction with the differential-liberation data. To accomplish this, the differential data are adjusted by the ratio of the bubblepoint properties during flash and differential conditions. The equations used to define the PVT properties used in reservoir simulation are[32]

$$B_o = (B_{obf}/B_{obd})B_{od} \quad \text{........................} \quad (10.42)$$

$$\text{and } R_s = R_{sbf} - (R_{sbd} - R_{sd})(B_{obf}/B_{obd}). \quad \text{..........} \quad (10.43)$$

Extrapolation of Oil Properties Above Bubblepoint Pressure. In numerical simulation, it is often necessary to extrapolate the saturated oil properties beyond the original bubblepoint pressure because, as gas is released from solution, its high mobility allows for easy migration from the point of evolution. This gas tends to accumulate in the upper regions of the reservoir. Consequently, there will be regions in the reservoir where the gas accumulates to values greater than the original solution-gas/oil ratio. If these regions are repressurized during waterflooding, not all of this gas goes back into solution at the original bubblepoint pressure. The pressure at which all the evolved gas goes back into solution is the saturation pressure.

The most accurate method of extending saturated-fluid properties beyond the original bubblepoint pressure is to run laboratory swelling tests. In these tests, gas above the original solution-gas/oil ratio is introduced into the PVT cell along with the reservoir oil. Then, the pressure is raised above the original bubblepoint pressure and the fluid properties required for the reservoir study are measured directly. The saturation pressure, p_s, is the pressure at which all the original gas and the introduced gas go into solution. This method has the disadvantage that additional tests and costs are required to extend the range of the PVT properties.

The next most accurate method of extrapolating oil properties beyond the initial bubblepoint pressure is the use of a cubic equation of state (EOS). EOS's form the basis of compositional fluid characterizations and are discussed later. In this method of extrapolation, measured oil properties are used to tune the EOS and the tuned EOS is used to extrapolate the hydrocarbon fluid properties beyond the measured range. However, tuning an EOS can be time consuming and may not be warranted by the objectives of the simulation study. In these cases, a less sophisticated method of extrapolating fluid properties is required.

A simple, graphical procedure for extrapolating hydrocarbon fluid properties is based on the $Y(p)$ function,[33]

$$Y(p) = \frac{(p_s - p)B_{oi}}{p(B_t - B_{oi})}. \qquad (10.44)$$

This extrapolation method is recommended as a quick, simple approach for extending reservoir fluid properties beyond the measured range.

Compositional Description. In most major oil companies, the application of compositional simulation is generally left to experienced simulation engineers because of the complex nature of the fluid description required. Because this book is intended for novice simulation users, only a limited discussion of EOS's is presented. Ref. 34 provides a detailed discussion of the use of EOS's.

For a compositional fluid description, the hydrocarbon phases are defined by their individual constituents or components. These constituents consist of both pure components, such as water, methane, ethane, and carbon dioxide, and lumped components, such as C_{7+}. The components are assigned mole fractions and physical properties (critical pressures and temperatures, acentricity factors, and molecular weights). In addition, the components are assigned binary interaction coefficients that are specific to the EOS.

The application of the EOS requires the use of a software package external to the reservoir simulator for the fluid characterization. The EOS package is run with the initial component properties and interaction coefficients. The calculated PVT properties are compared with the measured PVT properties. In general, the initial component properties need to be adjusted, or tuned, to attain a match. When a match is achieved, the final component properties can be entered into the compositional simulator for use in the simulation study.

10.3.3 Resolution of Data Conflicts. The manipulation of all data required for a simulation study inevitably leads to conflicts in the data obtained from different sources. Several potential conflicts have been discussed in this chapter: different transition-zone heights from well logs and core data, differences in drainage and imbibition capillary pressure and relative permeability curves, and differences in flash and differential PVT properties. The resolution of these data conflicts can be obtained by choosing the data that most accurately represent the process occurring in the reservoir and that are measured on the reservoir scale. With this rule, the height of the transition zone from well logs is more appropriate than the transition-zone height derived from core data because log data are measured at the reservoir scale. Imbibition capillary pressure and relative permeability data are preferable to drainage data, and differential-liberation PVT data are preferable to flash PVT data because, in most cases, these processes are believed to be the processes occurring in the reservoir. The examples in this chapter are not the only sources of data conflict that occur in reservoir simulation but are the more common ones.

In some cases, preliminary versions of the simulation model may be used to perform sensitivity analyses on conflicting data to determine whether the effort to resolve the conflict is warranted. For example, over a long oil column, PVT samples may indicate a bubblepoint pressure that is depth dependent, while a linear vertical pressure (from a wireline formation tester) gradient may imply that the bubblepoint pressure is depth invariant. To determine whether additional effort is required to resolve the conflict, the first two history-match cases should be run with a depth-dependent and a constant bubblepoint pressure. If the results of these two cases are in reasonable agreement, no additional effort may be required to resolve the conflict. If, however, the results of these cases differ, additional time and resources are required to resolve the conflict.

10.4 Model Construction

The data sources and data-manipulation methods discussed to this point are not limited to numerical simulation studies but are applicable to reservoir studies of all types. In other words, these data-manipulation techniques are independent of the imposed finite-difference grid and are applicable to the reservoir as a whole. Consequently, successful reservoir studies that use classic methods, such as material-balance techniques or Buckley-Leverett analysis, can benefit from the use of the techniques discussed.

For use in reservoir simulation, however, some data may require further manipulation because of the imposed numerical grid system. This is because some of the data required by the simulation model are dependent on the type of the model and the grid size used in the study. Before these model and grid-dependent techniques can be described, a discussion of the model-selection and -discretization processes is required.

10.4.1 Model Selection. The previous sections of this chapter discussed data manipulation for general reservoir studies. The construction of a simulation model is concerned with gathering these data to form an integrated, coherent mathematical representation of the subject reservoir. The first step in constructing the simulation model is selection of the modeling approach. This involves making decisions on several key, fundamental aspects of the model. **Table 10.13** lists these fundamental decisions. These decisions should be based on the physical characteristics of the subject reservoir, the physics of the recovery processes occurring in the reservoir, and the objectives of the simulation study.

Modeling Philosophy. Two fundamental approaches that can be used in reservoir simulation are conceptual and actual modeling. The choice of which modeling approach to use depends on the objectives of the study.

Conceptual modeling is based on the use of models that are not identical to actual reservoir areas but instead use average reservoir properties throughout the model. Conceptual studies use representative wells, well patterns, and preselected reservoir locations to obtain simulation results. These results must be scaled up for the entire reservoir by the use of scaling laws or engineering judgment. Because these idealized wells or reservoir units may not necessarily correspond to any actual wells or reservoir units in the field, the results generated from these models cannot be used directly to obtain information on any specific reservoir locations. Conceptual models, therefore, are used to perform sensitivity analyses on general uncertainties associated with the reservoir under study. The main advantage of conceptual modeling is that small, representative reservoir models can be used to obtain information on the reservoir. The disadvantage of conceptual modeling is that the results from the models cannot be used directly on any specific reservoir problem but must be considered representative of the reservoir as a whole.

Actual modeling refers to the use of models that represent genuine areas of the reservoir. These models are used to obtain information on the specific problems concerned with these reservoir areas. The advantage of actual models is that the model results can be used directly on real reservoir problems with little engineering interven-

TABLE 10.13—DECISIONS REQUIRED FOR MODELING APPROACH SELECTION

Modeling philosophy	Conceptual Actual
Fluid description	Black-oil fluid description Compositional fluid description

Reservoir type	Single-porosity-reservoir description
	Naturally-fractured-reservoir description
	  Dual-porosity formulation
	  Dual-permeability formulation

Recovery process	Primary depletion
	Secondary recovery/pressure maintenance
	EOR
	  Miscible displacement
	  Chemical flooding
	  Thermal recovery

Model scope	Single-well models Cross-sectional models Window models Full-field models
Model dimensionality	0D models (tank-type models) 1D models 2D models Stacked areal models 3D models

Equation solvers	Nonlinear-equation solver
	  IMPES
	  SEQ
	  SS
	  Fully implicit
	Linear-equation solver
	  Direct solution methods
	  Iterative solution methods

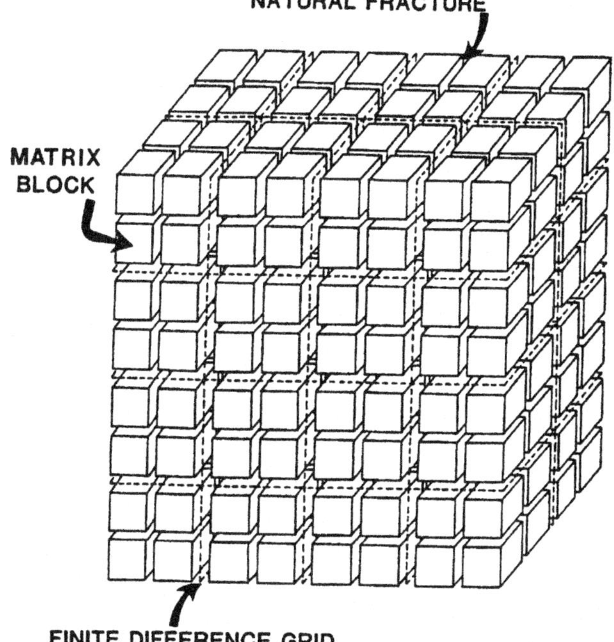

Fig. 10.21—Idealization of a naturally-fractured-reservoir model with the Warren and Root approach (after King *et al.*[35]).

tion. The disadvantage of actual models is that they are valid only for the modeled area. Extrapolating results to areas that are substantially different from the modeled area may be difficult, and additional modeling may be required to obtain identical information on other parts of the field.

Fluid Description. The two fluid descriptions that can be used in reservoir simulation, black-oil and compositional, were discussed in Sec. 10.3.2. The appropriate fluid description to use in a given study depends on the nature of the hydrocarbons in place and the processes used to recover these hydrocarbons. In discussing the recovery processes, we present guidelines for fluid description selection.

Reservoir Type. Two general reservoir types, each with a distinctly different reservoir behavior, that can be used in reservoir simulation studies are single-porosity and naturally fractured reservoirs. The most common formulation used in reservoir simulation is the single-porosity-reservoir approach. Single-porosity models contain only one pore system in which fluids can flow toward production wells. Single-porosity-reservoir behavior is the reservoir behavior discussed in most textbooks on reservoir engineering.

Naturally fractured reservoir models consider two pore systems open to fluid flow: the pore system made up of the fractures and the pore system contained within the rock matrix. **Fig. 10.21** is a schematic of naturally fractured reservoir models. Two formulations can be used for modeling the performance of naturally fractured reservoirs: dual-porosity and dual-permeability. The dual- porosity formulation allows for fluid flow from the rock matrix to the fractures only. That is, flow from one matrix gridblock to another cannot occur unless fluids first enter the fracture system. In this formulation, the fractures act as sinks to the rock matrix and as conduits to the production wells. The dual-permeability formulation is similar to the dual-porosity formulation; however, it also allows for direct matrix-gridblock-to-matrix-gridblock flow.

To some degree, most petroleum reservoirs are naturally fractured. The extent to which these fractures influence reservoir performance should determine which formulation to use in a simulation study. Again, this illustrates that a simulation model cannot be built blindly. Some knowledge of the reservoir and expected reservoir behavior is required before a proper simulation model can be constructed.

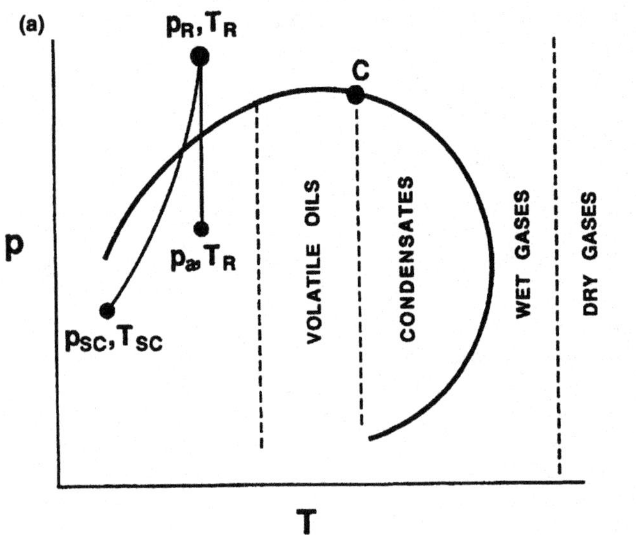

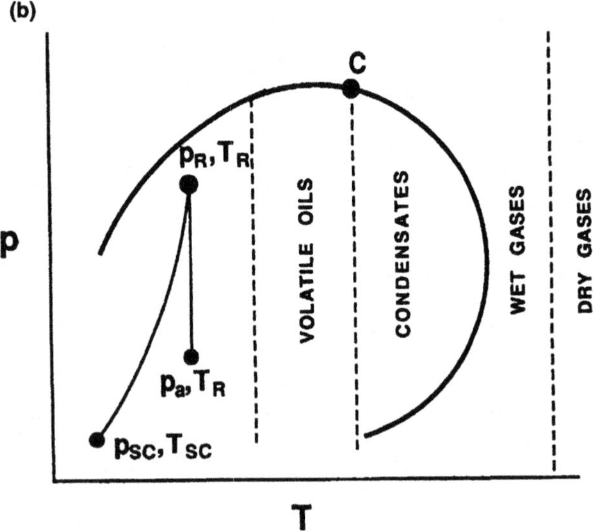

Fig. 10.22—Pressure/temperature diagrams for (a) undersaturated and (b) saturated black-oil reservoirs.

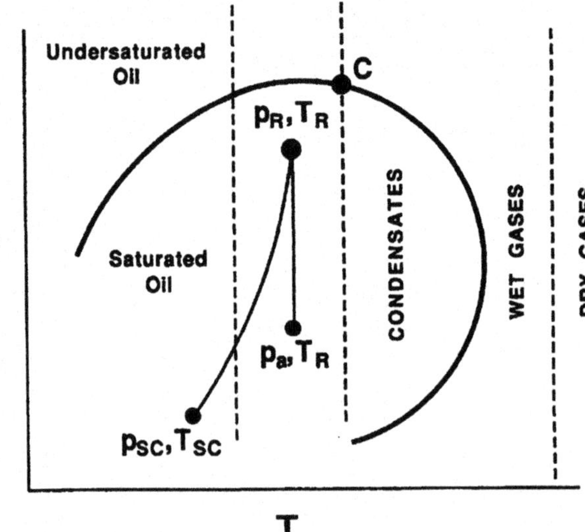

Fig. 10.23—Pressure/temperature diagram for a volatile-oil reservoir.

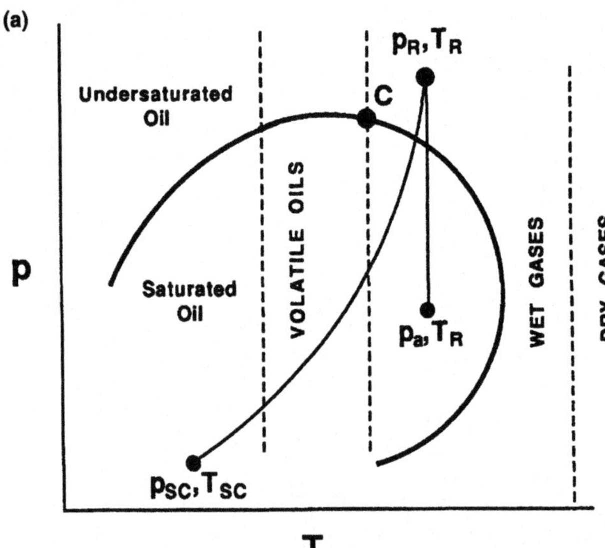

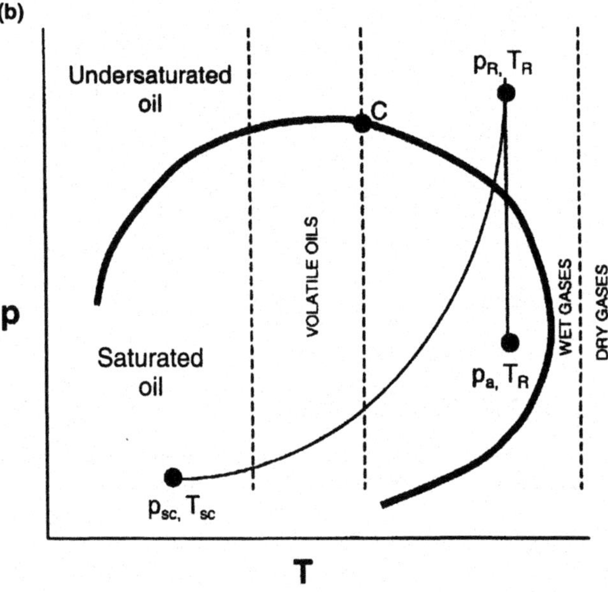

Fig. 10.24—Pressure/temperature diagrams for (a) rich-gas- and (b) lean-gas-condensate reservoirs.

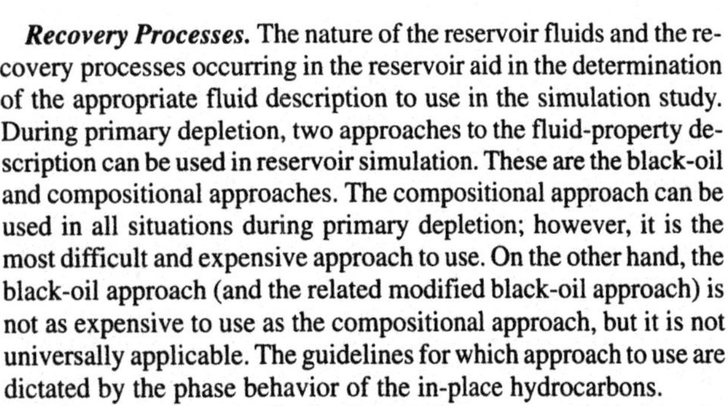

Recovery Processes. The nature of the reservoir fluids and the recovery processes occurring in the reservoir aid in the determination of the appropriate fluid description to use in the simulation study. During primary depletion, two approaches to the fluid-property description can be used in reservoir simulation. These are the black-oil and compositional approaches. The compositional approach can be used in all situations during primary depletion; however, it is the most difficult and expensive approach to use. On the other hand, the black-oil approach (and the related modified black-oil approach) is not as expensive to use as the compositional approach, but it is not universally applicable. The guidelines for which approach to use are dictated by the phase behavior of the in-place hydrocarbons.

Primary Depletion. Black-oil models are the most commonly used models in the oil industry. The fluids that can be represented by black-oil models are the crude oils discussed in most textbooks on reservoir engineering. **Fig. 10.22** shows the phase behavior of these fluids. Points (p_R, T_R), (p_{sc}, T_{sc}), and (p_a, T_R) in this figure represent initial reservoir conditions, surface conditions, and abandonment conditions, respectively. This figure shows the area of applicability of black-oil models. In black-oil reservoirs, fluid properties are considered to be strictly pressure dependent.

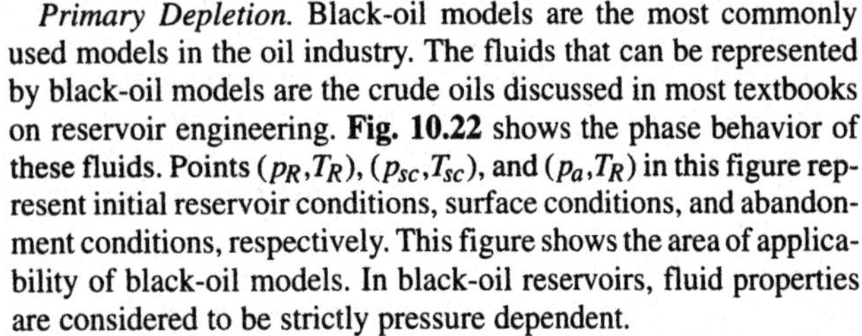

Volatile oils and gas condensates are composed of high concentrations of intermediate hydrocarbons (C_3 and C_4) that can partition easily into both gas and oil phases. The presence of these hydrocarbons allows for a large degree of mass transfer between the hydrocarbon

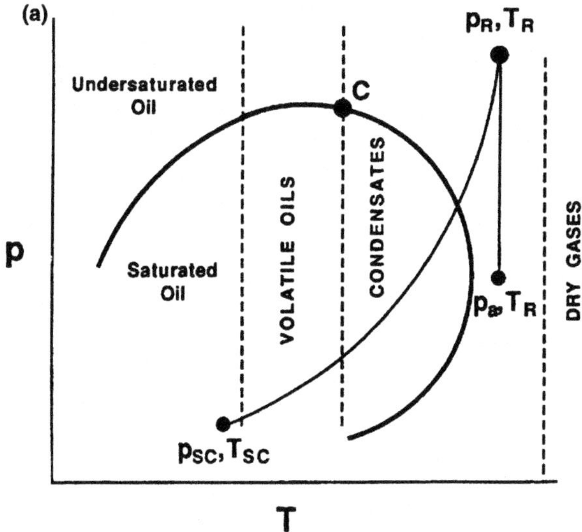

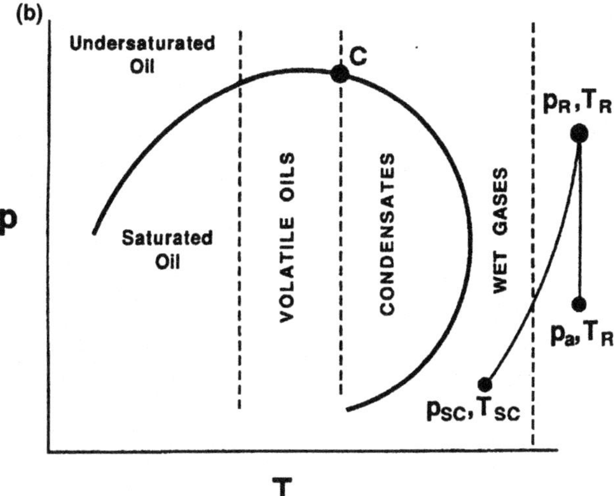

Fig. 10.25—Pressure/temperature diagrams for (a) wet- and (b) dry-gas reservoirs.

gas and liquid phases during primary depletion. When this occurs, fluid properties can become dependent on composition as well as on reservoir pressure and temperature. The simulation of volatile oils and gas condensates, therefore, may require the more computationally intensive compositional formulation. **Figs. 10.23 and 10.24** show the pressure/temperature (p-T) diagrams for a volatile oil and gas condensate, respectively.

In Fig. 10.23, no clear distinction can be observed between black and volatile oils other than the reservoir temperature, which is closer to the critical temperature for volatile oils. Therefore, for borderline cases, the study objectives determine which PVT formulation, black oil or compositional, to use in the simulation study.

Fig. 10.24 illustrates a rich gas condensate (Fig. 10.24a) and a lean gas condensate (Fig. 10.24b). For rich gas condensates, no real alternatives are available and the compositional PVT approach must be used. For lean gas condensates, an alternative PVT formulation, the modified black-oil approach, can be used. Like the black-oil approach, the modified black-oil approach uses PVT properties that are strictly pressure dependent. The modified black-oil approach, however, uses a liquid-dropout, r_s, property which is not considered in the black-oil approach. The liquid-dropout property is analogous to the solution-gas/oil ratio property for oils, R_s, but describes the volume of hydrocarbon liquids that drop out of the gas phase as a function of pressure during primary depletion.

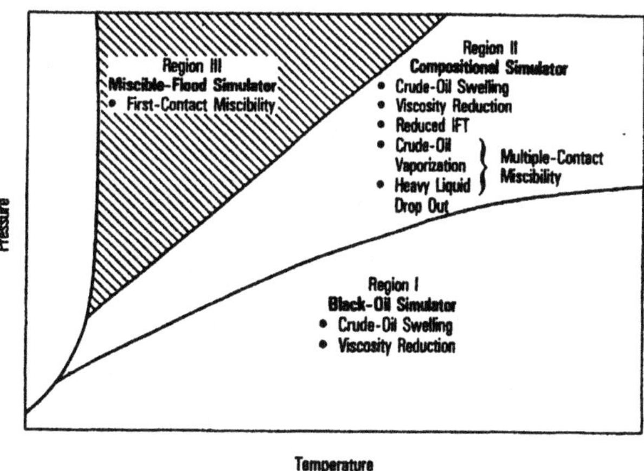

Fig. 10.26—Areas of application of a black-oil model, miscible-flooding model, and compositional model for miscible displacements (after Klins[38]).

Fig. 10.25 shows the p-T diagram for a wet and dry gas. For these gases, modified black-oil properties (for wet gases) or black-oil properties (for dry gases) generally are sufficient for the simulation of reservoir depletion.

Secondary Recovery and Pressure Maintenance. For gas-displacement processes in volatile-oil reservoirs and pressure-maintenance processes in gas-condensate reservoirs, mass transfer can affect reservoir behavior significantly and its influence may need to be incorporated into the simulation model. Incorporation of mass-transfer effects can be accomplished only with the compositional PVT approach.

EOR Processes. Miscible Displacement. Two different miscible-displacement methods, first-contact-miscibility (FCM) and multiple-contact-miscibility (MCM) processes, can be used for the EOR from oil reservoirs. FCM processes are processes in which the injected fluid is immediately miscible with the oil phase at the sand face, whereas MCM processes are those that require a certain degree of mass transfer before the injected fluid achieves miscibility with the crude oil. For reservoir simulation purposes, first-contact miscibility can be assumed if miscibility is achieved in the cell containing the injection well.

For FCM processes, special techniques have been developed[36,37] that are based on the use of empirical mixing laws that replace the rigorous compositional calculations for PVT properties. For MCM processes, the compositional approach is required because it is the only formulation that can model adequately the mass transfer required to achieve miscibility. **Fig. 10.26** provides guidelines for use of the special miscible techniques and the fully compositional approach for reservoir simulation. A plot, such as that shown in Fig. 10.26, must be determined in the laboratory for the crude oil of interest.

Chemical Flooding. Chemical-flooding recovery methods, such as polymer, alkali, and surfactant flooding, have specific characteristics, such as chemical reactions, adsorption, and non-Newtonian fluid behavior, that need to be addressed in the simulation study. Because most commercial black-oil reservoir simulators do not consider these phenomena, special simulators are required when a chemical flood is to be modeled.

Thermal-Recovery Processes. Thermal-recovery methods often are applied to heavy crude oils to reduce oil viscosity and improve flow behavior in the reservoir. For simulation purposes, thermal-recovery methods require a heat-balance equation and other special features (such as wellbore heat losses and temperature-dependent rock and fluid properties) in addition to the mass-balance equations described in Chap. 9. Again, most commercial black-oil simulators do not consider the energy balance necessary for thermal-recovery modeling, and special simulators or multipurpose simulators are required.

Model Scope. The model scope refers to the connectivity of the modeled reservoir area to the main reservoir area. The choice of the

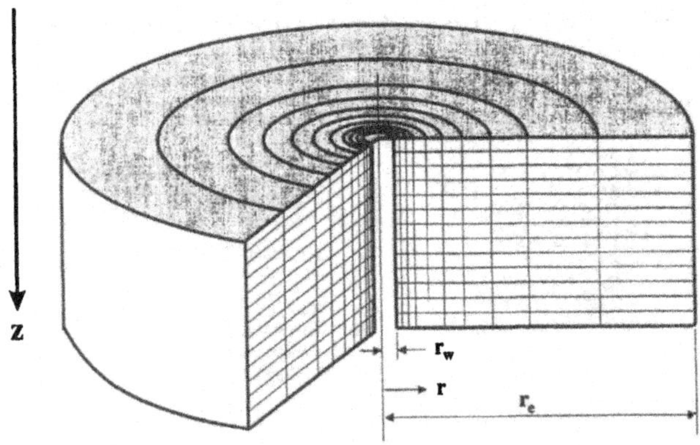

Fig. 10.27—Typical single-well model.

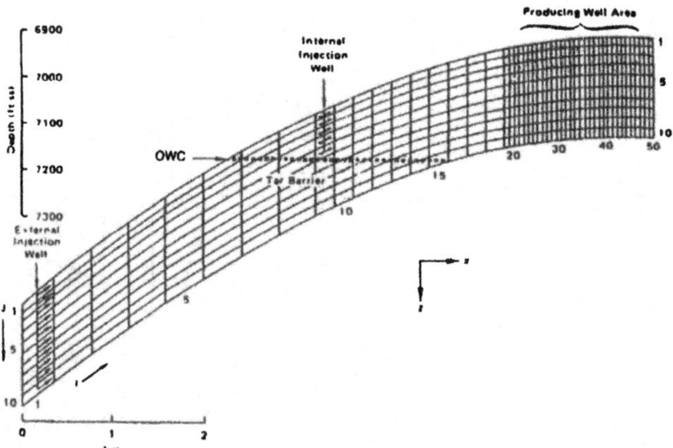

Fig. 10.28—Typical cross-sectional model in reservoir simulation (after Jacks *et al.*[39]).

scope of model to use in a simulation study is determined by the nature of the reservoir and the objectives of the study.

Single-Well Models. Single-well models (generally, *r-z* coordinates) consider only one well and drainage area in the reservoir. In these models, the volume drained by the well is assumed to be isolated from the main reservoir area. The study objectives that can be answered with a single-well model include evaluating various well-completion strategies, predicting coning behavior, and analyzing complex pressure-transient data. In addition, single-well models can be used to scale up relative permeability data for full-field models by aiding in the generation of well pseudofunctions (Sec. 10.4.3).

Single-well models can be either conceptual or actual in design. Single-well models of actual wells use the stratigraphy observed in well logs during the model-construction phase of the study. In general, the layering used in single-well models is kept uniform throughout the drainage area. **Fig. 10.27** shows a typical single-well model used in reservoir simulation studies.

Cross-Sectional Models. Cross-sectional models (generally, *x-z* coordinates) contain multiple wells along a cross section in the field. **Fig. 10.28** shows a typical cross-sectional model used in reservoir simulation studies. These studies assume that the modeled cross section is isolated from the main area of the field. Consequently, the model boundaries are chosen to lie on anticipated no-flow boundaries in the region of the cross section. These no-flow boundaries, therefore, should correspond to flow barriers observed in the field, such as the natural no-flow boundaries between production wells or along sealing faults.

Fig. 10.28 illustrates that a cross-sectional model can incorporate formation dip, reservoir stratigraphy, and anticipated well spacing. Therefore, the study objectives that can be addressed with a cross-sectional model are those concerned with the interplay of viscous, gravity, and capillary forces. Thus, cross-sectional models can be used to determine the effects of gravity override and underride along shales, edgewater encroachment, or gas-cap expansion. Cross-sectional models are used most commonly to generate interblock pseudofunctions in support of full-field simulation models.

The use of multiple wells in cross-sectional models requires that interwell properties be interpolated from those observed in well logs. Historically, simulation layers with uniform properties were used in cross-sectional models. With the recent advances in geostatistics,[14,15] however, the use of simulation layers with nonuniform properties is becoming the industry standard.

Window Models. Window models consider a representative area of the subject field rather than the entire field; therefore, a window model may consider a representative well pattern or an isolated fault block. Window models can be either 2D or 3D in nature and are used to provide a finer grid spacing and, consequently, greater model resolution in the areas of interest. Thus, window models can be used to track flood fronts in well patterns, establish new in-fill well locations in a portion of the field, or monitor gas-cap expansion or water encroachment.

Most window models assume that no-flow barriers exist on the boundaries of the windowed area; therefore, symmetry between well patterns commonly is used to define the window model. Some commercial simulators allow for fluid flux across the model boundaries, which, in turn, allows for the no-flow boundary condition to be relaxed. Also, imaginary flux wells on the model boundary can be used to simulate fluid migration into or out of the model area. With the advent of local grid refinement, finer grid spacing in areas of interest (which is the main objective of window models) can now be achieved in full-field models.

Full-Field Models. Full-field studies consider the entire field in the simulation model. Consequently, full-field models allow for all forms of hydraulic communication throughout a producing field. The types of communication that can be addressed in a full-field study include reservoir communication, wellbore communication, and communication through surface facilities; therefore, full-field models can be used to answer most, but not all, study objectives.

Model Dimensionality. Model dimensionality refers to the number of model directions in which fluids can flow in the subject reservoir. The number of directions required by a study depends on the reservoir and objectives of the study. Because the principal direction of flow in most reservoirs is horizontal or, more correctly, parallel to the reservoir dip, at least one horizontal direction usually is used in the simulation model. Because gravity always acts in the vertical direction, study objectives dealing with gravity forces always require inclusion of the vertical direction in the model. In addition, stratified reservoirs with large contrasts in formation properties may require the use of the vertical dimension even if horizontal flow dominates.

Zero-Dimensional (0D) Models. Zero-dimensional models, or tank-type models, consider only reservoir energy and cannot distinguish flow in any direction. These models form the basis of the material-balance approach discussed in Chaps. 1 and 11. Because these models consider average reservoir energy, they can be used to obtain information about the reservoir as a whole. The objectives that can be investigated with a 0D model include determination of initial fluids in place, prediction of fieldwide production, estimation of water encroachment, and determination of average reservoir pressure and saturation throughout time.

One-Dimensional Models. One-dimensional models allow for fluids to flow in a single direction. These models have limited applications for modeling field performance but commonly are used in research laboratories. Because all drive mechanisms, compositional effects, and chemical effects can be included in the simulator, 1D models can be used to study core and slim-tube displacements. Consequently, these models can be used to establish the contribution of various flow mechanisms in laboratory experiments. History matching of these core displacement processes can provide input data for miscible-flooding models.

Two-Dimensional Models. Historically, 2D models are the most commonly used models in reservoir simulation because 2D models can be applied to many of the model types discussed earlier. These include single-well models (*r-z*), cross-sectional models (*x-z*), and full-field models (*x-y*). Two-dimensional models are very versatile because they can be used to address many questions concerning reservoir behavior. With the advent of high-performance computers and improved reservoir-characterization techniques, many models that traditionally would have used two dimensions now use three dimensions.

Stacked Areal Models. Stacked areal models consist of several 2D areal models that are not in communication within the reservoir because of vertical transmissibility barriers but may be in communication through the wellbore because of commingled production or through the surface production or injection facilities. The reservoir objectives of stacked 2D models are the same as nonstacked 2D models. In addition, stacked areal models can be used to examine various commingling strategies, workover/recompletion strategies, and tubing/surface-facilities capacities. Although these objectives also can be achieved with 3D models, 3D models are more expensive to run than stacked areal models.

Three-Dimensional Models. Three-dimensional models are the standard models for full-field reservoir simulation in the oil industry. These models allow for flow in all spatial directions and can be used to address most study objectives. The disadvantage of 3D full-field models is that they are the most labor-, central-processing-unit (CPU)-, and resource-intensive models that can be used in a simulation study.

Equation Solvers. The choice of the equation solvers, for both nonlinear and linear equations considered by the reservoir simulator, is determined by the size of the model, the computer on which the study is conducted, and the stability and convergence properties of the model. The appropriate solver to use in a reservoir study is the one that uses the least amount of computer resources, provides a robust simulation model, and provides for acceptable run times.

Nonlinear-Equation Solvers. There are many choices available for the linearization and solution of the finite-difference equations generated by the reservoir simulator. These (listed in the order of increasing computational effort required) include the implicit-pressure/explicit-saturation (IMPES) method, the sequential-solution method, the simultaneous-solution method, the adaptive-implicit method, and the fully-implicit method. Most commercial simulators do not have options for all these methods, but most have options for the IMPES and fully-implicit methods.

IMPES Method. Of all the nonlinear methods, the IMPES method is the most computationally efficient method, requiring the simultaneous solution of only N coupled equations (where N is the number of active cells in the simulation model). In contrast, a fully-implicit black-oil model requires the simultaneous solution of $3N$ coupled equations, while a fully implicit compositional model requires the solution of $(n_c+1)\times N$ equations (where n_c is the number of hydrocarbon components). The disadvantage of the IMPES method is that it is applicable only when small saturation changes occur in the reservoir during a timestep because the IMPES method is based on the assumption that changes in relative permeability and capillary pressure are not large during a timestep. This restricts the IMPES method to physical situations where saturation changes are small, to simulation models with large grid cells (large-PV cells), or to simulation models that use small timestep sizes. Physical situations where the IMPES method cannot be used include gas or water coning and flood-front tracking.

Models with very small grid cells cannot, in most cases, use the IMPES formulation because, for a fixed fluid flux and timestep size, smaller grid cells exhibit larger saturation changes than larger grid cells. Thus, the IMPES method generally is limited to coarsely gridded and coarsely layered full-field models.

If there is doubt concerning the applicability of the IMPES method, it should be tried early in the model-construction phase. If it yields a robust model, its use should be continued. If it does not work, a more implicit method should be used.

Fully-Implicit Method. The fully-implicit method is universally applicable; however, it has the disadvantage that it is much more CPU intensive because of the additional $2N$ linear equations that must be solved in the method (for the black-oil case). Thus, the fully-implicit method should be used whenever the IMPES method fails to give adequate results.

Linear-Equation Solvers. The basic methods for the solution of the linear equations generated by the finite-difference approach are discussed in Chap. 7. These methods can be grouped into two categories: direct and iterative methods. Direct methods yield a solution after a fixed, predictable number of arithmetic operations. Iterative methods, on the other hand, require a nonfixed number of operations before a solution is obtained. When choosing a linear-equation solver, the following guidelines can be used.

Direct Solution Methods. The choice of the linear solution method used in the simulation model depends on the size of the model, the nonlinear method used, and the computer used for the study. Direct solution techniques generally outperform iterative methods on small models (less than 2,000 to 3,000 linear equations). Because the number of equations to be solved is dependent on the nonlinear solution method, direct solution methods can be used on larger IMPES models than fully-implicit models. In addition, for the same model run on vector computers, a banded option for direct linear solution techniques runs significantly faster than on a scalar computer. Because of the superior performance of direct methods on smaller models, direct methods are recommended for single-well, window, and coarsely gridded cross-sectional models.

Iterative Solution Methods. Iterative methods should be used on all large simulation models because of the superior performance of iterative methods in terms of storage and CPU time for large numbers of equations. If there is doubt about which method to use in a simulation model, both the direct and iterative methods should be tested early in the study to determine which method is superior for a given problem.

10.4.2 Model Discretization. Model discretization refers to the partitioning of the continuous spatial and time variables into discrete segments. Discretization of the space variables results in the finite-difference grid that gives the areal and geologic definitions to the simulation model. Discretization of time results in the timesteps used to advance the model through the simulation. Chaps. 5 and 9 discuss the mathematical description of the discretization process, but the discussion in this chapter focuses on the practical aspects of the model-discretization process.

Spatial Discretization. Discretization of the space variables includes the discretization of the horizontal dimensions, x-y or r-θ, and the vertical dimension, z. Discretization of the horizontal dimensions results in the areal grid, while discretization of the vertical dimension results in the model layering. The motivations for designing the areal grid and model-layering scheme differ slightly; however, there are several common requirements of the finite-difference grid. The grid system should be compatible with the study objectives, compatible with the mathematics of the finite-difference approach to ensure an accurate and stable solution, capable of providing an adequate determination of initial fluids in place, and capable of providing reasonable turnaround on the computer equipment used in the study.

The first feature of the grid system has been emphasized throughout this chapter. The second feature of the grid system is discussed in Chap. 5 in terms of mathematical-stability criteria, truncation error analysis, and compatibility analysis. The third feature of the grid system is determination of the initial-in-place-fluid volumes. The simulation grid should allow for a reasonable estimate of all reservoir fluids. In general, the simulation grid cannot be expected to give the exact in-place volumes determined from volumetric or material-balance studies but it should provide for an adequate estimate. The fourth feature implies that different grid systems may be required for the same reservoir, depending on the computer used in the study, because the computer resources required by a simulation model are proportional to the number of grid cells. Consequently, a model built for a supercomputer cannot be expected to run on a personal computer.

Areal Discretization. The practical objectives for designing the areal grid are (1) to provide information on the specific areas of interest in the field, (2) to define the internal and external boundaries of the subject reservoir, and (3) to model the dynamics of the recovery processes occurring in the reservoir.

Designing the areal grid to provide information on specific areas requires that gridblocks be placed over the areas of interest in the reservoir. These areas are determined by the objectives of the simulation study and are, in general, production and injection wells. Consequently, gridblock centers should be located as close as possible to all potential (current and future) well locations, including production-, injection-, and infill-well locations. If required, finer grids or a locally refined grid can be used in the areas of interest.

To define the internal and external boundaries, the areal grid must be designed so that the grid system provides an adequate description of the geometry of the reservoir. This implies that gridblock boundaries be placed on all limits of the reservoir including both internal and external reservoir boundaries. Consequently, gridblocks should be placed in the vicinity of all reservoir boundaries and internal faults.

Modeling the dynamics of the recovery process requires that the grid spacing be fine enough to model properly the physics of the recovery processes occurring in the subject reservoir. For example, depletion processes are governed principally by available reservoir energy. Consequently, fluid volumes and compressibilities dominate reservoir performance. This means that reservoir performance can be modeled adequately with relatively few areal grid cells provided that the vertical discretization is sufficient to describe reservoir geology. For displacement processes, however, additional grid cells may be required between producers and injectors to allow for a better description of flood fronts because coarse grid cells tend to smear flood fronts as they travel through the reservoir.

There are no rules on the proper cell size to use in a simulation study. The most appropriate method to determine the grid dimensions for the model is to perform a sensitivity analysis on the grid system early in the study. This is done by starting with an initial grid and reducing the grid dimensions in a systematic manner. When the simulation results are found to be independent of the grid system, the grid dimensions are appropriate for the study. As a rule of thumb, three to five gridblocks between offset wells may be adequate for primary production, while 5 to 10 gridblocks between offset wells may be adequate for displacement processes.

Grid Orientation. An additional consideration concerning the design of the areal grid that the reservoir engineer must consider is the orientation of the grid. The orientation of the finite-difference grid over the reservoir area requires both theoretical and practical considerations. The use of the five-point finite-difference formulation for areal models and the seven-point finite-difference formulation for 3D models has one important consequence on the selection of the orientation of the areal grid. To be mathematically correct, the finite-difference grid must be oriented in the directions of the principal permeability axes of the porous medium because the standard finite-difference formulations assume that all cross-derivative terms in the flow equations are zero. This is possible only if the grid is oriented in the directions of the principal permeability axes.

In practice, however, the directions of the principal permeability axes are not known in the field and generally cannot be used as an aid for defining the orientation of the finite-difference grid. Other considerations, therefore, may be used to help orient the grid. One that is used often for choosing the grid orientation is to select the orientation that minimizes the total number of active cells in the model. This criterion can be used to help run large models on computers with fixed storage. The use of this criterion also minimizes the computer time because CPU-time requirements are dependent on the number of active grid cells. A second consideration that can be used to determine grid orientation is to select the grid that maximizes the number of potential well locations that fall on or near gridblock centers. This ensures that the assumptions used in the mathematics of the well-management routines in the simulation packages are satisfied and therefore may minimize the errors in the inflow performance calculated in the simulator.

Some studies use grid systems oriented in the anticipated directions of fluid flow. The use of this criterion, however, is often difficult to implement in practice because, in many cases, the direction of fluid flow may change with time. This occurs when flood patterns are realigned during a displacement process, infill wells are drilled, or wells (or geologic zones) are shut in.

Finally, if strong areal permeability anisotropy is known to exist in the reservoir under study, the finite-difference grid must be oriented in the direction of the permeability trends. This is the only way that this anisotropy can be modeled.

It has been observed that the orientation of the grid can have a significant influence on the results of a simulation study.[40] This grid-orientation effect becomes more severe for adverse mobility ratios. This effect can be reduced by the use of a nine-point finite-difference formulation for areal flow and the use of an 11-point finite-difference formulation for 3D flow. The grid-orientation effect can only be minimized with these methods, not eliminated completely.

Vertical Discretization. The practical objective for vertical discretization is to provide enough simulation layers (1) to provide an appropriate description of the stratigraphy and geology of the reservoir under study, (2) to provide additional definition to thick reservoir flow units, (3) to match initial fluid contacts, (4) to match completion and perforation intervals, and (5) to provide adequate in-place-fluid-volume estimates in reservoirs with significant transition zones. In some cases, these goals may be in conflict and, in general, all cannot be achieved with the same layering scheme.

Providing an appropriate stratigraphic and geologic description is probably the most important goal in reservoir simulation because the principal reason reservoir simulation is such a powerful tool is that it is the only forecasting technique available to the reservoir engineer that considers reservoir geology. In the actual modeling approach (Sec. 10.4.1), at least one simulation layer can be placed over each major flow unit in the reservoir. In some cases, however, flow units with similar properties may be lumped into pseudolayers for reservoir simulation purposes.*

Providing additional definition to thick reservoir flow units refers to the use of multiple simulation layers within a single geological layer. The use of these additional layers can best be exemplified in coning studies where, even in a homogeneous reservoir, multiple simulation layers must be used to predict well behavior adequately.

Matching initial fluid contacts can be useful in conceptual modeling (Sec. 10.4.1). The disadvantage of attempting to match fluid contacts in actual full-field simulation is that matching GOC and OWC while simultaneously honoring reservoir stratigraphy is generally, if not always, impossible. This is also true when attempting to match completion and perforation intervals.

Fig. 10.29 shows three general approaches to layering that can be used in reservoir simulation: stratigraphic, proportional, and stacked layering. Generally, stratigraphic layering is used when geological considerations are the major concerns in the simulation study. In most cases, this is the main consideration in cross-sectional and full-field simulation models used in the petroleum industry. Consequently, stratigraphic layering is the most commonly used layering scheme in reservoir simulation.

Proportional layers are layers that retain their relative fraction of the total thickness throughout the reservoir (Fig. 10.29c). Proportional layering is used to incorporate additional vertical description to reservoir zones that do not exhibit strong geologic features.

Stacked layering is used to match fluid contacts and perforation intervals. Therefore, if these are the main considerations in the simulation study (for example, in a single-well coning study or a gas-cap-expansion study), then stacked layering can be used. Stacked layering is commonly used in conceptual models and single-well models.

Time Discretization. The practical objectives for time discretization are (1) to provide for a stable, accurate solution; (2) to place timesteps at key times in the reservoir history; (3) to place timesteps at key input/output times in the study; and (4) to provide for reasonable turnaround on the computer equipment used in the study.

To meet the first objective, the timestep sizes used in the study must not only meet all stability and compatibility criteria but must also be small enough to ensure that the physics of the recovery processes be preserved during the study. This implies that numerical dispersion is minimized, pressure and saturation changes are appropriate for modeling mobility changes during the timestep, and well-inflow calculations do not oscillate from timestep to timestep.

Placing timesteps at key times in the reservoir history requires that timesteps be selected whenever any major historical or anticipated well work is performed. This implies that a timestep is chosen when wells are to be drilled, worked over, or shut in or when major facilities

*Claridge, E.L.: "Pseudolayers in Reservoir Simulation," unpublished paper presented at the SPE Luncheon Series, Houston (21 November 1984).

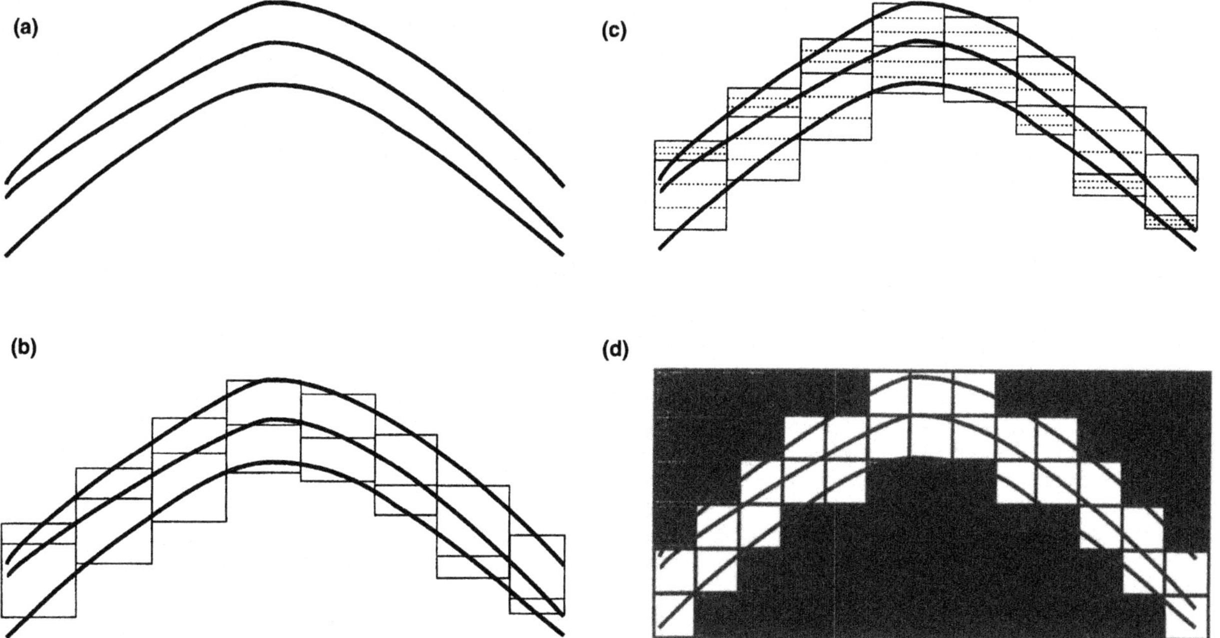

Fig. 10.29—Different strategies of layering used in reservoir simulation. (a) Reservoir to be modeled showing two distinct geologic layers, (b) layering strategy with stratigraphic layers, (c) layering strategy with proportional layering, and (d) layering strategy with stacked layering.

are brought on line. In practice, the dates of all well work cannot be matched exactly, but this objective still should be considered when timesteps are chosen.

The third objective for selecting the timestep size is to match times when input or output is to be written. In most simulation studies, results are required at regular intervals, such as monthly, quarterly, or yearly. Therefore, the simulation results must be written at these regular intervals.

In addition, restart records may need to be written at specific times during the simulation. Restarting a simulation run refers to writing the results of the simulation at a certain date to a data file that can be read during a second simulation run to restart the original simulation run. If important decisions are to be made on the subject reservoir, such as selection of an EOR process to apply at a certain time, then restart records need to be written at this time. The most common time to write these restart records is at the end of history/beginning of prediction. This allows for investigating multiple future operating alternatives without having to rerun the entire historical period for each prediction case.

Most commercial and in-house reservoir simulators have automatic timestep selectors that meet all the objectives listed. It is strongly recommended that these timestep selectors be used in all reservoir simulation studies.

10.4.3 Assignment of Grid-Cell Properties. ***Assignment of Reservoir Properties to Grid Cells From Reservoir Maps.*** Table 10.2 lists the map requirements for a simulation study. The maximum requirement for a simulation study is one map for each property listed in Table 10.2 for each simulation layer. All the map requirements listed in Table 10.2 would be necessary for the actual simulation of a large, complex reservoir. On the other hand, the minimum requirement for a simulation study would be the structure top of the first simulation layer; the net thickness of each simulation layer, which may be a constant value for each layer; and the porosity of each layer. Then, permeabilities can be obtained from porosity/permeability transforms. This minimum map requirement would be used, for example, in a conceptual, single-well model.

To maintain the variable nature of the properties defined by the geologic maps, map values must be assigned to the simulation model on a cell-by-cell basis. Many commercial software packages are available that can be used to assign map properties to the simulation grid cells. The theory behind these packages can be very sophisticated and is beyond the scope of this book; however, a brief discussion is presented.

In most studies, map properties are assigned by digitizing the geologic maps with digitizing software. In the digitizing process, variable x and y points on the map are entered into a computer program along a fixed contour value of the map. The map properties are gridded by assigning variable map properties for evenly spaced values of x and y points. After the map properties are gridded, they can be averaged and assigned to the simulation cells.

Although this digitizing process can be used on all reservoir properties, it is strongly advised that it be used only on rock properties, such as thickness, porosity, and permeability. To reflect lithology changes in the reservoir, endpoint fluid saturations, if they have been mapped by a geologist, may be digitized and entered into simulation models. Although there may be some exceptional cases, initial fluid saturations and reservoir pressures should not be digitized but should be calculated with the initialization routines that are internal to the simulator.

Assignment of Reservoir Properties to Grid Cells From a Fine-Grid Geocellular Model. Recent advances in reservoir characterization, particularly in geostatistics[14,15] and dynamic reservoir scaleup,[17] have revolutionized the methods used to construct reservoir simulation models since the mid-1980's. Although the theory of geostatistics is beyond the scope of this book, the application of these methods forms the basis of modern reservoir simulation.

The first step in the application of geostatistics is construction of a fine-grid geocellular model. The grid used in the geocellular model is similar to the block-centered grid systems discussed in Sec. 5.2.1. The objective of this model is to provide the following: a computational grid for geostatistical and scaleup calculations, a database for storing measured and derived reservoir properties and their spatial locations in the reservoir, and the basis for 3D visualization. Geocellular models of complex hydrocarbon reservoirs may contain several million cells.

Construction of the geocellular model begins with identifying marker surfaces in the reservoir of interest. A marker surface is a correlatable surface observed across the reservoir that has a distinctive log signature. Ideally, the marker surface should be observed in all wells that penetrate the subject reservoir (including wells that may target production from deeper reservoirs). The depths of these marker surfaces are contoured, digitized, and gridded as discussed earlier. The vertical spacing between the marker surfaces is dependent on the deposition of the reservoir and generally is nonuniform through the reservoir section. The marker surfaces are used to incorporate the reservoir structure and stratigraphy into the geocellular and reservoir simulation models.

Model layering is refined further by incorporating additional layers into the geocellular model. If there are few faults, pinchouts, or erosional surfaces in the reservoir, proportional layering (Fig. 10.29) can be used. If the reservoir contains many faults, pinchouts, or erosional surfaces, a more complex layering strategy may be required. In general, the layer spacing of the final model should be on the same order as the vertical resolution of the logging tools (typically 0.5 to 1.0 ft).

Areal spacing of the geocellular model is somewhat arbitrary. There are, however, computational advantages during the scaleup process in keeping the areal grid spacing of the model equal to a rational fraction of the areal simulation grid spacing (e.g., 1/1, 1/2, or 1/3 of the simulation model spacing). This allows several whole fine-grid cells to be combined to form one coarse-grid cell during scaleup.

Once the geocellular grid has been constructed, log-measured data (raw log traces; porosities; saturations; and, if appropriate, interpreted permeability traces) are imported into the model. Because the geocellular layer spacing has been selected to be the same as the resolution of the logging tool, no vertical averaging is required for the assignment of imported properties. The penetration points of the wells and the log-measured properties at these penetration points are then considered as hard data for the geostatistical computations.

Geostatistical techniques are then used to populate (assign) the cells with the reservoir property values. Cell-center locations are used in the geostatistical computations. If the location of the penetration point of a well within a cell differs from the cell-center location, the reservoir properties at the cell center will differ from the reservoir properties at the well. The principal geostatistical techniques used to populate a geocellular model for a full-field 3D reservoir simulation are conditional-simulation techniques.[14,15] For single-well or conceptual models, the kriging[15] technique may also be used. The difference in these methods is that conditional-simulation techniques consider both the statistics of the spatial variation of the data and the "noise" of the data, while the kriging technique considers only the statistics of the spatial variation of the data. Consequently, the conditional-simulation approach results in a more heterogeneous distribution of reservoir properties than does the kriging approach. Again, the theory of geostatistics is beyond the scope of this book and the interested reader is referred to Ref. 15.

After the geocellular model has been populated with the log-measured reservoir properties, external correlations may be applied to these properties on a cell-by-cell basis to develop derived reservoir properties. These correlations may also include calculations based on previously determined derived reservoir properties.

Once the geocellular model has been populated with both measured and derived reservoir properties, scaleup is performed. Scaleup is required because, even on the most current computer hardware, the number of grid cells in a typical geocellular model is too large for flow simulation. The scaleup step in most modern simulation studies is performed with dynamic scaleup methods.[17] In dynamic scaleup methods, unit mobility ratio displacement calculations (based on the solution of the single-phase, incompressible, flow equation with either specified inlet and outlet pressure boundary conditions or periodic boundary conditions) are run over the fine-grid geocellular model. The single-phase calculations on the fine grid provide the basis for determining which fine-grid cells to combine into a single coarse-grid cell. User-specified criteria, such as honoring of marker surface data, maximum/minimum number of fine-grid cells that can be combined to form a coarse-grid cell, and maximum percentage of total flow through a coarse-grid cell, are applied to form the coarse grid.

In addition, the results of the single-phase calculations over the fine grid are used to compare vs. the results over the coarse grid. This is done to evaluate the quality of the scaleup procedure and to determine the ability of the coarse grid and effective coarse-grid properties to mimic the behavior of the fine-grid solution.

Once the coarse grid is defined, the single-phase calculations are performed over the coarse grid. These displacement calculations are used to determine the effective permeabilities at the scale appropriate for the coarse grid. These single-phase-flow calculations take the place of the arithmetic averaging (Eq. 10.2) and harmonic averaging (Eq. 10.3) used in the static scaleup of permeability. Note that, if the coarse grid is known *a priori* and if the coordinates of the grid system align with the principal permeability axes of the porous media, the dynamic and static scaleup approaches should give comparable results. The effective porosity of the coarse grid is determined from Eq. 10.1. Finally, other scaleup rules, such as PV weighting, can be applied to derived reservoir properties. Once the dynamic scaleup has been completed, results of the fine- and coarse-grid calculations are compared to ensure that the coarse-grid system and effective properties at the coarse-grid scale are comparable. If satisfactory results are obtained, both the coarse grid and the effective coarse-grid properties are used in the simulation study.

One common method of improving the geocellular-model construction described in this section is use of facies-based geostatistical modeling. In facies-based modeling, a two-step procedure is used to populate the geocellular model. In the first step, geostatistcal techniques (indicator simulation) are used to populate the model with integers that represent (indicate) the spatial distribution of different rock facies (rock types). In the second step, the facies envelopes defined in the first step are populated with reservoir properties. The advantage of the facies-based approach is that such properties as spatial statistics, correlation lengths, and property correlations (permeability/porosity transforms and J functions among others) can be made specific to the different rock types present in the reservoir.

At this point, we reiterate our advice to retain the data at the scale at which they were measured until the scaleup step. We also advise not to average extremes in data if these extremes are believed to influence reservoir performance.

Assignment of Rock/Fluid Interaction Properties to Grid Cells. Sec. 10.3.2 discusses relative permeability and capillary pressure. These properties reflect interactions between the reservoir rock and fluids, and their laboratory measurements have been found to depend on both the porous medium and the fluids that flow through it. The properties measured directly from core samples are referred to as rock (or core) curves because the measured properties are applicable only at the scale with which they were measured.

Single-well simulation models and finely layered cross-sectional models commonly use layers that are approximately on the same scale as the core samples; therefore, rock curves are appropriate for these models. Full-field models, on the other hand, may not use simulation layers that are on the same scale as the core samples; consequently, scaleup of relative permeability and capillary pressure often is required for coarse-grid reservoir simulation. This scaleup is accomplished with relative permeability pseudofunctions and capillary pressure pseudofunctions.

Interblock Pseudofunctions. Interblock pseudofunctions are used to describe flow between adjacent grid cells in the simulation model. Two types of interblock pseudofunctions, analytical and dynamic, are available to the engineer working on a reservoir study.

Analytical Interblock Pseudofunctions. Analytical pseudofunctions can be determined by the use of simple analytical, or arithmetic, equations. The use of analytical pseudofunctions requires that certain assumptions be met in the reservoir under study. These assumptions are necessary for the derivation of the analytical expressions for the pseudofunctions. Analytical pseudofunctions assume that the volumetric average water saturation over the cell can be used as the water saturation of the finite-difference grid cell. The expression for the volumetric average water saturation is

$$\overline{S}_w = \frac{\int_0^{\Delta z} \phi S_w \mathrm{d}h}{\int_0^{\Delta z} \phi \mathrm{d}h}. \qquad (10.45)$$

Eq. 10.45 assumes that Δx and Δy of the simulation grid cell are constant. That is, the finite-difference grid cell is a rectangular

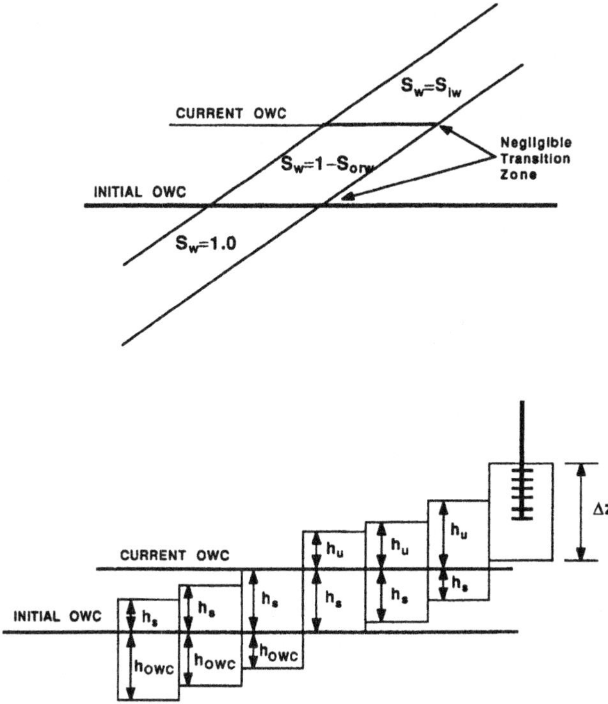

Fig. 10.30—Implementation of segregated-flow interblock pseudofunctions.

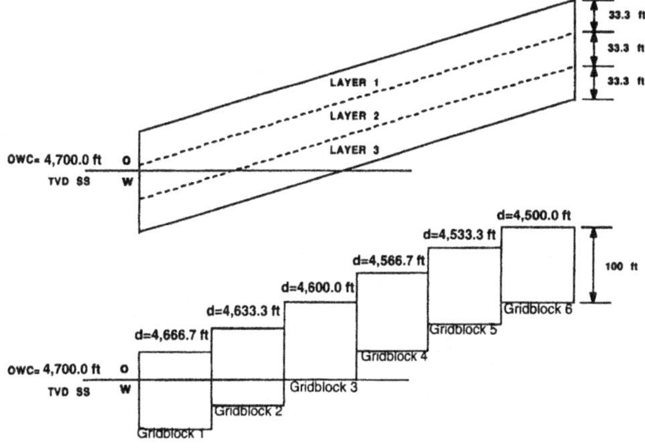

Fig. 10.31—Reservoir and finite-difference grid for segregated-flow pseudofunctions for Example 10.5.

parallelepiped. This water saturation is used as the x axis in the relative permeability and capillary pressure pseudofunction plots. The most common examples of analytical interblock pseudofunctions in use in the oil industry are segregated-flow pseudofunctions and vertical-equilibrium (VE) pseudofunctions.

Segregated-Flow Pseudofunctions. Segregated-flow interblock pseudofunctions assume that no transition zone exists in the reservoir; that is, capillary forces are negligible. For the purposes of reservoir simulation, this assumption is equivalent to assuming that the height of the simulation grid cell is very large compared with the height of the capillary transition zone. **Fig. 10.30** depicts three types of simulation grid cells: cells cut by the initial OWC, cells swept to S_{orw} by invading water (either partially or fully), and cells uninvaded by water.

For the assumptions of segregated flow in Fig. 10.30, the limits of integration in Eq. 10.45 can be set to the height of the initial OWC, h_{owc}; the height of the swept volume of the cell, h_s; and the height of the unswept volume of the cell, h_u. Fig. 10.30 shows these heights. Substituting these limits of integration into Eq. 10.45 results in

$$\overline{S}_w = \frac{h_{owc} + (1 - S_{orw})h_s + S_{iw}h_u}{h_{owc} + h_s + h_u}. \quad (10.46)$$

In Eq. 10.46, it is assumed that porosity is uniform throughout the grid cell, the water saturation below the initial OWC is 1.0, the water saturation in the swept zone is $(1 - S_{orw})$, and the water saturation in the unswept zone is S_{iw}. The selection of these water-saturation values is based on the fundamental assumption for segregated-flow pseudofunctions, which is that the height of the capillary transition zone is negligible in the simulation gridblock.

It should be noted that the total cell thickness, Δz, is equal to the sum of the thickness of the volume below the original OWC, the thickness of the swept volume, and thickness of the unswept volume.

$$\Delta z = h_{owc} + h_s + h_u. \quad (10.47)$$

Combining Eqs. 10.46 and 10.47 and rearranging results in

$$h_s = \frac{\overline{S}_w\Delta z - S_{iw}(\Delta z - h_{owc}) - h_{owc}}{(1 - S_{orw} - S_{iw})}. \quad (10.48)$$

Eq. 10.48 gives the height of the swept volume in the grid cell as a function of the average water saturation. In Eqs. 10.46 through 10.48, h_{owc}, Δz, S_{orw}, and S_{iw} are constant throughout time. Consequently, Eq. 10.48 is an equation of a straight line with h_s and $\overline{S}_w$ being the dependent and independent variables, respectively.

The equation for the relative permeability pseudofunction can be obtained by writing Darcy's law for oil in the unswept region of the grid cell,

$$q_{ou} = \frac{\beta_c k_{ro}(S_{iw})k_H \Delta y h_u}{\mu_o}\frac{\Delta\Phi_o}{\Delta x}, \quad (10.49)$$

and for oil in the grid cell in its entirety,

$$q_o = \frac{\beta_c k_{rop}(\overline{S}_w)k_H \Delta y \Delta z}{\mu_o}\frac{\Delta\Phi_o}{\Delta x}. \quad (10.50)$$

Equating Eq. 10.49 with Eq. 10.50 and applying Eq. 10.47 gives

$$k_{rop}(\overline{S}_w) = \frac{h_u}{\Delta z}k_{ro}(S_{iw}) \quad (10.51a)$$

$$\text{or } k_{rop}(\overline{S}_w) = \frac{(\Delta z - h_{owc} - h_s)}{\Delta z}k_{ro}(S_{iw}). \quad (10.51b)$$

In Eq. 10.51, $k_{ro}(S_{iw})$ is constant throughout time and represents the endpoint value of the relative permeability curve (rock curve).

Similarly, an equation for the water relative permeability pseudofunction can be obtained by considering water flow in the swept region and the region below the initial OWC for the grid cell.

$$q_{ws} = \frac{\beta_c k_{rw}(1 - S_{orw})k_H \Delta y h_s}{\mu_w}\frac{\Delta\Phi_w}{\Delta x}, \quad (10.52)$$

$$q_{wowc} = \frac{\beta_c k_{rw}(1.0)k_H \Delta y h_{owc}}{\mu_w}\frac{\Delta\Phi_w}{\Delta x}, \quad (10.53)$$

and, for the grid cell in its entirety,

$$q_w = \frac{\beta_c k_{rwp}(\overline{S}_w)k_H \Delta y \Delta z}{\mu_w}\frac{\Delta\Phi_w}{\Delta x}. \quad (10.54)$$

For parallel flow, the flow of water through the finite-difference grid cell is equal to the sum of the flow of water through the two regions containing mobile water. That is,

$$q_w = q_{ws} + q_{wowc}. \quad (10.55)$$

The equation for the water relative permeability pseudofunction can be obtained by combining Eqs.10.52 through 10.55.

$$k_{rwp}(\overline{S}_w) = \frac{h_{owc}}{\Delta z}k_{rw}(1.0) + \frac{h_s}{\Delta z}k_{rw}(1 - S_{orw}). \quad (10.56)$$

In Eq. 10.56, it is assumed that $k_{rw}(1.0)$ and $k_{rw}(1 - S_{orw})$ are constant throughout time.

Now the segregated-flow pseudofunctions can be generated for each gridblock by (1) assuming a value of $\overline{S}_w$, (2) calculating the

TABLE 10.14—DATA FROM EXAMPLE 10.2

$S_{orw} = 0.267$

$S_{iw} = 0.220$

$k_{row}(S_{iw}) = 0.45$

$k_{rw}(1 - S_{orw}) = 0.25$

$k_{rw}(1.0) = 1.0$

TABLE 10.15—DATA FOR EXAMPLE 10.5

Gridblock	Δz (ft)	h_{owc} (ft)	h_s (ft)	h_u (ft)
1	100.0	66.7	0.0	33.3
2	100.0	33.3	0.0	66.7
3	100.0	0.0	0.0	100.0

Current OWC = 4,700 ft TVD SS.

TABLE 10.16—RESULTS FOR EXAMPLE 10.5

Gridblock	h_s (ft)	h_u (ft)	$\bar{S}_w$	$k_{rop}(\bar{S}_w)$	$k_{rwp}(\bar{S}_w)$
1	20	13.3	0.84	0.06	0.72
2	20	46.7	0.58	0.21	0.38
3	20	80.0	0.32	0.36	0.05

Current OWC = 4,680 ft TVD SS.

height of the swept volume using Eq. 10.48, (3) calculating the relative permeability pseudofunctions with Eqs. 10.51 and 10.56, and (4) plotting the pseudofunctions vs. the assumed water saturation.

Because Eq. 10.48 is a straight line (h_s vs. $\bar{S}_w$), the resulting pseudofunctions vs. $\bar{S}_w$ are also straight lines. We originally assumed that capillary pressure was negligible; therefore, the corresponding capillary pressure pseudofunction is zero for all water saturations. A similar approach can be used to generate segregated-flow pseudofunctions for gas/oil systems. Segregated-flow pseudofunctions probably are the most commonly used analytical pseudofunctions in reservoir simulation.

Example 10.5. For the grid system shown in **Fig. 10.31** and the relative permeability data from Example 10.2, calculate the segregated-flow pseudofunctions for oil/water flow. Remember, segregated flow implies a small transition-zone height and, consequently, low capillary pressure values.

Solution. The data in **Table 10.14** are obtained from the solution of Example 10.2. To solve this problem, we need to consider only the first three gridblocks because Gridblocks 4 through 6 have relative permeability pseudofunctions identical to that of Gridblock 3. This is discussed later. For the first three gridblocks, the height of the original OWC, measured from the bottom of the gridblock, is, for Gridblock 1, $h_{owc} = 66.7$ ft; for Gridblock 2, $h_{owc} = 33.3$ ft; and for Gridblock 3, $h_{owc} = 0.0$ ft.

Because the height of the contact is measured from the bottom of the gridblock, Gridblocks 4 through 6 also have OWC heights, h_{owc}, of 0.0 ft, which is why these gridblocks have relative permeability pseudofunctions identical to that of Gridblock 3.

Table 10.15 presents data occurring when the current OWC is at 4,700 ft. That is, the current OWC is equal to the initial OWC. This table shows that, initially, the gridblocks are unswept (all swept heights, h_s, equal 0) and the height of the unswept zone, h_u, is equal to gridblock height minus the height of the original OWC, h_{owc}.

For Gridblock 1,

$$\bar{S}_w = \frac{h_{owc} + (1 - S_{orw})h_s + S_{iw}h_u}{h_{owc} + h_s + h_u} \quad \text{.............} \quad (10.46)$$

$$= \frac{66.7 + (1 - 0.267)0.0 + (0.22)33.3}{100}$$

$$= 0.74,$$

$$k_{rop}(\bar{S}_w) = \frac{h_u}{\Delta z} k_{ro}(S_{iw}) \quad \text{.......................} \quad (10.51a)$$

$$= \frac{33.3}{100.0}(0.45)$$

$$= 0.15,$$

$$\text{and } k_{rwp}(\bar{S}_w) = \frac{h_{owc}}{\Delta z} k_{rw}(1.0) + \frac{h_s}{\Delta z} k_{rw}(1 - S_{orw}) \quad \text{....} \quad (10.56)$$

$$= \frac{66.7}{100}(1.0) + \frac{0.0}{100}(0.25)$$

$$= 0.667.$$

For Gridblock 2, with the same equations,

$$\bar{S}_w = \frac{33.3 + (1 - 0.267)0.0 + (0.22)66.7}{100}$$

$$= 0.48,$$

$$k_{rop}(\bar{S}_w) = \frac{66.7}{100}(0.45)$$

$$= 0.30,$$

$$\text{and } k_{rwp}(\bar{S}_w) = \frac{33.3}{100}(1.0) + \frac{0.0}{100}(0.25)$$

$$= 0.33.$$

For Gridblock 3, with the same equations,

$$\bar{S}_w = \frac{0.0 + (1 - 0.267)0.0 + (0.22)100}{100}$$

$$= 0.22,$$

$$k_{rop}(\bar{S}_w) = \frac{100}{100}(0.45)$$

$$= 0.45,$$

$$\text{and } k_{rwp}(\bar{S}_w) = \frac{0.0}{100}(1.0) + \frac{0.0}{100}(0.25)$$

$$= 0.0.$$

Table 10.16 tabulates the results for a current OWC at 4,680 ft. The results for other current OWC heights are tabulated in **Table 10.17** and plotted in **Figs. 10.32 and 10.33**. Note that these relative permeability pseudofunctions are straight lines that can be characterized by two points. For example, for gridblocks not cut by the initial OWC (Gridblocks 3 through 6), the pseudofunctions can be generated graphically by connecting the endpoints. In other words, $k_{rop}(\bar{S}_w)$ can be generated by connecting points $[S_{iw}, k_{ro}(S_{iw})]$ and $[(1 - S_{orw}), 0.0]$, while $k_{rwp}(\bar{S}_w)$ can be generated by connecting points $[S_{iw}, 0.0]$ and $[(1 - S_{orw}), k_{rw}(1 - S_{orw})]$.

This example also illustrates that, when pseudofunctions are used in a simulation study, gridblocks with similar properties need to be grouped (in this case, Gridblocks 3 through 6) to minimize the amount of work required to generate the pseudofunctions and to minimize the number of curves entered into the model. For this example, the gridblocks are grouped by the relative heights, $h_{owc}/\Delta z$, of the initial OWC.

VE Pseudofunctions. The VE-pseudofunction approach assumes that the reservoir fluids are in a continuous state of capillary/gravity equilibrium.[41] Consequently, VE pseudofunctions cannot be used in situations where viscous forces dominate, such as preferential depletion or displacement in stratified reservoirs. **Fig. 10.34** shows the situations where VE pseudofunctions are applicable. Note the water-over-oil situation in Layers 1 (topmost layer) and 2 in Fig. 10.34b.

Again, the volumetric-average-water-saturation equation, Eq. 10.45, is used to begin the process of generating the relative permeability and capillary pressure pseudofunctions. For the geologic layers shown in Fig. 10.34, the limits of integration used in Eq. 10.45

TABLE 10.17—SOLUTION TO EXAMPLE 10.5

Initial Setup

Initial OWC, ft	4,700	$k_{ro}\ (S_{iw})$	0.450
S_{iw}	0.220	$k_{rw}\ (1 - S_{orw})$	0.250
S_{orw}	0.267	$k_{rw}\ (1.0)$	1.000

	Gridblock					
	1	2	3	4	5	6
Gridblock top, ft	4,666.7	4,633.3	4,600.0	4,566.7	4,533.3	4,500.0
Thickness, ft	100.00	100.00	100.00	100.00	100.00	100.00
h_{owc}, ft	66.7	33.3	0.0	0.0	0.0	0.0
Current OWC, 4,700.0 ft						
h_s, ft	0.00	0.00	0.00	0.00	0.00	0.00
h_u, ft	33.33	66.67	100.00	100.00	100.00	100.00
$\overline{S}_w$, fraction	0.74	0.48	0.22	0.22	0.22	0.22
k_{rop}, fraction	0.15	0.30	0.45	0.45	0.45	0.45
k_{rwp}, fraction	0.67	0.33	0.00	0.00	0.00	0.00
Current OWC, 4,680.0 ft						
h_s, ft	20.00	20.00	20.00	0.00	0.00	0.00
h_u, ft	13.33	46.67	80.0	100.00	100.00	100.00
$\overline{S}_w$, fraction	0.84	0.58	0.32	0.22	0.22	0.22
k_{rop}, fraction	0.06	0.21	0.36	0.45	0.45	0.45
k_{rwp}, fraction	0.72	0.38	0.05	0.00	0.00	0.00
Current OWC, 4,660.0 ft						
h_s, ft	33.33	40.00	40.00	6.67	0.00	0.00
h_u, ft	0.00	26.67	60.0	93.33	100.00	100.00
$\overline{S}_w$, fraction	0.91	0.69	0.43	0.25	0.22	0.22
k_{rop}, fraction	0.00	0.12	0.27	0.42	0.45	0.45
k_{rwp}, fraction	0.75	0.43	0.10	0.02	0.00	0.00
Current OWC, 4,640.0 ft						
h_s, ft	33.33	60.00	60.00	26.67	0.00	0.00
h_u, ft	0.00	6.67	40.00	73.33	100.00	100.00
$\overline{S}_w$, fraction	0.91	0.79	0.53	0.36	0.22	0.22
k_{rop}, fraction	0.00	0.03	0.18	0.33	0.45	0.45
k_{rwp}, fraction	0.75	0.48	0.15	0.07	0.00	0.00
Current OWC, 4,620.0 ft						
h_s, ft	33.33	66.67	80.00	46.67	13.33	0.00
h_u, ft	0.00	0.00	20.00	53.33	86.67	100.00
$\overline{S}_w$, fraction	0.91	0.82	0.63	0.46	0.29	0.22
k_{rop}, fraction	0.00	0.00	0.09	0.24	0.39	0.45
k_{rwp}, fraction	0.75	0.50	0.20	0.12	0.03	0.00
Current OWC, 4,600.0 ft						
h_s, ft	33.33	66.67	100.00	66.67	33.33	0.00
h_u, ft	0.00	0.00	0.00	33.33	66.67	100.00
$\overline{S}_w$, fraction	0.91	0.82	0.73	0.56	0.39	0.22
k_{rop}, fraction	0.00	0.00	0.00	0.15	0.30	0.45
k_{rwp}, fraction	0.75	0.50	0.25	0.17	0.08	0.00
Current OWC, 4,580.0 ft						
h_s, ft	33.33	66.67	100.00	86.67	53.33	20.00
h_u, ft	0.00	0.00	0.00	13.33	46.67	80.00
$\overline{S}_w$, fraction	0.91	0.82	0.73	0.66	0.49	0.32
k_{rop}, fraction	0.00	0.00	0.00	0.06	0.21	0.36
k_{rwp}, fraction	0.75	0.50	0.25	0.22	0.13	0.05
Current OWC, 4,560.0 ft						
h_s, ft	33.33	66.67	100.00	100.00	73.33	40.00
h_u, ft	0.00	0.00	0.00	0.00	26.67	60.00
$\overline{S}_w$, fraction	0.91	0.82	0.73	0.73	0.60	0.43
k_{rop}, fraction	0.00	0.00	0.00	0.00	0.12	0.27
k_{rwp}, fraction	0.75	0.50	0.25	0.25	0.18	0.10

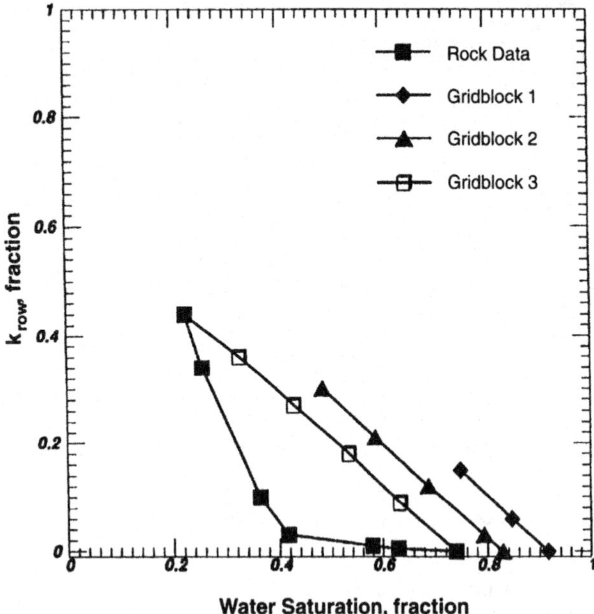

Fig. 10.32—Segregated-flow pseudofunctions for Example 10.5.

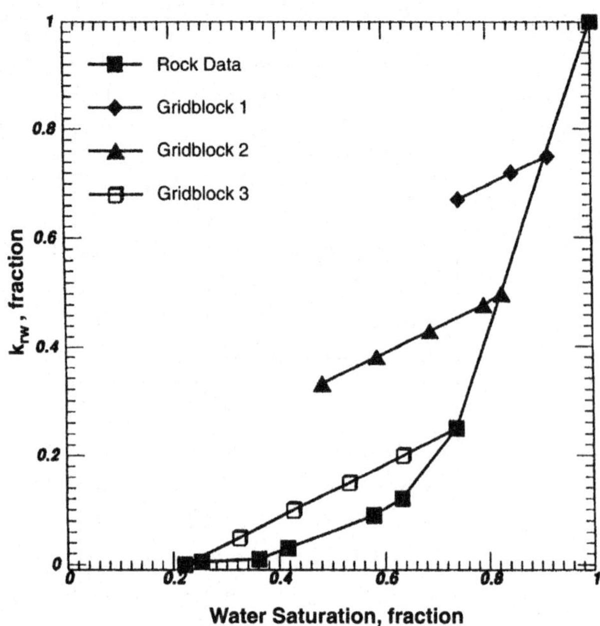

Fig. 10.33—Segregated-flow pseudofunctions for Example 10.5.

can be assigned at each geologic boundary, h_k. This results in a volumetric average water saturation described by

$$\overline{S}_w = \frac{\sum_{k=1}^{n_k} \phi_k S_{w_k} h_k}{\sum_{k=1}^{n_k} \phi_k h_k}, \qquad (10.57)$$

where Subscript k refers to the geologic layer within the simulation gridblock.

The values of porosity, ϕ_k, and thickness, h_k, for the geologic layers in Eq. 10.57 can be obtained from well log or core data, while the water saturation is obtained from the capillary pressure curve. This is done by use of the fundamental assumption of VE pseudofunctions: continuous capillary/gravity equilibrium. Capillary/gravity equilibrium is defined by

$$P_{c_k} = (\gamma_w - \gamma_o) h_k^*, \qquad (10.58)$$

where $\gamma_l = \gamma_c \rho_l g$ for $l = o$ or w and h_k^* = height of center of Layer k above the OWC.

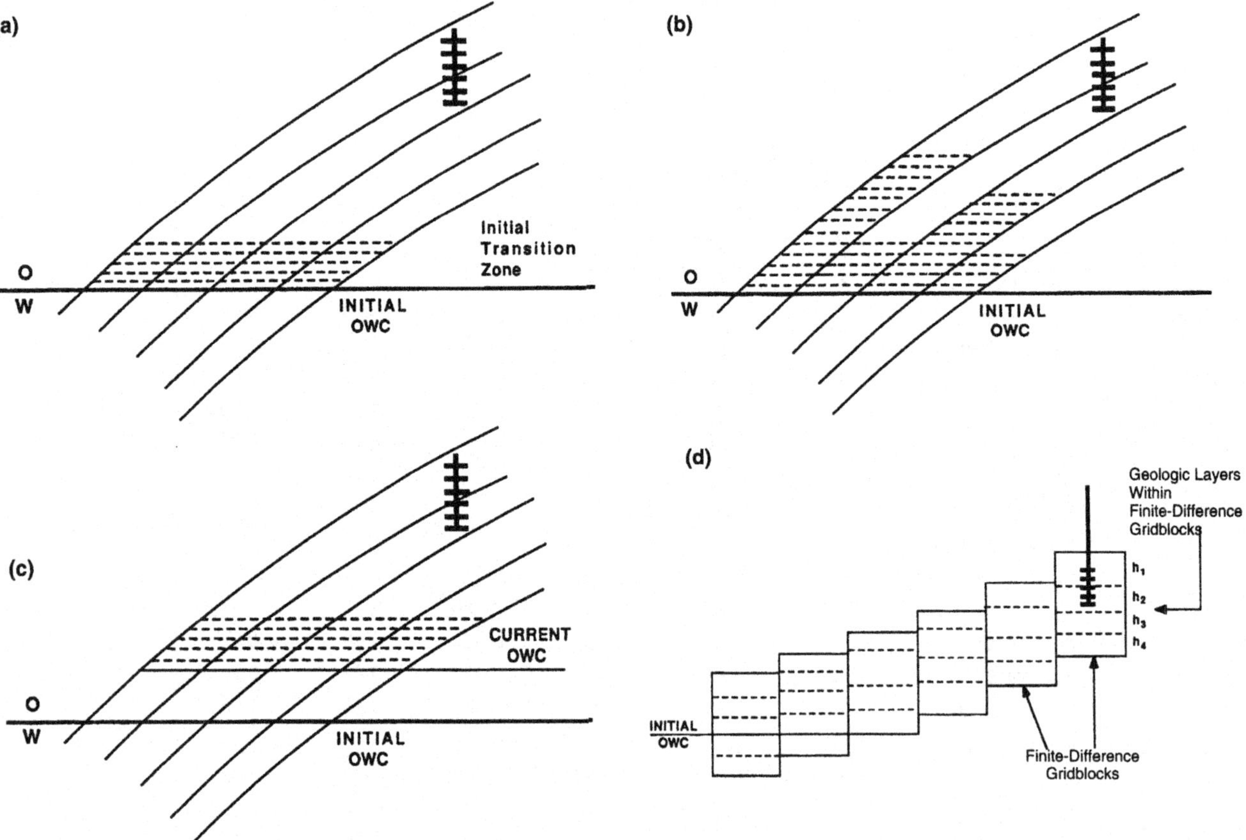

Fig. 10.34—VE-pseudofunction applications: (a) initial conditions; (b) preferential depletion, VE pseudofunctions are not applicable; (c) capillary/gravity equilibrium, VE pseudofunctions are applicable; and (d) grid system used to generate VE pseudofunctions.

If we substitute the height of the centers of the geologic layers above the OWC in Eq. 10.58 for h_k^*, then we can use the resultant value of P_c to determine the appropriate water saturations from the rock P_c curve, S_{w_k}, to use in Eq. 10.57. This procedure gives the average water saturation of the simulation gridblock.

To obtain the expressions for the relative permeability pseudofunctions, we write Darcy's law for each Phase l in the geologic layers.

$$q_{l_k} = \frac{\beta_c k_{rl}\left(S_{w_k}\right) k_{H_k} \Delta y h_k}{\mu_l} \frac{\Delta \Phi_l}{\Delta x}, \quad \text{(10.59)}$$

where $l = o$ or w, while Darcy's law for flow through the gridblock is

$$q_{lc} = \frac{\beta_c k_{rlp}(\bar{S}_w) k_H \Delta y \Delta z}{\mu_l} \frac{\Delta \Phi_l}{\Delta x}, \quad \text{(10.60)}$$

where $l = o$ or w. In addition,

$$q_{lc} = \sum_{k=1}^{n_k} q_{l_k} \quad \text{(10.61)}$$

$$\text{and } \Delta z = \sum_{k=1}^{n_k} h_k. \quad \text{(10.62)}$$

Combining Eqs. 10.59 through 10.62 results in

$$k_{rlp}(\bar{S}_w) = \frac{\sum_{k=1}^{n_k} k_{rl}\left(S_{w_k}\right) k_{H_k} h_k}{\sum_{k=1}^{n_k} k_{H_k} h_k}, \quad \text{(10.63)}$$

where $l = o$ or w and $k_{rlp}(\bar{S}_w)$ = relative permeability pseudofunction for Phase l at $\bar{S}_w$.

VE pseudofunctions can be generated with the following algorithm.

1. For each simulation gridblock, calculate the capillary pressure for each geologic layer within the gridblock using Eq. 10.58 and the height of the center of the geologic layer. For the geologic layers below OWC, $S_w = 1$, $k_{rw} = 1$, and $k_{ro} = 0$.
2. For each geologic layer within the simulation gridblock, calculate the water saturation, S_{w_k}, with the capillary pressure curve.
3. For each simulation gridblock, calculate a value of $\bar{S}_w$ with Eq. 10.57.
4. For each simulation gridblock, obtain $k_{ro}(S_{w_k})$ and $k_{rw}(S_{w_k})$ for all geologic layers and calculate the relative permeability pseudofunctions for oil and water with Eq. 10.63.
5. For each simulation gridblock, calculate the capillary pressure pseudofunction using the height of the center of the simulation gridblock in Eq. 10.58.
6. Plot the relative permeability and capillary pressure pseudofunctions vs. the gridblock average water saturation from Step 3. Each gridblock will yield one point on the pseudofunction curve. If more points are required, the initial OWC can be moved up and down arbitrarily to generate additional points.

Example 10.6. For the grid system in **Fig. 10.35** and with the rock properties given in **Table 10.18**, the relative permeability data from Example 10.2, and the capillary pressure data from Example 10.3, calculate the VE pseudofunctions for oil/water flow. Note that the grid system in this example is identical to that in Example 10.5. In this example, however, the effects of the capillary transition zone are incorporated into the pseudofunctions. In addition, the geologic sublayers are used. Assume $\rho_w = 65.0$ lbm/ft^3 and $\rho_o = 53.0$ lbm/ft^3.

Solution. The capillary pressure in Geologic Layer 1 can be obtained from Eq. 10.58.

$$P_c = (\gamma_w - \gamma_o)h^*, \quad \text{(10.64)}$$

where h^* = height above the OWC and $\gamma = \gamma_c \rho g$. Therefore,

$$\gamma_w = \left(0.21584 \times 10^{-3}\right)65.0 \times 32.174 = 0.4514 \text{ psi/ft},$$

$$\gamma_o = \left(0.21584 \times 10^{-3}\right)53.0 \times 32.174 = 0.3680 \text{ psi/ft},$$

$$\text{and } P_c = (0.4514 - 0.3680)(33.3/2) = 1.39 \text{ psi}.$$

In this expression, the height to the center of Layer 1 is equal to one-half the layer thickness because the OWC lies at the base of the geologic layer. Interpolating the capillary pressure data to obtain the corresponding S_w results in

$$\frac{1.39 - 1.177}{S_w - 0.626} = \frac{1.413 - 1.177}{0.573 - 0.626}$$

and $S_w = 0.578$. This is the water saturation in Layer 1 under VE conditions. Interpolating k_{ro} values with this value of S_w results in

$$\frac{0.578 - 0.573}{k_{ro} - 0.009} = \frac{0.626 - 0.573}{0.003 - 0.009}$$

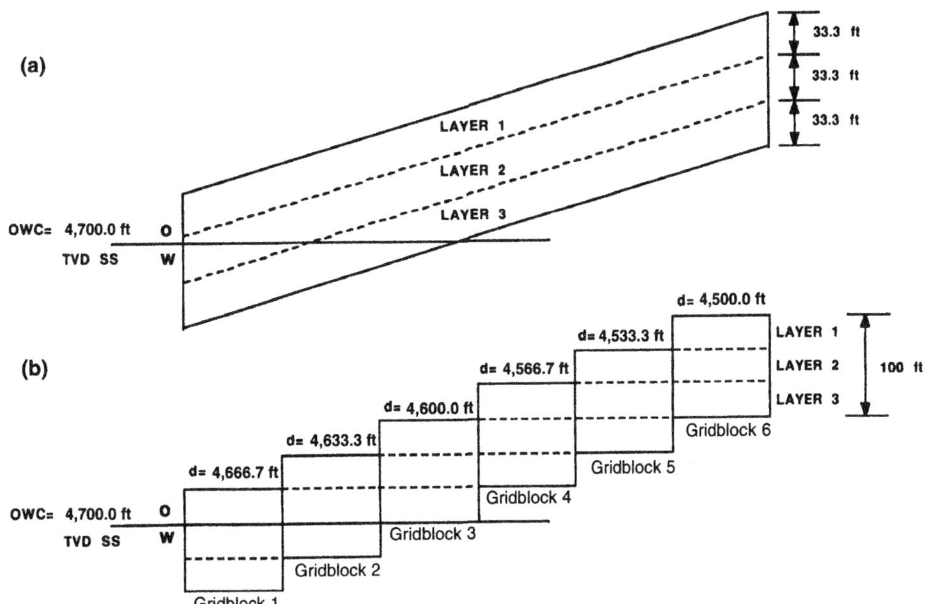

Fig. 10.35—(a) Reservoir and (b) finite-difference grid for VE pseudofunctions for Example 10.6.

TABLE 10.18—DATA AND INITIAL SETUP INFORMATION FOR EXAMPLE 10.6

Initial OWC, ft	4,700					
Oil density, lbm/ft^3	53.0					
Water density, lbm/ft^3	65.0					
	Gridblock					
	1	2	3	4	5	6
Gridblock top, ft	4,666.7	4,633.3	4,600.0	4,566.7	4,533.3	4,500.0
h_1, ft	33.3	33.3	33.3	33.3	33.3	33.3
ϕ_1, fraction	0.25	0.25	0.25	0.25	0.25	0.25
k_{H1}, md	300.0	300.0	300.0	300.0	300.0	300.0
h_2, ft	33.3	33.3	33.3	33.3	33.3	33.3
ϕ_2, fraction	0.23	0.25	0.25	0.25	0.25	0.23
k_{H2}, md	250.0	250.0	250.0	250.0	250.0	250.0
h_3, ft	33.3	33.3	33.3	33.3	33.3	33.3
ϕ_3, fraction	0.20	0.20	0.20	0.20	0.20	0.20
k_{H3}, md	200.0	200.0	200.0	200.0	200.0	200.0

and $k_{ro} = 0.008$. Similarly, for k_{rw} in Layer 1,

$$\frac{0.578 - 0.573}{k_{rw} - 0.090} = \frac{0.626 - 0.573}{0.125 - 0.090}$$

and $k_{rw} = 0.094$. Both Geologic Layers 2 and 3 are below the OWC; therefore, $S_w = 1.0$, $k_{ro} = 0.0$, and $k_{rw} = 1.0$.

Now, the average water saturation in Gridblock 1 can be calculated from Eq. 10.57 as

$$\bar{S}_w = \frac{h_1\phi_1 S_{w1} + h_2\phi_2 S_{w2} + h_3\phi_3 S_{w3}}{h_1\phi_1 + h_2\phi_2 + h_3\phi_3} \quad \text{............ (10.65)}$$

$$= [(33.0)(0.25)(0.578) + (33.3)(0.23)(1.0)$$

$$+ (33.3)(0.20)(1.0)]/[(33.3)(0.25) + (33.3)(0.23)$$

$$+ (33.3)(0.20)]$$

$$= 0.844.$$

The relative permeability pseudofunction for oil for Gridblock 1 can be obtained from Eq. 10.63 as

$$k_{rop}(\bar{S}_w) = \frac{h_1 k_{ro}(S_{w1})k_{H_1} + h_2 k_{ro}(S_{w2})k_{H_2} + h_3 k_{ro}(S_{w3})k_{H_3}}{h_1 k_{H_1} + h_2 k_{H_2} + h_3 k_{H_3}}$$

$$\text{.................... (10.66)}$$

$$= [(33.0)(0.008)(300) + (33.3)(0.0)(250)$$

$$+ (33.3)(0.0)(200)]/[(33.3)(300) + (33.3)(250)$$

$$+ (33.3)(200)]$$

$$= 0.003$$

and, similarly for $k_{rwp}(\bar{S}_w)$,

TABLE 10.19—SOLUTION TO EXAMPLE 10.6 AT CURRENT OWC OF 4,700 ft

	Gridblock					
	1	2	3	4	5	6
P_{c_1}, psi	1.390	4.170	6.940	9.720	12.500	15.280
S_{w_1}	0.578	0.308	0.240	0.220	0.220	0.220
k_{ro_1}	0.008	0.214	0.381	0.450	0.450	0.450
k_{rw_1}	0.094	0.005	0.001	0.000	0.000	0.000
P_{c_2}, psi	—	1.390	4.170	6.940	9.720	12.500
S_{w_2}	1.000	0.578	0.308	0.240	0.220	0.220
k_{ro_2}	0.000	0.008	0.214	0.381	0.450	0.450
k_{rw_2}	1.000	0.094	0.005	0.001	0.000	0.000
P_{c_3}, psi	—	—	1.390	4.170	6.940	9.720
S_{w_3}	1.000	1.000	0.578	0.308	0.240	0.220
k_{ro_3}	0.000	0.000	0.008	0.214	0.381	0.450
k_{rw_3}	1.000	1.000	0.094	0.005	0.001	0.000
P_{cp}, psi	−1.390	1.390	4.170	6.940	9.720	12.500
$\bar{S}_w$	0.844	0.602	0.361	0.252	0.226	0.220
k_{rop}	0.003	0.088	0.226	0.364	0.432	0.450
k_{rwp}	0.638	0.300	0.027	0.002	0.000	0.000

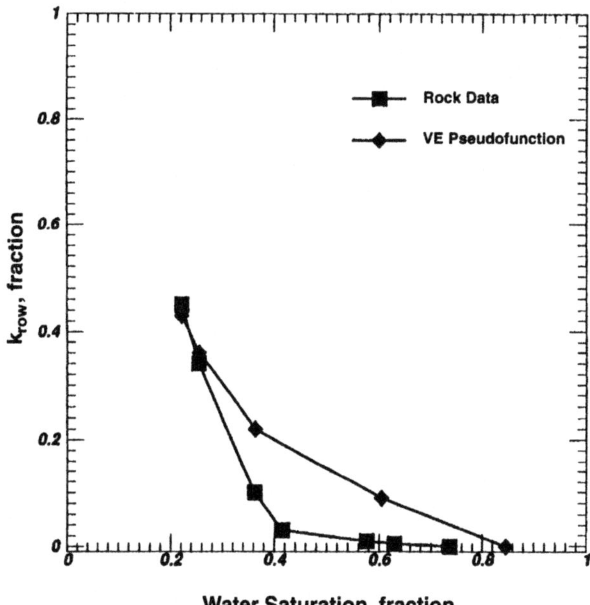

Fig. 10.36—VE pseudofunction for Example 10.6.

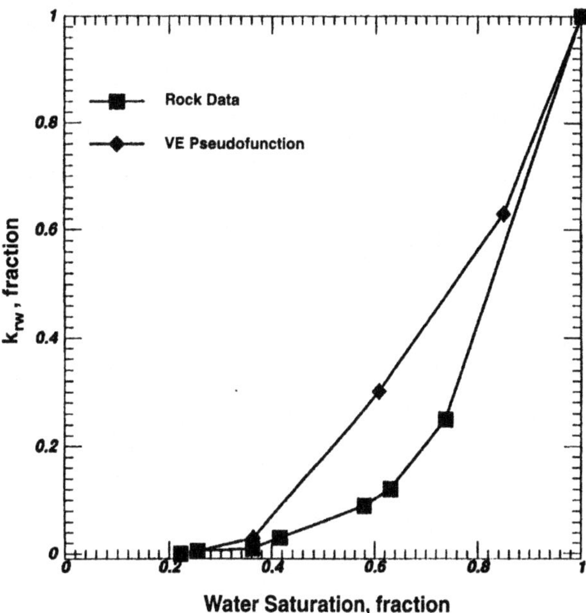

Fig. 10.37—VE pseudofunction for Example 10.6.

$$k_{rwp}(\overline{S}_w) = \frac{h_1 k_{rw}(S_{w1}) k_{H_1} + h_2 k_{rw}(S_{w2}) k_{H_2} + h_3 k_{rw}(S_{w3}) k_{H_3}}{h_1 k_{H_1} + h_2 k_{H_2} + h_3 k_{H_3}} \quad \text{.................... (10.67)}$$

$$= [(33.0)(0.094)(300) + (33.3)(1.0)(250)$$

$$+ (33.3)(1.0)(200)]/[(33.3)(300) + (33.3)(250)$$

$$+ (33.3)(200)]$$

$$= 0.638.$$

The capillary pressure pseudofunction is obtained using the distance from the gridblock center to the OWC, which completes the calculations for Gridblock 1.

$$P_{cp}(\overline{S}_w) = (\gamma_w - \gamma_o)\left[Z_{owc} - \left(Z_{top} + \frac{\Delta z}{2}\right)\right] \quad \text{........ (10.68)}$$

$$= (0.4514 - 0.3680)\left[4,700 - \left(4,666.7 + \frac{100}{2}\right)\right]$$

$$= -1.39 \text{ psi}.$$

These calculations yield one water saturation with one corresponding value of k_{rop}, k_{rwp}, and P_{cp}. Additional points can be obtained from the other gridblocks. **Table 10.19** tabulates these calculations.

In this example, the gridblock saturations span the entire range of water saturations. If additional water-saturation points are required, the OWC can be raised or lowered arbitrarily, as in Example 10.5. **Figs. 10.36 through 10.38** present these results.

Also note that, in this example, all the gridblocks have identical geologic-layer properties. If the gridblocks have significantly different geologic-layer properties, the gridblocks with similar properties need to be grouped together to generate the pseudofunctions. In the segregated-flow pseudofunctions, Example 10.5, the grouping criterion was the relative height of the initial OWC, $Z_{owc}/\Delta z$. For the VE pseudofunctions, the grouping criteria were the properties of the geologic layers within the gridblock.

Dynamic Interblock Pseudofunctions. The use of the analytical-pseudofunction approach requires that fundamental assumptions regarding reservoir behavior be met. These assumptions are used to derive the appropriate equations that describe interblock flow. Consequently, analytical pseudofunctions can be applied only in situations where the fundamental assumptions are valid. No single analytical-interblock-pseudofunction approach is universally applicable; however, the dynamic-pseudofunction approach is universally applicable. Although this approach is universally applicable, it is much more resource intensive than the analytical-pseudofunction approach because it requires construction of additional representative, cross-sectional simulation models.

The most common dynamic-pseudofunction approach used in reservoir simulation is the Kyte and Berry[42] approach. In this approach, the additional cross-sectional models required in the pseudofunction development are a fine-grid model (with a grid size that is much finer than the grid size of the full-field model), and a coarse-grid model (with a grid size equal to that used in the full-field model). The grid size of the fine-grid model is chosen so its grid layering is appropriate for rock relative permeability curves and capillary pressure curves, and the grid-cell boundaries of the cells coincide with the grid boundaries expected in the coarse-grid, cross-sectional and the full-field models.

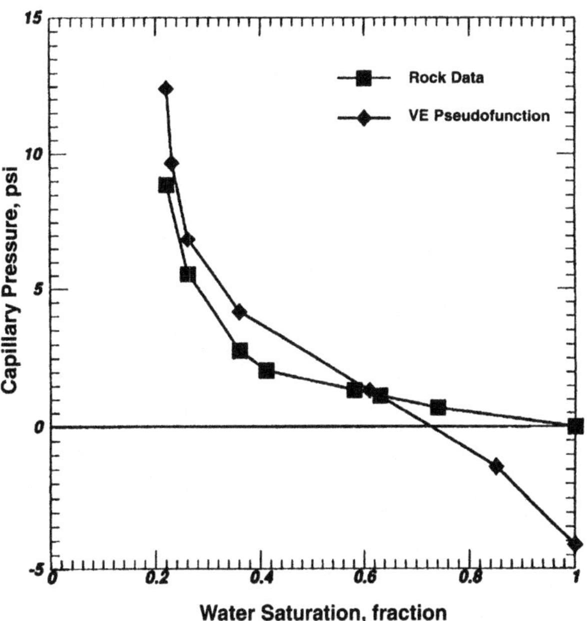

Fig. 10.38—VE pseudofunction for Example 10.6.

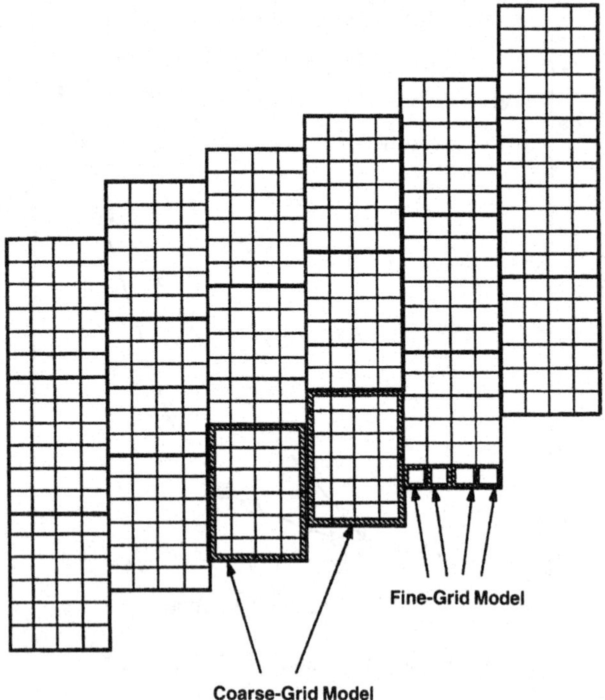

Fig. 10.39—Cross-sectional model to be used in generating dynamic interblock pseudofunctions.

The coarse-grid model is used to validate the pseudofunctions once they have been generated. **Fig. 10.39** shows a typical cross-sectional model used for the generation of dynamic interblock pseudofunctions.

The dynamic pseudofunctions are generated from the results of the fine-grid model. The fine-grid model may need to be run for a longer time period than the anticipated duration of the full-field model to ensure that the entire range of the pseudofunctions is adequate for the full-field simulation. During the fine-grid simulation run, the pressures, saturations, and fluid rates for each timestep are stored for post-processing.

Once the fine-grid cross-sectional model has been run, the results are averaged over the boundaries of the coarse-grid, cross-sectional model. This is accomplished by averaging only those results that fall within the boundaries of a coarse-grid cell and by assuming that these averaged results are representative of this cell. At this point, the averaged results can be assumed only to be representative of the coarse-grid cell because the coarse-grid model has not yet been run. This averaging process is performed for each coarse-grid cell for each timestep with PV-weighted averages.

$$\overline{p}_{lc} = \frac{\sum_{g_c} p_{lf} V_{pf}}{\sum_{g_c} V_{pf}}, \quad \text{(10.69)}$$

where $l = o$, w, or g for the average coarse-grid-cell phase pressure and

$$\overline{S}_{lc} = \frac{\sum_{g_c} S_{lf} V_{pf}}{\sum_{g_c} V_{pf}}, \quad \text{(10.70)}$$

where $l = o$, w, or g for the average coarse-grid-cell phase saturation.

In addition, the phase flow rates across the boundaries of the coarse-grid cells are summed from the fine-grid model for each phase in all coarse-grid cells. That is,

$$q_{lc} = \sum_{g_{cb}} q_{lf}, \quad \text{(10.71)}$$

where $l = o$, w, or g.

Rearranging Darcy's law for the coarse-grid cells (Eq. 10.60) results in the final expression for the dynamic pseudofunctions.

$$k_{rlp}(\overline{S}_l) = \frac{q_{lc}\mu_l \Delta x}{\beta_c k_H \Delta z \Delta y \Delta \Phi_l}, \quad \text{(10.72)}$$

where $l = o$, w, or g. In Eq. 10.72, the grid dimensions, Δx, Δy, and Δz, are the dimensions of the coarse grid.

The capillary pressure pseudofunction can be determined by the phase pressures

$$P_{cowp}(\overline{S}_w) = \overline{p}_{oc} - \overline{p}_{wc} \quad \text{(10.73)}$$

and $P_{cgop}(\overline{S}_g) = \overline{p}_{gc} - \overline{p}_{oc}$. (10.74)

This process is repeated for each coarse-grid cell for each timestep. Generally, the pseudofunctions are plotted for each coarse-grid cell. The results of each timestep provide one point on the coarse-grid-cell pseudofunction curve. The pseudofunction curves for all coarse-grid cells are grouped and one pseudofunction curve is chosen to represent a particular group of coarse-grid cells. Alternatively, these curves can be normalized and averaged with the techniques described in Sec. 10.3.2. The representative pseudofunction curves are assigned to the coarse-grid cross-sectional model, and the model is run to validate the pseudofunctions.

No assumptions are required to generate the dynamic interblock pseudofunctions because any fine-grid model can be constructed to represent the given reservoir geology and all reservoir mechanisms are considered in the fine-grid model. These dynamic interblock pseudofunctions are valid only for the cross section in which they were generated. Therefore, several representative cross sections may be required for a simulation study. Also, if the cross sections change (e.g., drilling of in-fill wells), the pseudofunctions may need to be regenerated.

Selection of Interblock Pseudofunctions. The selection of the proper interblock pseudofunctions to use in the simulation model requires some knowledge of the reservoir under study. The following rules can be used to determine which type of pseudofunctions to choose for a particular study.

If the grid-cell thicknesses are large compared with the capillary transition zone, segregated-flow pseudofunctions can be used. If the grid-cell thicknesses are approximately equal to the height of the capillary transition zone and viscous forces are not dominant, VE pseudofunctions can be used. Finally, if the grid-cell thicknesses are

TABLE 10.20—RECOMMENDED INTERBLOCK CURVES

Relative Permeability and Capillary Pressure Curves	Applicability	Additional Considerations
Rock curves	$h_{tz} \gg \Delta z$	
VE pseudofunctions	$h_{tz} \approx \Delta z$	Continuous capillary/gravity equilibrium exists. Viscous forces are not dominant.
Segregated-flow pseudofunctions	$h_{tz} \ll \Delta z$	Negligible capillary pressure.
Dynamic pseudofunctions	Universally applicable	Requires additional cross-sectional models. Only valid for the cross sections used in the cross-sectional models.

small compared with the transition-zone thickness, then the rock curves are appropriate. Dynamic pseudofunctions can be used in all cases. Generation of the dynamic pseudofunctions, however, requires additional cross-sectional modeling. **Table 10.20** provides a tabular form for these recommendations.

Well Pseudofunctions. Interblock pseudofunctions describe the flow of fluids from one gridblock to adjacent gridblocks. These pseudofunctions, however, do not necessarily describe flow from the gridblock to the wellbore. Well pseudofunctions are used to describe flow to the wellbore. The analytical-pseudofunction approaches discussed in the previous sections can be applied directly to well pseudofunctions, with the geometry of the wellbore replacing the interblock geometry. Emmanuel and Cook[43] developed a procedure for the generation of dynamic, well pseudofunctions that is similar to the Kyte and Berry[42] approach. In this approach, single-well radial models (r-z) are used instead of the cross-sectional models.

If both interblock and well pseudofunctions are used in a study, gridblocks containing well completions will have two sets of relative permeability and capillary pressure curves: a set for interblock calculations and a set for inflow-performance calculations.

Assignment of Well Properties to Grid Cells. *Field-Measured Productivity Indices.* In Chap. 6, the treatment of wells in reservoir simulation was discussed and the analytical expression for well inflow performance was derived as Eq. 6.23 for single-phase flow. For multiphase flow, the corresponding equation is

$$q_{lsc} = \frac{-2\pi\beta_c k_H k_{rl} h}{B_l\mu_l} \frac{1}{\left[\log_e(r_e/r_w) - F + s_t\right]}\left(\bar{p} - p_{wf}\right), \qquad (10.75a)$$

where $l = o$ or w, $F = 0.5$ for steady-state flow, and $F = 0.75$ for pseudosteady-state flow. A similar equation can be written for the gas phase that includes both free and solution gas.

Eq. 10.75a can be written as

$$q_{lsc} = -J_{wl}\left(\bar{p} - p_{wf}\right), \qquad (10.75b)$$

where $l = o$ or w and J_{wl} = well productivity index for Phase l defined by

$$J_{wl} = \frac{2\pi\beta_c k_H k_{rl} h}{B_l\mu_l} \frac{1}{\left[\log_e(r_e/r_w) - F + s_t\right]}, \qquad (10.76)$$

where $l = o$ or w.

Peaceman[24-26] showed that, in reservoir simulation, the inflow performance is given by

$$q_{lsc} = \frac{-2\pi\beta_c k_H k_{rl} h}{B_l\mu_l} \frac{1}{\left[\log_e(r_{eq}/r_w) + s_s\right]}\left(p_o - p_{wf}\right), \qquad (10.77a)$$

where $l = o$ or w, or by

$$q_{lsc} = \frac{-k_{rl}}{B_l\mu_l} G_w\left(p_o - p_{wf}\right), \qquad (10.77b)$$

where $l = o$ or w, G_w = well geometric factor, and r_{eq} in Eq. 10.77a is given by the expression

$$r_{eq} = 0.28 \frac{\left[\left(k_x/k_y\right)^{1/2}(\Delta y)^2 + \left(k_y/k_x\right)^{1/2}(\Delta x)^2\right]^{1/2}}{\left(k_x/k_y\right)^{1/4} + \left(k_y/k_x\right)^{1/4}}. \qquad (10.78)$$

Because r_{eq} is dependent on the grid dimensions Δx and Δy, the constant part of the well-inflow-performance equation that is defined by

$$G_w = 2\pi\beta_c k_H h \frac{1}{\left[\log_e(r_{eq}/r_w) + s_s\right]} \qquad (10.79)$$

also depends on the grid size. In Eq. 10.79, s_s is the skin factor that is appropriate for reservoir simulation and may be different from total skin, s_t, used in Eq. 10.76.

Most commercial simulators have Eqs. 10.78 and 10.79 incorporated into the well-management routines, and these equations can be used to supply default values if no information regarding the well is known (e.g., for wells that have not been tested or for wells that will be drilled during the prediction phase of the study). If, however, the well has been tested and the field-measured productivity index is to be incorporated into the simulation models, the well geometric factor must be calculated from field measurements. Eqs. 10.76 and 10.79 may be combined to give

$$\frac{G_w}{J_{wl}} = \frac{B_l\mu_l}{k_{rl}} \frac{\left[\log_e(r_e/r_w) - F + s_t\right]}{\left[\log_e(r_{eq}/r_w) + s_s\right]}, \qquad (10.80a)$$

where $l = o$ or w, or

$$G_w = \frac{B_l\mu_l}{k_{rl}} \frac{\left[\log_e(r_e/r_w) - F + s_t\right]}{\left[\log_e(r_{eq}/r_w) + s_s\right]} J_{wl}, \qquad (10.80b)$$

where $l = o$ or w. J_{wl} = field-measured well productivity index for Phase l (obtained from Eq. 10.75b); and B_l, μ_l, and k_{rl} = values of the phase properties at the time the well test was performed.

The well geometric factors, G_w, calculated to this point are valid for the entire well. The reservoir model, however, requires values for the individual simulation layers. One simple method of assigning the well geometric factor to individual layers is by a simple weighting scheme. The well geometric factor for Simulation Layer k can be obtained by

$$G_{w_k} = \frac{\dfrac{k_{H_k}\Delta z_k}{\left[\log_e(r_{eq}/r_w) + s_k\right]}}{\displaystyle\sum_i^{n_k} \frac{k_{Hi}\Delta z_i}{\left[\log_e(r_{eq}/r_w) + s_i\right]}} G_w. \qquad (10.81)$$

Note that, if the skin factors in all the simulation layers are assumed equal, Eq. 10.81 simplifies to simple $k_H\Delta z$ weighting. However, if the different layers in the actual wellbore can be isolated mechanically during the well test and individual total skin factors can be obtained for each layer, these skin factors can be used directly in Eq. 10.81.

Derived Productivity Indices. If Eq. 10.79 is to be used directly with skin factors derived from pressure-transient analysis, additional manipulation may be required. In 2D areal models, the skin value measured from a well test is appropriate and no adjustments are required. In multilayer simulation models, however, the proper skin factor for simulation must be backcalculated from the measured field value.

The total skin factor, s_t, is made up of the mechanical skin factor, s_m, and the skin caused by partial penetration, s_p. That is,

$$s_t = s_m + s_p. \qquad (10.82)$$

In a multilayer reservoir model, the pressure drop caused by partial penetration is, to some extent, accounted for in the simulator and a scaled version of the mechanical skin is appropriate. Rearranging Eq. 10.82 results in

$$s_m = s_t - s_p. \qquad (10.83)$$

The simulation skin value, s_s, can be assigned by scaling it to the permeability-thickness product, $k_H h$, obtained in the well test.

$$s_s = \frac{\displaystyle\sum_{k=1}^{n_k} \Delta z_k k_{H_k}}{\overline{k_H h}} s_m, \qquad (10.84)$$

where $\overline{k_H h}$ = permeability-thickness product determined from the well test. The use of Eq. 10.84 ensures that pressure drops in the simulation model equal the pressure drops in the actual well. It is now obvious why the total skin factor is appropriate for areal models while the mechanical skin factor is appropriate for multilayer models. Contrary to multilayer models, 2D areal models do not account for the pressure drop caused by partial penetration.

A similar procedure also may be required for condensate reservoirs in cases where the total skin factor from pressure-transient analysis exhibits a component resulting from liquid dropout. Because the physics of this skin mechanism are included in both 2D and 3D compositional simulation models, this component must also be removed from the total skin factor. The general rule is that, if the physics of the skin mechanism are included in the physics of the simulation model (in both the input data and the simulator itself), then that component of skin must be removed from the total skin measured in the field. In other words, only those components of the total skin with mechanisms excluded from the physics of the model should be included in the simulation skin factors, s_S.

10.5 History Matching

Previous sections of this chapter discussed the sources of the raw data required for a simulation model and the techniques for handling these data in the construction of a reservoir model. These techniques are used during the model-construction phase of the simulation study to provide the best estimates for the input data for the reservoir model of the field under study. These techniques, however, can be used only for data available from the relatively few wellbores that penetrate the reservoir. The vast majority of the reservoir remains unknown to the engineers and geologists working on the simulation study. Therefore, these initial data generally need to be adjusted, or tuned, for the simulation model to predict reservoir performance adequately. These data adjustments are performed during the history-matching phase of the simulation study.

Fig. 10.40 shows the steps performed during a history match. This procedure should lead to improved predictions from the simulation model; however, there is one detrimental feature to this procedure, as with any history-matching process. The final history-matched model is not unique. In other words, several different history-matched models may provide equally acceptable matches to past reservoir performance but may yield significantly different future predictions. There is no way to avoid this problem, but matching as much production data as available and adjusting only the least known reservoir data within acceptable ranges should yield a better match.

Although there are no rules for conducting a history match, several features are common to all successful history-matching exercises. The engineers, geologists, and operations staff of the subject field should be involved intimately in the history-matching phase of the simulation study. The role of the field staff should be to define the confidence intervals for the production data being matched (Step 3 in Fig. 10.40), to help select the reservoir data to be adjusted, and to determine the acceptable range for adjustment of the reservoir data (Step 4 in Fig. 10.40). In addition, the field staff should provide knowledge of the field that the simulation engineer may not have.

Ideally, only data that are least accurately known in the field or those not measured at reservoir scale should be changed during the history match. These data should be adjusted only within the acceptable limits defined by the field engineers and geologists.

Although relative permeability can be a powerful history-matching parameter, it should be used only as a last resort. The best approximation for relative permeability should be incorporated during the model-construction phase of the study and, if possible, should not be modified unless technically justified (for reasons other than to match past performance). This point is discussed in detail later.

10.5.1 Objectives of History Matching. The primary objectives of history matching are to improve and to validate the reservoir simulation model. In general, the use of the initial simulation input data does not match historical reservoir performance to a level that is acceptable for making accurate future forecasts. To improve the quality of the match, the iterative procedure shown in Fig. 10.40 can be used to adjust the initial simulation data systematically to provide an improved match. Once the historical production data are matched, a much greater confidence can be placed in the predictions made with the model.

There are also several beneficial byproducts or secondary objectives of a successful history match. The history-matching process invariably leads to a better understanding of the processes occurring in the reservoir. Levels of aquifer support, paths of fluid migration, and areas of bypassed oil can be identified during the history-matching phase of a simulation study. In addition, communication between different well pairs and reservoir areas are identified. This improved understanding is a result of the required observation of how changes in reservoir data affect simulated production.

A successful history match can identify opportunities to improve the reservoir description and the data-acquisition program. For example, it may become apparent during the history match that the simulation model is sensitive to data that are not currently available. These data can be collected in the field to improve the history match, model predictions, and general understanding of the reservoir.

Finally, the history-matching procedure may identify unusual operating conditions. For example, if the water cut or GOR from an individual well appears to go against areal trends, problems (such as behind-pipe communication) may be identified. Also, if production from an individual well appears to be significantly lower than that from offset wells, reservoir damage (skin) or mechanical wellbore problems may be suspected. On a field scale, areas of bypassed oil may be identified that can aid in an in-fill drilling program. Problems of this type are identified easily during a history match because the history-matching process forces the engineer to look for areal and temporal trends in production data that may be overlooked otherwise.

10.5.2 Selection of History-Matching Method. Two approaches are commonly used for the history-matching process: manual and automatic history matching. Of the two methods, manual history matching is used more often.

Manual history matching involves running the simulation model for the historical period and comparing the results to the known field behavior. Once the results of the history-match run are compared with field performance, the reservoir engineer can adjust the simulation data in an effort to improve the match. In the manual history-matching process, selection of the input data to adjust is made by the simulation engineer and requires knowledge of the field under study, engineering judgment, and reservoir-engineering experience. If the engineer performing the study does not have first-hand experience with the field, selection of reservoir data to adjust should be made with the aid of the field operations staff.

Automatic history matching is identical to manual history matching except that computer logic is used to adjust the reservoir data rather than direct engineering intervention. One detrimental feature of the automatic history-matching process is that it excludes the engineer from the history-matching phase of the simulation study. Consequently, the use of automatic history matching may remove engineering judgment and specific knowledge of the subject reservoir from the history match. For example, computer logic would not be able to identify wells undergoing behind-pipe communication but would blindly attempt to match higher water cuts or GOR's by adjusting reservoir data. Thus, even if an automatic history-matching procedure is used in a simulation study, the reservoir engineer must review the history-match results critically.

There are many approaches to automatic history matching, and each one attempts to minimize an error function (objective function). The error function is defined as a function of the difference between the observed reservoir performance and the simulated reservoir performance during the historical production period. The error function has the form

$$S_{\epsilon 2} = \sum_{i=1}^{n_{parm}} \left[w_i (X_{io} - X_{is})^2 \right], \quad \text{.................. (10.85)}$$

where X_i refers to any production parameters that are to be matched during the history-matching phase of the study. These production parameters are defined in Step 3 in Fig. 10.40 and may include static reservoir pressures, water cuts, GOR's, and breakthrough times, among others.

The automatic history-matching approach requires that the simulation model be run many times with slight adjustments to the input

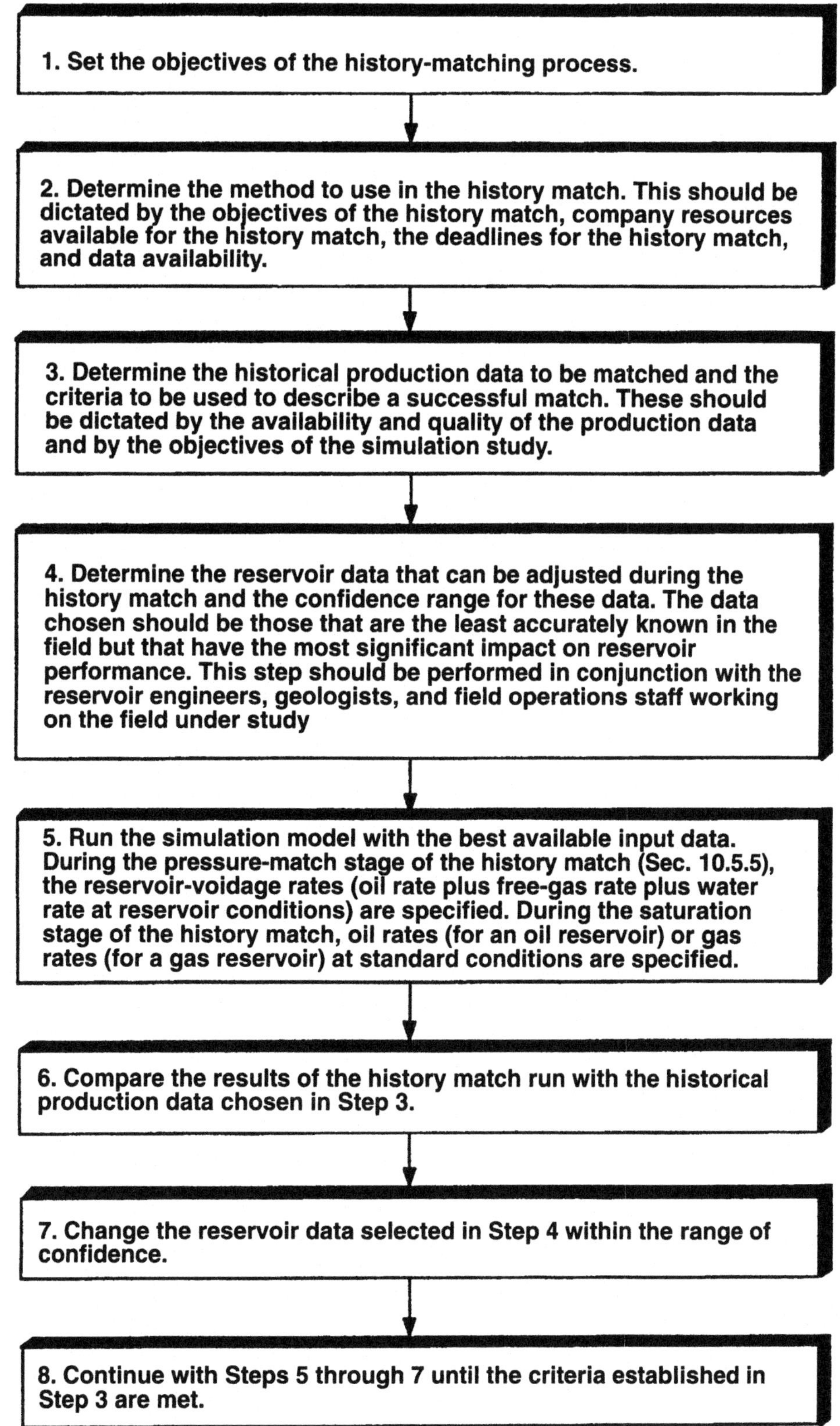

Fig. 10.40—Overall iterative procedure for a history match.

data. The purpose of these runs is to establish the functional relationship between the change in input data and the change in magnitude of the error function. The automatic history-matching logic then determines the set of input data that minimizes the error function defined by Eq. 10.85. Many methods can be used to obtain a data set that minimizes the error function. The differences in these methods depend on the assumptions of whether the error function is linear or nonlinear with changes to the reservoir data and on the technique used in the minimization of the error function (see Appendix A).

Selection of which history-matching method, manual or automatic, to use in the history-matching phase of a simulation study depends on the objectives of the history match, the company resources devoted to the history match, and the deadlines of the simulation study. If the secondary objectives of the history match, as discussed in Sec. 10.5.1, are to be emphasized, manual history matching may be required because some of the knowledge learned during history matching could be lost because of the nature of the automatic procedure. On the other hand, manual history matching can be very time-consuming and automatic history matching may be attempted to speed up the matching process.

No history-matching method, manual or automatic, guarantees a successful history match (one that meets all history-matching objectives). If unexpected difficulties arise during the history match, it may become apparent that both methods should be attempted to achieve the required match.

10.5.3 Selection of Production Data To Specify and Match. ***Selection of Production/Injection Data To Specify.*** *Production Wells.* To perform a history match, the production data to be specified (Step 5 in Fig. 10.40) and the data to be matched (Step 3 in Fig. 10.40) need to be selected. In general, the selection of the production data to specify depends on the stage of the history match and the hydrocarbons present in the reservoir. During the pressure-matching stage of the history match (see Sec. 10.5.5), the current reservoir energy and the reservoir-energy behavior with time are the most critical considerations. Consequently, the most appropriate production data to specify during this stage of the history match are the historical well-voidage rates. The voidage rate is the sum of the oil, free gas, and water rates at reservoir conditions. The use of reservoir voidage is the most convenient well specification during the pressure match because, by material balance, the available reservoir energy is determined by the amount of material removed from the reservoir. The reason that the reservoir voidage is specified is to ensure that the volume of reservoir fluids removed during the historical period is identical to that in the simulation model and the field. While this specification ensures that the total volume of produced fluid will match the historical reservoir volume, the proportion of fluids (oil, free gas, and water) will differ between the simulation model and the actual reservoir performance.

During the saturation-match stage of the history match, the production data to be specified are the oil production rates for an oil reservoir and the gas production rates for a gas reservoir. This specification ensures that the produced oil (or gas) volumes match historical reservoir performance. Unfortunately, with this specification, GOR, WOR, and voidage rates do not match actual reservoir performance nor do they match the results at the end of the pressure-match stage. Because the voidage rates have been altered, the pressures also differ from those obtained at the end of the pressure-match stage. The primary objective of the saturation match is to adjust reservoir data to match the well GOR and WOR. If the GOR and WOR can be matched, the oil (or gas) rates are matched (because they are specified), the voidage rates are matched (because the GOR and WOR are matched), and, consequently, the pressures from the end of the pressure match are recovered.

The rationale for decoupling the history match into pressure and saturation matches is straightforward. In practice, however, because the proportions of the oil, free gas, and water produced from the simulator differ at the end of the pressure match and at the end of the saturation match, the total compressibility of the fluids remaining in the reservoir also differ. Therefore, once the saturation match is achieved, the pressure match may need to be revisited to ensure that it is still acceptable.

The specified production data are required on a well-by-well basis for the history-matching process. If these data are metered at the field or reservoir level, they must be allocated back to the individual wells with one of the allocation methods discussed in Sec. 10.3.2 or with a field-specific allocation method. Generally, the operations staff in the field performs the allocation process if it is required.

The point where fluids are metered must also be considered when selecting the production/injection data to specify. If fluids are metered after significant changes to the produced stream, these changes need to be considered when specifying the well rates. For example, if crude oil or produced gas are diverted and used as lease fuel or if produced gas is exported and used as lift gas for other wells before metering, these fluids need to be accounted for in the well specifications. Also, if wet gas is produced and sent to a gas plant before metering, gas shrinkage needs to be considered. In this case, the proper specifications are the wet-gas volumes coming from the reservoir and not the metered lean-gas volumes coming from the gas plant. This discussion is also true for the production data that are selected to be matched.

Injection Wells. The selection of the injection data to specify for injection wells is not as critical as for production wells. In general, the specification of the historical surface injection rates is adequate for injection wells during all stages of the history match.

Selection of Production/Injection Data To Match. Selection of the production/injection data to be matched during a history match depends on the availability of production/injection data and the quality of the data. In general, the more data that can be matched during the history-matching process, the more confidence that can be placed in the simulation model during the prediction phase of the study. The quality of the production/injection data must also be considered during the history match. If the data are not measured accurately, then running excessive history-match cases to match the data exactly may not be warranted.

Production Wells. During the pressure match (Sec. 10.5.5), the main pressure data to match are shut-in buildup pressures (static pressures), p_{ws}, and pressures from a wireline formation tester. In full-field modeling, the flowing well pressures, p_{wf}, often are not included in the history match. This is discussed later.

Shut-in buildup pressures (static pressures), p_{ws}, are commonly used during the pressure-match stage of the history match. For full–field simulation, the use of these data requires some manipulation.[24–27] This is because (1) source/sink representation of wells is used in full-field simulation; (2) the timestep size used in the simulation model differs from the duration of the buildup test, and (3) often, wells in a full-field model are not shut in and reopened during the history match run to mimic an 8- to 24-hour buildup test (generally, the rates are adjusted downward to exclude production that would have occurred during the test period). The correction used in reservoir simulation takes the form of the pressure at a specific shut-in time to use in the match. The appropriate shut-in time to compare buildup pressures with simulated pressures is given by Odeh as[27]

$$\Delta t_{ws} = \left[\left(r_{eq}/r_w\right)^2\right]^{\frac{k_H h}{\sum_k \Delta z_k k_{H_k}}} \left(\frac{1.687 r_w^2 \phi \mu c_t}{k_H}\right) e^{-2s_p}, \quad \text{(10.86a)}$$

where the summation in the denominator of the exponent is performed over all layers open to the well. The constant 1.687 in Eq. 10.86a is for customary field units; it becomes 0.123563×10^6 for the metric units listed in Table 4.1. The appropriate model pressure to use for history-match comparisons is the pressure reported from the well-management reports (see Example 6.10). The simulator pressure may need further correction to ensure that the pressure reported by the simulator is adjusted to the gauge depth used in the test (or, equivalently, both pressures may be corrected to a common datum depth). To summarize, Eq. 10.86a is used in a history match to calculate the correct shut-in time, Δt_{ws}; for comparison, the buildup pressure from the test report at this time is obtained, the simulator pressure is corrected to the gauge depth (if required), and the two pressures are compared.

Note that, if the well is perforated through the full thickness, Δz, of every grid cell hosting the well, then $k_H h = \Sigma(\Delta z_k k_{H_k})$ and the skin caused by partial penetration is zero, $s_p = 0$. For these wells, $k_H h/\Sigma(\Delta z_k k_{H_k}) = 1$ and $-2s_p = 0$. If the definition of r_{eq} given by Peaceman[24], $r_{eq} = 0.2\Delta x$ (see Eq. 6.36b), is substituted into Eq. 10.86a along with the values of the exponents for a fully penetrating well, Eq. 10.86a reduces to the equation derived by Peaceman.

$$\Delta t_{ws} = \frac{0.0675 \phi \mu c_t}{k_H} (\Delta x)^2, \quad \text{(10.86b)}$$

The constant 0.0675 in Eq. 10.86b is for customary field units: it becomes 4.94251×10^3 for the metric units listed in Table 4.1.

One difficulty may be encountered when static pressures are used in the history match of wells perforated in multiple flow units or geologic layers. Shut-in buildup pressures in stratified reservoirs represent vertically averaged pressures. In these cases, the static pressures must be considered "soft" data. In cases where the well is perforated in one flow unit or geologic layer, the static pressures can be considered "hard" data if the completion integrity is adequate to provide zonal isolation.

Pressure data from a wireline formation tester always represents hard data, even in stratified reservoirs (as long as the tool has not failed during the survey). This is because wireline pressures are measured at the depths of interest (Fig. 10.19). Wireline pressure data are used in a history match by comparing the measured pressures at depth to the corresponding gridblock pressures. No corrections are required to wireline pressures because they are not associated with production and because the comparisons are made at depth.

Flowing well pressures, p_{wf}, have only limited application during the history-match phase of a simulation study because flowing pressures can be matched trivially in a full-field simulation model by adjusting the well-geometry factors, G_w. Flowing well pressures are, however, commonly used in history matching of single-well models where the study objectives include aiding in the interpretation of complicated pressure-transient tests.

During the saturation-match stage of the history match, the most common data selected to match are the well water cut (or, equivalently, WOR) and GOR. As discussed earlier, the water-cut and GOR data must be validated to ensure that water and gas production have not been influenced by tubing, cement, or casing leaks. In addition, when considering GOR as match data, the appropriate quantity to use is produced GOR. Consequently, all produced gas (sales, fuel, and flare gas) must be incorporated into the GOR and any gas introduced from an external source (lift gas) must be excluded.

Although water-cut and GOR data are measured routinely in the field, they may not always be available for the history match. For example, no water-production data are available before breakthrough; consequently, if the simulation study is performed before that time, the history match cannot benefit from water-production data.

Breakthrough times also are frequently used during a history match. The arrival time of a displacing fluid is dependent on the geology and zonation of the reservoir, interwell transmissibility, and mobility ratio of the displaced and displacing fluids. Breakthrough times generally are considered key match parameters in displacement processes, such as secondary-recovery and EOR processes.

Log-derived fluid saturations also can be used in a history match. Openhole logs from newly drilled infill wells can be compared with those of older offset wells to identify changes in fluid saturation in a given reservoir area throughout time. In addition, if wells are monitored routinely with cased-hole logging, such as PNC logging, the historical fluid saturations can be used in the history match. When comparing well-log data through time, the quality of the data must be scrutinized carefully. Changes in logging tools, analysis techniques, or service companies during the life of the field may yield results that appear to indicate changes in saturation but that are, in fact, only artifacts of the operational changes.

Injection Wells. The main injection-well data that are available to match during the history match are static pressures and zonal injection rates. Measurement of static pressures in injection wells is identical to that in production wells. These data, typically measured with a PLT, are important because accurate forecasts cannot be made during a displacement process unless good estimates of the injected volumes entering a flow unit can be made. Zonal injection rates can also be determined qualitatively with temperature surveys and acoustic logging (see Table 10.12).

Relationship Between Study Objectives and Data Availability. Because the availability and quality of historical data are beyond the control of the engineer performing the simulation study, it is the role of the simulation engineer to ensure that the study objectives are consistent and achievable with the available historical data. The following examples show the interrelationships between study objectives and historical data.

During the appraisal stage of field development, the only historical production data available from the field may be the results of several drillstem tests on exploration and appraisal wells. In this situation, the simulation model must be run without the benefit of an extensive history match. Therefore, the lack of historical data should be considered when the objectives of the simulation study

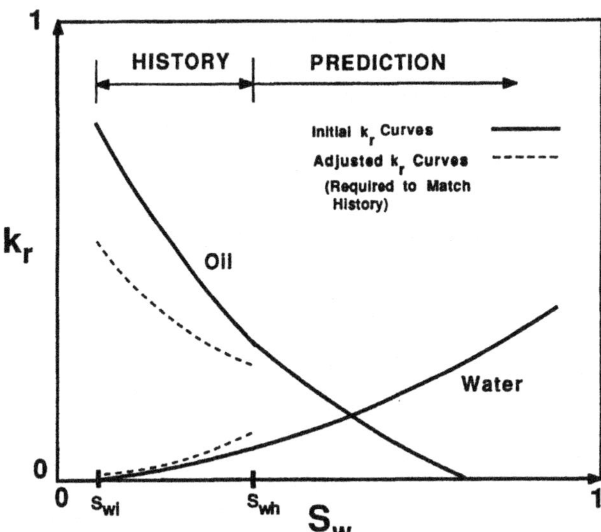

Fig. 10.41—Relative permeability curves adjusted for a history match of historical period S_{wi} through S_{wh}. How are the relative permeability curves extrapolated beyond S_{wh} for prediction?

are developed and a wide band of uncertainty should be placed on the predicted results.

A second example of the interrelationship of historical production data and study objectives is concerned with water production. Without sufficient historical water production to match, the predicted water production from the finite-difference simulator may not be any more accurate than that obtained from simple analytical methods. Again, in this case, the entire study approach and objectives may need to be re-evaluated.

As a final example, if a field is producing at the surface-facility capacity (constant peak capacity), the behavior during reservoir decline may not be forecast accurately. Again, the objectives of the study must be made consistent with the available production data.

10.5.4 Selection of Reservoir Data To Adjust. Because of the nature of reservoir simulation, virtually any reservoir parameter can be adjusted to achieve a history match. The selection of the parameters to be adjusted during a history match (Step 4 in Fig. 10.40), however, should be made judiciously and with the aid of the field engineers and geologists.

The more commonly used history-matching parameters are aquifer size and strength, the presence (or absence) of vertical permeability barriers, the $k_H h$ product (reservoir and well), the k_V/k_H ratio, PV, and relative permeability. There are no specific rules for choosing which reservoir parameters to adjust during a history match. The choice of the appropriate parameter to use depends on the given situation, which is discussed later in this chapter.

As stated earlier, caution should always be exercised when adjusting relative permeability data during a history match. **Fig. 10.41** illustrates the reason for this. In this figure, the original relative permeability (solid line) had to be adjusted (dashed line) through the historical period (saturation changes from S_{iw} to S_{wh}) to match production history. At the end of the historical period, there is no guidance as to how the relative permeability data should be extrapolated into prediction. For example, the relative permeability can be smoothed to intersect the endpoints of the original curve or extrapolated tangentially. The selection of how to continue the relative permeability curves is relatively arbitrary; however, this decision has a significant impact on the predictions made with the model. Consequently, it is recommended strongly that the best relative permeability data (at the reservoir scale) be selected at the beginning of the study and that these data be adjusted only as a last resort.

The range that the history-matching parameters can be adjusted varies from study to study. This range depends on many factors, including the quality of the acquired data, the geology (depositional environment and diagenetic processes) of the reservoir, and the degree of geological control in the subject field. In addition, the range for data changes does not need to be uniform throughout the field. For example, because the geologic control in the aquifer is generally not as good as that in the hydrocarbon-bearing areas, data in the aquifer often can be adjusted more liberally than those in the reservoir. The selection of the appropriate range for adjusting the history-match parameters should be made by the geologists and reservoir engineers working on the field.

10.5.5 Adjusting Reservoir Data To Match Historical Production. The actual adjustment of reservoir data during the history-matching process (Step 7 in Fig. 10.40) generally is performed in a two-stage procedure. Mattax and Dalton[1] refer to these two stages as gross and detailed, while Saleri and Toronyi[7] refer to these stages as a pressure match and a saturation match. Regardless of the names, the objective of the first stage is to match average reservoir pressures and the objective of the second stage is to match individual well histories.

The history-matching procedure is initiated by specifying the voidage, oil, or gas rates for the individual wells and running the simulation model with the best reservoir data available. The results of the history-match run are compared with historical field production and the input data adjusted in an effort to match the actual production history. The following discussion provides an overall strategy of how to adjust these input data. Each simulation study presents new problems, and no general strategy is guaranteed to work; therefore, the following strategy probably will need to be modified for most real history-matching situations.

The first stage of the history match, the gross stage or pressure match, is the easier of the two stages to perform. During this stage, the average reservoir pressure throughout time, regional pressure gradients, and well pressures are matched. To match average reservoir pressure, the most commonly adjusted reservoir parameters are aquifer size, PV, and total system compressibility (and its constituents). During this stage, material-balance studies and aquifer-influx studies can aid in obtaining insight into the data adjustments required for the history match. When matching reservoir pressures, any adjustments made to the PV affect the determination of in-place fluid volumes.

Regional pressures and pressure gradients are matched during the first stage of the history match (in addition to the average reservoir pressure). To match pressures and pressure gradients, the matching parameters most commonly used are aquifer connectivity, reservoir $k_H h$, transmissibilities across faults, and regional PV's. Changing aquifer connectivity and regional PV may affect the match to average reservoir pressures and the match to average reservoir pressure may need to be revised. At this point, coarsely gridded 3D models can be used to estimate the required adjustments in reservoir properties.

Matching individual well pressures throughout time can be attempted during the first stage of the history match. In full-field simulation, shut-in or buildup pressures should be used. When matching well pressures with time, the earliest detected problems should be corrected first. This prevents early-time errors from growing and masking later problems. If pressures are matched adequately early in the life of the well but the match progressively deteriorates, adjustments to reservoir data away from the wellbore may be required. Mattax and Dalton[1] suggest the use of the pressure-transient theory to aid in the determination of the appropriate adjustments to achieve the desired magnitude and timing of changes to well pressures.

Under single-phase, transient conditions, the solution to the transient-flow problem can be expressed in terms of the exponential integral function

$$p = p_i + \frac{q\mu B}{4\pi\beta_c k_H h}\left[E_i\left(-\frac{\phi c_t \mu r^2}{4\alpha_c \beta_c k_H t}\right)\right], \quad \ldots\ldots\ (10.87)$$

where Table 4.1 gives the units of all variables.

Although Eq. 10.87 has been derived for single-phase flow, there are two important observations that can be drawn from it for multiphase flow: the magnitude of the pressure drop, $p_i - p$, is scaled by the factor $(q\mu B)/(4\pi\beta_c k_H h)$ and the timing of these changes is scaled by the factor $(4\alpha_c\beta_c k_H)/(\phi c_t \mu r^2)$. With this analysis, estimates can be made for adjusting far-field data to alter the magnitude and timing of pressure changes at a given wellbore location.

Formation wireline tester pressures are also matched during this stage of the history match. The formation wireline pressures are used to match the model pressures on a flow-unit basis. The first step in matching the layer pressures is to match zonal injection rates in the model with field-measured injector PLT data. This ensures that each flow unit in the model is receiving the same level of injection support as that measured in the field. Layer $k_H h$ or PV (or any other property selected as an adjustable parameter) is then adjusted to match the flow-unit pressures. To match sharp discontinuities in the vertical pressure gradient (see Fig. 10.19), adjustments to the vertical transmissibility, T_{lz}, are required between the simulation layers that exhibit the discontinuity.

The second stage of the history match, the detailed stage or saturation match, is probably the most frustrating part of any simulation study because changes made to match individual well rates may affect the quality of the match obtained during the first stage or the quality of the match in other areas of the field.

The well histories that are matched during the second stage are water cuts, GOR's, and breakthrough times. Because of the nature of these data, all knowledge of the reservoir geology and recovery processes must be incorporated into the study during this stage.

To match water rates or arrival times, it is imperative that the mechanism of water production occurring in the reservoir be understood thoroughly. For example, the reservoir parameters required to match the water cuts of wells depend on whether water production is caused by water coning from a bottomwater aquifer, lateral water encroachment from an edgewater aquifer or an adjacent injection well, or water fingering.

If the mechanism of water or gas production is by coning, the water cuts or GOR's will be dominated by the degree of vertical communication, well drawdown, mobility ratio, and density differences between produced phases. Consequently, in coning situations, water cut and GOR can be matched by adjusting k_V or, if appropriate, by incorporating vertical permeability barriers, such as shales. This second option must, however, be confirmed by the field geologists. At this stage, analytical coning studies[44] or stand-alone single-well models may provide insight into required data changes.

If the water-production mechanism is lateral water encroachment from an aquifer or offset injection well, water production will be dominated by reservoir $k_H h$ and relative permeability. In addition, the regional PV may be used as a matching parameter because reservoir fill-up affects flood-front advancement and breakthrough times. In the first step of matching lateral water or gas migration, the layering used in the simulation model should be examined. If high-permeability streaks have been averaged with less permeable strata in the model-layering scheme, these streaks may need to be incorporated explicitly as separate layers. If the layering and permeability averaging appear suitable, changes to regional $k_H h$ or regional PV should be attempted. Changes to these reservoir properties should be made on a regional basis (as opposed to a well-by-well basis) to avoid simulating wells that were drilled into geologic anomalies. All changes to reservoir data must be confirmed by the field geologists. At this stage of the history match, Buckley-Leverett analysis, Stiles analysis, or stand-alone cross-sectional simulation models may aid in determining how much to change various reservoir properties and the resulting impact from these changes.

Relative permeability can be used as a last resort for matching well water cuts, GOR's, and breakthrough times. If relative permeabilities are to be used, the interblock curves can be used to match breakthrough times while the well curves can be used to match the shape of the water-cut performance curve. For the reasons discussed earlier, if the relative permeability curves are changed during a history match, these changes must be justified technically.

During the second stage of the history match, the adjusted reservoir parameters may alter the results from the first phase of the match. Consequently, reservoir pressures need to be rechecked to see whether they are still acceptable. If not, a second pass through the history-matching algorithm may be required.

When performing a history match, localized near-well changes are not recommended because they are not based on geologic considerations; sometimes, however, they cannot be avoided. There is a hierarchy of data adjustments, applicable in both the pressure- and saturation-match stages, that can be used to minimize the number of localized near-well changes in the model. When making adjustments vertically, the following order should be attempted.

1. Global (all simulation layers).
2. Reservoirs (in fields made up of vertically stacked reservoirs).
3. Flow units within a reservoir.
4. Facies (in laminated reservoirs or flow units).
5. Simulation layers.

When making adjustments areally, the following order should be attempted.

1. Global (all grid cells).
2. Reservoir/aquifer.
3. Fault blocks within a reservoir.
4. Facies (areal facies envelope).
5. Regional (groups of offset wells exhibiting a common history-match problem.
6. Individual wells.

Use of this hierarchy forces the history-match adjustments to be made in the most geologically sound manner.

Fig. 10.42 shows the general algorithm for adjusting reservoir data to match historical production behavior. Although every reservoir study is different, the guidelines in this section provide a first pass for most petroleum reservoirs.

10.5.6 History-Match Quality. There is no industry standard definition of what constitutes a successfully matched simulation model. The definition of a successful history match may vary from company to company, from individual to individual within a company, or from project to project by the same individual. What is important is that the history match be consistent with the objectives of the study. **Fig. 10.43** illustrates this point.

In Fig. 10.43, the actual historical water-cut performance of a well is plotted with the history-matched simulation performance. It must be determined whether the quality of the history match is acceptable to make future predictions. Quality determination depends on the objectives of the study. If, for example, the objectives of the study are to make future water-production forecasts to size additional water-handling facilities, then the match is probably acceptable because both the level of the water cut and the final trend are approximately correct. If, however, the objectives of the study are to identify future infill-well locations or future zones to perforate, then the quality of the match may not be adequate because the model is underpredicting water-cut performance early in the life of the well. If future predictions are to be made, this lost water may have a dramatic impact on the behavior of the infill wells or new perforations. Consequently, additional history-matching effort may be required to improve the early-time simulation performance.

10.6 Reservoir Performance Predictions

The prediction phase of a simulation study is the phase in which most of the study objectives are achieved. In this phase of the study, the simulation model is used to predict future reservoir performance, in contrast to history matching where the simulator is used to match historical performance. The remainder of this chapter discusses the fundamentals of running the reservoir simulator to obtain future reservoir forecasts.

10.6.1 Selection of Prediction Cases. Reservoir simulation is best used to compare changes in reservoir-management strategies (or entirely different development options) to assess the incremental impact of the projects under investigation. Reservoir simulation is best used on a comparative basis because of the nonunique nature of the history match. Because of the nonuniqueness of the history-matching process, predictions from even the most closely matched model are subject to some biased error. For models where no history match has been performed (newly discovered fields or fields in the appraisal stage of development), this error is even more pronounced. If the results of a base case are subtracted from the results of a second case (project case) and it is assumed that the error in both cases is approximately the same, the difference in the results (incremental results) is less sensitive to the nonunique history match than is either individual case. In other words, if the error is equal (exactly) in both cases, that error is removed from the incremental results. Therefore, reservoir simulation is best used to determine the incremental results of a project case compared with a base case.

Selection of the base case depends on the objectives of the simulation study. In general, the base case is selected as (1) a no future capital expenditure case (a "do-nothing" case), (2) the current reservoir-management strategy case (including future capital expenditures), or (3) an anticipated reservoir-management strategy case (for fields in the appraisal phase of development). For fields in the appraisal phase of development, a primary-depletion case is often selected as the base case.

Once selected, the results of the base case can be subtracted from other production forecasts to generate incremental results. For example, if an infill well program is to be evaluated, the results of the base case are subtracted from the infill-well case to determine the incremental reserves associated with the infill-well program.

Project Cases. One reason that reservoir simulation is such a powerful tool is because any production scenario can be investigated. When developing project cases, it is always a good practice to change only one variable or component at a time if possible. In the infill-well example just discussed, if two infill wells are scheduled to be drilled, the first prediction case should include only one of the infill wells. The results of this project case can be compared with the results of the base case to determine the incremental production associated with the first well. A second prediction case can then be run with both infill wells. The results of this second prediction can be compared to the results of the first prediction case (not with those of the base case) to determine the incremental reserves associated with the second infill well and with the results of the base case to determine total project reserves. With this method of evaluation, the total project reserves always equal the sum of the reserves of each component of the project.

To this point, we have discussed only incremental production. The simulation model can also be used to determine the level of interference between the project and base cases. In the infill-well example, the first project case may show that the cumulative production from the first infill well is 7.0 MMSTB oil (from the simulator's well reports) but that the incremental production (difference in results from the project and base cases) is only 5.0 MMSTB oil. This indicates that the well will produce 5.0 MMSTB of incremental oil plus the 2.0 MMSTB of oil already produced from the wells in the base case (well interference). Oil production caused by well interference is often related to accelerated production.

Proper use of simulator-generated results depends on the objectives of the study. For example, for project economics, the incremental results are the correct results to use, while the project rates (from the simulator's well reports) may be more appropriate to use for project design (tubing size, artificial-lift design, separator throughput, and other such factors).

Sensitivity Cases. Although reservoir simulation is best used as a comparative tool, situations exist where it cannot be used in this manner. For example, the objective of the simulation study may be to determine the reserves from a reservoir that is currently being appraised. In these situations, sensitivity cases can be run to determine the impact of uncertainties in reservoir data on the production forecast, to estimate the ranges of reserves, and to estimate the expected-value, v_E, reserves. Expected value is defined as the sum of the probability times the outcome ($v_E = \Sigma[PO]$) of different events, where P = probability and O = outcome.

Sensitivity cases differ from project cases in that, in sensitivity cases, the same project is investigated but uncertainties associated with that project are evaluated. For example, for the infill well example, if there is a 10% probability of encountering a skin factor of 0.5 (optimistic case), an 80% probability of encountering a skin factor of 1.0 (most likely case), and a 10% probability of encountering a skin factor of 2.0 (pessimistic case), all three cases must be evaluated. If the incremental results from these three sensitivity cases are 6.0, 5.0, and 3.0 MMSTB of oil, respectively, then the range of incremental reserves is 3.0 to 6.0 MMSTB, the most likely (deter-

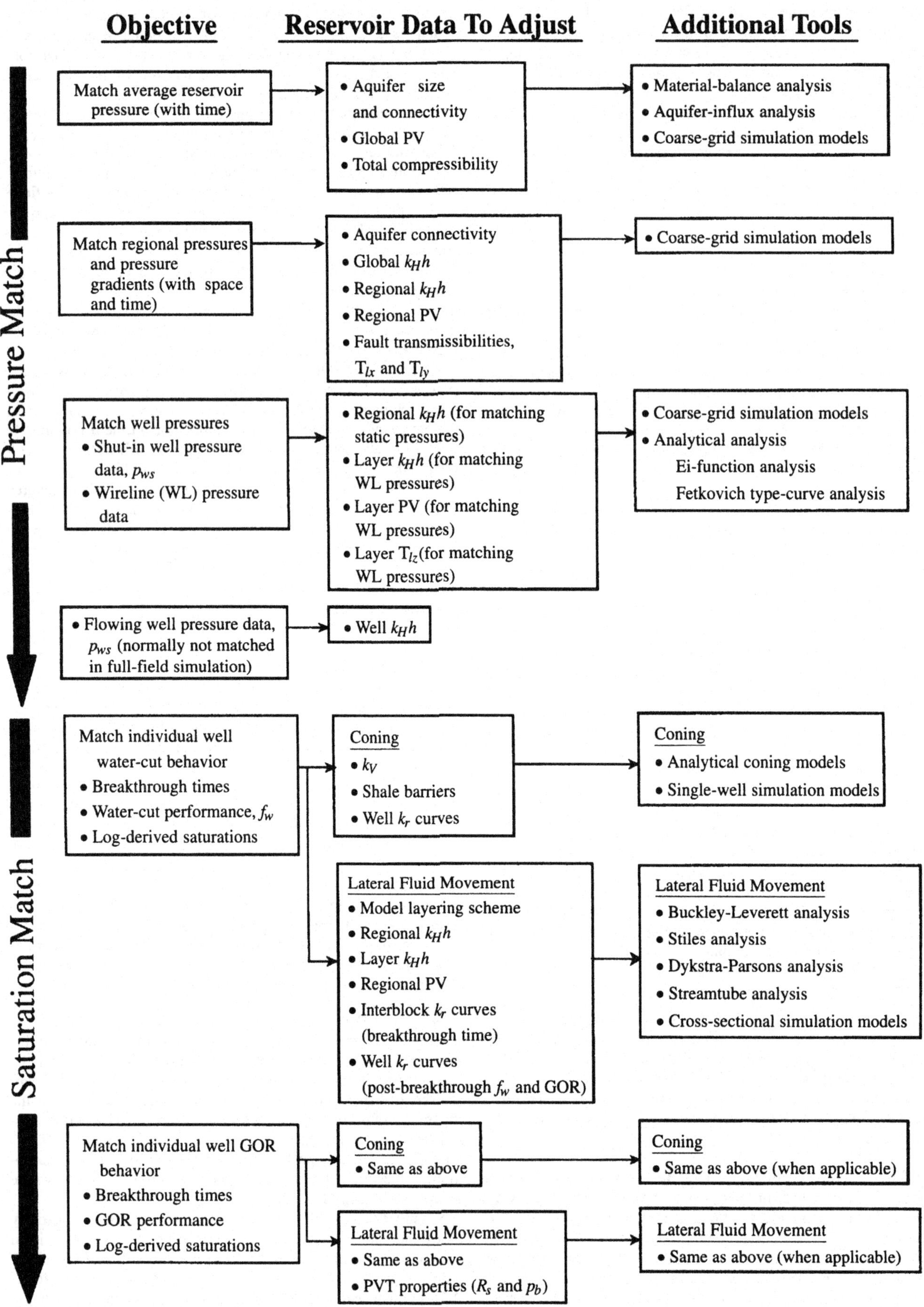

Fig. 10.42—General algorithm for manual history matching along with key reservoir data and additional history-matching tools.

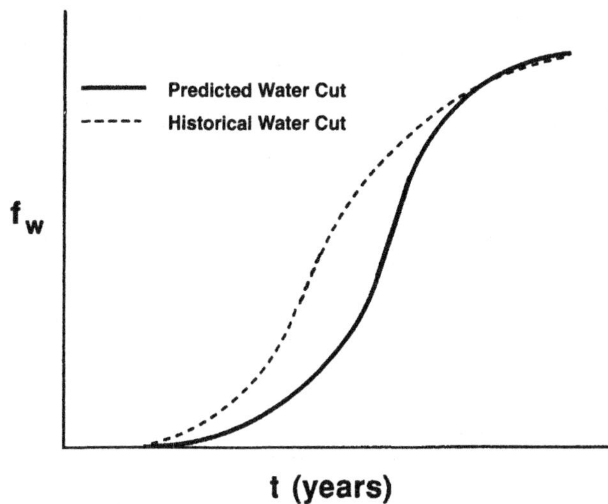

Fig. 10.43—Example of a history-matched simulation model. Is the match adequate for future predictions?

ministic) reserves are 5.0 MMSTB oil, and expected-value (probabilistic) incremental reserves are 4.9 MMSTB oil ($v_E = 0.1 \times 6.0 + 0.8 \times 5.0 + 0.1 \times 3.0$ MMSTB).

10.6.2 Reservoir Management in Reservoir Simulation. The main difference between running the reservoir simulator in prediction mode as opposed to history-matching mode is in the well specification and production constraints used in the model. During the history match, voidage, oil, or gas rates generally are specified because these rates are known in the field during the historical period. In prediction mode, the oil rates are not known and, in fact, must be forecast. Therefore, another well specification is required. In addition to the new well specification, production constraints may be imposed during the prediction phase to help model the reservoir-management strategy and operating practices in the field. In general, few (or no) production constraints are used in history mode.

There is a fundamental difference between well specifications and production constraints. Well specifications are used as targets for the individual wells, while production constraints are used to keep various production parameters within acceptable, realistic ranges. This difference is illustrated later in this section. Each well in the model requires one (and only one) well specification but can have any number of constraints.

The proper well specification to use in the prediction phase of a study depends on the strategy used for field management. If wells are produced into common surface facilities, such as a production separator, then these wells may need a tubinghead-pressure specification that is approximately equal to the separator pressure. (The pressure drop from the wellhead to the separator also may be included in the well specification.) If production is limited by a process capacity, such as the tubing throughput, then a total-fluid-rate specification may be required. Most commercial reservoir simulators have several options for well specifications. **Table 10.21** lists commonly used well specifications in reservoir simulation.

The proper production constraints to use in the prediction phase of a study also depend on the reservoir-management strategy used in the field. In the preceding paragraph, the example of a specified total fluid rate was discussed for the case of a well producing at the

TABLE 10.21—WELL SPECIFICATIONS AND THEIR COMMON USES IN RESERVOIR SIMULATION

Well Specification	Use in Reservoir Simulation
Oil rate, q_{osc}	Specify metered oil rates during history matching. Model wells producing at oil-processing capacity for predictions. Model wells producing at oil-allowable limits for predictions. Model oil flux across boundaries of window models through pseudowells.
Water rate, q_{wsc}	Specify metered water-injection rates during history matching. Rarely used for production wells during history matching. Model wells producing at water-treating capacity for predictions. Model injection wells injecting water at capacity. Model water flux across boundaries of window models through pseudowells. Model aquifer influx at boundaries of full-field, cross-sectional, and single-well models through pseudowells.
Liquid rate, q_{Lsc}	Specify metered liquid rates during history matching. Model wells producing at liquid capacity for predictions. Facility capacities. Tubing/flowline/pipeline throughput capacities. Model liquid flux across boundaries of window models through pseudowells.
Gas rate, q_{gsc}	Specify metered gas rates during history matching. Model wells producing at gas-processing capacity for predictions. Model gas wells producing at allowable limits. Model injection wells injecting gas at injection capacity. Model gas flux across boundaries of window models through pseudowells.
Voidage rate, q_t	Specify reservoir voidage from wells during history matching (useful for matching reservoir pressures when simulated water cuts or GOR's do not match actual water cuts or GOR's adequately). Used for voidage-balanced production/injection for predictions.
Flowing bottomhole pressure, p_{wf}	Rarely used during history matching. Model wells producing against a constant wellbore pressure for predictions. Model wells producing through an electrical submersible pump with a constant inlet pressure for predictions.
Tubinghead pressure, p_{th}	Rarely used during history matching. Model wells producing into facilities with fixed pressures. Headers. Separators. Pipelines. Compressors with fixed inlet pressures.

throughput capacity. The total fluid rate also can be used as a production constraint. The difference between a well specification and a production constraint is illustrated next.

If the oil rate is specified as 5,000 BOPD with a total fluid constraint of 15,000 BFPD, the reservoir will produce oil at the specified rate until the WOR reaches a value of two. At this point, the produced-fluid rate will reach the constraint of 15,000 BFPD. When this occurs, the simulator will take some remedial action.

Depending on the reservoir simulation program used in the study, production constraints can be placed at most levels of the reservoir/wellbore system. That is, production constraints can be placed on simulation layers, individual wells, groups of wells, and the entire field. For simulation layers, constraints on the layer water-cut and GOR values commonly are used to shut in the layer and let the simulator recomplete to drier or less gassy layers. Constraints at the well level include well water cuts and GOR's, bottomhole and tubinghead pressures, and fluid rates. Various well-intervention decisions based on internal computer logic can be made from these constraints. These decisions include whether to plug and abandon the well, whether to shut in the well, or whether to work over or stimulate the well. Constraints on groups of wells are used routinely in reservoir simulation. Group constraints can be used to control wells producing into (or injecting from) common surface facilities, producing into a common trunk line, or producing from an offshore production platform with limited fluid-processing capacity. Finally, field constraints are used to control fieldwide production and injection strategies. Field constraints can be used to set field targets and to determine when to drill new wells, simulate reinjection of produced gas or water, maintain voidage-balanced production/injection, limit production within the capacity of the surface facilities, or optimize fieldwide artificial-lift strategies.

The use of constraints at the various wellbore/reservoir levels provides the engineer with the ability to model complex reservoir-management strategies with relatively little manual intervention. For example, the simulation model does not have to be stopped and restarted to plug and abandon a well when its water cut reaches the economic limit of wells in the field. This not only is a convenience but also is a requirement if realistic simulations are to be performed on complex reservoirs.

Most commercial simulators have very sophisticated production-management routines that can be used to model most operating strategies.[1,45,46] These production-management routines often take as much coding effort as the mathematics of the finite-difference routines. **Table 10.22** provides a list of production constraints and well-intervention options commonly used in reservoir simulation.

As discussed earlier, switching from history to prediction mode requires that the well specifications be changed at the end of the historical period. This has the potential to create abrupt, unnatural changes in production rates during the transition from history to prediction. This is particularly true when a rate specification (either oil rate or total fluid rate) is changed to a tubinghead-pressure specification. **Fig. 10.44** illustrates an example. This abrupt change is not always encountered when changing well constraints, but when it does occur, it can be alleviated by the use of the well geometric factor, G_w. The process of smoothing the transition from history mode to prediction mode is known as calibrating wells.

If a rate specification is used for a well during history and a tubinghead-pressure specification is used in prediction, the calibration process can be performed graphically with the tubing lift curves. **Fig. 10.45** illustrates this.

In system-analysis plots, as Fig. 10.45 shows, the slope of the inflow-performance curve is equal to the negative reciprocal of the well-productivity index, J_w. To obtain the correct well geometric factor, G_w, for calibrating the well for the transition from history mode to prediction mode, Eq. 10.88 is used.

$$G_w = \frac{-\mu_p B_p}{k_{rp}} \frac{1}{m_B}, \qquad (10.88)$$

where m_B = the slope of the inflow-performance curve from the cell pressure, p_o, to the last rate in history mode on the lift curve corresponding to the specified tubinghead pressure. Fig. 10.45 shows this slope explicitly.

Once the wells have been calibrated, the simulator must be rerun during the historical period to determine the impact of this change on the history match. Changing the well geometric factor does not affect the pressures significantly during the history match; however, it may have a significant effect on the relative contribution to production from the different layers in the wellbore. Consequently, the detailed stage (or saturation match) of the history match may need to be re-evaluated before the prediction phase of the study can continue.

10.6.3 Validating and Analyzing Simulation Predictions. After running the simulation model in prediction mode, the results must be reviewed critically before they can be reported to management. The validation process is required to ensure that the simulation results make physical sense.

To check whether the simulation model is giving reliable forecasts, the simulation predictions should be compared with those from other sources. The most reliable check is to compare the results with analogous fields. For example, if the field under investigation is a reservoir undergoing a waterflood, the recovery factors (but not necessarily the production profiles) from the simulation study should be compared with those of actual waterfloods in reservoirs with comparable rock and fluid properties and with similar well patterns and spacings.

Another check on the reservoir data can be made against any past studies of the subject field. Although it is presumed that any new studies use additional information and, consequently, give more reliable results, any significant changes or anomalies from past studies should be noted. The causes for these changes should be identified to determine whether they result from improved data or from fundamental differences in the assumptions used in the studies or in the way the studies were conducted. A third source for validation of the reservoir data used in the prediction phase of the study is analytical approaches, such as material-balance studies.

The results of the well-management routines in the prediction cases must also be reviewed. The production-management routines in the reservoir simulation program allow complex operational practices to be modeled by the simulator without the intervention of the engineer performing the study. The well-management results often need to be inspected to ensure that they are modeling the field in a realistic manner. For example, if an automatic drilling or workover algorithm is used in the simulation study, the timing of the drilling or workover must be analyzed. In a situation where a very successful workover is performed months before field abandonment, the possibility of manually performing this workover earlier in the field life should be considered. Also, if a mediocre well is drilled months before field abandonment, removing it from the drilling queue should be considered because this well would probably not be drilled in the field. Also, all simulated well work should be reviewed to ensure that the well completion can support this work. For example, if an upper layer in a well waters out and is plugged back automatically by the internal well-management logic, then that plugback should be reviewed to ensure that it is mechanically possible with the current well completion. One example of this situation occurs when a well has been gravel packed or hydraulically fractured. In these completions, vertical reservoir units may not be mechanically isolated in the field but the internal computer logic may attempt to isolate these units.

These checks are always worth the additional effort because they can be used to catch data errors before they propagate to future prediction cases. This ensures that rework is minimized when errors are found and, more importantly, that decisions are based on valid simulation cases.

10.7 Final Advice

Aziz[8] reported 10 golden rules for engineers working on reservoir simulation studies. Some of these rules are discussed in detail in this chapter, while others were just mentioned. The complete rules are quoted here directly from the original article.

TABLE 10.22—PRODUCTION CONSTRAINTS AND THEIR COMMON USES IN RESERVOIR SIMULATION

Constraint Level	Production Constraint	Well-Intervention Options
Simulation layers	Layer water/oil ratio (WOR) Layer GOR	Shut in offending layer. Recomplete to additional layers.
Flow units	Layer water/oil ratio (WOR) Layer GOR	Shut in offending layer. Recomplete to additional layers.
Individual wells	Minimum oil rate	Plug and abandon well. Shut in well. Stimulate well. Work over well. Recomplete to additional layers. Apply artificial lift to low-rate wells.
	Maximum liquid rate	Choke back well.
	Minimum liquid rate	Plug and abandon well. Shut in well. Stimulate well. Recomplete to additional layers. Apply artificial lift.
	Maximum water rate	Choke back well. Shut in high-WOR layers. Shut in well. Perform tubing-changeout operation. Switch to higher-treatment-capacity system.
	Maximum gas rate	Choke back well. Shut in high-GOR layers. Shut in well. Switch to higher-treatment-capacity system.
	Minimum gas rate (for gas reservoirs)	Plug and abandon well. Shut in well. Stimulate well. Recomplete to additional layers.
	Well WOR	Plug and abandon well. Shut in well. Shut in high-WOR layers. Recomplete to low-WOR layers. Choke back well. Perform tubing-changeout operation.
	Well GOR	Plug and abandon well. Shut in well. Shut in high-GOR layers. Recomplete to low-GOR layers. Choke back well.
	Minimum flowing well pressure	Plug and abandon well. Shut in well. Apply artificial lift. Perform tubing-changeout operation.
	Minimum tubinghead pressure	Plug and abandon well. Shut in well. Switch to lower-pressure system.
Groups of wells	Minimum oil rate	Drill additional wells. Stimulate low-rate wells. Work over high-WOR/-GOR wells. Open shut-in wells. Apply artificial lift to low-rate wells.
	Maximum liquid rate	Shut in low-rate wells. Scale back all wells.
	Minimum liquid rate	Drill additional wells. Stimulate low-rate wells. Apply artificial lift to low-rate wells.
	Maximum water rate	Shut in high-WOR wells. Shut in high-water-rate wells. Scale back all wells. Drill disposal wells.
	Maximum gas rate	Shut in high-GOR wells. Shut in high-gas-rate wells. Scale back all wells. Drill injection wells.
	Minimum gas rate (for gas reservoirs)	Drill additional wells. Stimulate low-rate wells. Apply compressor to low-rate wells. Open shut-in wells.
Field	Same as group of wells	Same as group of wells.

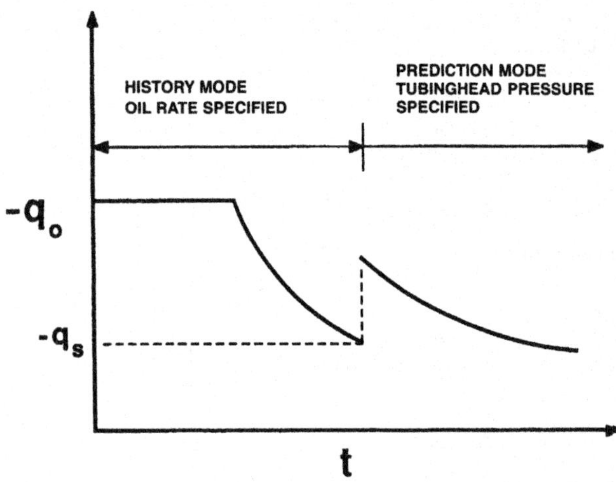

Fig. 10.44—Potential abrupt change in oil rates when switching from an oil-rate specification to a tubinghead-pressure specification during the transition from history mode to prediction mode. (Negative signs in this figure result from the naming convention used in this book.)

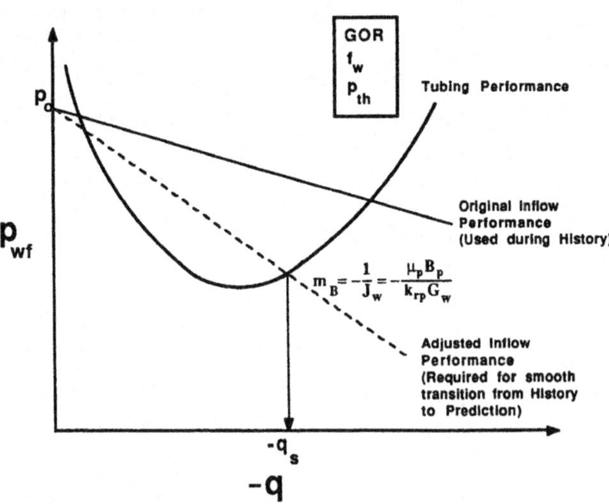

Fig. 10.45—Calibration of wells for smooth transition from history mode to prediction mode. Note that p_o, GOR, f_w, and q_s are the last values during history mode and p_{th} is the specified tubinghead pressure.

1. Understand Your Problem and Define Your Objectives. Before you do any simulation, understand the geological characteristics of your reservoir, the fluids it contains, and its dynamic behavior. Also clearly state the objectives of your study on paper before you start. Ask yourself if the objectives are realistic. These considerations will help you choose the most appropriate model for your study.

2. Keep It Simple. Start and end with the simplest model that is consistent with the nature of the reservoir, the objective of your study, and the availability of data. Classic reservoir engineering, simple analytical models, or single-block simulations are often all you need. At other times, the most sophisticated model available to you may not serve your needs. Understand model limitations and capabilities.

3. Understand Interaction Between Different Parts. Remember that a reservoir is not an isolated entity. It may connect with an aquifer and, through it, even to other reservoirs. Furthermore, reservoirs are connected through wells to the surface facilities. The isolation of different components of this system for separate study often may lead to inappropriate results by neglecting interaction between different parts of the system. However, when appropriate, don't be afraid to break a big problem into its smaller components. This can lead not only to substantial savings but to greater understanding of the mechanisms involved.

4. Don't Assume Bigger Is Always Better. Always question the size of a study that is limited by the computer resources or the budget. Simulation engineers often believe that no computer is big enough for what they want to do and tend simply to increase the size of the models to fit the computer. More blocks and components do not automatically translate into greater accuracy and reliability. In fact, in some situations the reverse is true. Insist on seeing appropriate justification for the number of blocks used in a given study.

5. Know Your Limitations and Trust Your Judgment. Remember that simulation is not an exact science. All models are based on assumptions and provide only an approximate answer to the real problem. Hence, a good understanding of both the problem and the model is essential for success. Numerical approximations may introduce "pseudophysical" phenomena like numerical dispersion. Use and trust your judgment, especially if it is based on your analysis of field or laboratory observations. Be careful to check your input and output. Do simple material-balance calculations to check simulation results. Pay particular attention to such things as negative compressibilities and permeabilities.

6. Be Reasonable in Your Expectations. Don't try to get from the simulator what it is incapable of producing. Often the most you can get from a study is some guidance on the relative merits of choices available to you. At other times you have the right to demand a lot more. But remember that if you exclude a mechanism during model development, you cannot study its effect with that model.

7. Question Data Adjustments for History Matching. Always question data adjustments during history matching. Remember that this process does not have a unique solution. The most reasonable solution will result from paying close attention to physical and geological reasonableness. A "good" history match with inappropriate adjustments to the data will lead to poor predictions. Don't be lulled into false security by a "good" or "close" match.

8. Don't Smooth Extremes. Pay attention to extremes in permeability (barriers and channels). Be careful in the process of averaging to avoid losing essential information when averaging the extremes. Never average out extremes.

9. Pay Attention to the Measurement and Use Scales. Measured values at the core scale may not apply directly at the larger block scale, but measurements do influence values at other scales. Remember that averaging may change the nature of the variables you average. For example, permeability may be a scalar at some small scale and a tensor at a larger scale. Even the meaning of capillary pressure and relative permeability can be different at different scales. Also, the dispersive terms in our equations are a result of the process of averaging.

10. Don't Skimp on Necessary Laboratory Work. Models do not replace good laboratory experiments that are designed to gain an understanding of the nature of the process being modeled or to measure essential parameters of the equations being solved by your simulator. Plan your laboratory work with the end use of this information in mind. Learn how to scale data.

10.8 Chapter Project

Whether involved in developing a simulator or conducting a simulation study, the simulation engineer needs to develop a full understanding of the capabilities and limitations of the model to be used. One common approach for increasing the knowledge of the reservoir under study is to conduct sensitivity analyses. From a broad prospective, sensitivity studies can be catalogued under two general groups. The first group focuses on understanding the variations in the performance of a model when the nonreservoir-specific parameters, such as gridblock sizes, timestep, and grid orientation, are changed. In this type of analysis, the specific rock and fluid properties, boundary-condition specifications, and initial saturation and pressure distributions remain intact while the problem is studied with, for example, different timestep sizes. In the second group of sensitivity studies, the simulation engineer attempts to develop a clear understanding of which rock and fluid properties become the most important parameters in solving a particular problem. In this way, the engineer develops a thorough understanding of the sensitivity of results to data accuracy and is in full control of the simula-

TABLE 10.23—AVERAGE PROPERTIES FOR A-1 RESERVOIR	
Permeability (SE-NW direction), $\bar{k}$, md	279.56
Porosity, $\bar{\phi}$, %	21.44
Formation thickness, $\bar{h}$, ft	25.72

tion study and, therefore, develops a thorough knowledge of the error range of the simulation.

In this chapter project, two studies are presented to increase our understanding of the sensitivity of the results to the level of data accuracy. In these exercises, the two-phase water-injection problem of Sec. 9.8.2 is revisited.

The two-phase injection simulation study discussed in Sec. 9.8.2 is repeated with homogeneous permeability, porosity, and thickness distributions throughout the A-1 reservoir. The homogeneous properties are obtained by use of volumetric averaging to the nonuniform-property distributions as given in Figs. 5.36 and 5.37 of Sec. 5.7. **Table 10.23** summarizes the average properties calculated for this exercise.

Fig. 10.46 shows the responses of Production Wells W-2 and W-4 to the various average properties used in this case and compares the calculated oil-production rates with the oil-production rates generated with actual data (see Tables 9.22 and 9.24). A close inspection of the oil-production rate of Well W-2 (plotted in Fig. 10.46) reveals that its calculated oil-production rates show some degree of disparity only when the gridblock thicknesses are averaged. Furthermore, no differences in oil-production rates from Well W-2 are observed when the homogeneous-thickness-case results are compared with the results in which all three properties (porosity, permeability, and thickness) were entered as averaged homogeneous properties. While these observations are correct for Well W-2, no significant differences in the calculated oil-production rates of Well W-4 were observed. This is expected because the average thickness value used in these cases is not significantly different from the actual thickness of Gridblock (3,2), which hosts Well W-4 (25.72 vs. 30.0 ft). However, in the case of Well W-2 this difference is much more significant. The actual thickness for Gridblock (9,3) is 15 ft, which is significantly smaller than the averaged value of 25.72 ft (see Figs. 5.36 and 6.19 for the actual wellblock thickness).

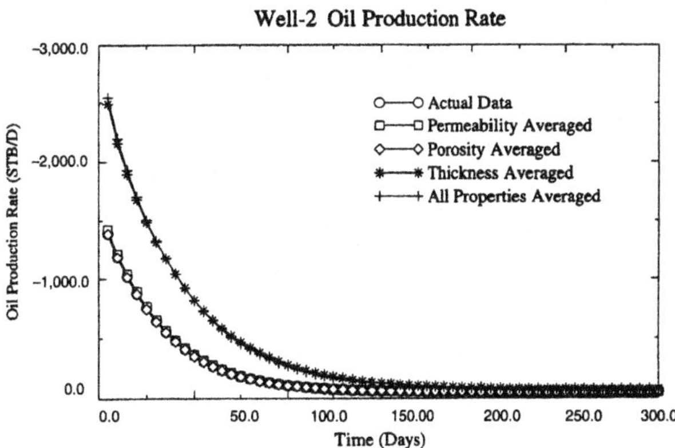

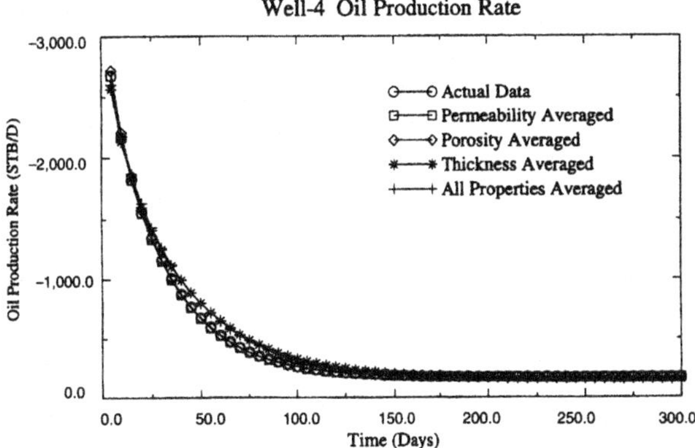

Fig. 10.46—Effect of homogeneous-property distribution on the calculated oil-production rates.

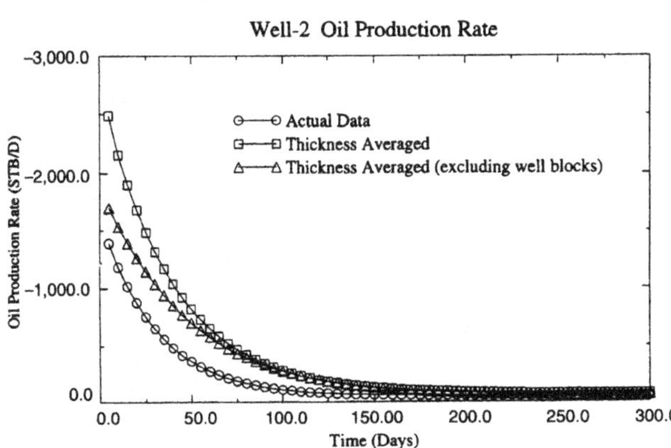

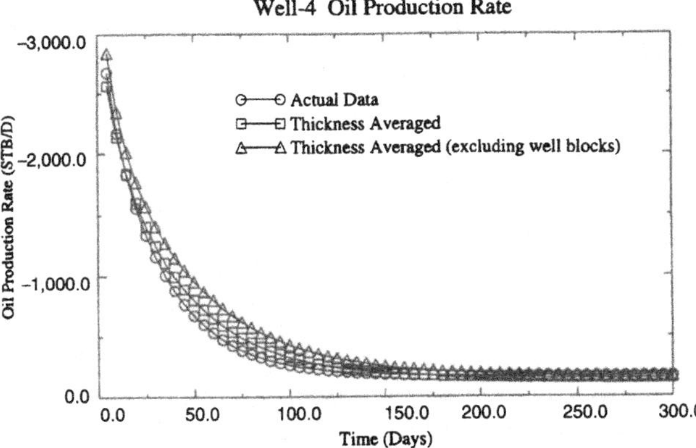

Fig. 10.47—Effect of wellblock thickness on the accuracy of the calculated oil-production rates.

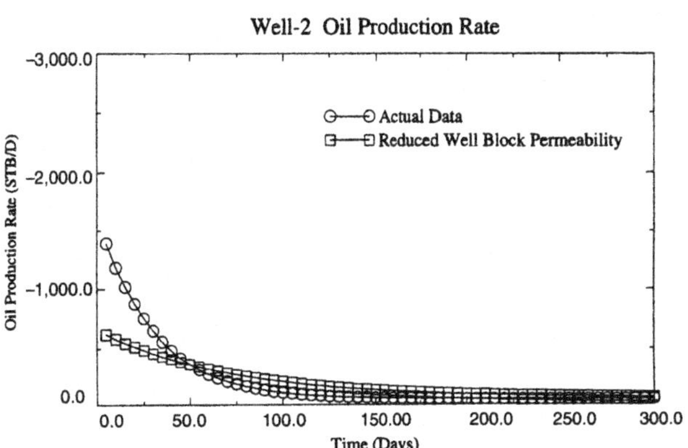

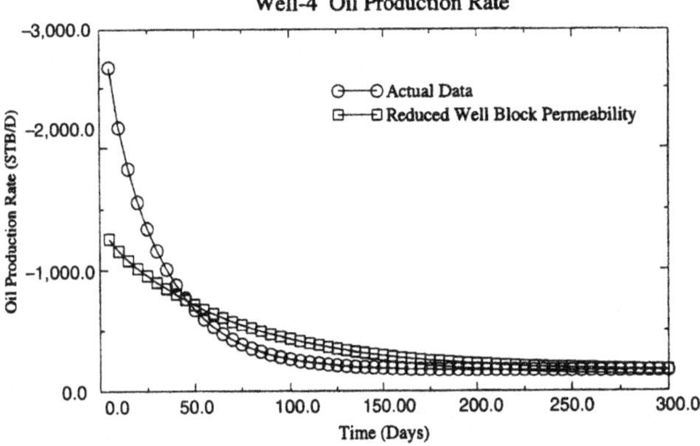

Fig. 10.48—Effect of wellblock permeability on the accuracy of the calculated oil-production rates.

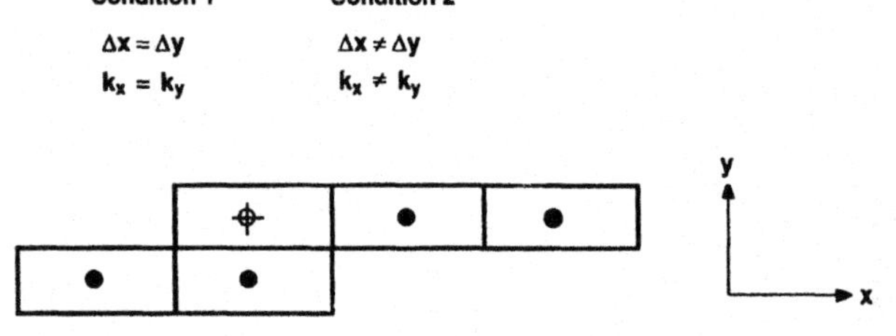

Fig. 10.49—Exercise 10.1.

To emphasize the importance of the accuracy of the wellblock entries, another series of runs is conducted. In this series of prediction cases, the average-thickness values are used uniformly in every gridblock except the wellblocks where the actual thicknesses were assigned. **Fig. 10.47** shows that for Well W-2, the calculated oil-production rates show better agreement with the results of the actual data case, especially during the early simulation times. Again, this is expected because, during early production times, Well W-2 is in direct communication with the wellblock. As the production continues, the radius of investigation of the well increases and oil-production rates become similar to those generated with the average-thickness values for the entire reservoir.

A third series of prediction cases shows the effect of another wellblock property on the calculated production rates. In these cases, the permeability values in the gridblocks that are hosting Production Wells W-2 and W-4 were reduced to one-third of their actual values ($k_{x_{3,2}}=93.33$ md and $k_{x_{9,3}}=90.0$ md vs. $k_{x_{3,2}}=280.0$ md and $k_{x_{9,3}}=270$ md). **Fig. 10.48** shows the results of these prediction cases. As expected, calculated oil flow rates were found to be significantly less than the actual flow rates at early times.

Exercises

10.1 Comment on the following statement regarding **Fig. 10.49.** Show the details of your analysis.

If Condition 1 is satisfied, it is possible to solve the flow problem as if it were a 1D problem. However, if Condition 2 applies, we cannot solve this system with a 1D fluid-flow formulation.

10.2 Fig. 10.50 represents a homogeneous, isotropic reservoir with uniform thickness. The depth to the top surface of the formation is 4,000 ft at every point, and the reservoir is 100% saturated with a slightly compressible liquid. The well in Gridblock 1 is put on production at a rate of 6,000 STB/D and produced at this constant rate for 20 days. A pressure survey in the wellbore at the end of 20 days

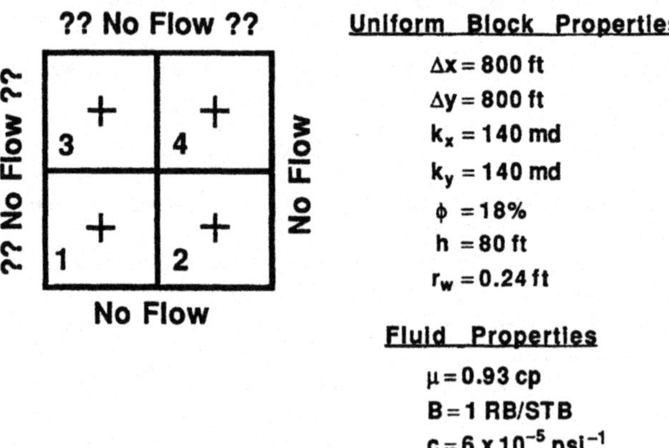

Fig. 10.50—Exercise 10.2.

reveals the sandface pressure as 3,590 psia, which represents a pressure drop of 850 psia from the initial pressure of the field. Your supervisor, after seeing this pressure drop, questions the validity of the no-flow conditions imposed on two of the boundaries, as shown in the figure. From seismic studies, it is certain that the other two boundaries are no-flow boundaries. Answer your supervisor's question on the validity of the no-flow boundary.

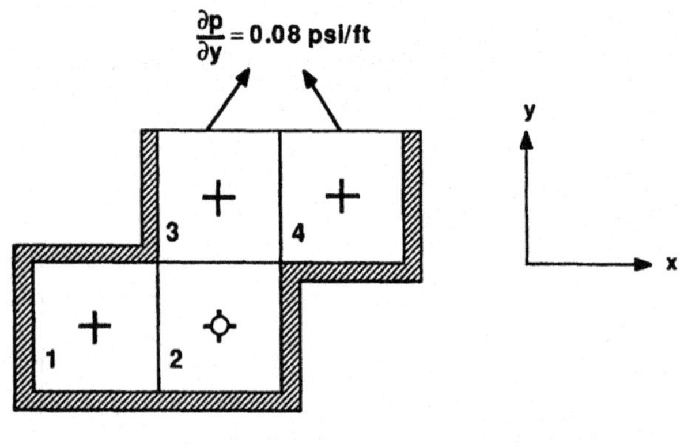

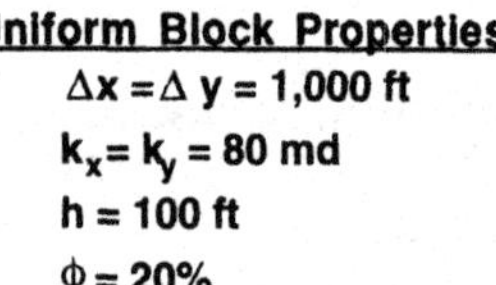

Fluid Properties

$\mu = 1.3$ cp

B = 1 RB/STB

$c = 1.0 \times 10^{5}$ psi^{-1}

Fig. 10.51—Exercise 10.3.

10.3 Consider the flow of a slightly compressible liquid in a 2D reservoir with no depth gradients (**Fig. 10.51**). The reservoir has homogeneous and isotropic property distribution and is at an initial pressure of 4,000 psia. The well in Gridblock 2 is produced at a rate of 4,000 STB/D. You are considering drilling a second production well in the center of Gridblock 4 if the average pressure in Gridblock 4 has not dropped more than 10% of the initial pressure when the well in Gridblock 2 is produced for 20 days.

1. Will you be able to drill the new well in Gridblock 4 on the basis of the proposed criterion?
2. Check the validity of your computations by performing a material balance on the solution. (Hint: Because $B=1$ RB/STB is assumed to remain constant, the conventional material-balance equation will not work; however, you can devise another approach).

10.4 Consider the 2D homogeneous and isotropic reservoir shown in **Fig. 10.52.** The well in Gridblock 4 was put on production 30 days before the well in Gridblock 5 was brought on line. Both wells were produced at a constant rate of 300 STB/D. **Table 10.24** contains available well-pressure survey data. Other pertinent data are $k_x = k_y = 100$ md, $\Delta x = \Delta y = 1{,}320$ ft, $h = 40$ ft, $\phi = 20\%$, $\mu_w = 1.0$ cp, $B_w = 1.0$ RB/STB, $c_w = 8 \times 10^{-7}$ psi^{-1}, and $r_w = 0.25$ ft (for both wells).

1. Find the nature of the boundary along A-B-C.
2. Find the pressure distribution in the reservoir at $t = 30$ and $t = 60$ days.

10.5 Consider the 1D, slightly-compressible-fluid flow problem detailed in **Fig. 10.53.** As the figure shows, a production well was completed in each gridblock; however, only the production well in Gridblock 2 was put on production at a rate of 1,400 STB/D. Wells in

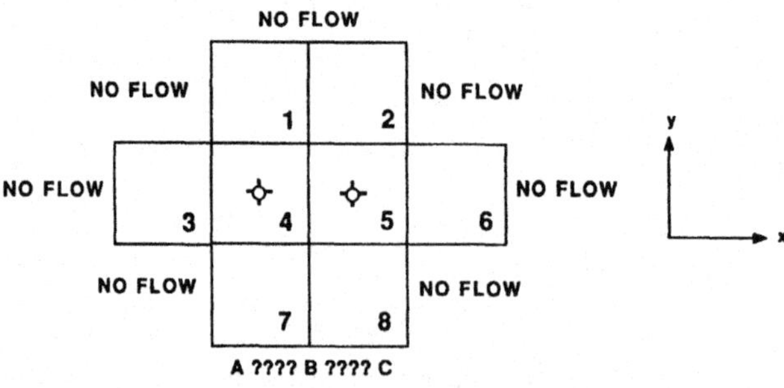

Fig. 10.52—Exercise 10.4.

TABLE 10.24—WELL PRESSURE DATA FOR EXERCISE 10.4

t (days)	p_{wf}, psia	
	Well 4	Well 5
0	5,000	N/A
30	3,697.0	3,783.5

Gridblocks 1 and 3 were kept shut in but pressures were monitored. Thirty days after Well 2 was put on production, a pressure survey was made in each well and the following measurements were recorded. At $t = 30$ days, the pressures of Wells 1, 2, and 3 are 1,514.3, 1,000, and 1,436.5 psia, respectively.

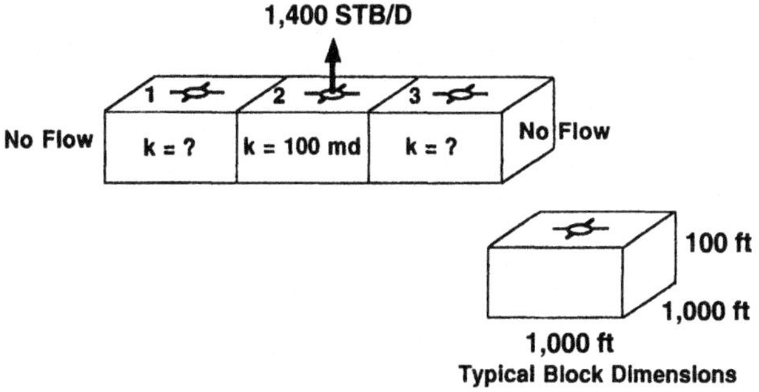

Fig. 10.53—Exercise 10.5.

Furthermore, a well-test analysis conducted in Well 2 revealed an average permeability of 100 md for Gridblock 2. With the pressure data given and the following additional information, estimate the permeabilities of Gridblocks 1 and 3. Other pertinent data are $p_i = 2{,}000$ psia, $\Delta x = \Delta y = 1{,}000$ ft, $h = 100$ ft, $\phi = 24\%$, $\mu = 2$ cp, $B = 1.0$ RB/STB, $c = 1 \times 10^{-5}$ psi^{-1}, and $r_w = 0.25$ ft.

10.6 Consider the system in **Fig. 10.54** where the permeability, thickness, and width of the gridblocks are uniform throughout. The sandface pressure in Gridblock 4 is 2,000 psia. A pressure gradient of -0.6 psi/ft is specified at the bottom of the reservoir. All other boundaries are considered to be completely sealed. The observed flow rate from the well in Gridblock 4 is measured as 2,255 STB/D. After conducting a simulation study, you realize that this rate does not match the simulated results. Going back to geological records of this reservoir, you find that there is a possibility that the right boundary of Gridblock 3 is active. Neglecting the depth gradients, assuming incompressible flow, and using the data provided, answer the following questions.

1. What is the nature of the boundary condition at the right boundary of Gridblock 3?
2. Assuming that the well is completed in Gridblocks 2 and 4, what will be the flow rate from the well if the same sandface pressure is specified? Find the pressure values in each gridblock and comment on the results.

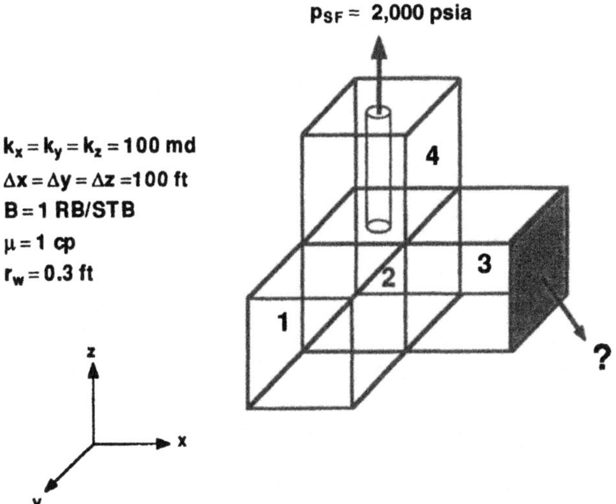

Fig. 10.54—Exercise 10.6.

10.7 Consider the slightly-compressible-fluid flow through the 2D homogeneous and isotropic porous medium shown in **Fig. 10.55**. All the boundaries are known to be no-flow boundaries except the right boundary of Gridblock 3. The well in Gridblock 2 has a flow-rate specification of 500 STB/D. The sandface pressure in the same gridblock is measured to be 2,028 psia at the end of 5 days of production.

1. What is the boundary condition specified at the right boundary of Gridblock 3?
2. Obtain the pressure distribution for this system at the end of the 5-day production period. Perform a material balance on your solution to check the accuracy of your computations.
3. Assume that the boundary conditions specified are maintained. Implement the line-successive overrelaxation (LSOR) solution technique to find the pressure distribution at the end of 10 days. Use an initial guess of 1,680 psia for the LSOR iteration. Use $\omega_{opt} = 1$ and a convergence criterion of 2 psi.

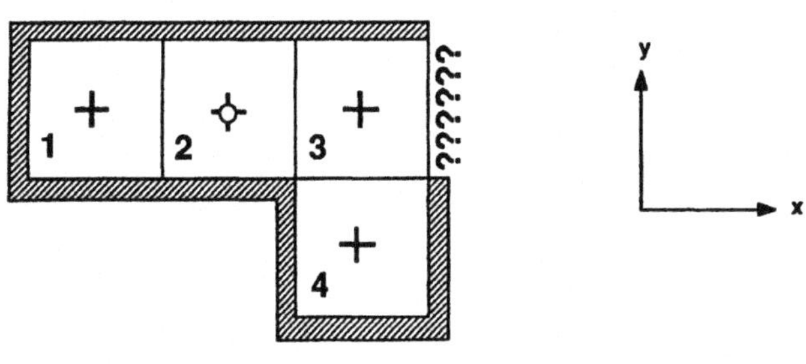

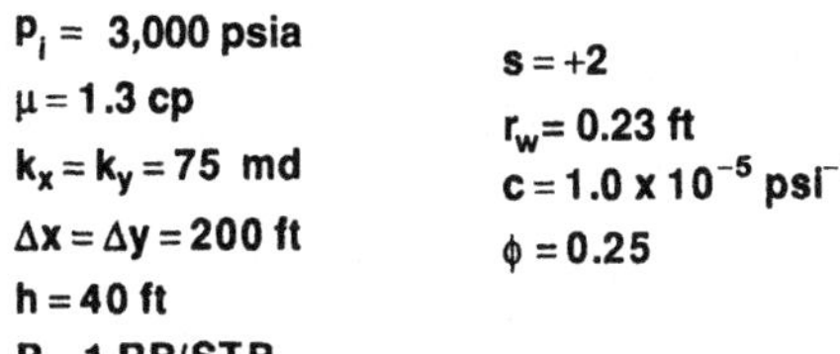

Fig. 10.55—Exercise 10.7.

10.8[47] Consider the 1D reservoir with no-depth gradients as shown in **Fig. 10.56**. Assume the existence of single-phase, slightly-compressible-fluid flow dynamics. It is concluded from seismic studies that the west boundary of the reservoir is completely sealed. There is a disagreement on the nature of the east boundary. Use the pressure and production data provided (reported pressure values were measured downhole at the sandface, and flow rates are surface flow rates) to complete the following tasks.

1. Determine the nature of the boundary condition along the east boundary.

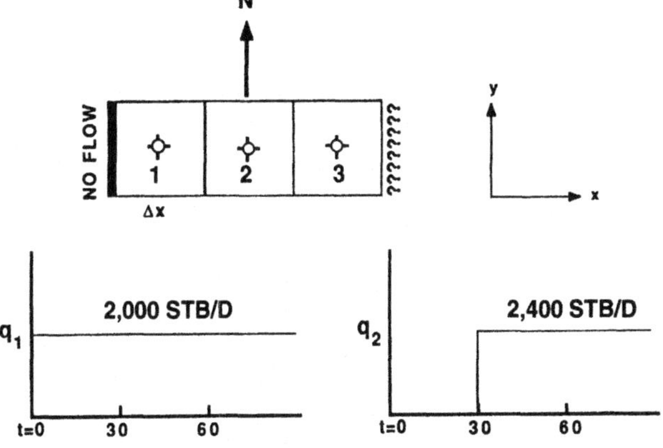

Fig. 10.56—Exercise 10.8.

TABLE 10.25—PRESSURE DATA FOR EXERCISE 10.8

t (days)	p_{sf}, psia	
	Well 1	Well 2
0	4,000	N/A
30	3,135.49	3,320.14

2. A third production well at $t = 60$ days is being considered. Your engineering manager indicates that the third production well should be drilled only if pressure at the location of the third well is not less than 50% of the initial formation pressure at $t = 60$ days. What would you recommend to your manager? Justify your recommendation. Use implicit finite-difference approximation in your solution.

Table 10.25 contains the available pressure survey data. Other relevant data are $k = 180$ md, $\phi = 17\%$, $\Delta x = \Delta y = 4{,}000$ ft, $h = 100$ ft, $\mu = 1$ cp, $B = 1$ RB/STB, $c = 6 \times 10^{-7}$ psi^{-1}, and $r_w = 0.2$ ft (wells were air drilled, hence no skin).

Nomenclature

B = FVF, L^3/L^3, reservoir volume/volume at standard conditions
B_g = gas FVF, L^3/L^3, RB/scf [m^3/std m^3]
B_l = FVF of Phase l, L^3/L^3, reservoir volume/volume at standard conditions
B_o = oil FVF, L^3/L^3, RB/STB [m^3/std m^3]
B_{ob} = oil FVF at bubblepoint pressure, L^3/L^3, RB/STB [m^3/std m^3]
B_{obd} = oil FVF at bubblepoint pressure obtained by differential liberation, L^3/L^3, RB/STB [m^3/std m^3]
B_{obf} = oil FVF at bubblepoint pressure obtained by flash expansion, L^3/L^3, RB/STB [m^3/std m^3]
B_{od} = oil FVF obtained by differential liberation, L^3/L^3, RB/STB [m^3/std m^3]
B_{of} = oil FVF obtained by flash expansion, L^3/L^3, RB/STB [m^3/std m^3]
B_{oi} = oil FVF at initial pressure, L^3/L^3, RB/STB [m^3/std m^3]
B_p = last value of FVF used in history mode, L^3/L^3, reservoir volume/volume at standard conditions
B_t = total (two-phase) FVF, L^3/L^3, RB/STB [m^3/std m^3]
B_w = water FVF, L^3/L^3, RB/B [m^3/std m^3]
c = compressibility, Lt^2/m, psi^{-1} [kPa^{-1}]
c_b = bulk compressibility, Lt^2/m, psi^{-1} [kPa^{-1}]
c_h = hydrostatic compressibility, Lt^2/m, psi^{-1} [kPa^{-1}]
c_o = oil compressibility, Lt^2/m, psi^{-1} [kPa^{-1}]
c_p = pore compressibility, Lt^2/m, psi^{-1} [kPa^{-1}]
c_R = reservoir-rock compressibility, Lt^2/m, psi^{-1} [kPa^{-1}]
c_s = rock-solids compressibility, Lt^2/m, psi^{-1} [kPa^{-1}]
c_t = total compressibility, Lt^2/m, psi^{-1} [kPa^{-1}]
c_u = uniaxial compressibility, Lt^2/m, psi^{-1} [kPa^{-1}]
c_μ = relative rate of change of oil viscosity with pressure above bubblepoint as used in Eq. 10.41, psi^{-1} [kPa^{-1}]
c_ϕ = porosity compressibility, Lt^2/m, psi^{-1} [kPa^{-1}]
E_{Dg} = microscopic gas-displacement efficiency, dimensionless
E_{Dw} = microscopic water-displacement efficiency, dimensionless
E_i = exponential integral function, dimensionless
f_{sh} = fraction of total thickness that is shale, dimensionless
f_w = water fractional-flow coefficient, dimensionless
F = specific function
g = gravitational acceleration, L/t^2, ft/sec^2 [m/s^2]
g_c = coarse grid
g_{cb} = coarse-grid boundary
G_w = well geometric factor, L^3, RB-cp/(D-psi) [m$^3\cdot$Pa$\cdot$s/(d$\cdot$kPa)]
G_{w_k} = well geometric factor for Simulation Layer k, L^3, RB-cp/(D-psi) [m$^3\cdot$Pa$\cdot$s/(d$\cdot$kPa)]
h = thickness (general and individual bed), L, ft [m]
h_g = gross reservoir thickness, L, ft [m]
h_k = thickness of kth layer, L, ft [m]
h_n = net pay thickness, L, ft [m]
h_{owc} = height of initial OWC contact in gridblock, L, ft [m]
h_s = height of swept portion of gridblock, L, ft [m]
h_t = gross pay (total) bed thickness, L, ft [m]
h_{tz} = transition-zone thickness, L, ft [m]
h_{tzc} = transition-zone thickness from core data, L, ft [m]
h_{tzl} = transition-zone thickness from well logs, L, ft [m]
h_u = height of the unswept portion of gridblock, L, ft [m]
h^* = height above OWC, L, ft [m]
h_k^* = height of center of Layer k above OWC, L, ft [m]
$h_{1\text{-}6}$ = thickness of Layers 1 through 6, L, ft [m]
J_w = well productivity (injectivity) index, L^4t/m, STB/(D-psi) [std m^3/(d$\cdot$kPa)]
J_{w_i} = productivity index of the ith well in a field, L^4t/m, STB/(D-psi) [std m^3/(d$\cdot$kPa)]
J_{w_l} = field-measured well productivity index for Phase l, L^4t/m, STB/(D-psi) [std m^3/(d$\cdot$kPa)]
J_{wn} = productivity index of nth well in a field, L^4t/m, STB/(D-psi) [std m^3/(d$\cdot$kPa)]
$J_{w_{n,k}}$ = productivity index for the kth zone of Well n in a field, L^4t/m, STB/(D-psi) [std m^3/(d$\cdot$kPa)]
J_{w_k} = productivity index of the kth zone in a well, L^4t/m, STB/(D-psi) [std m^3/(d$\cdot$kPa)]
$J(S_w)$ = Leverett J function defined by Eq. 10.31, dimensionless
k = permeability, L^2, darcy [μm^2]
k_a = absolute (air) permeability, L^2, darcy [μm^2]
k_H = horizontal permeability, L^2, darcy [μm^2]
k_{H_k} = horizontal permeability of kth layer, L^2, darcy [μm^2]
$k_{H_{1\text{-}6}}$ = horizontal permeability for Layers 1 through 6, L^2, darcy [μm^2]
k_o = effective permeability to oil, L^2, darcy [μm^2]
k_r = relative permeability, dimensionless
k_{rg} = relative permeability to gas, dimensionless
k_{rl} = relative permeability to Phase l, fraction
k_{rlp} = pseudorelative permeability to Phase l, dimensionless
k_{ro} = relative permeability to oil, dimensionless
k_{rog} = relative permeability to oil in oil/gas system, dimensionless
k_{rop} = pseudorelative permeability to oil, dimensionless
k_{row} = relative permeability to oil in oil/water system, dimensionless
k_{rw} = relative permeability to water, dimensionless
k_{rwp} = pseudorelative permeability to water, dimensionless
k_V = vertical permeability of clean reservoir rock, L^2, darcy [μm^2]
k_{V_e} = effective vertical permeability as defined by Eqs. 10.38 and 10.39, L^2, darcy [μm^2]
k_{V_k} = vertical permeability of Layer k, L^2, darcy [μm^2]
$k_{V_{1\text{-}6}}$ = vertical permeability of Layers 1 through 6, L^2, darcy [μm^2]

k_x = permeability in the direction of the x axis, L^2, darcy [μm^2]
$k_{x3,2}$ = permeability in x direction of Gridblock (3,2), L^2, darcy [μm^2]
$k_{x9,3}$ = permeability in x direction of Gridblock (9,3), L^2, darcy [μm^2]
k_y = permeability in the direction of the y axis, L^2, darcy [μm^2]
$\bar{k}_V$ = average vertical permeability, L^2, darcy [μm^2]
l = length, L, ft [m]
$\bar{l}_{sh}$ = average length of shale, L, ft [m]
m_B = slope of well flow performance curve, m/L^{4}t, D-psi/STB [d · kPa/std m^3]
n = index for well number
n_c = number of components, n
n_k = number of layers or intervals, n
n_{parm} = number of production parameters considered in history matching, n
n_{sh} = number of shale units per unit length of reservoir section, L^{-1}, ft^{-1} [m^{-1}]
n_w = number of wells in a field, n
N = initial oil-in-place, L^3, STB [std m^3]
o = oil
O = outcome
p = pressure, m/Lt^2, psia [kPa]
p_a = abandonment pressure, m/Lt^2, psia [kPa]
p_b = bubblepoint pressure, m/Lt^2, psia [kPa]
p_i = initial pressure, m/Lt^2, psia [kPa]
p_{gc} = coarse-gridblock pressure of gas phase, m/Lt^2, psia [kPa]
p_{lf} = fine-gridblock pressure for Phase l, m/Lt^2, psia [kPa]
p_o = oil pressure, pressure of gridblock containing a well, m/Lt^2, psia [kPa]
p_s = saturation pressure, m/Lt^2, psia [kPa]
p_{sc} = standard condition pressure, m/Lt^2, psia [kPa]
p_{sf} = well sandface pressure, m/Lt^2, psia [kPa]
p_{th} = tubinghead pressure, m/Lt^2, psia [kPa]
p_{wf} = flowing well bottomhole pressure, m/Lt^2, psia [kPa]
p_{ws} = shut in well bottomhole pressure, m/Lt^2, psia [kPa]
$\bar{p}$ = average reservoir (or gridblock) pressure, m/Lt^2, psia [kPa]
$\bar{p}_{lc}$ = average coarse-gridblock pressure of Phase l, m/Lt^2, psia [kPa]
$\bar{p}_{oc}$ = average coarse-gridblock pressure of oil phase, m/Lt^2, psia [kPa]
$\bar{p}_{wc}$ = average coarse-gridblock pressure of water phase, m/Lt^2, psia [kPa]
Δp_{gh} = pressure difference caused by height of fluid column, m/Lt^2, psi [kPa]
P = probability
P_c = capillary pressure, m/Lt^2, psi [kPa]
P_{c_c} = core-derived capillary pressure, m/Lt^2, psi [kPa]
P_{c_k} = capillary pressure of layer k, m/Lt^2, psi [kPa]
P_{cgo} = gas/oil capillary pressure, m/Lt^2, psi [kPa]
P_{cgop} = gas/oil capillary pressure pseudofunction, m/Lt^2, psi [kPa]
P_{cl} = log-derived capillary pressure, m/Lt^2, psi [kPa]
P_{cow} = oil/water capillary pressure, m/Lt^2, psi [kPa]
P_{cowp} = oil/water capillary pressure pseudofunction, m/Lt^2, psi [kPa]
P_{cp} = capillary pressure pseudofunction, m/Lt^2, psi [kPa]
P_{c_R} = reservoir scale capillary pressure as calculated by Eq. 10.33, m/Lt^2, psi [kPa]
q = production rate or flow rate, L^3/t, RB/D [m^3/d]
q_{gsc} = gas production rate at standard conditions, L^3/t, scf/D [std m^3/d]
$q_{i_{test}}$ = test production rate of Well i, L^3/t, STB/D [std m^3/d]
q_l = production rate of Phase l, L^3/t, RB/D [m^3/d]
q_{lc} = flow rate of Phase l in coarse grid, L^3/t, RB/D [m^3/d]
q_{lf} = flow rate of Phase l in fine grid, L^3/t, RB/D [m^3/d]
q_{l_k} = flow rate of Phase l from Layer k, L^3/t, RB/D [m^3/d]
q_{lsc} = production rate of Phase l at standard conditions, L^3/t, volume at standard conditions per day
q_n = prorated production rate from Well n, L^3/t, STB/D [std m^3/d]
$q_{n,k}$ = prorated production rate from Layer k in Well n, L^3/t, STB/D [std m^3/d]
$q_{n_{field}}$ = field production rate, L^3/t, STB/D [std m^3/d]
$q_{n_{test}}$ = production rate for Well n from a field test, L^3/t, STB/D [std m^3/d]
q_o = oil flow rate, L^3/t, RB/D [m^3/d]
q_{osc} = oil production rate at standard conditions, L^3/t, STB/D [std m^3/d]
q_{ou} = oil flow rate in unswept zone, L^3/t, RB/D [m^3/d]
q_s = last value of flow rate during history-matching mode, L^3/t, STB/D [std m^3/d]
q_t = total production rate or total flow rate, L^3/t, RB/D [m^3/d]
q_w = water flow rate, L^3/t, RB/D [m^3/d]
q_{wowc} = water flow rate in the zone below OWC in gridblock, L^3/t, RB/D [m^3/d]
q_{ws} = water flow rate in water-swept zone of gridblock, L^3/t, RB/D [m^3/d]
q_{wsc} = water flow rate at standard conditions, L^3/t, B/D [m^3/d]
$q_{1\text{-}6}$ = flow rate in Layers 1 through 6, L^3/t, RB/D [m^3/d]
r = drainage radius, L, ft [m]
r_e = radius of external boundary, L, ft [m]
r_{eq} = equivalent wellblock radius, L, ft [m]
r_s = liquid dropout, L^3/L^3, STB/MMscf
r_w = well radius, L, ft [m]
R_s = solution-gas/oil ratio, L^3/L^3, scf/STB [std m^3/std m^3]
R_{sbd} = bubblepoint solution-gas/oil ratio by differential liberation, L^3/L^3, scf/STB [std m^3/std m^3]
R_{sbf} = bubblepoint solution-gas/oil ratio by flash expansion, L^3/L^3, scf/STB [std m^3/std m^3]
R_{sd} = solution-gas/oil ratio by differential liberation, L^3/L^3, scf/STB [std m^3/std m^3]
R_{sf} = solution-gas/oil ratio by flash expansion, L^3/L^3, scf/STB [std m^3/std m^3]
R_{sw} = solution-gas/water ratio, L^3/L^3, scf/B [std m^3/std m^3]
s_k = skin factor for the kth layer, dimensionless
s_m = mechanical skin factor, dimensionless
s_p = partial penetration skin factor, dimensionless
s_s = skin factor used in reservoir simulation, dimensionless
s_t = total skin factor, dimensionless
S_g = gas saturation, fraction
S_g^* = gas saturation defined in Table 10.5, fraction
S_{gc} = critical gas saturation, fraction
S_{gi} = initial gas saturation, fraction
S_{gcn} = normalized critical gas saturation, fraction
S_{gn} = normalized gas saturation, fraction
S_{gn}^g = normalized gas saturation as defined by Eq. 10.27, fraction
S_{gn}^o = normalized gas saturation as defined by Eq. 10.26, fraction
S_{iw} = irreducible water saturation, fraction

S_{iwn} = normalized irreducible water saturation, fraction
S_l = saturation of Phase l, fraction
$\overline{S}_{lc}$ = average saturation of Phase l in coarse gridblock, fraction
S_{lf} = saturation of Phase l in fine gridblock, fraction
S_{li} = initial saturation of Phase l, fraction
S_{li_k} = initial saturation of Phase l in Layer k, fraction
S_{oi} = initial oil saturation, fraction
S_{org} = residual oil saturation in oil/gas system, fraction
S_{orgn} = normalized residual oil saturation in oil/gas system, fraction
S_{orw} = residual oil saturation in oil/water system, fraction
S_{orwn} = normalized residual oil saturation in oil/water system, fraction
S_w = water saturation, fraction
S_{w_k} = water saturation in Layer k, fraction
S_{wh} = historical water saturation, fraction
S_{wi} = initial water saturation, fraction
S_{wn} = normalized water saturation, fraction
$S_{\varepsilon 2}$ = sum of errors squared
t = time, t, days
Δt_{ws} = shut-in time for proper comparison of simulator pressure to buildup pressure during history matching, t, hours
T_R = reservoir temperature, T, °R [K]
T_{sc} = standard condition temperature, T, °R [K]
v = Poisson's ratio of reservoir rock
v_E = expected value
V = volume, L^3, ft^3 [m^3]
V_b = gridblock bulk volume, L^3, ft^3 [m^3]
V_p = PV, L^3, ft^3 [m^3]
V_{pf} = PV of fine gridblock, L^3, ft^3 [m^3]
V_s = rock solids volume, L^3, ft^3 [m^3]
w_i = weighting factor applied to Production Parameter i
x = distance in the x direction in the Cartesian coordinate system, L, ft [m]
Δx = size of gridblock along the x direction, L, ft [m]
X_{io} = production-history parameter (Eq. 10.85)
X_{is} = production parameter calculated by the simulator (Eq. 10.85)
y = distance in the y direction in the Cartesian coordinate system, L, ft [m]
Δy = size of gridblock along the y direction, L, ft [m]
$Y(p)$ = Y function, dimensionless
z = distance in the z direction in the Cartesian coordinate system, L, ft [m]
z = gas compressibility factor $z = pM/\varrho RT$, dimensionless
Δz = size of gridblock along the z direction, L, ft [m]
Δz_k = thickness of the kth layer, L, ft [m]
Z_{owc} = elevation of OWC referred to datum, L, ft [m]
Z_{top} = elevation of top of the formation referred to datum, L, ft [m]
α_c = volume conversion factor whose numerical value is given in Table 4.1
β_c = transmissibility conversion factor whose numerical value is given in Table 4.1
γ_c = gravity conversion factor whose numerical value is given in Table 4.1
γ_l = gravity of Phase l, m/L^2t^2, psi/ft [kPa/m]
γ_o = oil gravity, m/L^2t^2, psi/ft [kPa/m]
γ_w = water gravity, m/L^2t^2, psi/ft [kPa/m]
Θ_c = contact angle
μ = viscosity, m/Lt, cp [Pa · s]
μ_g = gas viscosity, m/Lt, cp [Pa · s]
μ_l = viscosity of Phase l, m/Lt, cp [Pa · s]
μ_o = oil viscosity, m/Lt, cp [Pa · s]
μ_{ob} = oil viscosity at bubblepoint pressure, m/Lt, cp [Pa · s]
μ_p = last value of viscosity used in the history mode, m/Lt, cp [Pa · s]
μ_w = water viscosity, m/Lt, cp [Pa · s]
ρ_g = gas-phase density, m/L^3, lbm/ft^3 [kg/m^3]
ρ_{gsc} = gas density at standard conditions, m/L^3, lbm/ft^3 [kg/m^3]
ρ_l = density of Phase l, m/L^3, lbm/ft^3 [kg/m^3]
ρ_o = oil-phase density, m/L^3, lbm/ft^3 [kg/m^3]
ρ_w = water-phase density, m/L^3, lbm/ft^3 [kg/m^3]
σ = interfacial tension, m/t^2, dyne/cm [mN/m]
σ_n = normal stress, m/Lt^2, psi [MPa]
σ_{nH} = normal stress in horizontal direction (Fig. 10.8), m/Lt^2, psi [MPa]
σ_{nV} = normal stress in vertical direction (Fig. 10.8), m/Lt^2, psi [MPa]
T_{lx} = transmissibility of Phase l in the x direction
T_{ly} = transmissibility of Phase l in the y direction
T_{lz} = transmissibility of Phase l in the z direction
ϕ = porosity, fraction
ϕ_k = porosity of Layer k, fraction
Φ = potential, m/Lt^2, psia [kPa]
Φ_l = potential for Phase l, m/Lt^2, psia [kPa]
Φ_o = oil phase potential, m/Lt^2, psia [kPa]
Φ_w = water phase potential, m/Lt^2, psia [kPa]
ω_{opt} = optimum overrelaxation parameter

Subscripts

g = gas
o = oil
w = water
$\varepsilon 2$ = error squared

References

1. Mattax, C.C. and Dalton, R.L.: *Reservoir Simulation,* Monograph Series, SPE, Richardson, Texas (1990) **13.**
2. Odeh, A.S.: "An Overview of Mathematical Modeling of the Behavior of Hydrocarbon Reservoirs," *SIAM Review* (July 1982) **24,** No. 3, 263.
3. Coats, K.H.: "Use and Misuse of Reservoir Simulation Models," *JPT* (November 1969) 1391.
4. Price, H.S.: "Let the Problem Dictate the Degree of Sophistication To Be Used in Reservoir Simulation," paper CIM 7110 presented at the 1971 Petroleum Soc. of CIM Annual Technical Meeting, Banff, Canada, 2–5 June.
5. Arnofsky, J.S. *et al.*: "Use and Abuse of Reservoir Simulation—1: Pressure Often Exists to Perform Expensive Reservoir Simulation," *Oil & Gas J.* (5 November 1984) 79.
6. Arnofsky, J.S. *et al.*: "Use and Abuse of Reservoir Simulation—2: Why Simulation Studies Can Be Good or Bad," *Oil & Gas J.* (19 November 1984) 109.
7. Saleri, N.G. and Toronyi, R.M.: "Engineering Control in Reservoir Simulation," paper SPE 18305 presented at the 1988 SPE Annual Technical Conference and Exhibition, Houston, 2–5 October.
8. Aziz, K.: "Ten Golden Rules for Simulation Engineers," *JPT* (November 1989) 1157.
9. *Petroleum Engineer Intl.* (May 1980).
10. *World Oil* (November 1978).
11. Campbell, J.M. Jr., Campbell, J.M. Sr., and Campbell, R.A.: *Analysis and Management of Petroleum Investments: Risk, Taxes and Time,* CPS, Norman, Oklahoma (1987).
12. Anstey, N.A.: *Simple Seismics,* Intl. Human Resources Development Corp., Boston, Massachusetts (1982) 168.
13. Harris, D.G.: "The Role of Geology in Reservoir Simulation Studies," *JPT* (May 1975) 625.
14. Hewitt, T.A.: "Fractal Distributions of Reservoir Heterogeneity and Their Influence on Fluid Transport," paper SPE 15386 presented at the 1986 SPE Annual Technical Conference and Exhibition, New Orleans, 5–8 October.
15. Hohn, M.E.: *Geostatistics and Petroleum Geology,* Van Nostrand Reinhold Co. Inc., New York City (1988).

16. Poston, S.W. and Gross, S.J.: "Numerical Simulation of Sandstone Reservoir Models," *SPERE* (July 1986) 423.
17. Durlofsky, L.J.: "Numerical Calculation of Equivalent Grid Permeability Tensors for Heterogeneous Porous Media," *Water Resources Res.* (1991) **27,** 699.
18. *A Course in Fundamentals of Core Analysis,* Core Laboratories, Dallas (1973) 54.
19. Morse, R.A., Terwilliger, P.L., and Yuster, S.T.: "Relative Permeability Measurements on Small Samples," *Oil & Gas J.* (1947) **46,** 109.
20. Leverett, M.C.: "Capillary Behavior of Porous Solids," *Trans.,* AIME (1941) **142,** 341.
21. Bear, J.: *Dynamics of Fluids in Porous Media,* Dover Publications Inc., New York City (1972).
22. Beaumont, E.A. and Foster, N.H.: *Reservoir I: Properties, Treatise of Petroleum Geology,* Reprint Series, American Assn. of Petroleum Geologists, Tulsa, Oklahoma (1987) **3,** 3.
23. Barbe, J.A.: "Reservoir Management at Dunlin," *JPT* (January 1983) 227.
24. Peaceman, D.W.: "Interpretation of Wellblock Pressures in Numerical Reservoir Simulation," *SPEJ* (June 1978) 183; *Trans.,* AIME, **265.**
25. Peaceman, D.W.: "Interpretation of Wellblock Pressures in Numerical Reservoir Simulation With Nonsquare Gridblocks and Anisotropic Permeability," *SPEJ* (June 1983) 531.
26. Peaceman, D.W.: "Interpretation of Wellblock Pressures in Numerical Reservoir Simulation—Part 3: Some Additional Well Geometries," paper SPE 16976 presented at the 1987 SPE Annual Technical Conference and Exhibition, Dallas, 27–30 September.
27. Odeh, A.S.: "The Proper Interpretation of Field Determined Buildup Pressure and Skin Values for Simulation Use," *SPEJ* (February 1985) 125.
28. Allan, T.O. and Roberts, A.P.: *Production Operations: Well Completions, Workover, and Stimulation,* Oil and Gas Consultants Intl. Inc., (1978) **1,** 274.
29. Halderson, H.H. and Chang, D.M.: "Notes on Stochastic Shales; From Outcrop to Simulation Model," *Reservoir Characterization,* L.W. Lake and H.B. Carroll (eds.), Academic Press Inc., Orlando, Florida (1986) 445–85.
30. Begg, S.H. and King, P.R.: "Modeling the Effects of Shales on Reservoir Performance: Calculation of Effective Vertical Permeability," paper SPE 13529 presented at the 1985 SPE Reservoir Simulation Symposium, Dallas, 10–13 February.
31. Phillips, J.L.: "Reservoir Simulation Technology—Results of a Survey," *Proc.,* Boeing Computer Services Spring 1984 Colloquium for the Geosciences, Houston (May 1984) 152.
32. *A Course in the Phase Behavior of Hydrocarbon Reservoir Fluids,* Core Laboratories, Dallas (1985).
33. *Petroleum Engineering Handbook,* H.B. Bradley (ed.), SPE, Richardson, Texas (1987) 40–46.
34. Ahmed, T.: *Hydrocarbon Phase Behavior,* Gulf Publishing Co., Houston (1989).
35. King, G.R., Ertekin, T., and Schwerer, F.C.: "Numerical Simulation of the Transient Behavior of Coal Seam Degasification Wells," *SPEFE* (April 1986) 165.
36. Koval, E.J.: "A Method for Predicting the Performance of Unstable Displacement in Heterogeneous Media," *SPEJ* (June 1963) 145; *Trans.,* AIME, **228.**
37. Todd, M.R. and Longstaff, W.J.: "The Development, Testing, and Application of a Numerical Simulator for Predicting Miscible Flood Performance," *JPT* (July 1972) 874; *Trans.,* AIME, **253.**
38. Klins, M.A.: *Carbon Dioxide Flooding: Basic Mechanisms and Project Design,* Intl. Human Resources Development Corp., Boston, Massachusetts (1984).
39. Jacks, H.H., Smith, O.J.E., and Mattax, C.C.: "The Modeling of a Three-Dimensional Reservoir With a Two-Dimensional Reservoir Simulator—The Use of Dynamic Pseudofunctions," *SPEJ* (June 1973) 175.
40. Todd, M.R., O'Dell, P.M., and Hirasaki, G.J.: "Methods for Increased Accuracy in Reservoir Simulators," *SPEJ* (December 1972) 515; *Trans.,* AIME, **253.**
41. Coats, K.H. *et al.*: "Simulation of Three-Dimensional, Two-Phase Flow in Oil and Gas Reservoirs," *SPEJ* (December 1967) 377; *Trans.,* AIME, **240.**
42. Kyte, J.R. and Berry, D.W.: "New Pseudofunctions To Control Numerical Dispersion," *SPEJ* (August 1975) 269.
43. Emmanuel, A.S. and Cook, G.W.: "Pseudorelative Permeability for Well Modeling," *SPEJ* (February 1974) 7.
44. Chappelear, J.E. and Hirasaki, G.J.: "A Model of Oil/Water Coning for Two-Dimensional Areal Reservoir Simulation," *SPEJ* (April 1976) 65; *Trans.,* AIME, **261.**
45. Emmanuel, A.S. and Ranney, J.C.: "Studies of Offshore Reservoir With an Interfaced Reservoir/Piping Network Simulator," *JPT* (March 1981) 399.
46. Wijesinghe, A.M. *et al.*: "A Comprehensive Well Management Program for Black-Oil Reservoir Simulation," paper SPE 12269 presented at the 1983 SPE Symposium on Reservoir Simulation, San Francisco, 16–18 November.
47. Ertekin, T. and Adewumi, M.A.: *Reservoir Simulation,* Video Library for E&P Specialists, Intl. Human Resources Development Corp., Boston, Massachusetts (1995).

SI Metric Conversion Factors

°API	141.5/(131.5 + °API)		= g/cm³
bbl	× 1.589 873	E − 01	= m³
cp	× 1.0*	E − 03	= Pa·s
ft	× 3.048*	E − 01	= m
ft³	× 2.831 685	E − 02	= m³
lbm	× 4.535 924	E − 01	= kg
md	× 9.869 233	E − 04	= μm²
psi	× 6.894 757	E + 00	= kPa
psi⁻¹	× 1.450 377	E − 01	= kPa⁻¹
°R	× .555 555		= K

*Conversion factor is exact.

Chapter 11
Relationships Between Numerical Reservoir Simulation and Classical Reservoir Engineering Approaches

11.1 Introduction

In Chap. 1, we briefly discussed some of the classical reservoir engineering techniques used by petroleum professionals to forecast reservoir performance. These classical techniques include material-balance and analytical methods and decline-curve analysis.

In Chaps. 2 through 10, we presented the concepts and procedures that form the basis of numerical reservoir simulation. Although many of these concepts and procedures appeared to be new, in many cases, they were generalizations of the methods used in the derivation of classical reservoir engineering techniques. The objective of this chapter is to demonstrate the relationships between numerical reservoir simulation and classical reservoir engineering approaches.

To facilitate the discussion, we use the following forms of the flow equations for a black-oil model, which are independent of grid geometry.

$$\vec{\nabla}\cdot\left(\beta_c \frac{kk_{rl}}{\mu_l B_l}\vec{\nabla}\Phi_l\right) + \frac{q_{lsc}}{V_b} = \frac{1}{\alpha_c}\frac{\partial}{\partial t}\left(\frac{\phi S_l}{B_l}\right), \quad \text{(11.1)}$$

where $l=o$ or w and

$$\vec{\nabla}\cdot\left(\beta_c \frac{kk_{rg}}{\mu_g B_g}\vec{\nabla}\Phi_g\right) + \vec{\nabla}\cdot\left(\beta_c \frac{R_s kk_{ro}}{\mu_o B_o}\vec{\nabla}\Phi_o\right) + \frac{q_{gsc}}{V_b} = \frac{1}{\alpha_c}\frac{\partial}{\partial t}\left(\frac{\phi S_g}{B_g} + \frac{R_s \phi S_o}{B_o}\right), \quad \text{(11.2)}$$

for gas. The operators $\vec{\nabla}\cdot\vec{u}$ and $\vec{\nabla}\Phi_l$ ($l=o$, w, or g) are defined by Eqs. 3.103 and 3.99, respectively, and the source/sink term, q_{lsc} ($l=o$, w, or g), is on a standard volume basis.

Eqs. 11.1 and 11.2 are derived by combining the continuity equation (a differential form of the mass-balance equation), an equation of state (EOS) [description of the pressure/volume/temperature (PVT) behavior of reservoir fluids], and a transport law (Darcy's law). These equations are coupled with the saturation constraint and capillary pressure equations

$$S_o + S_w + S_g = 1, \quad \text{(11.3)}$$

$$P_{cow} = p_o - p_w, \quad \text{(11.4)}$$

and $P_{cgo} = p_g - p_o$. .... (11.5)

This chapter demonstrates how Eqs. 11.1 through 11.5 are related to classical reservoir engineering approaches.

11.2 Relationship Between Numerical Reservoir Simulation and the Classical Material-Balance Approach

In the development of the classical material-balance approach, the mass-balance equation and an EOS are combined to derive the final forms of the governing equations for various types of reservoirs (see Table 1.2). There is a close relationship between the numerical-simulation and material-balance approaches because the only difference between the two is the exclusion of Darcy's law in the classical approach.

The derivation of the material-balance equation begins by assuming that the potential gradients and capillary pressure effects are negligible. These assumptions can be stated mathematically as

$$\vec{\nabla}\Phi_l \approx 0, \quad \text{(11.6)}$$

where $l=o,w$, or g, and

$$p_l = p, \quad \text{(11.7)}$$

where $l=o$, w, or g.

When we apply Eq. 11.6 to the partial-differential equations (PDE's) used in reservoir simulation, Eqs. 11.1 and 11.2, Darcy's law is removed from the formulation. Therefore, once we apply Eq. 11.6, the numerical-simulation and classical material-balance approaches are identical. Substituting Eq. 11.6 into Eqs. 11.1 and 11.2 results in

$$\frac{q_{osc}}{V_b} = \frac{1}{\alpha_c}\frac{\mathrm{d}}{\mathrm{d}t}\left(\frac{\phi S_o}{B_o}\right), \quad \text{(11.8)}$$

$$\frac{q_{wsc}}{V_b} = \frac{1}{\alpha_c}\frac{\mathrm{d}}{\mathrm{d}t}\left(\frac{\phi S_w}{B_w}\right), \quad \text{(11.9)}$$

and $$\frac{q_{gsc}}{V_b} = \frac{1}{\alpha_c}\frac{\mathrm{d}}{\mathrm{d}t}\left(\frac{\phi S_g}{B_g} + \frac{R_s \phi S_o}{B_o}\right). \quad \text{(11.10)}$$

When going from Eqs. 11.1 and 11.2 to Eqs. 11.8 through 11.10, the implicit assumption is made that average porosity, PVT properties, and saturations can be used to describe reservoir behavior. Multiplying Eqs. 11.8 through 11.10 by the bulk volume, V_b, results in

$$q_{osc} = \frac{V_b}{\alpha_c}\frac{d}{dt}\left(\frac{\phi S_o}{B_o}\right), \quad (11.11)$$

$$q_{wsc} = \frac{V_b}{\alpha_c}\frac{d}{dt}\left(\frac{\phi S_w}{B_w}\right), \quad (11.12)$$

and $$q_{gsc} = \frac{V_b}{\alpha_c}\frac{d}{dt}\left(\frac{\phi S_g}{B_g} + \frac{R_s\phi S_o}{B_o}\right). \quad (11.13)$$

Eqs. 11.11 through 11.13 form the basis of the classical material-balance approach.

11.2.1 General Material-Balance Equation. To begin our development of the general material-balance equation, we multiply Eq. 11.11 by dt and integrate. This results in

$$\int_o^t q_{osc}\,dt = \frac{V_b}{\alpha_c}\int_o^t \frac{d}{dt}\left(\frac{\phi S_o}{B_o}\right)dt \quad (11.14a)$$

or $$\int_o^t q_{osc}\,dt = \frac{V_b}{\alpha_c}\left(\frac{\phi S_o}{B_o}\right)\Bigg|_o^t$$

$$= \frac{V_b}{\alpha_c}\left(\frac{\phi S_o}{B_o} - \frac{\phi_i S_{oi}}{B_{oi}}\right). \quad (11.14b)$$

Recognizing that the integral term in Eq. 11.14b is the cumulative produced oil, N_p, and the second term in the parenthesis is related to the original oil in place, N, we can write

$$N_p = \int_o^t q_{osc}\,dt \quad (11.15)$$

and $$N = \frac{V_b}{\alpha_c}\frac{\phi_i S_{oi}}{B_{oi}}. \quad (11.16)$$

Substituting these equations into Eq. 11.14b yields

$$N_p = \frac{V_b}{\alpha_c}\frac{\phi S_o}{B_o} - N. \quad (11.17)$$

Because our sign convention is negative for production, the variable N_p is negative. This differs from the sign convention used in classical reservoir engineering, where production is positive.

With a similar procedure, we can develop a material-balance equation for water. For the rate term in the water equation, q_{wsc}, we must consider all sources of water entering or leaving the reservoir. That is,

$$q_{wsc} = q_{wpsc} + q_{wisc} + q_{esc}. \quad (11.18)$$

In Eq. 11.18, the water-production rate, q_{wpsc}, is negative, whereas the water-injection rate, q_{wisc}, and water-encroachment rate, q_{esc}, are positive. The explicit treatment for handling water encroachment is required because we set $\vec{\nabla}\Phi_w = 0$, which prevents water from entering the reservoir by natural migration. Substituting Eq. 11.18 into Eq. 11.12, multiplying by dt, and integrating results in

$$\int_o^t q_{wpsc}\,dt + \int_o^t q_{wisc}\,dt + \int_o^t q_{esc}\,dt = \frac{V_b}{\alpha_c}\left(\frac{\phi S_w}{B_w}\right)\Bigg|_o^t \quad (11.19)$$

or $$W_p + W_i + W_{esc} = \frac{V_b}{\alpha_c}\left(\frac{\phi S_w}{B_w} - \frac{\phi_i S_{wi}}{B_{wi}}\right). \quad (11.20)$$

Defining the initial water in place as

$$W = \frac{V_b}{\alpha_c}\frac{\phi_i S_{wi}}{B_{wi}} \quad (11.21)$$

and substituting into Eq. 11.20 yields

$$W_p + W_i + W_{esc} = \frac{V_b}{\alpha_c}\frac{\phi S_w}{B_w} - W. \quad (11.22)$$

Finally, we can develop a material-balance equation for gas with the identical approach used for oil and water. The gas material-balance equation becomes

$$G_p + G_i = \frac{V_b}{\alpha_c}\left(\frac{\phi S_g}{B_g} + \frac{R_s\phi S_o}{B_o} - \frac{\phi_i S_{gi}}{B_{gi}} - \frac{R_{si}\phi_i S_{oi}}{B_{oi}}\right). \quad (11.23)$$

In this equation, the gas production term, G_p, is negative, whereas the gas injection term, G_i, is positive. Eq. 11.23 can be rewritten as

$$G_p + G_i = \frac{V_b}{\alpha_c}\frac{\phi S_g}{B_g} + \frac{V_b}{\alpha_c}\frac{R_s\phi S_o}{B_o} - G - R_{si}N. \quad (11.24)$$

In this equation, N is defined by Eq. 11.16 and the initial free gas in place, G, is defined by

$$G = \frac{V_b}{\alpha_c}\frac{\phi_i S_{gi}}{B_{gi}}. \quad (11.25)$$

In classical reservoir engineering, G is defined in terms of the ratio of the initial free gas volume at reservoir conditions to the initial oil volume at reservoir conditions. That is,

$$m = \frac{GB_{gi}}{NB_{oi}} \quad (11.26)$$

or $$G = mN\frac{B_{oi}}{B_{gi}}. \quad (11.27)$$

Substituting Eq. 11.27 into Eq. 11.24 results in

$$G_p + G_i = \frac{V_b}{\alpha_c}\frac{\phi S_g}{B_g} + \frac{V_b}{\alpha_c}\frac{R_s\phi S_o}{B_o} - mN\frac{B_{oi}}{B_{gi}} - R_{si}N. \quad (11.28)$$

Rearranging Eq. 11.17 for $(V_b/\alpha_c)[(\phi S_o)/B_o]$ and substituting into Eq. 11.28 yields

$$G_p + G_i = \frac{V_b}{\alpha_c}\frac{\phi S_g}{B_g} + R_s(N + N_p) - mN\frac{B_{oi}}{B_{gi}} - R_{si}N. \quad (11.29)$$

To conform to the nomenclature of classical reservoir engineering, we define the cumulative produced-gas/oil ratio as

$$R_p = \frac{G_p}{N_p}. \quad (11.30)$$

Substituting into Eq. 11.29 results in

$$R_pN_p + G_i = \frac{V_b}{\alpha_c}\frac{\phi S_g}{B_g} + R_s(N + N_p) - mN\frac{B_{oi}}{B_{gi}} - R_{si}N. \quad (11.31)$$

Eq. 11.31 is the final form of the gas material balance. Rearranging Eqs. 11.17, 11.22, and 11.31 yields

$$\frac{V_b}{\alpha_c}\phi S_o = (N + N_p)B_o, \quad (11.32)$$

$$\frac{V_b}{\alpha_c}\phi S_w = (W + W_p + W_i + W_{esc})B_w, \quad (11.33)$$

and $$\frac{V_b}{\alpha_c}\phi S_g = \left[R_p N_p + G_i + mN\frac{B_{oi}}{B_{gi}} + R_{si}N - R_s(N + N_p)\right]B_g. \quad (11.34)$$

Summing Eqs. 11.32 through 11.34 results in

$$\frac{V_b}{\alpha_c}\phi(S_o + S_w + S_g) = (N + N_p)B_o + (W + W_p + W_i + W_{esc})B_w + \left[R_p N_p + G_i + mN\frac{B_{oi}}{B_{gi}} + R_{si}N - R_s(N + N_p)\right]B_g. \quad (11.35)$$

After applying the saturation constraint, Eq. 11.3, the material-balance equation becomes

$$\frac{V_b}{\alpha_c}\phi = (N + N_p)B_o + (W + W_p + W_i + W_{esc})B_w + \left[R_p N_p + G_i + mN\frac{B_{oi}}{B_{gi}} + R_{si}N - R_s(N + N_p)\right]B_g. \quad (11.36)$$

We can rearrange and sum Eqs. 11.16, 11.21, and 11.25 to obtain

$$\frac{V_b}{\alpha_c}\phi_i(S_{oi} + S_{wi} + S_{gi}) = NB_{oi} + WB_{wi} + GB_{gi}. \quad (11.37)$$

Applying Eqs. 11.3 and 11.27 to Eq. 11.37 results in

$$\frac{V_b}{\alpha_c}\phi_i = NB_{oi} + WB_{wi} + mNB_{oi}. \quad (11.38)$$

Subtracting Eq. 11.38 from Eq. 11.36 yields

$$\frac{V_b}{\alpha_c}(\phi - \phi_i) = (N + N_p)B_o + (W + W_p + W_i + W_{esc})B_w + \left[R_p N_p + G_i + mN\frac{B_{oi}}{B_{gi}} + R_{si}N - R_s(N + N_p)\right]B_g - NB_{oi} - WB_{wi} - mNB_{oi}. \quad (11.39)$$

Using the porosity dependence on pressure, Eq. 2.35, with initial pressure as reference pressure,

$$\phi = \phi_i\left[1 + c_\phi(p - p_i)\right] \quad (11.40)$$

results in

$$\frac{V_b}{\alpha_c}\phi_i c_\phi(p - p_i) = (N + N_p)B_o + (W + W_p + W_i + W_{esc})B_w + \left[R_p N_p + G_i + mN\frac{B_{oi}}{B_{gi}} + R_{si}N - R_s(N + N_p)\right]B_g - NB_{oi} - WB_{wi} - mNB_{oi}. \quad (11.41)$$

Performing multiplications in Eq. 11.41 and grouping similar terms yields

$$\frac{V_b}{\alpha_c}\phi_i c_\phi(p - p_i) = N\left[B_o + (R_{si} - R_s)B_g - B_{oi} + mB_{oi}\left(\frac{B_g}{B_{gi}} - 1\right)\right] + N_p(B_o + R_pB_g - R_sB_g) + W(B_w - B_{wi}) + (W_{esc} + W_p + W_i)B_w + G_iB_g. \quad (11.42)$$

To conform to the classical reservoir engineering approach, we add and subtract $R_{si}N_pB_g$ to Eq. 11.42. This results in

$$\frac{V_b}{\alpha_c}\phi_i c_\phi(p - p_i) = N\left[B_o + (R_{si} - R_s)B_g - B_{oi} + mB_{oi}\left(\frac{B_g}{B_{gi}} - 1\right)\right] + N_p\left[B_o + (R_{si} - R_s)B_g + (R_p - R_{si})B_g\right] + W(B_w - B_{wi}) + (W_{esc} + W_p + W_i)B_w + G_iB_g. \quad (11.43)$$

Defining the two-phase formation volume factor (FVF),

$$B_t = B_o + (R_{si} - R_s)B_g, \quad (11.44)$$

and substituting this definition into Eq. 11.43 yields

$$\frac{V_b}{\alpha_c}\phi_i c_\phi(p - p_i) = N\left[B_t - B_{oi} + mB_{oi}\left(\frac{B_g}{B_{gi}} - 1\right)\right] + N_p\left[B_t + (R_p - R_{si})B_g\right] + W(B_w - B_{wi}) + (W_{esc} + W_p + W_i)B_w + G_iB_g. \quad (11.45)$$

Solving Eq. 11.45 for N results in

$$N = \{(V_b/\alpha_c)\phi_i c_\phi(p - p_i) - N_p[B_t + (R_p - R_{si})B_g] - W(B_w - B_{wi}) - (W_{esc} + W_p + W_i)B_w - G_iB_g\} \div \{B_t - B_{oi} + mB_{oi}[(B_g/B_{gi}) - 1]\}. \quad (11.46)$$

Eq. 11.46 is the most general form of the material-balance equation that uses the assumptions discussed. Further assumptions can be applied to develop more common forms of the material-balance equation. In particular, we can apply the following assumptions to simplify Eq. 11.46.

1. The reservoir is undergoing primary production, which implies that $W_i = 0$ STB and $G_i = 0$ scf.
2. The reservoir rock is incompressible, which implies that $c_\phi = 0$ psi^{-1}.
3. The formation water is incompressible, which implies that $B_w = B_{wi} = 1$ RB/STB.

With these assumptions, Eq. 11.46 becomes

$$N = \frac{-N_p[B_t + (R_p - R_{si})B_g] - (W_{esc} + W_p)}{\{B_t - B_{oi} + mB_{oi}[(B_g/B_{gi}) - 1]\}}. \quad (11.47)$$

Eq. 11.47 is identical to the first equation listed in Table 1.2 with one exception, the sign difference of the production terms, N_p and W_p, which reflects the difference in the sign convention used by the two approaches. Additional simplifying assumptions can be applied to Eq. 11.47 for other reservoir conditions. Table 1.2 lists these assumptions and the resulting equations.

11.2.2 Muskat Method for Solution-Gas-Drive Reservoirs. For solution-gas-drive reservoirs, water production and water encroachment are negligible; therefore, we need to consider only Eqs. 11.1 (for oil only) and 11.2. After applying the assumptions of $\vec{\nabla}\Phi_l = 0$ ($l = o$ or g) and negligible capillary pressure effects and multiplying by the bulk volume, Eqs. 11.11 and 11.13 result. Applying the saturation constraint, Eq. 11.3, to Eq. 11.13 results in

$$q_{osc} = \frac{V_b}{\alpha_c}\frac{d}{dt}\left(\frac{\phi S_o}{B_o}\right) \quad \text{(11.48)}$$

$$\text{and } q_{gsc} = \frac{V_b}{\alpha_c}\frac{d}{dt}\left[\frac{\phi(1 - S_o - S_{iw})}{B_g} + \frac{R_s\phi S_o}{B_o}\right]. \quad \text{(11.49)}$$

In Eq. 11.49, we have replaced S_w with S_{iw} because of our assumption of negligible water movement. Applying the chain rule to Eqs. 11.48 and 11.49 yields

$$q_{osc} = \frac{V_b}{\alpha_c}\frac{d}{dp}\left(\frac{\phi S_o}{B_o}\right)\frac{dp}{dt} \quad \text{(11.50)}$$

$$\text{and } q_{gsc} = \frac{V_b}{\alpha_c}\frac{d}{dp}\left[\frac{\phi(1 - S_o - S_{iw})}{B_g} + \frac{R_s\phi S_o}{B_o}\right]\frac{dp}{dt}. \quad \text{(11.51)}$$

Expanding the derivatives in these equations results in

$$q_{osc} = \frac{V_b}{\alpha_c}\left(\frac{\phi}{B_o}\frac{dS_o}{dp} + \frac{S_o}{B_o}\frac{d\phi}{dp} - \frac{\phi S_o}{B_o^2}\frac{dB_o}{dp}\right)\frac{dp}{dt} \quad \text{(11.52)}$$

$$\text{and } q_{gsc} = \frac{V_b}{\alpha_c}\left[\frac{-\phi}{B_g}\frac{dS_o}{dp} + \frac{(1 - S_o - S_{iw})}{B_g}\frac{d\phi}{dp} - \frac{\phi(1 - S_o - S_{iw})}{B_g^2}\frac{dB_g}{dp} + \frac{R_s\phi}{B_o}\frac{dS_o}{dp} + \frac{R_sS_o}{B_o}\frac{d\phi}{dp} + \frac{\phi S_o}{B_o}\frac{dR_s}{dp} - \frac{R_s\phi S_o}{B_o^2}\frac{dB_o}{dp}\right]\frac{dp}{dt}. \quad \text{(11.53)}$$

Dividing Eq. 11.53 by Eq. 11.52 yields

$$\frac{q_{gsc}}{q_{osc}} = \left[\frac{-\phi}{B_g}\frac{dS_o}{dp} + \frac{(1 - S_o - S_{iw})}{B_g}\frac{d\phi}{dp} - \frac{\phi(1 - S_o - S_{iw})}{B_g^2} \times \frac{dB_g}{dp} + \frac{R_s\phi}{B_o}\frac{dS_o}{dp} + \frac{R_sS_o}{B_o}\frac{d\phi}{dp} + \frac{\phi S_o}{B_o}\frac{dR_s}{dp} - \frac{R_s\phi S_o}{B_o^2}\frac{dB_o}{dp}\right] \div \left(\frac{\phi}{B_o}\frac{dS_o}{dp} + \frac{S_o}{B_o}\frac{d\phi}{dp} - \frac{\phi S_o}{B_o^2}\frac{dB_o}{dp}\right). \quad \text{(11.54)}$$

Because we consider solution-gas drive only, injection is not considered in this formulation. For production wells, we can write

$$q_{gsc} = -\left(\frac{k_{rg}}{\mu_gB_g} + \frac{R_sk_{ro}}{\mu_oB_o}\right)G_w(p - p_{wf}) \quad \text{(11.55)}$$

$$\text{and } q_{osc} = -\frac{k_{ro}}{\mu_oB_o}G_w(p - p_{wf}), \quad \text{(11.56)}$$

where G_w = well geometric factor as discussed in Chap. 6. Substituting Eqs. 11.55 and 11.56 into Eq. 11.54 results in

$$\frac{k_{rg}\mu_oB_o}{k_{ro}\mu_gB_g} + R_s = \left[\frac{-\phi}{B_g}\frac{dS_o}{dp} + \frac{(1 - S_o - S_{iw})}{B_g}\frac{d\phi}{dp} - \frac{\phi(1 - S_o - S_{iw})}{B_g^2} \times \frac{dB_g}{dp} + \frac{R_s\phi}{B_o}\frac{dS_o}{dp} + \frac{R_sS_o}{B_o}\frac{d\phi}{dp} + \frac{\phi S_o}{B_o}\frac{dR_s}{dp} - \frac{R_s\phi S_o}{B_o^2}\frac{dB_o}{dp}\right] \div \left(\frac{\phi}{B_o}\frac{dS_o}{dp} + \frac{S_o}{B_o}\frac{d\phi}{dp} - \frac{\phi S_o}{B_o^2}\frac{dB_o}{dp}\right). \quad \text{(11.57)}$$

Solving Eq. 11.57 for dS_o/dp results in

$$\frac{dS_o}{dp} = \left\{\frac{S_o}{B_o}\frac{k_{rg}\mu_o}{k_{ro}\mu_g}\frac{dB_o}{dp} - \frac{(1 - S_o - S_{iw})}{B_g}\frac{dB_g}{dp} + \frac{B_gS_o}{B_o}\frac{dR_s}{dp} + \left[(1 - S_o - S_{iw}) - \frac{S_ok_{rg}\mu_o}{k_{ro}\mu_g}\right]\frac{1}{\phi}\frac{d\phi}{dp}\right\} \bigg/ \left(\frac{k_{rg}\mu_o}{k_{ro}\mu_g} + 1\right). \quad \text{(11.58)}$$

Applying the definition of formation compressibility,

$$c_\phi = \frac{1}{\phi}\frac{d\phi}{dp} \quad \text{(11.59)}$$

yields

$$\frac{dS_o}{dp} = \left\{\frac{S_o}{B_o}\frac{k_{rg}\mu_o}{k_{ro}\mu_g}\frac{dB_o}{dp} - \frac{(1 - S_o - S_{iw})}{B_g}\frac{dB_g}{dp} + \frac{B_gS_o}{B_o}\frac{dR_s}{dp} + c_\phi\left[(1 - S_o - S_{iw}) - \frac{S_ok_{rg}\mu_o}{k_{ro}\mu_g}\right]\right\} \bigg/ \left(\frac{k_{rg}\mu_o}{k_{ro}\mu_g} + 1\right). \quad \text{(11.60)}$$

Eq. 11.60 is the most general form of the Muskat equation that uses the assumptions discussed to this point. The more common version of the Muskat equation is obtained by assuming an incompressible formation ($c_\phi = 0$). With this assumption, Eq. 11.60 becomes

$$\frac{dS_o}{dp} = \frac{\frac{S_o}{B_o}\frac{k_{rg}\mu_o}{k_{ro}\mu_g}\frac{dB_o}{dp} - \frac{(1-S_o-S_{iw})}{B_g}\frac{dB_g}{dp} + \frac{B_gS_o}{B_o}\frac{dR_s}{dp}}{\frac{k_{rg}\mu_o}{k_{ro}\mu_g} + 1}, \quad \text{(11.61)}$$

Eq. 11.61 is the final form of the Muskat equation for solution-gas-drive reservoirs.

11.3 Relationship Between Numerical Reservoir Simulation and Analytical Methods

The equations that describe fluid flow through porous media, Eqs. 11.1 through 11.5, are too complex to solve analytically (exactly) because of the nonlinear nature of the equations. To obtain analytical solutions to the flow equations, simplifying assumptions must be applied to linearize the equations. In this section, we analyze the assumptions required to convert the flow equations to the equations used in pressure-transient and Buckley-Leverett analyses.

11.3.1 Pressure-Transient Analysis. For pressure-transient applications, we generally consider single-phase flow of either oil or gas. For this discussion, we consider the flow equation for the oil phase. The 1D radial form of the oil equation, Eq. 11.1, is

$$\frac{1}{r}\frac{\partial}{\partial r}\left[r\frac{\beta_ck_{ro}(S_{iw})k}{\mu_oB_o}\frac{\partial\Phi_o}{\partial r}\right] + \frac{q_{osc}}{V_b} = \frac{1}{\alpha_c}\frac{\partial}{\partial t}\left[\frac{\phi(1 - S_{iw})}{B_o}\right]. \quad \text{(11.62)}$$

To continue with the development of the well-test equation, several assumptions are required.

1. There are no external sources or sinks, which implies that $q_{osc} = 0$.
2. The reservoir is horizontal, which implies that $\partial\Phi_o/\partial r = \partial p/\partial r$.
3. The effective permeability to oil, $k_o = k_{ro}(S_{iw})k$, is independent of position (that is, a homogeneous distribution). For practical purposes, this implies that all three components (irreducible water saturation, S_{iw}; absolute permeability, k; and relative permeability characteristics) are independent of position.
4. The viscosity, μ_o, is constant.
5. The pressure gradient, $\partial p/\partial r$, is small.
6. The oil-phase compressibility, c_o, is small.

Applying Assumptions 1 through 4 to Eq. 11.62 results in

$$\frac{1}{r}\frac{\partial}{\partial r}\left(\frac{r}{B_o}\frac{\partial p}{\partial r}\right) = \frac{\mu_o(1 - S_{iw})}{\alpha_c\beta_c k_o}\frac{\partial}{\partial t}\left(\frac{\phi}{B_o}\right). \quad (11.63)$$

Expanding the derivative term on the right side of Eq. 11.63 yields

$$\frac{1}{r}\frac{\partial}{\partial r}\left(\frac{r}{B_o}\frac{\partial p}{\partial r}\right) = \frac{\mu_o(1 - S_{iw})}{\alpha_c\beta_c k_o}\left[\phi\frac{\partial}{\partial t}\left(\frac{1}{B_o}\right) + \frac{1}{B_o}\frac{\partial \phi}{\partial t}\right]. \quad (11.64)$$

Applying the chain rule to the right side of Eq. 11.64 results in

$$\frac{1}{r}\frac{\partial}{\partial r}\left(\frac{r}{B_o}\frac{\partial p}{\partial r}\right) = \frac{\mu_o(1 - S_{iw})}{\alpha_c\beta_c k_o}\left[\phi\frac{d}{dp}\left(\frac{1}{B_o}\right) + \frac{1}{B_o}\frac{d\phi}{dp}\right]\frac{\partial p}{\partial t} \quad (11.65a)$$

or $$\frac{1}{r}\frac{\partial}{\partial r}\left(\frac{r}{B_o}\frac{\partial p}{\partial r}\right) = \frac{\mu_o(1 - S_{iw})}{\alpha_c\beta_c k_o}\left[\frac{-\phi}{B_o^2}\frac{dB_o}{dp} + \frac{1}{B_o}\frac{d\phi}{dp}\right]\frac{\partial p}{\partial t}. \quad (11.65b)$$

Substituting the definitions of compressibility,

$$c_o = \frac{-1}{B_o}\frac{dB_o}{dp} \quad (11.66)$$

and $$c_\phi = \frac{1}{\phi}\frac{d\phi}{dp}, \quad (11.67)$$

into Eq 11.65b results in

$$\frac{1}{r}\frac{\partial}{\partial r}\left(\frac{r}{B_o}\frac{\partial p}{\partial r}\right) = \frac{\mu_o(1 - S_{iw})}{\alpha_c\beta_c k_o}\left(\frac{c_o\phi}{B_o} + \frac{c_\phi\phi}{B_o}\right)\frac{\partial p}{\partial t} \quad (11.68a)$$

or $$\frac{1}{r}\frac{\partial}{\partial r}\left(\frac{r}{B_o}\frac{\partial p}{\partial r}\right) = \frac{\mu_o\phi(1 - S_{iw})}{\alpha_c\beta_c k_o B_o}(c_o + c_\phi)\frac{\partial p}{\partial t}. \quad (11.68b)$$

In Eq. 11.66, the negative sign implies that, above the bubblepoint pressure, as the pore pressure increases, the oil-phase FVF decreases. Conversely, the positive sign in Eq. 11.67 implies that as the pore pressure increases, the porosity increases.

Defining the total system compressibility, c_t, as

$$c_t = c_o + c_\phi \quad (11.69)$$

and substituting Eq. 11.69 into Eq. 11.68b yields

$$\frac{1}{r}\frac{\partial}{\partial r}\left(\frac{r}{B_o}\frac{\partial p}{\partial r}\right) = \frac{\mu_o\phi(1 - S_{iw})c_t}{\alpha_c\beta_c k_o B_o}\frac{\partial p}{\partial t}. \quad (11.70)$$

Expanding the left side of Eq. 11.70 results in

$$\frac{1}{r}\left[\frac{r}{B_o}\frac{\partial^2 p}{\partial r^2} + \frac{1}{B_o}\frac{\partial p}{\partial r} - \frac{r}{B_o^2}\frac{dB_o}{dp}\left(\frac{\partial p}{\partial r}\right)^2\right] = \frac{\mu_o\phi(1 - S_{iw})c_t}{\alpha_c\beta_c k_o B_o}\frac{\partial p}{\partial t} \quad (11.71a)$$

or $$\frac{1}{B_o}\frac{\partial^2 p}{\partial r^2} + \frac{1}{rB_o}\frac{\partial p}{\partial r} - \frac{1}{B_o^2}\frac{dB_o}{dp}\left(\frac{\partial p}{\partial r}\right)^2 = \frac{\mu_o\phi(1 - S_{iw})c_t}{\alpha_c\beta_c k_o B_o}\frac{\partial p}{\partial t}. \quad (11.71b)$$

Substituting the definition of oil-phase compressibility, Eq. 11.66, into Eq. 11.71b yields

$$\frac{1}{B_o}\frac{\partial^2 p}{\partial r^2} + \frac{1}{rB_o}\frac{\partial p}{\partial r} + \frac{c_o}{B_o}\left(\frac{\partial p}{\partial r}\right)^2 = \frac{\mu_o\phi(1 - S_{iw})c_t}{\alpha_c\beta_c k_o B_o}\frac{\partial p}{\partial t}. \quad (11.72)$$

Multiplying Eq. 11.72 by B_o results in

$$\frac{\partial^2 p}{\partial r^2} + \frac{1}{r}\frac{\partial p}{\partial r} + c_o\left(\frac{\partial p}{\partial r}\right)^2 = \frac{\mu_o\phi(1 - S_{iw})c_t}{\alpha_c\beta_c k_o}\frac{\partial p}{\partial t}. \quad (11.73)$$

Assumptions 5 and 6, small pressure gradients and compressibility, imply that

$$c_o\left(\frac{\partial p}{\partial r}\right)^2 \approx 0. \quad (11.74)$$

Substituting Eq. 11.74 into Eq. 11.73 yields

$$\frac{\partial^2 p}{\partial r^2} + \frac{1}{r}\frac{\partial p}{\partial r} = \frac{\mu_o\phi(1 - S_{iw})c_t}{\alpha_c\beta_c k_o}\frac{\partial p}{\partial t}. \quad (11.75)$$

Substituting the identity

$$\frac{\partial^2 p}{\partial r^2} + \frac{1}{r}\frac{\partial p}{\partial r} = \frac{1}{r}\frac{\partial}{\partial r}\left(r\frac{\partial p}{\partial r}\right) \quad (11.76)$$

into Eq. 11.75 gives the diffusivity equation

$$\frac{1}{r}\frac{\partial}{\partial r}\left(r\frac{\partial p}{\partial r}\right) = \frac{\mu_o\phi(1 - S_{iw})c_t}{\alpha_c\beta_c k_o}\frac{\partial p}{\partial t}. \quad (11.77)$$

Eq. 11.77, when subject to appropriate initial and boundary conditions, forms the basis of classical buildup and drawdown testing. The most commonly used external-boundary conditions include no-flow, constant-pressure, and infinite-acting boundaries, while the most commonly used internal boundaries (wells) include constant-rate, constant-pressure, and multirate (with and without wellbore storage) specifications.

Although we list the constant-pressure well specification as an internal boundary condition, it is used rarely in well-test applications. It is, however, commonly used in the development of production type curves.[1,2] Production type curves are a form of decline curves and are discussed in Sec. 11.4.2.

11.3.2 Buckley-Leverett Analysis. The Buckley-Leverett analysis is the most common method for analyzing waterflood operations. Writing Eq. 11.1 for $l = o$ and w in a 1D, linear porous medium results in

$$\frac{\partial}{\partial x}\left(\beta_c\frac{k_x k_{ro}}{\mu_o B_o}\frac{\partial \Phi_o}{\partial x}\right) + \frac{q_{osc}}{V_b} = \frac{1}{\alpha_c}\frac{\partial}{\partial t}\left(\frac{\phi S_o}{B_o}\right) \quad (11.78)$$

and $$\frac{\partial}{\partial x}\left(\beta_c\frac{k_x k_{rw}}{\mu_w B_w}\frac{\partial \Phi_w}{\partial x}\right) + \frac{q_{wsc}}{V_b} = \frac{1}{\alpha_c}\frac{\partial}{\partial t}\left(\frac{\phi S_w}{B_w}\right). \quad (11.79)$$

The Buckley-Leverett technique uses the following assumptions.

1. There are no external sources or sinks in the porous medium, which implies that $q_{osc} = q_{wsc} = 0$ STB/D. (In the Buckley-Leverett technique, production and injection are handled through the boundary conditions.)
2. The oil and water phases are incompressible, which implies that B_o and B_w are constant.
3. The porous medium is incompressible, which implies that porosity is constant.
4. The cross-sectional area that is open to flow is constant.
5. The fractional flow of water is dependent on water saturation only.

Applying Assumptions 1 through 3 to Eqs. 11.78 and 11.79 results in

$$\frac{\partial}{\partial x}\left(\beta_c\frac{k_x k_{ro}}{\mu_o}\frac{\partial \Phi_o}{\partial x}\right) = \frac{\phi}{\alpha_c}\frac{\partial S_o}{\partial t} \quad (11.80)$$

and $$\frac{\partial}{\partial x}\left(\beta_c\frac{k_x k_{rw}}{\mu_w}\frac{\partial \Phi_w}{\partial x}\right) = \frac{\phi}{\alpha_c}\frac{\partial S_w}{\partial t}. \quad (11.81)$$

Multiplying both sides of Eqs. 11.80 and 11.81 by a constant cross-sectional area, A_x, yields

$$\frac{\partial}{\partial x}\left(\beta_c \frac{A_x k_x k_{ro}}{\mu_o}\frac{\partial \Phi_o}{\partial x}\right) = \frac{A_x \phi}{\alpha_c}\frac{\partial S_o}{\partial t} \quad (11.82)$$

and $$\frac{\partial}{\partial x}\left(\beta_c \frac{A_x k_x k_{rw}}{\mu_w}\frac{\partial \Phi_w}{\partial x}\right) = \frac{A_x \phi}{\alpha_c}\frac{\partial S_w}{\partial t}. \quad (11.83)$$

In Eqs. 11.82 and 11.83, we used the assumption of a constant cross-sectional area to move the A_x term inside the derivative operator. Noting that

$$q_l = \frac{-\beta_c A_x k_x k_{rl}}{\mu_l}\frac{\partial \Phi_l}{\partial x}, \quad (11.84)$$

where $l = o$ or w, is the equation of volumetric flow rate at reservoir conditions, we can write

$$\frac{-\partial q_o}{\partial x} = \frac{A_x \phi}{\alpha_c}\frac{\partial S_o}{\partial t} \quad (11.85)$$

and $$\frac{-\partial q_w}{\partial x} = \frac{A_x \phi}{\alpha_c}\frac{\partial S_w}{\partial t}. \quad (11.86)$$

Adding Eqs. 11.85 and 11.86 results in

$$-\frac{\partial}{\partial x}(q_o + q_w) = \frac{A_x \phi}{\alpha_c}\frac{\partial}{\partial t}(S_o + S_w). \quad (11.87)$$

Applying the saturation-constraint equation, Eq. 11.3, for two-phase flow gives

$$S_o + S_w = 1, \quad (11.88)$$

and differentiating with respect to time yields

$$\frac{\partial S_o}{\partial t} + \frac{\partial S_w}{\partial t} = 0 \quad (11.89a)$$

or $$\frac{\partial}{\partial t}(S_o + S_w) = 0. \quad (11.89b)$$

Substituting into Eq. 11.87 yields

$$\frac{\partial}{\partial x}(q_o + q_w) = 0. \quad (11.90)$$

Defining the total reservoir volumetric flow rate as

$$q_t = q_o + q_w \quad (11.91)$$

and substituting Eq. 11.91 into Eq. 11.90 results in

$$\frac{\partial q_t}{\partial x} = 0. \quad (11.92)$$

Eq. 11.92 implies that, for the assumptions used to this point (Assumptions 1 through 4 mentioned earlier in this section), the total liquid rate at reservoir conditions, q_t, is independent of location. To continue our discussion, we define the fractional flow of water as

$$f_w = \frac{q_w}{q_o + q_w} \quad (11.93a)$$

or $$f_w = \frac{q_w}{q_t}. \quad (11.93b)$$

Rearranging Eq. 11.93b and substituting into Eq. 11.86 yields

$$-\frac{\partial}{\partial x}(f_w q_t) = \frac{A_x \phi}{\alpha_c}\frac{\partial S_w}{\partial t}. \quad (11.94)$$

Expanding the left side of Eq. 11.94 yields

$$-q_t\frac{\partial f_w}{\partial x} - f_w\frac{\partial q_t}{\partial x} = \frac{A_x \phi}{\alpha_c}\frac{\partial S_w}{\partial t}. \quad (11.95)$$

Substituting Eq. 11.92 into Eq. 11.95 results in

$$-q_t\frac{\partial f_w}{\partial x} = \frac{A_x \phi}{\alpha_c}\frac{\partial S_w}{\partial t} \quad (11.96a)$$

or $$-\frac{\partial f_w}{\partial x} = \frac{A_x \phi}{\alpha_c q_t}\frac{\partial S_w}{\partial t}. \quad (11.96b)$$

With the assumption that f_w is a function of water saturation only, we can apply the chain rule to Eq. 11.96b to obtain

$$-\left(\frac{\partial f_w}{\partial S_w}\right)_t\left(\frac{\partial S_w}{\partial x}\right)_t = \frac{A_x \phi}{\alpha_c q_t}\left(\frac{\partial S_w}{\partial t}\right)_x. \quad (11.97)$$

Because S_w is a function of both location and time, the total change in the water saturation, dS_w, can be written as

$$dS_w = \left(\frac{\partial S_w}{\partial x}\right)_t dx + \left(\frac{\partial S_w}{\partial t}\right)_x dt. \quad (11.98)$$

If we are interested in a fixed value of water saturation, we can set $dS_w = 0$ and rearrange Eq. 11.98. This yields

$$\left(\frac{dx}{dt}\right)_{S_w} = \frac{-(\partial S_w/\partial t)_x}{(\partial S_w/\partial x)_t}. \quad (11.99)$$

Eq. 11.99 is the definition of the velocity at which a fixed water saturation, S_w, travels through the porous medium. Solving Eq. 11.99 for $(\partial S_w/\partial t)_x$ and substituting into Eq. 11.97 results in

$$\left(\frac{\partial f_w}{\partial S_w}\right)_t\left(\frac{\partial S_w}{\partial x}\right)_t = \frac{A_x \phi}{\alpha_c q_t}\left(\frac{\partial S_w}{\partial x}\right)_t\left(\frac{dx}{dt}\right)_{S_w} \quad (11.100)$$

or $$\left(\frac{dx}{dt}\right)_{S_w} = \frac{\alpha_c q_t}{A_x \phi}\left(\frac{\partial f_w}{\partial S_w}\right)_t, \quad (11.101)$$

where $(\partial f_w/\partial S_w)$ is assumed to be a known function. Eq. 11.101 is the Buckley-Leverett, or frontal-advance, equation. This equation forms the basis for the classical analysis of waterfloods.

11.4 Relationship Between Numerical Reservoir Simulation and Decline-Curve Analysis

Two forms of decline curves are commonly used in the petroleum industry: empirical-decline[3] and production type curves.[2] Empirical-decline curves are based on the rate/time relationship (see Eq. 1.1)

$$\frac{1}{q_{osc}}\frac{dq_{osc}}{dt} = -K(-q_{osc})^b, \quad (11.102)$$

where $$K = \frac{D_i}{\left(-q_{osc_i}\right)^b}. \quad (11.103)$$

Integration of Eq. 11.102 results in (see Table 1.3)

$$\frac{q_{osc}}{q_{osc_i}} = e^{-D_i t} \quad (11.104a)$$

for exponential decline ($b = 0$),

$$\frac{q_{osc}}{q_{osc_i}} = (1 + bD_i t)^{\frac{-1}{b}} \quad (11.104b)$$

for hyperbolic decline ($0 < b < 1$), and

$$\frac{q_{osc}}{q_{osc_i}} = (1 + D_i t)^{-1} \quad (11.104c)$$

for harmonic decline ($b = 1$).

Production type curves are analytical solutions to the diffusivity equation, Eq. 11.77, subject to a constant-wellbore-pressure specification. Fetkovich[2] showed that, under certain assumptions, the Arps' equations[3] are late-time solutions to the diffusivity equation. When this occurs, the two decline-curve approaches are identical.

11.4.1 Arps'[3] Decline Curves. Starting with Eq. 11.1 written for $l = o$,

$$\vec{\nabla}\cdot\left(\beta_c \frac{kk_{ro}}{\mu_o B_o}\vec{\nabla}\Phi_o\right) + \frac{q_{osc}}{V_b} = \frac{1}{\alpha_c}\frac{\partial}{\partial t}\left(\frac{\phi S_o}{B_o}\right). \quad (11.105)$$

To demonstrate the relationship between Eq. 11.105 and the classical Arps' equation, Eq. 11.102, we need to apply the following assumptions.

1. The effects of the potential gradient are negligible, which implies that $\vec{\nabla}\Phi_o \approx 0$.

2. The water saturation remains at the irreducible water saturation, S_{iw}, which implies that $S_o = 1 - S_{iw}$ throughout the production life of the well or field and that the reservoir is undergoing single-phase flow.

3. The well is produced at a constant bottomhole pressure, p_{wf}. To be consistent with the earlier assumption and $p_{wf} > p_b$.

4. The inflow performance parameters are constant with time, which implies that these parameters are also independent of pressure.

5. The group $\{[V_b\phi(1 - S_{iw})c_t]/(\alpha_c B_o)\}$ is constant with time.

6. The reservoir is in a boundary-dominated, pressure-depletion flow regime. This flow regime is discussed later in this section.

Chen and Poston[4] showed that, in many cases, these assumptions can be relaxed if pseudopressure and pseudotime are used in the solution of Eq. 11.105.

Applying Assumptions 1 and 2 to Eq. 11.105 results in

$$\frac{q_{osc}}{V_b} = \frac{1}{\alpha_c}\frac{d}{dt}\left[\frac{\phi(1 - S_{iw})}{B_o}\right]. \quad (11.106)$$

Multiplying by the bulk volume yields

$$q_{osc} = \frac{V_b}{\alpha_c}\frac{d}{dt}\left[\frac{\phi(1 - S_{iw})}{B_o}\right]. \quad (11.107)$$

Expanding the time derivative in a similar manner to Eq. 11.63 results in

$$q_{osc} = \frac{V_b}{\alpha_c}\frac{\phi(1 - S_{iw})c_t}{B_o}\frac{dp}{dt}. \quad (11.108)$$

As discussed in Chap. 6, the oil-production rate is modeled with an inflow-performance equation. In this discussion, we consider three different inflow-performance relationships:

$$q_{osc} = -J_o(p - p_{wf}), \quad (11.109)$$

$$q_{osc} = -C_p(p - p_{wf})^n, \quad (11.110)$$

and $$q_{osc} = -C_{p^2}(p^2 - p_{wf}^2)^n. \quad (11.111)$$

Eq. 11.109 is the inflow-performance relationship discussed in detail in Chap. 6, while Eqs. 11.110 and 11.111 are the backpressure equations in terms of pressures and pressures squared, respectively. In Eq. 11.109,

$$J_o = \frac{k_{ro}}{\mu_o B_o}G_w, \quad (11.112)$$

where G_w is defined by Eq. 6.28. For the special case $n = 1$, Eq. 11.110 becomes identical to Eq. 11.109 with

$$C_p = J_o. \quad (11.113)$$

Solving for p in Eq. 11.109 results in

$$p = p_{wf} - \frac{q_{osc}}{J_o}. \quad (11.114)$$

Substituting Eq. 11.114 into Eq. 11.108 yields

$$q_{osc} = \frac{V_b}{\alpha_c}\frac{\phi(1 - S_{iw})c_t}{B_o}\frac{d}{dt}\left(p_{wf} - \frac{q_{osc}}{J_o}\right). \quad (11.115)$$

Expanding the time derivative in Eq. 11.115 results in

$$q_{osc} = \frac{V_b}{\alpha_c}\frac{\phi(1 - S_{iw})c_t}{B_o}\left(\frac{dp_{wf}}{dt} - \frac{1}{J_o}\frac{dq_{osc}}{dt} + \frac{q_{osc}}{J_o^2}\frac{dJ_o}{dt}\right). \quad (11.116)$$

Because we have assumed that p_{wf} and J_o are constant with time,

$$\frac{dp_{wf}}{dt} = 0 \quad (11.117)$$

and $$\frac{dJ_o}{dt} = 0. \quad (11.118)$$

Substituting into Eq. 11.116 results in

$$q_{osc} = -\frac{V_b}{\alpha_c}\frac{\phi(1 - S_{iw})c_t}{B_o J_o}\frac{dq_{osc}}{dt}. \quad (11.119)$$

Separating variables and integrating yields

$$\int_{q_{osc_i}}^{q_{osc}} \frac{1}{q_{osc}}dq_{osc} = -\int_0^t \frac{\alpha_c}{V_b}\frac{B_o J_o}{\phi(1 - S_{iw})c_t}dt. \quad (11.120)$$

Applying the assumptions that J_o and $\{[V_b\phi(1 - S_{iw})c_t]/(\alpha_c B_o)\}$ are constant with time, we can remove these two groups from the integral on the right side of Eq. 11.120. This results in

$$\int_{q_{osci}}^{q_{osc}} \frac{1}{q_{osc}}dq_{osc} = -\frac{\alpha_c}{V_b}\frac{B_o J_o}{\phi(1 - S_{iw})c_t}\int_0^t dt. \quad (11.121)$$

Performing the integrations in Eq. 11.121 results in

$$[\log_e(q_{osc})]_{q_{osc_i}}^{q_{osc}} = \frac{-\alpha_c}{V_b}\frac{B_o J_o}{\phi(1 - S_{iw})c_t}(t)\Big|_0^t, \quad (11.122)$$

$$\log_e\left(\frac{q_{osc}}{q_{osc_i}}\right) = \frac{-\alpha_c}{V_b}\frac{B_o J_o}{\phi(1 - S_{iw})c_t}t, \quad (11.123)$$

or, finally,

$$\frac{q_{osc}}{q_{osc_i}} = e^{\frac{-\alpha_c}{V_b}\frac{B_o J_o}{\phi(1 - S_{iw})c_t}t}. \quad (11.124)$$

Comparing Eq. 11.124 with the equation for exponential decline, Eq. 11.104a, we can define

$$D_i = \frac{\alpha_c}{V_b}\frac{B_o J_o}{\phi(1 - S_{iw})c_t}. \quad (11.125)$$

Because we have assumed that p_{wf} and J_o are independent of time, we can define q_{osc_i} in Eq. 11.124 as

$$q_{osc_i} = -J_o(p_i - p_{wf}). \quad (11.126)$$

Eqs. 11.125 and 11.126 are the definitions of the decline-curve parameters D_i and q_{osc_i} in terms of reservoir properties and were first identified by Fetkovich.[2] These parameters can be made specific to a particular geometry by supplying appropriate definitions for V_b and J_o.

Note that we could have substituted Eq. 11.109 into Eq. 11.108 for q_{osc} to obtain

$$-J_o(p - p_{wf}) = \frac{V_b}{\alpha_c}\frac{\phi(1 - S_{iw})c_t}{B_o}\frac{dp}{dt} \quad (11.127a)$$

or $$\frac{V_b}{\alpha_c}\frac{\phi(1 - S_{iw})c_t}{B_o}\frac{dp}{dt} + J_o p = J_o p_{wf}. \quad (11.127b)$$

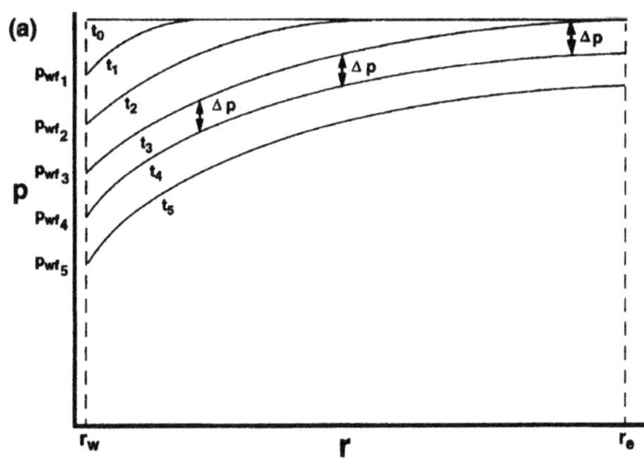

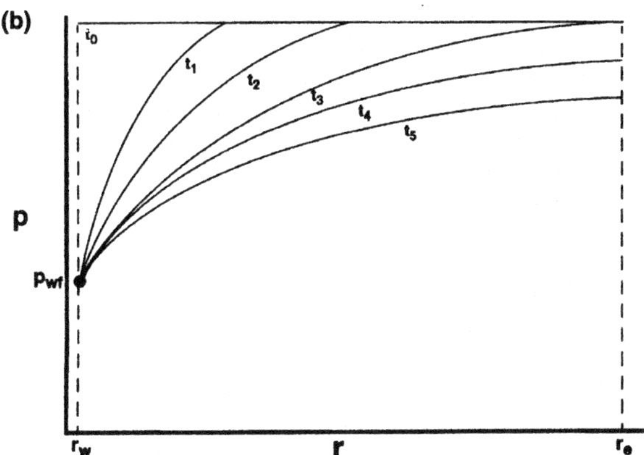

Fig. 11.1—(a) Pseudosteady state flow behavior with the onset of pseudosteady state occurring at $t_{pss} = t_3$. After t_{pss}, the pressure drop with respect to time, Δp, is independent of position, *r*. (b) Boundary-dominated pressure depletion. The onset of boundary-dominated pressure depletion occurs at t_3.

Under the assumptions listed previously, Eq. 11.127b is a linear, ordinary differential equation that, when subject to the initial condition $p = p_i$ at $t = 0$, has the formal solution

$$\frac{p - p_{wf}}{p_i - p_{wf}} = e^{-D_i t}, \qquad (11.128)$$

where D_i is defined by Eq. 11.125. This solution can be verified by solving Eq. 11.128 for p and substituting the result into Eq. 11.127b.

Eq. 11.128 gives the average pressure for reservoirs undergoing exponential decline that adhere to the previous assumptions. We could have derived Eq. 11.128 by substituting Eq. 11.109 into Eq. 11.124 to obtain

$$\frac{-J_o\left(p - p_{wf}\right)}{q_{osc_i}} = e^{\frac{-a_c}{V_b}\frac{B_o J_o}{\phi(1-S_{iw})c_t}t}. \qquad (11.129)$$

Substituting Eqs. 11.125 and 11.126 into Eq. 11.129 results in

$$\frac{J_o\left(p - p_{wf}\right)}{J_o\left(p_i - p_{wf}\right)} = e^{-D_i t} \qquad (11.130)$$

or $$\frac{p - p_{wf}}{p_i - p_{wf}} = e^{-D_i t}. \qquad (11.128)$$

Two points to this analysis need further discussion. The first is that this analysis is valid only for wells or reservoirs undergoing boundary-dominated pressure depletion. This type of depletion differs from pseudosteady-state behavior in that the wellbore pressure is fixed. **Fig. 11.1** illustrates this.

In this figure, two types of boundary-dominated flow behavior are depicted. Fig. 11.1a shows classic pseudosteady-state behavior. This figure illustrates that, after the onset of pseudosteady state ($t > t_{pss}$), the pressure drop with respect to time is independent of position. This figure also illustrates that the wellbore pressure, p_{wf}, is a function of time.

Fig. 11.1b shows boundary-dominated pressure depletion and that the wellbore pressure is fixed with time. This pressure depletion leads to the exponential-decline behavior described in this section. Eq. 11.128 describes the behavior of the average reservoir pressure of the pressure distribution shown in Fig. 11.1b as a function of time.

The second point is the possibility that other reservoir conditions exist that result in exponential decline. In this section, we demonstrate that the assumptions listed previously result in exponential decline. This does not imply that all reservoirs undergoing exponential decline must adhere to these assumptions. For example, Omoregie *et al.*[5] show that the Ninian field in the North Sea, which is undergoing a voidage-balanced peripheral waterflood, is experiencing exponential decline. A voidage-balanced waterflood violates at least two of the assumptions listed earlier: single-phase flow and boundary-dominated pressure depletion. If reservoir conditions other than the assumptions listed earlier are the cause of exponential decline, the definitions of the decline parameters, Eqs. 11.125 and 11.126, are not valid.

We now investigate the decline behavior of wells and reservoirs that obey the backpressure equation. Solving Eq. 11.110 for pressure results in

$$p = p_{wf} + \left(\frac{-q_{osc}}{C_p}\right)^{\frac{1}{n}}. \qquad (11.131)$$

Substituting Eq. 11.131 into Eq. 11.108 and applying the assumptions of constant inflow-performance parameters results in

$$q_{osc} = \frac{V_b}{a_c}\frac{\phi(1 - S_{iw})c_t}{B_o C_p^{1/n}}\frac{\mathrm{d}}{\mathrm{d}t}\left[(-q_{osc})^{\frac{1}{n}}\right]. \qquad (11.132)$$

To maintain our sign convention for production/injection, we work with the negative of production. That is,

$$q'_{osc} = -q_{osc}. \qquad (11.133)$$

Substituting Eq. 11.133 into Eq. 11.132 yields

$$q'_{osc} = \frac{-V_b}{a_c}\frac{\phi(1 - S_{iw})c_t}{B_o C_p^{1/n}}\frac{\mathrm{d}}{\mathrm{d}t}\left[(q'_{osc})^{\frac{1}{n}}\right]. \qquad (11.134)$$

Expanding Eq. 11.134 results in

$$q'_{osc} = \frac{-V_b}{a_c}\frac{\phi(1 - S_{iw})c_t}{nB_o C_p^{1/n}}(q'_{osc})^{\frac{1}{n}-1}\frac{\mathrm{d}q'_{osc}}{\mathrm{d}t}. \qquad (11.135)$$

Separating variables and integrating yields

$$\int_{q'_{osc_i}}^{q'_{osc}}(q'_{osc})^{\frac{1}{n}-2}\mathrm{d}q'_{osc} = \frac{-a_c}{V_b}\frac{nB_o C_p^{1/n}}{\phi(1 - S_{iw})c_t}\int_0^t \mathrm{d}t. \qquad (11.136)$$

The integral on the left side of Eq. 11.136 can have two forms of solutions, depending on the value of the exponent, n. For $n = 1$, which implies Darcy flow, Eq. 11.136 becomes

$$\int_{q'_{osc_i}}^{q'_{osc}}\frac{1}{q'_{osc}}\mathrm{d}q'_{osc} = \frac{-a_c}{V_b}\frac{B_o C_p}{\phi(1 - S_{iw})c_t}\int_0^t \mathrm{d}t, \qquad (11.121)$$

which was discussed in detail earlier. Performing the integrations in Eq. 11.121 results in the definition of exponential decline.

For $n \neq 1$, the integration of Eq. 11.136 results in

$$\frac{1}{\frac{1}{n} - 1}\left[(q'_{osc})^{\frac{1}{n}-1}\right]_{q'_{osc_i}}^{q'_{osc}} = \frac{-a_c}{V_b}\frac{nB_o C_p^{1/n}}{\phi(1 - S_{iw})c_t}(t)\Big|_0^t \qquad (11.137)$$

$$\text{or } (q'_{osc})^{\frac{1}{n}-1} - \left(q'_{osc_i}\right)^{\frac{1}{n}-1} = \frac{-\alpha_c}{V_b}\frac{(1-n)B_oC_p^{1/n}}{\phi(1-S_{iw})c_t}t. \quad \text{.................. (11.138)}$$

Dividing by $(q'_{osc_i})^{\frac{1}{n}-1}$ yields

$$\left(\frac{q'_{osc}}{q'_{osc_i}}\right)^{\frac{1}{n}-1} - 1 = \frac{-\alpha_c}{V_b}\frac{(1-n)B_oC_p^{1/n}}{\phi(1-S_{iw})c_t}\frac{t}{\left(q'_{osc_i}\right)^{\frac{1}{n}-1}} \quad \text{.................. (11.139)}$$

$$\text{or } \left(\frac{q'_{osc}}{q'_{osc_i}}\right)^{\frac{1}{n}-1} = 1 - \frac{\alpha_c}{V_b}\frac{(1-n)B_oC_p^{1/n}}{\phi(1-S_{iw})c_t}\frac{t}{\left(q'_{osc_i}\right)^{\frac{1}{n}-1}}. \quad \text{.................. (11.140)}$$

Finally,

$$\frac{q'_{osc}}{q'_{osc_i}} = \left[1 - \frac{\alpha_c}{V_b}\frac{(1-n)B_oC_p^{1/n}}{\phi(1-S_{iw})c_t}\frac{t}{\left(q'_{osc_i}\right)^{\frac{1}{n}-1}}\right]^{\frac{n}{1-n}}. \quad \text{.................. (11.141)}$$

Comparing Eq. 11.141 with Eq. 11.104b and noting that

$$\frac{q'_{osc}}{q'_{osc_i}} = \frac{q_{osc}}{q_{osc_i}} \quad \text{.............................. (11.142)}$$

indicates that

$$-\frac{1}{b} = \frac{n}{1-n} \quad \text{.......................... (11.143a)}$$

$$\text{or } b = \frac{n-1}{n}. \quad \text{.............................. (11.143b)}$$

Substituting Eq. 11.143b into Eq. 11.141 yields

$$\frac{q'_{osc}}{q'_{osc_i}} = \left[1 + \frac{\alpha_c}{V_b}\frac{nbB_oC_p^{1/n}}{\phi(1-S_{iw})c_t}\frac{t}{\left(q'_{osc_i}\right)^{\frac{1}{n}-1}}\right]^{\frac{-1}{b}}. \quad \text{..... (11.144)}$$

Again, comparing Eq. 11.144 with Eq. 11.104b indicates that

$$D_i = \frac{\alpha_c}{V_b}\frac{nB_oC_p^{1/n}}{\phi(1-S_{iw})c_t}\frac{1}{\left(q'_{osc_i}\right)^{\frac{1}{n}-1}}. \quad \text{............... (11.145)}$$

Defining the initial production rate,

$$q'_{osc_i} = -q_{osc_i} = C_p\left(p_i - p_{wf}\right)^n \quad \text{................ (11.146)}$$

and substituting into Eq. 11.145 results in

$$D_i = \frac{\alpha_c}{V_b}\frac{nB_oC_p\left(p_i - p_{wf}\right)^{n-1}}{\phi(1-S_{iw})c_t} \quad \text{................ (11.147a)}$$

$$\text{or } D_i = \frac{-\alpha_c}{V_b}\frac{nB_oq_{osc_i}}{\phi(1-S_{iw})c_t\left(p_i - p_{wf}\right)}. \quad \text{........... (11.147b)}$$

Eq. 11.147b indicates that, because of our sign convention of negative for production, D_i is positive. Using the definition of D_i given by Eq. 11.147b (or Eq. 11.145) and substituting Eq. 11.142 into Eq. 11.144 gives

$$\frac{q'_{osc}}{q'_{osc_i}} = \frac{q_{osc}}{q_{osc_i}} = \left(1 + bD_it\right)^{\frac{-1}{b}}, \quad \text{................ (11.148)}$$

which is the definition of hyperbolic decline. Eqs. 11.143b, 11.146, and 11.147b are the definitions of the decline parameters b, q_{osc_i}, and D_i, respectively. The corresponding pressure/time relationship for hyperbolic decline becomes

$$\left(\frac{p - p_{wf}}{p_i - p_{wf}}\right)^n = \left(1 + bD_it\right)^{\frac{b-1}{b}} \quad \text{................ (11.149a)}$$

in terms of b or

$$\frac{p - p_{wf}}{p_i - p_{wf}} = \left(1 + bD_it\right)^{\frac{1}{1-n}}. \quad \text{.................. (11.149b)}$$

in terms of n.

By inspecting Eq. 11.143b, we can see that a value of $b=1$ (harmonic decline) results in a value of $n \to \infty$. This implies that, under the conditions used in this analysis, harmonic decline will not occur. Also, note from Eq. 11.143b that values of $n<1$ result in negative values of b. Because this is physically impossible, this analysis is valid only for values of $n>1$.

With the same approach, we can analyze the decline behavior of wells and reservoirs in which the backpressure equation in terms of the pressure-squared formulation is valid. To obtain an integral that results in Arps' equation, we need to make the additional assumption that sufficiently high drawdowns exist so that

$$p^2 - p_{wf}^2 \approx p^2. \quad \text{.......................... (11.150)}$$

Substituting this approximation into Eq. 11.111 yields

$$q_{osc} = -C_{p^2}\,p^{2n} \quad \text{.......................... (11.151)}$$

$$\text{or } p = \left(\frac{-q_{osc}}{C_{p^2}}\right)^{\frac{1}{2n}}. \quad \text{...................... (11.152)}$$

Substituting Eq. 11.152 into Eq. 11.108 and applying Eq. 11.133 results in

$$q'_{osc} = -\frac{-V_b\,\phi(1-S_{iw})c_t}{\alpha_c\;2nB_o\,C_{p^2}^{1/2n}}(q'_{osc})^{\frac{1}{2n}-1}\frac{dq'_{osc}}{dt}. \quad \text{.................. (11.153)}$$

Separating variables and integrating yields

$$\int_{q'_{osc_i}}^{q'_{osc}}(q'_{osc})^{\frac{1}{2n}-2}dq'_{osc} = \frac{-\alpha_c}{V_b}\frac{2nB_oC_{p^2}^{1/2n}}{\phi(1-S_{iw})c_t}\int_0^t dt. \quad \text{.................. (11.154)}$$

Again, we must consider the value of the exponent on the left side of Eq. 11.154. For $n=½$, we have

$$\int_{q'_{osc_i}}^{q'_{osc}}\frac{1}{q'_{osc}}dq'_{osc} = \frac{-\alpha_c}{V_b}\frac{B_o\,C_{p^2}}{\phi(1-S_{iw})c_t}\int_0^t dt, \quad \text{........ (11.155)}$$

which is the definition of exponential decline.

For $n \neq ½$, we can integrate Eq. 11.154 to obtain

$$\frac{1}{(1/2n)-1}\left[(q'_{osc})^{\frac{1}{2n}-1}\right]_{q'_{osc_i}}^{q'_{osc}} = \frac{-\alpha_c}{V_b}\frac{2nB_o\,C_{p^2}^{1/2n}}{\phi(1-S_{iw})c_t}(t)\Big|_0^t \quad \text{.................. (11.156)}$$

$$\text{or } (q'_{osc})^{\frac{1}{2n}-1} - \left(q'_{osc_i}\right)^{\frac{1}{2n}-1} = \frac{-\alpha_c}{V_b}\frac{(1-2n)B_o\,C_{p^2}^{1/2n}}{\phi(1-S_{iw})c_t}t, \quad \text{.................. (11.157)}$$

and $\dfrac{q_{osc}}{q_{osc_i}} = \dfrac{q'_{osc}}{q'_{osc_i}} =$

$$= \left[1 - \frac{\alpha_c}{V_b}\frac{(1-2n)B_o C_{p^2}^{1/2n}}{\phi(1-S_{iw})c_t}\frac{t}{\left(C_{p^2}p_i^{2n}\right)^{\frac{1}{2n}-1}}\right]^{\frac{2n}{1-2n}}$$

$$\text{.......} (11.158)$$

$$\text{or } \frac{q_{osc}}{q_{osc_i}} = \left[1 - \frac{\alpha_c}{V_b}\frac{(1-2n)B_o C_{p^2}p_i^{2n-1}}{\phi(1-S_{iw})c_t}t\right]^{\frac{2n}{1-2n}}. \quad (11.159)$$

Comparing Eq. 11.159 with Eq. 11.104b indicates that

$$-\frac{1}{b} = \frac{2n}{1-2n} \quad (11.160a)$$

$$\text{or } b = \frac{2n-1}{2n}. \quad (11.160b)$$

Substituting Eq. 11.160a into Eq. 11.159 results in

$$\frac{q_{osc}}{q_{osc_i}} = \left[1 + \frac{\alpha_c}{V_b}\frac{2nbB_o C_{p^2}p_i^{2n-1}}{\phi(1-S_{iw})c_t}t\right]^{\frac{-1}{b}}. \quad (11.161)$$

Defining D_i as

$$D_i = \frac{\alpha_c}{V_b}\frac{2nB_o C_{p^2}p_i^{2n-1}}{\phi(1-S_{iw})c_t} \quad (11.162)$$

and substituting the initial production rate into Eq. 11.162 yields

$$D_i = \frac{-\alpha_c}{V_b}\frac{2nB_o q_{osc_i}}{\phi(1-S_{iw})c_t p_i}. \quad (11.163)$$

For a reference pressure of p_{sc}, the original oil in place can be defined as

$$N = \frac{V_b}{\alpha_c}\frac{\phi(1-S_{iw})}{B_o} \quad (11.164)$$

and substituting into Eq. 11.163 results in

$$D_i = \frac{-2nq_{osc_i}}{Nc_t p_i}. \quad (11.165)$$

Note again that D_i is positive because of our sign convention for production. Substituting Eq. 11.162 into Eq. 11.161 yields the definition of hyperbolic decline as

$$\frac{q_{osc}}{q_{osc_i}} = (1 + bD_i t)^{\frac{-1}{b}}. \quad (11.166)$$

Finally, the pressure/time relationship becomes

$$\left(\frac{p}{p_i}\right)^{2n} = (1 + bD_i t)^{\frac{-1}{b}}, \quad (11.167)$$

$$\frac{p}{p_i} = (1 + bD_i t)^{\frac{-1}{2nb}}, \quad (11.168)$$

or, after substituting Eq. 11.160,

$$\frac{p}{p_i} = (1 + bD_i t)^{\frac{b-1}{b}}. \quad (11.169)$$

Inspection of the definition of b, Eq. 11.160b, indicates that this analysis is valid for $n > ½$.

To this point, we have investigated cases where the inflow-performance parameters are constant during depletion. Fetkovich[2] also investigated the decline behavior of reservoirs in which C_{p^2} varies with reservoir pressure according to the relationship

$$C_{p^2} = C_{p_i^2}\frac{p}{p_i}. \quad (11.170)$$

For this case, the decline parameters become

$$-\frac{1}{b} = \frac{-2n}{2n+1} \quad (11.171a)$$

$$\text{or } b = \frac{2n+1}{2n} \quad (11.171b)$$

$$\text{and } D_i = \frac{-4n^2}{2n+1}\frac{q_{osc_i}}{Nc_t p_i}. \quad (11.172)$$

Inspection of Eq. 11.171b indicates that this analysis is valid for all positive values of n.

11.4.2 Production Type Curves. In Sec. 11.3.1, we derived the analytical-diffusivity equation, Eq. 11.77.

$$\frac{1}{r}\frac{\partial}{\partial r}\left(r\frac{\partial p}{\partial r}\right) = \frac{\mu_o\phi(1-S_{iw})c_t}{\alpha_c\beta_c k_o}\frac{\partial p}{\partial t}. \quad (11.77)$$

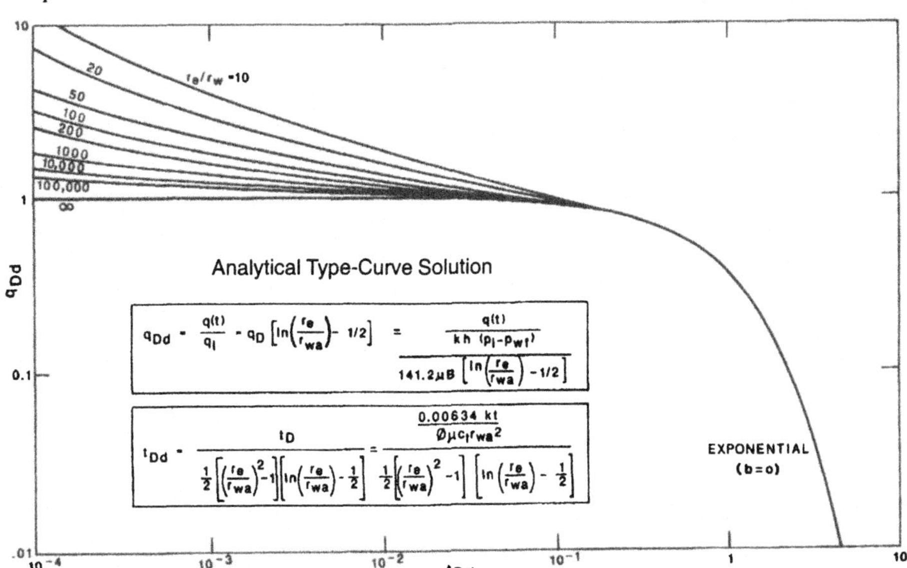

Fig. 11.2—Production type curves for well in the center of a cylindrical drainage area for transient and exponential decline periods (after Fetkovich[2]).

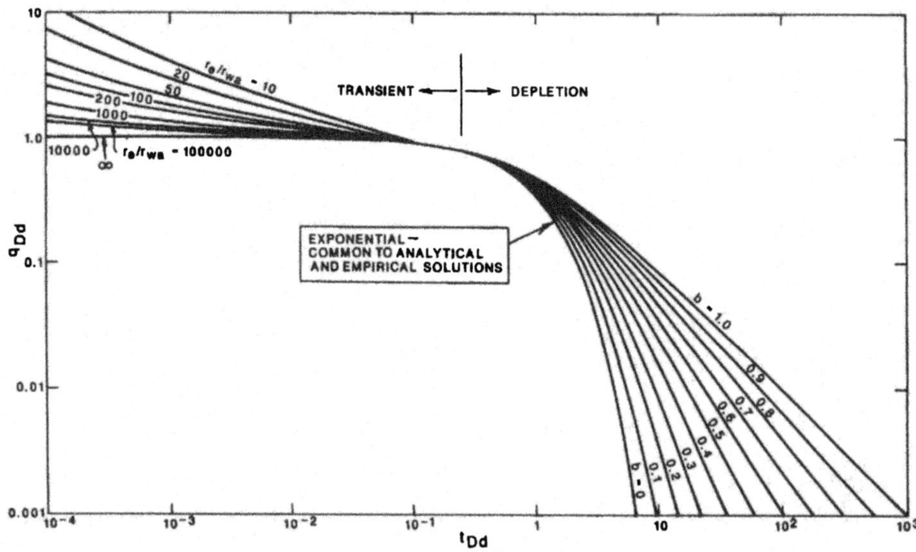

Fig. 11.3—Production type curves for a well in the center of a cylindrical drainage area for transient and depletion decline periods (after Fetkovich[2]).

Eq. 11.77, subject to a constant production rate or series of constant rates, forms the basis of pressure-transient analysis. However, when this equation is subject to a constant wellbore pressure, it forms the basis of production-type-curve analysis. Fetkovich[2] showed that, if Eq. 11.77 is subject to constant wellbore-pressure and no-flow external-boundary specifications and if the reservoir conditions adhere to the assumptions listed in Sec. 11.4.1, the late-time behavior is described by Arps' exponential-decline curve. **Fig. 11.2** illustrates this.

In Fig. 11.2, the early-time or transient-decline dimensionless rates are analytical solutions to Eq. 11.77, while the late-time or exponential-decline dimensionless rates are obtained from Eq. 11.124. The time at which these solutions converge is shown as $t=t_3$ in Fig. 11.1b. **Fig. 11.3** shows the same plot for the hyperbolic solutions during the boundary-dominated depletion period.

11.5 Summary

In this chapter, we discussed the relationships between numerical reservoir simulation and three of the more common classical reservoir engineering approaches: material-balance and analytical methods and decline-curve analysis. During this discussion, we demonstrated how the equations considered in numerical reservoir simulation can be reduced to the equations used in the classical methods.

The first objective for presenting this material is to review the assumptions of the classical approaches to demonstrate the general nature of numerical reservoir simulation. **Table 11.1** lists these assumptions. This review may help reservoir engineers unfamiliar with numerical simulation gain additional insight into how reservoir modeling relates to classical engineering approaches. The second objective is to illustrate that a numerical reservoir study incorporates all these analyses simultaneously. More important, however, is that, when a numerical reservoir study is conducted, the processes described by these analyses are modeled in the most consistent and general manner available to the reservoir engineer.

Nomenclature

A_x = cross-sectional area normal to the x direction, L^2, ft^2 [m^2]
b = decline parameter
B = FVF, L^3/L^3, reservoir volume/volume at standard conditions
B_g = gas FVF, L^3/L^3, RB/scf [m^3/std m^3]
B_{gi} = gas FVF at initial conditions, L^3/L^3, RB/scf [m^3/std m^3]
B_l = FVF of Phase l, L^3/L^3, reservoir volume/volume at standard conditions
B_o = oil FVF, L^3/L^3, RB/STB [m^3/std m^3]
B_{oi} = oil FVF at initial conditions, L^3/L^3, RB/STB [m^3/std m^3]
B_t = two-phase FVF, L^3/L^3, RB/STB [m^3/std m^3]
B_w = water FVF, L^3/L^3, RB/B [m^3/std m^3]
B_{wi} = water FVF at initial conditions, L^3/L^3, RB/B [m^3/std m^3]
c = compressibility, Lt^2/m, psi^{-1} [kPa^{-1}]
c_o = oil compressibility, Lt^2/m, psi^{-1} [kPa^{-1}]
c_t = total compressibility, Lt^2/m, psi^{-1} [kPa^{-1}]
c_w = water compressibility, Lt^2/m, psi^{-1} [kPa^{-1}]
c_ϕ = porosity compressibility, Lt^2/m, psi^{-1} [kPa^{-1}]
C_p = well productivity index for modified inflow performance relationship given by Eq. 11.110
D_i = initial decline rate, 1/t, D^{-1} [d^{-1}]
e = exponential
e^{-D_it} = exponential decline function
f_w = water fractional flow coefficient, dimensionless
G = initial gas in place, scf [std m^3]
G_i = cumulative volume of gas injected, L^3, scf [std m^3]
G_p = cumulative gas production, L^3, scf [std m^3]
G_w = well geometric factor, L^3, RB-cp/(D–psi) [$m^3 \cdot Pa \cdot s/(d \cdot kPa)$]
h = formation thickness, L, ft [m]
J_o = well productivity index for the oil phase, L^4t/m, STB/(D-psi) [std $m^3/(d \cdot kPa)$]
k = permeability, L^2, darcy [μm^2]
k_o = effective permeability to oil phase, L^2, darcy [μm^2]
k_{rg} = relative permeability to gas phase, dimensionless
k_{rl} = relative permeability to Phase l, dimensionless
k_{ro} = relative permeability to oil phase, dimensionless
k_x = permeability in the direction of the x axis, L^2, darcy [μm^2]
K = constant in generalized decline curve defined by Eq. 11.103
l = index for phase or component
m = gas-cap/oil-zone ratio, fraction
n = exponent for the inflow performance relationship (Eq. 11.110)
N = initial oil in place, L^3, STB [std m^3]
N_p = cumulative oil production, L^3, STB [std m^3]
p = pressure, m/Lt^2, psia [kPa]
p_b = bubblepoint pressure, m/Lt^2, psia [kPa]

TABLE 11.1—ASSUMPTIONS REQUIRED TO REDUCE NUMERICAL RESERVOIR SIMULATION EQUATION TO CLASSICAL RESERVOIR ENGINEERING APPROACHES

Reservoir Engineering Approach	Reservoir Geometry	Reservoir Rock Properties	Reservoir Fluids	Reservoir Fluid Properties
Generalized material-balance approach, Eq. 11.46	Arbitrary	Averaged properties	Oil, gas, and water	Averaged properties
Classical material-balance approach, Eq. 11.47	Arbitrary	Averaged properties $c_\phi = 0$ psi^{-1}	Oil, gas, and water	Averaged properties
Generalized Muskat method for solution-gas-drive reservoirs, Eq. 11.60	Arbitrary	Averaged properties	Oil and gas	Averaged properties
Classical Muskat method for solution-gas-drive reservoirs, Eq. 11.61	Arbitrary	Averaged properties $c_\phi = 0$ psi^{-1}	Oil and gas	Averaged properties
Pressure transient analysis, Eq. 11.77	Any regular geometry* One dimension	Homogeneous property distribution Small c_ϕ**	Single phase†	Constant viscosity** Small c_t**
Frontal advance (Buckley-Leverett), Eq. 11.101	Linear (1D Cartesian) Constant cross-sectional area	Homogeneous property distribution $c_\phi = 0$ psi^{-1} f_w is a function of water saturation only	Oil and water	Incompressible fluids: $c_o = 0$ psi^{-1} $c_w = 0$ psi^{-1}
Arps' decline curves	Arbitrary‡	Properties constant with time**	Single phase†	Properties constant with time**
Production type curves	Any regular geometry* One dimension	Homogeneous property distribution Small c_ϕ**	Single phase†	Constant viscosity** Small c_t**
Numerical reservoir simulation	Arbitrary geometry Three dimensions	Heterogeneous and anisotropic reservoir properties	Multiple phases and components	Pressure-dependent PVT and viscosity properties

*Eq. 11.77 assumes radial-cylindrical geometry.

**May be relaxed with the use of pseudopressure and pseudotime.

†May be relaxed with the use of multiphase pseudopressure and pseudotime.

‡The decline curves derived in this section can be made specific to a given geometry by applying appropriate definitions of V_b and J_o.

p_g = gas pressure, m/Lt^2, psia [kPa]
p_i = initial pressure, m/Lt^2, psia [kPa]
p_o = oil pressure, m/Lt^2, psia [kPa]
p_l = pressure of Phase l, m/Lt^2, psia [kPa]
p_{sc} = standard pressure, m/Lt^2, psia [kPa]
p_w = water pressure, m/Lt^2, psia [kPa]
p_{wf} = flowing well bottomhole pressure, m/Lt^2, psia [kPa]
P_{cgo} = gas/oil capillary pressure, m/Lt^2, psi [kPa]
P_{cow} = oil/water capillary pressure, m/Lt^2, psi [kPa]
q_D = dimensionless production rate
q_{Dd} = decline curve dimensionless production rate
q_{esc} = water-encroachment rate, L^3/t, B/D [std m^3/d]
q_{gsc} = gas production rate at standard conditions, L^3/t, scf/D [std m^3/d]
q_l = production rate of Phase l, L^3/t, RB/D [m^3/d]
q_{lsc} = production rate of Phase l at standard conditions, L^3/t, volume at standard conditions per day
q_o = oil production rate, L^3/t, RB/D [m^3/d]
q_{osc} = oil production rate at standard conditions, L^3/t, STB/D [std m^3/d]
q_{osc_i} = oil production rate at the start of production decline, L^3/t, STB/D [std m^3/d]
q'_{osc_i} = initial production rate as defined by inflow performance relationship, Eq. 11.146, L^3/t, STB/D [std m^3/d]
q'_{osc} = the negative of q_{osc} (Eq. 11.133)
q_t = total production rate or total flow rate, L^3/t, RB/D [m^3/d]
q_w = water flow rate, L^3/t, RB/D [m^3/d]
q_{wisc} = water injection rate at standard conditions, L^3/t, B/D [std m^3/d]
q_{wpsc} = water production rate at standard conditions, L^3/t, B/D [std m^3/d]
q_{wsc} = water flow rate at standard conditions, L^3/t, B/D [std m^3/d]
r = distance in radial direction in cylindrical coordinate system, L, ft [m]
r_e = radius of external boundary, L, ft [m]
r_w = wellbore radius, L, ft [m]
r_{wa} = effective wellbore radius, L, ft [m]
R_p = producing gas/oil ratio, L^3/L^3, scf/STB [std m^3/std m^3]
R_s = solution-gas/oil ratio, L^3/L^3, scf/STB [std m^3/std m^3]
R_{si} = initial solution-gas/oil ratio, L^3/L^3, scf/STB [std m^3/std m^3]
S_l = saturation of Phase l, fraction
S_g = gas saturation, fraction
S_{gi} = initial gas saturation, fraction
S_{iw} = irreducible water saturation, fraction
S_o = oil saturation, fraction
S_{oi} = initial oil saturation, fraction
S_w = water saturation, fraction
S_{wi} = initial water saturation, fraction
t = time, t, days
t_D = dimensionless time defined by Eq. 6.20
t_{Dd} = decline curve dimensionless time
t_{pss} = time to pseudosteady-state conditions, t, days
$t_{0\text{-}5}$ = times after start of production, t, days

TABLE 11.1—ASSUMPTIONS REQUIRED TO REDUCE NUMERICAL RESERVOIR SIMULATION EQUATIONS TO CLASSICAL RESERVOIR ENGINEERING APPROACHES (continued)

Reservoir Engineering Approach	Capillary Pressure	Pressure Gradients	Reservoir Dip	Inflow Performance Relationship	Drive Mechanism
Generalized material-balance approach, Eq. 11.46	No capillary pressures	No pressure gradients	No assumptions required	Arbitrary	Simultaneous drive with injection
Classical material-balance approach, Eq. 11.47	No capillary pressures	No pressure gradients	No assumptions required	Arbitrary	Simultaneous drive without injection
Generalized Muskat method for solution-gas-drive reservoirs, Eq. 11.60	No capillary pressures	No pressure gradients	No assumptions required	Arbitrary	Solution-gas drive
Classical Muskat method for solution-gas-drive reservoirs, Eq. 11.61	No capillary pressures	No pressure gradients	No assumptions required	Arbitrary	Solution-gas drive
Pressure transient analysis, Eq. 11.77	No capillary pressures	Small pressure gradients*	Horizontal reservoir	No external sources or sinks	Rock and fluid expansion with pressure depletion
Frontal advance (Buck-ley- Leverett), Eq. 11.101	No capillary pressures**	No assumptions required	Horizontal reservoir**	No external sources or sinks	Voidage-balanced water injection
Arps' decline curves	No capillary pressures	No pressure gradients	No assumptions required	Inflow performance parameters constant with time*	Rock and fluid expansion with pressure depletion
Production type curves	No capillary pressures	Small pressure gradients*	Horizontal reservoir	No external sources or sinks	Rock and fluid expansion with pressure depletion
Numerical reservoir simulation	Arbitrary capillary pressures	Arbitrary pressure gradients	Dipping reservoir	Any applicable well model (see Chap. 6)	Simultaneous drive with injection

*May be relaxed with the use of pseudopressure and pseudotime.

**May be relaxed with the use of a generalized definition of fractional flow.

$\vec{u}$ = velocity vector, L/t, volume at standard conditions per unit time per unit cross-sectional area
V_b = bulk volume, L^3, ft^3 [m^3]
W = initial water in place, L^3, B [std m^3]
W_i = cumulative volume of water injected at standard conditions, L^3, B [std m^3]
W_{esc} = cumulative volume of water encroached at standard conditions, L^3, B [std m^3]
W_p = cumulative volume of produced water at standard conditions, L^3, B [std m^3]
x = distance in the x direction in the Cartesian coordinate system, L, ft [m]
α_c = volume conversion factor whose numerical value is given in Table 4.1
β_c = transmissibility conversion factor whose numerical value is given in Table 4.1
μ_g = gas viscosity, m/Lt, cp [Pa·s]
μ_l = viscosity of Phase l, m/Lt, cp [Pa·s]
μ_o = oil viscosity, m/Lt, cp [Pa·s]
μ_w = water viscosity, m/Lt, cp [Pa·s]
ϕ = porosity, fraction
ϕ_i = porosity at initial pressure, dimensionless
Φ_g = gas-phase potential, m/Lt^2, psia [kPa]
Φ_l = potential of Phase l, m/Lt^2, psia [kPa]
Φ_o = oil-phase potential, m/Lt^2, psia [kPa]
Φ_w = water-phase potential, m/Lt^2, psia [kPa]

Subscripts

g = gas
o = oil
w = water

Superscripts

$'$ = negative of
$\rightarrow$ = vector

References

1. Fetkovich, M.J.: "A Simplified Approach to Water Influx Calculations—Finite Aquifer Systems," *JPT* (July 1971) 814.
2. Fetkovich, M.J.: "Decline Curve Analysis Using Type Curves," *JPT* (June 1980) 1065.
3. Arps, J.J.: "Analysis of Decline Curves," *Trans.*, AIME (1945) **160,** 228.
4. Chen, H.Y. and Poston, S.W.: "Application of a Pseudotime Function To Permit Better Decline-Curve Analysis," *SPEFE* (September 1989) 421.
5. Omoregie, Z.S. *et al.*: "Reservoir Management in the Ninian Field—A Case History," paper SPE 30443 presented at the 1995 Offshore Europe Conference, Aberdeen, 5–8 September.

Appendix A
Interpolation Techniques for Data Handling in Reservoir Simulation

This appendix provides a review of interpolation techniques that are candidates for data handling in reservoir simulation. Pressure/volume/temperature, transport properties, and relative permeability data are usually available in tabular forms. Internal calculations in simulators require the evaluation of properties (dependent variables) and their derivatives at given values of the corresponding variables (independent variables).

Although data handling can be achieved with table interpolation and curve fitting, the former method is used more commonly in reservoir simulation. Specifically, linear interpolation is used in almost all commercial simulators.

Table Interpolation

Data for a few property functions may not be represented easily by a single algebraic expression because the functions are not smooth, as is the case in B_o, R_s, and μ_o (see Sec. 2.3.2). Approximation of other property functions may require the use of high-degree polynomials. It is well-known, however, that high-degree polynomials may give bad representation of derivatives and their evaluation becomes expensive. The solution in these situations involves the use of table interpolation, in which a series of pairs of ordered data points is used to represent Function $y(x)$ over a given range of Parameter x.

Explicitly, given a table of data for Function $y(x)$ vs. Variable x, where $x_1 < x_2 < \ldots < x_n$, the evaluation of Function y^* that corresponds to x^* involves searching the array of data for Variable x until an interval is found in which x^* is bracketed; that is, $x_i \leqq x^* \leqq x_{i+1}$. This bracketing interval is $[x_i, x_{i+1}]$. Then, the value of Function y^* is calculated by interpolation. The following sections present various interpolation methods.

The two search techniques used to locate Interval $[x_i, x_{i+1}]$ in a table with nonuniform spacing are sequential and binary search. From our own tests and experience, we conclude that it is computationally efficient to use sequential search if the number of data points is less than or equal to 12 ($n \leqq 12$); otherwise, binary search is recommended. **Fig. A-1** gives a FORTRAN subroutine (search) that incorporates both search techniques and a linear interpolation function subroutine (fun1d) that uses the outcome of the search subroutine.

If the spacing of the elements in the table of properties is uniform, an efficient table-lookup algorithm can be developed. For uniformly spaced table entries, $x_1 < x_2 < \ldots x_n$, the values of x_i are separated by a constant value, Δx. That is,

$$\Delta x = x_{i+1} - x_i. \quad \text{(A–1)}$$

where $i = 1, 2, \ldots, n-1$.

The value of the indices (subscripts) of Interval $[x_i, x_{i+1}]$ that bracket x^* in a uniformly spaced table can be determined by

$$i = 1 + I\left(\frac{x^*}{\Delta x}\right), \quad \text{(A–2)}$$

where I = the function that truncates a real number into an integer.

One efficient strategy to use in reservoir simulation if input data are supplied in a nonuniformly spaced table is to use the routines listed in Fig. A-1 to process the original data into an internal table that uses uniform spacing. This can be done once at the beginning of the simulation. All subsequent table lookups can be performed with the internal data table. This procedure results in approximate values in the internal data table in Interval $[x_i, x_{i+1}]$, which straddles the original, nonuniform data points.

Linear Interpolation. In linear interpolation, an equation of a straight line that passes through the endpoints of Interval $[x_i, x_{i+1}]$ [that is, (x_i, y_i) and (x_{i+1}, y_{i+1})] is used for interpolation. The value of Function y^* that corresponds to a given value of Variable x^* is obtained with the interpolating equation

$$y^* = y_i + s(x^* - x_i), \quad \text{(A-3)}$$

where s, the slope of the chord connecting the two points, is

$$s = \frac{y_{i+1} - y_i}{x_{i+1} - x_i}. \quad \text{(A-4)}$$

The derivative of the function at x^* is given by the slope of the chord

$$\frac{dy}{dx}\Big|_{x^*} = s. \quad \text{(A-5)}$$

If the value of Variable x^* falls outside the range of table, the value of Function y^* is set equal to the function at the nearest endpoint of the table and the derivative of the function is set to zero to avoid overshoot in the predicted values of unknowns. That is,

$$y^* = y_1 \text{ and } \frac{dy}{dx}\Big|_{x^*} = 0 \quad \text{(A-6)}$$

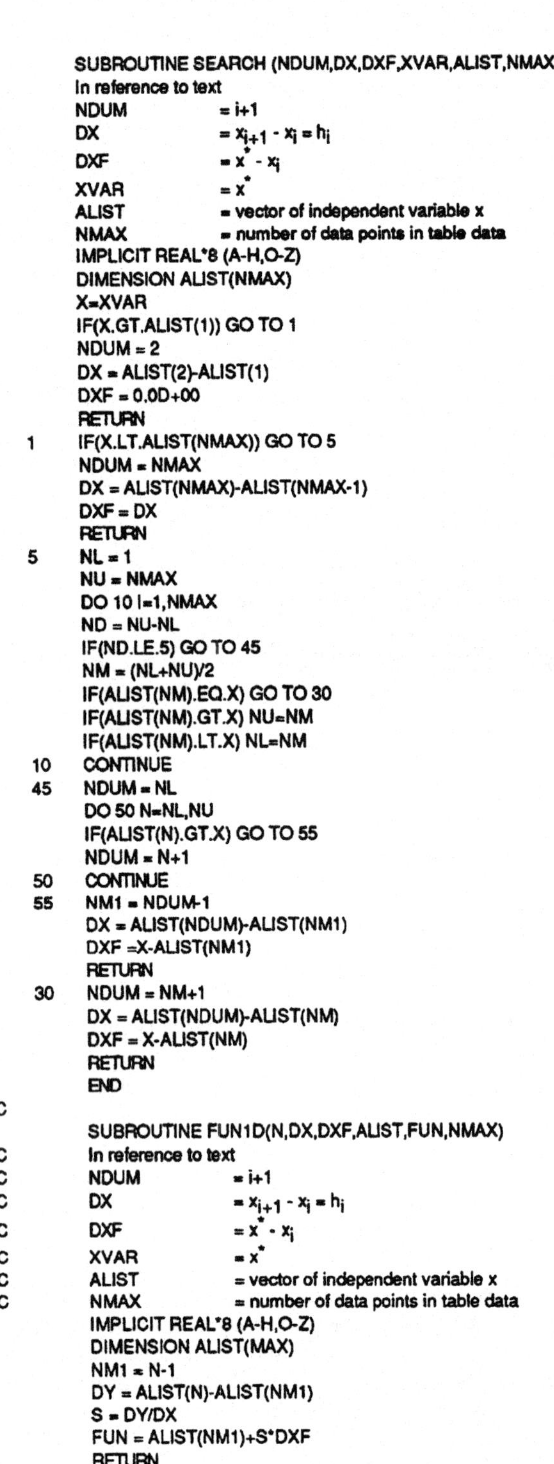

```
C
      SUBROUTINE SEARCH (NDUM,DX,DXF,XVAR,ALIST,NMAX)
C     In reference to text
C     NDUM          = i+1
C     DX            = x_{i+1} - x_i = h_i
C     DXF           = x* - x_i
C     XVAR          = x*
C     ALIST         = vector of independent variable x
C     NMAX          = number of data points in table data
      IMPLICIT REAL*8 (A-H,O-Z)
      DIMENSION ALIST(NMAX)
      X=XVAR
      IF(X.GT.ALIST(1)) GO TO 1
      NDUM = 2
      DX = ALIST(2)-ALIST(1)
      DXF = 0.0D+00
      RETURN
1     IF(X.LT.ALIST(NMAX)) GO TO 5
      NDUM = NMAX
      DX = ALIST(NMAX)-ALIST(NMAX-1)
      DXF = DX
      RETURN
5     NL = 1
      NU = NMAX
      DO 10 I=1,NMAX
      ND = NU-NL
      IF(ND.LE.5) GO TO 45
      NM = (NL+NU)/2
      IF(ALIST(NM).EQ.X) GO TO 30
      IF(ALIST(NM).GT.X) NU=NM
      IF(ALIST(NM).LT.X) NL=NM
10    CONTINUE
45    NDUM = NL
      DO 50 N=NL,NU
      IF(ALIST(N).GT.X) GO TO 55
      NDUM = N+1
50    CONTINUE
55    NM1 = NDUM-1
      DX = ALIST(NDUM)-ALIST(NM1)
      DXF =X-ALIST(NM1)
      RETURN
30    NDUM = NM+1
      DX = ALIST(NDUM)-ALIST(NM)
      DXF = X-ALIST(NM)
      RETURN
      END
C
      SUBROUTINE FUN1D(N,DX,DXF,ALIST,FUN,NMAX)
C     In reference to text
C     NDUM          = i+1
C     DX            = x_{i+1} - x_i = h_i
C     DXF           = x* - x_i
C     XVAR          = x*
C     ALIST         = vector of independent variable x
C     NMAX          = number of data points in table data
      IMPLICIT REAL*8 (A-H,O-Z)
      DIMENSION ALIST(MAX)
      NM1 = N-1
      DY = ALIST(N)-ALIST(NM1)
      S = DY/DX
      FUN = ALIST(NM1)+S*DXF
      RETURN
      END
```

Fig. A-1—Search and linear-interpolation-function subroutines.

if $x^* < x_1$

and $y^* = y_n$ and $\frac{dy}{dx}|_{x^*} = 0$ .... (A-7)

if $x^* \geqq x_n$.

Example A-1. Given the data in **Table A-1**, find the value and derivative of the function at $x^* = 0.5$ and 3.5 with linear interpolation.

Solution. For $x^* = 0.5$, searching the elements of Variable x reveals that $0 < x^* < 1$. Therefore, the bracketing interval is [0,1] and, as a result, $i = 1$. The slope of the chord is obtained by applying Eq. A-4 as

$$s = \frac{1 - (-5)}{1 - 0} = 6.$$

TABLE A-1—DATA FOR EXAMPLE A-1

i	x_i	y_i
1	0	–5
2	1	1
3	3	25

Therefore, application of Eq. A-3 gives

$$y^* = -5 + 6(0.5 - 0) = -2$$

and application of Eq. A-5 gives

$$\frac{dy}{dx}|_{x^*} = 6.$$

For $x^* = 3.5$, searching the elements of Variable x results in $x^* > 3$. That is, the value of $x^* = 3.5$ falls outside the table range. Application of Eq. A-7 gives $y^* = 25$ and

$$\frac{dy}{dx}|_{x^*} = 0.$$

Quadratic Interpolation. Quadratic interpolation uses a second-degree polynomial that passes through three points in Interval $[x_i, x_{i+2}]$ or $[x_{i-1}, x_{i+1}]$. Either of these intervals enclose the bracketing interval $[x_i, x_{i+1}]$ and an interval succeeding it, as in $[x_i, x_{i+2}]$, or preceding it, as in $[x_{i-1}, x_{i+1}]$. The following interpolating equation and slope are based on Interval $[x_i, x_{i+2}]$.

$$y^* = ax^{*2} + bx^* + c \qquad \text{(A-8)}$$

and $\frac{dy}{dx}|_{x^*} = 2ax^* + b.$ .... (A-9)

First, calculate

$$a_1 = (y_{i+1} - y_i)/[(x_{i+1} - x_i)(x_{i+2} - x_{i+1})] \qquad \text{(A-10)}$$

and $a_2 = (y_{i+2} - y_i)/[(x_{i+2} - x_i)(x_{i+2} - x_{i+1})],$ ..... (A-11)

then, $a = a_2 - a_1,$ .... (A-12)

$$b = a_1(x_{i+2} + x_i) - a_2(x_{i+1} + x_i), \qquad \text{(A-13)}$$

and $c = y_i - ax_i^2 - bx_i,$ .... (A-14)

If the value of Variable x^* falls in the last interval of the table, Parameters a, b, and c for Interval $[x_{n-2}, x_n]$ must be used. Again, Eqs. A-6 and A-7 apply if the value of Variable x^* falls outside the table range.

Example A-2. Resolve Example A-1 with quadratic interpolation.

Solution. For $x^* = 0.5$, the bracketing interval is [0,1] and, as a result, $i = 1$. Therefore, Eqs. A-8 through A-14 can be used to give

$$a_1 = (1 + 5)/[(1 - 0)(3 - 1)] = 3,$$

$$a_2 = (25 + 5)/[(3 - 0)(3 - 1)] = 5,$$

$$a = 5 - 3 = 2,$$

$$b = 3\,(3 + 0) - 5(1 + 0) = 4,$$

and $c = -5 - 2(0)^2 - 4(0) = -5.$

Therefore,

$$y^* = 2(0.5)^2 + 4(0.5) - 5 = -2.5$$

and $\frac{dy}{dx}|_{x^*} = 2(2)(0.5) + 4 = 6.$

TABLE A-2—DATA FOR EXAMPLE A-3

k	j	i	x_k, x_j, x_i	$y(x_k)$
0	0	0	0	-5
1	1	1	1	1
2	2	2	3	25

For $x^* = 3.5$, the value of Variable x^* falls outside the table range ($x^* > 3$); therefore, Eq. A-7 applies, which gives $y^* = 25$ and

$$\frac{dy}{dx}\Big|_{x^*} = 0,$$

as in the case of linear interpolation.

Lagrangian Interpolation. This interpolation technique uses a polynomial that passes through as many data points in the data table as desired. Therefore, an interpolating polynomial of degree m can be expressed as

$$y(x) = \sum_{k=0}^{m} y(x_k) l_k(x), \quad \text{(A-15)}$$

where
$$l_k(x) = \prod_{\substack{i=0 \\ \neq k}}^{m} \left(\frac{x - x_i}{x_k - x_i}\right); \quad \text{(A-16)}$$

therefore, the derivative of the function is

$$\frac{dy(x)}{dx} = \sum_{k=0}^{m} y(x_k) \sum_{\substack{j=0 \\ \neq k}}^{m} \frac{1}{(x_k - x_j)} \prod_{\substack{i=0 \\ \neq j,k}}^{m} \left(\frac{x - x_i}{x_k - x_i}\right). \quad \text{(A-17)}$$

m is the desired degree of the Lagrangian interpolating polynomial. If $m = 1$, linear interpolation is obtained. Likewise, if $m = 2$, quadratic interpolation is obtained. Lagrangian interpolation usually is used to obtain interpolating polynomials of higher degrees. The maximum degree possible equals the number of points in a table minus one ($m \leqq n - 1$). However, as the degree of the interpolating polynomial gets higher, the interpolated value of the function gets better but its derivative dy/dx gets worse.

Example A-3. Find the Lagrangian second-degree interpolating polynomial for the data in Example A-1. Also, find the interpolated value of the function and its derivative at $x^* = 0.5$.

Solution. A second-degree interpolating polynomial implies $m = 2$. Because the number of data points in the table is three, $m = 2$ represents the maximum possible degree of a Lagrangian interpolating polynomial.

Table A-2 shows the table of data rewritten to facilitate the application of Eqs. A-15 and A-16. Next, we apply Eq. A-16 to find $l_0(x)$, $l_1(x)$, and $l_2(x)$.

$$l_0(x) = \frac{(x-1)(x-3)}{(0-1)(0-3)} = \frac{x^2 - 4x + 3}{3},$$

$$l_1(x) = \frac{(x-0)(x-3)}{(1-0)(1-3)} = \frac{-x^2 + 3x}{2},$$

and
$$l_2(x) = \frac{(x-0)(x-1)}{(3-0)(3-1)} = \frac{x^2 - x}{6}.$$

Then, straightforward application of Eq. A-15 yields

$$y(x) = -5\left(\frac{x^2 - 4x + 3}{3}\right) + 1\left(\frac{-x^2 + 3x}{2}\right) + 25\left(\frac{x^2 - x}{6}\right),$$

which can be simplified to give the final form of the interpolating polynomial as

$$y(x) = 2x^2 + 4x - 5.$$

For $x^* = 0.5$,

$$y^* = 2(0.5)^2 + 4(0.5) - 5 = -2.5$$

and
$$\frac{dy}{dx}\Big|_{x^*} = 4x^* + 4 = 4(0.5) + 4 = 6.$$

Computer calculations, however, are carried out with Eqs. A-15 through A-17, rather than with the simplified forms. That is,

$$y^* = -5\left[\frac{(0.5-1)(0.5-3)}{(0-1)(0-3)}\right] + 1\left[\frac{(0.5-0)(0.5-3)}{(1-0)(1-3)}\right] + 25\left[\frac{(0.5-0)(0.5-1)}{(3-0)(3-1)}\right] = -2.5$$

and
$$\frac{dy}{dx}\Big|_{x^*} = -5\left\{\frac{1}{(0-1)}\left[\frac{(0.5-3)}{(0-3)}\right] + \frac{1}{(0-3)}\left[\frac{(0.5-1)}{(0-1)}\right]\right\} + 1\left\{\frac{1}{(1-0)}\left[\frac{(0.5-3)}{(1-3)}\right] + \frac{1}{(1-3)}\left[\frac{(0.5-0)}{(1-0)}\right]\right\} + 25\left\{\frac{1}{(3-0)}\left[\frac{(0.5-1)}{(3-1)}\right] + \frac{1}{(3-1)}\left[\frac{(0.5-0)}{(3-0)}\right]\right\}$$
$$= -5(-1) + 1(1) + 25(0) = 6.$$

Spline Interpolation. Spline interpolation is a mathematical representation of the use of a flexible strip for drawing a smooth curve through a set of points. Interpolating splines consist of a set of polynomials, each of which is defined over two neighboring data points so that any two adjacent polynomials, as well as their derivatives (except the mth derivative), are continuous at the joining point.

Background. This section provides the reader with background relevant to splines and enumerates the advantages of the use of splines instead of polynomials for interpolation and the use of natural cubic splines over other splines.

Definition 1. An interpolating spline $S(x)$ of degree m on Interval $[a,b]$, with respect to Knots (points) $a = x_1 < x_2 < \ldots < x_n = b$ and Ordinates $y(x_i)$, where $i = 1,2, \ldots, n$, is a function with the following properties.

1. $S(x_i) = y(x_i)$, where $i = 1,2, \ldots, n$.
2. $S(x) \in C^{m-1}[a,b]$. That is, $S(x)$ is piecewise continuous and is $(m-1)$ times differentiable.
3. $S(x)$ reduces to a polynomial of degree, at most, m on each Subinterval $x_i \leqq x \leqq x_{i+1}$, where $i = 1,2, \ldots, n-1$.

Definition 2. A spline $S(x)$ of odd degree $m = (2k-1)$ on Interval $[a,b]$ is a natural spline if it is given at each of the two intervals, $-\infty < x < x_1$, $x_n < x < \infty$, by some polynomial of degree $(k-1)$, rather than $(2k-1)$. That is, for a cubic interpolating natural spline, $m = 3$, $k = 2$, and $S(x) \in P_3$, where $a \leqq x \leqq b$, and $S(x) \in P_1$, where $-\infty < x < a$ and $b < x < \infty$. The last condition implies $S'(a) \neq 0$ and $S'(b) \neq 0$, but $S''(a) = S''(b) = 0$.

Theorem. There is a unique interpolating natural spline $S(x)$ of odd degree $m = 2k - 1$ interpolating Points $(x_1,y_1),(x_2,y_2), \ldots, (x_n,y_n)$, where $1 \leqq k \leqq n$, and Knots $x_1, x_2, \ldots, x_n$ are distinct.

Special Cases.

1. If $S(x)$ is of degree $n-1$, the interpolating natural spline reduces to the Lagrangian polynomial with maximum possible degree.
2. If $S(x)$ is of degree one, the interpolating natural spline reduces to linear interpolation.

Interpolating splines are preferred over interpolating polynomials for the following reasons.

1. Splines are smooth enough and do not suffer from oscillations between the knots.
2. Splines are less expensive to compute.
3. The degree of splines does not depend on the number of data points, which is not the case for interpolating polynomials.

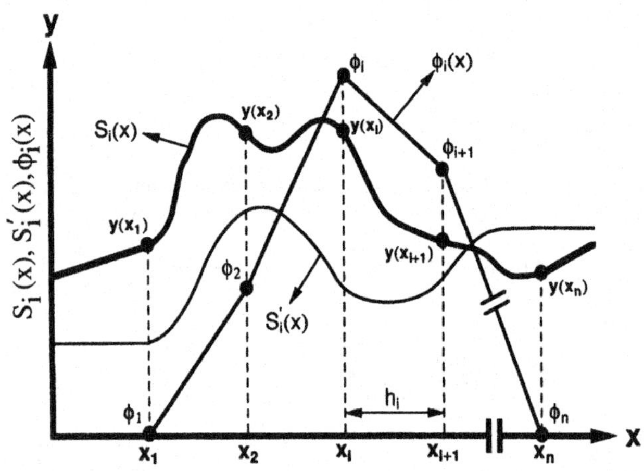

Fig. A-2—Sketch of interpolating natural cubic splines and their first and second derivatives.

Odd-degree interpolating splines are better than even-degree interpolating splines, and interpolating natural cubic splines are preferred over other odd-degree splines for many reasons.

1. Natural cubic splines are smoother and more realistic than linear splines.
2. Natural cubic splines are the smoothest of all cubic splines. They also offer unique representation without specifying end conditions necessary for cubic splines.
3. They are less expensive to compute than higher odd-degree splines.
4. Experience of other investigators in this area reveals that natural cubic splines are the best odd-degree interpolating splines.[1]

Equation for Interpolating Natural Cubic Spline. Referring to **Fig. A-2,** we define the following.

$$y_i = y(x_i), \quad \text{(A-18)}$$

where $i=1,2,\ldots,n$,

$$h_i = x_{i+1} - x_i, \quad \text{(A-19)}$$

where $i=1,2,\ldots,n-1$,

$$\phi_i = \frac{d^2S_{i-1}}{dx^2}\bigg|_{x_i} = \frac{d^2S_i}{dx^2}\bigg|_{x_i}, \quad \text{(A-20)}$$

where $i=2,3,\ldots,n$,

$$\phi_1 = \frac{d^2S_1}{dx^2}\bigg|_{x_1} = 0, \quad \text{(A-21)}$$

$$\text{and } \phi_n = \frac{d^2S_n}{dx^2}\bigg|_{x_n} = 0. \quad \text{(A-22)}$$

Let $S_i(x)$, the spline segment that is defined over $[x_i,x_{i+1}]$, be defined as

$$S_i(x) = \frac{a}{6}x^3 + \frac{b}{2}x^2 + cx + d, \quad \text{(A-23)}$$

where $x_i \leqq x \leqq x_{i+1}$. Differentiating Eq. A-23 twice with respect to x gives

$$\frac{d^2S_i(x)}{dx^2} = ax + b, \quad \text{(A-24)}$$

where $x_i \leqq x \leqq x_{i+1}$. Moment $\phi_i(x)$ over Interval $[x_i,x_{i+1}]$ can be expressed in terms of ϕ_i and ϕ_{i+1} as

$$\phi_i(x) = \left(\frac{x_{i+1}-x}{h_i}\right)\phi_i + \left(\frac{x-x_i}{h_i}\right)\phi_{i+1}. \quad \text{(A-25)}$$

Equating Eqs. A-24 and A-25 and integrating the resulting equation twice gives

$$S_i(x) = \frac{\phi_i}{6h_i}(x_{i+1}-x)^3 + \frac{\phi_{i+1}}{6h_i}(x-x_i)^3 + C_{1i}x + C_{2i}, \quad \text{(A-26)}$$

where $i=1,2,\ldots,n-1$. The use of $S_i(x_i)=y_i$ and $S_i(x_{i+1})=y_{i+1}$ to determine the constants of integration in Eq. A-26 gives

$$C_{1i} = \left(\frac{y_{i+1}}{h_i} - \frac{h_i}{6}\phi_{i+1}\right) - \left(\frac{y_i}{h_i} - \frac{h_i}{6}\phi_i\right) \quad \text{(A-27)}$$

$$\text{and } C_{2i} = -\left(\frac{y_{i+1}}{h_i} - \frac{h_i}{6}\phi_{i+1}\right)x_i + \left(\frac{y_i}{h_i} - \frac{h_i}{6}\phi_i\right)x_{i+1}. \quad \text{(A-28)}$$

Substituting Eqs. A-27 and A-28 into Eq. A-26 gives the ith spline equation in terms of Knots x_i and x_{i+1}, Ordinates y_i and y_{i+1}, Moments ϕ_i and ϕ_{i+1}, and Interval h_i as

$$S_i(x) = \frac{\phi_i}{6h_i}(x_{i+1}-x)^3 + \frac{\phi_{i+1}}{6h_i}(x-x_i)^3 + \left(\frac{y_{i+1}}{h_i} - \frac{h_i}{6}\phi_{i+1}\right) \times (x-x_i) + \left(\frac{y_i}{h_i} - \frac{h_i}{6}\phi_i\right)(x_{i+1}-x), \quad \text{(A-29)}$$

where $i=1,2,\ldots,n-1$ and $x_i \leqq x \leqq x_{i+1}$.

Computation of Moments (Second Derivatives) of Spline. From the definition of a natural cubic spline, we have Moments ϕ_1 and ϕ_n specified as

$$\phi_1 = \phi_n = 0. \quad \text{(A-30)}$$

Hence, we have to compute only Moments ϕ_i where $i=2,3,\ldots,n-1$. First, we differentiate $S_i(x)$ given by Eq. A-29 with respect to Variable x.

$$\frac{d}{dx}S_i(x) = -\frac{\phi_i}{2h_i}(x_{i+1}-x)^2 + \frac{\phi_{i+1}}{2h_i}(x-x_i)^2 + \left(\frac{y_{i+1}}{h_i} - \frac{h_i}{6}\phi_{i+1}\right) - \left(\frac{y_i}{h_i} - \frac{h_i}{6}\phi_i\right), \quad \text{(A-31)}$$

where $i=1,2,\ldots,n-1$.

Second, we apply the condition that the spline is smooth (that is, the first derivative is continuous) over the knots.

$$\frac{dS_i}{dx}\bigg|_{x_i} = \frac{dS_{i-1}}{dx}\bigg|_{x_i}, \quad \text{(A-32)}$$

where $i=2,3,\ldots,n-1$, which gives

$$\frac{h_{i-1}}{h_i}\phi_{i-1} + 2\left(1 + \frac{h_{i-1}}{h_i}\right)\phi_i + \phi_{i+1} = \frac{6}{h_i}\left(\frac{y_{i+1}-y_i}{h_i} - \frac{y_i - y_{i-1}}{h_{i-1}}\right), \quad \text{(A-33)}$$

where $i=2,3,\ldots,n-1$. Therefore, one can write Eq. A-33 for Knots $i=2,3,\ldots,n-1$. The resulting system of equations is a tridiagonal system in the unknowns $\phi_2, \phi_3, \ldots, \phi_{n-1}$, which can be solved with Thomas' algorithm[2] as presented in Sec. 7.3.1. Then, substituting the values of $\phi_1, \phi_2, \ldots, \phi_{n-1}$, and ϕ_n into Eq. A-29 for each value of Index i gives the ith spline, which completely defines the interpolating natural cubic splines.

Example A-4. Find the interpolating natural cubic spline for the data given in **Table A-3**. Also, find the interpolated value of the function and its first derivative at $x^*=3$.

Solution. $n=4$; therefore, the spline is defined over three intervals, $i=1, 2,$ and 3. The spline is given by Eq. A-29 and its first derivative is expressed by Eq. A-31.

TABLE A-3—DATA FOR EXAMPLE A-4		
i	x_i	y_i
1	1	1
2	2	3
3	4	4
4	5	2

TABLE A-4—DATA FOR SOLUTION TO EXAMPLE A-4	
i	h_i
1	1
2	2
3	1
4	—

First, calculate $h_i = x_{i+1} - x_i$ with the data in **Table A-4**. Applying Eqs. A-30 and A-33 gives the following. For $i = 1$,

$$\phi_1 = 0;$$

for $i = 2$,

$$\tfrac{1}{2}\phi_1 + 2\left(1 + \tfrac{1}{2}\right)\phi_2 + \phi_3 = \tfrac{6}{2}\left(\frac{4-3}{2} - \frac{3-1}{1}\right);$$

for $i = 3$,

$$\tfrac{2}{1}\phi_2 + 2\left(2 + \tfrac{2}{1}\right)\phi_3 + \phi_4 = \tfrac{6}{1}\left(\frac{2-4}{1} - \frac{4-3}{2}\right);$$

and for $i = 4$,

$$\phi_4 = 0.$$

Second, solve the previous system of equations, which gives $\phi_1 = 0$, $\phi_2 = -3/4$, $\phi_3 = -9/4$, and $\phi_4 = 0$.

As an example, $S_2(x)$ is obtained with Eq. A-29 for $i = 2$ as follows.

$$S_2(x) = \frac{-3/4}{6(2)}(4 - x)^3 + \frac{-9/4}{6(2)}(x - 2)^3 + \left[\tfrac{4}{2} - \tfrac{2}{6}\left(-\tfrac{9}{4}\right)\right](x - 2) + \left[\tfrac{3}{2} - \tfrac{2}{6}\left(-\tfrac{3}{4}\right)\right](4 - x),$$

where $2 \leqq x \leqq 4$, which reduces to

$$S_2(x) = -\tfrac{1}{8}x^3 + \tfrac{3}{8}x^2 + \tfrac{7}{4}x - 1,$$

where $2 \leqq x \leqq 4$. Likewise, one can proceed to compute $S_1(x)$ and $S_3(x)$. For $i = 1$,

$$S_1(x) = -\tfrac{1}{8}x^3 + \tfrac{3}{8}x^2 + \tfrac{7}{4}x - 1,$$

where $1 \leqq x \leqq 2$. For $i = 2$,

$$S_2(x) = -\tfrac{1}{8}x^3 + \tfrac{3}{8}x^2 + \tfrac{7}{4}x - 1,$$

where $2 \leqq x \leqq 4$. For $i = 3$,

$$S_3(x) = \tfrac{3}{8}x^3 - \tfrac{45}{8}x^2 + \tfrac{103}{4}x - 33,$$

where $4 \leqq x \leqq 5$.

To calculate the value of the function at $x^* = 3$, we find that $2 < x^* < 4$, so $i = 2$. Therefore, we use $S_2(x)$

$$S_2(3) = -\tfrac{1}{8}(3^3) + \tfrac{3}{8}(3^2) + \tfrac{7}{4}(3) - 1 = \tfrac{17}{4}.$$

Therefore, $y^* = 4.25$.

To calculate the value of the first derivative of the function at $x^* = 3$, we use Eq. A-31 for $i = 2$.

$$\frac{d}{dx}S_2(x^*) = -\frac{\phi_2}{2h_2}(x_3 - x^*)^2 + \frac{\phi_3}{2h_2}(x^* - x_2)^2 + \left(\frac{y_3}{h_2} - \frac{h_2}{6}\phi_3\right) - \left(\frac{y_2}{h_2} - \frac{h_2}{6}\phi_2\right).$$

Substituting the values of ϕ_2, ϕ_3, y_2, y_3, x_2, x_3, h_2, and x^* into the previous equation, one obtains

$$\frac{d}{dx}S_2(3) = -\frac{-3/4}{2(2)}(4-3)^2 + \frac{-9/4}{2(2)}(3-2)^2 + \left[\tfrac{4}{2} - \tfrac{2}{6}\left(-\tfrac{9}{4}\right)\right] - \left[\tfrac{3}{2} - \tfrac{2}{6}\left(-\tfrac{3}{4}\right)\right] = \tfrac{5}{8}.$$

Therefore,

$$\frac{dy}{dx}\Big|_{x^*} = \frac{5}{8}.$$

At $x^* = 3$, $y^* = 4.25$ and

$$\frac{dy}{dx}\Big|_{x^*} = 0.625$$

with spline interpolation, compared with $y^* = 3.5$ and

$$\frac{dy}{dx}\Big|_{x^*} = 0.50$$

with linear interpolation.

Data Handling With Curve Fitting

Thus far, the approximation of a function with interpolation between data points has been discussed. The interpolating functions in this case pass through all data points. There is another type of approximation in which the data are curve fitted to a function so that the function contains most of the information without necessarily passing through any of the data points. This type of approximation is very useful in handling data that belong to property functions that are known to be smooth.

Curve-Fitting Method. This method approximates the given data by some function f(x) such that f(x) contains or represents most of the information. This is accomplished by choosing a function that depends on x as well as on the set of parameters C_i, where $i = 1,2,\ldots,k$, that has to be determined later with the given data. Normally k is small compared with n. k should be large enough so that the information about f(x) in the data can be well-represented by proper choice of the parameters, $C_1, C_2, \ldots, C_k$ and, at the same time, small enough to allow for reproduction of the error.

Obtaining a curve fit for a given set of data points (x_1,y_1), $(x_2,y_2), \ldots, (x_n,y_n)$ involves the following five steps.

1. Choose an approximating function. The data should be plotted, analyzed, and studied carefully to choose an appropriate form of the approximating function. The selected function may have the form

$$\mathrm{f}(x) = \mathrm{f}(x, C_1, C_2, \ldots, C_k), \quad \text{(A-34)}$$

where x = independent variable and $C_1, C_2, \ldots, C_k$ = parameters with values that produce a good approximating function.

2. Define an error term. An error term that represents the deviation of the predicted value from the measured value is defined as

$$d_i = y_i - \mathrm{f}(x_i, C_1, C_2, \ldots, C_k), \quad \text{(A-35)}$$

where $i = 1,2,\ldots,n$.

3. Select a criterion for the fit. Parameters $C_1, C_2, \ldots, C_k$ are chosen to minimize one of the following expressions.

Sum of squares of errors: $S_s = \sum_{i=1}^{n} d_i^2$.

Maximum absolute error: $T = \max_{1 \leqq i \leqq n} |d_i|$.

Sum of absolute errors: $S_a = \sum_{i=1}^{n} |d_i|$.

The easiest and most widely used criterion is the minimization of the sum of squares of errors, commonly known as least-squares criterion. That is, minimize

$$S_s(C_1, C_2, \ldots, C_k) = \sum_{i=1}^{n} [y_i - f(x_i, C_1, C_2, \ldots, C_k)]^2. \quad \text{(A-36)}$$

4. Construct a minimization problem. The minimization of $S_s(C_1, C_2, \ldots, C_k)$ can be constructed as follows. First, $S_s(C_1, C_2, \ldots, C_k)$ is continuously differentiable as a function of its arguments. Second, at a minimum, all first partial derivatives must vanish.

Differentiating $S_s(C_1, C_2, \ldots, C_k)$ with respect to C_j gives

$$\frac{\partial}{\partial C_j} S_s(C_1, C_2, \ldots, C_k) = \sum_{i=1}^{n} \frac{\partial}{\partial C_j}[y_i - f(x_i, C_1, C_2, \ldots, C_k)]^2$$

$$= -2\sum_{i=1}^{n}[y_i - f(x_i, C_1, C_2, \ldots, C_k)] \times \frac{\partial}{\partial C_j} f(x_i, C_1, C_2, \ldots, C_k), \quad \text{(A-37)}$$

where $j = 1, 2, \ldots, k$. Equating each of the first partial derivatives to zero gives

$$\sum_{i=1}^{n}\left[y_i - f(x_i, C_1, C_2, \ldots, C_k)\right]\frac{\partial}{\partial C_j} f(x_i, C_1, C_2, \ldots, C_k) = 0, \quad \text{(A-38)}$$

where $j = 1, 2, \ldots, k$. Therefore, Eq. A-38 is a necessary condition for $C_1, C_2, \ldots, C_k$ to minimize Function $S_s(C_1, C_2, \ldots, C_k)$. It represents a system of k equations in the unknowns, $C_1, C_2, \ldots, C_k$, and usually is known as the normal equations of the least-squares approximation.

5. Solve the normal equations of least squares. The difficulty of solving these algebraic equations, Eq. A-38, for the unknowns $C_1, C_2, \ldots, C_k$, depends on the form of $f(x)$ given in Eq. A-34 (that is, the form of the chosen approximating function to represent the data). The particular form of $f(x, C_1, C_2, \ldots, C_k)$ may result in one of three types of fit: linear least squares, orthogonal polynomial, or nonlinear least squares.

Linear Least-Squares Fit. A linear least-squares fit is obtained if one selects a form of the approximating function $f(x, C_1, C_2, \ldots, C_k)$ so that it depends linearly on Parameters $C_1, C_2, \ldots, C_k$. Mathematically, this function can be expressed as

$$f(x, C_1, C_2, \ldots, C_k) = \sum_{m=1}^{k} C_m \phi_m(x), \quad \text{(A-39)}$$

where $\{\phi_m(x)\}$ = an *a priori* selected set of functions that depends only on x. $\{\phi_m(x)\}$ may, for example, be a set of monomials $\{x^{m-1}\}$ or a set of trigonometric functions $\{\sin(\pi m x)\}$.

With this particular form of $f(x, C_1, C_2, \ldots, C_k)$, as expressed in Eq. A-39, the normal equations can be obtained by application of Eq. A-38 as

$$\sum_{i=1}^{n}\left[y_i - \sum_{m=1}^{k} C_m \phi_m(x_i)\right]\frac{\partial}{\partial C_j}\sum_{m=1}^{k} C_m \phi_m(x_i) = 0, \quad \text{(A-40)}$$

where $j = 1, 2, \ldots, k$. Because

$$\frac{\partial}{\partial C_j}\sum_{m=1}^{k} C_m \phi_m(x_i) = \phi_j(x_i),$$

TABLE A-5—DATA FOR EXAMPLE A-5

i	x_i	y_i
1	1.0	0.0
2	2.0	0.6
3	3.0	1.77
4	4.0	1.92
5	5.0	3.31
6	6.0	3.52
7	7.0	4.59
8	8.0	5.31
9	9.0	5.79
10	10.0	7.06
11	11.0	7.17

where $j = 1, 2, \ldots, k$. Eq. A-40 can be rearranged and written as

$$\sum_{m=1}^{k} C_m \sum_{i=1}^{n} \phi_m(x_i)\phi_j(x_i) = \sum_{i=1}^{n} y_i \phi_j(x_i), \quad \text{(A-42)}$$

where $j = 1, 2, \ldots, k$.

Eq. A-42 represents a system of k linear equations in the k unknowns $C_1, C_2, \ldots, C_k$. The solution can be obtained by straightforward application of direct-solution methods (Sec. 7.3.1). However, Gaussian elimination may produce unreliable results if this system of equations is ill-conditioned. This can be avoided with the method presented in the next section.

Example A-5. Given the data in **Table A-5,** find the first-degree polynomial fit using least squares. Also, predict the values of the function and its first derivative at $x^* = 7.5$.

Solution. The approximating function is chosen as a first-degree polynomial

$$f(x, C_1, C_2) = C_1 + C_2 x.$$

Comparing this function with that of Eq. A-39 reveals that $k = 2$, $\phi_1(x) = 1$, $\phi_2(x) = x$, and $n = 11$. Application of Eq. A-42 for $j = 1$ gives

$$C_1 \sum_{i=1}^{11}(1)1 + C_2 \sum_{i=1}^{11}(x_i)1 = \sum_{i=1}^{11}(y_i)1,$$

which, on substitution of data, can be simplified to

$$11C_1 + 66C_2 = 41.04.$$

Likewise, application of Eq. A-42 for $j = 2$ gives

$$C_1 \sum_{i=1}^{11}(1)x_i + C_2 \sum_{i=1}^{11}(x_i)x_i = \sum_{i=1}^{11}(y_i)\, x_i,$$

which, on substitution of data, is simplified to

$$66C_1 + 506C_2 = 328.05.$$

Solving these two linear algebraic equations simultaneously, one obtains

$$C_1 = -0.7314 \text{ and } C_2 = 0.7437.$$

Therefore,

$$f(x) = -0.7314(1) + 0.7437(x)$$

at $x^* = 7.5$, and

$$f(x^*) = -0.7314(1) + 0.7437(7.5) = 4.85.$$

The first derivative of f(x) is

$$\frac{df(x)}{dx} = 0.7437;$$

therefore,

$$\frac{df(x^*)}{dx} = 0.7437.$$

Orthogonal Polynomial Fit. The linear least-squares fit often gives rise to normal equations that are ill-conditioned. To avoid this problem, the set of functions, $\{\phi_m(x)\}$, must be chosen to be orthogonal on Points $x_1, x_2, \ldots, x_n$.

For $\{\phi_m(x)\}$ to be orthogonal on the domain of x, the individual functions making up the set must satisfy

$$\sum_{i=1}^{n} \phi_j(x_i)\phi_m(x_i) = 0, \quad \text{(A-43)}$$

whenever $j \neq m; j = 1,2, \ldots, k$; and $m = 1,2, \ldots, k$. If Eq. A-43 holds, the normal equations of the least-squares fit, Eq. A-42, reduce to

$$C_j \sum_{i=1}^{n} \phi_j(x_i)\phi_j(x_i) = \sum_{i=1}^{n} y_i \phi_j(x_i), \quad \text{(A-44)}$$

where $j = 1,2, \ldots, k$, whose solution offers no further difficulty.

The problem now is to find orthogonal functions. In general, it is possible to construct such functions with the Gram-Schmidt[1] algorithm. If, however, the orthogonal functions are chosen to be polynomials, it is possible to construct such orthogonal polynomial functions quite efficiently with a three-term recurrence relation valid for the sequences of orthogonal polynomials. The Forsythe polynomials[3] are an example of a sequence of orthogonal polynomials.

Nonlinear Least-Squares Fit. A nonlinear least-squares fit is obtained if one finds it necessary to choose an approximating function f$(x, C_1, C_2, \ldots, C_k)$ such that it does not depend linearly on Parameters $C_1, C_2, \ldots, C_k$. In these situations, the normal equations of the least-squares approximation, Eq. A-38, form a set of nonlinear algebraic equations.

These nonlinear equations can be solved efficiently with the Newton-Raphson iterative method with the following application.

1. Define the left side of Eq. A-38 as F_j.

$$F_j = \sum_{i=1}^{n} \left[y_i - f(x_i, C_1, C_2, \ldots, C_k)\right] \frac{\partial}{\partial C_j} f(x_i, C_1, C_2, \ldots, C_k), \quad \text{(A-45)}$$

where $j = 1,2, \ldots, k$.

2. Define $C_1, C_2, \ldots, C_k$ as elements of $\vec{C}$ and $F_1, F_2, \ldots, F_k$ as elements of $\vec{F}$.

$$\vec{C} = \begin{bmatrix} C_1 \\ C_2 \\ \vdots \\ C_k \end{bmatrix} \quad \text{(A-46)}$$

$$\text{and } \vec{F} = \begin{bmatrix} F_1 \\ F_2 \\ \vdots \\ F_k \end{bmatrix}. \quad \text{(A-47)}$$

3. Define the Jacobian matrix, **[J]**, whose elements are F_{jm}.

$$[\mathbf{J}] = \begin{bmatrix} F_{11} & F_{12} & \cdots & F_{1k} \\ F_{21} & F_{22} & \cdots & F_{2k} \\ \vdots & \vdots & \ddots & \\ F_{k1} & F_{k2} & & F_{kk} \end{bmatrix}, \quad \text{(A-48)}$$

$$\text{where } F_{jm} = \frac{\partial F_j}{\partial C_m} = \frac{\partial}{\partial C_m}\left\{\sum_{i=1}^{n}\left[y_i - f\left(x_i, \vec{C}\right)\right]\frac{\partial}{\partial C_j} f\left(x_i, \vec{C}\right)\right\}, \quad \text{(A-49)}$$

where $j = 1,2, \ldots, k$ and $m = 1,2, \ldots, k$, which can be further expressed as

$$F_{jm} = \frac{\partial F_j}{\partial C_m} = \sum_{i=1}^{n}\left\{\left[y_i - f\left(x_i, \vec{C}\right)\right]\frac{\partial^2}{\partial C_m \partial C_j} f\left(x_i, \vec{C}\right) - \frac{\partial}{\partial C_m} f\left(x_i, \vec{C}\right)\frac{\partial}{\partial C_j} f\left(x_i, \vec{C}\right)\right\}, \quad \text{(A-50)}$$

where $j = 1,2, \ldots, k$ and $m = 1,2, \ldots, k$

4. The solution vector is obtained with the Newton-Raphson iterative equation.

$$\vec{C}^{(\nu+1)} = \vec{C}^{(\nu)} - [\mathbf{J}]^{-1\,(\nu)} \vec{F}^{(\nu)}, \quad \text{(A-51)}$$

where $\nu = 0,1,2, \ldots$.

The iteration is started by assuming an initial guess for the elements of $\vec{C}$. In other words, values for $\vec{C}^{(0)}$ are initially assumed. The elements of $\vec{F}(\vec{C}^{(0)})$ are calculated with Eq. A-45, and those for $[\mathbf{J}](\vec{C}^{(0)})$ are evaluated with either Eq. A-49 or A-50. Then, with Eq. A-51, the first estimate for the elements of $\vec{C}^{(1)}$ is obtained. This completes the first Newton-Raphson iteration for $\nu = 0$. At this stage, the elements of $\vec{C}^{(1)}$ can be used to execute a second iteration ($\nu = 1$) that yields a second estimate for the unknowns $C_1, C_2, \ldots, C_k$ [that is, $\vec{C}^{(2)}$]. Iteration proceeds in this manner until a specified convergence criterion is satisfied. The convergence criterion usually used with this iterative method is expressed as

$$\max_{1 \leqq m \leqq k} \left|\frac{C_m^{(\nu+1)} - C_m^{(\nu)}}{C_m^{(\nu)}}\right| \leqq \varepsilon, \quad \text{(A-52)}$$

where ε = a specified tolerance usually taken as 0.01 or 0.001.

Example A-6. Data for relative permeability of water, k_{rw}, as a function of water saturation, S_w, are available at n discrete points. Both k_{rw} and S_w are normalized with $y = k_{rw}/k_{rocw}$ and $x = (S_w - S_{iw})/(1 - S_{iw} - S_{or})$. The data, after being normalized, are given as $(x_1, y_1), (x_2, y_2), \ldots, (x_n, y_n)$.

Given that the approximating function is of the form $f(x, C_1, C_2) = C_1 x^{C_2}$, find the best estimate for Parameters C_1 and C_2 using nonlinear least-squares fit.

Solution. Although the approximating function f(x, C_1, C_2) does not depend linearly on Parameters C_1 and C_2, it can be made as such by taking the natural logarithm of f(x, C_1, C_2) as the approximating function.

$$\log_e f(x, C_1, C_2) = \log_e C_1 + C_2 \log_e x.$$

This new approximating function depends linearly on $\log_e C_1$ and C_2 and, as a consequence, the linear least-squares fit can be applied.

This procedure, however, is not recommended because errors in the best estimate of $\log_e C_1$ and the best fit $\log_e$ f are amplified when the antilog of these two is taken. Nevertheless, this example is given to demonstrate the use of nonlinear least-squares fit and is treated as such.

In this example, the number of data points is n and the number of parameters is $k = 2$. The approximating function is as given in the statement of the problem

$$f(x, C_1, C_2) = C_1 x^{C_2}.$$

Define F_1 and F_2 according to Eq. A-45.

$$F_1 = \sum_{i=1}^{n}\left(y_i - C_1 x_i^{C_2}\right)x_i^{C_2}$$

and $F_2 = \sum_{i=1}^{n}\left(y_i - C_1x_i^{C_2}\right)C_1x_i^{C_2}\log_e x_i.$

Define $\vec{C}$ and $\vec{F}$ according to Eqs. A-46 and A-47.

$$\vec{C} = \begin{bmatrix} C_1 \\ C_2 \end{bmatrix}$$

and $\vec{F} = \begin{bmatrix} F_1 \\ F_2 \end{bmatrix}.$

Define the Jacobian as in Eq. A-48.

$$[\mathbf{J}] = \begin{bmatrix} F_{11} & F_{12} \\ F_{21} & F_{22} \end{bmatrix},$$

where F_{jm} is defined by applying Eq. A-49. The resulting expressions for F_{jm} where $j=1,2$ and $m=1,2$ are

$$F_{11} = \frac{\partial F_1}{\partial C_1} = \sum_{i=1}^{n} - x_i^{2C_2},$$

$$F_{12} = \frac{\partial F_1}{\partial C_2} = \sum_{i=1}^{n}\left(y_i - 2C_1x_i^{C_2}\right)x_i^{C_2}\log_e x_i,$$

$$F_{21} = \frac{\partial F_2}{\partial C_1} = \sum_{i=1}^{n}\left(y_i - 2C_1x_i^{C_2}\right)x_i^{C_2}\log_e x_i,$$

and $F_{22} = \frac{\partial F_2}{\partial C_2} = \sum_{i=1}^{n}\left(y_i - 2C_1x_i^{C_2}\right)C_1x_i^{C_2}(\log_e x_i)^2.$

Assume an initial guess of $C_1^{(0)}$ and $C_2^{(0)}$ for the unknowns C_1 and C_2. At these assumed values, calculate $F_1^{(0)}$, $F_2^{(0)}$, $F_{11}^{(0)}$, $F_{12}^{(0)}$, $F_{21}^{(0)}$, and $F_{22}^{(0)}$, with the expressions given previously. Then, apply Eq. A-51 for $v=0$.

$$\vec{C}^{(1)} = \vec{C}^{(0)} - [\mathbf{J}]^{-1\,(0)}\vec{F}^{(0)}.$$

Solve Eq. A-51 repeatedly for $\vec{C}^{(2)}$, $\vec{C}^{(3)}$, ..., until convergence is obtained. Once convergence is achieved, the elements of the converged vector are the best estimates for C_1 and C_2. Therefore,

$$y = C_1x^{C_2}$$

or $\frac{k_{rw}}{k_{rocw}} = C_1\left(\frac{S_w - S_{iw}}{1 - S_{iw} - S_{or}}\right)^{C_2}.$

Nomenclature

a = constant
a_1–a_2 = functions defined in Eqs. A-10 and A-11
b = constant
B_o = oil formation volume factor, L^3/L^3, RB/STB [m^3/std m^3]
c = constant
$\vec{C}$ = vector composed of parameters of a least-squares fit
C = constant
C_i = the ith element of $\vec{C}$
C_j = the jth element of $\vec{C}$
C_k = the kth element of $\vec{C}$
C_m = the mth element of $\vec{C}$
C_1–C_k = parameters of fitted function
C_{1i} = constant of integration in Eq. A-26
C_{2i} = constant of integration in Eq. A-26
C^{m-1} = piecewise continuous and is $m-1$ times differentiable function
d = constant
d_i = deviation at Point i defined by Eq. A-35
f = function
F_j = specified function, jth element of $\vec{F}$
F_{jm} = (j,m) element of Jacobian defined by Eq. A-49 or A-50
$\vec{F}$ = residual vector
h_i = spacing of two independent variable data points
i = dummy index
I = function that truncates a real number into an integer
j = dummy index
[**J**] = Jacobian matrix
k = number of parameters, n
k_{rocw} = relative permeability to oil at irreducible water saturation, dimensionless
k_{rw} = relative permeability to water, dimensionless
$\log_e$ = natural logarithm, Base e
l_k = Lagrangian interpolating polynomial for the kth data point
l_0 = Lagrangian interpolating polynomial for the zero data point
l_1 = Lagrangian interpolating polynomial for the first data point
l_2 = Lagrangian interpolating polynomial for the second data point
m = degree of polynomial
n = number of data points, n
P_1 = polynomial of first degree
P_3 = polynomial of third degree
R_s = solution gas/oil ratio, L^3/L^3, scf/STB [std m^3/std m^3]
s = slope
S = spline
S_a = sum of absolute errors
S_i = cubic spline function for the ith interval
S_{or} = residual oil saturation, fraction
S_w = water saturation, fraction
S_{iw} = irreducible water saturation, fraction
S_s = sum of square of errors
S_1 = cubic spline function for first interval
T = maximum absolute error
v = index for iteration number
x = independent variable in a table of data
x_i = the ith element of Variable x
x_j = the jth element of Variable x
x_k = the kth element of Variable x
x_n = the nth (last) element of Variable x
x^* = specific value of Variable x
Δx = difference or interval ($\Delta x = x_{i+1} - x_i$)
y = dependent variable in a table of data
y_i = value of dependent variable at Point i
y_n = the nth (last) value in a table of data
y^* = dependent variable at x^*
ε = tolerance
μ_o = oil viscosity, m/Lt, cp [Pa·s]
ϕ_i = the ith moment of spline
ϕ_j = the jth moment of spline
ϕ_m = the mth moment of spline
ϕ_n = moment of spline at x_n defined by Eq. A-22

Superscripts

(v) = old iteration
$(v+1)$ = current iteration
$*$ = a specific value
$'$ = first derivative
$''$ = second derivative

References

1. Faires, J.D. and Burden, R.L.: *Numerical Methods,* PWS Publishing Co., Boston, Massachusetts (1993).
2. Aziz, K. and Settari, A.: *Petroleum Reservoir Simulation,* Applied Science Publishers Ltd., London (1979) 114–16.
3. Forsythe, G.E., Malcolm, M.A., and Moler, C.B.: *Computer Methods for Mathematical Computations,* Prentice-Hall Inc., Englewood Cliffs, New Jersey (1977) 89.

Appendix B
Solution Techniques Applied to Multiphase-Flow Equations

In solving multiphase-flow equations simultaneously, more than one unknown at each gridpoint needs to be solved. In general, two-phase-flow equations generate two unknowns at each node and three-phase-flow equations result in three unknowns per gridpoint. The general structure of the solution algorithms [for example, tridiagonal direct solver, successive overrelaxation (SOR), strongly implicit procedure (SIP), and alternating direction implicit procedure (ADIP)] remain the same; however, each matrix and vector entry is either a 2×2 or 3×3 submatrix and a subvector of dimension 2 or 3, depending on whether a two-phase- or three-phase-flow problem is under consideration. This appendix establishes the similarities between the single-phase- and multiphase-flow problems at the solution level of matrix equations generated by the finite-difference approximation.

Thomas' Algorithm Applied to Block Diagonal Matrices

Two-Phase-Flow Equations. Each block contributes two equations and has two unknowns. The characteristic equation for a typical gridpoint is

$$[\mathbf{a}]_i \vec{P}_{i-1} + [\mathbf{b}]_i \vec{P}_i + [\mathbf{c}]_i \vec{P}_{i+1} = \vec{d}_i, \quad \text{(B-1)}$$

where $[\mathbf{a}]_i = \begin{bmatrix} a_{1,1} & a_{1,2} \\ a_{2,1} & a_{2,2} \end{bmatrix}_i$,

$$[\mathbf{b}]_i = \begin{bmatrix} b_{1,1} & b_{1,2} \\ b_{2,1} & b_{2,2} \end{bmatrix}_i,$$

$$[\mathbf{c}]_i = \begin{bmatrix} c_{1,1} & c_{1,2} \\ c_{2,1} & c_{2,2} \end{bmatrix}_i,$$

$$\vec{P}_i = \begin{bmatrix} P_1 \\ P_2 \end{bmatrix}_i,$$

and $\vec{d}_i = \begin{bmatrix} d_1 \\ d_2 \end{bmatrix}_i$.

The equations generated from Eq. B-1 can be written in a matrix form as

$$[\mathbf{A}]\vec{P} = \vec{d}, \quad \text{(B-2)}$$

where $[\mathbf{A}] = \begin{bmatrix} [\mathbf{b}]_1 & [\mathbf{c}]_1 & & & & \\ [\mathbf{a}]_2 & [\mathbf{b}]_2 & [\mathbf{c}]_2 & & & \\ & \cdot & \cdot & \cdot & & \\ & & [\mathbf{a}]_i & [\mathbf{b}]_i & [\mathbf{c}]_i & \\ & & & \cdot & \cdot & \cdot \\ & & & & [\mathbf{a}]_n & [\mathbf{b}]_n \end{bmatrix}$,

$$\vec{P} = \begin{bmatrix} \vec{P}_1 \\ \vec{P}_2 \\ \bullet \\ \bullet \\ \vec{P}_i \\ \bullet \\ \bullet \\ \vec{P}_n \end{bmatrix}, \text{ and } \vec{d} = \begin{bmatrix} \vec{d}_1 \\ \vec{d}_2 \\ \bullet \\ \bullet \\ \vec{d}_i \\ \bullet \\ \bullet \\ \vec{d}_n \end{bmatrix}.$$

$[\mathbf{A}]$ is a bitridiagonal matrix with a form similar to that of the 1D, single-phase model with a_i, b_i, and c_i replaced by 2×2 matrices $[\mathbf{a}]_i$, $[\mathbf{b}]_i$, and $[\mathbf{c}]_i$, respectively.

In developing an algorithm for a coefficient matrix with the indicated structure, we proceed as in the case of Thomas' algorithm, but this time we are dealing with submatrices.

$$[\mathbf{w}]_1 = [\mathbf{b}]_1^{-1}[\mathbf{c}]_1,$$

$$\vec{g}_1 = [\mathbf{b}]_1^{-1}\vec{d}_1,$$

$$[\mathbf{w}]_i = \begin{bmatrix} w_{1,1} & w_{1,2} \\ w_{2,1} & w_{2,2} \end{bmatrix}_i = \left[[\mathbf{b}]_i - [\mathbf{a}]_i[\mathbf{w}]_{i-1}\right]^{-1}[\mathbf{c}]_i$$

where $i = 2, \ldots, n-1$, and

$$\vec{g}_i = \begin{bmatrix} g_1 \\ g_2 \end{bmatrix}_i = \left[[\mathbf{b}]_i - [\mathbf{a}]_i[\mathbf{w}]_{i-1}\right]^{-1}\left[\vec{d}_i - [\mathbf{a}]_i\vec{g}_{i-1}\right]$$

where $i = 2, \ldots, n$. During the backward substitution, the solution vectors $\vec{P}_i$ can be computed from

$$\vec{P}_n = \vec{g}_n$$

and $\vec{P}_i = \vec{g}_i - [\mathbf{w}]_i \vec{P}_{i+1}$,

where $i = n-1, n-2, \ldots, 2, 1$.

In the implementation of the algorithm, the inverses of ($[\mathbf{b}]_i - [\mathbf{a}]_i[\mathbf{w}]_{i-1}$) are required; therefore, these matrices cannot be singular.

Three-Phase-Flow Equations. Extension of the two-phase equations and Thomas' algorithm to three-phase applications is straightforward and involves recognizing that each submatrix is a 3 × 3 matrix and each subvector has three elements. The resulting coefficient matrix has a tritridiagonal structure.

SOR Procedure Applied to Multiphase-Flow Problems

The extension of an SOR procedure (for example, point SOR) to an SOR implementation for multiphase-flow equations is straightforward. The analog of Eq. 7.108 is

$$\vec{P}_i^{(k+1)} = \omega[\mathbf{A}]_{i,i}^{-1}\left[\vec{d}_i - \sum_{j=1}^{i-1}[\mathbf{A}]_{i,j}\vec{P}_j^{(k+1)} - \sum_{j=i+1}^{n}[\mathbf{A}]_{i,j}\vec{P}_j^{(k)}\right]$$

$$-(w-1)\vec{P}_i^{(k)}, \quad \ldots\ldots\ldots\ldots\ldots\ldots\ldots\ldots \text{(B-3)}$$

where $i = 1, \ldots, n$. In Eq. B-3, $[\mathbf{A}]_{i,j}$ are submatrices ($[\mathbf{A}]_{i,i}$ is the submatrix located on the main diagonal), and $\vec{P}_i$ and $\vec{d}_i$ are the subvectors of the unknown and right-side vectors, respectively. $[\mathbf{A}]_{i,j}$ are either 2 × 2 or 3 × 3 submatrices and $\vec{P}_i$ and $\vec{d}_i$ have two or three elements, depending on whether the problem is two or three phase. Subscript i represents the gridpoint for which Eq. B-3 is written. Aziz and Settari[1] indicate that the prediction of optimum ω is the same as the one used for single-phase problems. It is possible that, for multiphase problems, the optimum acceleration parameter will be close to one. In determining the value of the optimum acceleration parameter, a heuristic approach is necessary; therefore, the results of several numerical experiments need to be analyzed.

Block ADIP

The implementation of ADIP, as presented in Sec. 7.3.4 for single-phase-flow problems, can be extended readily to multiphase-flow problems. For a 2D problem, the coefficients of the left sides of Eqs. 7.142 (Stage 1) and 7.143 (Stage 2) become 2 × 2 or 3 × 3 submatrices for two-phase- and three-phase-flow problems, respectively. These equations are

$$[\mathbf{W}]_{i,j}\vec{P}^*_{i-1,j} + [\mathbf{C}^*]_{i,j}\vec{P}^*_{i,j} + [\mathbf{E}]_{i,j}\vec{P}^*_{i+1,j} = \vec{Q}^*_{i,j} \quad \ldots\ldots \text{(B-4)}$$

for Stage 1 (x-direction sweep) and

$$[\mathbf{S}]_{i,j}\vec{P}^{(k+1)}_{i,j-1} + [\mathbf{C}^{**}]_{i,j}\vec{P}^{(k+1)}_{i,j} + [\mathbf{N}]_{i,j}\vec{P}^{(k+1)}_{i,j+1} = \vec{Q}^{**}_{i,j}$$

$$\ldots\ldots\ldots\ldots\ldots\ldots\ldots\ldots \text{(B-5)}$$

for Stage 2 (y-direction sweep). When Eqs. B-4 and B-5 are written at each stage, a block tridiagonal-matrix equation (similar to Eq. B-2) is generated. These equations can be solved with Thomas' algorithm as applied to block tridiagonal systems.

Block SIP

Again, in adopting the SIP method presented in Sec. 7.3.4 to multiphase-flow problems, it is necessary to replace the scalar coefficients by $p \times p$ matrices and the unknown and right-side scalars by vectors of dimension p. This similarity makes the extension of the single equation SIP to the multiple-equation case straightforward.

Nomenclature

a_i = coefficient of P_{i-1} in single-phase model
$[\mathbf{a}]_i$ = lower codiagonal submatrix entry of a block tridiagonal system
$[\mathbf{A}]$ = coefficient matrix in a matrix equation
$[\mathbf{A}]_{i,i}$ = codiagonal submatrix entry of a block tridiagonal system
$[\mathbf{A}]_{i,j}$ = offdiagonal submatrix entry of a block tridiagonal system
b_i = coefficient of P_i in single-phase model
$[\mathbf{b}]_i$ = submatrix located on the main diagonal of a block tridiagonal system
c_i = coefficient of P_{i+1} on single-phase model
$[\mathbf{c}]_i$ = upper codiagonal submatrix entry of a block tridiagonal system
$[\mathbf{C}^*]_{i,j}$ = submatrix located on the main diagonal during the x-direction sweep of ADIP
$[\mathbf{C}^{**}]_{i,j}$ = submatrix located on the main diagonal during the y-direction sweep of ADIP
$\vec{d}$ = right-side vector of Eq. B-2
$\vec{d}_i$ = right-side vector for Gridblock i
$[\mathbf{E}]_{i,j}$ = submatrix located on the upper codiagonal during the x-direction sweep
$\vec{g}_i$ = intermediate vector for Gridblock i in Thomas' algorithm
$\vec{g}_1$ = intermediate vector obtained during Thomas' algorithm application for Gridblock 1
n = Gridblock n
$[\mathbf{N}]_{i,j}$ = submatrix located on the upper codiagonal during the y-direction sweep of ADIP
p = number of phases
$\vec{P}^*_{i,j}$ = unknown vector of the ADIP during the x-direction sweep
$\vec{P}$ = vector of unknowns
$\vec{P}_i$ = vector of unknowns for Gridblock i
$\vec{P}_{i,j}$ = vector of unknowns for Gridblock (i,j)
$\vec{P}_j$ = vector of unknowns for Gridblock j
$\vec{P}_n$ = vector of unknowns for Gridblock n
$\vec{Q}^*_{i,j}$ = right-side vector of the ADIP during the x-direction sweep
$\vec{Q}^{**}_{i,j}$ = right-side vector of the ADIP during the y-direction sweep
$[\mathbf{S}]_{i,j}$ = submatrix located on the lower codiagonal during the y-direction sweep of ADIP
$[\mathbf{w}]_i$ = an intermediate submatrix for Gridblock i
$[\mathbf{w}]_1$ = an intermediate submatrix for Gridblock 1
$[\mathbf{W}]_{i,j}$ = submatrix located on the lower codiagonal during the x-direction sweep of ADIP
ω = overrelaxation parameter

Subscripts

i = Gridblock i, dummy index in x direction
j = dummy index in y direction
n = Gridblock n

Superscripts

(k) = old iteration
n = old timestep
$(k+1)$ = current iteration
$*$ = intermediate value during the x-direction sweep of ADIP

Reference

1. Aziz, K. and Settari, A.: *Petroleum Reservoir Simulation*, Applied Science Publishers Ltd., London (1979).

Appendix C
Computer Architecture

Since the mid-1970's, rapid changes in computer architectures have significantly influenced various trends in the oil industry and reservoir simulation. These trends include the structure in which reservoir simulation programs are developed, the manner in which these programs are used, and the people responsible for performing the simulation studies.

In the early days of digital computing, the mainframe computer was essentially the only type of computer in use. These computers tended to be large, expensive machines that processed data in a sequential, or scalar, manner.

Because of the cost of these mainframe computers, reservoir simulation was limited to the major oil companies and specialized consulting houses. In addition, these computers usually were located in corporate computer centers or research laboratories, which limited their accessibility. Consequently, reservoir simulation often was conducted only by research engineers working at corporate computer centers, research laboratories, consulting firms, and universities. Keeping reservoir simulation in the research laboratories, consulting firms, and universities probably was appropriate during the early years of reservoir simulation because it was an emerging technology. However, performing simulation studies away from the field offices became less attractive as reservoir simulation technology matured because engineers in the research laboratories were not always the personnel most familiar with the subject field.

Two computer architecture trends in the late 1970's and early 1980's impacted the course of reservoir simulation. These trends were the emergence of personal computers (PC's) and the emergence of supercomputers. The emergence of the PC brought the power of the computer to smaller oil companies and to district and field offices in the major oil companies. This was primarily because of the low cost of PC's. Like the mainframe computers, early PC's processed data in a scalar manner. In addition, the PC's had limited memory and disk storage capability; therefore, reservoir simulation studies could not be performed on early PC's.

This is not to say that PC's did not have an influence on reservoir simulation at this time. The emergence of the PC brought the daily use of the computer to the oil industry, and the development of computer networks gave access to the mainframe computers through the PC. In addition, although the simulation runs could not be performed on the PC, much of the simulation pre- and post-processing could be performed on these machines. Thus, some elements of a simulation study could be performed on the PC. Finally, the software purchased for the PC was very reliable and user friendly. These standards began to be incorporated into reservoir simulation software. Thus, the emergence of the PC had an indirect impact on reservoir simulation.

The emergence of the supercomputer, however, had a direct impact on reservoir simulation. The main difference between the first supercomputers and the conventional computers of the day was the manner in which these computers processed data. While early mainframe computers processed data in a scalar mode, supercomputers processed data in a vector mode.

The use of vector processing impacted reservoir simulation in the way simulation programs were written and in the way these programs were used. Reservoir simulation programs had to be written to take advantage of the power and capabilities of the supercomputer. Two methods were used to take advantage of vector-processing capability. First, algorithms, which were not necessarily the most optimal algorithm on scalar computers, were found to be optimal on vector machines because of the vector qualities of the algorithm. Consequently, these optimal vector algorithms were incorporated into the simulation programs. Second, the simulation programs were restructured, or vectorized, to take maximum advantage of vector processing. These two steps increased the execution speed of simulation programs by approximately one order of magnitude.

The increased speed of the simulation programs, resulting from the use of supercomputers, provided the capability to construct larger, more sophisticated simulation models than was possible on the scalar processors. In full-field simulation models, the ability to construct larger simulation models allowed for the use of more grid cells than previously possible. Thus, finer resolution in both the areal and vertical dimensions was incorporated into the models. Detailed areal studies of displacement processes were conducted (because more grid cells between offset wells were possible), 3D models replaced 2D areal models, and greater geological detail (more simulation layers) became an industry standard.

In cross-sectional models, the ability to construct larger simulation models allowed for studying the effects of small-scale reservoir features on displacement processes. Simulation models with layer spacing on the order of inches to feet became practical. Consequently, cross-sectional models were used for direct study of the effect of small-scale reservoir heterogeneities, such as cross-bedding, on fluid-displacement processes. The effects of these small-scale features were incorporated into full-field models by the use of appropriate scaling methods[1] and relative permeability and capillary pressure pseudofunctions.

Finally, the use of supercomputers in reservoir simulation allowed for the use of improved fluid characterization in reservoir studies. Three-dimensional, compositional simulation models became practical at the field scale.

In the early to mid-1980's, two more trends in computer architecture had an impact on reservoir simulation. These were the advent of parallel-processing computers and the reduced instruction set computer (RISC) systems.

Parallel processing, a natural extension of vector processing, is often referred to as the next generation of supercomputers. The use of these computers allows even larger, more sophisticated models to be built. Consequently, the trends in reservoir simulation can be expected to continue with the use of parallel processors.

Although the use of vector- and parallel-processing computers has increased the complexity of the models that can be built and run, their cost has done little to remove complex reservoir simulation from the research laboratories of the major oil companies. The benefit of the RISC systems is that they have enabled more complex, full-field models to be run by the smaller oil companies and in the field and district offices of the major oil companies. Thus, simulation studies can be conducted by the reservoir engineers who are most familiar with the subject field.

RISC systems are a new generation of computers that, at least at the present, have been adapted successfully to high-performance workstations. Workstations are relatively inexpensive computers designed for access by a limited number of simultaneous users (in the range of one to five users per computer). These high-performance workstations are powerful enough to run large simulation models in a relatively short time period. Currently, simulation models can be run on RISC workstations that would have taken up all the resources of a large mainframe computer just a decade ago.

Because changes in computer architectures have had a dramatic impact on the course of reservoir simulation, it is appropriate to provide a brief description of the various architectures. The fundamental principles of scalar, vector, and parallel processing and RISC system computers are presented.

Scalar, vector, and parallel processors differ in the timing in which instructions are carried out during computation. These processing methods are sometimes referred to as single-instruction/single-data, single-instruction/multiple-data, and multiple-instructions/multiple-data processing methods, respectively.[2] The basis for this naming convention will become apparent as the various methods are described.

Before the differences in the processing methods are discussed, several definitions are provided. A scalar quantity is a single value quantity. For example, π is a scalar quantity. A vector quantity is a 1D array of values. For example, in FORTRAN, the quantity A(I) is a vector quantity. The stride of a vector is the number of locations in memory between successive elements of the vector. The following FORTRAN do loop illustrates the stride of a vector.

```
      DO 10 I = 1, N
            C(2*I) = A(I) + B(I)
10    CONTINUE
```

In this example, Vectors A(I) and B(I) have a stride of one, while Vector C(2*I) has a stride of two. A vector with a stride of one is said to be contiguous.

Scalar-Processing Computers

Scalar processing (also referred to as sequential processing) performs all instructions sequentially, acting as if all quantities, including the elements of a vector, are scalars. The following simple FORTRAN do loop illustrates this.

```
      DO 10 I = 1, N
            C(I) = A(I) + B(I)
10    CONTINUE
```

Clearly, the quantities A(I), B(I), and C(I) are all vector quantities. In a scalar-processing machine, one instruction is performed during each cycle of the computer; consequently, the do loop shown would be executed in the following manner.

1. Load A(I) into buffer.
2. Load B(I) into buffer.
3. Add A(I) to B(I).
4. Store the result in C(I).

Clock Cycle	OPERATION			
	LOAD A	LOAD B	ADD A to B	STORE C
1	Load A(1)	-	-	-
2	-	Load B(1)	-	-
3	-	-	A(1) + B(1)	-
4	-	-	-	C(1)
5	Load A(2)	-	-	-
6		Load B(2)	-	-
7	-	-	A(2) + B(2)	-
8	-	-	-	C(2)
9	Load A(3)	-	-	-
10	-	Load B(3)	-	-
11	-	-	A(3) + B(3)	-
12	-	-	-	C(3)
.	.	.	.	.
.	.	.	.	.
.	.	.	.	.
4N-3	Load A(N)	-	-	-
4N-2	-	Load B(N)	-	-
4N-1	-	-	A(N) + B(N)	-
4N	-	-	-	C(N)

Fig. C-1—Schematic diagram of addition of two vectors on a scalar (or sequential) -processing computer.

This process is repeated n_e times to complete the do loop. **Fig. C-1** shows the scalar-processing method schematically. (This figure should be considered a schematic representation only because floating-point operations, such as addition, take several clock cycles to execute.)

For conventional scalar processors, the only way to improve the computer's speed is to reduce the cycle time. In addition, the amount of work required to restructure the software to optimize a computer program generally is not warranted because the benefits, measured in terms of execution speedup, are often not very substantial. Speedup factors of approximately two can be expected to be achieved by significant software restructuring on a scalar machine.[2,3]

Vector-Processing Computers

Vector processing differs from scalar processing in that some instructions that act on vectors can be executed concurrently. This is best illustrated with the earlier FORTRAN do loop example, which added two vectors. On a vector-processing machine, the do loop would be executed in the following manner.

1. Load A(1) into buffer.
2. Load A(2) into buffer while loading B(1) into buffer.
3. Load A(3) into buffer while loading B(2) into buffer while adding A(1) to B(1).
4. Load A(4) into buffer while loading B(3) into buffer while adding A(2) to B(2) while storing result into C(1).

This process is continued n_e times to complete the do loop; **Fig. C-2** shows this process schematically. The chain of instructions shown in Fig. C-2 is often referred to as a vector pipeline. In general, a more efficient program can be written if a large number of computations can be put into the vector pipelines and if longer vector lengths, n_e, are used in the program.

Clock Cycle	OPERATION			
	LOAD A	LOAD B	ADD A to B	STORE C
1	Load A(1)	-	-	-
2	Load A(2)	Load B(1)	-	-
3	Load A(3)	Load B(2)	A(1) + B(1)	-
4	Load A(4)	Load B(3)	A(2) + B(2)	C(1)
5	Load A(5)	Load B(4)	A(3) + B(3)	C(2)
6	Load A(6)	Load B(5)	A(4) + B(4)	C(3)
7	Load A(7)	Load B(6)	A(5) + B(5)	C(4)
8	Load A(8)	Load B(7)	A(6) + B(6)	C(5)
.	.	.	.	.
.	.	.	.	.
.	.	.	.	.
N	Load A(N)	Load B(N-1)	A(N-2) + B(N-2)	C(N-3)
N+1	-	Load B(N)	A(N-1) + B(N-1)	C(N-2)
N+2	-	-	A(N) + B(N)	C(N-1)
N+3	-	-	-	C(N)

Fig. C-2—Schematic diagram of addition of two vectors on a vector-processing computer.

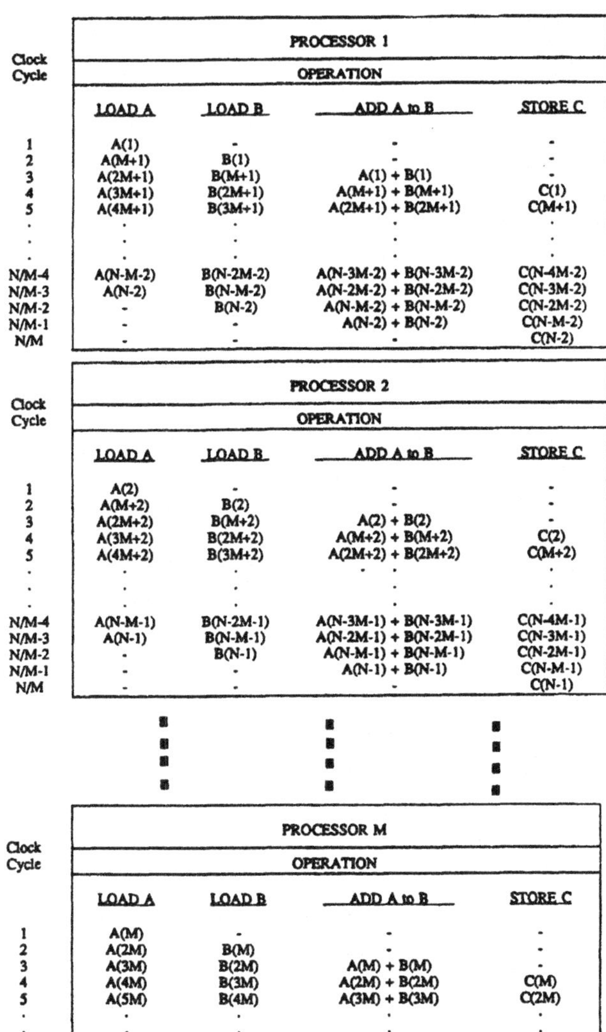

Clock Cycle	PROCESSOR 1			
	OPERATION			
	LOAD A	LOAD B	ADD A to B	STORE C
1	A(1)	-	-	-
2	A(M+1)	B(1)	-	-
3	A(2M+1)	B(M+1)	A(1) + B(1)	-
4	A(3M+1)	B(2M+1)	A(M+1) + B(M+1)	C(1)
5	A(4M+1)	B(3M+1)	A(2M+1) + B(2M+1)	C(M+1)
.	.	.	.	.
N/M-4	A(N-M-2)	B(N-2M-2)	A(N-3M-2) + B(N-3M-2)	C(N-4M-2)
N/M-3	A(N-2)	B(N-M-2)	A(N-2M-2) + B(N-2M-2)	C(N-3M-2)
N/M-2	-	B(N-2)	A(N-M-2) + B(N-M-2)	C(N-2M-2)
N/M-1	-	-	A(N-2) + B(N-2)	C(N-M-2)
N/M	-	-	-	C(N-2)

Clock Cycle	PROCESSOR 2			
	OPERATION			
	LOAD A	LOAD B	ADD A to B	STORE C
1	A(2)	-	-	-
2	A(M+2)	B(2)	-	-
3	A(2M+2)	B(M+2)	A(2) + B(2)	-
4	A(3M+2)	B(2M+2)	A(M+2) + B(M+2)	C(2)
5	A(4M+2)	B(3M+2)	A(2M+2) + B(2M+2)	C(M+2)
.	.	.	.	.
N/M-4	A(N-M-1)	B(N-2M-1)	A(N-3M-1) + B(N-3M-1)	C(N-4M-1)
N/M-3	A(N-1)	B(N-M-1)	A(N-2M-1) + B(N-2M-1)	C(N-3M-1)
N/M-2	-	B(N-1)	A(N-M-1) + B(N-M-1)	C(N-2M-1)
N/M-1	-	-	A(N-1) + B(N-1)	C(N-M-1)
N/M	-	-	-	C(N-1)

Clock Cycle	PROCESSOR M			
	OPERATION			
	LOAD A	LOAD B	ADD A to B	STORE C
1	A(M)	-	-	-
2	A(2M)	B(M)	-	-
3	A(3M)	B(2M)	A(M) + B(M)	-
4	A(4M)	B(3M)	A(2M) + B(2M)	C(M)
5	A(5M)	B(4M)	A(3M) + B(3M)	C(2M)
.	.	.	.	.
N/M-4	A(N-M)	B(N-2M)	A(N-3M) + B(N-3M)	C(N-4M)
N/M-3	A(N)	B(N-M)	A(N-2M) + B(N-2M)	C(N-3M)
N/M-2	-	B(N)	A(N-M) + B(N-M)	C(N-2M)
N/M-1	-	-	A(N) + B(N)	C(N-M)
N/M	-	-	-	C(N)

Fig. C-3—Schematic diagram of addition of two vectors on a parallel-processing computer.

The speedup of vector processing over scalar processing can be calculated from Amdahl's law,[2]

$$S_v = \frac{1}{(f_s - f_v/V)}. \quad \text{(C-1)}$$

Amdahl's law illustrates why the most efficient algorithm on a scalar-processing machine may not be the most efficient algorithm on a vector-processing machine. If an algorithm is efficient on a scalar machine but cannot be vectorized to a high degree (that is, the algorithm can only be restructured in such a way that a low value of f_v in Eq. C-1 results), it may not be the most efficient algorithm on a vector machine.

The key to restructuring the software to take full advantage of vector processing is to ensure the following.

1. As many do loops as possible are made candidates for vectorization.
2. The vector pipelines contain as many computations as possible.
3. The vector lengths are as long as possible.

Not all do loops are candidates for vectorization. Vectorization will not occur in the following situations.

1. The do loop contains a recursive element.
2. The do loop contains a call to a subroutine or function.
3. The do loop contains an I/O or GO TO statement.
4. The do loop contains a complex IF statement.

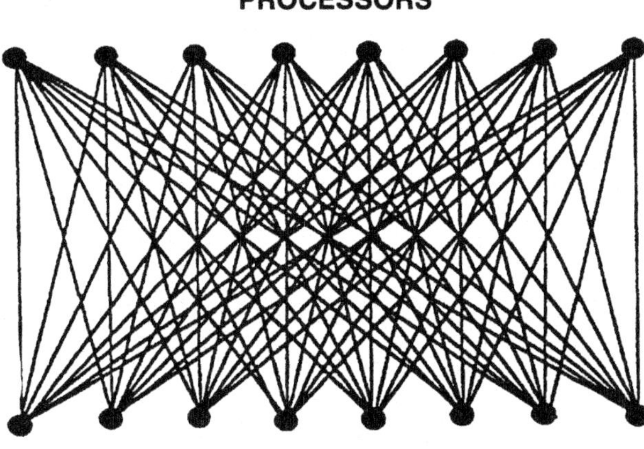

Fig. C-4—Parallel computing with shared memory.[4]

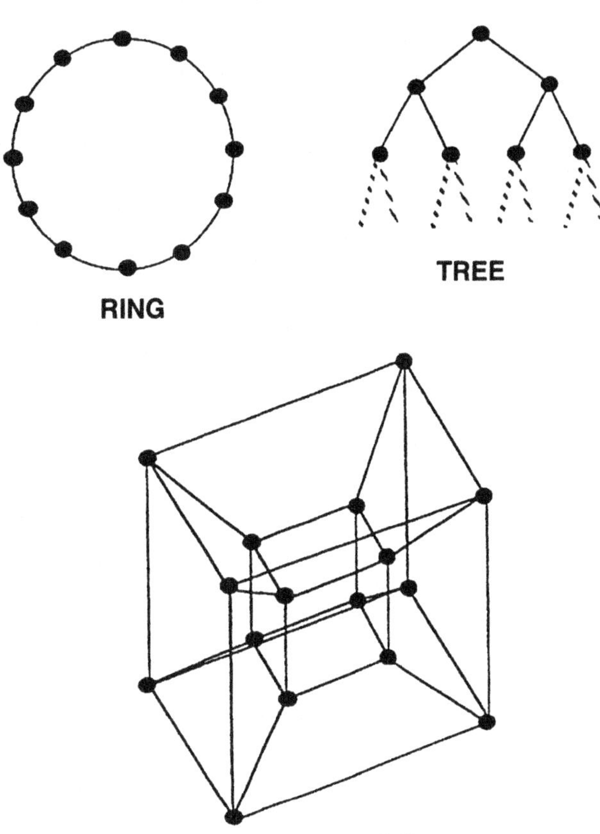

Fig. C-5—Parallel computing with distributed memory.[4]

Parallel-Processing Computers

Parallel processing is considered an extension of vector processing, in that it attempts to perform even more computations simultaneously. This is accomplished by creating computers with multiple processing units that share common memory. The work can be divided among the processing units and executed concurrently. Thus, the FORTRAN example of the addition of two vectors is executed as in **Fig. C-3**. The major concern of parallel processing is to balance the computations performed on all processors, particularly if n_e/n_p is not an integer.

Parallel-processing computers can be classified by the manner in which the processing units have access to memory. A parallel computer where all processors have access to all memory is called a shared-memory computer. **Fig. C-4** shows the architecture of a shared-memory computer schematically. Parallel processors that have access to only portions of the memory are called distributed-memory computers (because the memory is distributed among the processors). **Fig. C-5** shows the architecture of a distributed-memory computer schematically.

The speedup of parallel processing over scalar processing can be calculated from the parallel-processing form of Amdahl's law,

$$S_p = \frac{1}{(f_s - f_p/n_p)}. \qquad \text{(C-2)}$$

RISC

As stated earlier, the processes shown in Figs. C-1 through C-3 can be considered schematic diagrams only because the operations shown often take several clock cycles to execute. RISC systems improve execution time with fewer, faster executing instructions. Often, these instructions are executed in one clock cycle.[4]

Unlike the computer architectures discussed earlier [sometimes referred to as complex instruction set computer (CISC) systems] that attempt to provide generalized computer systems, RISC systems are designed for more specialized applications. The design of RISC systems is based on the following principles.[2]

1. Analyze the software applications to be performed on the computer system to identify the key operations in these applications.
2. Design a data path that is optimal for the key operations of the target software applications.
3. Design efficient instructions that perform the key operations of the target software applications with the optimal data path.
4. Add nonessential instructions (for the target software applications) only if they do not slow down the computer.

Therefore, CISC architectures can be thought of as high-performance generalized computers, while RISC architectures can be thought of as specialized computers customized for the software applications that run on them.

Nomenclature

f_p = fraction of operations performed in parallel mode ($f_p = 1 - f_s$)
f_s = fraction of operations performed in scalar mode
f_v = fraction of operations performed in vector mode
n_e = number of elements in vector, n
n_p = number of processors, n
S_p = speedup of parallel processing over scalar processing
S_v = speedup of vector processing over scalar processing
V = vector operator

References

1. Durlofsky, L.J.: "Modeling Fluid Flow Through Complex Reservoir Beds," *SPEFE* (December 1992) 315; *Trans.,* AIME, **293.**
2. Tanenbaum, A.S.: *Structured Computer Organization*, Prentice-Hall Inc., Englewood Cliffs, New Jersey (1990) 36 and 436.
3. Brode, B.Q. *et al.*: *FORTRAN Programming on Cray Computers*, Pacific Sierra Research Corp., Los Angeles, California (1984).
4. Killough, J.: "Vector and Parallel Computing in Reservoir Simulation," paper presented at the 1990 Intl. Forum on Reservoir Simulation, Baden, Austria, 17–23 July.

Author Index

Subject Index

D

E

F

G

H

I

J

K

L

M

N

O

P

Q

R

S

T

U

V

W-Z

CPSIA information can be obtained
at www.ICGtesting.com
Printed in the USA
LVOW06s0007050816
498980LV00001B/1/P

9 781555 630898